Τό βιβλίο αὐτό τό ἀφιερώνω
στή θεία μου Φανή
καί στό θεῖο μου Κώστα

A.D.P.

ELECTROMAGNETICS

Classical and Modern Theory and Applications

ELECTRICAL ENGINEERING AND ELECTRONICS

A Series of Reference Books and Textbooks

Editors

Marlin O. Thurston
Department of Electrical
Engineering
The Ohio State University
Columbus, Ohio

William Middendorf
Department of Electrical
and Computer Engineering
University of Cincinnati
Cincinnati, Ohio

Electronics Editor

Marvin H. White
Westinghouse Electric Corporation
Defense and Space Center
Baltimore, Maryland

1. Rational Fault Analysis, *edited by Richard Saeks and S. R. Liberty*
2. Nonparametric Methods in Communications, *edited by P. Papantoni-Kazakos and Dimitri Kazakos*
3. Interactive Pattern Recognition, *Yi-tzuu Chien*
4. Solid-State Electronics, *Lawrence E. Murr*
5. Electronic, Magnetic, and Thermal Properties of Solid Materials, *Klaus Schröder*
6. Magnetic -Bubble Memory Technology, *Hsu Chang*
7. Transformer and Inductor Design Handbook, *Colonel Wm. T. McLyman*
8. Electromagnetics: Classical and Modern Theory and Applications, *Samuel Seely and Alexander D. Poularikas*

Other Volumes in Preparation

ELECTROMAGNETICS

Classical and Modern Theory and Applications

SAMUEL SEELY / ALEXANDER D. POULARIKAS
Department of Electrical Engineering
University of Rhode Island
Kingston, Rhode Island

MARCEL DEKKER, INC.   New York and Basel

Library Of Congress Cataloging in Publication Data

Seely, Samuel, [Date]
Electromagnetics.

(Electrical engineering and electronics ; 8)
Bibliography: p.
Includes index.
1. Electromagnetism. I. Poularikas, Alexander D., [Date] joint author. II. Title. III. Series.
QC760.S44 537 79-11641
ISBN 0-8247-6820-5

MARCEL DEKKER, INC.
270 Madison Avenue, New York, New York 10016

Current Printing (last digit):
10 9 8 7 6 5 4 3 2 1

PRINTED IN THE UNITED STATES OF AMERICA

PREFACE

The objectives of this book are more ambitious than those of the usual book on electromagnetics. Not only does it seek to provide the essential introductory aspects of electricity and magnetism, but it also seeks to provide examples of how these basic principles are employed in an understanding and description of a wide range of electromagnetic applications. Because many of these important applications overlap electromagnetics with other fields, we have included certain details of acoustics, thermal, plasmas, elasticity, physical and geometrical optics. Such applications often require extensive mathematical sophistication in their description, and we have attempted to provide sufficient mathematical material, either within the text or in appendixes, to permit the reader to follow the developments. Moreover, we also recognize that exact solutions to certain problems are often not possible, and we have included some material to show how one would approach the solution of problems using graphical, numerical or approximate analytical methods.

In the development of the text material, we proceed from basic concepts to particular specialized viewpoints. Thus we devote considerable attention to fields and field configurations from graphical numerical and analytical viewpoints before we seek to apply these to a traditional discipline. Because of subsequent needs, we seek ideas and examples from a wide variety of disciplines in these early chapters and find them in thermal, acoustic, mechanical, and fluids as well as in electricity. It is not until we have explored the general properties of fields do we turn our attention to a detailed study of electricity and magnetism. Once we have discussed these areas and have developed an understanding of electromagnetism and the important aspects of Maxwell's equations, we then turn to the various important areas of application of such fields. These studies range from plane waves in free space, in bounded space, and in confined regions such as in waveguides and in resonators. As one changes the wavelength of the fields, one is led from radiation problems from simple configurations to a more extensive discussion of simple and multiple radiators and the broad aspects of diffraction. The physical optics problems, and these are often referred to as Fourier Optics, are brought into focus through a variety of applications including optical filtering and signal processing, holography, and some aspects of fiber optics.

The introduction of anisotropic mediums into the fields, either through birefrigent crystals or by introducing plasmas with and without applied magnetic fields (as in the ionosphere), leads to questions of the generation of ordinary and extraordinary waves, the polarization of waves, and dispersion, as inevitable consequences.

It must be understood, however, that it is not our purpose to discuss in detail every aspect of every field that we introduce. Specifically, we are not trying to include a complete discussion of many disciplines within one pair of covers. We are trying to show some of the logical directions which the broad field of electromagnetics has impacted, and to present enough content so that the broad concepts are understood. We recognize that the mathematical sophistication often becomes more demanding with more detailed studies, and in consequence we might not consider all of the practical aspects of a given field. This occurs, for example, when we discuss problems having rectangular configurations but do little with cylindrical configurations. Hence, our discussion of cylindrical waveguides, cylindrical resonators, and cylindrical fibers is limited. It is our expectation that if we can provide an understanding in the mathematically less complicated cases that the reader will be able to develop an understanding of the comparable situations with different geometrical constraints.

With objectives such as these, some material is introductory and other is rather advanced. The use of the book will be dictated by the objectives of a particular course of study. The instructor is provided with a wide choice of topics, and the demands on the student will be dictated by his course objectives. Thus the book can be used in fields courses at the junior level, and it can also be used in more specialized courses at more advanced levels. In addition, practicing engineers will greatly benefit from this book because of its wide scope and coverage.

The authors wish to express their appreciation to Mrs. Ada Willis for her patience in typing the original manuscript and its numerous revisions, and to Mrs. Katherine MacDougall for her expert typing of the final manuscript.

CONTENTS

ELECTROMAGNETICS

Classical and Modern Theory and Applications

CHAPTER 1

POTENTIAL-FLOW FIELDS

This chapter introduces classes of field problems which are characterized as potential-flow fields. The physical conditions which lead to such classes of behavior are considered to constitute a phenomenological class. The features of such potential-flow fields, which are classified as conservative, irrotational or curl-free fields are described by Laplace's equation.

1-1. Field Versus Lumped Parameter Description

The study of lumped, linear systems analysis proceeds by modeling the system elements in terms of through (flow) and across (potential) variables. Linear physical elements which constitute such systems fall into three classes when described in mathematical terms relating the terminal through and across variables: proportional, derivative, integral. When an array of elements are interconnected, the equilibrium equations of the connected array are deduced by imposing known physical laws: Kirchoff's laws for electrical networks; conservation of energy for thermal systems, conservation of mass for fluid systems. The formulations prove to be analogs of each other, and the general physical considerations often parallel each other sufficiently well to allow understanding in one field to aid in an understanding in an analogous field. Often this understanding is improved by performing experiments in an analogous system since experiments may be more easily carried out and interpreted in one system than another. To elaborate on this point, we shall consider some familiar examples.

Example 1-1.1. Develop the equations and the network representation of a linear system consisting of a spring, a mass, and a dashpot interconnected as shown in Fig. 1-1.1. The dashpot consists of a piston immersed in a viscous fluid.

Solution. The equation of motion for an applied force f, is written as follows:

$$M \frac{dv}{dt} + Dv + K \int v \, dt = f \qquad (1\text{-}1.1)$$

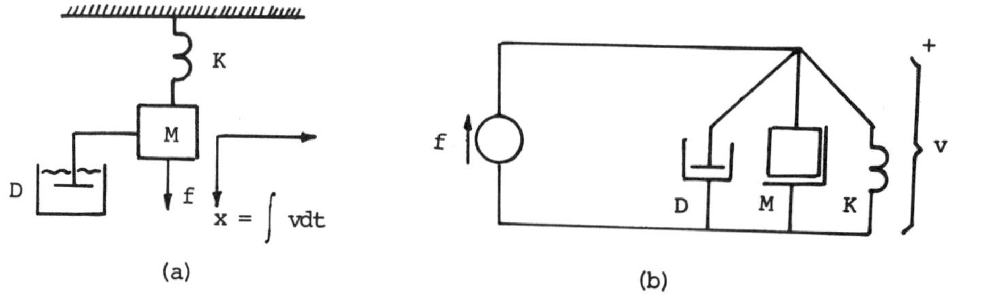

Figure 1-1.1. Representations of a spring, mass, dashpot system. (a) Physical system. (b) Equivalent network representation.

where K is the spring constant and D is the damping constant. This equation may be written explicitly in terms of x, since $dx/dt = v$. Thus

$$M \frac{d^2x}{dt^2} + D \frac{dx}{dt} + Kx = f \qquad (1\text{-}1.2)$$

Solution of one or the other of these equations, subject to two specified initial conditions, will serve to determine uniquely the motion of the mass as a function of time.

ΔΔΔ

The lumped parameter analysis discussed in the example is concerned only with the bulk or overall behavior of the system. It does not concern itself with questions such as:

1. How does the spring constant depend on the material and construction of the spring?
2. Under what conditions will the elongation of the spring be directly proportional to the displacement?
3. What is the maximum elongation of the spring before it weakens?
4. How does the viscous force produced by the dashpot depend on the physical properties of the fluid used?
5. In what way should the dimensions of the dashpot be changed in order to double the viscous force?
6. Under what conditions will the viscous force be proportional to the velocity?

These questions, and others of a similar nature, are those that field analysis attempts to answer. In other words, field analysis is the link between the physical properties of all of the elements of a system and the lumped parameter model that described the gross behavior of the system.

A complete field analysis of the spring would give the relation between the stress and strain at each point in the spring as a function of the external elongation of the spring. The field analysis of the dashpot would provide a solution for the velocity field in the fluid as a function of piston velocity and position. In terms of this velocity field and the viscosity of the fluid of the field the overall damping force could be obtained.

Clearly, field analysis describes fields that are functions of the spatial coordinates as well as time. As a result, the description is given as partial differential equations as contrasted with the ordinary type of differential equation that occurs in a lumped parameter analysis.

Example 1-1.2. Develop the equilibrium equation for a parallel RLC circuit as shown in Fig. 1-1.2.

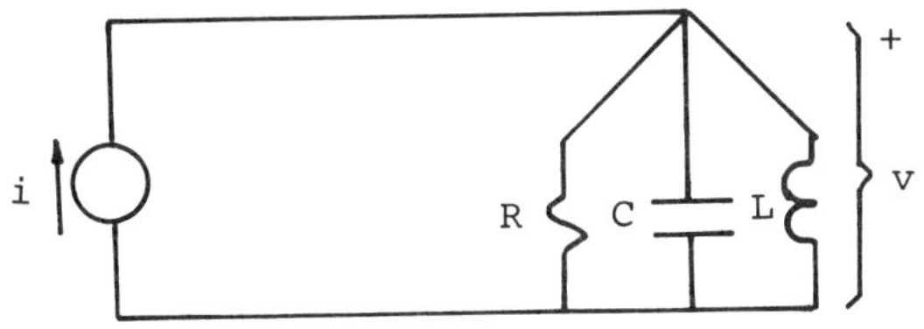

Figure 1-1.2. A parallel RLC circuit.

Solution. For ideal elements, the current-voltage terminal relations for three elements are:

$$i = \frac{v}{R}; \quad i = C\,\frac{dv}{dt}; \quad i = \frac{1}{L}\int v\,dt \tag{1-1.3}$$

By an application of the Kirchoff current law to the node or junction, the equation giving the relation between the applied current and the voltage across the elements, is:

$$C\,\frac{dv}{dt} + \frac{v}{R} + \frac{1}{L}\int v\,dt = i \tag{1-1.4}$$

The exact parallelism between Figs. 1-1.1 and 1-1.2, and Eqs. (1-1.1) and (1-1.4) for the mechanical and electrical systems clearly illustrates the analogy between the two systems. ΔΔΔ

Just as in the mechanical MDK system, the lumped parameter analysis of the CRL electrical circuit does not provide answers to many questions of fundamental importance. Among these unanswered questions are:

1. Under what conditions can circuit elements such as resistors, inductors and capacitors be assumed to have an electrical behavior according to the current-voltage terminal relations given in Eq. (1-1.3)?
2. Do the circuit parameters, resistance R, inductance L, and capacitance C, depend on frequency or are they truly constants?

3. What is the maximum voltage that can be applied across the capacitor before dielectric breakdown occurs?
4. How should an inductor be constructed in order to obtain a maximum value of inductance L in a given volume?
5. Why is the current in an inductor related to the terminal voltage according to the expression $i = (1/L) \int v\, dt$?
6. Is the lumped parameter description of the circuit valid for frequencies greater than 10^{10} Hz?
7. Will the circuit radiate electromagnetic waves?
8. For a resistor with a non-uniform cross section, what is the temperature distribution throughout the resistor? Will hot spots develop?
9. How can the capacitance C be increased?

All of these questions and many more of similar type are of utmost importance not only to the engineer concerned with the design of resistors, inductors and capacitors, but also to the circuit applications engineer. An analysis to determine the electric and magnetic fields existing in the space around and within these elements will permit answers to all of the questions posed. In addition, the studyh of the fields associated with these devices is necessary for a proper understanding of the operation of circuit elements and the limitations inherent in the lumped parameter model. Again, the importance of field theory in providing the link between the detailed physical phenomena taking place in a circuit and the lumped parameter model used to describe the terminal behavior is apparent.

1-2. Definition of a Physical Field

We have noted that the lumped parameter system is intimately related to and an approximation to the more general distributed parameter case, and that an analogy exists among different physical systems (mechanical, electrical, fluid, thermal, elastic). However, no short and concise definition of what constitutes a physical field can be given. A general understanding and feeling for the field concept is perhaps best obtained from a consideration of a number of typical fields and the attributes that they have in common. However, because we shall be interested in a description of the behavior of the system at all points in the field, the description must be given in terms of *point* variables and not in terms of *terminal* variables.

Let us consider a certain volume or region in which the state of a physical system can be described by a function $f(x,y,z,t)$ of the spatial rectangular coordinates x,y,z and the time t. The function f is a point function; that is, it has a definite value at each point in the region and represents a field quantity. As an example, the temperature distribution throughout a body is a field quantity; likewise the pressure distribution in a fluid is a field quantity. Thus one important attribute of a field is that it has "extent," i.e., it describes a physical property as a continuous function of space and time coordinates. If the physical property is independent of time, the corresponding describing function represents a *static* or *time independent* field quantity. On the other hand, if the property being described varies with time, then the field is a *dynamic* or *time dependent* field.

When the property in question, be it temperature, pressure, density, etc. can be uniquely described at each point in space at a given time by a single number or scalar quantity, the collection of these scalar numbers defines a *scalar field.* Not all physical fields are scalar fields. Many of the properties of physical systems require not only a magnitude but also a direction to be specified, e.g., the velocity distribution in a fluid. In this case the property in question is described by a vector point function $\overline{F}(x,y,z,t)$ and the field is a *vector field.* Note that both the magnitude and direction of a vector field changes from point to point throughout the region of interest and, in general, also with time. A vector field may always be decomposed into three scalar fields. For example, the velocity field which describes the flow of a fluid can be decomposed into three scalar fields that give the components of the velocity in the x,y,z directions at each point.

Although vectors are used in a geometrical sense in static mechanics and in geometry, such vectors do not constitute a vector field. A vector field has extent and is an infinite collection of vectors, one at each point, describing a physical property throughout a region of space rather than, for example, a single force applied at a specific point along a truss or beam. Thus one might pictorially show a field by associating a number (to denote the magnitude or strength of the field at a point) and an arrow (to denote the direction of the field at a point) at every point in the field. In a less general case one might consider a three dimensional grid structure. At each point of intersection of the grid there would be both a number and a unit vector to specify the magnitude and direction of the field at that point.

In addition to scalar and vector fields, there are further generalizations that lead to what is termed a *tensor field.* An example of a tensor field is the stress distribution throughout an elastic solid. In an elastic body forces may exist that tend to elongate or compress the body along each coordinate direction x,y,z at each point. In addition, shear forces may exist that tend to shear the body along different planes. The complete description of the state of stress in the body thus requires more than three scalar quantities (if there were no shear stress, 3 scalar quantities would suffice) in order to describe it. In this particular case a 3 by 3 matrix, or nine scalar quantities are required, and the resultant matrix with elements that are point functions of the coordinates represents a tensor field of order two. On this general basis, scalars are tensors of order zero while vectors are tensors of order one.

1-3. Occurrence of Physical Fields in Engineering and Science

There is virtually no branch of engineering that is not concerned, to some extent, with field phenomena. The vibration of strings, beams, membranes, etc., is described by field quantities that give the displacement from equilibrium and the velocity at each point throughout the body. The flow of any fluid or gas is described by various field quantities such as velocity, pressure, density, etc. The temperature distribution and flow of heat is a field problem. Likewise any physical process depending on a diffusion mechanism requires a field description. Examples of diffusion are those that occur in filtration problems, in chemical mixing problems, in the flow of electrons and holes in semiconductors, and the diffusion of neutrons in reactors.

The propagation of waves or wave phenomena is intimately associated with fields. There are many examples of waves occurring in nature, among which are: the common acoustic or sound waves in air, water waves on the ocean, electro-magnetic waves, waves on strings and beams, ultrasonic waves in material bodies, magnetohydrodynamic waves in conducting fluids, etc. All wave problems have many features in common so that the detailed study of one or more types helps to provide a background for the understanding of other kinds of waves as well.

Many of the fields that occur in engineering are qualitatively familiar to us because of their common occurrence and our ability to detect their presence with our physical senses. An intuitive feeling for the nature of the velocity field in a flowing fluid or the temperature field throughout a room is held by most students in engineering or science. On the other hand, there are many fields that are a good deal more abstract in nature and even at times might be regarded more as mathematical inventions rather than as having physical reality. For example, Newton's law of gravitation states that two bodies attract each other with a force that is proportional to the product of their masses and inversely proportional to the square of the distance between their centers. From this basic law has arisen the concept of a gravitational field. That is, the ability of one mass to attract another is attributed to the existence of a force field set up by the first mass and vice versa. Any other mass situated in the force field of the first mass will then experience a force, with this force being communicated to it through the gravitational force field. We could regard the notion of this gravitational force field that pervades all of space around a given mass as a fictitious field. However, even if we adhered to this viewpoint, we would still have to admit that the concept was an extremely useful one, and simplifies the solution of problems such as evaluating the flight trajectory of an interplanetary space ship, or the motions of the planets.

In many branches of modern physics such abstract fields are introduced in order to describe natural physical processes. To the extent that the field can be endowed with all the necessary properties to describe correctly all of the observed physical phenomena, it can be said to have physical reality, even though our senses of touch, sight, and hearing, are inadequate to detect it. In the case of the gravitational force field a basic requirement or property that had to be imposed was that the correct force acting on an arbitrary mass must be obtained by the use of the field concept.

Enough has been said to show that field phenomena do occur in all areas of physical endeavor. We shall now begin our detailed study of fields, their definition and their description, with particular emphasis on the electromagnetic field.

1-4. Simple Flow Fields

To introduce our detailed consideration of fields and field configurations, we consider five physical problems. These have been selected to show that classes of fields exist in different areas of physical science which are phenomenologically the same (the basic phenomena are physically similar and are described mathematically by similar equations).

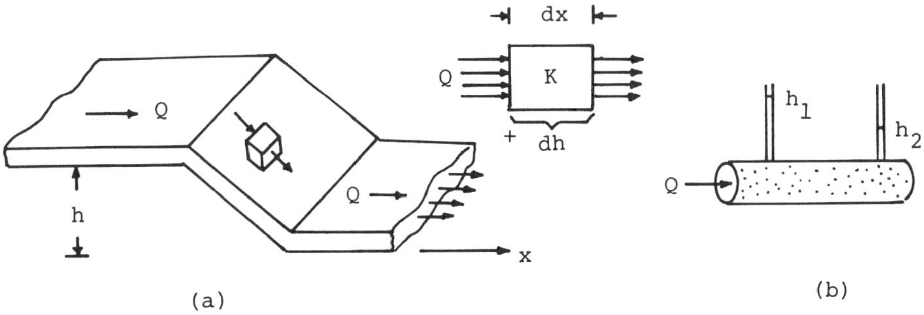

Figure 1-4.1. Idealized model of flow of a brook through a porous bed.

Refer to Fig. 1-4.1a which represents a brook which passes down a sloping porous bed. For our present purposes this situation is idealized as uniform flow of unlimited extent through a uniform porous bed. We consider a unit strip of the flow field within the porous bed, and we view an incremental length dx. Experimental and theoretical studies show that the flow rate through the porous bed is related to the properties of the bed and the difference in head across the incremental length. Mathematically the relation is written

$$Q = -K \frac{dh}{dx} \qquad \text{kg/m}^2\text{-sec} \tag{1-4.1}$$

for the case of one-dimensional flow. This relation, which is known as Darcy's law, states that the flow rate depends on the properties of the porous bed and the slope of the hill down which the water flows. This same equation applies for the case of fluid flow through a packed horizontal pipe, as illustrated in Fig. 1-4.1b.

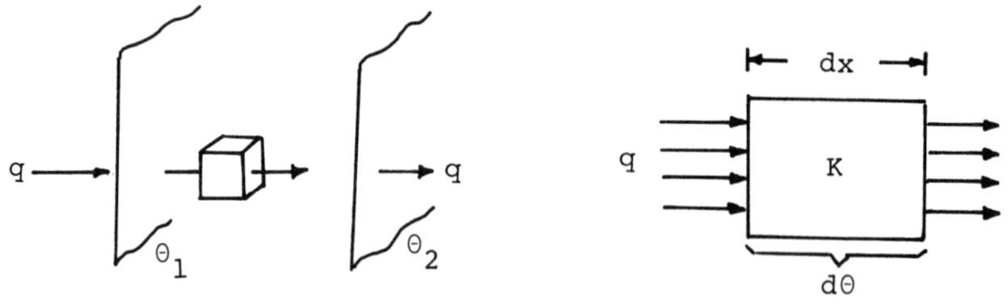

Figure 1-4.2. Heat flow through a heat conducting medium.

Now refer to Fig. 1-4.2. which illustrates a thermal system. It might represent a furnace wall that is maintained at a temperature Θ_1 and which is separated from a heat shield that is assumed to be maintained at temperature Θ_2 by an insulating material of known thickness and properties. Experimental studies show that the heat conduction rate is related to the properties of the material and to the thermal gradient across the insulating material. The relationship, which is known as the Fourier law, is

$$q = -K \frac{d\Theta}{dx} \qquad \text{Joule/m}^2\text{-sec} \tag{1-4.2}$$

for the one-dimensional heat transfer system illustrated.

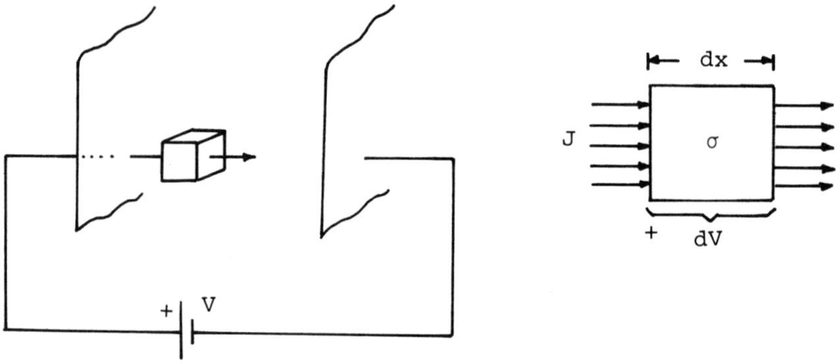

Figure 1-4.3. Electric current through a resistive medium.

As a third example, we consider the electrical problem illustrated in Fig. 1-4.3, which shows two parallel electrical electrodes a distance d apart with a material of electrical *conductivity* σ between them. A voltage source is applied to establish a known difference of electrical potential between the electrodes. Experimental studies show that the current is related to the potential gradient across the conducting medium as described by Ohm's law, which is

$$J = -\sigma \frac{dV}{dx} \qquad \text{Coulomb/m}^2\text{-sec} = \text{Amp/m}^2 \tag{1-4.3}$$

for the one-dimensional current illustrated.

As a fourth example, we consider the one-dimensional diffusion problem described by Fick's law

$$M = -D \frac{d\eta}{dx} \qquad \text{particles/m}^2\text{-sec} \tag{1-4.4}$$

where M is the rate of *particle transport* per unit area, η is the concentration of diffusing constituent and D is the *diffusion constant*. This law relates the diffusion of particles from a region of high concentration or density to one of lower concentration.

As a final example, consider the simple elastic problem illustrated in Fig. 1-4.4 which shows a homogeneous medium under simple tensile stress. In this appli-

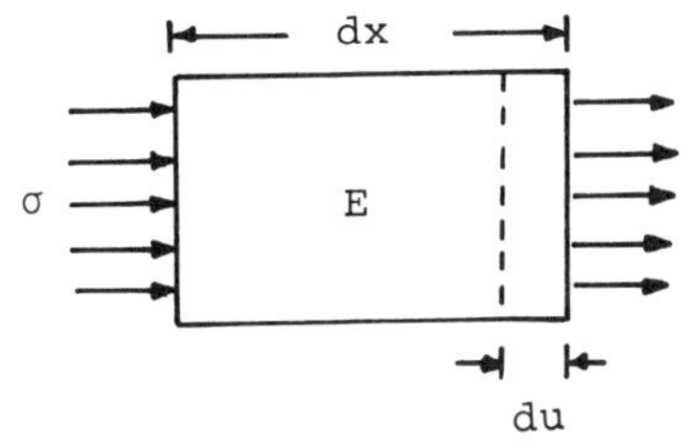

Figure 1-4.4. Elastic expansion of a stressed medium.

cation a tensile stress σ produces a certain elongation $\varepsilon = du/dx$ or *strain*. Below the elastic limit the relationship between stress and strain is given by a simple form of Hooke's law

$$\sigma = E\varepsilon = E \frac{du}{dx} \qquad \text{kg/m}^2 \tag{1-4.5}$$

where E is the *bulk modulus* of elasticity.*

These five examples (and others of similar nature exist) show that a common phenomenon of "diffusion" exists in fluids, heat, electric current, molecular concentration and elastic flow. Moreover, the experimental laws relating the flow (*through*) variable with the potential (*across*) variable have identical form. Consequently these situations are exactly analogous ones, and the study of the field properties of any one of them will allow immediate interpretation for the others. For convenience, we tabulate the analogous quantities in Table 1-4.1.

---

*Repetition of symbols with different meaning is unavoidable when several physical fields are treated simultaneously. However, in context little confusion should result. The symbolism we are using is more or less standard in each area.

Table 1-4.1. Analogous Field Quantities

Area	Variable		Conduction law	Coefficient
	through	across		
Fluid	Q, $\frac{m^3}{m^2\text{-sec}}$	h, meter	$Q = -K \frac{dh}{dx}$	K
Thermal	q, $\frac{\text{Joule}}{m^2\text{-sec}}$	Θ, deg K	$q = -K \frac{d\Theta}{dx}$	K, thermal conductivity
Electric	J, Amp/m^2 = $\frac{\text{Coulomb}}{m^2\text{-sec}}$	V, Volt	$J = -\sigma \frac{dV}{dx}$	σ, conductivity
Particle Transport	M, $\frac{\text{Particle}}{m^2\text{-sec}}$	η, concentration	$M = -D \frac{d\eta}{dx}$	D, diffusion constant
Elastic	σ, $\frac{kg}{m^2}$	u, meter	$\sigma = E \frac{du}{dx}$	E, bulk modulus

1-5. The Current Flow-Field

We wish to study in some detail the properties of the current flow-field. This will be done with the aid of a flux plotter, a device that will allow the field to be mapped experimentally. Flux plotting equipment, which is available commercially, or which can be readily prepared, often consists of a sheet of conducting Teledeltos paper, a paper having a uniform surface conductivity. This paper may be cut to any desired shape to represent a specified configuration. Electrodes of prescribed shape can be attached to the paper in specified positions or painted on with a highly conducting silver paint. By applying a known source of voltage between the electrodes, a current, known as a *conduction* current, will exist between the electrodes. By means of a high impedance voltmeter it is possible to explore the potential distribution over the surface of the conducting sheet. Of course, similar field plotting equipment may consist of a sheet of metal on an insulated support. It might also consist of a nonconducting shallow tank which contains a uniform layer or conducting liquid.

Suppose that a flux plotting assembly consists of a large rectangular conducting surface with small circular electrodes which have been attached to it. If the conducting sheet is sufficiently large, then the system approximates a pair of conducting electrodes immersed in an infinite conducting plane. This assembly is closely analogous to a pair of wires immersed in an infinite conducting medium, a

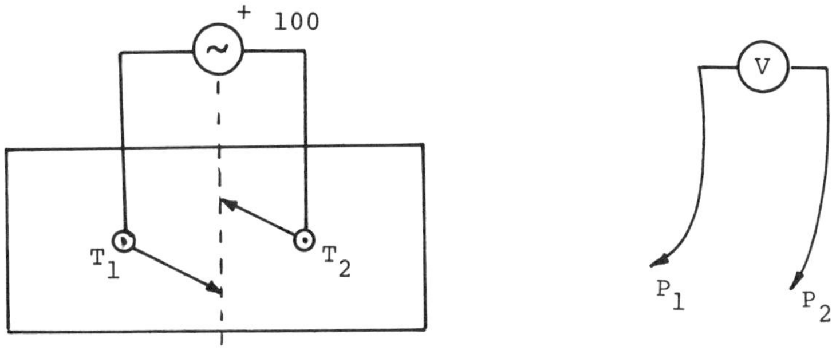

Figure 1-5.1. Flux plotting equipment for the system under survey.

cross section of which is being explored. Analogously, of course, this may also represent corresponding problems in thermal, fluid, or elastic fields, e.g., it could represent two steam pipes embedded in concrete, each pipe being at a different temperature. The geometric situation is substantially that illustrated in Fig. 1-5.1. The electrode terminals are connected to the source of power, and the voltmeter will be used to explore the field. That a potential variation should be expected follows from the fact that a current will exist between the terminals attached to the conducting sheet. It is this current flow field that is to be studied carefully.

Suppose that it is possible to adjust the source so that the indicating voltmeter reads 100 scale divisions when connected between the two electrodes. For convenience, suppose that each scale division is 1 Volt, so that the maximum scale reading is 100 Volt. Suppose now that one of the voltmeter probes, say P_1, is attached to terminal T_1, and it is desired to search for all points on the sheet which will indicate 50 Volt on the voltmeter V (refer to Fig. 1-5.2). By actually performing this experiment, it will be found that the 50 Volt level occurs on the perpendicular bisector of the line between the two terminals T_1 and T_2. Such a result would be expected from the symmetry of the configuration. Clearly, if probe P_1 is placed anywhere along this line and probe P_2 is placed on terminal T_2 a 50-Volt reading will also result.

Now a systematic exploration of the field is to be undertaken. Connect probe P_1 to terminal T_1 and search the field for the curve of 10 Volt by moving probe P_2 over the field. When this has been completed and the curve of the 10 Volt potential difference has been drawn, the process will be repeated for the 20 Volt curve, then the 30 Volt curve, etc., until the entire field has been explored. The curves of constant potential are referred to as *equipotential lines* or curves. A system of curves will result, somewhat as illustrated in Fig. 1-5.2. Clearly, if both probes are applied to two points of the same equipotential, no deflection will be noted on the voltmeter. This is, in fact, the real meaning of the term equipotential.

If the conducting material were of substantial thickness, then points of equal potential difference could be found within the material. These points constitute

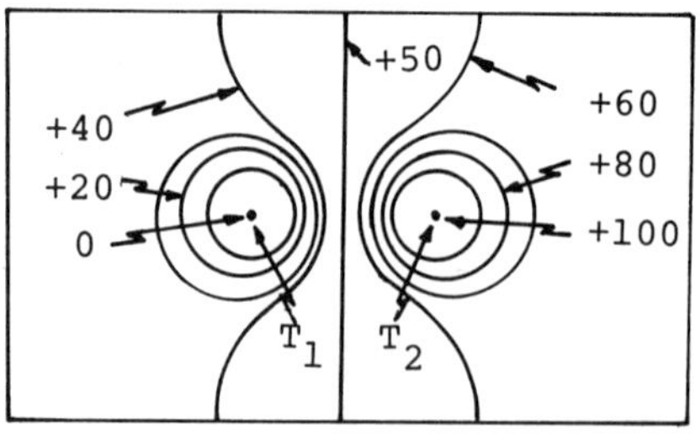

Figure 1-5.2. Equipotential lines in the current field.

surfaces whose base lines are equipotentials on the surface of the sheet. The surfaces are referred to as *equipotential surfaces*. As an extension of the above, there is no difference of potential between any two points on the same equipotential surface.

1-6. Potential and Potential Difference

Each equipotential curve of Fig. 1-5.2 has been labeled with a number which specifies the potential difference relative to T_1 which has been assigned the value zero; T_1 is thus being chosen as the reference or datum of potential. Also, the + sign applied to the numerical value of potential difference has been chosen to be consistent with the designated reference positive potential. Similarly, the reference current direction is here being chosen to coincide with the requirement that the direction of conventional current shall be from a region of higher to a region of lower potential. That is, the current in the conducting sheet will be from T_2 to T_1 when the applied potential difference has the reference polarity. Clearly, if the terminal connections are interchanged, the direction of the current will reverse although the same distribution of equipotentials will result. Now, however, the equipotentials will carry minus signs in order to denote that they are the negatives of the previous values.

The reference point or datum of potential is entirely arbitrary, as all effects depend only on the differences of potential. That is, T_1 may be chosen at any desired reference level without in any way affecting the equipotentials in the field. All that happens is that the equipotentials in the field will either increase or decrease, depending upon the specified reference level of T_1. Conversely, any point of the field may be chosen as the reference point or datum of potential. For example, suppose that a point on the bisector (shown as the +50 Volt curve in Fig. 1-5.2) is chosen as the zero level of potential. In this case, all potential values of Fig. 1-5.2 will be reduced by the constant value of 50 Volt. T_1 will now be designated -50 volts and T_2 will be designated as +50 Volt. All other values will change correspondingly. The potential difference between any two points in the field is independent of the choice of reference level of potential. Clearly, the potential at any point of the field is equal to the potential difference between this point and a reference point.

Consider, therefore, that the potential of a point a of the field is given by the symbol Φ_a relative to some arbitrary point as reference. Correspondingly, the potential of some other point b of the field relative to the same arbitrary reference point is given as Φ_b. The potential difference between these two points is

$$V_{ab} = \Phi_a - \Phi_b \tag{1-6.1}$$

The numerical value given by Eq. (1-6.1) may be positive or negative depending on whether Φ_a is greater or less than Φ_b. To avoid confusion in what follows, V_{ab} will denote the *potential drop* from point a to point b. If, therefore, V_{ab} is negative, this merely means that the potential of point a is less than the potential of point b relative to the same reference point.

1-7. Potential Gradient and Line Integral

In addition to considerations of the potential distribution over the field, it is often convenient to consider the *gradient* of the potential at all points of the field. To understand the meaning of this term consider two adjacent equipotential surfaces, one of which is denoted Φ and the second $\Phi + d\Phi$, as shown in Fig. 1-7.1. Consider a point a on one equipotential and two points b and c on the adjacent equipotential. Point b is chosen to lie along the normal drawn to the equipotential at point a and at a distance $|d\bar{n}| = dn$. The magnitude of the normal $\bar{n}$ will be chosen to be unity, by definition, and in the present case the positive direction of the normal is taken in the direction of increasing potential.

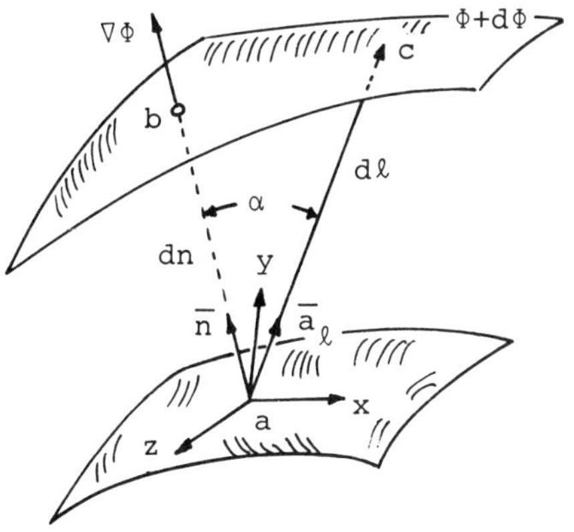

Figure 1-7.1. Adjacent equipotentials in a potential field.

Consider now the quantity $d\Phi/dn$ which specifies the space rate of change of potential in the direction $\bar{n}$. This is the slope or gradient of the potential field at the point $\underline{a}$. $d\Phi/dn$ when written with its associated direction $\bar{n}$ is called the *gradient of the potential*, or in symbols

$$\text{grad } \Phi = \frac{d\Phi}{dn}\bar{n} \tag{1-7.1}$$

Physically therefore, the potential gradient, grad Φ, is a measure of the maximum slope or the maximum rate of change of potential with distance in the direction of increasing potential. For example, if one were to stand on the side of a hill, the gradient would be a measure of the slope at that point in the direction of steepest ascent. In any other direction the slope specifies what is called the *directional derivative* at the point. In the case considered, the gradient is the tangent of the angle between the horizontal and the side of the hill at the point. Often in practice the slope is specified as, say, 1/100. This means that the ground rises 1 m. in each 100 m. of horizontal distance in the specified direction. Note particularly that, since the direction of steepest ascent is specified, the gradient has both magnitude and direction and is a vector quantity. In vector analysis it is usual to write the symbol ∇ instead of the letters *grad*, where the symbol ∇ is called the *del* operator. Using this notation, Eq. (1-7.1) can be written as

$$\text{grad } \Phi = \nabla\Phi = \frac{d\Phi}{dn}\bar{n} \tag{1-7.2}$$

Note further from Fig. 1-7.1 that

$$dn = d\ell \cos\alpha$$

and thus*

$$\frac{d\Phi}{d\ell} = \frac{d\Phi}{dn}\frac{dn}{d\ell} = \frac{d\Phi}{dn}\cos\alpha = \frac{d\Phi}{dn}\frac{\bar{n}\cdot d\bar{\ell}}{d\ell} = \nabla\Phi \cdot \bar{a}_\ell = \frac{\nabla\Phi\cdot d\bar{\ell}}{d\ell} \tag{1-7.3}$$

is the directional derivative of the potential Φ. This is the rate of change of Φ in the particular direction $\bar{a}_\ell$, the direction specified. If a rectangular system of axes were to be specified which was fixed at point $\underline{a}$, then the directional derivative of Φ in the direction of the X-axis would be

$$\frac{\partial\Phi}{\partial x} = |\text{grad } \Phi| \cos\alpha_x = \bar{a}_x \cdot \nabla\Phi$$

where α_x is the angle between $\bar{n}$ and the X axis, with corresponding terms $\partial\Phi/\partial y$ and $\partial\Phi/\partial z$ along the Y and Z directions. For a general direction which possesses

*See Appendix I for a discussion of vector algebra.

components along the three axes, it follows that

$$\text{grad}\ \Phi = \nabla\Phi = \bar{a}_x \frac{\partial\Phi}{\partial x} + \bar{a}_y \frac{\partial\Phi}{\partial y} + \bar{a}_z \frac{\partial\Phi}{\partial z} \tag{1-7.4}$$

The basic laws listed in Table 1-4.1 in general form involve the gradient function.

It is now possible to reverse the foregoing considerations and consider the question of the difference of potential between two points, given the gradient of the potential at a point. According to Eq. (1-7.1) the potential difference is $d\Phi$, so that

$$d\Phi = (\text{grad}\ \Phi)_n\ dn \tag{1-7.5}$$

where the subscript n denotes that the component of grad Φ in the direction $\bar{n}$ is chosen. This is, of course, just grad Φ itself. The total potential difference between the points a and b is given by the expression

$$V_{ba} = \Phi_b - \Phi_a = \int_a^b d\Phi = \int_a^b (\text{grad}\ \Phi)_n\ dn \tag{1-7.6}$$

In general, proceeding from Eq. (1-7.3), this equation then becomes

$$V_{ba} = \int_a^b \nabla\Phi \cdot d\bar{\ell} \tag{1-7.7}$$

In this expression $d\bar{\ell}$ denotes a vector element along path ℓ.

Suppose that the two points a and b now denote any two points of the field, as illustrated in Fig. 1-7.2. The system of lines is to denote equipotentials of the field. The total potential difference between the points a and b along path 1 is simply the summation of the potential differences along all elements of this path. That is

$$V_{ba} = \Phi_b - \Phi_a = \int_{a\ \text{path 1}}^b d\Phi = \int_{a\ \text{path 1}}^b \nabla\Phi \cdot d\bar{\ell} \tag{1-7.8}$$

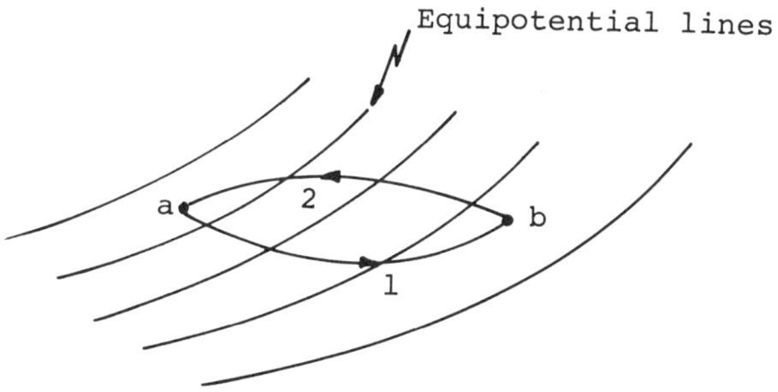

Figure 1-7.2. Line integral of the potential gradient over a closed path.

In a similar way, the total potential difference between points b and a along path 2 is given by the expression

$$V_{ab} = \Phi_a - \Phi_b = \int_{b\ \text{path 2}}^{a} d\Phi = \int_{b\ \text{path 2}}^{a} \nabla\Phi \cdot d\overline{\ell} \tag{1-7.9}$$

These two quantities are the negative of each other, and so

$$V_{ba} = -V_{ab} \tag{1-7.10}$$

The integrals in Eqs. (1-7.8) and (1-7.9) are referred to as the *line integrals* of the potential gradient. In a potential field in which these equations are valid, the line integral is independent of the path of integration and is equal to the difference of the potentials at the two end points of integration. Note that the indicating voltmeter in Fig. 1-5.1 actually measures the line integral of the potential gradient between the two points where the probes are applied.

Attention is called to the fact that the physical fields herein being discussed satisfy the condition

$$\oint_C \nabla\Phi \cdot d\overline{\ell} = 0 \tag{1-7.11}$$

where the symbol $\oint_C$ denotes an integration taken around a complete path. Fields of the type which can be expressed as the gradient of a scalar potential are classified as *conservative, irrotational,* or *curl-free fields*. The significance of the names irrotational or curl-free will become more evident at a later point in our study. The names are chosen to imply that fields are not necessarily conservative, irrotational or curl-free. Nonconservative fields will be studied later.

Example 1-7.1. Find the line integral from P_1 to P_2 when the force field is given by (see Fig. 1-7.3)

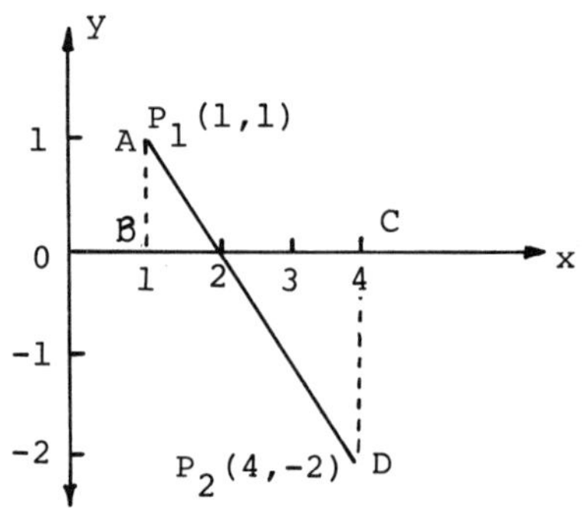

Figure 1-7.3. The integration path for this example.

$$\overline{F}(x,y,z) = \overline{a}_x x^2 + \overline{a}_y y^2 + \overline{a}_z z^2 \tag{1-7.12}$$

Solution: In the present case, the equation of the curve from P_1 to P_2 is

$$y = -x + 2 \tag{1-7.13}$$

If we eliminate y in the expression for $\overline{F}$, we have

$$\overline{F} = x^2 \overline{a}_x + (-x+2)^2 \overline{a}_y \tag{1-7.14}$$

since z = 0 in the XY plane. The element of path length $d\overline{\ell}$ is

$$d\overline{\ell} = dx\ \overline{a}_x + dy\ \overline{a}_y + dz\ \overline{a}_z$$

But in the XY plane dz = 0, and from the equation of the curve we find that dy = -dx. Then

$$d\overline{\ell} = dx\ \overline{a}_x - dx\ \overline{a}_y = (\overline{a}_x - \overline{a}_y)\ dx \tag{1-7.15}$$

Using Eqs. (1-7.14) and (1-7.15) we write that

$$I = \int_{P_1}^{P_2} \overline{F} \cdot d\overline{\ell} = \int_1^4 [x^2\ \overline{a}_x + (-x+2)^2\ \overline{a}_y] \cdot [\overline{a}_x - \overline{a}_y]\ dx$$
$$= \int_1^4 [x^2 - (-x+2)^2]\ dx = (2x^2 - 4x)\Big|_1^4 = 18 \tag{1-7.16}$$

We can follow the path ABCD in this integration, and we now have

$$I = \int_A^B + \int_B^C + \int_C^D = \int_A^B \overline{F} \cdot (-\overline{a}_y dy) + \int_B^C \overline{F} \cdot (\overline{a}_x dx) + \int_C^D \overline{F} \cdot (-\overline{a}_y dy)$$
$$= \int_0^1 (-)y^2 dy + \int_1^4 x^2 dx + \int_{-2}^0 (-)y^2 dy = -\frac{1}{3} + \frac{63}{3} - \frac{8}{3} = 18 \tag{1-7.17}$$

ΔΔΔ

This example shows that in evaluating line integrals *either, but not both,* of the following two procedures can be used:

1. Include the direction of integration in the expression for $d\overline{\ell}$ and integrate from the smallest algebraic value of the coordinate to the larger value.
2. Use a general expression for $d\overline{\ell}$ without regard to the direction of integration. Introduce the direction of traversal of the path by using the initial and final points of the path as the lower and upper limits of integration, respectively.

1-8. Current and Flow Fields

Consider a small area dS on an equipotential surface, as shown in Fig. 1-8.1, and this is supposed to be one of the equipotentials of Fig. 1-5.2. If the total current from electrode to electrode is denoted I, then a portion dI of the total current passes through this area. The magnitude of the *current density* $\overline{J}$ is the quantity

$$J = \frac{dI}{dS} \qquad \text{Amp/m}^2 \tag{1-8.1}$$

which is assumed constant over the surface element dS. The current density can be represented as the density of so-called *current lines* or *current flux* lines if one chooses the arbitrary convention that the number of flux lines passing through the element of area dS of the equipotential surface is proportional to the current intensity per unit area. If the flux lines converge, this signifies that the current is increasing. Should the flux lines diverge, this signifies that the current density is decreasing. This general representation of flow or flux densities by line densities is often used in describing field phenomena.

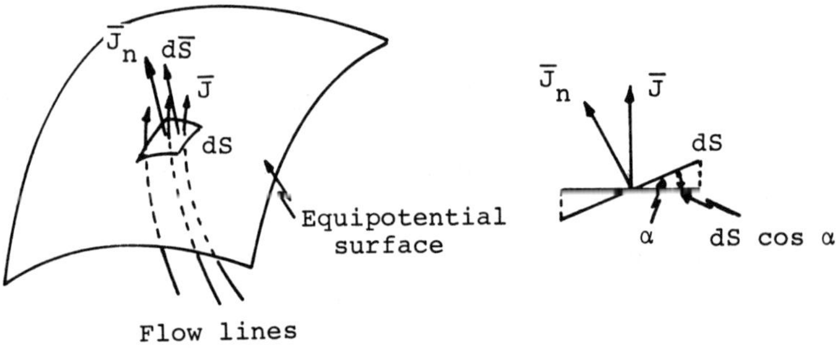

Figure 1-8.1. Current lines through a surface element.

Now refer to Fig. 1-8.2 which represents the flux plotting equipment of Fig. 1-5.2. It is apparent that the current density may have a different direction at every point in the field. It is convenient to interpret the current density as a vector which indicates the direction of the current at any point in space. Refer again to Fig. 1-8.1, which represents a bundle of current flux lines passing through an element of area dS of an equipotential surface. Since dS denotes a very minute area, the current passing through it is to be homogeneous and constant. The current flow lines will be normal to the equipotentials. This statement is not obvious but its validity is established by stream-function consideration (see Sec. 2-4).

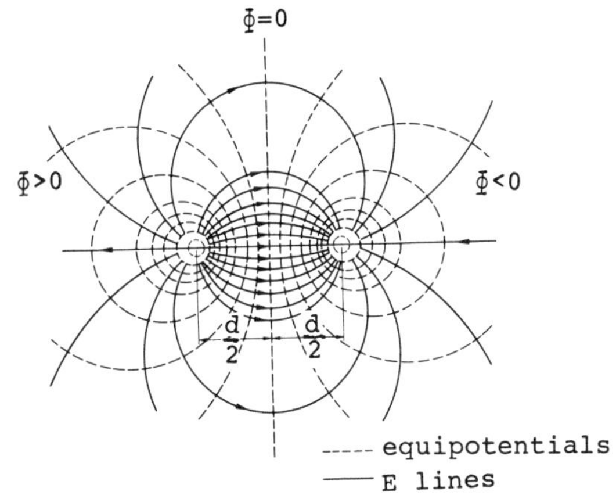

Figure 1-8.2. Current flow lines of the current field.

Suppose that the area dS is now turned through a small angle α relative to its original position. In this case, the element of area is no longer on an equipotential surface. The number of current lines, and so the current through the element of area dS, will be reduced. The current will be proportional to the projection (dS cos α) of the area dS on its original position on the equipotential. Thus in this case

$$dI = J \cos \alpha \, dS = J_n \, dS = \bar{J} \cdot d\bar{S} \tag{1-8.2}$$

where $d\bar{S} = \bar{n}\, dS$ is the vector representation of the element of area dS, and $\bar{n}$ is the unit normal giving a specific direction for the area. It then follows from Eq. (1-8.2) that

$$I = \int_S J_n \, dS = \int_S \bar{J} \cdot \bar{n} \, dS = \int_S \bar{J} \cdot d\bar{S} \tag{1-8.3}$$

1-9. Electric Field Intensity

It is convenient to define a vector function $\bar{E}$, called the *electric field intensity*, which is the negative of the potential gradient; thus

$$\bar{E} = -\text{grad}\, \Phi = -\nabla\Phi \qquad \text{Volt/m} \tag{1-9.1}$$

The current density vector $\bar{J}$ is parallel to $\nabla\Phi$, and the vectors $\bar{J}$ and $\bar{E}$ are in the same direction. But two related vectors which have the same direction are related by a constant factor which gives the ratio of their magnitudes. This is written in the present case as

$$\overline{J} = \sigma \overline{E} \tag{1-9.2}$$

where σ, the proportionality constant, is the electrical conductivity of the medium. This formula is Ohm's law and was first introduced in Eq. (1-4.3).

The line integral of the field $\overline{E}$ between two points is given by

$$\int_{P_1}^{P_2} \overline{E} \cdot d\overline{\ell} = -\int_{P_1}^{P_2} \nabla\Phi \cdot d\overline{\ell} = -\int_{P_1}^{P_2} \frac{d\Phi}{dn}\overline{n} \cdot d\overline{\ell} = -\int_{P_1}^{P_2} \frac{d\Phi}{d\ell}\, d\ell = -\int_{P_1}^{P_2} d\Phi$$

$$V_{21} = \Phi_{P_2} - \Phi_{P_1} = -\int_{P_1}^{P_2} \overline{E} \cdot d\overline{\ell} \tag{1-9.3}$$

This constitutes one of the fundamental equations in electromagnetic field theory. We shall use this result on a number of different occasions.

1-10. Properties of the Flow Field

It is now possible to formulate other properties of flow fields. A very important property of such a field is given by the Kirchhoff current law, KCL. This law states that a *stationary* electric current behaves like an incompressible fluid; that is, current is neither created nor destroyed in the absence of sources or sinks. This means that if a closed surface is chosen in a multidimensional flow field, then the total current into the region bounded by the closed surface must be exactly equal to the total current leaving the region. Alternatively, this result may be expressed in the following way: the algebraic sum of the currents entering any finite closed surface in the multidimensional field must be zero. If the flow comprises a group of filamentary conductors connected at a junction instead of the continuous space distribution then the total current to the junction, assuming that a closed surface contains this junction, must be zero (Kirchhoff's current law in circuit theory). It will later be found that the foregoing must be modified if nonstationary or time-varying currents exist.

This theorem may be formulated mathematically by reference to Fig. 1-10.1. The current density vector $\overline{J}$ over the surface area $d\overline{S}$ is considered constant. Since the total current passing through an element of area dS is, by Eq. (1-8.2)

$$dI = J_n\, dS = \overline{J} \cdot \overline{n}\, dS$$

the current passing through the entire closed surface is zero by the Kirchhoff current law, or

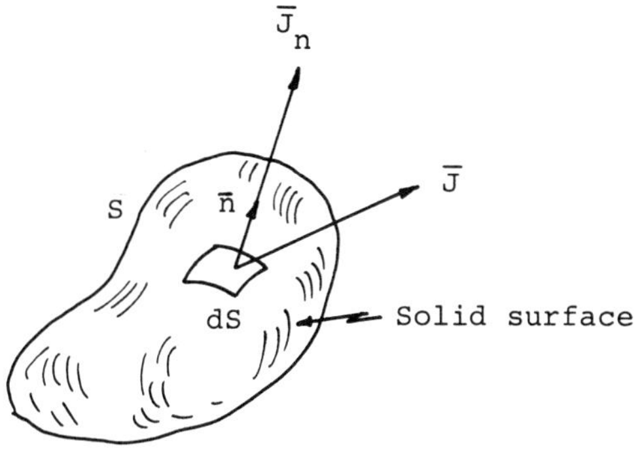

Figure 1-10.1. Vector representation of an area and current density.

$$\oint_S \bar{J} \cdot \bar{n} \, dS = 0 \tag{1-10.1}$$

where $\oint_S$ denotes that the integration is to be carried out over the entire closed surface which defines a volume in the multidimensional space. The difference between this expression and that in Eq. (1-8.3) must be clearly understood since they represent quite different quantities.

Equation (1-10.1) is an integral representation of the fact that the current (flux of current) is incompressible. A differential representation of this same fact is possible. To determine this, we shall select a particular surface, in this case a rectangular parallelopiped, as shown in Fig. 1-10.2. We now wish to apply Eq. (1-10.1) to this particular region within the current field. We do this by first considering the pair of faces shown. We can write directly the following:

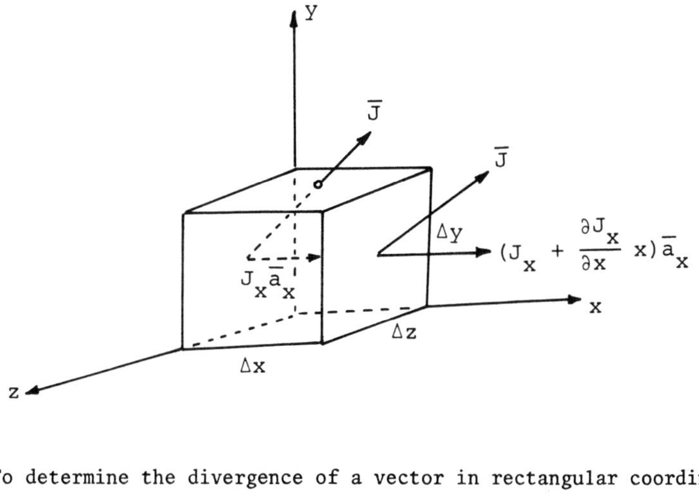

Figure 1-10.2. To determine the divergence of a vector in rectangular coordinates.

1. The flux of current into the volume element in the X-direction is $J_x \Delta y \Delta z$ where J_x is the current density in the X-direction and $\Delta y \Delta z$ is the area of the parallelopiped face.
2. The flux of current out of the volume element in the X-direction can be written from a knowledge of the current density at the second face. This current density can be written in terms of that at the first face by means of a Taylor expansion relative to a point on the first face. Now, because the second point is a differential distance Δx away from the first point, we retain only the leading terms in the Taylor expansion. The flux of current at the second face is thus $(J_x + \frac{\partial J_x}{\partial x} \Delta x)\Delta y \Delta z$.
3. The net contribution to the flux of current from sources, if any, within the volume element will be the difference between the outward and inward flows, thus the net contribution to the current flux from sources in the volume element = $\frac{\partial J_x}{\partial x} \Delta x \Delta y \Delta z$. For the geometry selected, the partial derivative is evaluated at the left face.

An entirely similar procedure allows an evaluation of the net contribution to the flux from sources in the volume element through the other two pairs of faces. The results are $(\frac{\partial J_y}{\partial y} \Delta y \Delta x \Delta z)$ and $(\frac{\partial J_z}{\partial z} \Delta z \Delta x \Delta y)$, respectively. The total change of current flux from sources in the volume element is written

$$\oint_{\Delta S} \bar{J} \cdot \bar{n}\, dS = \left(\frac{\partial J_x}{\partial x} + \frac{\partial J_y}{\partial y} + \frac{\partial J_z}{\partial z} \right) \Delta x \Delta y \Delta z \tag{1-10.2}$$

where ΔS denotes the closed surface of the parallelopiped.

If we divide Eq. (1-10.2) by $\Delta x \Delta y \Delta z$ and shrink the volume element $\Delta x \Delta y \Delta z$ to zero, the left hand side becomes the net output flow per unit volume at the *point* corresponding to the center of the volume element. This is written

$$\text{div } \bar{J} = \lim_{\Delta V \to 0} \frac{\oint_{\Delta S} \bar{J} \cdot \bar{n}\, dS}{\Delta V} = \frac{\partial J_x}{\partial x} + \frac{\partial J_y}{\partial y} + \frac{\partial J_z}{\partial z} \tag{1-10.3}$$

The *divergence* (div) may be thought of as equal to the rate of increase of lines of flow per unit volume. Thus div $\bar{J}$ is a scalar field which, at each point, is a measure of the strength of the source of the vector field $\bar{J}$ at that point. However, for the stationary current flow field which we are examining, we can show by Eq. (1-10.1) that

$$\text{div } \bar{J} = 0 \tag{1-10.4}$$

since for a region without sources the rate of increase of lines of flow per unit volume will be zero. Eq. (1-10.4) is the point statement that describes the field that is described in integral form by Eq. (1-10.1). A vector $\bar{A}$ for which its divergence is zero is sometimes referred to as a *solenoidal* vector.

Reference is made to Eq. (1-7.4) which introduced the del operator

$$\nabla = \bar{a}_x \frac{\partial}{\partial x} + \bar{a}_y \frac{\partial}{\partial y} + \bar{a}_z \frac{\partial}{\partial z} \tag{1-10.5}$$

Since we chose a rectangular configuration with

$$\bar{J} = \bar{a}_x J_x + \bar{a}_y J_y + \bar{a}_z J_z \tag{1-10.6}$$

this allows us to write:

$$\begin{aligned} \text{div } \bar{J} = \nabla \cdot \bar{J} &= (\bar{a}_x \frac{\partial}{\partial x} + \bar{a}_y \frac{\partial}{\partial y} + \bar{a}_z \frac{\partial}{\partial z}) \cdot (\bar{a}_x J_x + \bar{a}_y J_y + \bar{a}_z J_z) \\ &= \frac{\partial J_x}{\partial x} + \frac{\partial J_y}{\partial y} + \frac{\partial J_z}{\partial z} = 0 \end{aligned} \tag{1-10.7}$$

as the differential statement of the Kirchhoff current law.

A very important result known as the *divergence theorem* follows from Eq. (1-10.3). This is the relationship

$$\oint_S \bar{J} \cdot \bar{n} \, dS = \int_V \text{div } \bar{J} \, dV = \int_V \nabla \cdot \bar{J} \, dV \tag{1-10.8}$$

This is a transformation integral which permits the integral of the normal components of a vector field over a surface S to be expressed in terms of the volume integral of the derivatives of the components of the vector field, where the volume V is that enclosed by the given surface S.

We now refer to Eqs. (1-9.1) and (1-9.2) which are combined to

$$\nabla \cdot \bar{J} = \nabla \cdot \sigma \bar{E} = -\sigma\nabla \cdot \nabla\Phi = -\sigma\nabla^2\Phi \tag{1-10.9}$$

We have here defined the symbol $\nabla^2 \triangleq \nabla\cdot\nabla$. This will permit us to find an explicit form for ∇^2. We find directly

$$\begin{aligned} \nabla \cdot \nabla\Phi &= (\bar{a}_x \frac{\partial}{\partial x} + \bar{a}_y \frac{\partial}{\partial y} + \bar{a}_z \frac{\partial}{\partial z}) \cdot (\bar{a}_x \frac{\partial\Phi}{\partial x} + \bar{a}_y \frac{\partial\Phi}{\partial y} + \bar{a}_z \frac{\partial\Phi}{\partial z}) \\ &= \frac{\partial^2\Phi}{\partial x^2} + \frac{\partial^2\Phi}{\partial y^2} + \frac{\partial^2\Phi}{\partial z^2} \end{aligned}$$

The same result is obtained if we think of $\nabla \cdot \nabla$ as a new operator ∇^2 with the representation in rectangular coordinates

$$\nabla^2 = \frac{\partial^2}{\partial x^2} + \frac{\partial^2}{\partial y^2} + \frac{\partial^2}{\partial z^2} \tag{1-10.10}$$

The operator ∇^2 is called the *Laplacian*, and it is a scalar operator. We see that for the stationary current flow field

$$\nabla^2\Phi = 0 \tag{1-10.11}$$

This is known as *Laplace's equation*.

This development shows that Laplace's equation will provide a description of the potential field distribution of static field problems. Further details of Laplace's equation and techniques for its solution will be deferred until Chaps. 3 and 4 when we shall examine these techniques in some detail. Particular attention is called to the fact that the experimental technique which was used to explore the potential and flow field for the example which has been the basis of our study did, in fact, yield a potential distribution which is a solution of Laplace's equation for the particular geometry of our problem. Note specifically, therefore, that the results using teledeltos paper give a solution to Laplace's equation.

1-11. Simple Sources

In the foregoing sections we developed the general properties of conservative fields. We now proceed to a study of distributions which can be described analytically, as a basis for expanding our understanding of static fields. We note that source distributions are ordinarily of finite extent and are continuous over their dimensions. It is convenient from a mathematical standpoint to assume that the source distribution is discontinuous. In particular, we shall consider here the characteristics of fields which are set up by point sources, since we can then properly superimpose such point sources to arrive at an arbitrary source distribution.

Example 1-11.1. An infinitely thin insulated wire provides current to a conducting sphere which is embedded in a homogeneous, poorly conducting material, as shown in Fig. 1-11.1. Find the potential distribution and the flow characteristics of the field.

Solution: From considerations of symmetry, we see that the current density at a distance r from the center of the electrode is

$$\overline{J} = \frac{I}{4\pi r^2}\,\overline{a}_r \tag{1-11.1}$$

Note that the Kirchhoff current law (conservation of charge) has been invoked since the total current from the electrode is assumed to pass through a spherical surface at a distance r. The electric field intensity in the conducting medium is obtained from $\overline{J}$ by Ohm's law ($\overline{J} = \sigma\overline{E}$) and is

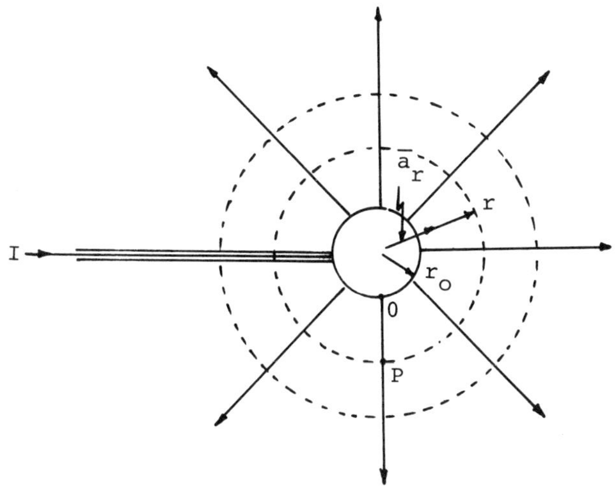

Figure 1-11.1. Current flow in the neighborhood of a spherical electrode embedded in a homogeneous conducting medium.

$$\bar{E} = \frac{\bar{J}}{\sigma} = \frac{I}{4\pi r^2 \sigma} \bar{a}_r \tag{1-11.2}$$

The potential difference between the surface of the metallic sphere and any field point P in the region at a distance r from the center of the electrode can be determined using Eq. (1-9.3). This is given by

$$V_{PO} = -\int_{r_o}^{r} \bar{E} \cdot d\bar{r} = -\frac{I}{4\pi\sigma} \int_{r_o}^{r} \frac{dr}{r^2}$$

or

$$V_{OP} = \frac{I}{4\pi\sigma} \left(\frac{1}{r_o} - \frac{1}{r}\right) \tag{1-11.3}$$

It is interesting to note that the potential difference between the metallic sphere and an arbitrary point P approaches a limiting value as the distance r increases. The limiting value of this potential difference is

$$V_O = \frac{I}{4\pi\sigma r_o} \tag{1-11.4}$$

This value is correct within 1 percent if the point P is $100r_o$ from the center of the metallic sphere.

For the potential difference between the electrode and a point at a distance r therefrom, Eq. (1-11.3) can be combined with Eq. (1-11.4) to give the potential difference V_{OP} in terms of the total potential difference V_O. The result is

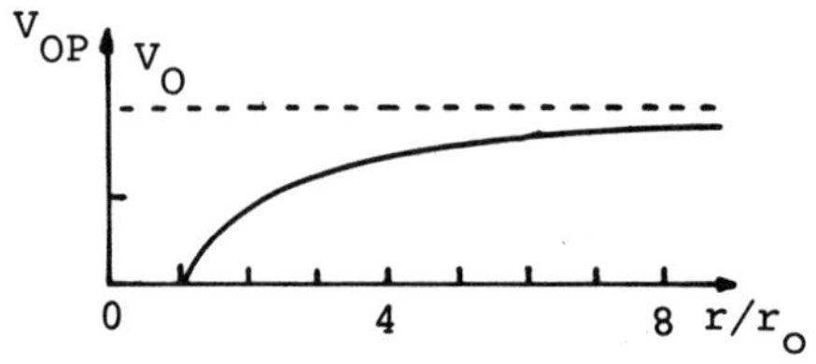

Figure 1-11.2. Potential in the neighborhood of a spherical electrode.

$$V_{OP} = V_0 \left(1 - \frac{r_o}{r} \right) \tag{1-11.5}$$

This function has the form shown in Fig. 1-11.2.

It is convenient to find an expression for the potential at any point of the field. According to our previous discussion, this is equal to the potential difference between this point and a reference point. From Eq. (1-11.3) it appears that the potential of any point at a distance r from the center of the spherical electrode is

$$\Phi = \frac{I}{4\pi\sigma r} + k \tag{1-11.6}$$

where k is an arbitrary constant. Observe that at large distances the potential Φ is just equal to k. Therefore k is the potential of a point at a large distance from the electrode. If this remote point is chosen as the zero or datum, then the potential at any point in space is simply

$$\Phi = \frac{I}{4\pi\sigma r} \tag{1-11.7}$$

This formula shows that Φ is independent of the radius of the electrode, and this is true even for a point electrode for which $r_o \to 0$.

ΔΔΔ

Example 1-11.2. Consider two point electrodes that are embedded in a homogeneous and isotropic medium of conductivity σ and which are separated by a distance L. Suppose also that a current I is conducted to one electrode, designated as Q_1, and the current is conducted away from the second electrode Q_2. It is required to find the equipotential distribution in the medium.

Solution: The geometry of the system is illustrated in Fig. 1-11.3. The potential at the point P is obtained by combining the potentials at P due to each electrode separately. This simple procedure for combining potentials is possible because of the *linear* relationship that exists between the current and the potential. This allows simple linear superposition of the effects of each electrode. This is a broad principle that applies for linear systems and is known as the *superposition* principle. The potential at point P is given by:

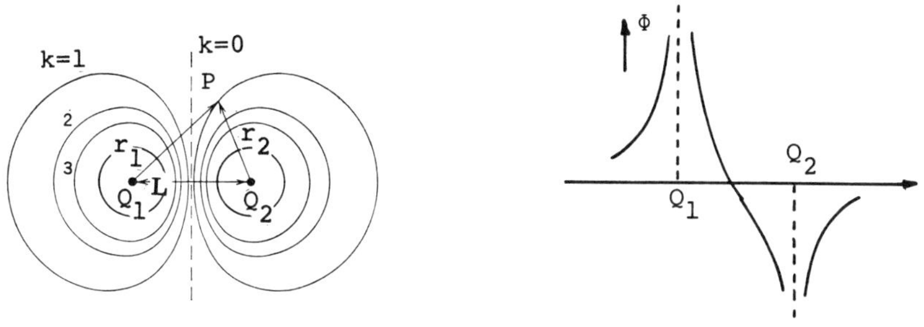

Figure 1-11.3. Equipotentials of two point charges of opposite sense.

$$\Phi_P = \frac{I}{4\pi\sigma}\left(\frac{1}{r_1} - \frac{1}{r_2}\right) \tag{1-11.8}$$

To find the equipotential surfaces, it is recalled that these must satisfy the condition that Φ = constant over the equipotential surface. This permits us to write

$$\frac{1}{r_1} - \frac{1}{r_2} = \frac{4\pi\sigma\Phi}{I} = \frac{k}{L} \tag{1-11.9}$$

where k is a constant. It follows from this that

$$r_1 = \frac{r_2}{1 + kr_2/L} \tag{1-11.10}$$

This equation relates the distance from each source to the equipotential surfaces and allows these surfaces to be drawn. If k is given the values k = 0,1,2... equipotential surfaces having equal potential differences will result. Fig. 1-11.3 gives a sketch of these potential surfaces. ΔΔΔ

Example 1-11.3. As an extension of Ex. 1-11.1, consider the line source illustrated in Fig. 1-11.4 to be embedded in a homogeneous, infinite, conducting

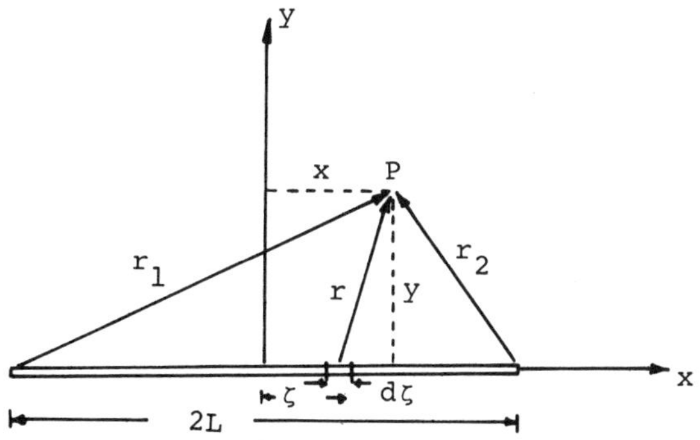

Figure 1-11.4. A line source.

medium. It is required to find an expression for the potential at any point P and the equipotential surfaces.

Solution: To solve the problem it is supposed that the line source is a continuous and uniform current leak away from the conductor, and that this can be resolved into an array of point sources which are in a line and spaced at infinitely small distances. In particular, it is supposed that the line source can be resolved into a large number of very small line elements $d\zeta$, each of which is considered as constituting a point source. If the total current supplied by the line is I, then the current supplied by the element $d\zeta$ is $I\, d\zeta/2L$, where 2L is the total length of the line, as illustrated.

The potential at point P due to the current element $I\, d\zeta/2L$ is given by

$$d\Phi = \frac{Id\zeta}{2L}\,\frac{1}{4\pi\sigma r}$$

which, by making use of the geometry of the figure, can be expressed as

$$d\Phi = \frac{I}{8\pi\sigma L}\,\frac{d\zeta}{\sqrt{(x-\zeta)^2 + y^2}} \tag{1-11.11}$$

where ζ is the distance from the origin to the line element $d\zeta$. The total potential of the line source at point P is obtained directly as

$$\Phi = \frac{I}{8\pi\sigma L}\int_{-L}^{L}\frac{d\zeta}{\sqrt{(x-\zeta)^2 + y^2}}$$

which integrates to the expression

$$\Phi = \frac{I}{8\pi\sigma L}\ln\frac{(x+L) + \sqrt{(x+L)^2 + y^2}}{(x-L) + \sqrt{(x-L)^2 + y^2}} \tag{1-11.12}$$

The equipotential lines in the XY plane are ellipses if we set $r_1 + r_2 = 2a$, where a is the semimajor axis and where the foci are at the end points of the line 2L (refer to any book on analytic geometry). In this case

$$\begin{aligned} r_1 &= a + \frac{xL}{a} = \sqrt{(x+L)^2 + y^2} \\ r_2 &= a - \frac{xL}{a} = \sqrt{(x-L)^2 + y^2} \end{aligned} \tag{1-11.13}$$

If these are introduced into Eq. (1-11.12) the expression for the potential becomes

$$\Phi = \frac{I}{8\pi\sigma L}\ln\frac{a+L}{a-L} \tag{1-11.14}$$

Clearly, for each arbitrary value of a, the potential will be a constant. Owing to

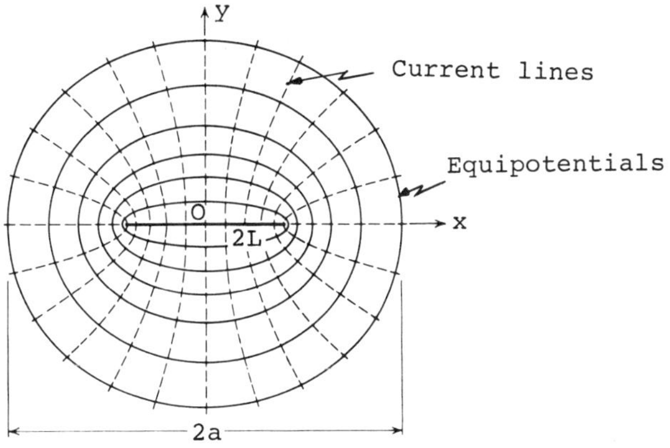

Figure 1-11.5. Equipotential and current flow lines for the line source.

symmetry, it is clear that the equipotential surfaces are ellipsoids of revolution which are obtained by rotating the ellipses about the X-axis. Also, the current lines, which must be normal to the ellipsoids, are hyperboloids of two sheets having the same foci as the equipotential ellipsoids. The equipotential ellipses and the current flow hyperbolas are shown in Fig. 1-11.5. ΔΔΔ

Example 1-11.4. Consider a coaxial cable that is long compared with the spacing between the inner and outer electrodes, as shown in Fig. 1-11.6. Find expressions for the field lines and the potential for a current, I, between the two electrodes. The medium between the two electrodes has a conductivity σ.

Solution: The potential distribution will be substantially that due to a cylindrical electrode with rounded ends, but with a specified potential at the outer boundary of the field. The situation will be somewhat like that in Example 1-11.3, but with equipotential surfaces that will be nearly cylindrical in shape, except at

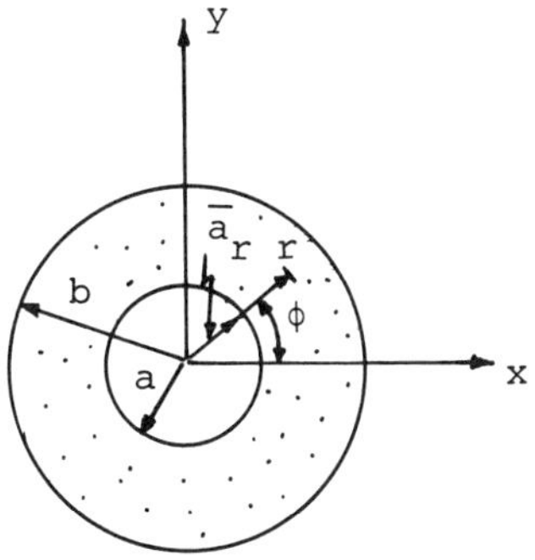

Figure 1-11.6. Two coaxial cylinders.

the ends. The current will be uniform in the radial direction over the whole length of the cylinder through each equipotential surface. However, because of the symmetry of the field, the current density will be

$$\bar{J} = \frac{I}{2\pi r L}\,\bar{a}_r \qquad \text{Amp/m}^2 \tag{1-11.15}$$

The current density vector will be directed outward if the current is out of the line conductor.

The electric field intensity is given by

$$\bar{E} = \frac{1}{\sigma}\,\bar{J} = \frac{I}{2\pi\sigma L}\,\frac{1}{r}\,\bar{a}_r \tag{1-11.16}$$

Therefore, the potential difference between the inner conductor (radius a) and the outer conductor (radius b) will be given by

$$V_{ab} = \int_a^b \bar{E}\cdot d\bar{r} = \frac{I}{2\pi\sigma L}\ln\frac{b}{a} \tag{1-11.17}$$

Attention is again called to the differences in formulas for the electric field intensity and potential variations for point sources and line sources. For the point source these are respectively $1/r^2$ and $1/r$ variations, whereas for the line source these are $1/r$ and $\ln r$ variations. It is for these reasons that Figs. 1-5.2 and 1-11.3, even though they show somewhat similar type of variation, are in fact quite different.

ΔΔΔ

REVIEW QUESTIONS

1. What does field analysis seek to accomplish?
2. When is a field called static and when is it called dynamic?
3. Give several examples of scalar and of vector fields.
4. What is the common phenomenon which exists in fluids, heat, electric current, molecular concentration, and elastic flow?
5. If the two terminals of a voltmeter are set on two equipotential lines of values 115 and 132, what will be the reading of the instrument?
6. What is the difference between equipotential lines and equipotential surfaces?
7. Define the scalar and the vector product of two vectors.
8. Explain the meaning of the gradient $\nabla\Phi$ of a scalar.
9. What is a directional derivative?
10. How do we define an irrotational field?
11. At what angle do the current lines cut the equipotential lines?
12. Define the electric field intensity $\bar{E}$. Is the field $\bar{E}$ perpendicular or parallel to the current lines?

13. What is the physical meaning of the divergence of a vector field?
14. State the divergence theorem.
15. Write Laplace's equation.

PROBLEMS

1-7.1. The potential distribution is given by $\Phi = 3x + 2y^2$. What is the expression for $\nabla\Phi$? What is the directional derivative in the X-direction at the points (1,1) and (1,3)?

1-7.2. The potential distribution is given by $\Phi = 3r^{-1} + r$. Find $\nabla\Phi$ at the point (1,1,1) and its direction with respect to the positive Z-axis. [Hint: $r = (x^2+y^2+z^2)^{1/2}$.]

1-7.3. Find the line integral from $P_1(1,2)$ to $P_2(2,4)$ when the nonconservative force field is given by $\overline{F}(x,y) = (x^2+y^2)\overline{a}_x + 3\overline{a}_y$. (a) Choose the straight line from P_1 to P_2, and (b) follow the path $(1,2) \rightarrow (2,2) \rightarrow (2,4)$.

1-7.4. Show that the following relations are true: $\nabla(\Phi_1+\Phi_2) = \nabla\Phi_1 + \nabla\Phi_2$, and $\nabla(\Phi_1\Phi_2) = \Phi_1\nabla\Phi_2 + \Phi_2\nabla\Phi_1$, where $\Phi_1 = \Phi_1(x,y,z)$ and $\Phi_2 = \Phi_2(x,y,z)$.

1-7.5. Show that

$$\nabla\left(\frac{1}{r}\right) = +\frac{\overline{a}_r}{r^2} \quad \text{and} \quad \nabla'\left(\frac{1}{r}\right) = -\frac{\overline{a}_r}{r^2}$$

if $\overline{a}_r$ is a unit vector from the point (x,y,z) to the point (x',y',z'). The prime sign on the del operator indicates differentiation with respect to the independent variables x', y' and z'.

1-8.1. If the potential distribution is given by $\Phi = 3x + y^2 + z$, find the current density and its direction at the point (1,1,1) of a medium with conductivity $\sigma = 0.5$ mhos/m.

1-8.2. A constant current exists between two perfect conductors attached to a thin conducting sheet of conductivity σ. Show explicitly that $\oint \overline{E} \cdot d\overline{\ell} = 0$ around a circle and an isosceles triangle.

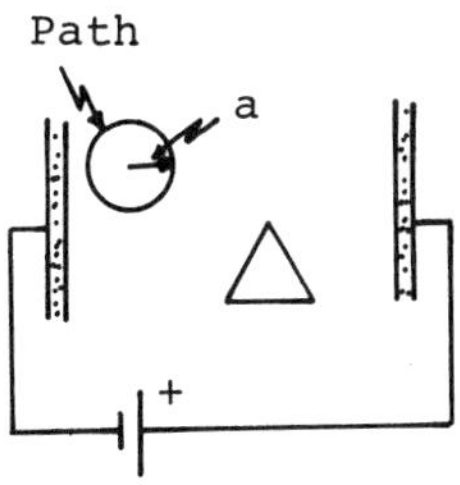

Figure P1-8.2.

1-9.1. The electric field $\overline{E}$ of a radio wave in the sea is 100 microvolt/m. Determine the current density due to this wave. σ of sea water $\doteq 5 \frac{\text{mho}}{\text{m}}$.

1-9.2. (a) Show that the steady state heat flow in three dimensions is governed by the equation $\overline{q} = -K\nabla\Theta$, which is a generalization of Eq. (1-4.2).

(b) Find the heat flow per unit length from a long cylinder of radius a kept at a temperature Θ_1 and which is placed along the axis of a second cylinder of radius b maintained at a temperature Θ_2. The material between the cylinders has a thermal conductivity K.

(c) Find the temperature distribution between the cylinders. Refer to Fig. P1-9.2.

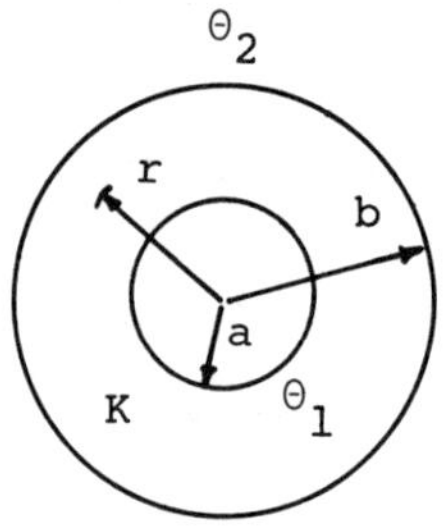

Figure P1-9.2.

1-9.3. Find the resistance of a composite disc made of two different conducting media as shown in Fig. P1-9.3. The current I enters at the center by means of a small wire and leaves uniformly via the edge of the disc.

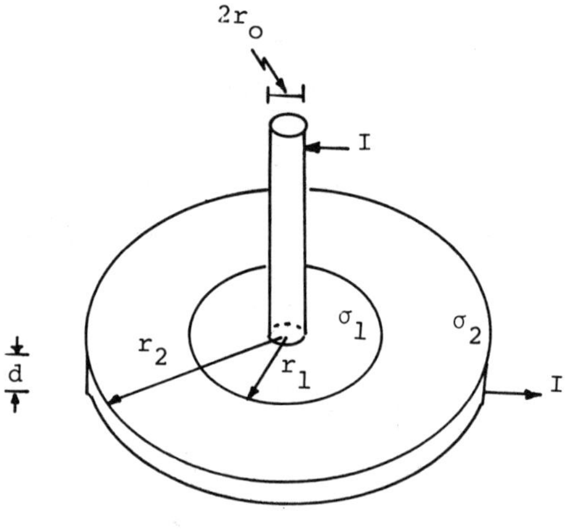

Figure P1-9.3.

1-9.4. Find the resistance of a homogeneous poorly conducting material if a current I exists between two hemispherical electrodes shown in the figure.

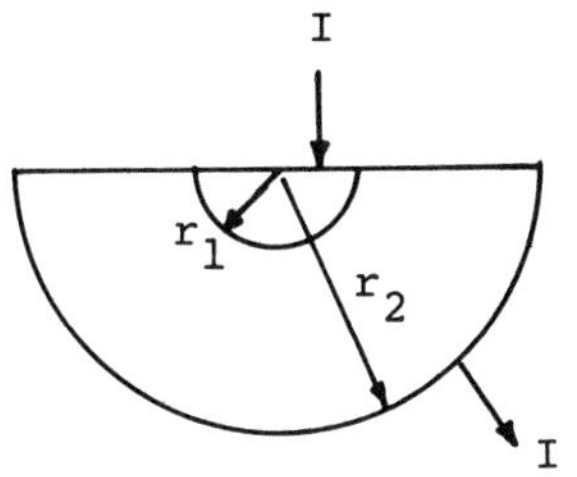

Figure P1-9.4.

[Ans: $\frac{1}{2\pi\sigma}\left(\frac{1}{r_1} - \frac{1}{r_2}\right)$]

1-10.1. Find the divergence of the following vectors at points (0,0,0) and (1,1,1)

a. $\overline{J} = (3x + 1)\overline{a}_x + (y^2 + 1)z\overline{a}_y + 4z\overline{a}_z$

b. $\overline{J} = 3yz\,\overline{a}_x + (2y + x)\overline{a}_y + (x + z)\overline{a}_z$

c. $\overline{J} = 2x\overline{a}_x + (x + y)\overline{a}_y + z^3\overline{a}_z$

1-10.2. Find the divergence of the vector fields at the two points in Prob. 1-10.1 by using the definition

$$\lim_{\Delta V \to 0} \frac{\oint_S \overline{J} \cdot d\overline{S}}{\Delta V}$$

The surface S belongs to cubes centered at those two points and having sides 1, 0.5, 0.1, 0.01.

1-11.1. A long conducting wire of radius 1 mm. and conductivity $\sigma = 10^7$ mho/m has a steady axial current of 100 Amp. through it. The rate of heat generation will be I^2R Watt by Joule's law, where R is the resistance per unit length. The wire is surrounded by a porcelain insulating jacket of radius 2mm. The outside of the jacket is maintained at a temperature of 30° C. The thermal conductivity of the porcelain jacket is 1 Watt/m^2-$^\circ$C/m, i.e., $K = 1\,\frac{\text{Watt}}{m^2}\,\frac{1}{{}^\circ C/m} = 1$ Watt/m-$^\circ$C. Find the steady state temperature of the wire in order that the heat flow from the wire in the radial direction per unit length will equal the rate of heat generation.

1-11.2. Two coaxial cylinders as illustrated in Fig. 1-11.6 have a potential difference V_o between them, i.e., the inner cylinder is at a potential V_o and the outer cylinder is at zero potential. The potential field between the cylinders is a solution of Laplace's equation $\nabla^2\Phi = 0$. This equation becomes an ordinary differential equation when Φ is independent of the angle ϕ and the axial coordinate Z, i.e., $\frac{1}{r}\frac{\partial}{\partial r}(r\frac{\partial\Phi}{\partial r}) = 0$. Integrate this equation to obtain a solution for Φ between the cylinders. The constants of integration are evaluated from the given boundary conditions at $r = a$ and $r = b$. From the solution for Φ find the electric field between the cylinders.

1-11.3. Steady state diffusion is another example of a potential flow field analogous to those described in Sec. 1-4. As an example, consider the injection of a dye into a beaker of water. The dye will disperse or diffuse from the point of injection until it uniformly fills the beaker. Under steady state conditions (e.g., dye being injected at a constant rate) the rate at which the particles diffuse is proportional to the gradient of the diffusing particles concentrate. The particles diffuse from regions of high concentration to regions of low concentration. This phenomenon is described by Fick's law $M = -D\nabla\eta$, where M is the rate of particle flow in particles per unit area per sec., η is the particle density in particles per unit volume, and D is the diffusion coefficient.

(a) What are the units of D?

(b) A fluid diffuses uniformly from a spherical source of radius <u>a</u> at a rate q_1 particles per sec. per m^2. At $r = b$ the particle density is measured and found to be N particles per m^3. Find the steady state particle density $\eta(r)$ in terms of q_1, D, and N.

[Hint: Conservation of particles requires that the total flow $4\pi a^2 q_1$ from the source must be equal to the total steady state flow $4\pi r^2 q(r)$ across any other spherical surface. Combine this conservation law with Fick's law to obtain an equation for $\eta(r)$.]

CHAPTER 2

GENERAL PROPERTIES OF VECTOR FIELDS

The concept of a potential flow field was introduced in Chap. 1 and the properties of such fields were examined by a detailed study of electric current flow fields. A key factor in potential flow fields was that the vector field that represents the flow is proportional to the gradient of a scalar potential field. There is a second type of flow, called rotational flow, for which the flow field cannot be obtained from the gradient of a scalar potential. In this chapter we shall examine the more general situation involving both rotational and irrotational fields. That is, the mathematical description of different types of vector fields and of volume and surface sources will be examined. This will be accompanied by considering derivations of the equations governing a variety of potential type fields, such as: electrostatic fields, irrotational fluid flow, and heat flow. We shall find that such fields are governed by Poisson's and Laplace's equations.

2-1. Irrotational Fields

We shall approach the idea of an irrotational field from a somewhat different point of view from that discussed in Chap. 1. The approach to be discussed is, of course, equivalent to what has already been said. Now we begin by stating that a vector field $\overline{F}(x,y,z,t)$ is said to be an irrotational field if it has zero "circulation" everywhere. The circulation of a field is the value of the line integral of the field around a closed contour C. Thus by definition

$$\text{Net circulation integral} = \oint_C \overline{F} \cdot d\overline{\ell} \tag{2-1.1}$$

If the line integral in Eq. (2-1.1) is zero for all arbitrary contours C, the vector field $\overline{F}$ is irrotational. If we think of $\overline{F}$ as representing the flow of some ideal fluid, then for an irrotational field there is no circulation of the flow around any closed path.

We found, in connection with Eq. (1-7.8), that the gradient of a scalar potential Φ has the property that its line integral around a closed path vanishes, i.e.,

$$\oint \nabla\Phi \cdot d\bar{\ell} = \oint \frac{d\Phi}{d\ell}\, d\ell = \oint d\Phi = 0 \tag{2-1.2}$$

Consequently by Eq. (2-1.1) $\nabla\Phi$ is an irrotational vector field. This allows us to state an important result for irrotational fields: "all irrotational fields can be derived from the gradient of a scalar potential," so that in general,

$$\bar{F} = -\nabla\Phi \tag{2-1.3}$$

The negative sign is chosen by convention for later convenience. Note, therefore, that irrotational fields are precisely those that we previously referred to as potential flow fields. The irrotational property is not a general one, as already mentioned, since fields for which the circulation integral does not vanish also exist. We shall discuss such fields in the next section.

We noted previously that a useful pictorial representation of a vector field could be obtained by drawing in flow lines - also called flux lines or streamlines. These are lines which are everywhere tangent to the vector field $\bar{F}$. The relative magnitude of $\bar{F}$ can also be represented by varying the density of the flow lines. A typical field map of this type is shown in Fig. 2-1.1a. If the field varies with time, the flow pattern also changes with time. In this case Fig. 2-1.1a would represent the field at a particular instant of time. The mapping of a vector field by means of flow lines is clearly applicable, quite independently of whether or not the field represents the actual flow of some quantity, such as a fluid. It is mainly for conceptual reasons that it is useful to think of any vector field as representing a flow.

Another property of a vector field was previously noted in terms of the divergence of the field, i.e.,

$$\text{div}\,\bar{F} = \nabla \cdot \bar{F} = \lim_{\Delta V \to 0} \frac{\oint_S \bar{F} \cdot d\bar{S}}{\Delta V} \tag{2-1.4}$$

where the divergence represents the net outflow per unit volume. In any region where the flow lines are continuous, there will be just as much flow into a given volume element ΔV as there is outward flow, with the divergence being zero. In a region where flow lines are generated or terminated, as illustrated in Fig. 2-1.1b, the divergence is non-zero. The value of the *divergence* $\nabla \cdot \bar{F}$ *at a given point is a measure of the source strength* (*or strength of a sink*) *at that point*, since flow lines begin at a source point and terminate at a sink. A sink may equally well be regarded as a negative source.

It should be clear that all physical fields must arise from a suitable set of

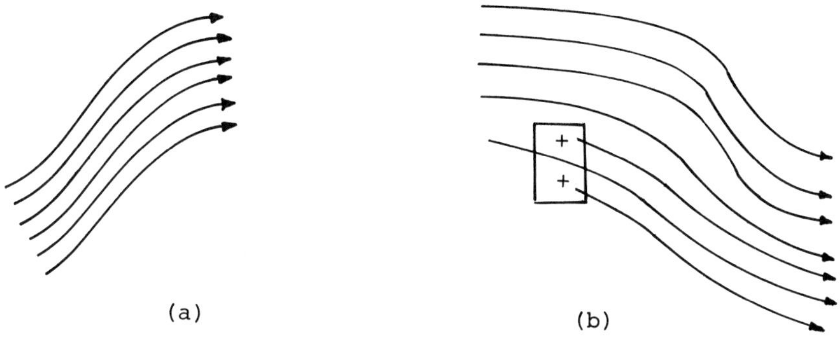

Figure 2-1.1. (a) Flow lines in a vector field. (b) A region where flow lines are generated.

sources. Thus for an *irrotational* field, $\nabla \cdot \overline{F}$ cannot be identically zero everywhere or else the field itself would vanish (in the next section we discuss *rotational* fields for which the divergence is always zero). If we denote the source strength by the scalar field function $\rho(x,y,z,t)$ we can write over the region containing the sources [Poisson's equation]

$$-\nabla \cdot \overline{F} = \nabla^2\Phi = -\rho \tag{2-1.5}$$

since $\overline{F} = -\nabla\Phi$. In a region where $\rho = 0$ we have Laplace's equation:

$$\nabla^2\Phi = 0 \tag{2-1.6}$$

We see therefore that simple irrotational fields are described by a scalar potential which for the region containing sources is a solution of Poisson's equation (2-1.5), and in a source free region it is a solution of Laplace's equation.

We point out, however, that there are irrotational fields for which the governing equations are more elaborate than Poisson's or Laplace's equation. Such elaborations arise from more involved relationships to the sources, from time retardation effects such as occur in wave phenomena, and from coupling to other fields. Various examples of these more involved fields will be discussed in later chapters. Nevertheless, Poisson's and Laplace's equations do describe a large variety of physical fields of engineering importance.

2-2. Rotational Fields and Curl

In accordance with the discussion in connection with Eq. (2-1.1), if the circulation integral $\oint \overline{F} \cdot d\overline{\ell}$ does not vanish, the field is said to have circulation or rotation. Other words used to denote the same rotation property are *vorticity* and *curl*.

To understand the physical significance of the vorticity property, the following "thought" experiment may be performed. Imagine a large body of fluid, say water, in which a velocity field $\overline{v}$ exists. If we place in this fluid a small buoyant paddle wheel that is free to rotate about an axis, as in Fig. 2-2.1 (often called the curl meter), we would most likely find that for a certain orientation of its axis the paddle wheel would rotate. If it does rotate, the velocity field has a net circulation or rotation at the position of the paddle wheel. If we orient the axis to give maximum rate of rotation, this maximum rotation rate is a

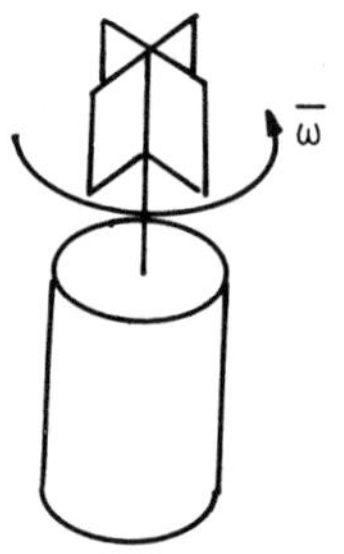

Figure 2-2.1. A paddle wheel used to measure the vorticity of a fluid.

relative measure of the circulation or vorticity strength at the given point. Since the rotation rate does depend on the orientation of the paddle wheel, the vorticity strength is a vector quantity. If the velocity field were purely irrotational, there would be no location in the fluid at which the paddle wheel would rotate.

If the paddle wheel were rotated by some external means, it would stir up the fluid and produce a rotational velocity field. In this case the paddle wheel would represent a *vortex* source. The vector direction of the source is taken as that of the axis of the paddle wheel, with the positive direction such that rotation is counterclockwise about the positive axis, as in Fig. 2-2.1.

With this description of vorticity of a field, we are in a position to specify a differential quantity that gives the vorticity or circulation of the field at a point. This is the following: the rotation or curl of the field is defined to be the net value of the circulation integral taken around the boundary of a differential element of area dS divided by the element of area. To be more precise, the quantity defined gives the component of the curl in the direction of the normal to

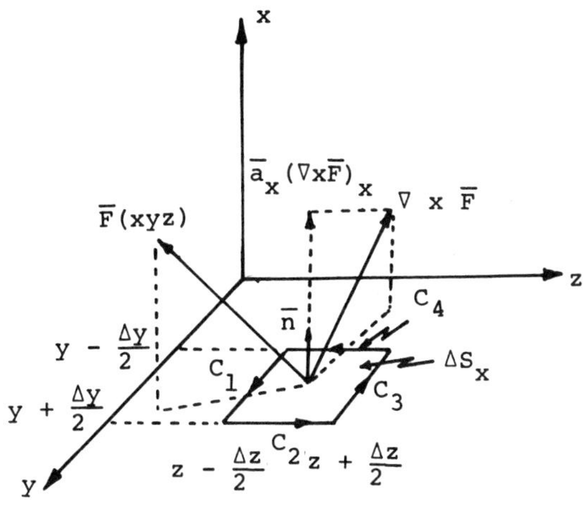

Figure 2-2.2. The procedure used to evaluate the curl of a vector field.

the element of area considered. To define this mathematically, consider an element of area ΔS_x located in a plane parallel to the YZ plane. If the contour C is traversed in the sense shown in the Fig. 2-2.2 the positive normal to the surface element is upward (right-hand rule). The component of the curl of a vector field $\bar{F}$ in the direction of $\bar{n}$, which in this case is in the positive X direction, is

$$(\text{curl } \bar{F})_x = \bar{a}_x \cdot (\nabla \times \bar{F}) = (\nabla \times \bar{F})_x = \lim_{\Delta S_x \to 0} \frac{\oint_{C_{\Delta S_x}} \bar{F} \cdot d\bar{\ell}}{\Delta S_x} \tag{2-2.1}$$

To evaluate this expression, we can write, to first order on the several sides

$$\bar{F} = \bar{F}(xyz) + (-\frac{\Delta z}{2})\frac{\partial \bar{F}}{\partial z} \qquad \text{on } C_1$$

$$\bar{F} = \bar{F}(xyz) + (\frac{\Delta z}{2})\frac{\partial \bar{F}}{\partial z} \qquad \text{on } C_3$$

when we evaluate $\bar{F}$ at the center of the sides C_1 and C_3. The contribution to the line integral from C_1 and C_3 is given by

$$\int_{C_1+C_3} \bar{F} \cdot d\bar{\ell} = (\bar{F} - \frac{\partial \bar{F}}{\partial z}\frac{\Delta z}{2}) \cdot \bar{a}_y \Delta y + (\bar{F} + \frac{\partial \bar{F}}{\partial z}\frac{\Delta z}{2}) \cdot (-\bar{a}_y)\,\Delta y$$

$$= -\frac{\partial F_y}{\partial z}\Delta z \Delta y$$

By a similar procedure we find that

$$\int_{C_2+C_4} \bar{F} \cdot d\bar{\ell} = \frac{\partial F_z}{\partial y}\Delta z \Delta y$$

Therefore

$$(\text{curl } \overline{F})_x = \overline{a}_x \cdot (\nabla \times \overline{F}) = \lim_{\Delta y \Delta z \to 0} \frac{\left(\frac{\partial F_z}{\partial y} - \frac{\partial F_y}{\partial z}\right) \Delta z \Delta y}{\Delta z \Delta y} = \frac{\partial F_z}{\partial y} - \frac{\partial F_y}{\partial z} \tag{2-2.2}$$

If the same procedure is followed to evaluate the components of the curl of $\overline{F}$ along the Y and Z directions, the total result is, in vector form,

$$\text{curl } \overline{F} = \overline{a}_x \left(\frac{\partial F_z}{\partial y} - \frac{\partial F_y}{\partial z}\right) + \overline{a}_y \left(\frac{\partial F_x}{\partial z} - \frac{\partial F_z}{\partial x}\right) + \overline{a}_z \left(\frac{\partial F_y}{\partial x} - \frac{\partial F_x}{\partial y}\right) \tag{2-2.3}$$

The curl of $\overline{F}$ in rectangular coordinates can be obtained in a formal way by evaluating the vector product of the del operator ∇ with $\overline{F}$, which is

$$\text{curl } \overline{F} = \nabla \times \overline{F} = \overline{a}_x \left(\frac{\partial}{\partial x} + \overline{a}_y \frac{\partial}{\partial y} + \overline{a}_z \frac{\partial}{\partial z}\right) \times (\overline{a}_x F_x + \overline{a}_y F_y + \overline{a}_z F_z) \tag{2-2.4}$$

The evaluation is carried out by noting that

$$\overline{a}_x \times \overline{a}_x = \overline{a}_y \times \overline{a}_y = \overline{a}_z \times \overline{a}_z = 0$$

$$\overline{a}_x \times \overline{a}_y = -\overline{a}_y \times \overline{a}_x = \overline{a}_z; \quad \overline{a}_y \times \overline{a}_z = -\overline{a}_z \times \overline{a}_y = \overline{a}_x; \quad \overline{a}_z \times \overline{a}_x = -\overline{a}_x \times \overline{a}_z = \overline{a}_y$$

and yields the expression in Eq. (2-2.3). Conveniently, therefore, curl $\overline{F}$ is also written as $\nabla \times \overline{F}$. A convenient way to remember the curl expression is to relate it to the expansion of the determinant

$$\nabla \times \overline{F} = \begin{vmatrix} \overline{a}_x & \overline{a}_y & \overline{a}_z \\ \frac{\partial}{\partial x} & \frac{\partial}{\partial y} & \frac{\partial}{\partial z} \\ F_x & F_y & F_z \end{vmatrix} \tag{2-2.5}$$

Although we have evaluated the curl of $\overline{F}$ in rectangular coordinates, the basic definition given in Eq. (2-2.1) for the component of the curl normal to an arbitrary element of area is a general one and may be used to evaluate the curl in other coordinate systems. The expressions for the curl in cylindrical and in spherical coordinates are given in Appendix I, where a number of formulas from vector analysis are summarized.

If we replace $\overline{F}$ by the vector field $\nabla\Phi$ in Eq. (2-2.3) or Eq. (2-2.5) we will find that

$$\nabla \times \nabla\Phi \equiv 0 \tag{2-2.6}$$

For example, the x-component is given by

$$(\nabla \times \nabla\Phi)_x = \bar{a}_x \cdot (\nabla \times \nabla\Phi) = \frac{\partial}{\partial y}\frac{\partial\Phi}{\partial z} - \frac{\partial}{\partial z}\frac{\partial\Phi}{\partial y} = 0$$

because the order of taking the partial derivatives may be interchanged. Thus whenever a vector field can be represented by the gradient of a scalar potential, this field will be irrotational and will have an identically zero curl.

We note that a pure rotational field has a non-vanishing curl, at least at some point, but will have identically zero divergence. The flow lines must then be continuous and form closed loops since there are no scalar sources or sinks on which flow lines begin or terminate. Of course, if the curl were also identically zero, the field would vanish. The regions where the curl is not zero are the regions where the vortex sources which produce the rotational field must exist. A field with identically zero divergence is also called a *solenoidal* field.

If the divergence of the curl of a vector $\bar{A}$ is evaluated, it would be found to be identically zero; that is

$$\nabla \cdot \nabla \times \bar{A} = 0 \tag{2-2.7}$$

This result is easily established by taking the divergence of the curl in rectangular coordinates. From this mathematical identity, an easy way to ensure that a field should be solenoidal (pure rotational) is to express it as the curl of some other vector quantity. Thus, a velocity field $\bar{v}$ obtained from the relation $\bar{v} = \nabla \times \bar{A}$ will have zero divergence. In fluid mechanics $\bar{A}$ is called the *vorticity vector potential*, and in electromagnetic theory it is called the *magnetic vector potential* $(\bar{B} = \nabla \times \bar{A})$.

We have already noted that a solenoidal field cannot have zero curl everywhere or else it would vanish. Thus, we must have $\nabla \times \bar{F}$ equal to a vector vortex source. If we derive $\bar{F}$ from the curl of a vector potential $\bar{A}$ then

$$\nabla \times \bar{F} = \nabla \times \nabla \times \bar{A} = \bar{J} \tag{2-2.8}$$

where $\bar{J}$ is the vector vortex source (not necessarily an electric current density). In rectangular coordinates $\nabla \times \nabla \times \bar{A}$ can be expanded into the form (see Sec. I-2 in Appendix I)

$$\nabla \times \nabla \times \bar{A} = \nabla\nabla \cdot \bar{A} - \nabla^2\bar{A} \tag{2-2.9}$$

Usually $\nabla \cdot \bar{A}$ can be chosen as zero (this will be explained in later chapters), and in this case Eq. (2-2.8) becomes

$$\nabla^2\bar{A} = -\bar{J} \tag{2-2.10}$$

This is the vector Poisson equation and corresponds to three scalar Poisson equations; e.g., the X-component is

$$\nabla^2 A_x = -J_x$$

This again shows that Poisson's equation is of fundamental importance in field theory.

It can be shown that a general vector field $\overline{W}$ can be split into the sum $\overline{W} = \overline{U} + \overline{V}$ of an irrotational field ($\nabla \times \overline{U} = 0$) and a solenoidal or rotational field ($\nabla \cdot \overline{V}) = 0$). This result, which is known as Helmholtz's theorem, provides us with further insight into the mathematical structure of vector fields.

Physical fields with non-zero curl will be studied in detail in later chapters, so we will not go into further detail in this section. In order to clarify many of the concepts introduced above, we will discuss three examples of field phenomena where a finite curl exists.

Example 2-2.1. Evaluate the curl of the velocity field of a rigid body in rotation.

Solution: Refer to Fig. 2-2.3 which illustrates a rigid body that is rotating with a constant angular velocity $\overline{\omega}$ about an axis denoted by the unit vector $\overline{n}$, so that

$$\overline{\omega} = \omega\overline{n} \tag{2-2.11}$$

Consider now an arbitrary point in the body at a position specified by the position vector $\overline{r}$. The linear speed of this point will be

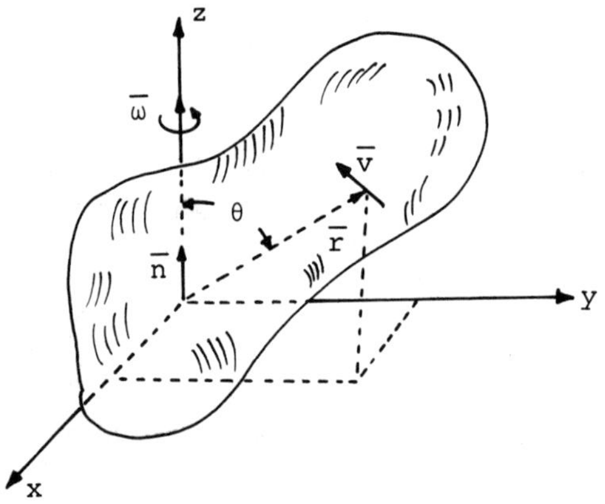

Figure 2-2.3. A rotating rigid body.

$$v = \omega r \sin \theta$$

which in vector form is

$$\bar{v} = \bar{\omega} \times \bar{r} \tag{2-2.12}$$

The curl of this velocity field is given by

$$\nabla \times \bar{v} = \nabla \times (\bar{\omega} \times \bar{r})$$

Suppose now that our coordinate reference frame is so oriented that $\bar{\omega}$ is along the Z-axis. This means that

$$\bar{\omega} \times \bar{r} = \omega \bar{a}_z \times (\bar{a}_x x + \bar{a}_y y + \bar{a}_z z) = \omega(x\bar{a}_y - y\bar{a}_x)$$

and by Eq. (2-2.3) we find that

$$\nabla \times (\bar{\omega} \times \bar{r}) = \omega \bar{a}_z \left(\frac{\partial x}{\partial x} + \frac{\partial y}{\partial y}\right) = 2\omega \bar{a}_z = 2\bar{\omega} \tag{2-2.13}$$

This shows that the curl of the velocity field $\bar{v}$ is equal to twice the angular rotational velocity $\bar{\omega}$. This example illustrates the appropriateness of the term curl or rotation for the vector quantity $\nabla \times \bar{v}$.

An equivalent situation arises when a beaker of water is placed on a turntable, all rotating at constant angular velocity ω. But $\bar{v} \perp d\bar{\ell}$ along C_2 and C_4 and so

$$\oint \bar{v} \cdot d\bar{\ell} = \int_{C_1+C_3} = [\omega(r+dr)(r+dr)d\theta - \omega r\, r d\theta] = 2\,\omega r dr\, d\theta$$

and therefore

$$\bar{a}_z \cdot \nabla \times \bar{v} = \lim_{r dr d\theta \to 0} \frac{\oint \bar{v} \cdot d\bar{\ell}}{r dr d\theta} = 2\omega$$

where the Z-axis is taken to be perpendicular to the page. ΔΔΔ

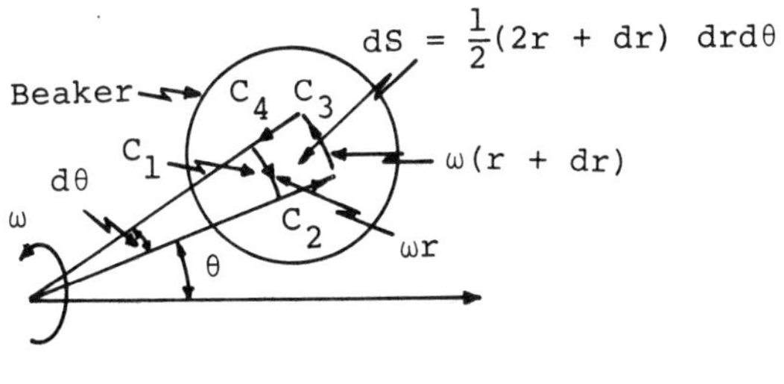

Figure 2-2.4. A rotating fluid system.

Example 2-2.2. Find the magnetic field intensity produced by a current filament carrying a current I.

Solution: Refer to Fig. 2-2.5a which represents an infinitely long cylinder of radius carrying a uniform current of density $\overline{J} = I/\pi a^2\ \overline{a}_z$, where I is the total current.

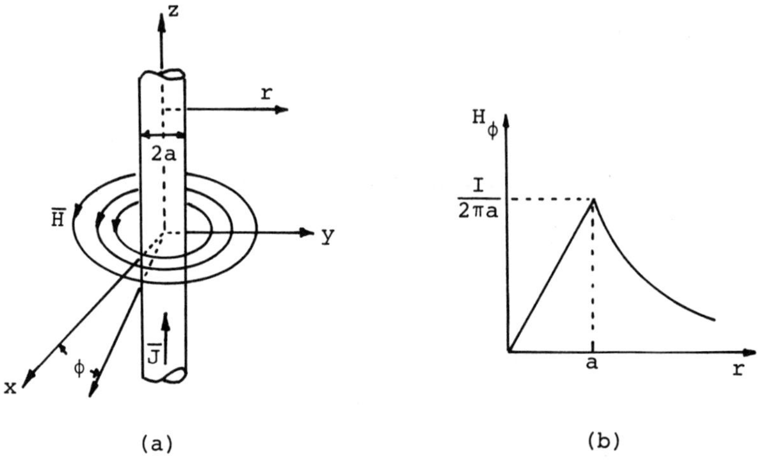

Figure 2-2.5. Magnetic field due to a line current.

Since magnetic fields have not yet been studied, we state without proof at this point that the static magnetic field $\overline{H}$ is related to the current density by the formula

$$\nabla \times \overline{H} = \overline{J} \tag{2-2.14}$$

Here the current density $\overline{J}$ acts as a line vortex source for the magnetic field $\overline{H}$. Outside the cylinder, that is, for $r > a$, the curl of $\overline{H}$ is zero since $\overline{J} = 0$ in this region. However, for $0 \le r \le a$, $\overline{J} \neq 0$, and a finite curl exists.

Since $\overline{J}$ has only a Z-component, then $\nabla \times \overline{H}$ will also have a Z-component only. In cylindrical coordinates (see Appendix I) we have that

$$(\nabla \times \overline{H})_z = \frac{1}{r}\frac{\partial}{\partial r}(rH_\phi) - \frac{1}{r}\frac{\partial H_r}{\partial \phi} = J_z \tag{2-2.15}$$

In view of the existing symmetry, there can be no variation with angle and so we have that

$$\frac{\partial}{\partial r}(rH_\phi) = \begin{cases} rJ_z & r \le a \\ 0 & r > a \end{cases} \tag{2-2.16}$$

Integrating these expressions once gives

$$rH_\phi = \begin{cases} \dfrac{r^2 J_z}{2} + C_1 & r \leq a \\ C_2 & r > a \end{cases} \tag{2-2.17}$$

where C_1 and C_2 are constants of integration to be evaluated. These constants are readily evaluated. We see that at $r = 0$, the field must vanish, which requires that $C_1 = 0$. Also, at $r = a$ the field is continuous. This requires that

$$\frac{a^2 J_z}{2} = \frac{I}{2\pi} = C_2 \tag{2-2.18}$$

Thus our solution for $\overline{H}$ is

$$\overline{H} = \overline{a}_\phi H_\phi = \begin{cases} \dfrac{I}{2\pi a^2} r\overline{a}_\phi & r \leq a \\ \dfrac{I}{2\pi r} \overline{a}_\phi & r \geq a \end{cases} \tag{2-2.19}$$

The magnitude of $\overline{H}$ versus r is plotted in Fig. 2-2.5b. It is seen from these expressions that the field lines are concentric circles enclosing the current line source. The density of the lines for $r > a$ decreases inversely with the radially outward distance from the center line of the source. The field lines form closed loops, and $\overline{H}$ therefore is a solenoidal field. This result may also be deduced by noting that the divergence $\nabla \cdot \overline{H}$ is identically zero, since in the present case the $\overline{H}$-field is H_ϕ and the divergence in cylindrical form becomes

$$\nabla \cdot \overline{H} = \frac{1}{r} \frac{\partial H_\phi}{\partial \phi} = 0 \tag{2-2.20}$$

This example shows that a pure rotational or solenoidal field can have zero curl in certain regions, but there must exist at least one region where the curl does not vanish. This means that a vortex source must exist somewhere in the field. Common vortex sources include water swirling through the drain hole in a bathtub having an air column in the center; a tornado which consists essentially of a core of air rotating as a solid body surrounded by a free vortex flow.

2-3. Gauss and Stokes Theorems

There are two integral transformations, the Gauss theorem and Stokes' theorem, that are of considerable importance in field analysis. We wish to discuss these theorems in some detail.

The Gauss theorem is essentially the divergence theorem, which was discussed in some detail in Sec. 1-10, and given in Eq. (1-10.8). We rewrite this result as

$$\oint_S \overline{F} \cdot d\overline{S} = \int_V \nabla \cdot \overline{F}\, dV \tag{2-3.1}$$

Gauss law is obtained by replacing $\nabla \cdot \overline{F}$ by the scalar source ρ,

$$\nabla \cdot \overline{F} = \rho$$

Eq. (2-3.1) then becomes

$$\oint_S \overline{F} \cdot d\overline{S} = \int_V \rho\, dV = Q \tag{2-3.2}$$

where Q is the total source strength enclosed by the closed surface S. This theorem states that the total outward flux or flow of a vector field through a closed surface S is equal to the enclosed source strength.

Stokes' theorem relates the outward flux of the curl of a field, say $\nabla \times \overline{F}$ through an open surface S to the net circulation of $\overline{F}$ around the contour C that bounds S

$$\int_S (\nabla \times \overline{F}) \cdot d\overline{S} = \oint \overline{F} \cdot d\overline{\ell} \tag{2-3.3}$$

This theorem is readily proved by using the basic definition of the curl, as discussed in Sec. 2-2. Refer to Fig. 2-3.1 which shows a cap of area S defined by the contour C and let the open surface S be divided into a large number of differential surface elements S_i with boundaries C_i. From this definition of the curl, we have

$$(\nabla \times \overline{F}) \cdot \overline{n}\, \Delta S_i = \oint_{C_i} \overline{F} \cdot d\overline{\ell}$$

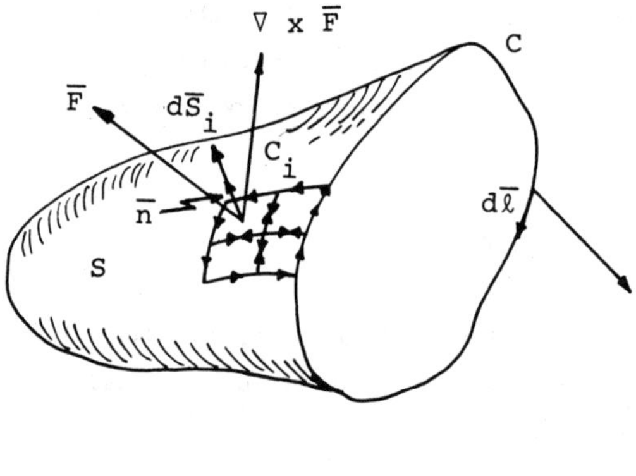

Figure 2-3.1. For proving Stokes' theorem.

If we sum the contributions from all elements, we obtain

$$\sum_i (\nabla \times \overline{F}) \cdot \overline{n}\, \Delta S_i \doteq \sum_i \oint_{C_i} \overline{F} \cdot d\overline{\ell} = \oint_C \overline{F} \cdot d\overline{\ell}$$

Notice that all the internal contours C_i are traversed twice, but in opposite directions. Because of this, the line integral reduces to that around the boundary C. In the limit as ΔS_i goes to zero, the left hand side becomes

$$\int_S (\nabla \times \overline{F}) \cdot \overline{n}\, dS = \int_S (\nabla \times \overline{F}) \cdot d\overline{S}$$

which proves the result Eq. (2-3.3).

The Gauss and Stokes theorems can often be applied to obtain solutions in a direct manner to certain field problems that exhibit sufficient symmetry. The following two examples illustrate these techniques.

Example 2-3.1. Find the current density $\overline{J}$ between two concentric spherical electrodes.

Solution: Figure 2-3.2 illustrates two concentric spheres of respective radii a and b. The inner sphere is kept at the potential V_o relative to the outer sphere. The medium between the spheres is assumed to be homogeneous of conductivity σ.

The configuration has perfect spherical symmetry, and we may assume that the current density $\overline{J}$ is in the radial direction and is a function of r only. Let the total current supplied by the center electrode be I; thus I is the total source strength. Now we apply Gauss law, Eq. (2-3.2), to the spherical surface of radius r, and we have that

$$\oint_S \overline{J} \cdot d\overline{S} = I$$

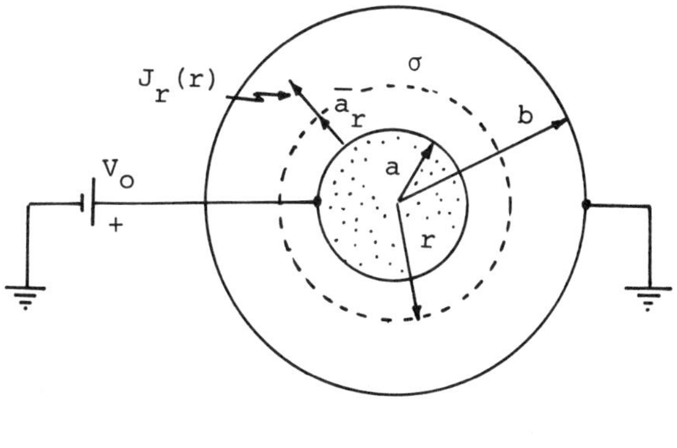

Figure 2-3.2. Current flow between concentric spheres.

Because of the symmetry, we can perform the integration to get

$$\oint_S \bar{J} \cdot d\bar{S} = J_r(r) \oint \bar{a}_r \cdot d\bar{S} = 4\pi r^2 J_r(r) = I$$

The existence of symmetry is a crucial requirement in order to assume that the radial current density $J_r(r)$ is constant everywhere on the spherical surface of radius r and to permit us to perform the integration.

From the above result, we obtain

$$J_r(r) = \frac{I}{4\pi r^2} \tag{2-3.4}$$

We can now write that (see Appendix I for the gradient in spherical coordinates)

$$\bar{J}_r(r) = \sigma\bar{E} = -\sigma \frac{\partial \Phi}{\partial r} \bar{a}_r$$

and so we have

$$\frac{\partial \Phi}{\partial r} = \frac{-I}{4\pi\sigma r^2}$$

from which, by integration,

$$\Phi = \frac{I}{4\pi\sigma r} + C \tag{2-3.5}$$

From Fig. 2-3.2 we have the boundary condition: $r = b$, $\Phi = 0$; from this we find that $C = -I/4\pi\sigma b$. Further, for Φ to equal V_o at $r = a$, the current I must then have the value

$$I = \frac{4\pi\sigma ab}{b-a} V_o \tag{2-3.6}$$

and the current density is

$$J_r(r) = \frac{\sigma ab V_o}{(b-a)r^2} \tag{2-3.7}$$

The ratio of V_o to the total current I is the total or effective lumped resistance to current flow. From Eq. (2-3.6) we find that

$$R = \frac{V_o}{I} = \frac{b-a}{4\pi\sigma ab} \tag{2-3.8}$$

for the resistance between the two concentric spheres. This is a simple example of how a lumped parameter, the resistance R, can be derived from field theory. ΔΔΔ

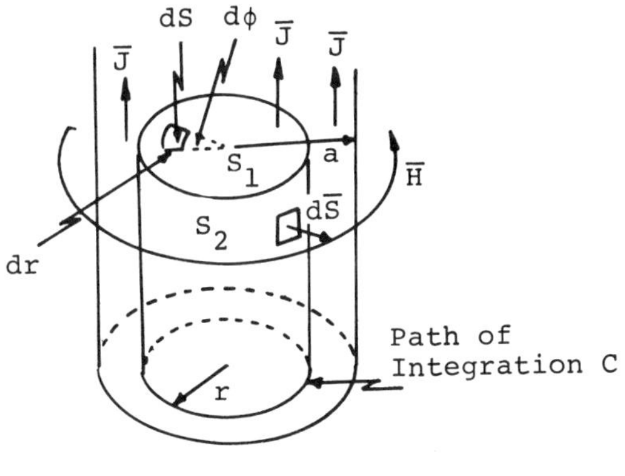

Figure 2-3.3. Application of Stokes theorem to a current source.

Example 2-3.2. Find the magnetic field due to a line source.

Solution. In this example we shall use Stokes' theorem to solve the magnetic field problem discussed earlier as Ex. 2-2.2 and illustrated in Fig. 2-2.5. Consider an enlarged view of the conductor of radius a and consider as a Stokes' surface a small concentic cylinder of radius r with S_1 denoting the end cup and S_2 denoting the cylindrical surface. We observe the symmetry of the field, and see that $\overline{H}$ has a ϕ-component which is a function of r only. We apply Stokes' theorem to the cup consisting of a cylindrical cup of side area S_2 and top area S_1 that is defined by the circular boundary C of radius r (see Fig. 2-3.3). This yields

$$\int_S (\nabla \times \overline{H}) \cdot d\overline{S} = \oint_C \overline{H} \cdot d\overline{\ell} = H_\phi(r) \int_0^{2\pi} r\, d\phi = 2\pi r\, H_\phi(r)$$

However, since $\nabla \times \overline{H} = \overline{J}$, then the integral relation becomes

$$2\pi r\, H_\phi(r) = \int_S \overline{J} \cdot d\overline{S} = \int_{S_1} \overline{J} \cdot d\overline{S} + \int_{S_2} \overline{J} \cdot d\overline{S}$$

But $\overline{J}$ is perpendicular to $d\overline{S}$ over S_2 and the second integral vanishes. Thus

$$2\pi r\, H_\phi(r) = \int_0^{2\pi} \int_0^r J_z r\, dr\, d\phi$$

For $r < a$, we get $I/\pi a^2\, (\pi r^2)$ for the surface integral, while for $r > a$ we get I, because $J_z = 0$ for $r > a$. The solution for H_ϕ is

$$H_\phi = \begin{cases} \dfrac{Ir}{2\pi a^2} & r \leq a \\[2ex] \dfrac{I}{2\pi r} & r \geq a \end{cases}$$

Note that a condition of symmetry was necessary in order for us to evaluate the line integral of $\overline{H}$ in a simple manner; specifically, $\overline{H} \cdot d\overline{\ell} = H_\phi \overline{a}_\phi \cdot \overline{a}_\phi \, r \, d\phi = H_\phi \, r \, d\phi$ could be integrated because H_ϕ did not vary with the angle.

ΔΔΔ

2-4. Stream Functions

We have already noted that vector fields are conveniently represented pictorially by a flow map. The flow lines or streamlines are curved lines that are everywhere tangent to the vector field at the given point. The function that describes the family of streamlines is called the *stream function*. The equation satisfied by the stream function can be obtained from the vector field whose flow lines are mapped by the stream function. Consider a vector field $\overline{F}(x,y,z)$ and let $d\overline{r}$ be a differential element of length along a streamline. It is necessary for $d\overline{r}$ to be parallel to $\overline{F}$ at all points, a condition which can be expressed mathematically by the relation

$$\overline{F} \times d\overline{r} = 0 \tag{2-4.1}$$

Clearly, this equation requires that $\sin\theta = 0$, where θ is the angle between $\overline{F}$ and $d\overline{r}$, and this requires that $\overline{F}$ and $d\overline{r}$ be parallel vectors. If we expand Eq. (2-4.1) into rectangular coordinates, we obtain

$$F_y dz - F_z dy = 0$$

$$F_z dx - F_x dz = 0$$

$$F_x dy - F_y dx = 0$$

which is equivalent to the set of equations

$$\frac{dx}{F_x} = \frac{dy}{F_y} = \frac{dz}{F_z} \tag{2-4.2}$$

A solution of these equations will give a function $\psi(x,y,z)$ which is the stream function. Equating ψ to a constant will give the equation of a particular streamline.

For irrotational fields, we know that we can derive $\overline{F}$ from the gradient of a scalar potential Φ, i.e., $\overline{F} = -\nabla\Phi$. In this case, Eq. (2-4.1) gives

$$\nabla\Phi \times d\overline{r} = 0 \tag{2-4.3}$$

This equation states that the flow lines are parallel to $\nabla\Phi$, and so are perpendicular to the constant Φ surfaces since $\nabla\Phi$ is normal to the constant potential surfaces.

We can establish certain interesting properties of the stream functions which map the flow characteristics of the field, as already discussed in Sec. 1-8. Let us restrict ourselves to a two dimensional field. The stream function ψ will take on constant values along the stream or flow lines. Let the magnitude $|\nabla\psi|$ be proportional to the strength of $\overline{F}$ at any point in the field. This requires that

$$\nabla\psi \times \overline{a}_z = \lambda\overline{F} \tag{2-4.4}$$

where we have assumed that our vector field $\overline{F}$ has a zero Z-component, and where λ is a constant of proportionality. For the two dimensional field $\partial\psi/\partial z = 0$ and by expansion

$$\frac{\partial\psi}{\partial y} = \lambda F_x; \quad \frac{\partial\psi}{\partial x} = -\lambda F_y \tag{2-4.5}$$

Actually a field so defined is source-free since

$$\nabla \cdot (\nabla\psi \times \overline{a}_z) = \frac{\partial^2\psi}{\partial x\partial y} - \frac{\partial^2\psi}{\partial y\partial x} = 0$$

which means that

$$\nabla \cdot \overline{F} = 0$$

In regions where $\nabla \cdot \overline{F} \neq 0$, flow lines begin and end so that a flow map would not be meaningful in such regions.

Note also that by taking the curl of both sides of the equation (see Sec. I-2 in Appendix I)

$$\nabla \times (\nabla\psi \times \overline{a}_z) = (\nabla \cdot \overline{a}_z)\nabla\psi - (\nabla \cdot \nabla\psi)\overline{a}_z = \lambda\nabla \times \overline{F}$$

or

$$\nabla^2\psi = -\lambda(\overline{a}_z \cdot \nabla \times \overline{F}) \tag{2-4.6}$$

Clearly $\nabla \times \overline{F} \neq 0$ is permitted and moreover, it forms a source function for Poisson's equation. For irrotational fields $\nabla \times \overline{F} = 0$, and ψ satisfies Laplace's equation. This means that for irrotational fields the potential function Φ and the stream function ψ both satisfy Laplace's equation. Actually this is a fundamental property of conjugate functions, a matter that is best discussed through the Cauchy-Riemann equations of complex function theory. Observe that increments in ψ

represent the flux of $\lambda\overline{F}$, and a flux tube bounded by ψ_1 and ψ_2 and a unit dimension along Z carries an amount $\psi_2-\psi_1$ of flux (or fluid).

2-5. Potential Flow in Fluids

Chapters 3 and 4 are devoted to the study of methods for solving Laplace's and Poisson's equations. In order to present meaningful examples in those chapters, it is desirable to show that the Laplace and Poisson equations describe a number of physical fields of engineering importance. We shall, in this section and the two following sections, give a phenomenological derivation of the equations governing potential flow in fluids, heat conduction, and the electrostatic field. Later chapters will develop the physical properties of these fields in greater detail.

The concepts of streamlines and flow tubes have already been introduced, and we apply them to fluid flow. The streamlines are the lines that give the direction of the velocity field at each point in space. The lines may be uniformly spaced, converge, or diverge, depending on whether or not the flow field is uniform, converging or diverging. The flow tube is a tube whose boundary is made up of flow lines or streamlines, as illustrated in Fig. 2-5.1. A given volume element of fluid always remains within the same flow tube. If the velocity field varies with time, then the streamlines and consequently the flow tubes are continually changing in configuration but the fluid within the flow tube will never cross the boundary of the tube since, by definition the velocity is always along the tube.

The motions of streamlines and flow tubes provides a useful pictorial representation of the flow field. As long as the flow can be mapped by a system of smooth non-intersecting streamlines, the flow is called *laminar* (layered) flow. For practical fluids it is found that when the velocity exceeds a certain maximum value, depending on viscosity and other effects, the flow lines break up and become highly irregular and interlaced. In this high velocity regime the flow is said to be turbulent. For turbulent flow no straightforward mathematical description of the flow is possible.

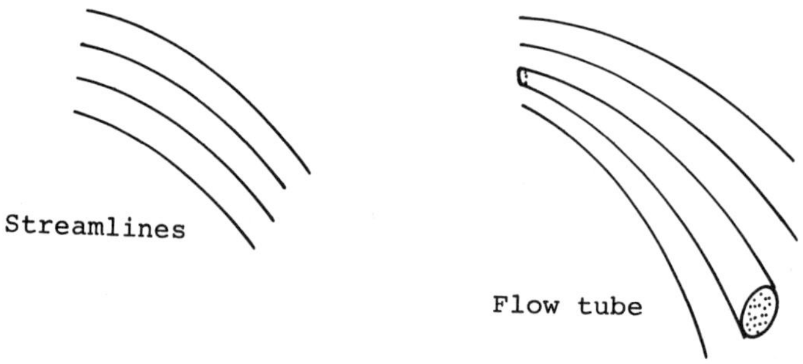

Figure 2-5.1. Streamlines and a flow tube in a fluid.

The smooth laminar flow can be classified into two distinct types, irrotational flow and rotational flow, as noted earlier in Secs. 2-1 and 2-2. For irrotational flow the fluid undergoes no circulation. This means that the circulation integral, which is the line integral of the velocity $\overline{v}$ around a closed contour C is always zero. That is

$$\oint_C \overline{v} \cdot d\overline{\ell} = -\oint_C \nabla\Phi \cdot d\overline{\ell} = 0 \tag{2-5.1}$$

In this equation we have set $\overline{v}$ equal to the negative gradient of a potential since $\nabla\Phi$ has the property that its line integral around a closed contour is zero. Consequently, it follows that potential flow is irrotational flow. The converse is also true, that is, irrotational flow can always be described in terms of the gradient of a scalar potential function. A physical feeling for what is meant by irrotational flow is possible by noting that if a small paddle wheel (see Sec. 2-2) is immersed at any point in the fluid and the paddle wheel never rotates, then the flow has no circulation, and is irrotational.

In rotational flow, the second type of flow field, the paddle wheel in the fluid would be found to rotate. The rate at which the paddle wheel rotates when oriented so as to give maximum rotation, is a measure of the circulation or rotation of the fluid at the given point.

Our main purpose in this section is to study potential flow fields, and in particular, to establish the conditions under which such flow will exist in a fluid. There are essentially two requirements: (1) no external forces that can produce fluid circulation are present, and (2) the fluid has zero viscosity. The presence of viscosity in a fluid causes rotational flow to develop, and in consequence, viscous fluids cannot be adequately described in terms of a scalar potential theory alone.

To show that irrotational flow is governed by Laplace's equation, we consider a small volume element ΔV, commonly called the *control volume*, within the fluid at a point P. Conservation of mass flow or transport out of the control volume requires that

$$\nabla \cdot (\rho\overline{v}) = \rho_g - \frac{\partial\rho}{\partial t} \tag{2-5.2}$$

The net mass flow per unit volume out of the control volume is given by the divergence of $\rho\overline{v}$ where ρ denotes mass density Kg/m^3. The net outward mass flow per unit volume must equal the rate of decrease $-\partial\rho/\partial t$ of density or mass per unit volume, plus the rate of mass generation ρ_g per unit volume. This is the mass conservation law, and is given by Eq. (2-5.2). The density rate of mass generation ρ_g might, for example, denote the generation of the fluid component by a chemical reaction that occurs within the control volume.

If the fluid is incompressible, and many fluids such as water, oil, etc. may be treated as such, then $\partial\rho/\partial t$ will be zero since the density cannot change in time. If also the flow is irrotational, then $\overline{v} = -\nabla\Phi$, where Φ is called the *velocity potential*. Thus for incompressible irrotational flow (ρ = constant) we have

$$\nabla \cdot (\rho\overline{v}) = \rho\nabla \cdot \overline{v} = -\rho\nabla^2\Phi = \rho_g$$

or

$$\nabla^2\Phi = -\frac{\rho_g}{\rho} \tag{2-5.3}$$

which is Poisson's equation. If there is no fluid generation or source ρ_g present, then $\nabla\rho \cdot \overline{v} = 0$ and Φ is a solution of Laplace's equation

$$\nabla^2\Phi = 0 \tag{2-5.4}$$

Thus Laplace's equation governs irrotational flow in an incompressible fluid.

The boundary conditions for fluid flow are quite complicated. At a rigid surface the normal component of the velocity must be zero since there can be no flow into a rigid or solid surface. The tangential components of the fluid velocity near solid surfaces are more difficult to specify. Since all fluids have finite viscosity, there is no relative slip between a solid boundary and the fluid flowing past it. Fluids like air and water have a small viscosity and the transition from no relative velocity at the wall to the velocity that would prevail in potential flow takes place in a very thin layer. This thin layer is known as the boundary layer. In the case of high speed flow, such as might exist in aircraft or missiles, the boundary layer is rarely more than one-tenth of an inch thick. The flow in the general body of the fluid outside of the boundary layer is irrotational, and our foregoing considerations apply. As a result, the approximation of irrotational flow within the body of the fluid is valid, except directly at the surface of the solid boundary (up to, but not through the boundary layer).

2-6. Heat Conduction

In any material body at a finite absolute temperature the molecules constituting the body will execute continual random motions. The kinetic energy associated with this random motion is the thermal or heat energy stored in the material. In a unit volume of material with mass density ρ, the amount of heat energy stored is given by $c_p\rho\Theta$ where c_p is the specific heat of the material. If some portion of a body is at a higher temperature than the surrounding regions, the molecules with greater kinetic energy in this region will impart or give up by collisions some of their energy to the less energetic molecules in the lower temperature surrounding regions. Thus heat energy flows from a region of high temperature to one of lower temperature. The Fourier law states that the rate of heat energy flow is proportional to the gradient of the temperature, or

$$\bar{q} = -K\nabla\Theta \qquad \text{Joule/m}^2\text{-sec} \tag{2-6.1}$$

This result has already been introduced [see Eq. (1-4.2)]. When heat generation exists, we must relate this to the divergence of $\bar{q}$,

$$\nabla \cdot \bar{q} = \rho_g$$

By combining this with Eq. (2-6.1) we have that

$$\nabla^2\Theta = -\frac{\rho_g}{K} \tag{2-6.2}$$

which is Poisson's equation. If there is no heat generation, then the temperature distribution Θ is governed by Laplace's equation

$$\nabla^2\Theta = 0 \tag{2-6.3}$$

The boundary conditions for heat flow are, for two adjacent regions in contact with each other

$$\Theta_1 = \Theta_2$$

$$K_1 \frac{\partial\Theta_1}{\partial n} = K_2 \frac{\partial\Theta_2}{\partial n} \tag{2-6.4}$$

where K_1, Θ_1 and K_2, Θ_2 refer respectively to regions 1 and 2. The first boundary condition (2-6.4) states that the temperature is a continuous function across the boundary. The second condition states that the heat flux that flows across the surface between two mediums is a continuous function at the surface.

2-7. Electrostatic Fields

In Chap. 1 it was noted that an electric field is associated with the electric current flow field. This electric field is, in fact, the physical cause for current in a medium with finite conductivity. In this section we will develop the basic equations governing the static electric field itself. In Chap. 5 a more detailed study of the physical properties of the electrostatic field is presented.

The development proceeds from the experimental law of Coulomb which shows that two electric charges Q_1 and Q_2 a distance R apart attract each other if they are of opposite sign and repel each other if they have the same sign. The force of attraction or repulsion in vacuum is given yby

$$F = \frac{Q_1 Q_2}{4\pi\varepsilon_o R^2} \tag{2-7.1}$$

where $4\pi\varepsilon_o$ is a constant of proportionality, and ε_o [= $(1/36\pi) \times 10^{-9}$ Farad/meter] is the *permittivity* of free space. The force is measured in Newton, the charge is in Coulomb, and the distance R is in meters. The force acting between two point charges is conveniently regarded from the field point of view as arising from a vector force field set up by each charge. This vector force field is called the *electric field intensity* and is denoted by the symbol $\overline{E}$. Thus the electric field set up by a point charge in vacuum is given by the expression

$$\overline{E} = \frac{Q}{4\pi\varepsilon_o R^2}\,\overline{a}_R \tag{2-7.2}$$

where $\overline{a}_R$ is a unit vector directed radially outward from Q. A test charge Q_t placed in the force field $\overline{E}$ of Q at a distance R from Q will experience a force

$$\overline{F} = Q_t\overline{E} = \frac{Q\,Q_t}{4\pi\varepsilon_o R^2}\,\overline{a}_R \tag{2-7.3}$$

This equation is the vector form of Coulomb's law given by Eq. (2-7.1).

If we consider the charge Q to be specified with respect to a reference frame by $\overline{r}'$, and that of the test charge to be specified by $\overline{r}$, then it is easily verified that

$$\frac{\overline{a}_R}{R^2} = \frac{\overline{r}-\overline{r}'}{|\overline{r}-\overline{r}'|^3} = -\nabla\frac{1}{R} = -\nabla\frac{1}{|\overline{r}-\overline{r}'|}$$

where

$$R = [(x-x')^2 + (y-y')^2 + (z-z')^2]^{1/2} \tag{2-7.4}$$

$$\overline{r} = x\,\overline{a}_x + y\,\overline{a}_y + z\,\overline{a}_z$$

$$\overline{r}' = x'\overline{a}_x + y'\overline{a}_y + z'\overline{a}_z$$

In the light of this, it follows that

$$\overline{E} = -\frac{Q}{4\pi\varepsilon_o}\nabla\left(\frac{1}{R}\right) \tag{2-7.5}$$

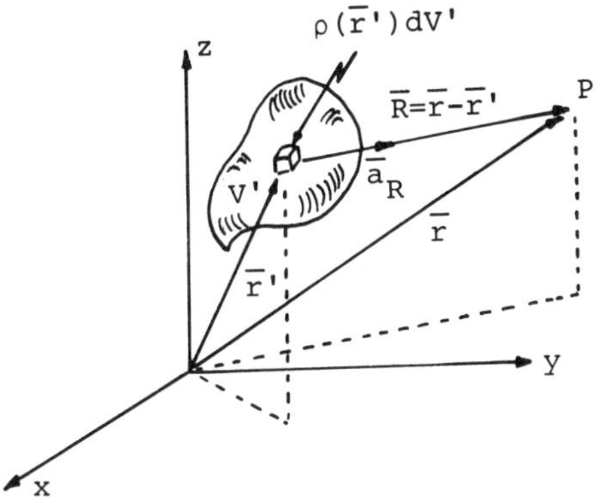

Figure 2-7.1. The general charge distribution.

But since the curl of the gradient is identically zero, we find that

$$\nabla \times \overline{E} = -\frac{Q}{4\pi\varepsilon_o} \nabla \times \nabla \frac{1}{R} = 0 \tag{2-7.6}$$

We are thus able to express $\overline{E}$ as the gradient of a scalar potential Φ. From Eq. (2-7.5) we see that

$$\overline{E} = -\nabla\Phi \qquad \text{a)}$$

where (2-7.7)

$$\Phi = \frac{Q}{4\pi\varepsilon_o R} \qquad \text{b)}$$

Suppose that we have a colume distributionof charge, with density $(\overline{r}')$ as shown in Fig. 2-7.1. The resultant electric field as obtained by superposition is

$$\overline{E}(\overline{r}) = \int_{V'} \frac{\rho(\overline{r}')(\overline{r}-\overline{r}')}{4\pi\varepsilon_o|\overline{r}-\overline{r}'|^3} dV' \tag{2-7.8}$$

$\overline{E}(\overline{r})$ is more readily evaluated as the negative gradient of the potential Φ,

$$\overline{E} = -\nabla\Phi = -\nabla \int_{V'} \frac{\rho(\overline{r}')}{4\pi\varepsilon_o|\overline{r}-\overline{r}'|} dV' \tag{2-7.9}$$

where the integral represents the potential at point P at a distance r due to the contribution of all charges distributed in the volume V. The integral on the right is a solution of Poisson's equation

$$\nabla^2\Phi = -\frac{\rho}{\varepsilon_o}$$

and analytic methods for carrying out the solution will be discussed in some detail in Chap. 4. That Poisson's equation applies is an expected result since the total flux of $\epsilon_o \overline{E}$ from a point charge is given by

$$\oint_S \epsilon_o \overline{E} \cdot d\overline{S} = Q \oint_S \frac{\overline{a}_R \cdot d\overline{S}}{4\pi R^2} = Q \oint_S \frac{d\Omega}{4\pi} = Q \tag{2-7.10}$$

where Q equals the source strength and where $d\Omega = \overline{a}_R \cdot d\overline{S}/R^2$ defines the solid angle subtended by dS. Thus $\nabla \cdot \overline{E}$ will equal $1/\epsilon_o$ times the source density. This states that

$$-\nabla \cdot \overline{E} = \nabla \cdot \nabla\Phi = \nabla^2\Phi = -\frac{\rho}{\epsilon_o}$$

which is Poisson's equation.

The electrostatic field is set up by a distribution of electric charges. If the material has a finite conductivity, the force of the electric field will cause the negative charge (electrons) in a normal conductor to flow towards the positive charge. The rate of charge flow is the current, with the positive sense chosen to conform to the direction of positive charge flow. The current density is related to the electric field by Ohm's law, i.e.,

$$\overline{J} = \sigma\overline{E} \tag{2-7.11}$$

as already discussed in Chap. 1.

The current density $\overline{J}$ is related to the charge density ρ by an equation called the charge *continuity* equation. If we consider a small volume element dV, then the rate at which charge flows out of this volume element per unit volume is given by $\nabla \cdot \overline{J}$ and must equal the rate of decrease of the charge density within dV. The continuity equation for conduction charges is then

$$\nabla \cdot \overline{J} = -\frac{\partial\rho}{\partial t} \tag{2-7.12}$$

Under steady state conditions $\partial\rho/\partial t = 0$ and so $\nabla \cdot \overline{J} = 0$. But since $\overline{J} = \sigma\overline{E}$ and $\overline{E} = -\nabla\Phi$, we find that $\overline{J}$ is determined by a solution of Poisson's equation. Since $\partial\rho/\partial t$ is required to be zero under steady state conditions, then it is required that some external source of charge must be present to replenish the charge that is drained from a given region by the current. This external source is very often a battery in which a chemical reaction provides the generation of the required charge. The steady state current field is always solenoidal, i.e., $\nabla \cdot \overline{J} = 0$, and flows in continuous tubes from one battery terminal through the external region and back to the other terminal, and subsequently through the battery.

At times it is convenient to regard the battery terminals or any other set of electrodes as the equivalent source region for the current field. In this case the normal component $\overline{J} \cdot \overline{n}$ at the electrode surface is the equivalent surface source strength. However, the true physical source is the charge distribution ρ maintained by a battery (or other equivalent source) which sets up an electrostatic field and thereby a steady flow of charge.

The boundary conditions for the steady state current field are the same as those for seepage flow and heat conduction. Thus at a boundary between mediums with conductivities σ_1 and σ_2 the condition that there shall be no change in the charge density at the boundary requires that the normal component of the flow be continuous, or

$$J_{1n} = J_{2n} \qquad \text{a)}$$

or equivalently (2-7.13)

$$\sigma_1 \frac{\partial \Phi_1}{\partial n} = \sigma_2 \frac{\partial \Phi_2}{\partial n} \qquad \text{b)}$$

In addition, the potential Φ must be a single valued function and hence is continuous at the boundary, so that

$$\Phi_1 = \Phi_2$$

at the common boundary.

REVIEW QUESTIONS

1. Why cannot the divergence be identically zero everywhere for an irrotational field? What are the fields which may violate this condition?
2. Write explicitly the form for $\nabla \times \overline{F}$ in rectangular coordinates.
3. For a rotating body with angular velocity $\overline{\omega}$ the following relation holds $\nabla x \overline{v} = 2\overline{\omega}$ where $\overline{v}$ is the velocity of a point of the rotating body. What does this relation tell us?
4. If a conductor of radius a carries a current density $\overline{J}$, how does the magnetic field intensity $\overline{H}$ vary with respect to the distance r?
5. Since $\nabla \cdot \overline{H} = 0$ is always true throughout all of space, what basic conclusion can we deduce from it?
6. State Gauss theorem.
7. State the Stokes theorem.
8. What do we call a field whose streamlines do not intersect?
9. What type of an equation governs steady state heat flow?
10. What is the force equation between two charges separated by a distance R?

11. State the continuity equation for charges.

12. State Ohm's law.

13. What type of equation relates the potential in an electric field that is produced by a static charge distribution?

PROBLEMS

2-2.1. A vector field $\overline{A}$ is defined by: $\overline{A} = x^2\overline{a}_x + xyz\,\overline{a}_y + y^2z^2\overline{a}_z$. Find the magnitude and direction of $\nabla \times \overline{A}$, and its components $(\nabla \times \overline{A})_x$, $(\nabla \times \overline{A})_y$, and $(\nabla \times \overline{A})_z$.

2-2.2. Find the curl of the following fields:

a. $\overline{F} = xy\overline{a}_x + yz\overline{a}_y + xyz\overline{a}_z$

b. $\overline{F} = (x^2 + y^2 + z^2)\overline{a}_x + y\overline{a}_z$

c. $\overline{F} = 3x\overline{a}_x + 3y\overline{a}_y + 3z\overline{a}_z$.

2-2.3. Show that for any vector $\overline{A}$, $\nabla \cdot \nabla \times \overline{A} = 0$.

2-2.4. From the definition of curl, show that the components of the curl of a vector field $\overline{F}(x,y,z)$ along Y and Z directions are given respectively by:

$$\frac{\partial F_x}{\partial z} - \frac{\partial F_z}{\partial x}\,; \quad \frac{\partial F_y}{\partial z} - \frac{\partial F_x}{\partial y}\,.$$

2-2.5. Plot the field $\nabla \times \overline{F}$ at the following points: $(1,45^\circ)$, $(1,65^\circ)$, $(2,45^\circ)$ and $(2,65^\circ)$ for $\overline{F} = x\overline{a}_x + z^2\overline{a}_y + x^3\overline{a}_z$.

2-2.6. If the magnetic vector potential is $\overline{A} = xy\overline{a}_x + xyz\overline{a}_z$, what is the component of the magnetic field $\overline{B}$ along the X-direction at point (1,2,4)?

2-2.7. The fluid velocity across a channel is given by $\overline{v} = v_0\, y(d-y)\,\overline{a}_x$ where $\underline{d}$ is its width. Plot the angular velocity $\overline{\omega}$ (vorticity) versus distance across the channel, $0 \leq y \leq d$.

2-2.8. Find and plot the magnetic field intensity $\overline{H}$ in the region $0 \leq r \leq \infty$ if a composite conductor carries opposite currents I_1 and I_2 as shown in Fig. P2-2.8.

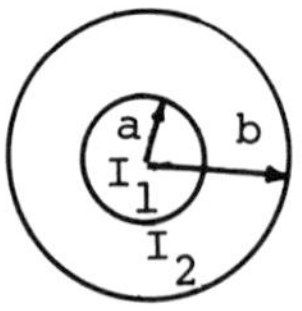

Figure P2-2.8.

2-2.9. A vector $\overline{A}$ is defined by: $\overline{A} = (x^2 - y^2)\overline{a}_x - 2xy\,\overline{a}_y$.

(a) Can the vector $\overline{A}$ be represented as the gradient of a scalar function?

(b) Find the value of the line integral of $\overline{A}$ over the contour of a square in the xy plane with sides parallel to the two axes and one corner located at the origin and another corner at x = y = 2.

2-2.10. Find the $\nabla \times \overline{H}$ and magnitude of $\nabla \times \overline{H}$ at the cylindrical coordinate point $(1, \pi/4, 1)$ for $\overline{H} = (1 - 1/r)\cos\phi\,\overline{a}_r + (1 - 1/r)\sin\phi\,\overline{a}_\phi + rz\,\overline{a}_z$, and at the spherical coordinate point $(1, \pi/4, \pi/4)$ for $\overline{H} = r\cos\phi\,\overline{a}_r + r^2\overline{a}_\theta + r\sin\theta\,\overline{a}_\phi$.

2-3.1. Given the function $\overline{F} = 3x\overline{a}_x + 2xy^2\overline{a}_y$, find the value of the integrals $\int_S \nabla \times \overline{F} \cdot d\overline{S}$ and $\oint_C \overline{F} \cdot d\overline{\ell}$ over the areas and the contours shown:

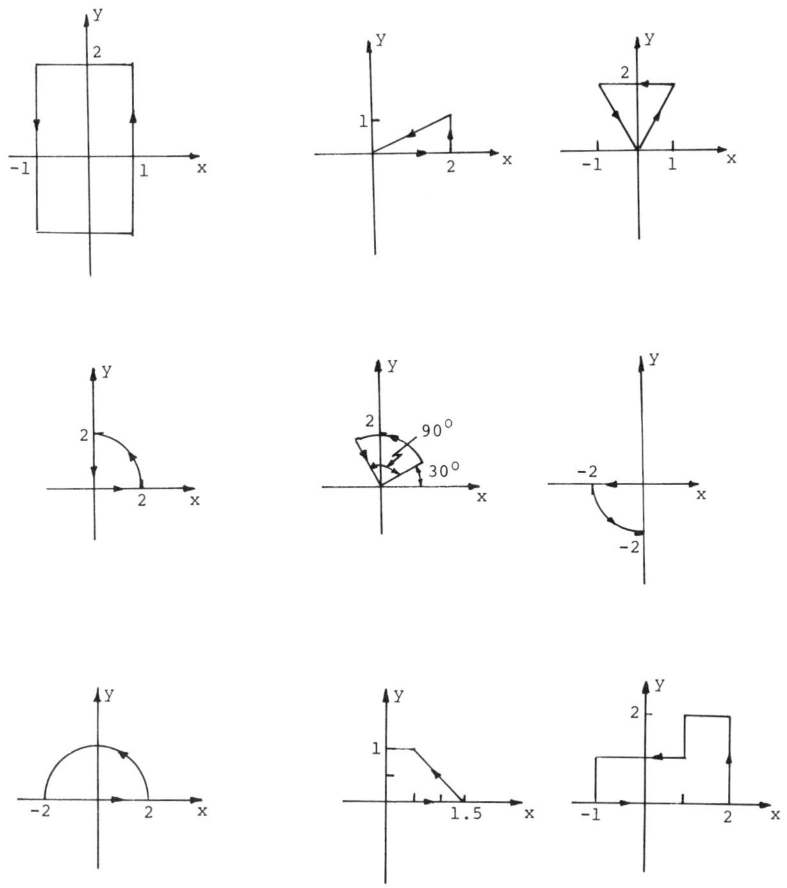

Figure P2-3,1.

2-3.2. A scalar source of strength ρ is producing a vector field $\overline{F} = x^2y^2\overline{a}_x + x^3y^3\overline{a}_y + xyz\ \overline{a}_z$. Find the total source strength $Q = \int_V \rho\ dV$ within a cube 10 cm on a side lying in the first octant and having three of its sides coincide with the three coordinate planes.

2-3.3. A total quantity Q of source stuff is uniformly distributed throughout a sphere of radius a.

(a) By an application of Gauss' law find expressions for the potential at all points in space from r = 0 outward.

(b) Sketch the variation of the potential and the potential gradient with r.

(c) Show that the potential function satisfies Poisson's equation within the sphere, and Laplace's equation outside of the sphere.

2-3.4. What is the resistance between the inner and outer surfaces of concentric spherical shells of radii 10 cm. and 25 cm. that is filled with sea water?

2-3.5. By how much must we increase the current or decrease the area so that the field inside of a conductor increases by 10 percent.

2-3.6. Find the curl of the following vector field in cylindrical coordinates r, ϕ, z: $\overline{A} = \overline{a}_z kr^2 \cos 2\phi$, where k is a constant. Show that the line integral of $\overline{A}$ around the contour C equals the flux of $\nabla \times \overline{A}$ through C (Stokes' law), i.e., $\oint_C \overline{A} \cdot \overline{d\ell} = \int_S \nabla \times \overline{A} \cdot \overline{dS}$.

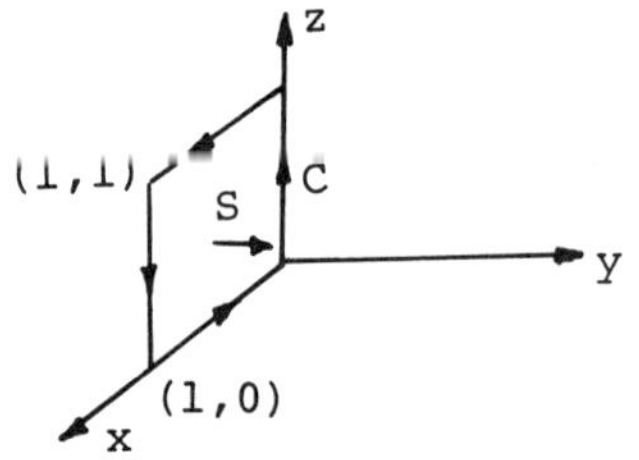

Figure P2-3.6.

2-3.7. Evaluate the curl of $\overline{a}_z\ e^{-jkr}/r$ in spherical coordinates r, θ, ϕ by first expressing $\overline{a}_z$ in terms of components along the unit vectors $\overline{a}_r$, $\overline{a}_\theta$, $\overline{a}_\phi$, i.e., $\overline{a}_z = a_1\overline{a}_r + a_2\overline{a}_\theta + a_3\overline{a}_\phi$ where a_1, a_2, a_3 are to be found.

2-4.1. Find and sketch the stream function and the potential function Φ if the velocity field is given by

$$\overline{v} = \frac{x}{x^2+y^2}\overline{a}_x + \frac{y}{x^2+y^2}\overline{a}_y.$$

[Ans: y = Cx.]

2-4.2. If the electric field is given by $\overline{E} = 1.5\ \overline{a}_x + 2.5\ \overline{a}_y$, find the stream function and sketch the streamlines if the constant of integration takes the values 1, 2, and 3.

2-4.3. If the magnetic field is given by: $\overline{H} = (y + b)\ \overline{a}_x - (x + a)\ \overline{a}_y$, find the stream function and sketch the streamlines if the constant of integration takes the values 1, 2, and -4.

2-4.4. The two dimensional velocity field is given by $\overline{v} = r\ \overline{a}_r$. Find the stream function and sketch the field.
[Hint: change $\overline{v}$ to cartesian coordinates.]

2-7.1. If it were possible for 1 per cent of the atoms of two humans, each weighing 60 Kg, to be charged, what would be the force developed if they were standing 10 m apart?

2-7.2. If the electric field between the plates of a capacitor is 10^3 Volt/cm, what is the force exerted on a singly ionized He atom, and on an electron, located within this field?

2-7.3. Find the force on an electron and the corresponding electric field at the point P due to the charge array shown in Fig. P2-7.3a. Repeat for the charge array shown in Fig. P2-7.3b.

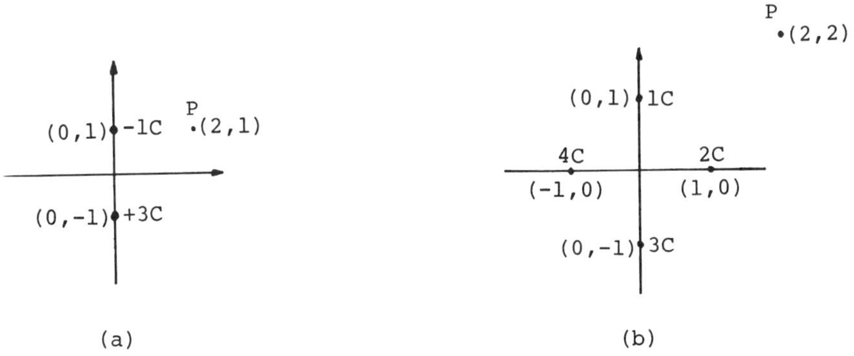

Figure P2-7.3.

2-7.4. Consider two media with conductivities σ_1 and σ_2 separated by a plane boundary. Electric current flows toward the boundary at an angle θ_1 relative to the interface normal in the medium with conductivity σ_1. Show that the current flow lines are bent or refracted away from the normal in medium two if $\sigma_2 > \sigma_1$ and that the expression describing the refraction of the current flow lines is: $\sigma_1 \tan\theta_2 = \sigma_2 \tan\theta_1$, where θ_2 is the angle of the flow lines relative to the interface normal in the medium with conductivity σ_2.

CHAPTER 3

BOUNDARY VALUE PROBLEMS - APPROXIMATE SOLUTIONS

When the boundary conditions are such that analytic methods for solving Laplace's equations cannot be used, recourse to certain approximate techniques is possible. It is the purpose of this chapter to examine such important methods, even before considering analytic methods.

3-1. The Method of Curvilinear Squares

Several fundamental features of conservative fields have already been established. These are noted again for convenience:

1. Stream lines or flow lines and equipotential surfaces must everywhere intersect at right angles.
2. The flow lines meet all equipotential boundary surfaces at right angles.
3. At all boundary surfaces at which the boundary condition is $\partial\Phi/\partial n = 0$ the flow lines are parallel to the boundary surface.

If, in addition to satisfying the boundary conditions, the field lines and the equipotentials can be made to form *curvilinear squares*, the result can be shown to be a true picture of the field distribution. A curvilinear square is a four-sided figure usually, the sides of which intersect at right angles. When properly subdivided into smaller units by the use of additional flow lines and equipotentials, the resulting curvilinear squares approach true squares. Although it will be convenient to continue the discussion in this chapter in terms of electric current and heat conduction, the principles involved apply to all problems which are described by Laplace's equation.

In order to examine the technique in greater detail, consider Fig. 3-1.1a, which represents a portion of a field distribution. In one part of this figure the

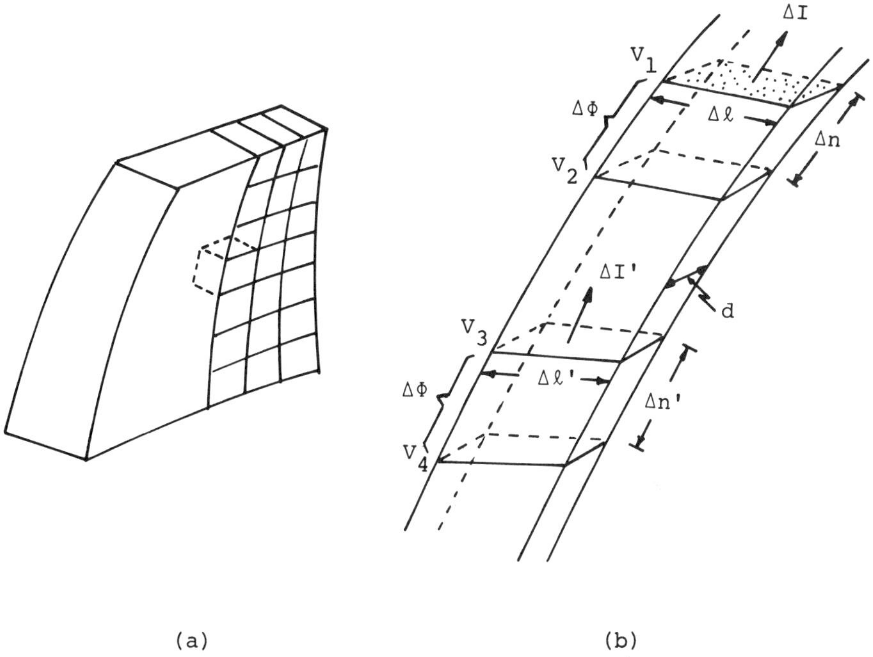

Figure 3-1.1. A representative field distribution.

curvilinear squares are large, and there is considerable curvature to the sides of the square. The right hand section shows the effect of using more equipotential and flow lines. It is clear that the squares in this center section approach more nearly perfect squares. If this subdivision were carried to the limit, the resulting curvilinear squares would become perfect squares.

Let us calculate the total current ΔI through an elementary area or tube of the current flow field in the region marked 1. From Fig. 3-1.1b it is clear that the total current through the area $\Delta\ell$ wide and $\underline{d}$ deep is, since the current density vector is normal to this area,

$$\Delta I = J d \Delta\ell$$

If, for simplicity, $\underline{d}$ is chosen equal to unity, then

$$\Delta I = J\Delta\ell \quad \text{per unit depth} \tag{3-1.1}$$

Also, the magnitude of the electric field strength E is given by

$$E = \frac{d\Phi}{dn} \doteq \frac{\Delta\Phi}{\Delta n} \tag{3-1.2}$$

Hence, from Ohm's law it follows that

$$J = \sigma E = \sigma \frac{d\Phi}{dn} \doteq \sigma \frac{\Delta\Phi}{\Delta n} \tag{3-1.3}$$

Now combine Eq. (3-1.3) with Eq. (3-1.1), which yields

$$\Delta I = \sigma \frac{\Delta\Phi}{\Delta n} \Delta\ell = \sigma\Delta\Phi\left(\frac{\Delta\ell}{\Delta n}\right) \tag{3-1.4}$$

A similar analysis may be carried out on some other square, say that labeled 2 in Fig. 3-1.1b. Suppose that the values of all quantities in this region are denoted by primes. Then, following the same development as above, it follows that

$$\Delta I' = J'\Delta\ell' \qquad \text{a)}$$

$$J' = \sigma E' = \sigma \frac{\Delta\Phi'}{\Delta n'} \qquad \text{b)} \tag{3-1.5}$$

$$\Delta I' = \sigma\Delta\Phi' \left(\frac{\Delta\ell'}{\Delta n'}\right) \qquad \text{c)}$$

From the definition or significance of a current line, the tube of current, and Ohm's law, the currents ΔI and $\Delta I'$ must be equal since no sources exist in the region being considered. Then

$$\sigma\Delta\Phi \frac{\Delta\ell}{\Delta n} = \sigma\Delta\Phi' \frac{\Delta\ell'}{\Delta n'}$$

or

$$\Delta\Phi = \frac{\Delta\ell'/\Delta n'}{\Delta\ell/\Delta n} \Delta\Phi' \tag{3-1.6}$$

In general, $\Delta\ell$, Δn, and $\Delta\ell'$, $\Delta n'$ vary with the convergence or divergence of the current lines and the equipotentials. But, by the method of construction here contemplated, their ratio is everywhere constant and chosen equal to unity for convenience in drawing. Thus,

$$\Delta\Phi = \Delta\Phi' \tag{3-1.7}$$

As a result, the potential difference between adjacent equipotentials is constant, whence

$$V_4 - V_3 = V_3 - V_2 = V_2 - V_1 = \Delta V = \Delta\Phi$$

Moreover, since by construction the ratio $\Delta\ell/\Delta n$ is unity, it follows that the total current through each tube of the current field is the same, and from Eq. (3-1.4)

$$\Delta I = \sigma\Delta\Phi \left(\frac{\Delta \ell}{\Delta n}\right) = \sigma\Delta\Phi \tag{3-1.8}$$

This is a very important result since it implies that only one field distribution exists for a given set of boundary conditions, and this field satisfies Ohm's law. If, therefore, the current lines and equipotentials are laid out so that they form curvilinear squares in the region of the specified boundaries, the resulting field distribution is the true field distribution, since it satisfies the boundary conditions and Ohm's law. But we have already found that Ohm's law implies Laplace's equation; consequently, the method of curvilinear squares is a means for solving Laplace's equation.

3-2. Technique of Field Mapping

To develop a facility in field mapping requires a considerable amount of practice and experience. Often a complex field can be reduced to a series of simple special cases which can be properly associated and correlated. This requires experience with a number of special forms and the field distribution associated with them. Two special forms are illustrated:

1. The 90° corner. This is illustrated in Fig. 3-2.1a. It should be observed that two symmetries exist, flow-line symmetry and construction symmetry. The second electrode is assumed at an infinite distance from the corner.
2. The 270° corner. This is illustrated in Fig. 3-2.1b. As in item 1, the second electrode is at an infinite distance from the corner.

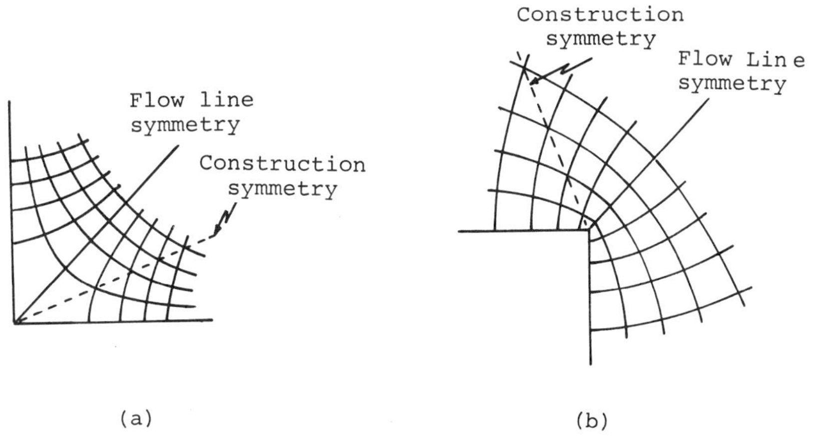

Figure 3-2.1. (a) The 90° corner. (b) The 270° corner.

The mechanics of field plotting are best described by a series of rules of procedure:

1. Begin with several sheets of tracing paper, a soft pencil, and an eraser.
2. Lay out in ink the boundaries around which or within which the field is to be mapped.
3. Examine the geometry carefully to take advantage of any symmetries that may exist.
4. Cover the entire field with large curvilinear squares, however erroneous they may be. At the outset, it is advisable to concentrate on the orthogonality property rather than on the equilateral property. The number of equipotential lines should be small initially, since subdivision can be effected later, when the general nature of the field distribution has been established.
5. Make successive corrections to the map, maintaining the ultimate curvilinear square objective in mind. It may be necessary after a number of corrections to transfer the field plot to a new sheet of paper, for subsequent and continued subdivision. The use of tracing paper facilitates this transfer.
6. Continue the process of revision and subdivision until the orthogonal quadrilaterals become curvilinear squares.

These rules of procedure are general guides, and may be modified for specific problems. The accuracy of the resulting field map is a function of the artistic skill, the patience and perseverance, and the available time of the sketcher.

3-3. Determination of Resistance From Field Sketch

We continue our study by casting the field plot into a means for determining the resistance of the configuration under survey. This will allow the determination of the resistance of conductors of all plane shapes of constant thickness from graphically determined curvilinear square plots. To examine the situation, refer to a unit depth of a two dimensional field, as illustrated in Fig. 3-3.1.

From Eq. (3-1.8) the number of current lines per tube (the total current through the specified tube) is given by

$$\Delta I = \sigma \left(\frac{\Delta \ell}{\Delta n}\right) \Delta \Phi$$

But since the field is constructed of curvilinear squares $\Delta \ell/\Delta n = 1$. Thus,

$$\Delta I = \sigma \Delta \Phi$$

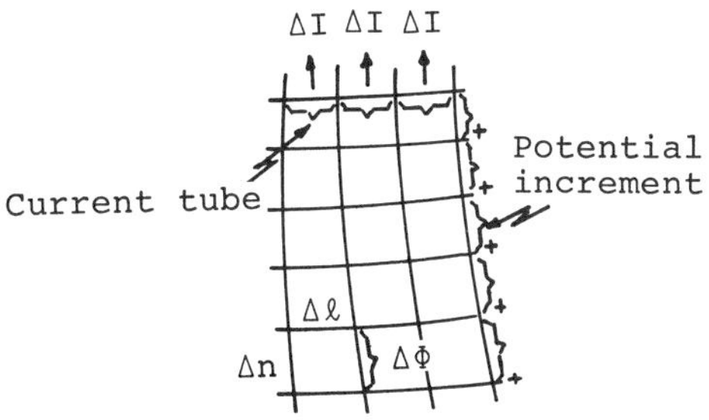

Figure 3-3.1. A two dimensional field.

But the total number of current lines must equal the number of current lines per tube times the number of tubes. If there are N_i tubes, then the total current is

$$I = N_i \Delta I = N_i \sigma \Delta \Phi \qquad (3\text{-}3.1)$$

Moreover, the potential difference between all equipotential lines is equal, and the total potential difference between the specified boundaries is

$$V = N_v \Delta \Phi \qquad (3\text{-}3.2)$$

where N_v is the total number of potential increments between the specified boundaries. Thus, dividing Eq. (3-3.2) by Eq. (3-3.1) gives, for the resistance

$$r = \frac{V}{I} = \frac{N_v}{\sigma N_i} \text{ Ohm-m of depth} \qquad (3\text{-}3.3)$$

The units are those of $1/\sigma$ since the number ratio is dimensionless, and the depth of thickness has been chosen as 1 m. For a specified depth d the resistance is

$$R = \frac{N_v}{\sigma d N_i} \text{ Ohm} \qquad (3\text{-}3.4)$$

An alternative approach is the following: Suppose that it is desired to determine the resistance of an individual curvilinear square. This is given by

$$\Delta R = \frac{\Delta \Phi}{d \Delta I} = \frac{\Delta \Phi}{d \sigma \Delta \Phi} = \frac{1}{\sigma d} \qquad (3\text{-}3.5)$$

Thus, $1/\sigma d$ is the resistance of a prism of depth d whose base is the curvilinear square. The total resistance may be considered as consisting of the resistance of N_i parallel paths each containing N_v resistors in series. Hence

$$R = \frac{N_v}{N_i} \Delta R = \frac{N_v}{\sigma d N_i} \tag{3-3.6}$$

which is the same result determined from the total field picture.

Attention is called to the fact that the resistance of an individual curvilinear square is $1/\sigma d$ and is independent of the physical dimensions of the square. This comes about because the influence on the resistance of an increased physical length is cancelled by the effect on the resistance of an increased width. Because of this, conducting material such as Teledeltos paper is specified in units of Ohm/square.

Example 3-3.1. Determine the resistance between faces A and B of the uniformly thick conductor illustrated in Fig. 3-3.2.

Solution. The resistance is found by mapping the field in this conductor and determining the resistance from the field map. From Fig. 3-3.2 we see that

$$N_i = 4 \qquad N_v = 14$$

Thus we get $R = (1/\sigma d)(14/4)$ Ohm.

For the case of a regular figure, such as a rod or a bar of uniform cross section, Eq. (3-3.6) attains a well known form. Remembering that the squares are of the same physical dimensions, then the number of N_v squares is proportional to L, and the number of N_i units is proportional to W, the width. Thus,

$$R = \frac{1}{\sigma} \frac{L}{Wd} = \frac{L}{\sigma A} \tag{3-3.7}$$

where A is the cross sectional area of the rod, and L is its length.

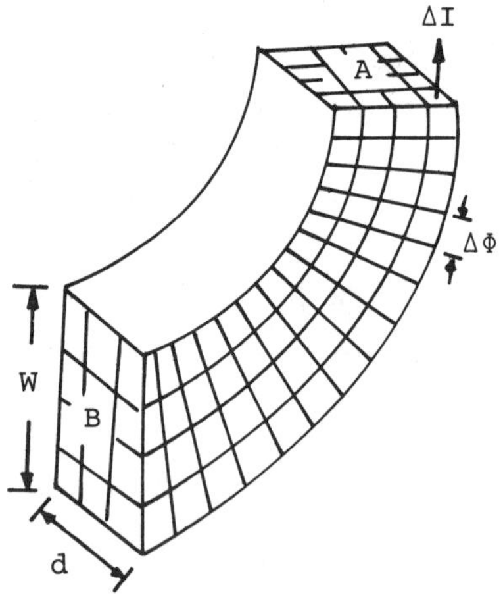

Figure 3-3.2. A conductor of specified shape.

ΔΔΔ

3-4. Resistance Net Approximation

In principle, the method of curvilinear squares yields an exact plot of the field, and hence is an exact solution of Laplace's equation. The inaccuracies in the method arise from the mechanics of deducing the field plot. In some cases it is possible to use a somewhat cruder approximation by dividing the field into larger sections, finding the resistance of each section, and then combining the resistances to find the resultant resistance of the entire structure. This method is best described by means of a specific example.

Example 3-4.1. A heat conducting specimen is illustrated in Fig. 3-4.1. It consists of two different materials and is situated between regions of constant temperature, as indicated. Determine a resistance net approximation for finding the heat flow through the specimen.

Solution. In order to understand the approximations to be made in the resistance net approximation, a curvilinear square plot is shown in Fig. 3-4.2.

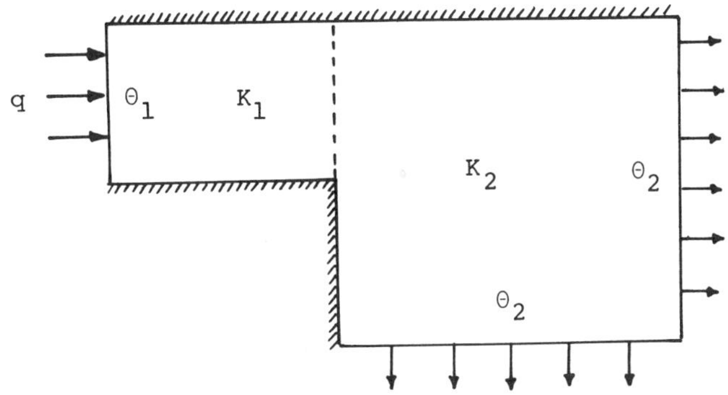

Figure 3-4.1. The two material thermal conductor under study.

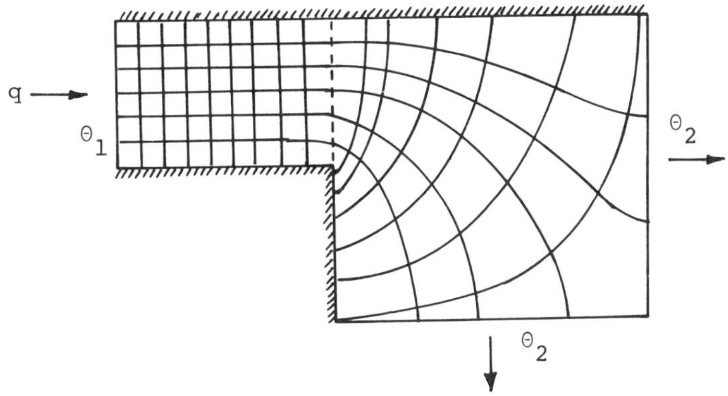

Figure 3-4.2. The curvilinear square field of the heat conductor of Fig. 3-4.1.

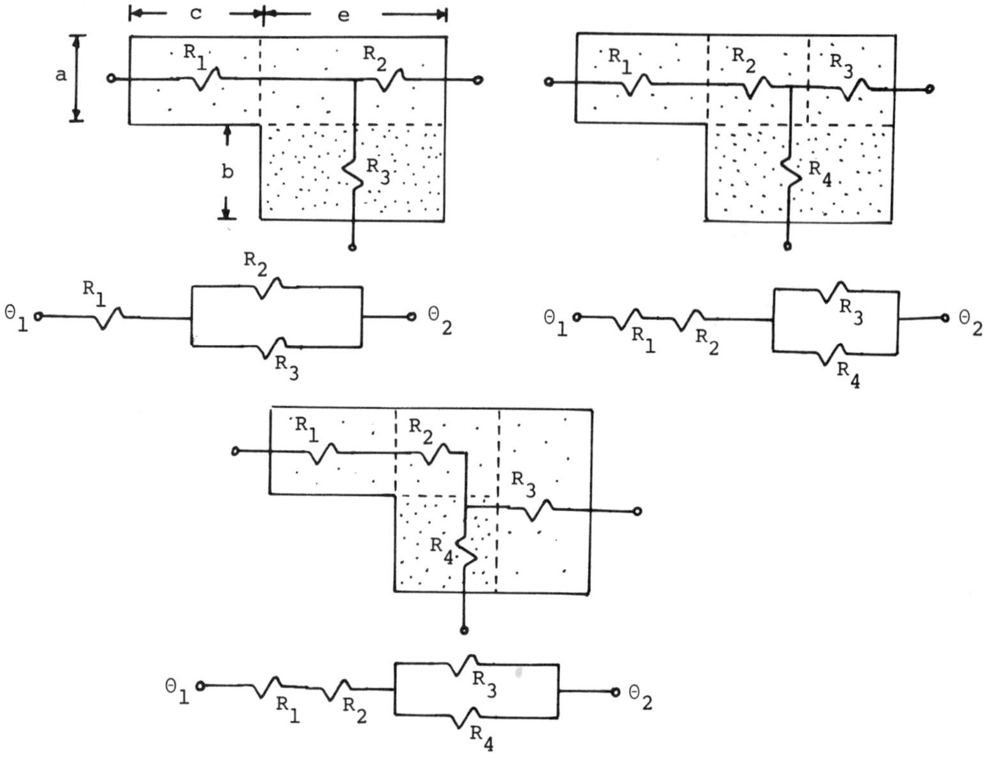

Figure 3-4.3. Three alternative resistance net approximations corresponding to Fig. 3-4.2.

The sketches of Fig. 3-4.3 show a number of possible resistance net approximations. The lines included on these figures represent approximations to the thermal flow lines. Clearly, the approximations arise from the manner in which the field plot in each selected section is chosen. The errors result from the discontinuities that are introduced. As might be surmised, the greater the number of sections into which the specimen is divided, the more nearly will it equal the curvilinear square plot, and the less will be the error. For a block of unit depth the values of R_1, R_2, and R_3 for the first figure are given by [see Eq. (3-3.7)]

$$R_1 = \frac{c}{K_1 a} \qquad R_2 = \frac{e}{K_2 a} \qquad R_3 = \frac{b}{K_2 d}$$

and the total heat flow will be

$$q = \frac{\Theta_1 - \Theta_2}{R}$$

where R is the total resistance given by $R_1 + R_2R_3/(R_2 + R_3)$. Note that in heat flow problems the thermal conductivities K_1 and K_2 replace the electrical conductivity σ for resistance calculations. A procedure similar to the above is followed to evaluate the individual resistances in the other resistance nets in Fig. 3-4.3.

It might be well to note that despite the crudeness of the approximations that may result, a method such as this will ordinarily be within 50 percent of the exact result; often it is considerably better. Approximations of this order are often sufficient to judge the feasibility of a particular engineering design in the early stages of development.

ΔΔΔ

3-5. Numerical Methods - Iteration

Numerical trial and error methods for the solution of Laplace's equation in two dimensions are very commonly used. Various variations of these methods are known as *Relaxation* and *Iteration*. The methods usually begin with a finite difference approximation to Laplace's equation. To find this form, refer to Fig. 3-5.1 which shows a node point 0 at any point in the field which is described by the two-dimensional equation

$$\frac{\partial^2 \Phi}{\partial x^2} + \frac{\partial^2 \Phi}{\partial y^2} = 0 \tag{3-5.1}$$

The potential Φ has different values in general at each of the points marked 1, 2, 3, 4, which are equally spaced at the distances h from the point 0. The value of Φ at each of these points can be written in terms of the potential Φ_0, the value at point 0, by an appropriate application of Taylor's theorem. Initially we consider

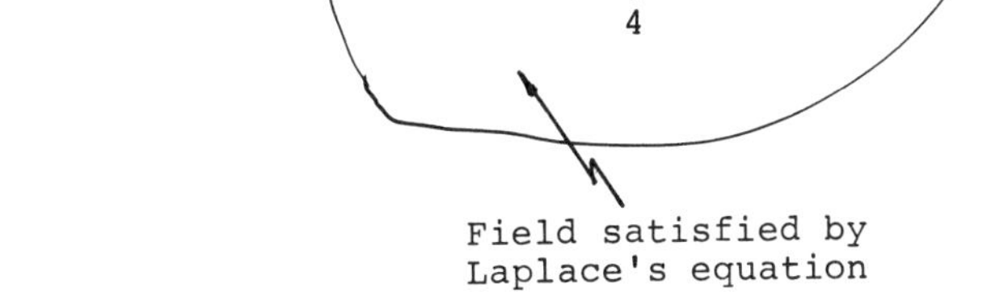

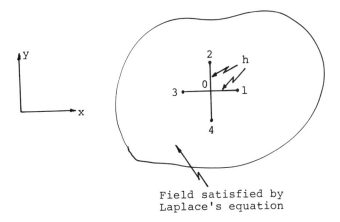

Figure 3-5.1. A four point mesh group in a finite difference approximation to Laplace's equation.

the points 3,0,1, with coordinates $x_o - h$, x_o, $x_o + h$, respectively. The general Taylor series expansion is

$$\Phi(x,y) = \Phi(x_o,y_o) + \left(\frac{\partial\Phi}{\partial x}\right)_o (x-x_o) + \left(\frac{\partial\Phi}{\partial y}\right)_o (y-y_o) + \frac{1}{2!}\left[\left(\frac{\partial^2\Phi}{\partial x^2}\right)_o (x-x_o)^2 + \left(\frac{\partial^2\Phi}{\partial y^2}\right)_o (y-y_o)^2 + 2\left(\frac{\partial^2\Phi}{\partial x\partial y}\right)_o (x-x_o)(y-y_o)\right] + \ldots \qquad (3\text{-}5.2)$$

where the derivatives are evaluated at the point 0 where $x = x_o$, $y = y_o$. This expansion gives for the potential at points 1 and 3

$$\Phi_1 = \Phi_o + \left(\frac{\partial\Phi}{\partial x}\right)_o h + \left(\frac{\partial^2\Phi}{\partial x^2}\right)_o \frac{h^2}{2} + \ldots \qquad \text{a)}$$

$$\Phi_3 = \Phi_o - \left(\frac{\partial\Phi}{\partial x}\right)_o h + \left(\frac{\partial^2\Phi}{\partial x^2}\right)_o \frac{h^2}{2} + \ldots \qquad \text{b)} \qquad (3\text{-}5.3)$$

These equations are added, with the result

$$\Phi_1 + \Phi_3 = 2\Phi_o + h^2 \left(\frac{\partial^2\Phi}{\partial x^2}\right)_o + \text{remainder} \qquad (3\text{-}5.4)$$

But if h is very small the remainder being of order h^4 can be neglected so that

$$h^2\left(\frac{\partial^2\Phi}{\partial x^2}\right)_o \doteq \Phi_1 + \Phi_3 - 2\Phi_o \qquad (3\text{-}5.5)$$

Now proceed in precisely the same way for the y coordinate, with the points labeled 4,0,2, with coordinates $y_o - h$, y_o, $y_o + h$, respectively. The resulting expression corresponding to Eq. (3-5.5) is

$$h^2 \left(\frac{\partial^2\Phi}{\partial y^2}\right)_o = \Phi_2 + \Phi_4 - 2\Phi_o \qquad (3\text{-}5.6)$$

Thus Laplace's equation at point 0 will be satisfied in finite difference form if

$$\left(\frac{\partial^2\Phi}{\partial x^2} + \frac{\partial^2\Phi}{\partial y^2}\right)_o = \frac{\Phi_1 + \Phi_3 + \Phi_2 + \Phi_4 - 4\Phi_o}{h^2} = 0$$

or

$$\Phi_1 + \Phi_2 + \Phi_3 + \Phi_4 = 4\Phi_o \qquad (3\text{-}5.7)$$

Therefore, the potential at point 0 in the center of points 1,2,3,4, is the average of the potentials at these points or

$$\Phi_o = \frac{\Phi_1 + \Phi_2 + \Phi_3 + \Phi_4}{4} \qquad (3\text{-}5.8)$$

To apply these results, the field is divided by a grid into a series of squares which establishes the mesh groups. Three methods exist for establishing the values at the cross-over node or net points. In one, a set of equations is written, yielding a large number of simultaneous equations for the values at each net point. By the nature of the problem, since only nearest neighbor terms exist, sparse matrix methods for solution can be used. The second is an iteration process, and the third is called the relaxation method which is considered in Sec. 3-8.

In the iteration process the known boundary conditions, in terms of known potentials are applied, and starting from the points of known potential, a systematic trial and error or *iteration* process is set up for determining the potential at any point by the use of Eq. (3-5.8). The method consists of assuming a given potential distribution and systematically going back and forth across the grid to adjust the potential distribution according to Eq. (3-5.8). This requires that at each net point the potential be adjusted to be the average of that at the four surrounding points.

The accuracy of this method is dependent on the fineness of the grid and also the amount of time that is spent refining the potentials. If one is to complete such a calculation by hand it is generally best to start with a large grid, get a good estimate of potentials and then subdivide into smaller units and continue the process.

A physical understanding of the process is possible by reference to Fig. 3-5.2 which shows the conducting body replaced by a network or grid of resistors. This configuration might be looked upon as the equivalent of the curvilinear plot with each curvilinear square replaced by its equivalent resistor. Now consider any point 0 in the grid. This is redrawn in Fig. 3-5.3, but in this case we have extended the considerations to include a flow into the node, and q_g might denote the rate of heat flow into point 0 from an external source or due to internal heat generation. Hence we are considering Poisson's equation rather than Laplace's equation. Under

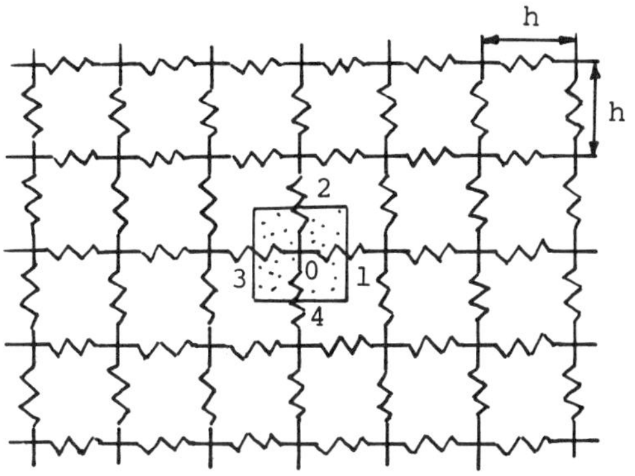

Figure 3-5.2. A conducting body replaced by a network of thermal resistors.

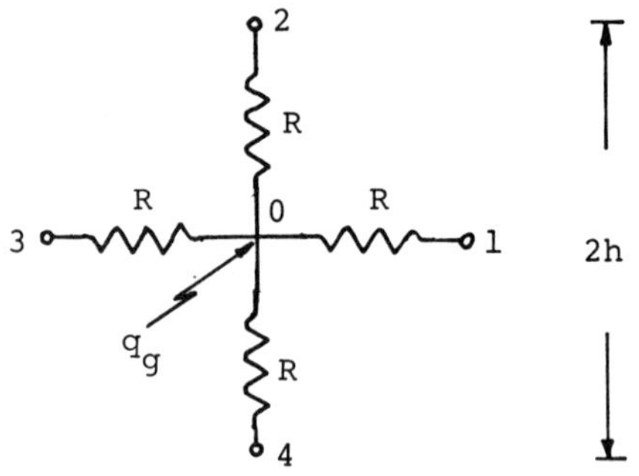

Figure 3-5.3. An element of the thermal network

steady state conditions the rate of heat flow into point 0 must be equal to the rate of heat flow away from point 0. Thus for equilibrium with R = 1/Kd for square cells with depth d,

$$q_g = \frac{1}{R}(\Theta_0 - \Theta_1) + \frac{1}{R}(\Theta_0 - \Theta_2) + \frac{1}{R}(\Theta_0 - \Theta_3) + \frac{1}{R}(\Theta_0 - \Theta_4) \qquad (3\text{-}5.9)$$

The temperature Θ_0 at the node point 0 is thus

$$\Theta_0 = \frac{\Theta_1 + \Theta_2 + \Theta_3 + \Theta_4}{4} + \frac{q_g R}{4} \qquad (3\text{-}5.10)$$

for the case where heat generation is included. When $q_g = 0$, the relationship for Θ_0 is

$$\Theta_0 = \frac{\Theta_1 + \Theta_2 + \Theta_3 + \Theta_4}{4} \qquad (3\text{-}5.11)$$

which is precisely the form of Eq. (3-5.8) which was obtained from purely mathematical considerations. Note that Eq. (3-5.10) leads to a solution of Poisson's equation.

Equations (3-5.8) and (3-5.10) are the finite difference formulas for the Laplacian and Poisson fields for the case of a square grid. If the region being studied is not rectangular in shape, the square grid may not be the most appropriate one. In such a case, some other form of grid can be used, but the finite difference formulas appropriate to the grid would have to be derived. Specifically, refer to Fig. 3-5.4 which shows a hexagonal mesh configuration, a form that is especially useful when the physical boundaries involved are circular. Consider point 0 in the mesh. Again let q_g be the rate of heat flow into point 0 from an external heat source or due to internal heat generation. Under steady state conditions, the rate of heat flow into point 0 must equal the rate of heat flow out of the point 0. Thus

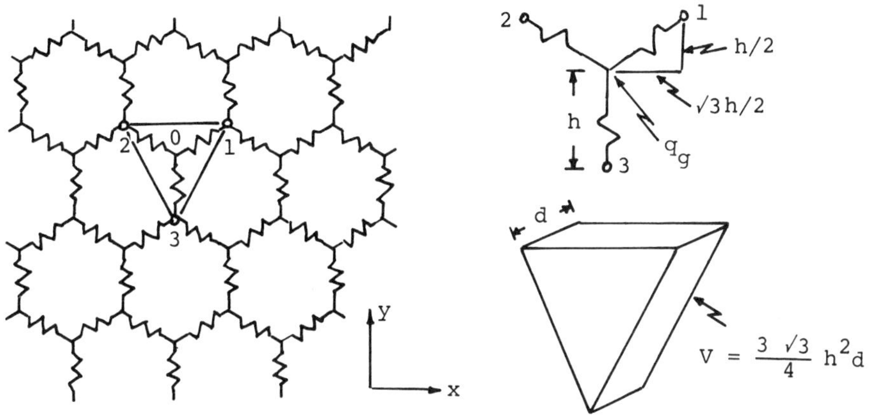

Figure 3-5.4. A hexagonal mesh, and the conditions at a typical point 0 in the mesh.

$$q_g = \frac{1}{R}(\Theta_0 - \Theta_1) + \frac{1}{R}(\Theta_0 - \Theta_2) + \frac{1}{R}(\Theta_0 - \Theta_3) \qquad (3\text{-}5.12)$$

where R is yet to be determined. We solve Eq. (3-5.12) for the temperature Θ_0 of the node 0 when there is heat flow at the rate q_g into the node, thus

$$\Theta_0 = \frac{\Theta_1 + \Theta_2 + \Theta_3}{3} + \frac{q_g R}{3} \qquad (3\text{-}5.13)$$

When $q_g = 0$ we obtain

$$\Theta_0 = \frac{\Theta_1 + \Theta_2 + \Theta_3}{3} \qquad (3\text{-}5.14)$$

which again gives the temperature at the point 0 as the average of that at the three surrounding points. An extension of this method to heat transfer with storage is available in the literature.

It is instructive to derive Eq. (3-5.13) by means of the Taylor expansion since this will also serve to establish the value of the thermal resistance R between any two nodes. For convenience let us choose the origin of the X,Y coordinate system at the node 0. The coordinates of the nodes 1,2,3, are then ($\sqrt{3}$ h/2, h/2), (-$\sqrt{3}$ h/2, h/2), and (0,-h) respectively. To order h^2 the Taylor series expansion gives the following values of the temperatures Θ_1, Θ_2, Θ_3, at nodes 1,2,3:

$$\Theta_1 = \Theta_0 + \left(\frac{\partial\Theta}{\partial x}\right)_0 \frac{\sqrt{3}}{2} h + \left(\frac{\partial\Theta}{\partial y}\right)_0 \frac{h}{2} + \frac{1}{2}\left[\left(\frac{\partial^2\Theta}{\partial x^2}\right)_0 \frac{3h^2}{2} + \left(\frac{\partial^2\Theta}{\partial y^2}\right)_0 \frac{h^2}{4} + 2\left(\frac{\partial^2\Theta}{\partial x \partial y}\right)_0 \frac{\sqrt{3}\, h^2}{4}\right]$$

$$\Theta_2 = \Theta_0 - \left(\frac{\partial\Theta}{\partial x}\right)_0 \frac{\sqrt{3}}{2} h + \left(\frac{\partial\Theta}{\partial y}\right)_0 \frac{h}{2} + \frac{1}{2}\left[\left(\frac{\partial^2\Theta}{\partial x^2}\right)_0 \frac{3h^2}{4} + \left(\frac{\partial^2\Theta}{\partial y^2}\right)_0 \frac{h^2}{4} - 2\left(\frac{\partial^2\Theta}{\partial x \partial y}\right)_0 \frac{\sqrt{3}\, h^2}{4}\right]$$

$$\Theta_3 = \Theta_0 - \left(\frac{\partial\Theta}{\partial y}\right)_0 h + \frac{1}{2}\left(\frac{\partial^2\Theta}{\partial y^2}\right)_0 h^2$$

Upon addition of these three equations we obtain

$$\Theta_1 + \Theta_2 + \Theta_3 = 3\Theta_0 + \frac{3h^2}{4}\left[\left(\frac{\partial^2\Theta}{\partial x^2}\right)_0 + \left(\frac{\partial^2\Theta}{\partial y^2}\right)_0\right]$$

or

$$(\nabla^2\Theta)_0 = \frac{4}{h^2}\left(\frac{\Theta_1 + \Theta_2 + \Theta_3}{3} - \Theta_0\right) \tag{3-5.15}$$

The rate of heat flow form the node, because of the temperature gradient, is $\overline{q} = -K\nabla\Theta$. The heat flow away from the node per unit volume is given by $\nabla \cdot \overline{q} = -K\nabla^2\Theta$ and must equal the heat generation per unit volume. Since q_g denotes the total heat generation or input from a source in a volume $V = 3\sqrt{3}\, h^2 d/4$ (see Fig. 3-5.4) we have at the point 0

$$\nabla \cdot \overline{q} = -K(\nabla^2\Theta)_0 = \frac{q_g}{V} = \frac{4q_g}{3\sqrt{3}\, h^2 d} \tag{3-5.16}$$

where d is the depth of the material being considered. Now combine Eq. (3-5.16) with Eq. (3-5.15) to eliminate $(\nabla^2\Theta)_0$, getting

$$\frac{4}{h^2}\left(\frac{\Theta_1 + \Theta_2 + \Theta_3}{3} - \Theta_0\right) = -\frac{4q_g}{3\sqrt{3}\, h^2 Kd}$$

or

$$\Theta_0 = \frac{\Theta_1 + \Theta_2 + \Theta_3}{3} + \frac{q_g}{3\sqrt{3}\, Kd} \tag{3-5.17}$$

This is the same equation as Eq. (3-5.13) and shows that for the hexagonal mesh under consideration the thermal resistance between nodes separated a distance h is given by

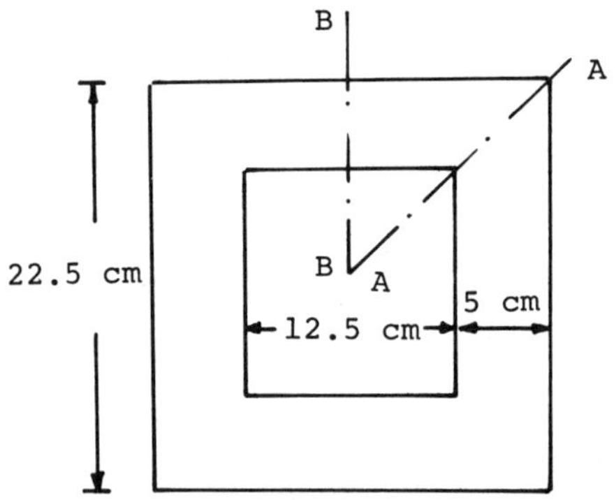

Figure 3-5.5. A section of a hydrogen furnace.

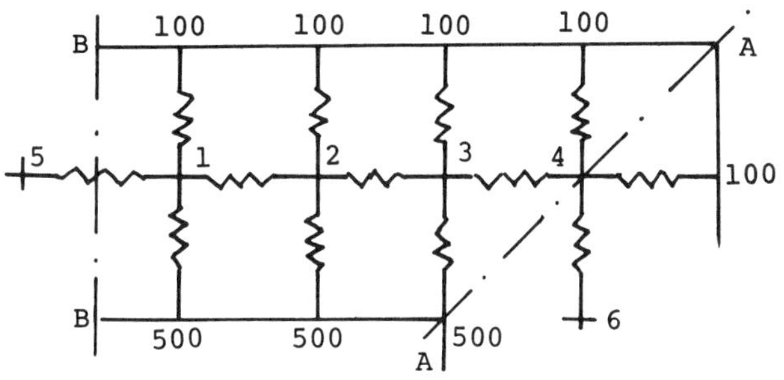

Figure 3-5.6. A 14 point mesh superimposed on the furnace section.

$$R = \frac{1}{\sqrt{3}\ Kd} \tag{3-5.18}$$

Example 3-5.1. Consider Fig. 3-5.5 which represents a square tube of a hydrogen annealing furnace. The temperature of the inner surface is 500° C, and the temperature of the outer surface is 100° C. The problem is to find the rate of heat flow through the furnace walls. End effects are to be neglected.

Solution. Because of conditions of symmetry, it is only necessary to analyze one eighth section bounded by plane AA and BB.

We might begin by superimposing a 14 point mesh on the cross section, as shown in Fig. 3-5.6. It is noted that the temperatures of six of these points are not known. With the mesh arranged in the manner shown, to find Θ_2 requires Θ_1 and Θ_3. These could be assumed, and subsequently checked. However, if the assumptions were not good, the trial and error solutions for Θ_1, Θ_2, etc., would be lengthy.

It is actually desirable to rearrange the mesh, as shown in Fig. 3-5.7. It is now possible to solve for Θ_2, Θ_4, Θ_5. Thus

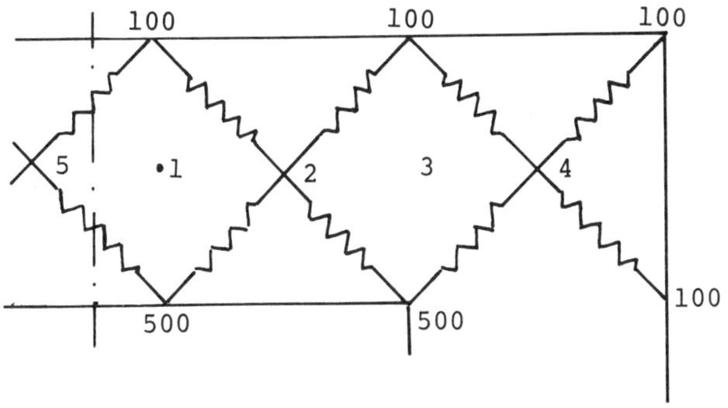

Figure 3-5.7. A rearrangement of the mesh in Figure 3-5.6.

$$\Theta_2 = \frac{1}{4}(500 + 500 + 100 + 100) = 300$$

$$\Theta_4 = \frac{1}{4}(500 + 100 + 100 + 100) = 200$$

$$\Theta_5 = \frac{1}{4}(500 + 500 + 100 + 100) = 300$$

With these temperatures known, we may return to the mesh of Fig. 3-5.6 and find Θ_1 and Θ_3. We readily find that

$$\Theta_3 = \frac{1}{4}(300 + 100 + 200 + 500) = 275$$

$$\Theta_1 = \frac{1}{4}(300 + 100 + 300 + 500) = 300$$

These are first trial results.

As a second trial, Θ_4, which was determined using the very coarse mesh of Fig. 3-5.7, is now recalculated using the finer mesh of Fig. 3-5.6. This gives

$$\Theta_4 = \frac{1}{4}(275 + 100 + 100 + 275) = 187$$

since by symmetry $\Theta_6 = \Theta_3$. Likewise, Θ_2 and Θ_5 can be recalculated, and these values can, in turn, be used to recalculate Θ_1 and Θ_3. This process is then repeated (iterated) and continued until the values which are obtained do not vary with additional checking. When this is done, the temperature distribution is found to be that shown in Fig. 3-5.8.

One may now superimpose a finer mesh structure on the cross section, and solve for the temperatures at intermediate points. Figure 3-5.9 shows the finer mesh structure and the temperature distribution that results after a few trials. A still finer mesh structure can be used, but for the particular problem in question the rate of heat flow as found from Fig. 3-5.9 is only about 3 percent in error.

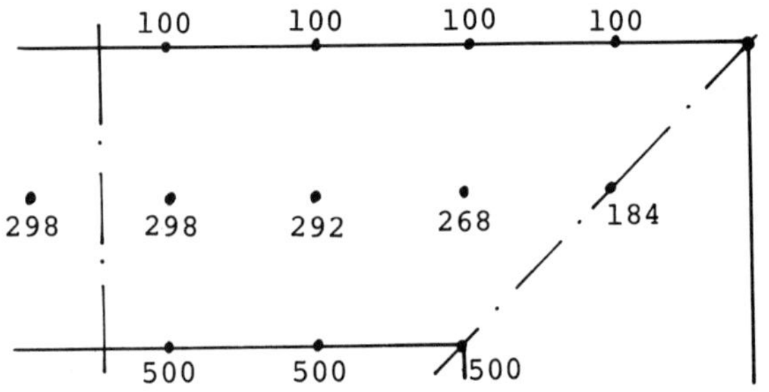

Figure 3-5.8. The temperatures at the mesh points of Figure 3-5.6.

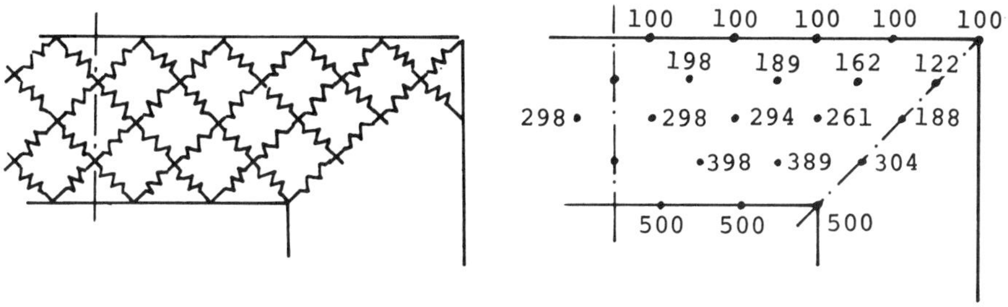

Figure 3-5.9. A finer mesh network superimposed on the furnace section.

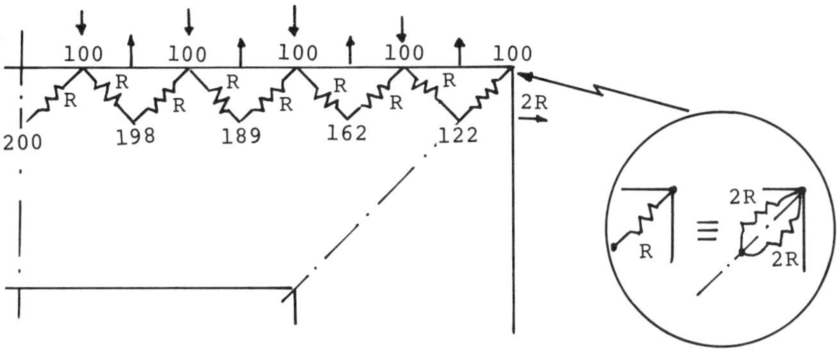

Figure 3-5.10. The resistance net for the evaluation of heat flow.

To calculate the heat flow through this 1/8 section of the furnace wall, any layer can be used. Since a greater number of temperature points are known along the outer layer than on any inner layer, the outer one shown in Fig. 3-5.10 is more satisfactory. The thermal resistance on the extreme right is 2R for the line of symmetry divides it lengthwise into two parts. The heat flow through any branch equals the temperature difference divided by R. Thus, the heat flow Q to the outer boundary will be

$$Q = \frac{122-100}{2R} + \frac{122-100}{R} + \frac{2(162-100)}{R} + \frac{2(189-100)}{R} + \frac{2(198-100)}{R} + \frac{200-100}{R}$$

$$= \frac{631}{R} = 631 \text{ Kd}$$

for the 1/8 section since $R = (Kd)^{-1}$ for a square mesh. For the eight sections the flow Q_t will be

$$Q_t = 8Q = 5032 \text{ Kd}$$

where d is the depth of the furnace.

Using the rough methods of Sec. 3-4, we have

$$R \doteq \frac{5}{8.75\ \text{Kd}}$$

and

$$Q = \frac{8 \times (500-100)}{5/8.75\ \text{Kd}} = 5600\ \text{Kd}$$

Note that for the sake of simplicity the dimensions of the furnace section were chosen so that the mesh fits exactly within the boundaries. In actual cases this would generally not be the case, and an extrapolation and interpolation would probably be necessary at some of the boundaries. The case of curved boundaries is treated in a later section.

ΔΔΔ

Example 3-5.2. Apply Eq. (3-5.8) to deduce a set of simultaneous equations for the configuration in Ex. 3-5.1, and solve for the unknown Θ's at the indicated points of Fig. 3-5.6.

Solution. Relative to the points marked 1,2,3,4, the desired set of equations is

$$\begin{aligned}
-3\Theta_1 + \Theta_2 + 0\Theta_3 + 0\Theta_4 &= -600 \\
\Theta_1 - 4\Theta_2 + \Theta_3 + 0\Theta_4 &= -600 \\
0\Theta_1 + \Theta_2 - 4\Theta_3 + \Theta_4 &= -600 \\
0\Theta_1 + 0\Theta_2 + 2\Theta_3 - 4\Theta_4 &= -200
\end{aligned} \tag{3-5.19}$$

where conditions of symmetry permit us to write $\Theta_5 = \Theta_1$ and $\Theta_3 = \Theta_6$. From this set of equations we write the augmented matrix, which is

$$\begin{bmatrix} -3 & 1 & 0 & 0 & -600 \\ 1 & -4 & 1 & 0 & -600 \\ 0 & 1 & -4 & 1 & -600 \\ 0 & 0 & 2 & -4 & -200 \end{bmatrix}$$

We now employ the Gauss reduction method for determing the values of Θ_i. This requires that we transform this matrix into more convenient form, which we do by employing the row (column) operations which are:

i. the interchange of any two rows (columns)
ii. the addition of a multiple of one row (column) to another row (column)
iii. the multiplication of a row (column) by a nonzero constant.

The aim of the procedure is to convert the series of equations into an upper triangular form, that is, to have all entries below the diagonal to be zero. This establishes the resulting equations into a set that can be readily evalauated, as discussed below.

Divide the first row by 3, add the new values to the second row, and then multiply it by 3. We find the following values:

$$\begin{bmatrix} -3 & 1 & 0 & 0 & -600 \\ 0 & -11 & 3 & 0 & -2400 \\ 0 & 1 & -4 & 1 & -600 \\ 0 & 0 & 2 & -4 & -200 \end{bmatrix}$$

Follow the same procedure between the second and the third row and then between the third and the last row. We find the final values:

$$\begin{bmatrix} -3 & 1 & 0 & 0 & -600 \\ 0 & -11 & 3 & 0 & -2400 \\ 0 & 0 & -41 & 11 & -9000 \\ 0 & 0 & 0 & -142 & -26200 \end{bmatrix}$$

Each row specifies an equation. Begin with the bottom row to obtain Θ_4, then use this value in row 3 to find Θ_3. Continue this so-called back-substitution successively until all temperatures are found. We obtain the following temperatures:

$$\Theta_4 = 26200/142 = 184.507; \quad \Theta_3 = 269.014; \quad \Theta_2 = 291.549; \quad \Theta_1 = 297.183$$

These values should be compared with the values shown in Fig. 3-5.8. ΔΔΔ

Example 3-5.3. Find the potentials at the indicated points in Fig. 3-5.11,

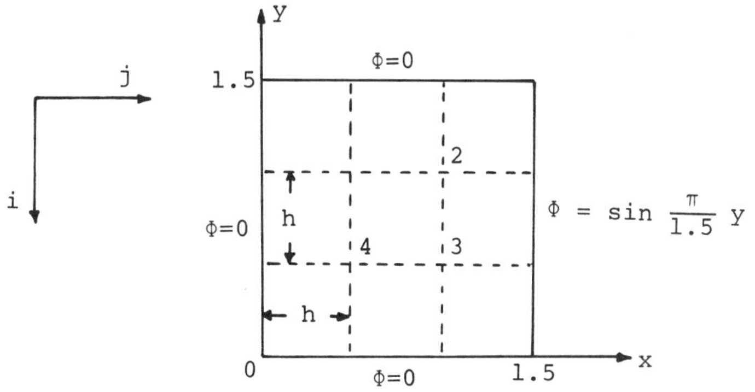

Figure 3-5.11. A two-dimensional boundary value problem.

assuming that there is a surface charge density $\rho_s(x,y) = x^2 y$.

Solution. Combine Eqs. (3-5.5) and (3-5.6) with Poisson's equation

$$\frac{\partial^2\Phi}{\partial x^2} + \frac{\partial^2\Phi}{\partial y^2} = -\rho(x,y)$$

which is the general description of the situation shown, to obtain

$$h^2 \left(\frac{\partial^2\Phi}{\partial x^2} + \frac{\partial^2\Phi}{\partial y^2}\right) = \Phi_{i+1,j} + \Phi_{i-1,j} + \Phi_{i,j+1} + \Phi_{i,j-1} - 4\Phi_{ij} = -\rho(x_i,y_j)h^2 \qquad (3\text{-}5.20)$$

In this difference equation the point (i,j) denotes the point 0 in our previous development. In this example the indexes are $i = 1,2$ and $j = 1,2$. An application of this equation to the net points given in the figure yields the following system of equations

$$\begin{aligned}
-4\Phi_1 + \Phi_2 + 0\Phi_3 + \Phi_4 &= -(0.5)^2\,(0.5^2 \times 1) \\
\Phi_1 - 4\Phi_2 + \Phi_3 + 0\Phi_4 &= -(0.5)^2\,(1^2 \times 1) - \sin\frac{\pi}{1.5} \\
0\Phi_1 + \Phi_2 - 4\Phi_3 + \Phi_4 &= -(0.5)^2\,(1^2 \times 0.5) - \sin\left(\frac{\pi}{1.5}\,0.5\right) \\
\Phi_1 + 0\Phi_2 + \Phi_3 - 4\Phi_4 &= -(0.5)^2\,(0.5^2 \times 0.5)
\end{aligned} \qquad (3\text{-}5.21)$$

These can be solved by employing the row operations with the augmented matrix, as in the foregoing example.

Initially, consider the simple case where the surface charge density $\rho_s(x,y) = 0$. The values of the potentials are found to be

$$\Phi_1 = 0.10825 \qquad \Phi_2 = 0.32476 \qquad \Phi_3 = 0.32476 \qquad \Phi_4 = 0.10825$$

These values are compared with the values deduced from an analytic solution to this problem (see Pr. 4-2.1) which are given by the equation

$$\Phi = \frac{\sinh \frac{\pi}{1.5} x}{\sinh \left(\frac{\pi}{1.5}\,1.5\right)} \sin \frac{\pi}{1.5} y = \frac{\sinh \frac{\pi}{1.5} x}{\sinh \pi} \sin \frac{\pi}{1.5} y$$

The results are

$$\Phi_1 = 0.093688 \qquad \Phi_2 = 0.299857 \qquad \Phi_3 = 0.299857 \qquad \Phi_4 = 0.093688$$

Owing to the coarse mesh that has been used, a considerable difference exists between the values from the analytic expression and the approximate values from the net calculation.

To obtain the values of the Φ_i's from the set of equations (3-5.20) the Jacobi method of iteration can be used. This method is seldom used in practice because the rate at which successive iterates converge to the exact solution is slower than that possible using other methods. However, the Jacobi method provides a valuable means for comparing optimum rates of convergence of other methods.

We denote the nth iterative value of Φ_{ij} by $\Phi_{i,j}^{(n)}$. Thus Eq. (3-5.20) becomes

$$\Phi_{i,j}^{(n+1)} = \frac{1}{4}[\Phi_{i-1,j}^{(n)} + \Phi_{i+1,j}^{(n)} + \Phi_{i,j-1}^{(n)} + \Phi_{i,j+1}^{(n)} + h^2\rho_{i,j}] \qquad (3\text{-}5.22)$$

which must include the boundary value points. The initial interior points may be quite arbitrarily selected. When this is done, Table 3-5.1 results, which shows the iteration for this example.

Table 3-5.1

	$\Phi_{1,1}$	$\Phi_{1,2}$	$\Phi_{2,2}$	$\Phi_{2,1}$
n	1	2	3	4
0	0.2	0.4	0.4	0.2
1	0.15	0.366507	0.366507	0.15
2	0.1291268	0.3456342	0.3456342	0.1291268
3	0.1186922	0.3351977	0.3351977	0.1186922
4	0.1134724	0.3299799	0.3299799	0.1134724
5	0.1108630	0.3273705	0.3273705	0.1108630
6	0.1095583	0.3260658	0.3260658	0.1095583
7	0.1089060	0.3254135	0.3254135	0.1089060
8	0.1085798	0.3250873	0.3250873	0.1085798

A more rapid rate of convergence results when the most recent value for a point is used in the equation. Now the difference equation is the following:

$$\Phi_{i,j}^{(n+1)} = \frac{1}{4}[\Phi_{i-1,j}^{(n+1)} + \Phi_{i+1,j}^{(n)} + \Phi_{i,j-1}^{(n+1)} + \Phi_{i,j+1}^{(n)} + h^2\rho_{i,j}] \qquad (3\text{-}5.23)$$

The results obtained using this equation are contained in Table 3-5.2.

Example 3-5.4. The configuration shown in Fig. 3-5.12a represents a circular conducting cyclinder surrounded by a square conducting cylinder. Determine the capacitance per unit length of this capacitor.

Solution. If the total charge per unit length on the outer cylinder is Q when the potential difference between the cylinders is V, the capacitance is given by

$$C = \frac{Q}{V} \qquad (3\text{-}5.24)$$

Table 3-5.2

n	$\Phi_{1,1}$ 1	$\Phi_{1,2}$ 2	$\Phi_{2,2}$ 3	$\Phi_{2,1}$ 4
0	0.2	0.4	0.4	0.2
1	0.15	0.3540075	0.3550093	0.1262523
2	0.1200649	0.335276	0.3318895	0.1129886
3	0.1120661	0.3274964	0.3266287	0.1096737
4	0.1092925	0.3254878	0.3252978	0.1086475
5	0.1085338	0.3249654	0.3249107	0.1083611
6	0.1083316	0.3248180	0.32488022	0.1082834
7	0.1082753	0.3247768	0.3247725	0.1082619

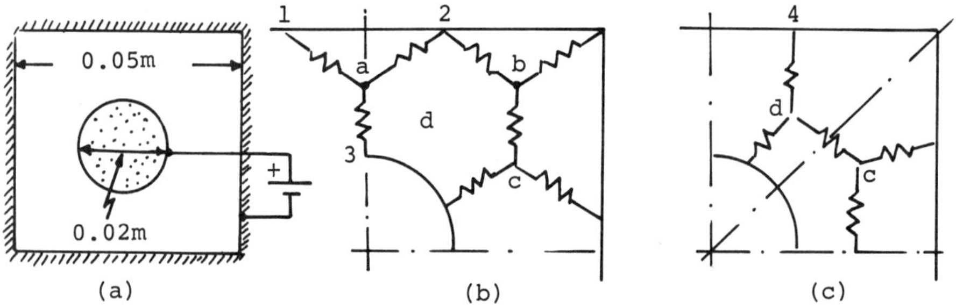

Figure 3-5.12. Cylindrical capacitor, and the method for calculating the electric flux.

Capacitance will be considered at some length in Sec. 5-7. Let Φ denote the potential distribution between the two cylinders. The corresponding electric field is given by Eq. (2-7.7a) as

$$\overline{E} = -\nabla\Phi \tag{3-5.25}$$

The total flux of $\overline{E}$ crossing a closed surface equals $1/\varepsilon_0$ times the enclosed charge according to Eq. (2-7.10). At the boundary of a conductor the lines of electric force terminate on surface charges distributed with density ρ_s given by

$$\rho_s = \varepsilon_0 \overline{n}\cdot\overline{E} \qquad (\text{Coulomb/m}^2) \tag{3-5.26}$$

where $\overline{n}$ is a unit normal directed out from the conductor. The total charge on the outer boundary may thus be viewed as being equal to the total normal flow of $\varepsilon_0\overline{E} = -\varepsilon_0\nabla\Phi$ towards the boundary. Hence capacitance calculations are formally the same as thermal or electrical total conductance calculations with ε_o replacing K and σ, respectively.

For the indicated potential of the inner cylinder at 100 volts and the outer cylinder at zero volts, and for the meshes illustrated in Fig. 3-5.12, we find [see Eq. (3-5.14)]

$$\Phi_a = \frac{1}{3}(\Phi_1 + \Phi_2 + \Phi_3) = \frac{1}{3}(0 + 0 + 100) = 33$$

$$\Phi_b = \frac{1}{3}(0 + 0 + \Phi_c)$$

$$\Phi_c = \frac{1}{3}(100 + 0 + \Phi_b)$$

The latter two equations give approximately $\Phi_b = 13$, $\Phi_c = 38$. For Φ_d we obtain

$$\Phi_d = \frac{1}{3}(100 + 0 + 38) \doteq 46$$

We can now calculate the total flux of $\varepsilon_o\overline{E}$ to the outer wall using the numbered meshes in Fig. 3-5.12b and 3-5.12c. There results, considering each half-face for a total of 8 half-faces

$$Q = 8\sqrt{3}\,\varepsilon_o\left(\Phi_a + \Phi_b + \Phi_d + \frac{1}{2}\Phi_b\right)$$

$$= 8\sqrt{3}\,\varepsilon_o(33 + 13 + 46 + 6.5) = 1360\,\varepsilon_o \quad \text{(Coulomb/m)}$$

and $R = (\sqrt{3}\,Kd)^{-1}$ is replaced by $(\sqrt{3}\,\varepsilon_o)^{-1}$. Hence the capacitance per unit length is

$$C = \frac{Q}{V} = 13.6\,\varepsilon_o \qquad \text{(Farad/m)}$$

It is of some interest to compare this value with that of a coaxial capacitor for which an exact formula is possible [see Eq. (5-7.7)]. If we select the inner radius as given and select an equivalent outer radius of .0257 m, the capacitance is

$$C = \frac{2\pi\varepsilon_o}{\ln\frac{.0257}{.01}} = 6.7\varepsilon_o \qquad \text{(Farad/m)}$$

ΔΔΔ

3-6. Curved Boundaries

The examples discussed in Sec. 3-5 were carefully selected to allow the basic mesh to fit exactly within the boundaries to be studied. Figure 3-6.1 illustrates the situation which arises when one string of a square net cuts a boundary. As shown, node 1 extends beyond the boundary, and is, therefore, an unknown quantity. As a result, it is not possible to find the value of the function at node 0. We need an expression for Φ_o in terms of Φ_b and not Φ_1. We may accomplish this result in a manner that parallels that leading to Eq. (3-5.8).

We begin with the Taylor series expansion, Eq. (3-5.2), and put x equal, in turn, to $x_o + \xi h$ and $x_o - h$. Thus we have

$$\Phi_b = \Phi_o + \left(\frac{\partial \Phi}{\partial x}\right)_o \xi h + \frac{1}{2}\left(\frac{\partial^2 \Phi}{\partial x^2}\right)_o \xi^2 h^2 + \cdots \tag{3-6.1}$$

and

$$\Phi_3 = \Phi_o - \left(\frac{\partial \Phi}{\partial x}\right)_o h + \frac{1}{2}\left(\frac{\partial^2 \Phi}{\partial x^2}\right)_o h^2 + \cdots$$

Upon multiplying the second equation by ξ and adding to the first, the result is

$$\Phi_b + \xi\Phi_3 = (1 + \xi)\Phi_o + \frac{\xi(1 + \xi)}{2}\left(\frac{\partial^2 \Phi}{\partial x^2}\right)_o h^2 \tag{3-6.2}$$

This is the finite difference approximation for the second derivative of Φ with respect to x, instead of the usual approximation, Eq. (3-5.4). In the solution of Laplace's equation, Eq. (3-6.2) together with Eq. (3-5.6) yields

$$h^2(\nabla^2\Phi)_o = \frac{2\Phi_b}{\xi(1+\xi)} + \frac{2\Phi_3}{1 + \xi} + \Phi_2 + \Phi_4 - \left(2 + \frac{2}{\xi}\right)\Phi_o = 0 \tag{3-6.3}$$

When $\xi = 1$, Eq. (3-6.3) reduces to Eq. (3-5.7) as it should.

In the limiting case when $\xi = 0$, the approach must be altered. Begin again with Fig. 3-6.1 where point 1 is a fictitious point. By appropriate Taylor expansion for potentials Φ_2, Φ_3, Φ_4, and combining in the manner above, the result becomes

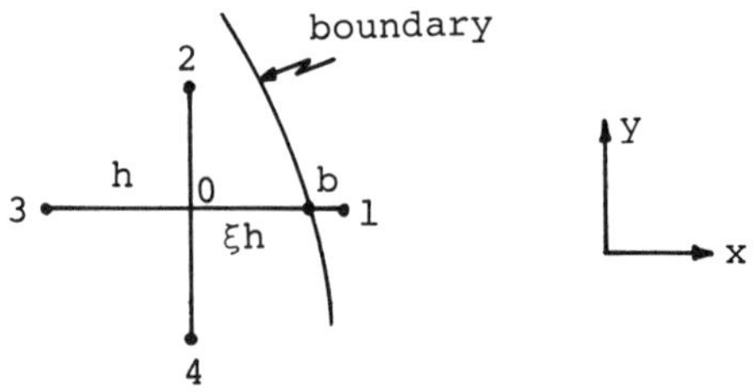

Figure 3-6.1. A net point extending beyond the boundary.

$$\frac{\Phi_2 + \Phi_4}{2} - \Phi_o = 0 \tag{3-6.4}$$

If two strings are cut by the boundary, as in Fig. 3-6.2, then a generalization of Eq. (3-6.3) will be found to be

$$\frac{2\Phi_b}{\xi(1+\xi)} + \frac{2\Phi_a}{\eta(1+\eta)} + \frac{2\Phi_3}{1+\xi} + \frac{2\Phi_4}{1+\eta} - \left(\frac{2}{\xi} + \frac{2}{\eta}\right)\Phi_o = 0 \tag{3-6.5}$$

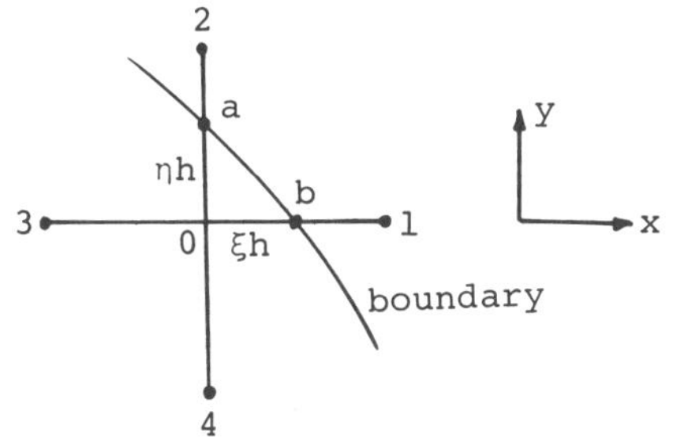

Figure 3-6.2. A curved boundary cutting two strings of a rectilinear net.

3-7. Normal Gradient Boundary Conditions

When a specified normal gradient is given as a boundary condition rather than a specified functional value for the potential the problem becomes rather involved, except when the boundary is rectilinear. For the rectilinear case to order h^3, we have, by subtracting Eq. (3-5.3b) from Eq. (3-5.3a),

$$\Phi_1 - \Phi_3 = 2h\left(\frac{\partial\Phi}{\partial x}\right)_o \tag{3-7.1}$$

as the finite difference at 0 of the normal gradient condition on the boundary. In this case Φ_1 is a fictitious quantity (see Fig. 3-7.1a). But Φ_1 can be eliminated from Eq. (3-5.8) to yield an expression that involves only real nodal values of Φ. The final expression is

$$\Phi_2 + 2\Phi_3 + \Phi_4 - 4\Phi_o + 2h\left(\frac{\partial\Phi}{\partial x}\right)_o = 0 \tag{3-7.2}$$

and serves as one of the equations needed to determine the Φ_i in terms of the known values of the normal gradient. When the normal gradient is not zero the flow at the boundary either leaves or enters the region through the boundary. It may be viewed as arising from an equivalent source or terminating in an equivalent sink outside the boundary. Alternatively, the flow may be thought of as originating or terminat-

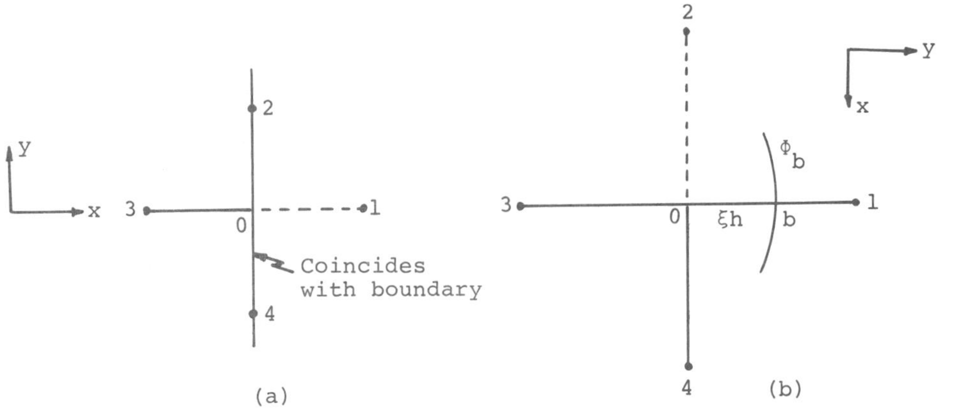

Figure 3-7.1. Voltage gradient at a plane boundary.

ing in an equivalent source or sink located on the boundary, and having a strength $(2h/R)(\partial\Phi/\partial n)$ at each node as may be seen by comparing Eq. (3-7.2) with Eq. (3-5.10).

If in addition to zero gradient there exists a cut as shown in Fig. 3-7.1b, then Eq. (3-7.1) becomes

$$\Phi_2 - \Phi_4 = 2h \left(\frac{\partial\Phi}{\partial x}\right)_o \tag{3-7.3}$$

But Φ_2 can be eliminated from Eq. (3-6.3) to yield the following expression

$$\frac{2\Phi_b}{\xi(1+\xi)} + \frac{2\Phi_3}{1 + \xi} + 2\Phi_4 - (2 + \frac{2}{\xi})\Phi_o = 0 \tag{3-7.4}$$

3-8. Relaxation Techniques

The numerical method known as the relaxation method for solving boundary value problems is a somewhat more systematic and efficient method (particularly after becoming experienced with the technique) than the iteration process described in Sec. 3-5. In this section we will develop the essential features of the method. There are many ramifications involved so we refer the interested student to the books by Southwell and Allen (see References) for further details.

The method begins by dividing the region of interest by a rectangular or hexagonal mesh as in the iteration process. Using whatever knowledge or intuition that is available, a preliminary assignment of the potentials at all of the net points is then made. These values of the potentials will generally not satisfy the finite difference form of Laplace's equation, that is, Eq. (3-5.8) or Eq. (3-5.14) will not hold at every node in the mesh. Likewise, Eq. (3-6.3) will in general not hold at the boundary nodes in the case of curved boundaries. To describe what is to be done

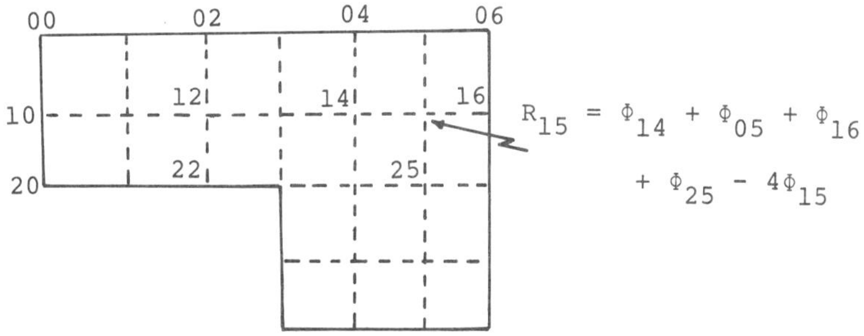

Figure 3-8.1. A mesh for applying the relaxation method.

about this situation it will be convenient to assume that a square mesh is being used as in Fig. 3-8.1. A quantity called the *residual* or *residue* is introduced that gives a measure of the amount by which Eq. (3-5.8) fails to hold, i.e., at node ij the residual R_{ij} is

$$R_{ij} = \Phi_{i-1,j} + \Phi_{i+1,j} + \Phi_{i,j-1} + \Phi_{i,j+1} - 4\Phi_{ij} \tag{3-8.1}$$

The potentials at all nodes must now be modified in such a manner as to *relax* or reduce the residuals to zero or as near zero as is deemed necessary for sufficient accuracy (this process gives the method its name). Since Φ_{ij} in Eq. (3-8.1) is multiplied by a factor of 4 it is clear that R_{ij} can be reduced to zero with the smallest change in the potentials by changing the value of Φ_{ij} only. At times it is preferable to over relax and reduce the residual to be close to zero but of opposite sign since the potentials at the adjacent nodes are also going to be changed. When R_{ij} is relaxed by changing Φ_{ij} the residuals at the surrounding four nodes also change but by only 1/4 the amount of the change in R_{ij}. Thus, the initial over-relaxation is usually compensated for when the residuals at adjacent nodes are being relaxed. The relaxation process is repeated at each node and then the whole grid is gone over again and again until all of the residuals are essentially zero. The following example will clarify the steps to be taken.

Example 3-8.1. Repeat Ex. 3-5.3 using the relaxation technique. Find the potentials at the same points as in Ex. 3-5.3.

Solution. It is preferable to make a large drawing of the configuration so that all of the numerical work may be recorded on the drawing. For conveience in discussion we have numbered the nodes although this would not be necessary in practice. For lack of any better information at the beginning, we assume that the temperature varies linearly along temperature varying directions. The assumed temperatures are recorded on the left-hand side of each node multiplied by 100 so that we

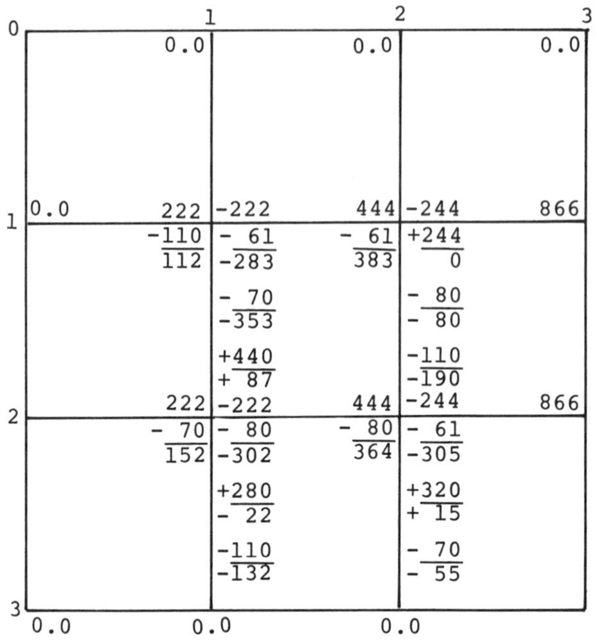

Figure 3-8.2. The relaxation solution for the potentials of Ex. 3-5.3.

can work to two decimal places with simplified arithmetic. The initial residuals are recorded on the right-hand side.

One method of procedure is to reduce the largest current residual to zero at every relaxation. If we choose to change Φ at the point 12 (row 1, column 2) by (-244)/4 = -61, the residual at 12 will change by +244, thus making the residual at 12 equal to zero. Simultaneously we will have changes of the residuals at points 11 and 22, each one changed by -61.

The largest residual is now -305 at 22 and could be reduced to approximately zero if Φ changes by -80 ($\sim$ - 305/4). The other two points which are affected are 21 and 22. Next selecting the point 21 we change its potential by -70 ($\sim$ -302/4) and tabulate the changes. The largest current residual is now -353 at 11 and could become approximately zero by a change of -88 in Φ at this point. However, when the residuals at adjacent points have the same sign, the rate of convergence is increased by changing Φ by about one-quarter to one-half more than is necessary to reduce the residual to zero; this is known as over-relaxation. Thus, changing Φ at 11 by -110 gives a residual +87 at this point and of -190 at 12 and -132 at 21. Proceeding in the same way we find accurate results within five minutes of computation. The residuals will range between -5 to +5.

In our analysis no changes of the residuals at the boundaries were attempted, because the values of Φ at the boundaries are correct and thus the associated residuals are always zero. In addition, the reader should remember to divide his final values by 100 in this example.

ΔΔΔ

Example 3-8.2. Using the relaxation technique, find the temperature distribution for the furnace described in Ex. 3-5.1.

Solution. It is desirable to make a large drawing of the configuration so that all of the numerical work may be recorded on the drawing. Symmetry considerations should be taken into account to reduce the configuration to the smallest possible section that has to be dealt with. Thus, in Fig. 3-8.3 we illustrate a 1/8 section of the furnace together with a rectangular grid chosen as in Fig. 3-5.9. We have numbered the nodes, although this would not be necessary in practice. Also we assume initially that the temperature varies linearly from the inner to the outer wall. The assumed temperatures are recorded on the left side of each node and the residuals on the right hand side. The residuals resulting from the initial temperatures assigned are calculated by using Eq. (3-8.1). For example, the residual at node 27 is (row 2, column 7)

$$R_{27} = 200 + 200 + 200 + 400 - 4 \times 300 = -200$$

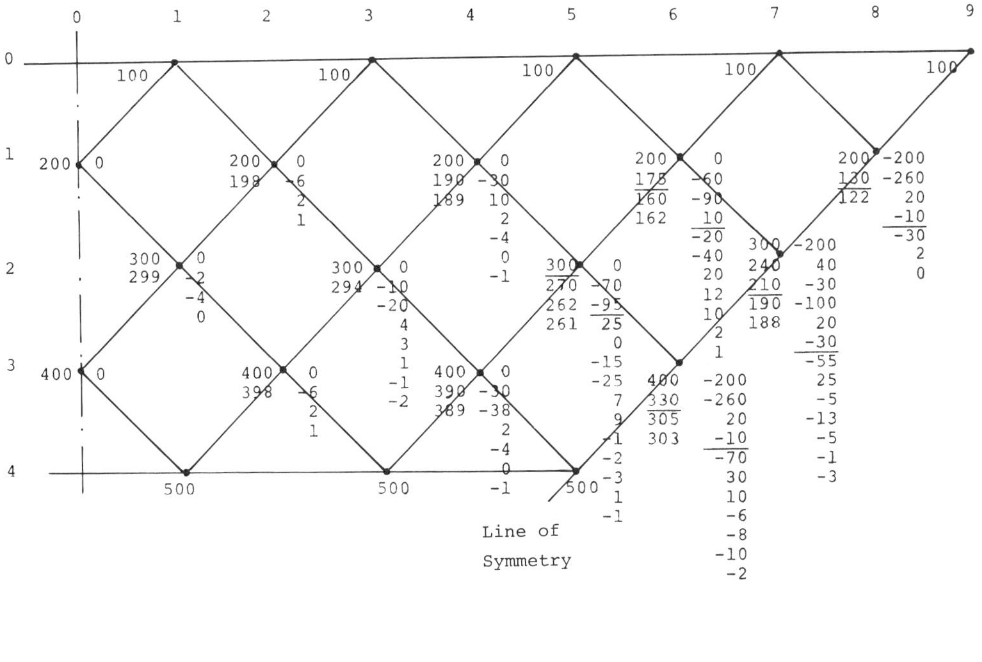

Figure 3-8.3. The relaxation solution for a 1/8 section of the furnace in Fig. 3-5.5.

since the temperature at the node which is not present in the 1/8 section is 200 because of its symmetrical position about the line of symmetry relative to node 16. The initial temperature distribution for this example happens to make all of the residuals except those along the right hand side line-of-symmetry zero (this normally does not happen).

Usually it is preferable to relax the largest residuals first. Since there are three of equal size, we arbitrarily choose node 27 first and overrelax it by about 20 percent by reducing $\Theta_{27} = 300$ by an amount $240/4 = 60$ to 240. The resulting new residuals R_{16}, R_{18}, R_{27}, R_{36}, which are effected by the change in the residual R_{27}, become $0 - 60 = -60$, $-200 - 60 = -260$, $-200 + 4 \times 60 = 40$ and $-200 - 60 = -260$, respectively. Next we relax R_{18} by reducing Θ_{18} by an amount $280/4 = 70$ (again over relaxed). The resulting new residuals appear as the third figures in the residual columns. Next we relax R_{36} by changing Θ_{36} by amount -70. The new residuals R_{25}, R_{27}, and R_{36} become -70, -100, +20, respectively. Now we return to node 27 and reduce Θ_{27} by an amount $120/4 = 30$ which changes the residual R_{27} by amount +120 and that at the surrounding nodes by amount $-(1/4)\Delta R_{27} = -30$. We now move to node 16 and change Θ_{16} by $-100/4$ to effect a change of +100 in R_{16}. It is very important to note that this will change the residue R_{27} by *twice the usual amount*, i.e., by $-(1/2)\Delta R_{16}$, since it is implied by symmetry that when the temperature Θ_{16} is changed a similar change is simultaneously made at the node which is located on the opposite side of the line-of-symmetry but is not included in the 1/8 section. Similarly, a change in Θ_{25} changes the residue R_{25} by $\Delta R_{25} = -4\Delta\Theta_{25}$ and changes the residue at node 36 by $2\Delta\Theta_{25}$, while the residues R_{16} and R_{34} both change by the usual amount $\Delta\Theta_{25}$.

The above process is continued and if the nodes are relaxed in the sequence 25,36,27,16,18,14,25,27,16,34,23,14,12,32,21,34,25, and 36 the results tabulated in Fig. 3-8.2 are obtained. At this point all of the residues lie between -3 and 1 which results in 3 figure accuracy for the Θ_{ij}. The resultant values of Θ_{ij} agree within one place in the third figure with the values calculated by the iteration method and given in Fig. 3-5.9. However, this does not necessarily mean that a solution to Laplace's equation has been obtained with the same accuracy since only a finite difference approximation has been used.

ΔΔΔ

Two significant features of the relaxation method are (a) Only simple addition, subtraction, and multiplication are involved so the calculations can be done mentally and only the results need to be tabulated. (b) When all of the residues have been relaxed so that the remaining R_{ij} divided by 4 are less than the maximum error desired, the final values should be checked. That is, the residues should be evaluated in terms of the final values of the potentials at the nodes. If errors are found *it is not necessary to go back and correct these*. The correct residues are simply tabulated and the relaxation process continued.

In the application of the method it is preferable to begin with a relatively coarse mesh. As a guide to choosing the initial values of the potentials it is helpful to make a rough curvilinear plot of the constant potential contours first. Linear interpolation by eye may then be used between the estimated constant potential contours to fix the initial values of the potentials at the nodes. When the coarse mesh has been relaxed a finer mesh should be introduced. If each square of the original mesh is divided in four, the initial values of the potentials at the center are chosen as the average of those at the surrounding four points.

The relaxation method can be applied to Poisson's equation also. The only change required is the inclusion of the source term which modifies the equation for the residues. Thus, for a square mesh

$$R_{ij} = \Phi_{i-1,j} + \Phi_{i+1,j} + \Phi_{i,j-1} + \Phi_{i,j+1} - 4\Phi_{ij} + q_g R \tag{3-8.2}$$

as obtained from Eq. (3-5.9). For a square mesh $R = (Kd)^{-1}$. For a hexagonal mesh the equations corresponding to Eqs. (3-8.1) and (3-8.2) are

$$R_o = \Phi_1 + \Phi_2 + \Phi_3 - 3\Phi_o \qquad \text{a)}$$

$$R_o = \Phi_1 + \Phi_2 + \Phi_3 - 3\Phi_o + q_g R \qquad \text{b)} \tag{3-8.3}$$

where $R = (\sqrt{3}\ Kd)^{-1}$ with d being the depth of the material and K the conductivity and q_g the source strength at each node. The subscripts 1,2,3 denote the three nodes connected to node 0.

If curved boundaries are involved, then the equations for the residues at the boundary nodes are obtained from Eq. (3-6.3) or Eq. (3-6.4) when $q_g = 0$. Thus, with reference to Fig. 3-6.1 where the boundary cuts one string only, Eq. (3-6.3) gives

$$R_o = \frac{2\Phi_b}{\xi(1+\xi)} + \frac{2\Phi_3}{1+\xi} + \Phi_2 + \Phi_4 - (2 + \frac{2}{\xi})\ \Phi_o \tag{3-8.4}$$

for the residue at node 0. When the potential at node 3 is changed by amount $\Delta\Phi_3$ the residue at this node will change by $-4\Delta\Phi_3$ since this is an ordinary node, but the change in the residue at node 0 will be $2\Delta\Phi_3/(1+\xi)$ as Eq. (3-8.4) shows. When the boundary cuts two strings as in Fig. 3-6.2, the residue equation is

$$R_o = \frac{2\Phi_b}{\xi(1+\xi)} + \frac{2\Phi_a}{\eta(1+\eta)} + \frac{2\Phi_3}{1+\xi} + \frac{2\Phi_4}{1+\eta} - (\frac{2}{\xi} + \frac{2}{\eta})\ \Phi_o \tag{3-8.5}$$

Finally, if the normal component of the gradient is given at the boundary, Eq. (3-7.2) applies (see Fig. 3-7.1) and we have

$$R_o = \Phi_2 + 2\Phi_3 + \Phi_4 - 4\Phi_o + 2h\ (\frac{\partial\Phi}{\partial x})_o \tag{3-8.6}$$

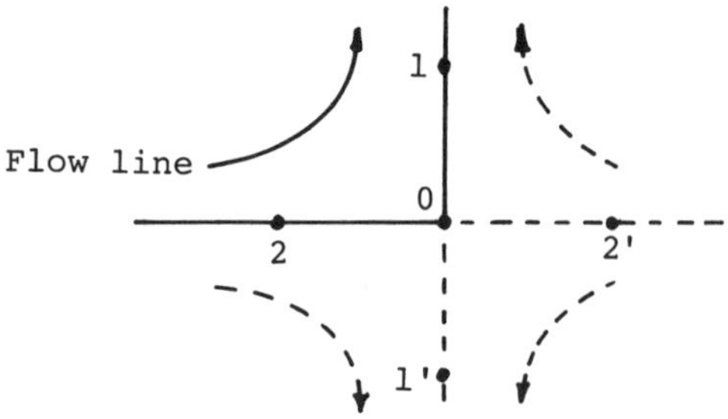

Figure 3-8.4. A right angle boundary with zero normal gradient.

A special case is that when the normal gradient is zero which then gives

$$R_o = \Phi_2 + \Phi_4 + 2\Phi_3 - 4\Phi_o \tag{3-8.7}$$

This equation was actually used in solving Ex. 3-8.2. Along the line of symmetry the normal gradient is zero and this may be considered as the reason why the residues at nodes 27 and 36 change by twice the change in the potentials at nodes 16 and 25, respectively.

A similar situation arises when the normal gradient is zero along two boundaries that meet at right angles as shown in Fig. 3-8.4. This corner can be viewed as a 1/4 section of a larger structure in which the boundaries coincide with the lines of symmetry. It is then easy to see that the residue at node 0 is given by

$$R_o = 2\Phi_1 + 2\Phi_2 - 4\Phi_o \tag{3-8.8}$$

since the absent nodes 1' and 2' contribute the same amount to R_o as do nodes 1 and 2 in order to maintain the required symmetry in the field configuration for the larger structure. Thus, for the true physical structure the change in the potentials at nodes 1 and 2 are counted twice to compute the change in the residue at node 0.

Similarly, from Eq. (3-7.4) we find that the residual when one side has zero gradient and the other is cut by an amount ξ is given by

$$R_o = \frac{2\Phi_b}{\xi(1+\xi)} + \frac{2\Phi_3}{1+\xi} + 2\Phi_4 - \left(2 + \frac{2}{\xi}\right)\Phi_o = 0 \tag{3-8.9}$$

Example 3-8.3. Find the resistance of a semi-conductor block shown in Fig. 3-8.5.

Solution. The resistance of a semi-conductor sample is measured by clamping it between an electrode and a flat plate as in Fig. 3-8.5. The total resistance R_t between the electrodes is measured and from this the intrinsic conductivity σ is to

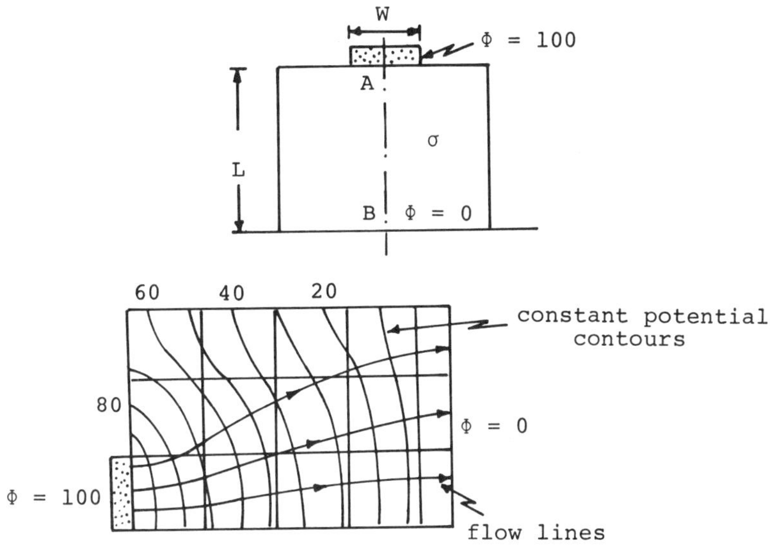

Figure 3-8.5. A semi-conductor resistor.

be determined. If the current flow were uniform from surface A to surface B then $R_t = L/(\sigma Wd)$ where d is the depth of the material. But, because the current spreads out over a width greater than W the resistance will be smaller and the simple expression $\sigma = L/(R_t Wd)$ will not give an accurate determination of σ. We will calculate a more accurate expression for R_t by using the relaxation method.

In view of the symmetry we need to consider only a 1/2 section. The length L equals 2.25 W. The mesh is chosen with h = W/2 which gives 4.5 meshes along the length of the sample as shown in Fig. 3-8.5. A rough sketch of the constant potential contours and current flow lines also shown in Fig. 3-8.5 is used to estimate the initial values of the potentials by linearly interpolating between constant potential contours. We thus arrive at the initial starting point for the half section shown in Fig. 3-8.6.

This example has been chosen to illustrate a number of the modifications discussed above. All of the nodes except those at which the potentials are either 100 or 0 (the applied potentials) lie on boundaries where the normal component of the gradient is zero. Thus, for the corner node 00 the residue is given by Eq. (3-8.8)

$$R_{00} = 2\Phi_{01} + 2\Phi_{10} - 4\Phi_{00}$$

$$= 2 \times 48 + 2 \times 70 - 4 \times 64 = -20$$

For nodes 01, 02, 03, 10, 31, 32, and 33, the residues are given by Eq. (3-8.7). For example,

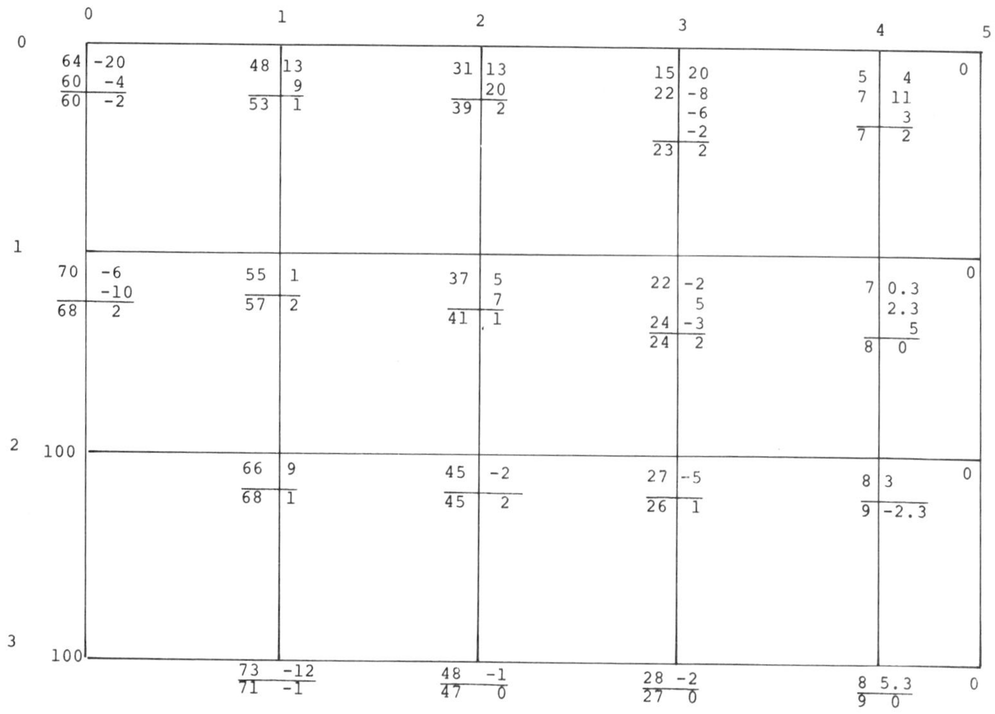

Figure 3-8.6. Relaxation solution for the configuration in Fig. 3-8.5.

$$R_{01} = 64 + 31 + 2 \times 55 - 4 \times 48 = 13$$

The nodes 04, 14, 24, and 34 have one string each cut by the boundary, so Eq. (3-8.9) must be used with $\xi = 1/2$ in this case. Since $\Phi_b = 0$ we get, for example,

$$R_{04} = \frac{4}{3} \times 15 + 2 \times 7 - 6 \times 5 = 4$$

In relaxing the residues towards zero the above equations must be kept in mind in order to correctly evaluate the change in residues at the neighboring nodes.

Let us begin by reducing the potential at node 00 by 4. This changes R_{00} by +4 × 4 = +16, R_{10} by -4, and R_{01} by -4. Next, increase Φ_{03} by 7 which changes R_{03} from 20 to 20 - 4 × 7 = -8, changes R_{02} from 13 to 20, changes R_{13} from -2 to 5 and R_{04} from 4 to 11. We now raise Φ_{04} from 5 to 7 and thereby change R_{04} from 11 to 11 - 8 = 3, R_{03} from -8 to -6 and R_{14} from 0.3 to 2.3. If we now raise Φ_{13} from 22 to 24 we change R_{13} from 5 to -3, R_{12} from 5 to 7, R_{03} from -6 to -6 + 2 × 2 = -2, and R_{14} from 2.3 to 2.3 + 4/3 × 2 = 5. It is important to note how the latter two residues were evaluated. According to Eq. (3-8.7) a change $\Delta\Phi_{13}$ in Φ_{13} is reflected by a change of $2\Delta\Phi_{13}$ in the residue at the boundary node 03. Similarly, according

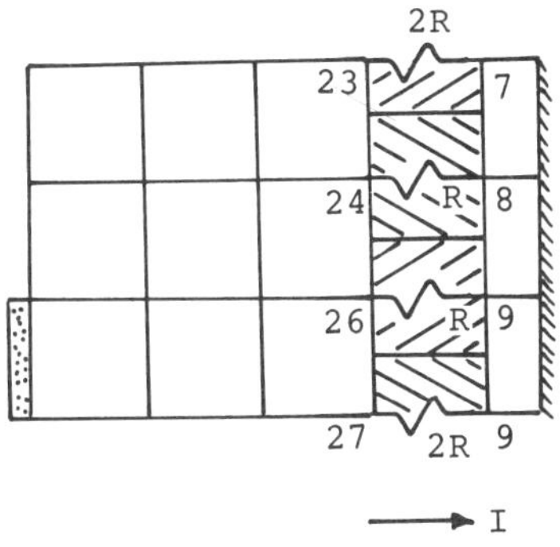

Figure 3-8.7. Resistance net for finding the total current.

to Eq. (3-8.4) a change $\Delta\Phi_{13}$ in Φ_{13} gives a change $2/(1 + \xi)\Delta\Phi_{13} = (4/3)\Delta\Phi_{13}$ in the residue R_{14}. The above process when continued gives the final results tabulated in Fig. 3-8.6.

We are now in a position to calculate the total current I and from this the resistance R_t. To evaluate the current we use the resistance net shown in Fig. 3-8.7, that is, we divide the speciman into resistance blocks to calculate the total current flowing through a cross section.

From Fig. 3-8.7 it is clear that

$$I = 2\left[\frac{23-7}{2R} + \frac{24-8}{R} + \frac{26-9}{R} + \frac{27-9}{2R}\right] = \frac{100}{R}$$

where $R = 1/\sigma d$. Note that the uppermost and lowermost blocks are of width h/2 and hence have a resistance of 2R. The total resistance between electrodes is given by

$$R_t = \frac{100}{I} = \frac{100}{100} R = \frac{1}{\sigma d}$$

from which we obtain

$$\sigma = \frac{1}{R_t d}$$

If this is compared with $\sigma = L/(R_t Wd)$, which is based on assuming uniform current flow without spreading, and we note that L = 2.25 W we see that the latter gives a value of σ which is a factor of 2.25 too large. We should, of course, use a finer mesh if we want a more accurate result for R_t. The calculation given above is probably accurate to only within ±10 percent but is a great improvement over the value obtained by assuming uniform current flow since this is in error by at least 100 percent.

The total current I can also be evaluated by finding the total flow across sections intersecting nodes 03 and 33 or nodes 05 and 35. These latter two alternatives give

$$I = 2\left[\frac{39-23}{2R} + \frac{41-24}{R} + \frac{45-26}{R} + \frac{47-27}{2R}\right] = \frac{108}{R}$$

and

$$I = 2\left[\frac{7}{R} + \frac{8}{R/2} + \frac{9}{R/2} + \frac{9}{R}\right] = \frac{100}{R}$$

The last result agrees with the first but the second is 8 percent higher. The most accurate results are those obtained by using sections close to the right hand side in Fig. 3-8.7 since the current flow at this end is more uniform and more nearly parallel to the resistance blocks and hence makes the resistance net approximation better. If an extreme left hand side section is used the greatest error would occur, i.e., one finds that I = 151/R which is very high.

ΔΔΔ

3-9. Computer Techniques

If a digital computer is used for carrying out the relaxation process, a slightly modified procedure is employed. The procedure begins, as before, by numbering the net points, say as shown in Fig. 3-9.1. Now we begin by setting up a matrix array of the initial values of the array. If initial values cannot be written, set the values to zero. If the boundary values are given, include these. Hence one may begin with an array as shown in Fig. 3-9.2. Now one proceeds systematically along the rows, moving as shown in Fig. 3-9.3, changing the values according to Eq. (3-5.7). After a first trial run, go through the listing again, making changes as a second trial run. Continue with this procedure until stationary values are achieved. The successive trials at a given point, say Φ_{ij}, will vary

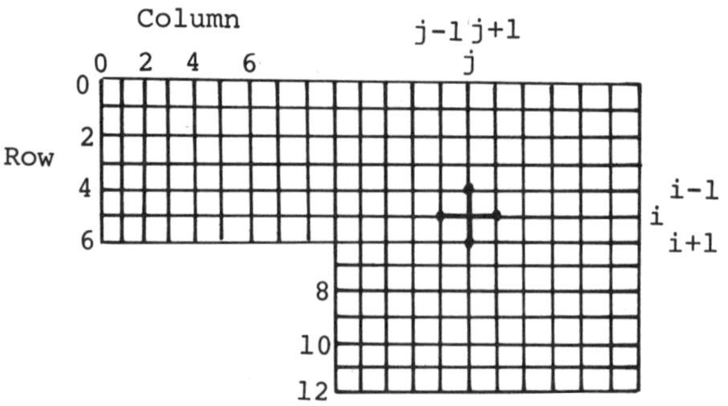

Figure 3-9.1. The net point numering for computer calculation.

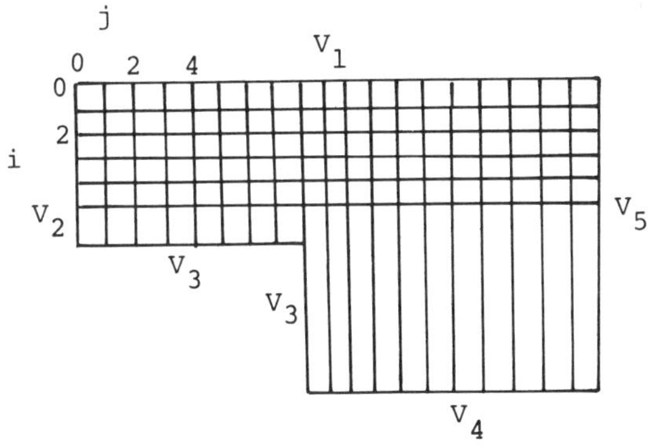

Figure 3-9.2. Initial values for the relaxation process.

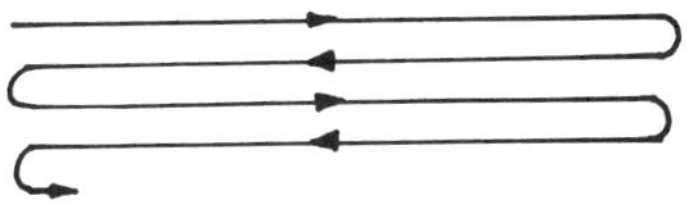

Figure 3-9.3. The order of relaxation computations.

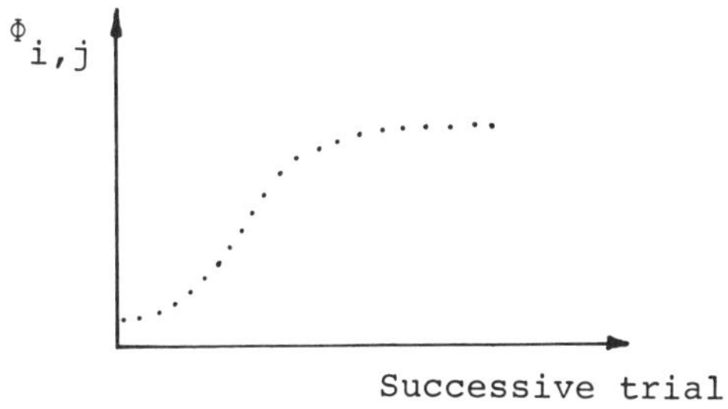

Figure 3-9.4. The convergence of the relaxation process.

somewhat in the manner shown. In carrying out the calculations, there exists in computer memory at any given time values for $\Phi_{i-1,j}$, $\Phi_{i+1,j}$, $\Phi_{i,j-1}$, $\Phi_{i,j+1}$. As the calculation will tackle each mesh point in turn working through the mesh, two of these values will be recently updated values while the other two still have to be calculated in this round of calculations.

The direct use of Eq. (3-5.7) for the solution of any problem will lead to an unnecessarily lengthy calculation. Hence an important question is - can one multiply the updated and/or current values by some constant other than 1 that will cause a convergent consistent solution to occur in a shorter number of calculations? It has been found that an accelerating factor ω of 1.5 applied to the available values does significantly reduce the computation time. Higher values of the factor ω can result in overshoot and ultimate settling, with a relaxation constant of 2 or higher resulting in unstable calculations.

We note that here, as in the hand-performed relaxation method, corrections must be made if the mesh does not fit exactly within the boundaries of the specified configuration.

To carry out the complete field distribution requires that a computer program be written to calculate $\Phi_{i,j}$ from Eq. (3-5.7) at each point i,j in the mesh in turn and to continue the calculation until the change in $\Phi_{i,j}$ at each point is less than a given quantity.

REVIEW QUESTIONS

1. At what angle do the flow lines and the equipotential surfaces intersect each other?
2. What is the significant feature of the curvilinear squares?
3. Describe the steps in field mapping.
4. Discuss why the equation $R = N_v/\sigma dN_i$ is equivalent to $R = L/\sigma A$ for a cylindrical or rectangular homogeneous resistor.
5. Describe the method of resistance net approximation.
6. What is the constant in problems involving heat flow which replaces the conductivity in electrical current problems?
7. Discuss the procedure in applying the iteration process.
8. If the field in a region satisfies Laplace's equation, specify the formula for the potential at a point due to an array of point charges.
9. What limits the accuracy of the iteration process?
10. Are the resistance values to be associated with the square and the hexagonal grids the same?
11. How do we modify the connections at a node in order that the numerical solution corresponds to the Poisson equation?
12. Specify the row and the column operations, and explain why we use them?
13. What is the residual?
14. What is meant by over-relaxation?

PROBLEMS

3-3.1. One method used for transferring heat from a hot fluid to a cold fluid is to pass the hot fluid through a hollow tube that is immersed in a cool fluid. A cross-sectional view of a typical heat transfer tube is shown in Fig. P3-3.1. In order to obtain some idea of the relative merit of the heat

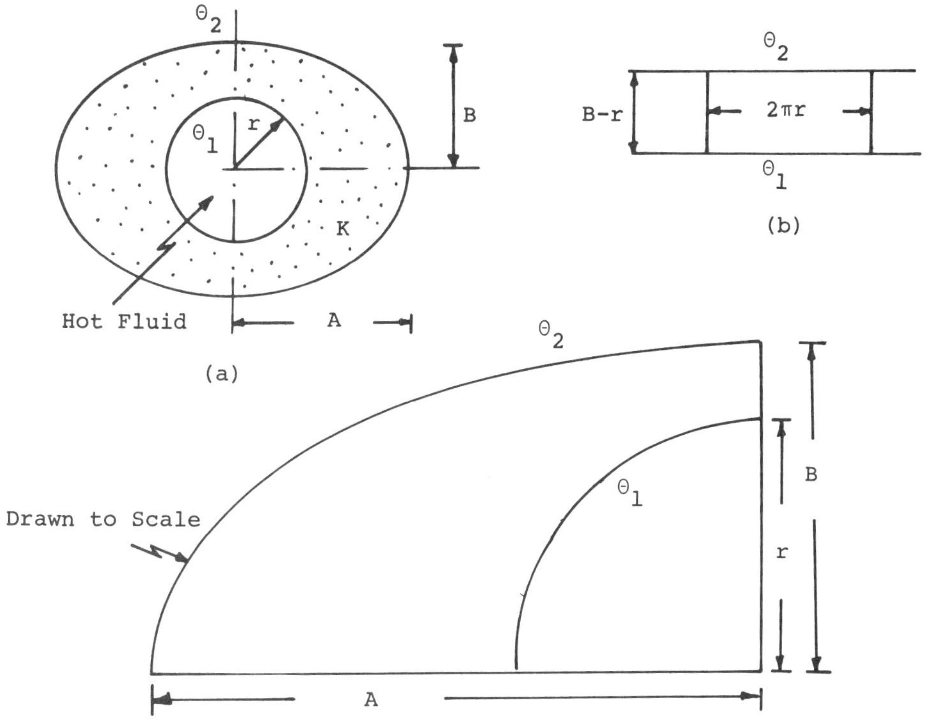

Figure P3-3.1

transfer tube, determine the ratio of the heat transfer rate of the tube in Fig. P3-3.1a to that of a flat plate with a width equal to the inner circumference of the heat transfer tube and a thickness equal to the smallest wall dimension of the heat transfer tuee as in Fig. P3-3.1b. You may consider that the outside of the tube is at a constant temperature Θ_2 and that the surface of the passing wall is at a constant temperature Θ_1. Carry out a flux plot, and from this deduce the relative merit factor.

Data: Conductivity of tube wall = K Watt/C^o-m

$r = 3.75$ cm $B = 5.10$ cm $A = 10.0$ cm

A scale drawing of a quarter section of the tube is included on the preceding page.

3-4.1. To obtain a highly stable (constant frequency) oscillator it is common practice to use a quartz crystal as the frequency determining element and to house it in a constant temperature oven. Figure P3-4.1 illustrates the cross section of a constant temperature oven. The outside dimensions of the copper box are 5 cm × 5 cm × 8 cm. The insulating liner is 1 cm thick and has a thermal conductivity K = 0.03 Watt/^{o}C-meter. Six wires connect the

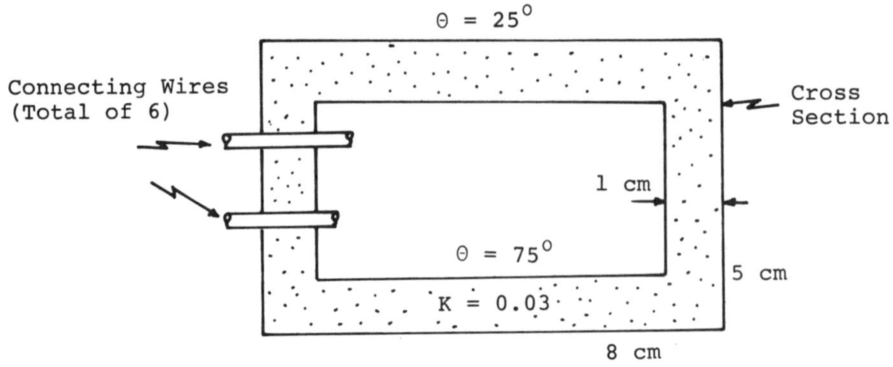

Figure P3-4.1

oscillator and heater circuits to the outside circuitry. These wires are made of copper with a thermal conductivity of 384 Watt/°C-meter and have a radius of 0.3 mm. By using a simple resistance net obtain an estimate of the heater power required to maintain the interior temperature at 75°C for an outside temperature of 25°C. What fraction of the heat loss is due to the six wires?

3-8.1. Figure P3-8.1 shows a parallel plate capacitor of width W, spacing d, and length L >> W. If the electric field is assumed to be uniform between the plates the capacitance per unit length is given by $C = \varepsilon_o W/d$. A theoretical formula which takes fringing effects into account gives

$$C = \frac{\varepsilon_o W}{d} + \frac{\varepsilon_o}{\pi} \ln \frac{\pi W}{d}$$

Use the relaxation method to evaluate C and compare your results with those given by the theoretical formulas. Choose the illustrated mesh with W = 2d. Note that C = Q/200 where the potential between the plates is 200 volts and Q is the total flux or flow of $\varepsilon_o E$ towards one plate. The latter may be found using the method employed in Ex. 3-8.2, i.e., to find the flow across the symmetry plane where $\Phi = 0$. The mesh should extend to infinity but for practical purposes a mesh just large enough to provide a reasonably accurate solution for the potential along the symmetry line $\Phi = 0$ in the vicinity of the capacitor is sufficient. Use the approximate constant potential contours to specify the initial values of the potentials at the nodes. Note that the potentials at the nodes along the upper and right hand sides cannot be relaxed since the mesh has been chosen to be finite in size. The potentials at these nodes as given were obtained by relaxing a larger mesh and should be assumed as known for this problem.

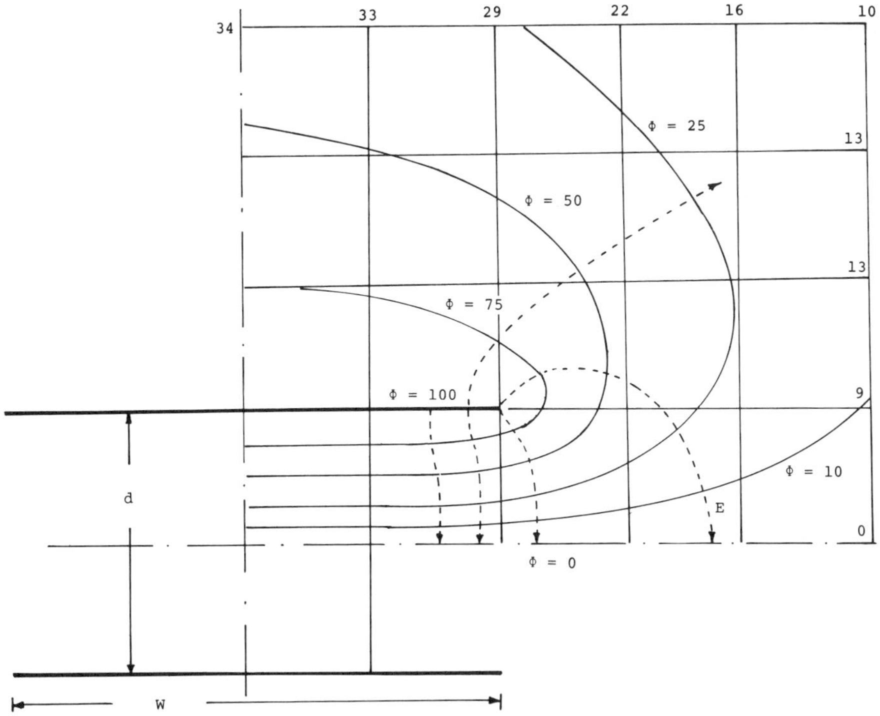

Figure P3-8.1

3-8.2. Use the relaxation method to find the resistance between faces A and B of the specimen illustrated in Fig. P3-8.2. The material has a depth d = 2 cm and a width W = 16 cm. The conductivity $\sigma = 10^5$ mhos per meter. Note that if the suggested mesh is used there will be four nodes that have strings cut by the boundary. Also note that along the right and left faces the normal gradient is zero. Compare your answer with $R_t = L/\sigma Wd$ where L is the average length of the speciman (L = 6 cm).

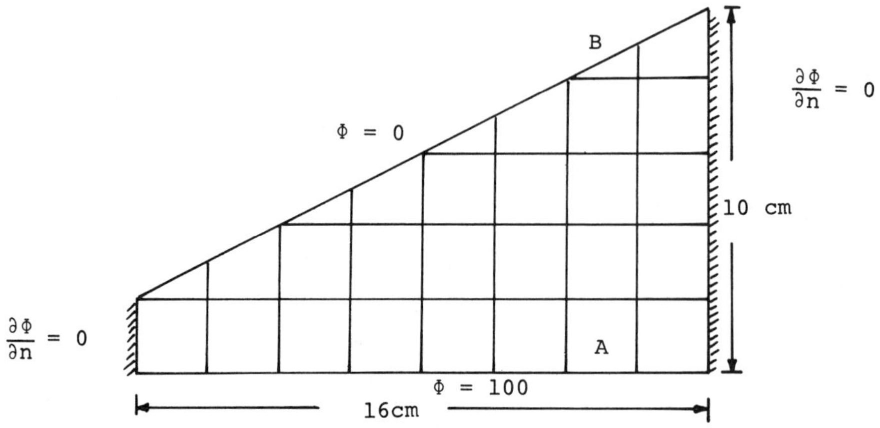
B
$\frac{\partial \Phi}{\partial n} = 0$
$\Phi = 0$
10 cm
$\frac{\partial \Phi}{\partial n} = 0$
A
$\Phi = 100$
16cm

Figre P3-8.2

CHAPTER 4

ANALYTIC SOLUTION OF BOUNDARY VALUE PROBLEMS
(Laplace's and Poisson's Equations)

In the previous chapters our aim was to introduce a number of field problems of engineering importance, and to consider some specific approximate and numerical methods for solving these field problems. In this chapter we will develop analytic techniques for the solution of such problems that have considerable generality and applicability. In addition, a deeper insight into some of the physical properties of fields will be obtained through the detailed study of the analytical solution of the examples that are solved.

In general, potential fields which are governed by Laplace's and Poisson's equations, and also all other types of field problems, are described by partial differential equations, in contrast to the ordinary differential equations that described lumped parameter systems, e.g., mechanical and electrical networks. The solution of these equations will assume forms that depend critically on the boundary configuration and on the boundary conditions that must be met. It is for this reason that such problems are often referred to as boundary value problems. Often the techniques are called harmonic analysis, because of the character of the mathematical forms of the solutions.

4-1. General Considerations

To introduce some general features of boundary value problems, consider the problem of finding a solution to the potential field $\Phi(x,y,z)$ which is described by Laplace's equation

$$\nabla^2\Phi = 0 \tag{4-1.1}$$

that exists in the region V defined by the two surfaces S_1 and S_2 shown in Fig. 4-1.1.

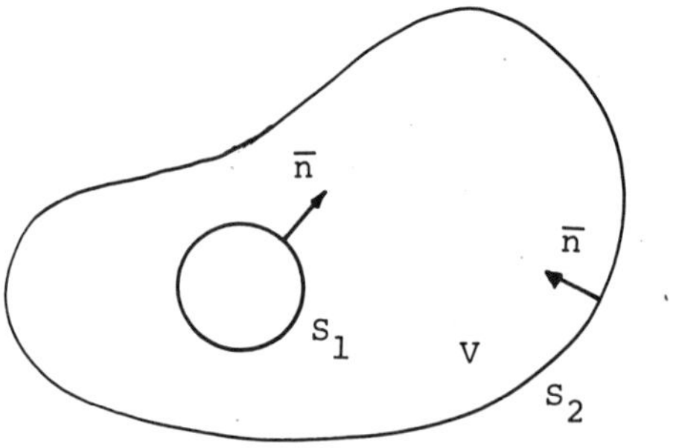

Figure 4-1.1. A potential field boundary value problem.

The boundaries play a very important role in determining the potential field variation everywhere throughout the enclosed volume V. Further, specifying the value of the potential everywhere on the boundary is sufficient to make the solution unique. In other words, if we can find a solution to the partial differential equation (4-1.1) such that the potential assumes the specified values on the boundaries S_1 and S_2, then this solution is unique; that is, there is no other solution. Uniqueness can be proved quite easily by mathematical methods, but for the present, we shall rely on the physical argument that there can be only one possible correct solution to a given problem. For example, Φ could represent the steady state temperature distribution in the region V, and when we hold the boundaries at specified temperatures, there will be only one possible temperature distribution in the region V. Mathematical proof of uniqueness (see Sec. 4-9) assumes two different solutions, and it is then shown that these must be equal.

There are three different types of boundary conditions that are applicable. These are summarized in Table 4-1.1. Any one of the three boundary conditions may be specified over a given portion of the boundary, and thus leading to a unique solution.

Table 4-1.1. Boundary Condition Descriptions

Name	S_1	S_2	Comments
Dirichlet boundary conditions	$\Phi = \Phi_1$ = const. on S_1	$\Phi = \Phi_2$ = const. on S_2	$\Phi(x,y,z)$ is the known general solution that becomes Φ_1 on S_1 and Φ_2 on S_2
Neumann boundary conditions	$\frac{\partial\Phi}{\partial n} = \Phi_1(x,y,z)$	$\frac{\partial\Phi}{\partial n} = \Phi_2(x,y,z)$	The general function $\Phi(x,y,z)$ must satisfy the gradient conditions on S_1 and S_2
Mixed boundary conditions	$\Phi = \Phi_1(x,y,z)$ on part of S_1 and $\partial\Phi/\partial n = \Phi_{11}(x,y,z)$ on the rest of S_1	$\Phi = \Phi_2(x,y,z)$ on part of S_2 and $\partial\Phi/\partial n = \Phi_{22}(x,y,z)$ on the rest of S_2	$\Phi_1, \Phi_2, \Phi_{11}$ and Φ_{22} are the forms assumed by $\Phi(x,y,z)$ on the boundary surfaces to satisfy the specified boundary conditions

4-2. Method of Separation of Variables in Cartesian Coordinates

The several approximate methods of solving boundary value problems in Chap. 3 are general, and may be applied in a straightforward manner for almost any boundary configuration. The analytic methods now to be explored are more critical in application than these approximate methods, since the form of the analytic solution depends critically on the specified boundary configuration.

The principal analytic procedure for solving boundary value problems is the method of *separation of variables*. In this procedure, we assume that the solution for Φ can be expressed as a product of three separate functions, each of which depends on only one coordinate variable. For example, in rectangular coordinates we assume that the solution will be of the form

$$\Phi(x,y,z) = f(x)\, g(y)\, h(z) \tag{4-2.1}$$

If, when we substitute this assumed solution into the partial differential equation we obtain thereby three independent ordinary differential equations for the functions $f(x)$, $g(y)$, $h(z)$, the method works. We then say that the partial differential equation is separable in that coordinate system. If the partial differential equation is not separable, the method of separation of variables is not applicable. Fortunately, Laplace's equation is separable in many of the common coordinate systems, including rectangular, cylindrical and spherical coordinates. However, for fields described by partial differential equations of a form more complex than Laplace's equation, the number of coordinate systems in which separability occurs is more restricted.

To illustrate the method of separation of variables, we shall consider several specific examples that involve rectangular, cylindrical and spherical coordinate systems. We shall show all details in some of these examples in order that the procedure in the solution is clearly indicated.

Example 4-2.1. Find the potential distribution inside the rectangular region shown in Fig. 4-2.1, for the boundary conditions noted.

Solution. The boundaries coincide with constant coordinate surfaces in rectangular coordinates and, therefore, the appropriate coordinate system to be used in the analysis is the rectangular coordinate system. Further, there are no volume sources, so the potential Φ is a solution of Laplace's equation in two dimensions (Φ is independent of z)

$$\frac{\partial^2\Phi(x,y)}{\partial x^2} + \frac{\partial^2\Phi(x,y)}{\partial y^2} = 0 \tag{4-2.2}$$

with the boundary conditions as noted:

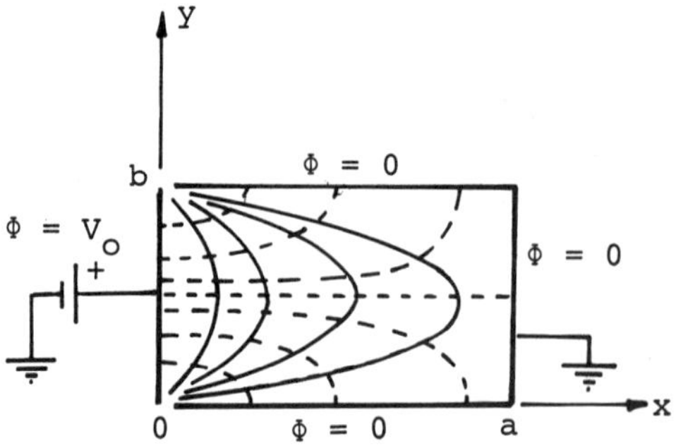

Figure 4-2.1. A two-dimensional problem with Dirichlet boundary conditions.

C-1. $\Phi = V_o$ at $x = 0$ $\quad 0 \leq y \leq b$

C-2. $\Phi = 0$ at $x = a$ $\quad 0 \leq y \leq b$

C-3. $\Phi = 0$ at $y = 0$, $y = b$ $\quad 0 \leq x \leq a$

To apply the method of separation of variables, we assume a product solution

$$\Phi(x,y) = f(x)\, g(y) \tag{4-2.3}$$

When we substitute this functional form into Eq. (4-2.2) we obtain

$$g \frac{d^2f}{dx^2} + f \frac{d^2g}{dy^2} = 0$$

since $\partial^2 fg/\partial x^2 = g\, d^2f/dx^2$, etc. We now divide by fg with the resultant equation

$$\frac{1}{f}\frac{d^2f}{dx^2} + \frac{1}{g}\frac{d^2g}{dy^2} = 0 \tag{4-2.4}$$

We observe that each of these terms depends on one coordinate variable only. Since we can vary x without changing y, and vice versa, the sum of the two terms can equal zero only if each term is equal to a constant, and the two constants add up to zero. Thus we can write

$$\frac{1}{f}\frac{d^2f}{dx^2} = k_x^2 \qquad \text{a)}$$

$$\frac{1}{g}\frac{d^2g}{dy^2} = k_y^2 \qquad \text{b)} \tag{4-2.5}$$

$$k_x^2 + k_y^2 = 0 \quad \text{or} \quad k_x^2 = -k_y^2 \qquad \text{c)}$$

where k_x^2 and k_y^2 are constants.

The general solution for f and g are hyperbolic functions of the form

$$f(x) = C_1' \sinh k_x x + C_2' \cosh k_x x \tag{4-2.6}$$

$$g(y) = D_1 \sinh k_y y + D_2 \cosh k_y y \tag{4-2.7}$$

where C_1', C_2', D_1 and D_2 are arbitrary constants. However, Eq. (4-2.5c) indicates that either k_x^2 or k_y^2 must be negative. Thus if k_x is real k_y must be imaginary, and vice versa; their magnitudes must be the same. For the case of k_x imaginary (and written jk_y) with k_y real, Eqs. (4-2.6) and (4-2.7) take the form

$$f(x) = C_1 \sin k_y x + C_2 \cos k_y x \tag{4-2.8}$$

$$g(y) = D_1 \sinh k_y y + D_2 \cosh k_y y \tag{4-2.9}$$

where $C_1 = jC_1'$ and $C_2 = C_2'$; $\sinh jx = j \sin x$; $\cosh jx = \cos x$. A second set of equations is obtained if we take k_x real and k_y imaginary ($= jk_x$). This set takes the form

$$f(x) = C_1 \sinh k_x x + C_2 \cosh k_x x \tag{4-2.8a}$$

$$g(y) = D_1 \sin k_x y + D_2 \cos k_x y \tag{4-2.9a}$$

We observe that in these solutions the trigonometric and hyperbolic forms are exchanged. The choice of the two sets to be used depends on the nature of the boundary conditions. If the potential is required to have repeated zeros as a function of x, then Eqs. (4-2.8) and (4-2.9) are used. If zeros are specified in the y-direction, the second set is used. If, however, the boundaries extend to infinity in one direction, the hyperbolic functions are replaced by real exponentials.

In our problem the potential is zero at $y = 0$ and at $y = b$; we thus select the second set of equations. We write for the potential Φ the form

$$\Phi(x,y) = f(x)g(y) = (C_1 \sinh k_x x + C_2 \cosh k_x x)(D_1 \sin k_x y + D_2 \cos k_x y) \tag{4-2.10}$$

We first impose boundary condition C-3. When $y = 0$, we obtain

$$\Phi = D_2(C_1 \sinh k_x x + C_2 \cosh k_x x)$$

To force this equation to be zero for all values of x along the surface $y = 0$ we must choose $D_2 = 0$. We do not choose $C_1 = C_2 = 0$ which is the other alternative, since this would make Φ independent of x, and would make it impossible to satisfy boundary conditions C-1 and C-2. The solution which satisfies C-3, y = 0, is then

$$\Phi = D_1 \sin k_x y \, (C_1 \sinh k_x x + C_2 \cosh k_x x)$$

To make $\Phi = 0$ when $y = b$, independent of x, we must choose either $D_1 = 0$ or $\sin k_x b = 0$. We cannot choose $D_1 = 0$ or Φ will be identically zero. Hence we must choose the second alternative which is satisfied if

$$k_x = \frac{n\pi}{b} \qquad n = 1,2,3,4,\ldots \tag{4-2.11}$$

n cannot have the value zero for reasons of orthogonality to be discussed below. Consequently, a solution for Φ that satisfies the total boundary condition C-3 is

$$\Phi_n = D_n \sin \frac{n\pi y}{b} \left[\sinh \frac{n\pi}{b} x + C_n \cosh \frac{n\pi}{b} x\right]$$

where we have replaced the coefficients D_1, C_1 and C_2 by new coefficients D_n and C_n. Since all integral values of n give a valid solution, at this stage the general solution must be chosen as a superposition of all the possible solutions corresponding to different values of n, thus

$$\Phi = \sum_{n=1}^{\infty} D_n \sin \frac{n\pi y}{b} \left[\sinh \frac{n\pi x}{b} + C_n \cosh \frac{n\pi x}{b}\right] \tag{4-2.12}$$

Before proceeding further, we point out an important aspect of the solution procedure that is a general feature of boundary value problems. The imposition of the boundary conditions leads to the allowed values of the separation constants, in the present case $k_x = n\pi/b$. Each allowed value is an *eigenvalue* (proper value) and the corresponding solution is the *eigenfunction*, with the set of eigenvalues and eigenfunctions being characteristic of the particular boundary value problem. The general solution is a superposition of all the eigenfunctions, each multiplied by an arbitrary amplitude factor.

The next step in completing the solution is to restrict further the potential given by Eq. (4-2.12). This is done by imposing the other boundary conditions. Now we apply boundary condition C-2 which requires that

$$\sum_{n=1}^{\infty} D_n \sin \frac{n\pi y}{b} \left[\sinh \frac{n\pi a}{b} + C_n \cosh \frac{n\pi a}{b}\right] = 0 \qquad 0 \le y \le b \tag{4-2.13}$$

This equation requires that the quantity in the square brackets must vanish. This requires that we choose $C_n = -\tanh n\pi a/b$, and Eq. (4-2.12) becomes

$$\Phi = \sum_{n=1}^{\infty} D_n \sin\frac{n\pi y}{b}\left[\sinh\frac{n\pi x}{b} - \tanh\frac{n\pi a}{b}\cosh\frac{n\pi x}{b}\right]$$

$$= \sum_{n=1}^{\infty} D_n \sin\frac{n\pi y}{b}\,\frac{\sinh\frac{n\pi x}{b}\cosh\frac{n\pi a}{b} - \sinh\frac{n\pi}{b}\cosh\frac{n\pi x}{b}}{\cosh\frac{n\pi a}{b}}$$

We write this in the form

$$\Phi = \sum_{n=1}^{\infty} A_n \sin\frac{n\pi y}{b}\sinh\frac{n\pi(a-x)}{b} \tag{4-2.14}$$

where $A_n = D_n/\cosh n\pi a/b$.

Eq. (4-2.14) satisfies the conditions of the problem subject to all boundary conditions except C-1. The imposition of condition C-1 requires that

$$V_o = \sum_{n=1}^{\infty} A_n \sinh\frac{n\pi a}{b}\sin\frac{n\pi y}{b} \tag{4-2.15}$$

This is seen to be a Fourier series for V_o in terms of the eigenfunctions $\sin(n\pi y/b)$. The eigenfunctions $\sin n\pi y/b$ are *orthogonal* over the range $0 \leq y \leq b$. Orthogonality of functions is an extension of the same concept as orthogonality of two vectors. Two functions $\psi_1(\mu)$ and $\psi_2(\mu)$ are said to be orthogonal over the interval $\mu_1 \leq \mu \leq \mu_2$ if the following integral vanishes

$$\int_{\mu_1}^{\mu_2} \sigma(\mu)\,\psi_1(\mu)\,\psi_2(\mu)\,d\mu = 0 \tag{4-2.16}$$

$\sigma(\mu)$ is a suitable weighting function which, in some cases, is equal to unity. The eigenfunctions that occur in the solution of boundary value problems almost always are mutually orthogonal. This orthogonality property is a very important one, as we shall see, since it enables an arbitrary function to be expanded as a Fourier series in terms of the infinite set of eigenfunctions. It is assumed that the reader is already familiar with Fourier series involving the trigonometric sine and cosine functions. To proceed we multiply Eq. (4-2.15) by $\sin m\pi y/b\, dy$, integrate over y from 0 to b, and use the orthogonality property for trigonometric functions

$$\int_0^b \sin\frac{n\pi y}{b}\sin\frac{m\pi y}{b}\,dy = \begin{cases} 0 & n \neq m \\ \frac{b}{2} & n = m,\ n \neq 0 \end{cases} \tag{4-2.17}$$

We obtain

$$\frac{b}{2} A_m \sinh\frac{m\pi a}{b} = \int_0^b V_o \sin\frac{m\pi y}{b}\,dy = \frac{V_o b(1 - \cos m\pi)}{m\pi} \tag{4-2.18}$$

Solving for A_m from this equation and combining it with Eq. (4-2.16) we obtain finally the required solution for Φ which is

$$\Phi = \sum_{n=1,3,5,\ldots}^{\infty} \frac{4V_o}{n\pi} \sin \frac{n\pi y}{b} \frac{\sinh \frac{n\pi}{b}(a-x)}{\sinh \frac{n\pi a}{b}} \qquad n = 1,3,5,\ldots \tag{4-2.19}$$

since $(1 - \cos n\pi) = 2$ for $n = 1,3,5,\ldots$ and zero otherwise. The equipotential lines and flow lines of $\overline{E}$ are shown in Fig. 4-2.1.

ΔΔΔ

Example 4-2.2. To include time as one of the variables in the problem, consider a uniform slab of homogeneous material that is bounded by planes $x = 0$ and $x = a$. Let the initial temperature be $\Theta = \Theta(x)$ and suppose that the two faces are maintained at temperature zero, as shown. We are required to find the temperature at any point of the slab at any time. See Fig. 4-2.2.

Solution. The solution to this problem requires solving the thermal (diffusion) equation. This equation arises by considering a small volume element dV. The rate at which heat flows out of this volume element per unit volume is $\nabla \cdot \overline{q}$, and this must equal the time rate of change of heat concentration within dV. The continuity equation is then

$$\nabla \cdot \overline{q} = -\frac{\partial}{\partial t}(c_t \rho_v \Theta)$$

where c_t is the specific heat of the material (Joule/kg-^{o}K) and ρ_v is the mass density (kg/m^3). Combine this with the Fourier law $\overline{q} = -K\nabla\Theta$, and there results

$$\frac{K}{c_t \rho_v} \nabla^2\Theta = c^2\nabla^2\Theta = -\frac{\partial\Theta}{\partial t} \tag{4-2.20}$$

To solve this equation, assume the product solution

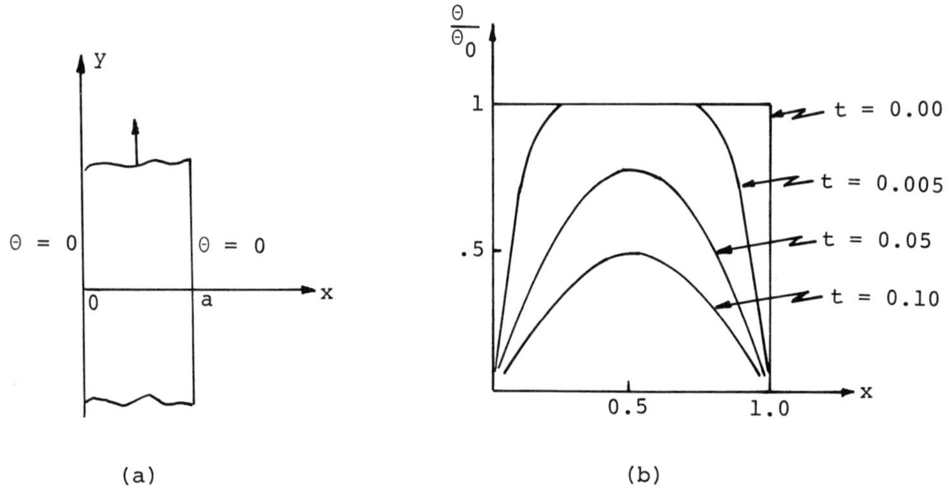

Figure 4-2.2. An initially heated homogeneous slab.

$$\Theta(x,t) = X(x)\,T(t) \tag{4-2.20}$$

which must satisfy the boundary conditions

C-1.	$\Theta(x,t) = 0$	$x = 0$	$t = t$
C-2.	$\Theta(x,t) = 0$	$x = a$	$t = t$
C-3.	$\Theta(x,t) = \Theta(x)$	$x = x$	$t = 0$

This equation is combined with the defining equation to get

$$X \frac{dT}{dt} = c^2 T \frac{d^2X}{dx^2} \qquad \text{or} \qquad \frac{1}{c^2 T}\frac{dT}{dt} = \frac{1}{X}\frac{d^2X}{dx^2}$$

We separate these expressions by writing:

$$\frac{1}{c^2 T}\frac{dT}{dt} = -k^2 \qquad \text{a)}$$

$$\frac{1}{X}\frac{d^2X}{dx^2} = -k^2 \qquad \text{b)} \tag{4-2.21}$$

The general solution of the differential equation, Eq. (4-2.21a), is the expression

$$T = A\, e^{-k^2c^2t} \tag{4-2.22}$$

The solution to Eq. (4-2.21b) is

$$X = B_1 \cos kx + B_2 \sin kx \tag{4-2.23}$$

The general solution to Eq. (4-2.20a) is then of the form

$$\Theta(x,t) = (B'' \cos kx + C'' \sin kx)\, e^{-k^2c^2t} \tag{4-2.24}$$

where $B'' = B_1A$ and $C'' = B_2A$.

We wish to evaluate the arbitrary constants for our particular problem. We apply the boundary conditions. We write, according to C-1,

$$0 = e^{-k^2c^2t}\,(B'' + 0)$$

which requires that $B'' = 0$, and so

$$\Theta(x,t) = C''\, e^{-k^2c^2t} \sin kx \tag{4-2.25}$$

By condition C-2 we have

$$0 = C''\, e^{-k^2c^2t} \sin ka$$

which requires that

$$\sin ka = 0, \quad ka = n\pi \qquad n = 1,2,\ldots$$

so that

$$k = \frac{n\pi}{a} \qquad n = 1,2,\ldots$$

Subject to C-1 and C-2 the solution will be of the general form

$$\Theta(x,t) = \sum_{n=1}^{\infty} C_n e^{-(\frac{n\pi}{a})^2 c^2 t} \sin \frac{n\pi}{a} x \tag{4-2.26}$$

Upon imposing condition C-3, Eq. (4-2.26) becomes

$$\theta(x) = \sum_{n=1}^{\infty} C_n \sin \frac{n\pi}{a} x$$

We find the constants C_n by multiplying both sides by $\sin n\pi/a\ x\ dx$ and integrating,

$$C_n = \frac{2}{a}\int_0^a \theta(x) \sin \frac{n\pi}{a} x\, dx \tag{4-2.27}$$

Taken together, Eqs. (4-2.26) and (4-2.27) constitute the complete solution.

We examine the form of the solution for the special case when $\theta(x) = \Theta_o$, a constant. The explicit form for C_n is

$$C_n = \frac{2\Theta_o}{a}\int_0^a \sin \frac{n\pi}{a} x\, dx = \frac{2\Theta_o}{n\pi}[- \cos n\pi + 1]$$

From this we see that

$$C_n = 0 \quad \text{for n even} \qquad \text{and} \qquad C_n = \frac{4\Theta_o}{n} \quad \text{for n odd.}$$

The complete solution in this case has the explicit form

$$\Theta(x,t) = \frac{4\Theta_o}{\pi}\sum_{n=1}^{\infty} \frac{1}{n} e^{-(\frac{n\pi}{a})^2 c^2 t} \sin \frac{n\pi}{a} x, \qquad n = 1,3,5,\ldots$$

and it is plotted in Fig. 4-2.2b for the case $c/a = 1$.

ΔΔΔ

Examples 4-2.1 and 4-2.2 have been discussed in considerable detail because they illustrate most of the essential features involved in the separation of variables method of solving boundary value problems. To provide an overall view, we summarize the main steps involved.

1. Choose a coordinate system for which the boundaries coincide with the constant coordinate surfaces.
2. Express the solution in product form, i.e., as a product of functions each depending on one coordinate only. If the partial differential equation separates, an ordinary differential equation for each function is obtained and the solution can proceed.
3. Choose the separation constants and coefficients in the general solution so as to satisfy the prescribed boundary conditions. A certain amount of skill and experience is needed in order to adapt the general solution to fulfill the requirements of the specific problem being considered. However, when all the boundary conditions have been satisfied, the solution will be unique. Frequently it will be necessary to utilize the orthogonality properties of the eigenfunctions that arise in order to determine all of the unknown amplitude coefficients that occur.

To illustrate further procedures involved when other boundary conditions are specified, we will consider several variations of the basic problem shown in Fig. 4-2.1. The variations to be considered are illustrated in Fig. 4-2.3.

For the problem illustrated in Fig. 4-2.3a, we have a situation that is an obvious extension of Example 4-2.1, with the requirement that the potential Φ be equal to $V_1(y)$ at $x = 0$ and $V_2(y)$ at $x = a$. This problem is readily solved by using the

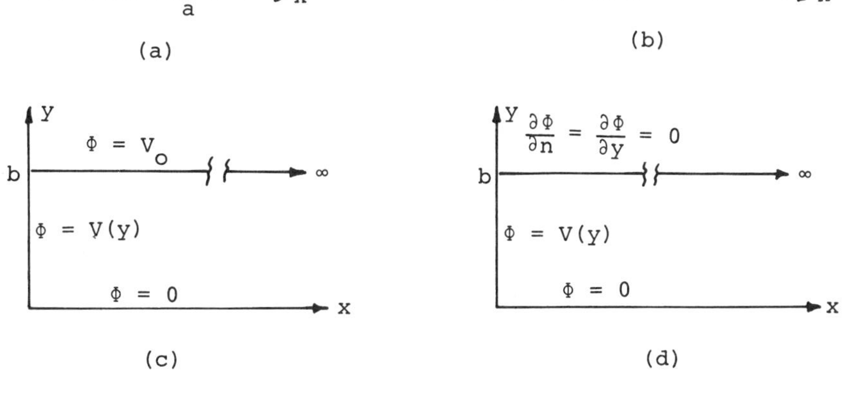

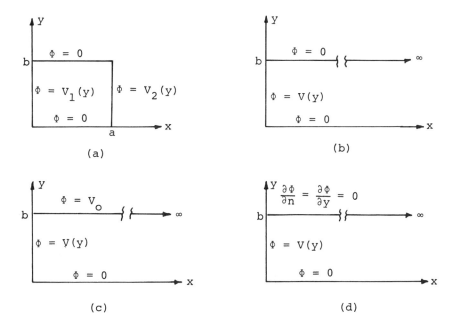

Figure 4-2.3. Some two dimensional potential field configurations.

principle of superposition. This involves constructing two solutions Φ_a and Φ_b with the properties

$$\Phi_a = 0 \qquad y = 0, b \qquad 0 \le x \le a$$

$$\Phi_a = 0, \qquad x = a \qquad 0 \le y \le b$$

$$\Phi_a = V_1(y), \quad x = 0 \qquad 0 \le y \le b$$

and

$$\Phi_b = 0 \qquad y = 0, b \qquad 0 \le x \le a$$

$$\Phi_b = 0, \qquad x = 0 \qquad 0 \le y \le b$$

$$\Phi_b = V_2(y), \quad x = a \qquad 0 \le y \le b$$

Each of these is essentially a problem of the form solved in Example 4-2.1. The superposition of Φ_a and Φ_b gives a potential $\Phi = \Phi_a + \Phi_b$ that is a solution of Laplace's equation and satisfies all boundary conditions. Thus the basic procedure involved here is to find partial solutions that satisfy the non zero value of potential on one side only, and superimpose these partial solutions to obtain the final required solution.

The configuration in Fig. 4-2.3b requires a solution for Φ that will vanish as x becomes infinite. This requirement can be met by using the exponential function $e^{-n\pi x/b}$ in place of the hyperbolic functions sinh $n\pi x/b$ and cosh $n\pi x/b$ used to obtain Eqs. (4-2.12) and (4-2.19). It is readily found that this solution is

$$\Phi = \sum_{n=1}^{\infty} \frac{4V_0}{n\pi} \sin \frac{n\pi y}{b} \; e^{-n\pi x/b} \tag{4-2.28}$$

for the case when $V(y) = V_0$.

To solve the problem shown in Fig. 4-2.3c, we seek two partial solutions Φ_a and Φ_b with $\Phi = \Phi_a + \Phi_b$ which satisfy the following boundary conditions

C-1.	$\Phi_a = V_0$	at	$y = b$	C-5.	$\Phi_b = 0$	at	$y = b$
C-2.	$\Phi_a = 0$	at	$x = 0$	C-6.	$\Phi_b = V(y)$	at	$x = 0$
C-3.	$\Phi_a = 0$	at	$x = \infty$	C-7.	$\Phi_b = 0$	at	$x = \infty$
C-4.	$\Phi_a = 0$	at	$y = 0$	C-8.	$\Phi_b = 0$	at	$y = 0$

The solution Φ_a which becomes V_0 at $y = b$ and zero at $y = 0$ is obtained if the constant k_y is zero. As a consequence of Eq. (4-2.5c) k_x is also zero and thus we obtain

$$f = A_1 x + A_2 \qquad \text{a)}$$
$$g = B_1 y + B_2 \qquad \text{b)} \tag{4-2.29}$$

If we apply the boundary conditions C-4 and C-1 we find that $A_1 = 0$, $B_2 = 0$, and $A_2 B_1 = V_o/b$. Hence we obtain

$$\Phi_a = \frac{V_o y}{b} \tag{4-2.30}$$

For Φ_b we can choose the general form (see previous case)

$$\Phi_b = \sum_{n=1}^{\infty} C_n \sin \frac{n\pi y}{b} e^{-n\pi x/b} \tag{4-2.31}$$

since this form satisfies the boundary conditions $\Phi_b = 0$ for $y = 0,b$ and vanishes at infinity. The constants C_n are still to be determined. But it is noted that the total potential is given by

$$\Phi = \Phi_a + \Phi_b = \frac{V_o y}{b} + \sum_{n=1}^{\infty} C_n \sin \frac{n\pi y}{b} e^{-n\pi x/b} \tag{4-2.32}$$

Now employing the remaining boundary condition at $x = 0$ requires that

$$V(y) = \frac{V_o y}{b} + \sum_{n=1}^{\infty} C_n \sin \frac{n\pi y}{b}$$

and hence

$$\sum_{n=1}^{\infty} C_n \sin \frac{n\pi y}{b} = V(y) - \frac{V_o y}{b}$$

The coefficients C_n may now be determined by Fourier analysis techniques (see Eq. 4-2.27) and are given by

$$C_n = \frac{2}{b} \int_0^b \left[V(y) - \frac{V_o y}{b}\right] \sin \frac{n\pi y}{b} dy \tag{4-2.33}$$

When $V(y)$ is given, the integral can be evaluated and the solution is then completed.

In the previous problems we have chosen the separation constant k_y equal to $n\pi/b$ in order to make $\sin k_y y$, and hence the potential, vanish at $y = 0,b$. For the problem illustrated in Fig. 4-2.3d we require instead that the normal derivative be zero at $y = b$. To satisfy this condition, we must choose

$$\frac{d}{dy} \sin k_y y = k_y \cos k_y y = 0 \qquad y = b$$

Hence k_y is given by

$$k_y = \frac{\pi}{2b}, \frac{3\pi}{2b}, \ldots, \frac{n\pi}{2b} \qquad n = 1,3,5,\ldots$$

The general solution for Φ is thus of the form

$$\Phi = \sum_{n=1,3,\ldots}^{\infty} C_n \sin \frac{n\pi y}{2b} e^{-n\pi x/b} \tag{4-2.34}$$

As before, the coefficient C_n can be determined by a Fourier analysis technique from the boundary condition at $x = 0$. Note that the functions $\sin n\pi y/2b$ are orthogonal for odd values of n, i.e.,

$$\int_0^b \sin \frac{n\pi y}{2b} \sin \frac{m\pi y}{2b}\, dy = 0 \qquad n \neq m$$

so that we obtain

$$C_n = \frac{2}{b}\int_0^b V(y) \sin \frac{n\pi y}{2b}\, dy \tag{4-2.35}$$

4-3. Method of Separation of Variables in Cylindrical Coordinates

If the boundaries coincide with constant coordinate surfaces in a cylindrical coordinate system, Laplace's and Poisson's equations are then expressed in terms of cylindrical coordinates r, ϕ, z. For Laplace's equation we have (see Appendix I)

$$\nabla^2\Phi = \frac{1}{r}\frac{\partial}{\partial r}\left(r\frac{\partial\Phi}{\partial r}\right) + \frac{1}{r^2}\frac{\partial^2\Phi}{\partial\phi^2} + \frac{\partial^2\Phi}{\partial z^2} = 0 \tag{4-3.1}$$

We assume a product solution $\Phi = f(r)g(\phi)h(z)$, and we find that

$$\frac{r}{f}\frac{d}{dr}\left(r\frac{df}{dr}\right) + \frac{1}{g}\frac{d^2g}{d\phi^2} + r^2\frac{1}{h}\frac{d^2h}{dz^2} = 0 \tag{4-3.2}$$

after substituting fgh for Φ into Eq. (4-3.1) and dividing by fgh and multiplying by r^2.

In this equation, the second term is a function of ϕ only while the other terms do not vary with ϕ. Hence Eq. (4-3.2) can hold for all values of ϕ only if

$$\frac{1}{g}\frac{d^2g}{d\phi^2} = -\nu^2$$

or

$$\frac{d^2g}{d\phi^2} + \nu^2 g = 0 \tag{4-3.3}$$

where ν^2 is the separation constant.

If we replace the second term in Eq. (4-3.2) by $-\nu^2$ and divide by r^2 we obtain

$$\frac{1}{rf}\frac{d}{dr}\left(r\frac{df}{dr}\right) - \frac{\nu^2}{r^2} + \frac{1}{h}\frac{d^2h}{dz^2} = 0$$

For this equation to hold for all values of r and z we must have

$$\frac{d^2h}{dz^2} - k_z^{\ 2}h = 0 \qquad \text{a)}$$

$$\frac{1}{r}\frac{d}{dr}\left(r\frac{df}{dr}\right) + \left(k_z^{\ 2} - \frac{\nu^2}{r^2}\right)f = 0 \qquad \text{b)} \qquad (4\text{-}3.4)$$

where k_z is another separation constant which at present is assumed real. Equations (4-3.3) and (4-3.4a) may be easily solved to give

$$g = A_1 \sin \nu\phi + A_2 \cos \nu\phi \ (\text{or } A_1 e^{j\nu\phi} + A_2 e^{-j\nu\phi}) \qquad (4\text{-}3.5a)$$

$$h = B_1 e^{-k_z z} + B_2 e^{k_z z} \qquad (4\text{-}3.5b)$$

Equation (4-3.4b) which defines f is known as Bessel's equation and its solutions are given by

$$J_\nu(k_z r) = \left(\frac{k_z r}{2}\right)^\nu \sum_{i=0}^{\infty} \frac{(-1)^i}{i!\Gamma(i+\nu+1)} \left(\frac{k_z r}{2}\right)^{2i} \qquad (4\text{-}3.6a)$$

$$J_{-\nu}(k_z r) = \left(\frac{k_z r}{2}\right)^{-\nu} \sum_{i=0}^{\infty} \frac{(-1)^i}{i!\Gamma(i-\nu+1)} \left(\frac{k_z r}{2}\right)^{2i} \qquad (4\text{-}3.6b)$$

which are called Bessel functions of the first kind and order $\pm\nu$. By definition of the Γ-function $\Gamma(n+1) = \int_0^\infty e^{-x}x^n dx = n!$ for n integer. In our study we shall take $\nu = n$ to be an integer, which is the appropriate form for problems spanning the whole range in ϕ, $0 \le \phi \le 2\pi$; and so the function g, and as a consequence the value of Φ, must be the same at points ϕ and $(\phi + n2\pi)$ apart. For integral values of ν, J_ν and $J_{-\nu}$ are dependent; hence we must use another independent solution, and this is known as the Neumann function. For $\nu = n$, the two solutions are

$$J_n(k_z r) = \sum_{m=0}^{\infty} \frac{(-1)^m (k_z r/2)^{n+2m}}{m!\ (n+m)!} \qquad (4\text{-}3.7a)$$

$$Y_n(k_z r) = \frac{2}{\pi}\left(\gamma + \ell n \frac{k_z r}{2}\right) J_n(k_z r) - \frac{1}{\pi}\sum_{m=0}^{n-1} \frac{(n-m-1)!}{m!}\left(\frac{2}{k_z r}\right)^{n-2m}$$
$$- \frac{1}{\pi}\sum_{m=0}^{\infty} \frac{(-1)^m (k_z r/2)^{n+2m}}{m!\ (n+m)!}\left(1 + \frac{1}{2} + \cdots \frac{1}{m} + 1 + \frac{1}{2} + \cdots \frac{1}{n+m}\right) \qquad (4\text{-}3.7b)$$

where $\gamma = 0.5772$ is Euler's constant and the series $(1 + \frac{1}{2} + \dots + \frac{1}{m})$ is taken to be zero when $m = 0$. A notable feature of Neumann's function is that it becomes infinite at $r = 0$, and would not be present in a physical problem that requires a finite value of potential along the axis where r = 0.

If k_z now written k_z' becomes imaginary, $k_z' = jk_z$, then the solution of Eq. (4-3.4a) becomes

$$h = C_1 \sin k_z z + C_2 \cos k_z z \tag{4-3.8}$$

However, Bessel's equation now takes a new form

$$\frac{1}{r}\frac{d}{dr}\left(r\frac{df}{dr}\right) - \left(k_z^2 + \frac{n^2}{r^2}\right) f = 0 \tag{4-3.9}$$

which is known as the modified Bessel's equation. The solutions of Eq. (4-3.9) are the modified Bessel functions of the first and second kind, and are, respectively,

$$I_n(k_z r) = j^{-n} J_n(jk_z r) = j^n J_n(-jk_z r) \tag{4-3.10a}$$

$$K_n(k_z r) = \frac{\pi}{2} j^{n+1} [J_n(jk_z r) + jY_n(jk_z r)] \tag{4-3.10b}$$

The modified Bessel functions are defined in such a way that they are real when $k_z r$ is real. A sketch of the first few Bessel functions is given in Fig. 4-3.1. Tables of numerical values for the functions are widely available.

The Bessel functions for larger values of the argument approximate damped sine and cosine functions. In fact, for $k_z r$ large compared with the order n, the Bessel functions approximate to

$$J_n(k_z r) \doteq \sqrt{\frac{2}{k_z r\pi}} \cos\left(k_z r - \frac{\pi}{4} - \frac{n\pi}{2}\right) \tag{4-3.11}$$

$$Y_n(k_z r) \doteq \sqrt{\frac{2}{k_z r\pi}} \sin\left(k_z r - \frac{\pi}{4} - \frac{n\pi}{2}\right) \tag{4-3.12}$$

For large values of $k_z r$, i.e., $k_z r >> n$, the asymptotic forms of the modified functions are

$$I_n(k_z r) \doteq \frac{e^{k_z r}}{\sqrt{2\pi k_z r}} \tag{4-3.13a}$$

$$K_n(k_z r) \doteq \sqrt{\frac{\pi}{2k_z r}}\, e^{-k_z r} \tag{4-3.13b}$$

Only the function K_n remains bounded at infinity. The modified functions do not have any zeros, i.e., there are no real values of $k_z r$ which make I_n or K_n vanish. For later use, we list some useful relations among Bessel functions:

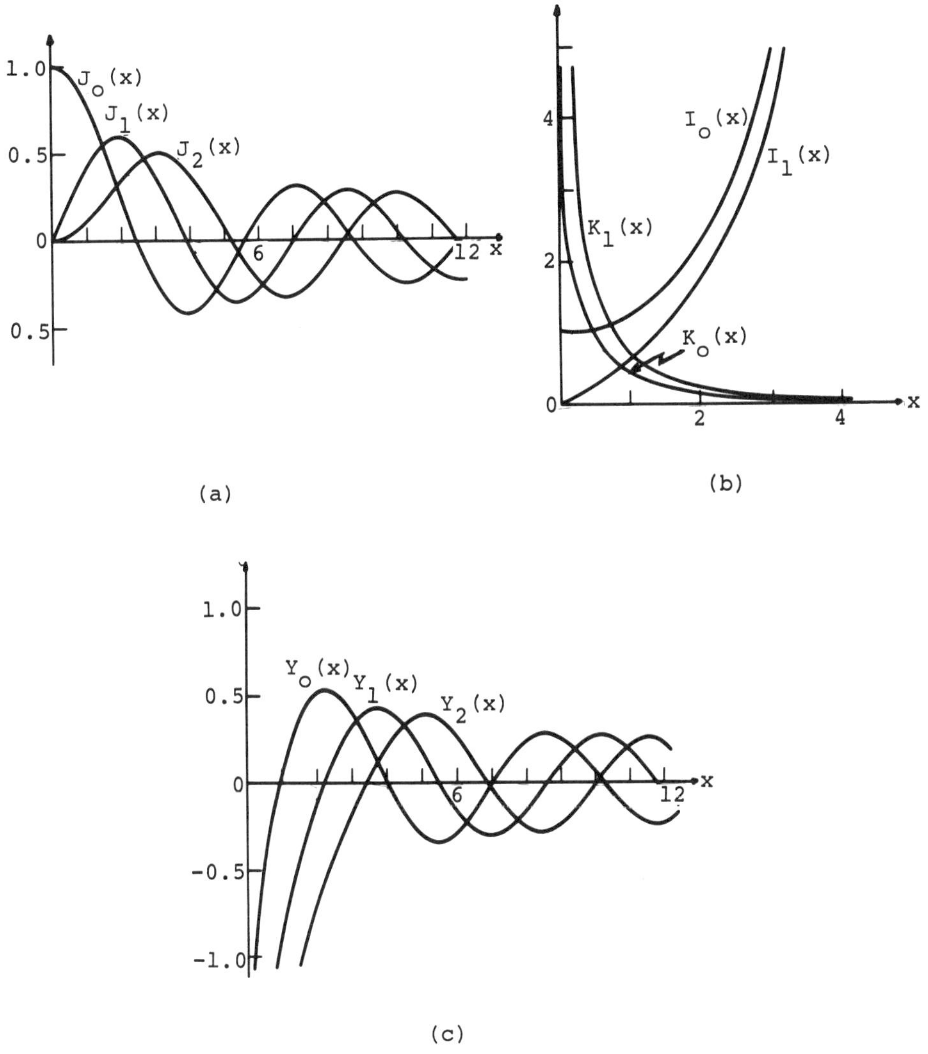

Figure 4-3.1. Sketches of a few Bessel functions. (a) Bessel functions of the first kind. (b) Modified Bessel functions. (c) Bessel functions of the second kind.

Table 4-3.1. Properties of Bessel Functions

Differentiation Formulas

$$J_0'(x) = \frac{dJ_0}{dx} = -J_1(x) \quad \text{a)}$$

$$J_0'(ax) = -aJ_1(ax) \quad \text{b)}$$

$$xJ_n'(x) = nJ_n(x) - xJ_{n+1}(x) \quad \text{c)}$$

$$I_0'(x) = I_1(x) \quad \text{d)} \qquad (4\text{-}3.14)$$

$$xI_n'(x) = nI_n(x) + xI_{n+1}(x) \quad \text{e)}$$

$$K_0'(x) = -K_1(x) \quad \text{f)}$$

$$xK_n'(x) = nK_n(x) - xK_{n+1}(x) \quad \text{g)}$$

Recurrence Formulas

$$J_{n+1}(x) = \frac{2n}{x} J_n(x) - J_{n-1}(x) \quad \text{a)}$$

$$J_{-n}(x) = (-1)^n J_n(x) = J_n(-x) \quad \text{for } n = \text{integer} \quad \text{b)} \qquad (4\text{-}3.15)$$

$$I_{n+1}(x) = \frac{-2n}{x} I_n(x) + I_{n-1}(x) \quad \text{c)}$$

$$K_{n+1}(x) = \frac{2n}{x} K_n(x) + K_{n-1}(x) \quad \text{d)}$$

Integrals

$$\int_0^x xJ_n(\alpha x)\, J_n(\beta x)\, dx$$

$$= \frac{x}{\alpha^2-\beta^2} [\beta J_n(\alpha x) J_{n-1}(\beta x) - \alpha J_n(\beta x) J_{n-1}(\alpha x)]; \quad \alpha \neq \beta \quad \text{a)}$$

$$\int_0^x xJ_n^{\,2}(\alpha x)\, dx = \frac{x^2}{2} [J_n^{\,2}(\alpha x) - J_{n+1}(\alpha x)\, J_{n-1}(\alpha x)] \quad \text{b)} \qquad (4\text{-}3.16)$$

$$\int_0^x x^n J_{n-1}(x)\, dx = x^n J_n(x) \quad \text{c)}$$

$$\int_0^x x^{n+1}\, J_n(\alpha x)\, dx = \frac{x^{n+1}}{\alpha} J_{n+1}(\alpha x) \quad \text{d)}$$

Observe that the Bessel function $Y_n(x)$ satisfies the same relations as $J_n(x)$.

The foregoing discussion has presented the general forms of the solutions of Laplace's equation in cylindrical coordinates. We shall now illustrate in specific detail the adaptation of these general considerations to the solution of a number of typical boundary value problems that can be described in terms of cylindrical coordinates.

Attention is called to the fact that not all problems with cylindrical geometry will necessarily require Bessel functions in their solution. Only those problems that lead, upon separation, to the Bessel differential equation will involve Bessel functions in their solution. We shall examine several such problems.

Example 4-3.1. Find the potential distribution between two concentric cylinders as shown in Fig. 4-3.2.

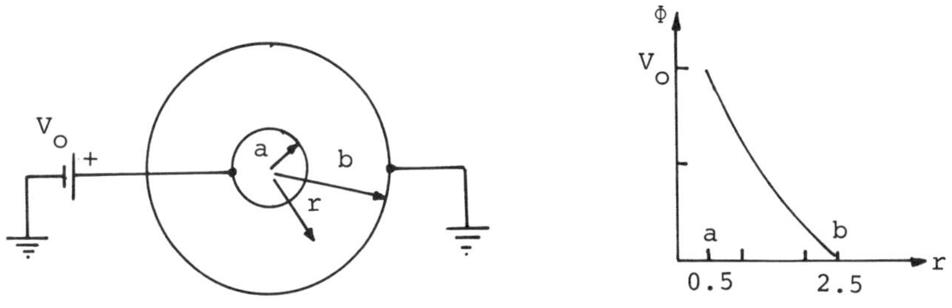

(a) (b)

Figure 4-3.2. Infinitely long cylindrical capacitor.

Solution. Since in this problem we have invariance in the z direction and symmetry in the ϕ direction, Laplace's equation takes the simple form ($\Phi = f$)

$$\frac{d}{dr}\left(r\frac{df}{dr}\right) = 0$$

which can be easily solved to give

$$f = C_1 \ln r + C_2 \tag{4-3.17}$$

Applying the boundary conditions $f = 0$ at $r = b$ and $f = V_o$ at $r = a$ we obtain

$$\Phi = f = \frac{V_o}{\ln \frac{a}{b}} \ln \frac{r}{b} \tag{4-3.18}$$

This procedure should be compared with that used in solving Ex. 1-12.4.

Note that Laplace's equation in this case reduces to a one-dimensional equation that is not of the Bessel form. The solution is not given in terms of Bessel functions.

ΔΔΔ

Example 4-3.2. Find the temperature distribution everywhere within a solid cylinder if the surface of half the cylinder is kept at temperature Θ_1 and the

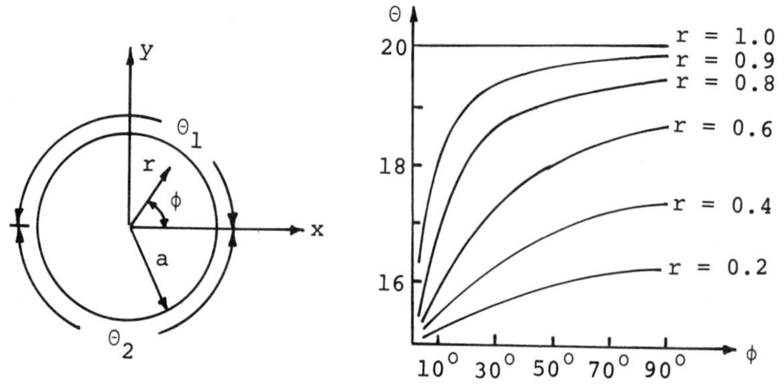

(a) (b)

Figure 4-3.3. A cylinder in two temperature baths.

other half is maintained at temperature Θ_2, as shown in Fig. 4-3.3a.

Solution. We showed that the steady state temperature distribution is described by Laplace's equation $\nabla^2\Theta = 0$. Because of independence in the z direction, Eq. (4-3.2) takes the form ($\Theta = fg$)

$$\frac{r}{f}\frac{d}{dr}\left(r\frac{df}{dr}\right) + \frac{1}{g}\frac{d^2g}{d\phi^2} = 0 \tag{4-3.19}$$

Following the standard separation procedure discussed previously this equation can be separated into the following two equations

$$\frac{d^2g}{d\phi^2} + n^2 g = 0 \tag{4-3.20a}$$

$$\frac{1}{r}\frac{d}{dr}\left(r\frac{df}{dr}\right) - \frac{n^2}{r^2} f = 0 \tag{4-3.20b}$$

Observe that Eq. (4-3.20b) is not the Bessel differential equation. The solutions to these equations are, respectively,

$$g = A_1 \sin n\phi + A_2 \cos n\phi \tag{4-3.21a}$$

$$f = B_1 r^n + B_2 r^{-n} \tag{4-3.21b}$$

The temperature at r = 0 must be finite, which requires that $B_2 = 0$. Hence the general solution is given by

$$\begin{aligned}\Theta(r,\phi) &= fg = \sum_{n=0}^{\infty} r^n (A_{1n} \sin n\phi + A_{2n} \cos n\phi) \\ &= A_0 + \sum_{n=1}^{\infty} r^n (A_{1n} \sin n\phi + A_{2n} \cos n\phi)\end{aligned} \tag{4-3.22}$$

where we have set $B_1A_1 = A_{1n}$ and $B_1A_2 = A_{2n}$. It is noted that Eq. (4-3.22) is a Fourier series representation of the function $\Theta(\phi)$ at $r = a$.

Multiply Eq. (4-3.22) by $\sin n\phi \, d\phi$ and then perform the integration in the range $0 \leq \phi \leq 2\pi$. We obtain

$$A_{1n} = \frac{2}{n}\frac{1}{\pi a^n}(\Theta_1 - \Theta_2) \qquad n = 1,3,5,\ldots \tag{4-3.23}$$

Similarly, if we multiply Eq. (4-3.22) by $\cos n\phi \, d\phi$ and integrate we find that $A_{2n} = 0$. Finally multiplying by $d\phi$ and integrating we obtain $A_0 = (\Theta_1 + \Theta_2)/2$. Hence the solution inside the cylinder is given by

$$\Theta = \frac{\Theta_1 + \Theta_2}{2} + \frac{2(\Theta_1 - \Theta_2)}{\pi} \sum_{n=1}^{\infty} \left(\frac{r}{a}\right)^n \frac{1}{n} \sin n\phi \qquad n = 1,3,5,\ldots \tag{4-3.24}$$

The temperatures at different radii and with $\Theta_1 = 20$ and $\Theta_2 = 10$ are plotted in Fig. 4-3.3b.

ΔΔΔ

Example 4-3.3. The convex surface and one base of a cylinder of radius a and length b are kept at constant temperature zero, the temperature of each point of the other base is given as a function of the distance from the center of the base. Find the temperature at any point of the cylinder under steady state conditions.

Solution. The boundary conditions are seen to be

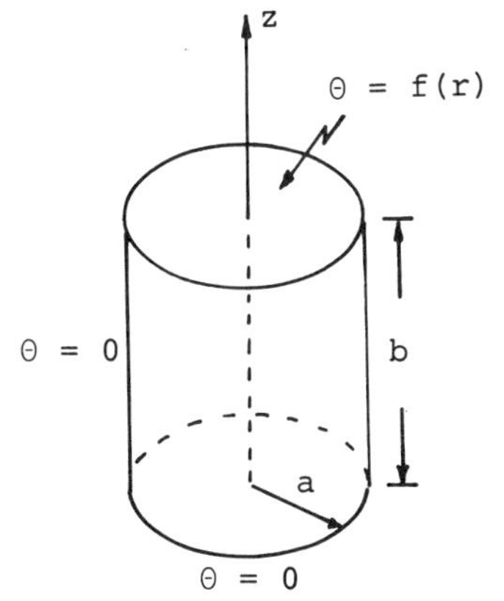

Figure 4-3.4. A problem with cylindrical geometry.

C-1. $\Theta = 0$ when $z = 0$

C-2. $\Theta = 0$ when $r = a$

C-3. $\Theta = f(r)$ when $z = b$

For such a cylindrical problem, the general solution is, as discussed above,

$$\Theta = (A_1 \cos \nu\phi + A_2 \sin \nu\phi)(B_1 \cosh k_z z + B_2 \sinh k_z z)[C_1 J_\nu(k_z r) + C_2 Y_\nu(k_z r)]$$

But we note the following:

a. The solution is independent of ϕ because of symmetry, then $\nu = 0$.
b. The problem allows $r \to 0$, then $C_2 = 0$ to avoid a singularity at the origin since $Y_\nu \to \infty$ as $r \to 0$.
c. By C-1, $B_1 = 0$.

Subject to these conditions, the solution has the form

$$\Theta = A \sinh k_z z \; J_0(k_z r)$$

By C-2, it is required that k_z be chosen such that $J_0(k_z a) = 0$. But there are an infinite number of values which satisfy this condition, whence we introduce the quantity k_{zm}, such that $J_0(k_{zm} a) = 0$ ($k_{z1} a = 2.405$, $k_{z2} a = 5.520$, etc.; see Table 4-3.2).

Table 4-3.2. Roots of $J_n(x) = 0$

n	m=1	2	3	4
0	2.405	5.520	8.654	11.792
1	3.832	7.016	10.174	13.324
2	5.135	8.417	11.620	14.796
3	6.380	9.761	13.015	
4	7.588	11.065	14.372	

The solution satisfying C-1 and C-2 is now

$$\Theta(z,r) = \sum_m A_m \sinh(k_{zm} z) \; J_0(k_{zm} r)$$

Condition C-3 requires additionally that

$$f(r) = \sum_m A_m \sinh (k_{zm}b)\ J_0(k_{zm}r)$$

This expression allows us to proceed with an evaluation of the constants A_m, since Bessel functions form an orthogonal set. We proceed with a Fourier type analysis, often called a Fourier-Bessel expansion. To do this, multiply both sides of this equation by $rJ_0(k_{zm}r)\,dr$ and integrate to get

$$\int_0^a f(r)rJ_0(k_{zm}r)dr = A_m \sinh(k_{zm}b) \int_0^a rJ_0^2(k_{zm}r)dr$$
$$+ \sum_{n\neq m} \sin(k_{zm}b) \int_0^a rJ_0(k_{zn}r)J_0(k_{zm}r)dr$$
$$= A_m \sinh(k_{zm}b)\ \frac{a^2}{2}\ [J_0^2(k_{zm}a) - J_1(k_{zm}a) - J_{-1}(k_{zm}a)]$$

Using Eq. (4-3.15b) and the identity $J_0(k_{zm}a) = 0$ found above, the quantity in the bracket is $J_1^2(k_{zm}a)$; hence it follows that

$$A_m = \frac{1}{\sinh(k_{zm}b)\ \frac{a^2}{2}\ J_1^2(k_{zm}a)} \int_0^a r\ f(r)\ J_0(k_{zm}r)\ dr$$

Case 1a. If there is no temperature variation in the upper face, i.e., $f(r) = \Theta_0$, a constant then using Eq. (4-3.16d)

$$\int_0^a r\ \Theta_0\ J_0(k_{zm}r)dr = \Theta_0 a\ J_1(k_{zm}a)\ \frac{1}{k_{zm}}$$

and now the constants A_m have the values

$$A_m = \frac{\Theta_0 a\ J_1(k_{zm}a)}{\sinh(k_{zm}b)\ \frac{a^2}{2}\ J_1^2(k_{zm}a)k_{zm}} = \frac{2\Theta_0}{k_{zm}a\ \sinh(k_{zm}b)} \cdot \frac{1}{J_1(k_{zm}a)}$$

Case 1b. Suppose that the convex surface is surrounded by an insulated jacket. The boundary conditions are now

C-1. $\Theta = 0$ when $z = 0$

C-2. $\partial\Theta/\partial r = 0$ when $r = a$

C-3. $\Theta = f(r)$ when $z = b$

The solution, subject to C-1 is, as before,

$$\Theta(z,r) = A \sinh k_z z\ J_0(k_z r)$$

By C-2 and Eq. (4-3.14b)

$$\frac{\partial\Theta}{\partial r} = -k_z A \sinh(k_z z)\, J_1(k_z r)$$

and for

$$\left.\frac{\partial\Theta}{\partial r}\right|_{r=a} = 0 \qquad J_1(k_z a) = 0$$

The roots of $J_1(k_z a) = 0$ are called k_{zm} and the solution, subject to C-1 and C-2, is now

$$\Theta(z,r) = \sum_m A_m \sinh(k_{zm} z)\, J_0(k_{zm} r)$$

with $k_{z1} = 3.832$, $k_{z2} = 7.016$, etc., being the roots of $J_1(k_{zm} a) = 0$ (see Table 4-3.2).

Applying condition C-3

$$f(r) = \sum_m A_m \sinh(k_{zm} b)\, J_0(k_{zm} r)$$

A direct calculation then leads to

$$\int_0^a f(r) r\, J_0(k_{zm} r) dr = A_m \sinh(k_{zm} b) \int_0^a r[J_0(k_{zm} r)]^2\, dr$$

$$= A_m \sinh(k_{zm} b)\, \frac{a^2}{2}\, [J_0(k_{zm} a)]^2$$

by using Eq. (4-3.16b) and the identity $J_1(k_{zm} a) = 0$ found above. The value for A_m then becomes

$$A_m = \frac{1}{k_{zm} \sinh k_{zm} b\, \frac{a^2}{2}\, [J_0(k_{zm} a)]^2} \int_0^a r\, f(r)\, J_0(k_{zm} r) dr$$

ΔΔΔ

Example 4-3.4. Find the potential and the $\overline{E}$ field distribution outside of an infinitely long conducting cylinder of radius a placed in a previously uniform electric field $\overline{E} = E_o \overline{a}_x$, as shown in Fig. 4-3.5.

Solution. The axis of the cylinder coincides with the Z-axis. Since the applied field is independent of the Z-coordinate and the structure is uniform along z, the induced electric field will also be independent of z.

Moreover, the applied electric field must induce such a charge distribution on the surface of the cylinder that the field produced by this charge distribution will cancel the applied field inside the cylinder. This is required since, under static conditions, the electric field in a conducting medium must be zero for zero current.

The applied electric field will be considered to arise from a scalar potential

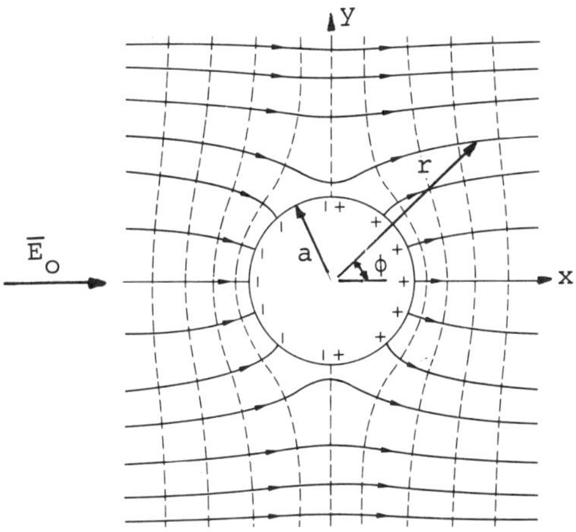

Figure 4-3.5. Resultant total electric field for a cylinder in a uniform applied electric field.

$$\Phi_o = -E_o x = -E_o r \cos\phi \qquad (4\text{-}3.25)$$

since $-\nabla\Phi = E_o\overline{a}_x$. For the geometry of this problem the induced potential will be of the form (see Ex. 4-3.2)

$$\begin{aligned} \Phi_i &= \sum_{n=0}^{\infty} (A_n \cos n\phi + B_n \sin n\phi)\, r^n \qquad r \le a \qquad \text{a)} \\ &= \sum_{n=0}^{\infty} (C_n \cos n\phi + D_n \sin n\phi)\, r^{-n} \qquad r \ge a \qquad \text{b)} \end{aligned} \qquad (4\text{-}3.26)$$

where we choose r^n for the interior of the cylinder and r^{-n} for the exterior region, since Φ_i must remain bounded at $r = 0$ and $r = \infty$. The total potential $\Phi = \Phi_o + \Phi_i$ must be continuous at $r = a$. Since Φ_o varies as $\cos\phi$, Φ_i will also. This implies that B_n and D_n must be zero. Furthermore, $\cos\phi$ is orthogonal to $\cos n\phi$ and $\sin n\phi$ for all n. To find A_n, B_n, C_n, D_n, the expression for $\Phi = \Phi_o + \Phi_i$ must be multiplied by $\cos\phi\, d\phi$ and be integrated from 0 to 2π. The coefficients A_n, B_n, C_n, D_n, except for A_1 and C_1, all become zero. In other words, the induced potential will have the same ϕ dependence as the applied potential. Thus the acceptable forms for the induced potentials are

$$\begin{aligned} \Phi_i &= A_1 r \cos\phi \qquad r \le a \qquad \text{a)} \\ \Phi_i &= C_1 r^{-1} \cos\phi \qquad r \ge a \qquad \text{b)} \end{aligned} \qquad (4\text{-}3.27)$$

Continuity of the total potential at r = a requires that

$$-E_0 a \cos\phi + A_1 a \cos\phi = -E_0 a \cos\phi + C_1 a^{-1} \cos\phi$$

or

$$C_1 = a^2 A_1 \tag{4-3.28}$$

In addition, the induced potential must cancel the applied potential inside the cylinder; thus $A_1 = E_0$. The induced potential and the resultant induced electric field are now given by

$$\Phi_i = E_0 r \cos\phi = E_0 x \qquad r \le a \qquad \text{a)}$$
$$\Phi_i = a^2 E_0 r^{-1} \cos\phi \qquad r \ge a \qquad \text{b)} \tag{4-3.29}$$

and

$$\overline{E}_i = -\nabla\Phi_i = E_0 \overline{a}_x \qquad r \le a \qquad \text{a)}$$
$$\overline{E}_i = E_0 \frac{a^2}{r^2} (\cos\phi\, \overline{a}_r + \sin\phi\, \overline{a}_\phi) \qquad r \ge a \qquad \text{b)} \tag{4-3.30}$$

The total electric field inside the cylinder is clearly zero. Outside of the cylinder the total electric field is the superposition of the uniform applied field $E_0\overline{a}_x$ and the induced field given by Eq. (4-3.30b).

The induced charge ρ_s per unit area on the surface of the cylinder is easily found from the value of the normal electric field at the surface by direct application of the Gauss' law to coin-shaped volume at the surface (refer to Sec. 5-3). We then have that

$$\rho_s = \varepsilon_0 E_r = \varepsilon\, \overline{a}_r \cdot (E_0 \overline{a}_x + \overline{E}_i) = 2\varepsilon_0 E_0 \cos\phi \tag{4-3.31}$$

However, the total charge induced on the cylinder is zero, there being only a relative displacement of the negative charges. The induced charge distribution and resultant total electric field are illustrated in Fig. 4-3.5.

ΔΔΔ

Example 4-3.5. Find the steady state temperature distribution inside a semi-infinite rod of radius a. The end face at z = 0 is kept at a temperature Θ_2 and the walls of the rod are kept at temperature $\Theta_1 = 0$, as shown in Fig. 4-3.6.

Solution. Because of symmetry, the solution must clearly be independent of the angle ϕ, and this specifies that n = 0. Therefore Eqs. (4-3.4) take the form

$$\frac{d^2h}{dz^2} - k_z^2 h = 0 \qquad \text{a)}$$
$$\frac{1}{r}\frac{d}{dr}\left(r \frac{df}{dr}\right) + k_z^2 f = 0 \qquad \text{b)} \tag{4-3.32}$$

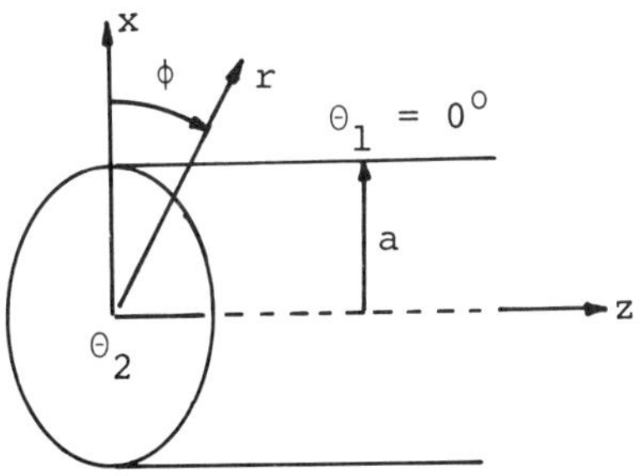

Figure 4-3.6. Cylindrical rod heated at one end.

where the second equation has as its solution the Bessel function of zero order, $J_o(k_z r)$. Furthermore, the origin is not excluded, and Θ must not be infinite at $r = 0$. This requires that we set the constant multiplier of the term $Y_n = 0$. From physical conditions Θ must vanish for large values of z. This imposes the requirement that $k_z = \Gamma$ (Γ = real) and Eq. (4-3.32a) will give two exponential solutions from which we retain only $e^{-\Gamma z}$. This establishes as the complete general solution in cylindrical coordinates

$$\Theta = A_o J_o(\Gamma r)\, e^{-\Gamma z} \tag{4-3.33}$$

We must take account of the fact that various values of Γ may yield equally acceptable solutions. These values are denoted Γ_m. Equation (4-3.33) becomes

$$\Theta = \sum_{m=1}^{\infty} A_{mo} J_o(\Gamma_m r)\, e^{-\Gamma_m z} \qquad z > 0; \quad r < a \tag{4-3.34}$$

Now, as a boundary condition, we see that $\Theta(a,z) = 0$, so that

$$\sum_{m=1}^{\infty} A_{mo} J_o(\Gamma_m a)\, e^{-\Gamma_m z} = 0 \tag{4-3.35}$$

This formula shows that the values of Γ_m must be so chosen that $(\Gamma_m a)$ are the zeros of $J_o(\Gamma a)$. Several of the zeros of some Bessel functions $J_n(x) = 0$ are contained in Table 4-3.2 (see also Fig. 4-3.1). The values of Γ_m in the table are simply (roots/a).

We now employ the second evident boundary condition $\Theta(r,0) = \Theta_2$. This requires that

$$\Theta_2 = \sum_{m=1}^{\infty} A_{mo} J_o(\Gamma_m r) \tag{4-3.36}$$

We also make use of the mathematical result that the function $J_o(\Gamma_m r)$ with respect to the weighting factor r over the range $0 \le r \le a$ requires that

$$\int_0^a J_o(\Gamma_m r)\, J_o(\Gamma_n r)\, r\, dr = 0 \qquad n \neq m$$
$$= \frac{a^2}{2} J_1^{\,2}(\Gamma_m a) \qquad n = m$$

as was the case in Ex. 4-3.3. This allows us to evaluate the coefficient A_{mo} from Eq. (4-3.36) by a conventional Fourier-Bessel expansion. If we multiply both sides by $rJ_o(\Gamma_m r)\,dr$ and integrate, we obtain

$$\Theta_2 \int_0^a rJ_o(\Gamma_m r)dr = A_{mo} \int_0^a rJ_o^{\,2}(\Gamma_m r)\, dr$$

from which we find that

$$A_{mo} = \frac{\Theta_2 J_1(\Gamma_m a)\, a/\Gamma_m}{\frac{1}{2} a^2 \,[J_o^{\,2}(\Gamma_m a) + J_1^{\,2}(\Gamma_m a)]} = \frac{2\Theta_2}{\Gamma_m a\, J_1(\Gamma_m a)} \tag{4-3.37}$$

since $(\Gamma_m a)$ are the roots of J_o. The reduction was effected through the use of Eqs. (4-3.16b), (4-3.16e) and (4-3.15b). The solution, which is independent of ϕ is given by

$$\Theta(r,z) = 2\,\Theta_2 \sum_{m=1}^{\infty} \frac{e^{-\Gamma_m z}\, J_o(\Gamma_m r)}{\Gamma_m a\, J_1(\Gamma_m a)} \qquad z \ge 0 \tag{4-3.38}$$

Results specified by this equation are given in Fig. 4-3.7 which shows plots of temperature versus distance z at different radii.

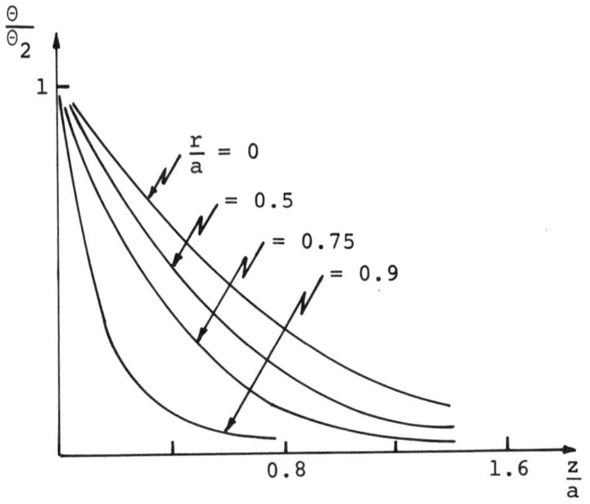

Figure 4-3.7. Temperature distribution in a rod.

ΔΔΔ

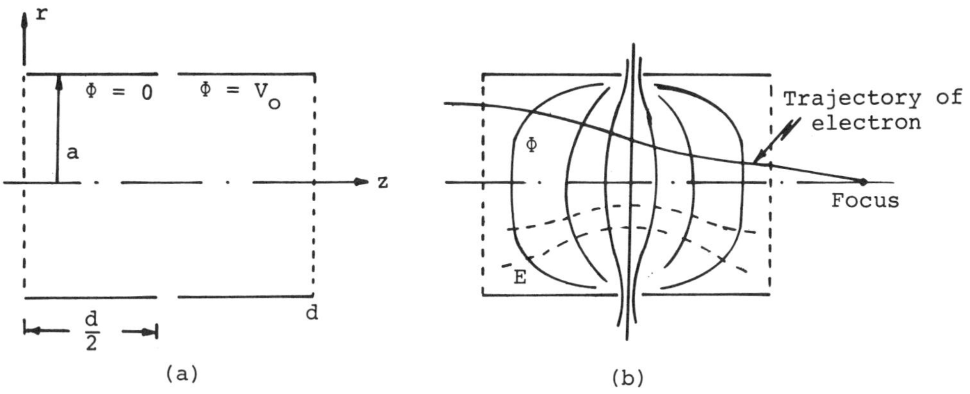

Figure 4-3.8. (a) An electrostatic lens. (b) Constant potential lines.

Example 4-3.6. Find the potential inside of the electrostatic lens system shown in Fig. 4-3.8. The lens consists of two cylinders each of length d/2 and radius a. The cylinders are separated by a small gap at the center. The end surfaces consist of a fine mesh wire grid which permits electrons to pass through into the lens region. The right half of the structure is kept at a potential V_o relative to the left half.

Solution. The wire grid end surfaces may be assumed to impose the boundary conditions $\Phi = 0$ and $\Phi = V_o$ at $z = 0$ and $z = d$, respectively, for $r \leq a$. To satisfy the boundary conditions at $z = 0,d$ we can use the simple solution

$$\Phi_1 = \frac{V_o z}{d} \tag{4-3.39}$$

We must then superimpose another partial solution Φ_2 with the property that

C-1. $\Phi_2 = 0, \quad z = 0,d \quad \text{for } r \leq a$

C-2. $\Phi_2 + \Phi_1 = 0, \quad r = a \quad 0 \leq z \leq d/2$

C-3. $\Phi_2 + \Phi_1 = V_o, \quad r = a \quad d/2 < z \leq d$

C-2 plus C-3 means that we must fulfill the conditions

$$\Phi_2 = -\frac{V_o z}{d} \qquad 0 \leq z < \frac{d}{2} \qquad \text{a)}$$

$$\Phi_2 = V_o - \frac{V_o z}{d} \qquad \frac{d}{2} < z \leq d \qquad \text{b)} \tag{4-3.40}$$

To satisfy condition C-1, we can use the sin $k_z z$ ($k_z = n\pi/d$) functions for the Z-dependence. In this case the separation constant is jk_z and the radial dependence is described by the modified Bessel functions [see Eqs. (4-3.8) and (4-3.10)]. Only $I_0(k_z r)$ can be used since K_0 becomes infinite at the origin. Also, there is no ϕ variation, so only the zero order function is needed. The solution for Φ_2 is then of the form $\Phi_2 = A \sin(k_z z) I_0(k_z r)$. To satisfy C-1 we must choose $k_z d = n\pi$ when $r = a$. The general solution for Φ_2 is, therefore,

$$\Phi_2 = \sum_{n=1}^{\infty} A_n I_0 \left(\frac{n\pi r}{d}\right) \sin \frac{n\pi z}{d} \tag{4-3.41}$$

When we set r = a, we get a simple Fourier series involving sin $n\pi z/d$ functions, which we equate to Eq. (4-3.40). We can solve for the coefficients A_n in the usual manner. We find

$$A_n \frac{d}{2} I_0 \left(\frac{n\pi a}{d}\right) = -\int_0^{d/2} \frac{V_o z}{d} \sin \frac{n\pi z}{d}\, dz + \int_{d/2}^{d} \left(V_o - \frac{V_o z}{d}\right) \sin \frac{n\pi z}{d}\, dz$$

$$= \begin{cases} \dfrac{V_o d}{n\pi} (-1)^{n/2} & n = 2,4,6,\ldots \\ 0 & n = 1,3,5,\ldots \end{cases} \tag{4-3.42}$$

The complete solution for Φ is given by

$$\Phi = \Phi_1 + \Phi_2 = \frac{V_o z}{d} + \sum_{n=2,4,6,\ldots}^{\infty} \frac{2V_o}{n\pi} (-1)^{n/2} \frac{I_0(n\pi r/d)}{I_0(n\pi a/d)} \sin \frac{n\pi z}{d} \tag{4-3.43}$$

ΔΔΔ

4-4. Spherical Coordinates

Laplace's equation in spherical coordinates is written in terms of the coordinates r,θ,ϕ where θ is the polar angle and ϕ is the aximuthal angle (see Appendix I). It has the form

$$\nabla^2\Phi = \frac{1}{r^2} \frac{\partial}{\partial r} \left(r^2 \frac{\partial\Phi}{\partial r}\right) + \frac{1}{r^2 \sin\theta} \frac{\partial}{\partial\theta} \left(\sin\theta \frac{\partial\Phi}{\partial\theta}\right) + \frac{1}{r^2 \sin^2\theta} \frac{\partial^2\Phi}{\partial\phi^2} = 0 \tag{4-4.1}$$

Spherical coordinates are illustrated in Fig. 4-4.1. We now substitute a product solution $\Phi = f(r)g(\theta)h(\phi)$ into Eq. (4-4.1) and divide by $fgh/(r^2\sin^2\theta)$. This leads to

$$\frac{\sin^2\theta}{f} \frac{d}{dr} \left(r^2 \frac{df}{dr}\right) + \frac{\sin\theta}{g} \frac{d}{d\theta} \left(\sin\theta \frac{dg}{d\theta}\right) + \frac{1}{h} \frac{d^2h}{d\phi^2} = 0 \tag{4-4.2}$$

The last term is a function of ϕ only, while the first two terms depend only on r

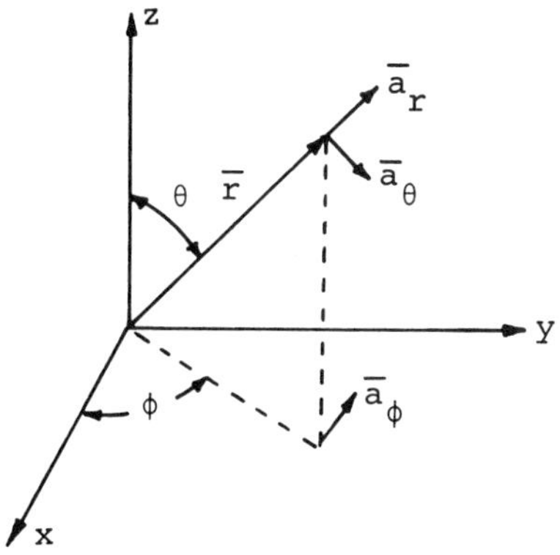

Figure 4-4.1. Spherical coordinates

and θ. To provide for periodicity in the ϕ-direction we select the separation constant as $-n^2$, with n real,

$$\frac{1}{h}\frac{d^2h}{d\phi^2} = -n^2$$

or

$$\frac{d^2h}{d\phi^2} + n^2h = 0 \tag{4-4.3}$$

Usually the whole range $0 \le \phi \le 2\pi$ is involved so that n must be an integer to make $h(\phi)$ single-valued, i.e., $h(\phi + 2\pi) = h(\phi)$. The solutions for h are of the form

$$h = A_1 \cos n\phi + A_2 \sin n\phi \quad (\text{or } A_1e^{jn\phi} + A_2e^{-jn\phi}) \tag{4-4.4}$$

When we use Eqs. (4-4.3) and (4-4.2) and divide by $\sin^2\theta$, we find

$$\frac{1}{f}\frac{d}{dr}\left(r^2\frac{df}{dr}\right) + \frac{1}{g \sin\theta}\frac{d}{d\theta}\left(\sin\theta\frac{dg}{d\theta}\right) - \frac{n^2}{\sin^2\theta} = 0$$

Since this equation consists of the sum of terms depending on r alone or θ alone, these will separate to the following expressions

$$\frac{d}{dr}\left(r^2\frac{df}{dr}\right) - m(m+1)\,f = 0 \tag{4-4.5}$$

$$\frac{d}{d\theta}\left(\sin\theta\frac{dg}{d\theta}\right) + \left[m(m+1)\sin\theta - \frac{n^2}{\sin\theta}\right] g = 0 \tag{4-4.6}$$

by using the usual procedure on separation. The separation constant is chosen as m(m+1) for later convenience.

The reader can readily verify that the solutions of Eq. (4-4.5) are of the form

$$f(r) = B_1 r^m + B_2 r^{-m-1} \tag{4-4.7}$$

where B_1 and B_2 are arbitrary constants.

The equation for $g(\theta)$ is known as Legendre's equation. The solutions of this equation remain finite at $\theta = 0,\pi$ only if m is an integer, and it was for this reason that we chose the separation constant as m(m+1). The two solutions are called Associated Legendre polynomials, and are denoted by the symbols $P_m^n(\cos\theta)$ and $Q_m^n(\cos\theta)$. The solution for $g(\theta)$ is

$$g(\theta) = C_1\, P_m^n(\cos\theta) + C_2\, Q_m^n(\cos\theta) \tag{4-4.8}$$

The functions Q_m^n are Associated Legendre polynomials of the second kind, and these become infinite at $\theta = 0,\pi$. Problems that include the polar axis will have solutions that involve only Associated Legendre polynomials of the first kind P_m^n. When $n = 0$, the solutions P_m^0, which are written P_m, are called Legendre polynomials. The first few polynomials are listed in Table 4-4.1.

Table 4-4.1. Associated Legendre Polynomials

$P_0^0 = 1$	$P_1^1 = \sin\theta$	$Q_0(\cos\theta) = \frac{1}{2}\,\ell n\,\frac{1+\cos\theta}{1-\cos\theta}$
$P_1^0 = \cos\theta$	$P_2^1 = \frac{3}{2}\sin 2\theta$	$Q_1(\cos\theta) = \frac{1}{2}\cos\theta\,\ell n\frac{1+\cos\theta}{1-\cos\theta} - 1$
$P_2^0 = \frac{3}{4}\cos 2\theta + \frac{1}{4} = \frac{3}{2}\cos^2\theta - \frac{1}{2}$	$P_2^2 = \frac{3}{2}(1-\cos 2\theta)$	$Q_2(\cos\theta) = \frac{3\cos^2\theta-1}{4}\ell n\,\frac{1+\cos\theta}{1-\cos\theta} - \frac{3\cos\theta}{2}$
$P_3^0 = \frac{1}{2}(5\cos^3\theta - 3\cos\theta)$	$P_3^1 = \frac{3}{8}(\sin\theta + 5\sin 3\theta)$	
	$P_m^n = 0,\ n > m$	

The Legendre functions form an orthogonal set and these possess the following properties:

$$\int_0^\pi P_m^n(\cos\theta)\, P_\ell^n(\cos\theta)\,\sin\theta\, d\theta = 0 \qquad m \neq \ell \qquad \text{a)}$$

$$\int_0^\pi P_m^n(\cos\theta)\, P_m^\ell(\cos\theta)\,\frac{d\theta}{\sin\theta} = 0 \qquad n \neq \ell \qquad \text{b)} \tag{4-4.9}$$

The normalization integral is given by

$$\int_0^{\pi} [P_m^n(\cos\theta)]^2 \sin\theta \, d\theta = \frac{2}{2m+1}\frac{(m+n)!}{(m-n)!} \tag{4-4.10}$$

For the more usual problems, the general solution to Laplace's equation in spherical coordinates is of the form

$$\Phi = \sum_{m=0}^{\infty}\sum_{n=0}^{m} P_m^n(\cos\theta)(A_n \cos n\phi + B_n \sin n\phi)(C_m r^m + D_m r^{-m-1}) \tag{4-4.11}$$

when the polar axis is included in the region of interest. The sum over n terminates at n = m because $P_m^n = 0$ for n > m.

We shall consider two examples that will illustrate the solutions to problems involving spherical coordinates.

Example 4-4.1. Find the induced field $\overline{E}_i$ and the induced charge on the surface of a conducting sphere of radius a placed in a previously uniform electric field $\overline{E} = E_o\overline{a}_z$, as illustrated in Fig. 4-4.2 (see Ex. 4-3.4 for the analogous cylindrical problem).

Solution. We must find a solution to Laplace's equation in spherical coordinates in order to meet the spherical boundary conditions. The applied field may be assumed to arise from an applied potential

$$\Phi_o = -E_o z = -E_o r\cos\theta = -E_o r\, P_1(\cos\theta) \tag{4-4.12}$$

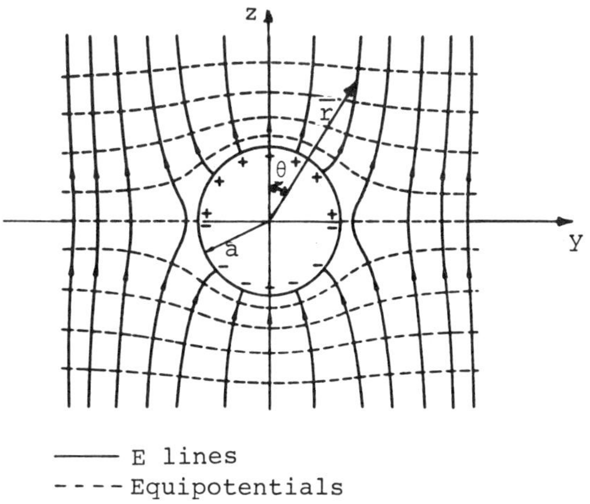

Figure 4-4.2. A conducting sphere in a uniform electric field.

since $-\nabla\Phi_o = E_o \bar{a}_z$ in this case. The induced potential will have no variation with the azimuthal angle ϕ since Φ_o does not depend on ϕ, and so $n = 0$. Also the structure has rotational symmetry about the Z axis. Therefore, the induced potential has the form

$$\Phi_i = \sum_{m=0}^{\infty} A_m r^m P_m(\cos\theta) \qquad r \le a \tag{4-4.13a}$$

$$\Phi_i = \sum_{m=0}^{\infty} B_m r^{-m-1} P_m(\cos\theta) \qquad r \ge a \tag{4-4.13b}$$

At $r = a$ the total potential $\Phi = \Phi_o + \Phi_i$ is continuous, and so

$$-E_o a P_1 + \sum_{m=0}^{\infty} A_m a^m P_m = -E_o a P_1 + \sum_{m=0}^{\infty} B_m a^{-m-1} P_m$$

or

$$\sum_{m=0}^{\infty} A_m a^m P_m = \sum_{m=0}^{\infty} B_m a^{-m-1} P_m$$

If we multiply both sides by $P_n \sin\theta\, d\theta$ and integrate over the range 0 to π, and this process is called the Fourier-Legendre expansion, we obtain, by virtue of the orthogonality property Eq. (4-4.9a)

$$A_n a^n = B_n a^{-n-1} \tag{4-4.14}$$

We could have anticipated this result from the following argument: if two series of orthogonal functions are equal, then the coefficients of like functions on each side must be equal. In other words, each term is analogous to a component of a vector in an infinite dimensional space, and the series is analogous to the total vector in this space. Since the components are mutually orthogonal, the two vectors, i.e., the two series, can be equal only if the individual components are equal, i.e., if $A_m a^m P_m = B_m a^{-m-1} P_m$. The orthogonal functions P_m are analogous to the unit vectors in a mutually orthogonal infinite dimensional set of cartesian coordinates.

In the interior of the sphere, the total potential must vanish (or reduce to a constant, since the reference potential is arbitrary) so as to yield a zero total electric field. Thus

$$-E_o r P_1 + \sum_{m=0}^{\infty} A_m r^m P_m = 0$$

which gives

$$A_1 = E_o; \quad A_m = 0 \quad \text{for} \quad m \neq 1$$

because of the mutual orthogonality of the eigenfunctions P_m. From Eq. (4-4.14) we now have

$$B_1 = a^3 A_1 = a^3 E_o; \quad B_n = 0 \quad \text{for} \quad n \neq 1$$

Because of these results, the induced potential is given by

$$\Phi_i = E_o r P_1 = E_o r \cos\theta = E_o z \qquad r \leq a \qquad \text{a)}$$

$$\Phi_i = \frac{E_o a^3}{r^2} \cos\theta \qquad r \geq a \qquad \text{b)} \qquad (4\text{-}4.15)$$

Inside of the sphere the total electric field is zero, while outside of the sphere it is given by

$$\bar{E} + \bar{E}_i = -\nabla(\Phi_o + \Phi_i) = -\bar{a}_r \frac{\partial}{\partial r}(\Phi_o + \Phi_i) - \frac{\bar{a}_\theta}{r}\frac{\partial}{\partial\theta}(\Phi_o + \Phi_i)$$

$$= E_o \cos\theta\, \bar{a}_r \left(1 + \frac{2a^3}{r^3}\right) - E_o \sin\theta\, \bar{a}_\theta \left(1 - \frac{a^3}{r^3}\right) \qquad (4\text{-}4.16)$$

The induced surface charge density is given by

$$\rho_s = \varepsilon_o \bar{a}_r \cdot (\bar{E} + \bar{E}_i) = 3E_o\varepsilon_o \cos\theta \qquad (4\text{-}4.17)$$

since r = a at the surface. ΔΔΔ

Example 4-4.2. Find the steady state temperature distribution Θ within a sphere, if the surface of the sphere is held at a temperature $\Theta(\theta,\phi)$ which varies from point to point.

Solution. Since Θ must be finite at $r = 0$, the general solution is

$$\Theta = \sum_{m=0}^{\infty} \sum_{n=0}^{m} P_m^n(\cos\theta)(A_m \cos n\phi + B_n \sin n\phi)\, r^m \qquad (4\text{-}4.18)$$

At $r = a$ we have

$$\Theta = \Theta(a,\theta,\phi) = \sum_{m=0}^{\infty} \sum_{n=0}^{m} P_m^n(\cos\theta)\, a^m (A_{mn} \cos n\phi + B_{mn} \sin n\phi)$$

If we multiply both sides by $P_\ell^s \cos s\phi \sin\theta\, d\theta\, d\phi$ and integrate, we get

$$A_{\ell s} a^\ell \frac{2\pi}{2\ell+1} \frac{(\ell+s)!}{(\ell-s)!} = \int_0^{2\pi}\int_0^{\pi} \Theta(a,\theta,\phi) P_\ell^s \cos s\phi \sin\theta\, d\theta\, d\phi$$

by using the orthogonality relation Eq. (4-4.9a), the normalization integral Eq. (4-4.10), and the orthogonality property of $\cos n\phi$ and $\sin n\phi$. For $s = 0$ we must replace π by 2π in the above.

A similar expression holds for $B_{\ell s}$ with $\cos s\phi$ replaced by $\sin s\phi$ in the integral. Thus we again see that the orthogonality properties of the eigenfunctions enable us to determine the amplitude coefficients A_{mn} and B_{mn} by means of a two-dimensional Fourier-Legendre series analysis from the equation expressing the boundary conditions on Θ at $r = a$.

ΔΔΔ

4-5. The Impulse (Dirac Delta) Function

Physical fields arise from sources that are distributed throughout a finite volume of space or over a finite surface. Such source distributions may be built up by a suitable superposition of point sources. From a mathematical point of view, it is very convenient to consider the existence of ideal point sources of unit strength and the nature of the fields that they produce. One function which will help to represent the source distributions is the impulse function, known also as the Dirac delta function, or just the delta function. For the one-dimensional case, the delta function is defined by the following properties

$$\delta(x) = 0 \qquad x \neq 0 \qquad \text{a)}$$

$$\int_{-\infty}^{\infty} \delta(x)dx = 1 = \text{Area associated with the } \delta\text{-function} \qquad \text{b)}$$

$$\int_{-\infty}^{\infty} f(x)\delta(x)dx = f(0) \qquad \text{c)} \qquad (4\text{-}5.1)$$

$$\begin{cases} \delta(x) = \lim\limits_{n\to\infty} f_n(x) \\ \int_{-\infty}^{\infty} f_n(x)dx = 1, \quad \lim\limits_{n\to\infty} f_n(x) = 0 \quad \text{for} \quad x \neq 0 \end{cases} \qquad \text{d)}$$

We note that the delta function is not an ordinary function; the integral and the function $\delta(x)$ are defined by the number $f(0)$ assigned to the function $f(x)$, and they have no independent meaning.

The delta function can be obtained as a limiting case of either analytic continuous or piecewise continuous functions. The following are three of many possible representations of the delta function, and are illustrated in Fig. 4-5.1.

$$\delta(x) = \lim_{a\to 0} \frac{1}{\sqrt{a\pi}} e^{-x^2/a} \qquad \text{a)}$$

$$\delta(x) = \lim_{a\to 0} \begin{cases} 0 & x < 0 \\ 1/a & 0 < x < a \\ 0 & x > 0 \end{cases} \qquad \text{b)} \qquad (4\text{-}5.2)$$

$$\delta(x) = \lim_{a\to\infty} \frac{\sin ax}{\pi x} = \lim_{a\to\infty} \frac{1}{2\pi} \int_{-a}^{a} e^{jxt}\, dt \qquad \text{c)}$$

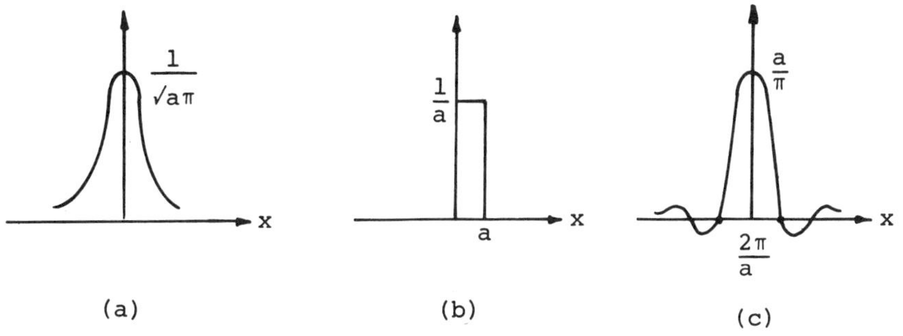

Figure 4-5.1. Dirac delta function representations.

By representing the delta function by means of ordinary mathematical functions, we are able to give meaning to the definition Eq. (4-5.1c). Consider, for example, the rectangular pulse given in Fig. 4-5.1b which we describe in terms of singularity step functions $u_{-1}(x)$ where $u_{-1}(x) = 1$ for $x > 0$, and $u_{-1}(x) = 0$ for $x < 0$

$$p_a(x) = \frac{1}{a}\,[u_{-1}(x) - u_{-1}(x-a)]$$

Assuming a continuous function f(x), it follows that

$$\lim_{a\to 0} \int_{-\infty}^{\infty} p_a(x)f(x)dx = \lim_{a\to 0} \frac{1}{a}\int_0^a f(x)dx \doteq f(0) \lim_{a\to 0} \frac{1}{a}\int_0^a dx = f(0)$$

and Eq. (4-5.1c) is true.

The following are some properties of the delta function:

a. Shifting property

$$\int_{-\infty}^{\infty} \delta(x-x')\ f(x)\ dx = f(x') \qquad \text{a)}$$

b. Linearity of the delta function

$$\int_{-\infty}^{\infty} \delta(x)\,[a_1f_1(x) + a_2f_2(x)]dx = a_1 \int_{-\infty}^{\infty} \delta(x)f_1(x)dx + a_2 \int_{-\infty}^{\infty} \delta(x)f_2(x)dx \qquad \text{b)}$$

c. Even property of the delta function. Begin with the expression

$$\int_{-\infty}^{\infty} \delta(x)f(x)dx = f(0) \qquad (4\text{-}5.3)$$

Since f(x) is continuous, this implies that if f(x) is an odd function, then f(0) = 0; this requires that δ(x) be an even function.

d. Convolution property

$$\delta(x-x') * \delta(x-x'') = \int_{-\infty}^{\infty} \delta(\tau-x')\,\delta(x-\tau-x'')\,d\tau = \delta[x-(x'+x'')] \qquad c)$$

e. Derivative

$$\int_{-\infty}^{\infty} \frac{d\delta(x)}{dx} f(x)dx = \delta(x)f(x)\Big|_{-\infty}^{\infty} - \int_{-\infty}^{\infty} \delta(x)\,\frac{df(x)}{dx} = -\left.\frac{df(x)}{dx}\right|_{x=0} \qquad d)$$

In field theory, as already discussed, it is necessary to distinguish clearly between the coordinates that specify the location of the source and the coordinates that specify the point at which the field is being evaluated. In this book we use primed coordinates x',y',z' to designate the source point, while unprimed coordinates x,y,z are used to designate the field point, as shown in Fig. 4-5.2. The vector $\overline{r}' = x'\overline{a}_x + y'\overline{a}_y + z'\overline{a}_z$ is a vector from the specified origin to the source point, while $\overline{r} = x\overline{a}_x + y\overline{a}_y + z\overline{a}_z$ is a vector from the origion to the field point, as illustrated. The vector from the source point to the field is

$$\overline{r} - \overline{r}' = (x-x')\,\overline{a}_x + (y-y')\,\overline{a}_y + (z-z')\,\overline{a}_z \qquad a)$$

with the magnitude of the distance given by (4-5.4)

$$|\overline{r}-\overline{r}'| = [(x-x')^2 + (y-y')^2 + (z-z')^2]^{1/2} \qquad b)$$

We shall also use an abbreviated notation, as noted below, when there is no danger of of confusion. In this notation, the magnitude $|\overline{r}-\overline{r}'|$ will be designated by R and a unit vector directed from the source point to the field point by $\overline{a}_R$; thus

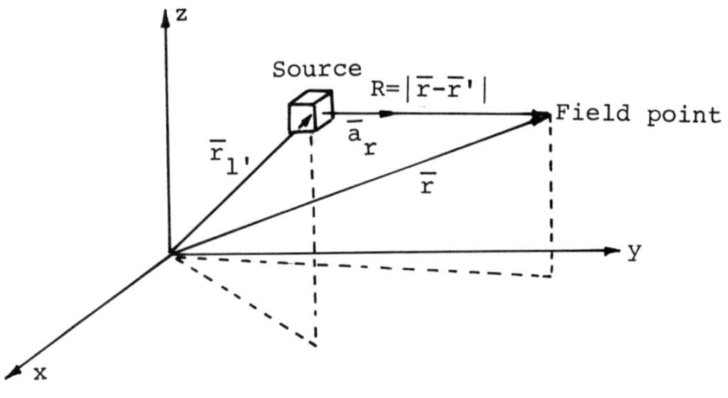

Figure 4-5.2. Illustrating source and field coordinates.

$$|\bar{r}-\bar{r}'| = R \qquad \text{a)}$$
$$\frac{\bar{r}-\bar{r}'}{|\bar{r}-\bar{r}'|} = \bar{a}_R \qquad \text{b)} \qquad (4\text{-}5.5)$$

The capital letter R is used in order to avoid confusion with the usual notation for spherical coordinates.

In field theory, a point source is localized along three coordinates and can be represented by a product of three delta functions. That is, a point source of unit strength at x', y' and z' is represented by

$$\delta(x-x')\ \delta(y-y')\ \delta(z-z') = \delta(\bar{r}-\bar{r}') \qquad (4\text{-}5.6)$$

where $\delta(\bar{r}-\bar{r}')$ is a *short-hand* notation for the three-dimensional delta function. The three-dimensional delta function has properties analogous to those given by Eq. (4-5.3a) for the one-dimensional function. Now the conditions are written

$$\delta(\bar{r}-\bar{r}') = 0 \qquad \bar{r} \neq \bar{r}'$$
$$\int_V f(x',y',z')\delta(\bar{r}-\bar{r}')dV' = \int_V f(\bar{r}')\delta(\bar{r}-\bar{r}')dV' = \begin{cases} f(\bar{r}), & x,y,z \text{ in } V \\ 0, & x,y,z \text{ outside } V \end{cases} \qquad (4\text{-}5.7)$$

In this integral the limits of integration are over the primed coordinates x',y',z' and *$f(\bar{r}')$ is a short-hand notation* meaning that f is a function of x',y',z'. For this equation to hold, f must be continuous at x,y,z. This equation will also apply if f is replaced by a vector function which is continuous at x,y,z. Also note that the primed and unprimed variables may be interchanged without invalidating Eq. (4-5.7).

The three-dimensional delta function unit source can be thought of as the limit of a volume source distributed throughout a sphere of radius a with density $(4\pi a^3/3)^{-1}$ as the radius goes to zero. The total source strength thus remains equal to unity although the density becomes infinite, and the product of the volume and density equals unity for any radius a.

In coordinate systems other than the rectangular one, the three-dimensional delta function has a somewhat different form. In cylindrical coordinates r,θ,z

$$\delta(\bar{r}-\bar{r}') = \delta(r-r')\ \frac{\delta(\phi-\phi')}{r'}\ \delta(z-z') \qquad (4\text{-}5.8)$$

The extra factor 1/r' is introduced so that the volume integral will yield unity. The element of volume is dV' = r'dr'dϕ'dz' so

$$\int_V \delta(\bar{r}-\bar{r}')dV' = \int_r \int_\phi \int_z \delta(r-r')\delta(\phi-\phi')\delta(z-z')\ dr'd\phi'dz' = 1 \qquad (4\text{-}5.9)$$

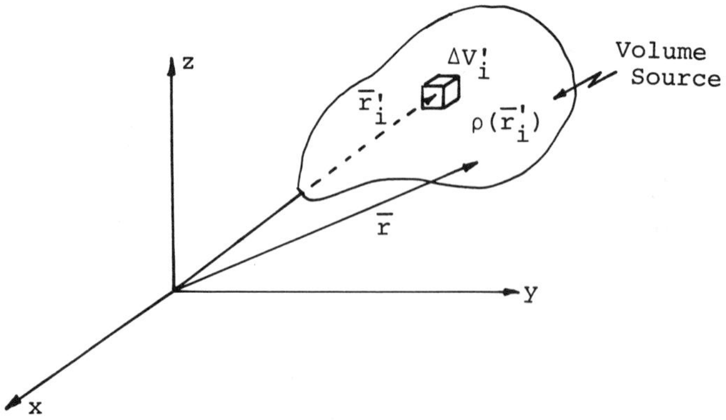

Figure 4-5.3. A volume distribution of sources.

since for any of the one-dimensional delta functions

$$\int_u \delta(u-u')du' = 1$$

where $u = r, \phi$ or z. If the factor $1/r'$ were not introduced, the volume integral would give r, which does not correspond to a source of unit strength. For the same reasons, the unit source in spherical coordinates is given by

$$\delta(\bar{r}-\bar{r}') = \frac{\delta(r-r')\delta(\theta-\theta')\delta(\phi-\phi')}{(r')^2 \sin\theta'} \tag{4-5.10}$$

because the element of volume is

$$dV' = (r')^2 \sin\theta' dr' d\theta' d\phi'$$

Let us now consider a general volume distribution of sources. We shall show that it may be regarded as the superposition of suitably weighted unit sources. Refer to Fig. 4-5.3. Let the volume density of the source be $\rho(x',y',z') = \rho(\bar{r}')$ so that the total source strength of a volume element $\Delta V_i'$ located at $\bar{r}_i'$ is $\Delta V_i' \rho(\bar{r}_i')$. We may regard this as equivalent to a point source at $\bar{r}_i'$ with the total strength $\Delta V_i' \rho(\bar{r}_i')$, and we may express it in the form

$$\Delta V_i' \rho(\bar{r}_i') \delta(\bar{r}-\bar{r}_i')$$

The total source is the sum of the contributions from each volume element and is

$$\sum_i \rho(r_i') \delta(\bar{r}-\bar{r}_i') \Delta V_i'$$

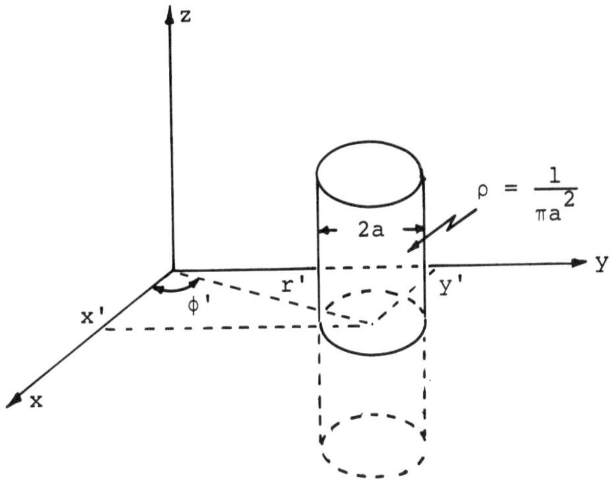

Figure 4-5.4. The unit line source

This is, in the limit as all $\Delta V_i'$ approach zero,

$$\rho(\overline{r}) = \int_V \rho(\overline{r}') \, \delta(\overline{r}-\overline{r}') \, dV' \tag{4-5.11}$$

This result could have been written down immediately from the property Eq. (4-5.7) of the three-dimensional delta function. However, the detailed derivation shows that $\rho(\overline{r})$ can be regarded as a superposition or linear sum of weighted unit sources.

In two-dimensional field problems the unit source is a line source. Such a line source that is infinitely long in the Z-direction and localized at x',y' is represented by

$$\delta(x-x') \, \delta(y-y') = \frac{\delta(r-r') \, \delta(\phi-\phi')}{r'} \tag{4-5.12}$$

in rectangular and cylindrical coordinates respectively, where $x' = r' \cos \phi'$, $y' = r' \sin \phi'$. The unit line source can be regarded as a source with density $(\pi a^2)^{-1}$ throughout a cylinder of radius $\underline{a}$ as the radius goes to zero. In this case, the density times the cross-sectional area equals unity. The line source is illustrated in Fig. 4-5.4.

4-6. Integration of Poisson's Equation

In this section we will consider the solution of Poisson's equation with unit point sources, with line sources, and with volume distributions of such sources. The essential features of these solutions have already been discussed, but we shall here adopt a more general point of view.

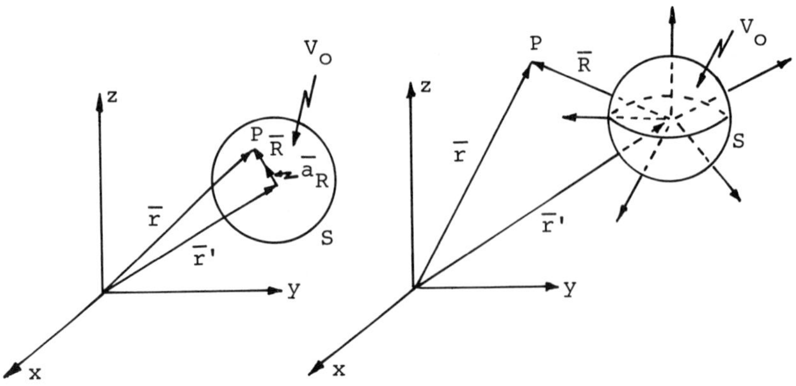

Figure 4-6.1. Outward flux from a point source with the field point inside and outside of the defined region of the source.

Consider the equation

$$\nabla \cdot \nabla\Phi = \nabla^2\Phi = -\delta(\bar{r}-\bar{r}') = -\delta(x-x')\ \delta(y-y')\ \delta(z-z') \tag{4-6.1}$$

which is Poisson's equation with a unit point source at $\bar{r}'$. Since $\nabla^2\Phi$ is equal to the divergence of the gradient of Φ, this equation states that the net outward flux of the vector field $-\nabla\Phi$ at the point $\bar{r}'$ is unity, the total source strength. Refer to Fig. 4-6.1; the flux (or flow) of $-\nabla\Phi$ through the surface of the small sphere of volume V_o centered on the source point $\bar{r}'$ must equal unity by Gauss law, as given by Eq. (2-7.10). We can verify this property directly from Eq. (4-6.1) by integrating both sides of the equation throughout the volume V_o. This yields

$$\int_{V_o} \nabla \cdot \nabla\Phi\ dV = -\int_{V_o} \delta(\bar{r}-\bar{r}')\ dV = -1 \tag{4-6.2}$$

because of the basic property of the delta function when the point x',y',z' is inside the volume V_o over which we are integrating (see Eq. (4-5.7) with f replaced by unity). If we use the divergence theorem on the left hand side, we obtain

$$-\oint_S \nabla\Phi \cdot d\bar{S} = 1 \tag{4-6.3}$$

which shows that the total flux of $-\nabla\Phi$ through the surface S surrounding the source equals unity.

We now return to Eq. (4-6.1) and consider all points $\bar{r} \neq \bar{r}'$ for which $\nabla^2\Phi = 0$. In view of the spherical symmetry, Φ should be a function only of the radial distance R away from the point source. In spherical coordinates with R regarded as the radial coordinate, $\nabla^2\Phi = 0$ has the form

$$\frac{1}{R^2}\frac{d}{dR}\left(R^2\frac{d\Phi}{dR}\right) = 0$$

since there is no variation with the angles θ and ϕ [see Eq. (4-4.1)]. This equation is readily integrated to give

$$\Phi = \frac{C_1}{R} + C_2$$

where C_1 and C_2 are constants to be determined. Now we require Φ to be zero at infinity, if we choose this to be the potential reference point, so that $C_2 = 0$. The constant C_1 is determined by the total flux relation Eq. (4-6.3). We note that

$$\nabla\Phi = \nabla\frac{C_1}{R} = \bar{a}_R\frac{d}{dR}\left(\frac{C_1}{R}\right) = -\bar{a}_R\frac{C_1}{R^2}$$

Also, the element of surface area $d\bar{S}$ equals $\bar{a}_R R^2\,d\Omega$ where $d\Omega$ is the element of solid angle. Equation (4-6.3) gives

$$\oint_\Omega \frac{C_1}{R^2}R^2\,d\Omega = 4\pi C_1 = 1$$

or $C_1 = 1/4\pi$. The required solution for Φ is thus

$$\Phi = \frac{1}{4\pi R} = \frac{1}{4\pi|\bar{r}-\bar{r}'|} = \frac{1}{4\pi[(x-x')^2 + (y-y')^2 + (z-z')^2]^{1/2}} \tag{4-6.4}$$

If we refer back to Eq. (4-6.1) we now see that the function

$$-\nabla^2\left(\frac{1}{4\pi R}\right) = -\nabla^2\frac{1}{4\pi|\bar{r}-\bar{r}'|}$$

has the essential properties of the three-dimensional delta function, Eq. (4-5.7). The reader may verify directly that $\nabla^2(1/4\pi R)$ is zero when $R \neq 0$ by using rectangular coordinates and the last form given for Φ in Eq. (4-6.4). At $R = 0$, the function $\nabla^2(1/4\pi R)$ becomes infinite in such a way that the volume integral equals unity, the strength of the delta function.

Let us now consider two point sources of strengths Q_1 and Q_2 and located at $\bar{r}_1'$ and $\bar{r}_2'$. By superposition, the resultant potential is

$$\Phi(\bar{r}) = \frac{Q_1}{4\pi R_1} + \frac{Q_2}{4\pi R_2} \tag{4-6.5}$$

where

$$R_1 = |\bar{r}-\bar{r}_1'| = [(x-x_1')^2 + (y-y_1')^2 + (z-z_1')^2]^{1/2}$$

and

$$R_2 = |\bar{r}-\bar{r}_2'|$$

If we have a volume distribution of sources with density $\rho(\overline{r}')$ then, from the volume element dV', the contribution to the potential will be

$$\frac{\rho(\overline{r}')dV'}{4\pi|\overline{r}-\overline{r}'|}$$

Clearly, from the total source distribution, the resultant potential is obtained by superposition and is

$$\Phi(\overline{r}) = \int_V \frac{\rho(\overline{r}')dV'}{4\pi|\overline{r}-\overline{r}'|} \tag{4-6.6}$$

In the case of a volume source of density ρ, the potential is a solution of

$$\nabla^2\Phi = -\rho(\overline{r}) \tag{4-6.7}$$

We can verify directly that Eq. (4-6.6) does indeed satisfy this equation. Substituting Eq. (4-6.6) for Φ in Eq. (4-6.7) gives

$$\nabla^2 \int_V \frac{\rho(\overline{r}')dV'}{4\pi|\overline{r}-\overline{r}'|} = \int_V \nabla^2 \frac{\rho(\overline{r}')}{4\pi|\overline{r}-\overline{r}'|} dV'$$

The ∇^2 operator differentiates the x,y,z coordinates only, while the integration is over the primed coordinates. Furthermore, we have seen that $-\nabla^2(1/4\pi|\overline{r}-\overline{r}'|)$ has the properties of $\delta(\overline{r}-\overline{r}')$ so we can write

$$\nabla^2 \int_V \frac{\rho(\overline{r}')}{4\pi|\overline{r}-\overline{r}'|} dV' = -\int_V \rho(\overline{r}')\ \delta(\overline{r}-\overline{r}')dV' = -\rho(\overline{r})$$

because of Eq. (4-5.7). But this last step has reproduced the right hand side of Eq. (4-6.7) and thus verifies that the solution of Eq. (4-6.6) which we obtained by using the superposition principle satisfies Eq. (4-6.7).

The solution $1/4\pi R$ for the potential from a unit point source is analogous to the unit impulse response in network theory. In field theory such solutions for unit sources are called *Green's functions*. The Green's function for Poisson's equation is, and in this form it is for unbounded space only,

$$G(\overline{r},\overline{r}') = \frac{1}{4\pi R} = \frac{1}{4\pi|\overline{r}-\overline{r}'|} \tag{4-6.8}$$

The notation $G(\overline{r},\overline{r}')$ is used to show that the Green's function is a function of the coordinates of the source point and the observation or field point. For a general distribution of sources, we can now express the solution for Φ in the form [see Eq. (4-6.6)]

$$\Phi(\overline{r}) = \int_V G(\overline{r},\overline{r}')\ \rho(\overline{r}')\ dV' \tag{4-6.9a}$$

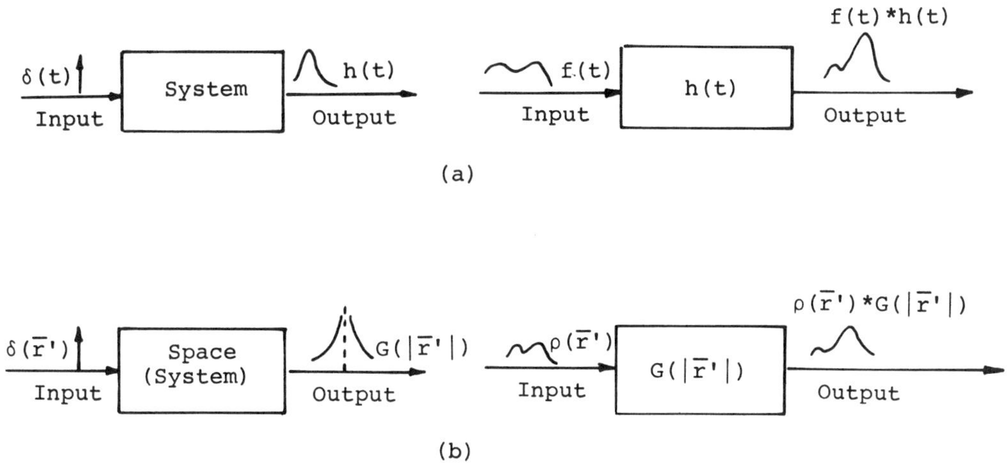

Figure 4-6.2. System representation of field problems.

which is the superposition integral giving the response Φ in terms of the response G due to a unit source and the general applied source distribution ρ.

In circuit theory the impulse response of a system to a unit time impulse or delta function input can be represented as shown in Fig. 4-6.2. The symbol * in the figure denotes convolution of the input and the impulse response functions. In a parallel way to that involving the time signals in circuit theory, in field theory the output of a system (potential) to a general input signal (charge) is also given by the convolution of the systems impulse response signal and its input, as shown in Fig. 4-6.2b. Using the definition of the convolution integral, the output $\rho(\bar{r}) * G(|\bar{r}|)$ is

$$\Phi(\bar{r}) = \int_V \rho(\bar{r}')\, G(|\bar{r}-\bar{r}'|)\, dV' \tag{4-6.9b}$$

which is Eq. (4-6.9a).

If the sources are distributed over a surface S with density $\rho_s(\bar{r}')$ it is only necessary to replace the volume integral by a surface integral, with the result

$$\Phi(\bar{r}) = \int_S G(\bar{r},\bar{r}')\, \rho_s(\bar{r}')dS' = \int_S \frac{\rho_s(\bar{r}')dS'}{4\pi|\bar{r}-\bar{r}'|} \tag{4-6.10}$$

The solution for Φ from a unit line source, i.e., the solution of

$$\nabla^2\Phi(x,y) = -\delta(x-x')\,\delta(y-y') \tag{4-6.11}$$

can be found by following a similar procedure. However, we can obtain the solution in a very direct way by using Gauss' law. Consider a cylinder of unit length

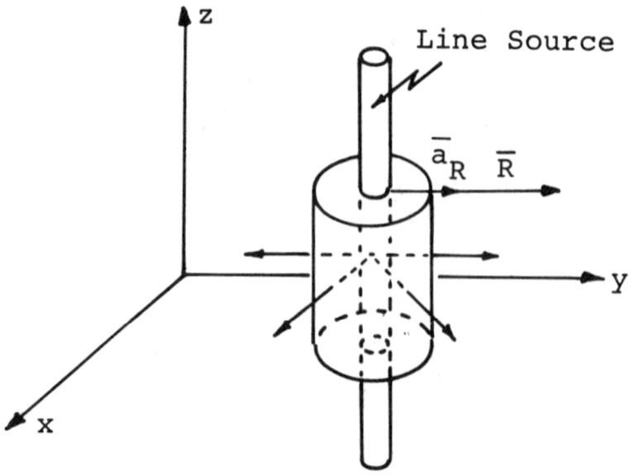

Figure 4-6.3. Flux from a unit line source.

surrounding the line source, as shown in Fig. 4-6.3. Because of symmetry, Φ is a function of $R = [(x-x')^2 + (y-y')^2]^{1/2}$ only. Thus $\nabla\Phi$ has only a radially outward component. The flux of $-\nabla\Phi$ per unit length through the cylindrical surface is $-\nabla\Phi \cdot \bar{a}_R 2\pi R$ and must equal unity since $-\int_V \nabla \cdot (\nabla\Phi)dV' = \int_V \delta(\bar{r}-\bar{r}')dV' = 1$. Then

$$\nabla\Phi \cdot \bar{a}_R = \frac{\partial\Phi}{\partial R} = \frac{1}{2\pi R}$$

and

$$\Phi = \frac{1}{2\pi} \ln R + C \tag{4-6.12}$$

for a negative line charge. The constant C can be taken equal to zero if the potential datum point is chosen as the surface R = 1, which it is convenient to do. For a distribution of line sources the solution is

$$\Phi(x,y) = \int_S \frac{\ln[(x-x')^2 + (y-y')^2]^{1/2}}{2\pi} \rho(x',y')dx'dy' \tag{4-6.13}$$

as obtained by superposition. The function $(\ln R)/2\pi$ is the two-dimensional Green's function for Poisson's equation.

We extend the results, and consider the solution to the vector Poisson's equation

$$\nabla^2\bar{A} = -\bar{J} \tag{4-6.14}$$

The result is readily written down since it is the sum of three scalar equations for A_x, A_y, and A_z for which the solutions have the form given in Eq. (4-6.6). By vector addition, the result is given by

$$\overline{A}(\overline{r}) = \int_V \frac{\overline{J}(\overline{r}')}{4\pi R} \, dV' \tag{4-6.15}$$

as the solution for $\overline{A}$.

4-7. Green's Function and the Solution of Poisson's Equation

The use of Green's function in the solution of boundary value problems has physical appeal because, as discussed in the foregoing section, the field at a point caused by a source can be considered to be the total effect due to each elementary portion of the source. If $G(x,x')$ is the field at a point x due to a unit *point* source located at x', then the total field at x due to a distributed source $\rho(x')$ is the integral of $G\rho$ over the range of x' occupied by the source.

As already noted, the discussion in Sec. 4-6 applies only to an unbounded space. In a bounded region the solution is more difficult to obtain, but can still be found for those boundary configurations for which Laplace's equation can be solved. As already discussed, the essential method used is to expand both Φ and ρ in terms of a suitable set of eigenfunctions. There is no loss in generality in finding a solution for the special case of a unit source $\delta(\overline{r}-\overline{r}')$ since the solution for a general source is then readily obtained by superposition. Thus, if we let $G(\overline{r},\overline{r}')$ be the solution for a unit source, such that

$$\nabla^2 G(\overline{r},\overline{r}') = -\delta(\overline{r}-\overline{r}') \tag{4-7.1}$$

the solution for a general source will be

$$\Phi(\overline{r}) = \int_V G(\overline{r},\overline{r}') \, \rho(\overline{r}') \, dV' \tag{4-7.2}$$

with the Green's function so chosen that it satisfies the same boundary conditions that apply to Φ.

We may also modify Eq. (4-7.2) so as to make G satisfy either the boundary condition $G = 0$ or $\partial G/\partial n = 0$ even though Φ does not necessarily satisfy these boundary conditions. To elaborate further on these remarks, consider a region V bounded by a closed surface S, as in Fig. 4-7.1. Let ρ be a source distribution in V, and suppose that Φ is required to satisfy the boundary conditions

$$\Phi = \Phi_s(x,y,z) \qquad \text{on } S_1$$

$$\frac{\partial \Phi}{\partial n} = \sigma(x,y,x) \qquad \text{on } S_2$$

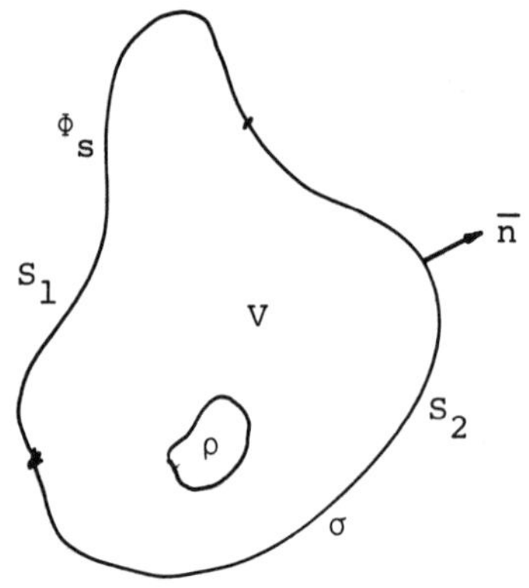

$S = S_1 + S_2$

Figure 4-7.1. Boundary value problem for Poisson's equation.

Consider the expression

$$\nabla \cdot (\Phi\nabla G - G\nabla\Phi) = \nabla\Phi \cdot \nabla G - \nabla G \cdot \nabla\Phi + \Phi\nabla^2 G - G\nabla^2\Phi = G\rho - \Phi\delta(\bar{r}-\bar{r}')$$

If we integrate over the volume V and use the divergence theorem on the left hand member, we obtain

$$\oint_S (\Phi\nabla G - G\nabla\Phi) \cdot \bar{n}dS = \oint_S (\Phi \frac{\partial G}{\partial n} - G \frac{\partial \Phi}{\partial n}) \, dS$$

$$= \int_V G\rho \, dV - \int_V \Phi\delta(\bar{r}-\bar{r}') \, dV$$

$$= \int_V G\rho \, dV - \Phi(\bar{r}')$$

In the surface integral we know the value of Φ on S_1 and $\partial\Phi/\partial n$ on S_2. Hence we can evaluate this integral provided that G has been constructed so as to satisfy the boundary conditions

$G = 0$ on S_1 where Φ is known

$\partial G/\partial n = 0$ on S_2 where $\partial\Phi/\partial n$ is known

We now find for the bounded space that

$$\Phi(r) = \int_V G(\bar{r},\bar{r}')\rho(\bar{r}')dV' + \int_{S_1} \Phi_S(x',y',z') \frac{\partial G}{\partial n} dS' - \int_{S_2} G\sigma(x',y',z')dS' \quad (4\text{-}7.3)$$

where we have interchanged the primed and unprimed variables (this is simply a relabeling of the variables so as to make $\bar{r}$ correspond to the field point and $\bar{r}'$ correspond to the source point). We thus see that by imposing proper boundary conditions on the Green's function we are able to take care of the required boundary conditions on Φ. As a further extension, if $\Phi + k\,\partial\Phi/\partial n$ is specified on a part of the boundary, then G should be chosen to satisfy the condition $G + k\,\partial G/\partial n$ on this part of the boundary.

In view of the foregoing results, we may restrict our further analysis without any loss in generality, to that of finding solutions for Poisson's equation with a unit source, i.e., to constructing Green's functions. There are two main techniques that are used to construct the Green's function, and these will be developed by considering several particular examples.

Example 4-7.1. Investigate the electric potential distribution $\Phi(x)$ between two parallel plates of infinite extent. The electric charge $\rho(x)$ is distributed between the two plates in a known form, as shown in Fig. 4-7.2.

Solution. The problem here considered requires the solution of Poisson's equation

$$\nabla^2\Phi = -\frac{\rho}{\varepsilon}$$

subject to the boundary conditions

C-1. $\Phi(0) = 0$

C-2. $\Phi(1) = 0$

But owing to the symmetry that exists in the Y- and Z- directions, Poisson's equation reduces to the simple form

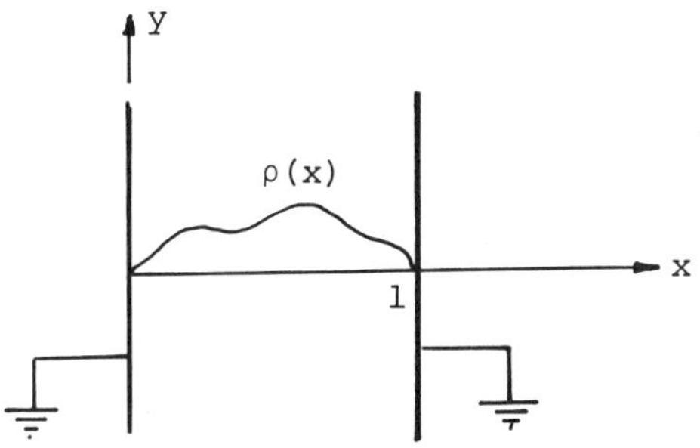

Figure 4-7.2. The assumed charge density distribution.

$$\frac{d^2\Phi}{dx^2} = -\frac{\rho(x)}{\varepsilon} \tag{4-7.4}$$

To proceed, we multiply this equation by G(x,x') and integrate. We obtain

$$-\int_0^1 G\,\frac{d^2\Phi}{dx^2}\,dx = \int_0^1 \frac{\rho(x)G}{\varepsilon}\,dx$$

We now find the following relation

$$-\int_0^1 G(x,x')\,\frac{d^2\Phi}{dx^2}\,dx = \frac{dG(1,x')}{dx}\,\Phi(1) - G(1,x')\,\frac{d\Phi(1)}{dx} - \frac{dG(0,x')}{dx}\,\Phi(0) + G(0,x')\,\frac{d\Phi(0)}{dx}$$

$$-\int_0^1 \frac{d^2G}{dx^2}\,\Phi dx = G(0,x')\,\frac{d\Phi(0)}{dx} - G(1,x')\,\frac{d\Phi(1)}{dx} - \int_0^1 \frac{d^2G}{dx^2}\,\Phi dx$$
$$= \int_0^1 \frac{\rho(x)G(x,x')}{\varepsilon}\,dx \tag{4-7.5}$$

where integration by parts was applied twice. We must now choose a Green's function G(x,x') for this problem. Guided by our former considerations, and choosing boundary conditions dictated by C-1 and C-2, we select the following

$$-\frac{d^2G}{dx^2} = \delta(x-x') \qquad \text{a)}$$

$$G(0,x') = 0 \qquad \text{b)} \qquad (4\text{-}7.6)$$

$$G(1,x') = 0 \qquad \text{c)}$$

Combining these results with Eq. (4-7.5) we find the solution to be

$$\Phi(x') = \int_0^1 \frac{\rho(x)G(x,x')}{\varepsilon}\,dx \tag{4-7.7}$$

It remains now to find G(x,x'). The exact form can be found from Eq. (4-7.6a) by direct integration, since

$$\frac{dG}{dx} = -\int \delta(x-x')dx + C_1 = -u_{-1}(x-x') + C_1 \tag{4-7.8}$$

where $u_{-1}(x)$ is the unit step function. We integrate again to obtain

$$G(x,x') = -\int u_{-1}(x-x')dx + \int C_1 dx + C_2 = -(x-x')u_{-1}(x-x') + C_1 x + C_2 \tag{4-7.9}$$

Imposing the boundary conditions (4-7.6b) and (4-7.6c) on this general solution yields the two equations

$$G(0,x') = x'u_{-1}(-x') + C_1 \cdot 0 + C_2 = 0 + 0 + C_2 = 0$$

$$G(1,x') = -(1-x')u_{-1}(1-x') + C_1 + C_2 = 0$$

from which

$$\begin{aligned} C_1 &= (1-x')u_{-1}(1-x') \\ C_2 &= 0 \end{aligned} \tag{4-7.10}$$

Hence the Green's function for Eq. (4-7.4) is equal to

$$G(x,x') = -(x-x')u_{-1}(x-x') + (1-x')x \tag{4-7.11}$$

This gives the response at x' due to a unit impulse source at x. Interchanging the role of x and x' in Eqs. (4-7.7) and (4-7.11) we find the solution of Eq. (4-7.4) to be

$$\Phi(x) = \int_0^1 \frac{\rho(x')}{\varepsilon} G(x',x)dx' = \int_0^1 \frac{\rho(x')}{\varepsilon}[-(x'-x)u_{-1}(x'-x) + (1-x)x']dx' \tag{4-7.12}$$

We note that the Green's function in Eq. (4-7.12) can be written in the form (show it!)

$$G(x,x') = \begin{cases} (1-x')x & x < x' \\ (1-x)x' & x > x' \end{cases} \tag{4-7.13}$$

ΔΔΔ

Based on our discussion of Green's functions and in the light of Appendix II, we observe the following:

I. Green's function of a self-adjointing operator is symmetric $G(x,x') = G(x',x)$ [see Eq. (4-7.13)].
II. $G(x,x')$ is continuous
III. $\tilde{A}G(x,x') = 0$ except at $x = x'$ (for the definition of $\tilde{A}$ see Appendix II)
IV. $G(x,x')$ satisfies homogeneous boundary conditions
V. $G(x,x')$ has a change of its slope at $x = x'$.

Example 4-7.2. The electric charge distribution between two conducting plates is given by $\rho(x)$. If a battery is connected as shown in Fig. 4-7.3, find the potential distribution between the plates.

Solution. We must find a solution of Poisson's equation subject to the boundary conditions

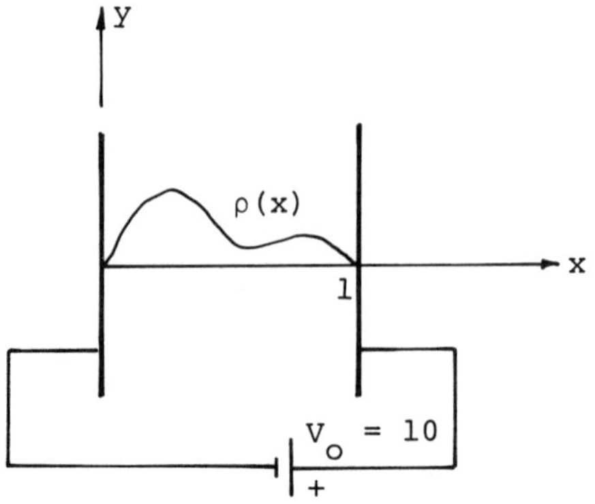

Figure 4-7.3. The system configuration.

$$\nabla^2\Phi = -\frac{\rho(x)}{\varepsilon}$$

$$\Phi(0) = 0$$

$$\Phi(1) = 10$$

We proceed by employing the same procedure as that in Ex. 4-7.1. We now find that

$$\Phi(x') = -10\,\frac{dG(1,x')}{dx} - \int_0^1 \frac{\rho(x)}{\varepsilon}\, G(x,x')\, dx \tag{4-7.14}$$

where it was assumed that $G(0,x') = G(1,x') = 0$. From Eq. (4-7.11) we find

$$\frac{dG(1,x')}{dx} = -u_{-1}(1-x') - (1-x')\,\delta(1-x') + (1-x')$$

$$= -1 - (1-x')\cdot 0 + (1-x') = -x' \qquad 0 \le x' \le 1$$

and Eq. (4-7.14) becomes

$$\Phi(x) = -10x + \int_0^1 \frac{\rho(x')}{\varepsilon}\, G(x',x)dx' \tag{4-7.15}$$

ΔΔΔ

For the case of multidimensional problems, different approaches to the determination of the appropriate Green's function exist. We shall consider two examples.

Example 4-7.3. Method I. Find the Green's function for an infinitely long rectangular pipe of dimensions a and b with a unit source located at x', y', as shown in Fig. 4-7.4.

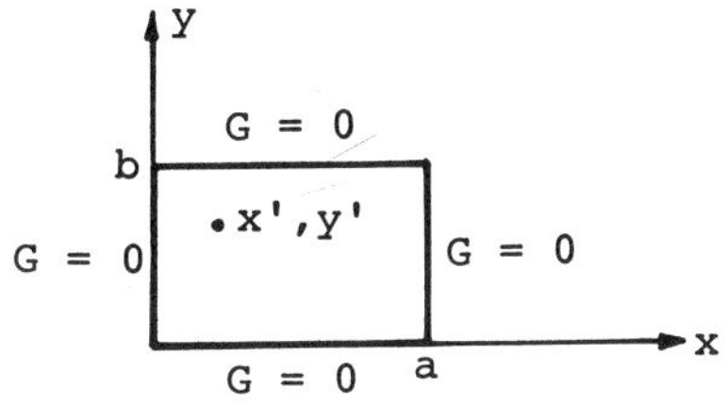

Figure 4-7.4. Line source in a rectangular pipe.

Solution. Our problem now is to find a solution for G that satisfies

$$\frac{\partial^2 G}{\partial x^2} + \frac{\partial^2 G}{\partial y^2} = -\delta(x-x')\,\delta(y-y') \qquad \text{a)}$$

subject to the boundary conditions

$$G = 0, \quad x = 0,a \quad 0 \le y \le b \qquad \text{b)}$$

$$G = 0, \quad y = 0,b \quad 0 \le x \le a \qquad \text{c)} \qquad (4\text{-}7.16)$$

For the present problem, we note that the eigenfunctions

$$\sin\frac{n\pi x}{a} \qquad n = 1,2,3,\ldots$$

$$\sin\frac{m\pi y}{b} \qquad m = 1,2,3,\ldots$$

satisfy the required boundary conditions. We select for G the complete set given by the Fourier expansion. Thus, let

$$G = \sum_{n=1}^{\infty}\sum_{m=1}^{\infty} A_{nm} \sin\frac{n\pi x}{a} \sin\frac{m\pi y}{b}$$

where the A_{nm} are coefficients to be determined. When we substitute the assumed expansion for G into the differential equation (4-7.16) we obtain

$$\sum_{n=1}^{\infty}\sum_{m=1}^{\infty} - A_{nm}\left[\left(\frac{n\pi}{a}\right)^2 + \left(\frac{m\pi}{b}\right)^2\right] \sin\frac{n\pi x}{a} \sin\frac{m\pi y}{b} = -\delta(x-x')\,\delta(y-y')$$

after performing the differentiations. To determine the coefficients A_{nm} we use the usual Fourier expansion technique. We multiply both sides by sin $s\pi x/a$ sin $r\pi y/b$ and integrate over x and y; this leads to

$$-A_{sr}\left[\left(\frac{s\pi}{a}\right)^2 + \left(\frac{r\pi}{b}\right)^2\right]\frac{ab}{4} = -\int_0^a\int_0^b \sin\frac{s\pi x}{a} \sin\frac{r\pi y}{b}\,\delta(x-x')\,\delta(y-y')\,dx\,dy$$

$$= -\sin\frac{s\pi x'}{a} \sin\frac{r\pi y'}{b}$$

because of the orthogonality property of the sin functions and the singular property of the delta functions. Our solution for G is now given by

$$G(x,y;x',y') = \frac{4}{ab} \sum_{n=1}^{\infty} \sum_{m=1}^{\infty} \frac{\sin \frac{n\pi x}{a} \sin \frac{n\pi x'}{a} \sin \frac{m\pi y}{b} \sin \frac{m\pi y'}{b}}{(\frac{n\pi}{a})^2 + (\frac{m\pi}{b})^2} \tag{4-7.17}$$

Note that G is symmetric in the primed and unprimed variables, i.e., $G(x,y;x',y') = G(x',y';x,y)$. This symmetry property expresses the reciprocity property of the solution to Poisson's equations. Physically it means that the potential at a point x,y due to a unit source at x',y' is the same as the potential at x',y' when the source is moved to the original field point x,y. In other words, interchanging the source point and field point does not change the value of the potential. ΔΔΔ

The foregoing solution has illustrated one method of constructing the Green's function, namely, form a Fourier series expansion for G in terms of a complete set of eigenfunctions that satisfy the boundary conditions. The solution, Eq. (4-7.7) is in the form of a double infinite series. If we could sum the series over n, we could express the solution as a single infinite series. The second procedure to be illustrated will yield a solution for G which has a closed form expression for the x-dependence and will be equal to the solution given above, if the series over n is summed.

Example 4-7.4. Method II. Repeat Ex. 4-7.3, but express G in closed form for the x-dependence.

Solution. Since Laplace's equation is separable in rectangular coordinates, we assume that the solution for G can be expressed in the form

$$G = \sum_m f_m(x)\, g_m(y) \tag{4-7.18}$$

To satisfy the boundary conditions at y = 0,b, we choose $g_m(y) = \sin m\pi y/b$. We now substitute this equation into Eq. (4-7.16a) and obtain

$$\sum_{m=1}^{\infty} \left(\frac{d^2 f_m}{dx^2} - \frac{m^2\pi^2}{b^2} f_m\right) \sin \frac{m\pi y}{b} = -\delta(x-x')\, \delta(y-y')$$

To obtain an equation for $f_m(x)$, we multiply both sides by $\sin r\pi y/b$ and integrate over y to obtain

$$\frac{b}{2} \left[\frac{d^2 f_m}{dx^2} - \frac{m^2\pi^2}{b^2} f_m\right] = -\sin \frac{m\pi y'}{b}\, \delta(x-x') \tag{4-7.19}$$

For $x \neq x'$, we see that

$$\frac{d^2 f_m}{dx^2} - \frac{m^2\pi^2}{b^2} f_m = 0$$

since $\delta(x-x') = 0$ for $x \neq x'$. Solutions of this latter equation are $\sinh m\pi x/b$ and $\cosh m\pi x/b$ or linear combinations of these functions. To satisfy the boundary conditions at $x = 0,a$, we choose

$$f_m(x) = A_m \sinh \frac{m\pi x}{b} \qquad x < x'$$
$$f_m(x) = B_m \sinh \left[\frac{m\pi}{b}(a-x)\right] \qquad x > x' \qquad (4\text{-}7.20)$$

Let us consider Eq. (4-7.19) carefully. A little though will show that for d^2f_m/dx^2 to have a delta function behavior at x' (see Fig. 4-7.5) the slope df_m/dx will correspond to a step function change at x'. Hence, f_m will be continuous but has a discontinuous slope at x'. To determine the required discontinuity in df_m/dx at x' we integrate Eq. (4-7.19) over the region $x'-\tau < x < x'+\tau$ and let τ approach zero. Since f_m is chosen to be continuous at x', we use the result

$$\lim_{\tau\to 0} \int_{x'-\tau}^{x'+\tau} f_m(x)\,dx = \lim_{\tau\to 0} 2\tau\, f_m(x') = 0$$

and thus find that

$$\lim_{\tau\to 0} \frac{b}{2} \int_{x'-\tau}^{x'+\tau} \frac{d^2 f_m}{dx^2}\,dx = \frac{b}{2} \frac{df_m}{dx}\Bigg|_{x'-\tau}^{x'+\tau} = -\sin\frac{m\pi y'}{b} \int_{x'-\tau}^{x'+\tau} \delta(x-x')\,dx = -\sin\frac{m\pi y'}{b}$$

Hence the discontinuity in df_m/dx at x' is given by

$$\frac{df_m}{dx}\Bigg|_{x'-\tau}^{x'+\tau} = -\frac{2}{b}\sin\frac{m\pi y'}{b} \qquad (4\text{-}7.21)$$

From the jump condition Eq. (4-7.21) and Eq. (4-7.20) we find that

$$-A_m \frac{m\pi}{b}\cosh\frac{m\pi x'}{b} - B_m \frac{m\pi}{b}\cosh\frac{m\pi}{b}(a-x') = -\frac{2}{b}\sin\frac{m\pi y'}{b}$$

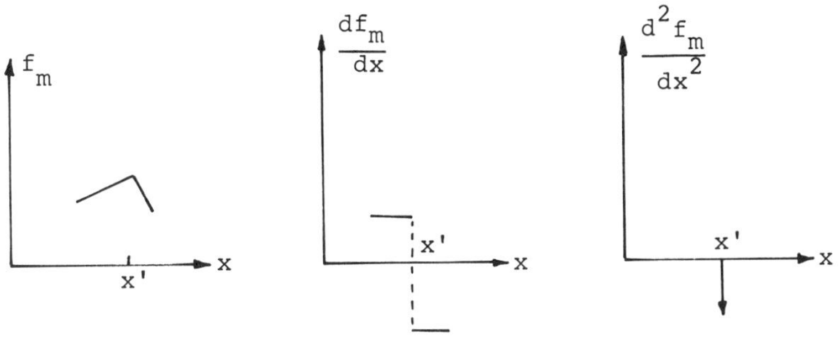

Figure 4-7.5. Behavior of f_m and its derivatives at $x = x'$.

From Eq. (4-7.20) the continuity condition at x' requires that

$$A_m \sinh \frac{m\pi x'}{b} = B_m \sinh \frac{m\pi}{b}(a-x')$$

These last two equations, when solved for A_m and B_m, yield

$$A_m = \frac{2}{m\pi} \frac{\sinh \frac{m\pi}{b}(a-x') \sin \frac{m\pi y'}{b}}{\sinh \frac{m\pi a}{b}} \quad \text{a)}$$

$$B_m = \frac{2}{m\pi} \frac{\sinh \frac{m\pi}{b} x' \sin \frac{m\pi y'}{b}}{\sinh \frac{m\pi a}{b}} \quad \text{b)} \qquad (4\text{-}7.22)$$

The solution for G is now completed and is given by

$$G = \sum_{m=1}^{\infty} \frac{2}{m\pi} \frac{\sin \frac{m\pi y}{b} \sin \frac{m\pi y'}{b}}{\sinh \frac{m\pi a}{b}} \begin{cases} \sinh \frac{m\pi x}{b} \sinh \frac{m\pi(a-x')}{b} & x \le x' \\ \sinh \frac{m\pi x'}{b} \sinh \frac{m\pi(a-x)}{b} & x \ge x' \end{cases} \qquad (4\text{-}7.23)$$

This solution is equivalent to that given in Eq. (4-10.6) but has the feature that the x-dependence is exhibited in closed form.

ΔΔΔ

4-8. The Method of Images

As has been discussed, to find the potential to a static boundary value problem requires a solution to Laplace's equation which satisfies the prescribed boundary conditions. This involves writing Laplace's equation in the set of orthogonal curvilinear coordinates which is best suited to the description of the surfaces bounding the region in which the value of Φ is desired. The solution of the problem is expressed in terms of Fourier series, Bessel functions, etc., depending on the system of orthogonal curvilinear coordinates.

There are many problems of importance which do not yield readily to solution by the methods of harmonic analysis. Special methods have been devised for solving some of these problems. One such method is due to Lord Kelvin, and is of great value in solving for the forms of the lines of force around conductors suspended parallel to the earth. The essence of the method in its applications to electric field problems is the following: suppose that a given charge distribution produces a constant potential over a known surface (and this potential is usually taken as zero at the surface). The solution to the problem of finding the electric field intensity at all points in space by means of the method of electrical images involves finding a simple charge distribution reflected in the conductor which, with the distribution of charges outside, will produce the same specified potential surface. From uniqueness considerations of the solution of Laplace's equation, the

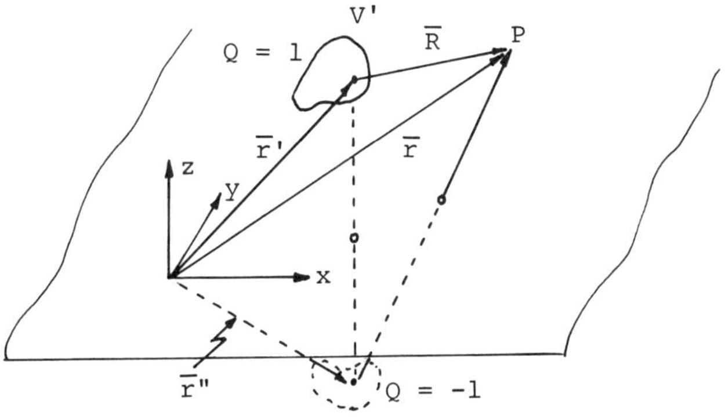

Figure 4-8.1. A volume charge distribution above a ground plane.

field will be the same when the conductor is removed and is replaced by the new charge distribution. The solution of the problem in the region normally outside of the conductor is obtained by considering the field due to the two charge distributions alone.

When distributed charges are present, a logical extension of the method is employed. This requires first finding the potential due to a point charge and its image and then using the resulting potential, which is actually the Green's function, to determine the potential due to the total charge distribution. As a specific case refer to Fig. 4-8.1 which shows a volume charge distribution above a ground plane. The potential at point P due to the single charge Q in V' is

$$\Phi_1(\overline{r}) = \frac{1}{4\pi\varepsilon|\overline{r}-\overline{r}'|} \tag{4-8.1}$$

To find the potential due to the image charge, we note that the potential due to both charges must be zero on the plane Z = 0. This requires that

$$G(x,y,z)\Big|_{z=0} = \Phi_1(x,y,0) + \Phi_2(x,y,0) = 0$$

from which we must have

$$\Phi_2(x,y,0) = -\frac{1}{4\pi\varepsilon[(x-x')^2 + (y-y')^2 + z'^2]^{1/2}} \tag{4-8.2}$$

Evidently this is the potential due to a point charge with Q = -1 and $x'' = x'$ and $y'' = y'$. The choice for z'' is narrowed to $z'' = -z'$, since $z'' = z'$ will yield the original position. By Eqs. (4-8.1) and (4-8.2) the required Green's function is

$$G(\overline{r},\overline{r}') = \frac{1}{4\pi\varepsilon|\overline{r}-\overline{r}'|} = \frac{1}{4\pi\varepsilon[(x-x')^2 + (y-y')^2 + (z+z')^2]^{1/2}} \tag{4-8.3}$$

For the charge distribution $\rho(\overline{r}')$, we use Eq. (4-6.9) to find that the potential is

$$\Phi(\overline{r}) = \int_V G(\overline{r},\overline{r}')\, \rho(\overline{r}')\, dV' \tag{4-8.4}$$

where $G(\overline{r},\overline{r}')$ is given in Eq. (4-8.3). Clearly, of course, this result is a special case of the general solution given by Eq. (4-7.3).

Example 4-8.1. Refer to Fig. 4-8.2, and suppose that a point charge +Q is placed a distance d in front of an infinite plane conductor which is grounded. It is required to find an expression for the charge density induced in the conductor.

Solution. Based on the discussion above, the choice of an image charge -Q at a distance -d yields a pair of charges which together satisfy the presribed boundary condition $\Phi = 0$ at all points of the conductor.

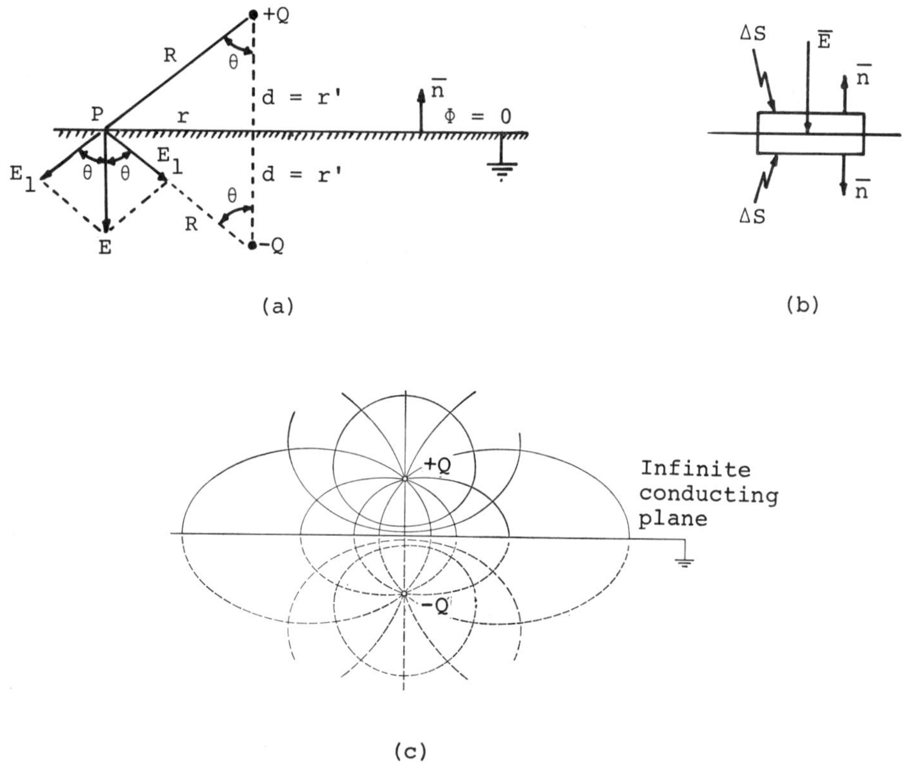

Figure 4-8.2. The image of a point charge in an infinite conducting plane: (a) Gives the geometry for analysis; (b) Shows the field at the boundary surface; (c) Shows the lines of force drawn to show the symmetry of the field at the charge.

It is seen from this figure that the field intensity at the point P is

$$\bar{E} = 2\bar{E}_1 \cos\theta = 2\bar{E}_1 \frac{d}{R} = 2E_1 \frac{d}{R}(-\bar{n}) \tag{4-8.5}$$

But since the magnitude of the electric field of the point charge is

$$E_1 = \frac{Q}{4\rho\varepsilon_0|\bar{r}-\bar{r}'|^2}$$

then we have

$$\bar{E} = \frac{Q}{2\pi\varepsilon_0|\bar{r}-\bar{r}'|^2}\frac{d}{R}(-\bar{n})$$

which is

$$\bar{E} = \frac{Qd}{2\pi\varepsilon_0|\bar{r}-\bar{r}'|^3}(-\bar{n}); \qquad (R = |\bar{r}-\bar{r}'|) \tag{4-8.6}$$

Suppose that we now consider a very shallow coin-shaped Gaussian surface in the air-conductor interface at point P, as shown in Fig. 4-8.2b. Because $\bar{E}$ is parallel to $\bar{n}$, there is no flux through the shallow sides; all of the flux is related to the surface, say ΔS. Therefore, using Gauss' theorem, it follows that

$$\oint_{\Delta S} \bar{E} \cdot \bar{n}\, dS = \frac{Q_s}{\varepsilon_0}$$

where Q_s is the charge within the volume. But $\bar{E}$ is a constant over the infinitesimal area ΔS and exists only on the upper surface of the coin-shaped surface. Then

$$\bar{E} \cdot \bar{n} = \frac{Q}{\Delta S\varepsilon_0} = \frac{\rho_s}{\varepsilon_0}$$

where the surface charge density is given by $\rho_s = Q_s/\Delta S$. Thus it follows that

$$\bar{E} = \frac{\rho_s}{\varepsilon_0}\bar{n}$$

Combining this result with the above gives

$$\frac{\rho_s}{\varepsilon_0} = -\frac{Qd}{\varepsilon_0 2\pi|\bar{r}-\bar{r}'|^3}$$

and the surface charge density is given by

$$\rho_s = -\frac{Qd}{2\pi|\bar{r}-\bar{r}'|^3} \tag{4-8.7}$$

ΔΔΔ

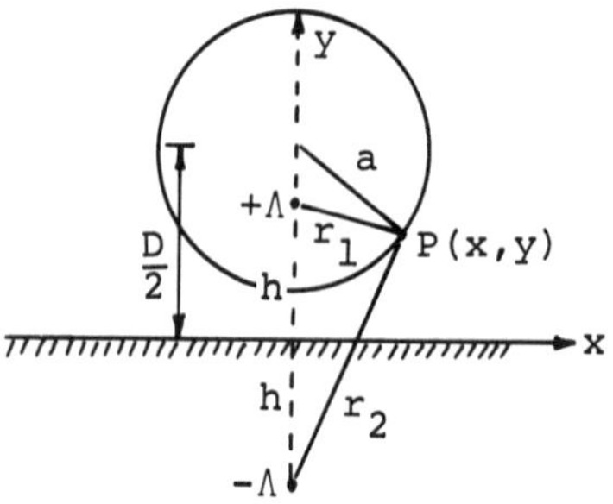

Figure 4-8.3. A line source above the ground, and the locus for constant potential.

Example 4-8.2. Find the electric field pattern produced by an infinite line charged to Λ Coulomb/m at a distance h above the ground.

Solution. The procedure parallels that in Ex. 4-8.1 in some measure, with the image of the line source appearing a distance h below the ground, as illustrated. The potential at point P due to the +Λ line of charge is (see Pr. 4-8.3)

$$V_{P_o}^{+} = \frac{2\Lambda}{4\pi\varepsilon_o} \ln \frac{h}{r_1}$$

and the potential at P due to the -Λ line of charge is

$$V_{P_o}^{-} = -\frac{2\Lambda}{4\pi\varepsilon_o} \ln \frac{h}{r_2}$$

Hence the total electric potential at point P due to both lines of charge (line plus image) is

$$V = V_{P_o}^{+} + V_{P_o}^{-} = \frac{2\Lambda}{4\pi\varepsilon_o} \ln \frac{r_2}{r_1} \tag{4-8.8}$$

It is noted from this that the potential at all points along the X axis is zero, as required.

In order to determine the locus of an equipotential surface, V is considered constant. This requires that r_2/r_1 = constant = A. Then

$$r_2 = r_1 A \tag{4-8.9}$$

From the figure it is seen that

$$r_1^2 = x^2 + (y-h)^2 \qquad \text{a)}$$
$$r_2^2 = x^2 + (y+h)^2 \qquad \text{b)} \tag{4-8.10}$$

and from Eq. (4-8.9)

$$r_2^2 = A^2 r_1^2$$

Combining these latter equations we get

$$x^2 + (y+h)^2 = A^2 [x^2 + (y-h)^2]$$

By expansion and rearrangement is is found that

$$x^2 + y^2 + 2hy \frac{1 + A^2}{1 - A^2} = -h^2$$

Completing the square by adding the quantity $h^2(1+A^2)^2/(1-A^2)^2$ on both sides of the equation, this expression may be written

$$x^2 + \left(y + h \frac{A^2 + 1}{A^2 - 1}\right)^2 = \frac{(2hA)^2}{(A^2 - 1)^2} \tag{4-8.11}$$

This expression is the equation of a circle of radius $a = 2hA/(A^2-1)$ with its center at the point $[0, h(A^2+1)/(A^2-1)]$. A plot of these results is shown in Fig. 4-8.3. We note that this is the analytic solution to the problem first introduced in Sec. 1-5 by flux plotting methods.

For convenience, the distance from the origin 0 to the center of the circle (the equipotential curve) is denoted D/2, as shown in the figure. By writing

$$\frac{D}{2} = h \frac{A^2 + 1}{A^2 - 1} \qquad \text{a)}$$

then (4-8.12)

$$a = \frac{2Ah}{A^2 - 1} = \sqrt{\left(\frac{D}{2}\right)^2 - h^2} \qquad \text{b)}$$

ΔΔΔ

4-9. Uniqueness of Solutions to Poisson's Equation

When a solution to Poisson's equation

$$\nabla^2 \Phi = -\rho$$

has been found such that Φ satisfies Dirichlet, Neumann, or mixed boundary conditions on the surface S bounding the region V of interest, this solution is unique. That is, a second solution satisfying the same boundary conditions and differing from Φ within V does not exist. To prove this uniqueness property, we assume that two different solutions have been found, and we must then show that these must, indeed, be identical.

Let Φ_1 and Φ_2 be two solutions of Poisson's equation with the same source function,

$$\nabla^2\Phi_1 = -\rho \qquad \nabla^2\Phi_2 = -\rho$$

Also, let Φ_1 and Φ_2 satisfy the same boundary conditions on S. The difference solution $\Phi_D = \Phi_1 - \Phi_2$ satisfies Laplace's equation $\nabla^2\Phi_D = 0$. Consider

$$\nabla \cdot (\Phi_D\nabla\Phi_D) = |\nabla\Phi_D|^2 + \Phi_D\nabla^2\Phi_D = |\nabla\Phi_D|^2$$

and integrate over the volume V to obtain

$$\int_V \nabla \cdot (\Phi_D\nabla\Phi_D)dV = \oint_S \Phi_D \frac{\partial\Phi_D}{\partial n} dV = \int_V |\nabla\Phi_D|^2 dV$$

The surface integral vanishes since Φ_1 and Φ_2 satisfy the same boundary conditions, and so either Φ_D or $\partial\Phi_D/\partial n$ is zero on S. We therefore conclude that

$$\int_V |\nabla\Phi_D|^2 dV = 0$$

which requires that $\nabla\Phi_D = 0$. Therefore, the difference solutions can, at most, equal a constant. But the constant will be zero if Dirichlet boundary conditions have been specified since in this case $\Phi_D = 0$ on S. If the Neumann condition, that is, $\partial\Phi/\partial n$, is specified everywhere on S, then Φ_D may equal a constant, and the solution is unique only to within an additive constant. However, this is just the result of not having a specified potential reference or datum point. Consequently, there is only one solution to Poisson's equation which satisfies the prescribed boundary conditions. The uniqueness proof given is clearly applicable to solutions of Laplace's equation, as well. This result may be interpreted to mean that only one unique solution is possible for a specified problem, a condition that is expected from purely physical considerations. It would, in fact, by terribly disconcerting to find more than one solution to a given problem. However, the solution may be expressed in more than one equivalent form, as discussed in connection with the solutions in Ex. 4-7.4.

Uniqueness is a very important result and provided the basis for the nonanalytic techniques already considered. This follows because it shows that a solution, however determined, be it by formal analytic methods, by numerical methods, by experimental or graphical techniques, or in fact, by divine inspiration or guessing, will be a unique solution. With uniqueness, the solution to problems with very complicated geometry and boundaries is made possible.

REVIEW QUESTIONS

1. State the Dirichlet, Neumann, and the maxed boundary conditions.
2. Describe the method of separation of variables.
3. What conditions in a boundary value problem determine its eigenvalues?
4. What is meant by the statement that two functions are orthogonal in a specified range?
5. What steps must be followed in order to solve a boundary value problem?
6. Sketch a few lower order Bessel and Neumann functions.
7. What is the range over which the Neumann functions are not used in physical problems?
8. What forms do the Bessel and Neumann functions take for large values of their arguments?
9. What functions are used in solving problems with spherical symmetry?
10. What is the relation between the Legendre polynomials and the Associated Legendre functions?
11. State some of the fundamental properties of the impulse (Dirac delta) function.
12. State Green's function for the Poisson equation.
13. Do Green's functions exist for boundary value problems?

PROBLEMS

4-2.1. Find the potential distribution for the boundary value problem shown in the figure.

[Ans: $\Phi = V_o \dfrac{\sinh[(\pi/b)x]}{\sinh[(\pi/b)a]} \sin \dfrac{\pi}{b} y$]

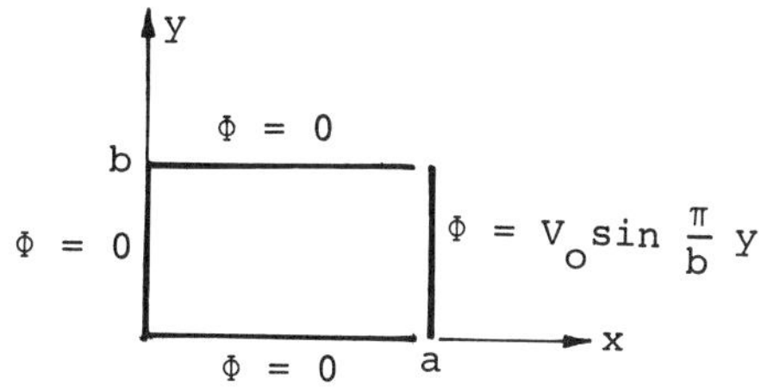

Figure P4-2.1.

4-2.2. Find the potential distribution for the boundary value problem shown in the figure.

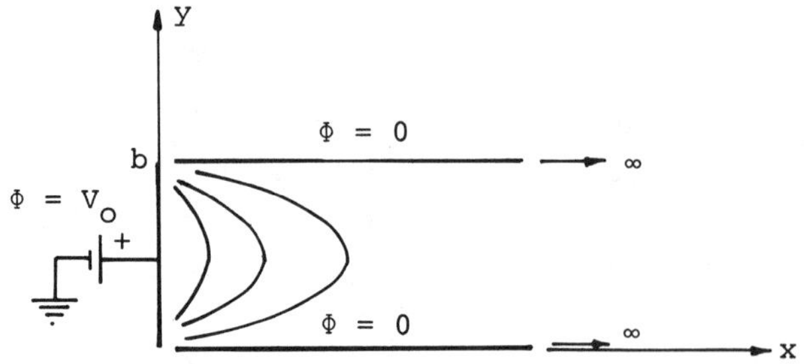

Figure P4-2.2.

[Hint: Use the exponential form for the $f(x) = C_1 e^{-k_x x}$;

[Ans: $\Phi(x,y) = \sum_{n=1,3,5,\ldots}^{\infty} \frac{4V_o}{n\pi} e^{-n\pi x/b} \sin \frac{n\pi}{b} y$]

4-2.3. Show that

$$\lim_{a\to\infty} \frac{\sinh[\frac{n\pi}{b}(a-x)]}{\sinh \frac{n\pi a}{b}} = e^{-n\pi x/b}$$

and compare it with the solution of Pr. 4-2.2 and Ex. 4-2.1.

[Hint: Use the exponential form of the hyperbolic functions.]

4-2.4. Find the potential distribution for the boundary value problem shown in the figure.

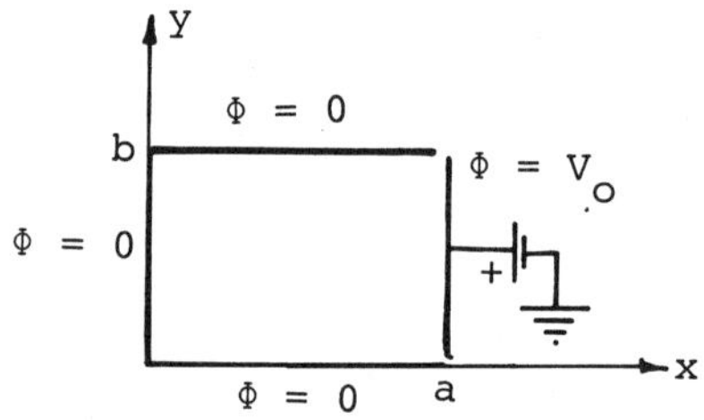

Figure P4-2.4.

[Ans: $\Phi(x,y) = \sum_{n=1,3,5,\ldots}^{\infty} \frac{4V_o}{n\pi} \frac{\sinh(n\pi x/b)}{\sinh(n\pi a/b)} \sin \frac{n\pi}{b} y$]

4-2.5. Find the potential distribution for the boundary value problem shown in the figure. [Use the results from Pr. 4-2.4 and Ex. 4-2.1 and apply the theorem of superposition.]

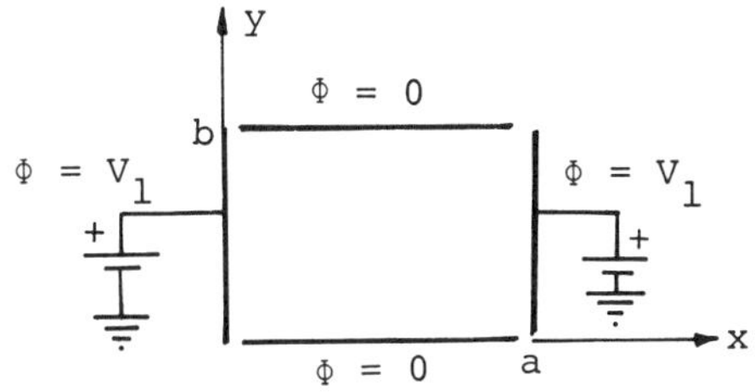

Figure P4-2.5.

4-2.6. Find the potential distribution for the boundary value problem shown in the figure.

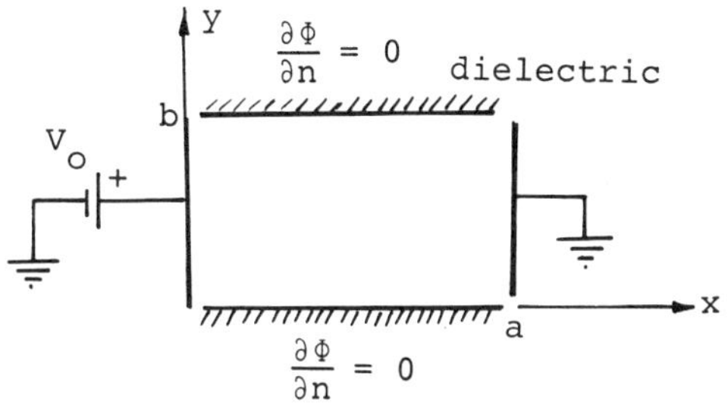

Figure P4-2.6.

[Ans: $\Phi(x,y) = V_0 \frac{a-x}{a}$]

4-2.7. Find the expression for the potential function $\Phi(x,y)$ at any point in the plane for the two-dimensional boundary value problem shown.

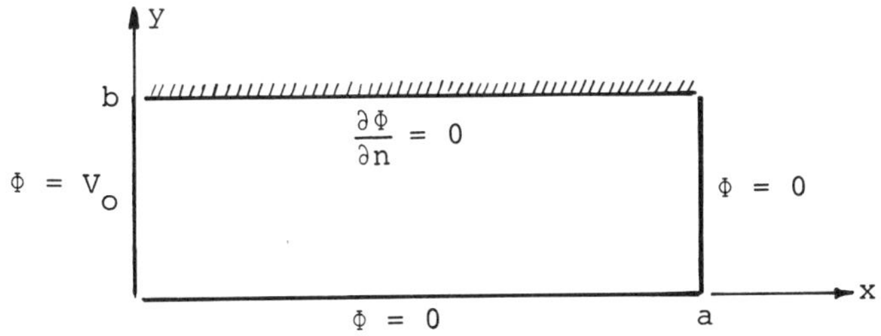

Figure P4-2.7.

4-2.8. A metal lamination of thickness h and infinite extent is insulated on each surface by a material of thickness d/2, as illustrated. Heat is generated within the lamination at a constant rate of W_0 Watt/m^3. No heat is generated in the insulating layers. Find the temperatures in the three regions.

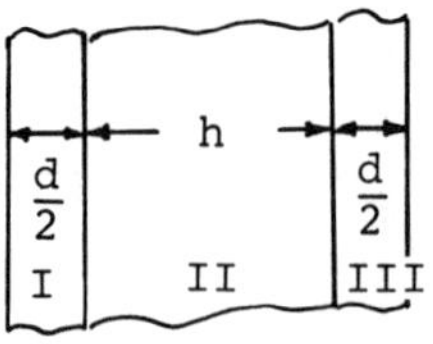

Figure P4-2.8.

4-3.1. Show that $J_o(\Gamma r)$ is a solution of the equation

$$\frac{d^2 J_o}{dr^2} + \frac{1}{r}\frac{dJ_o}{dr} + \Gamma^2 J_o = 0$$

4-3.2. A cylindrical capacitor is shown in the figure. Find the potential distribution inside and outside the capacitor.

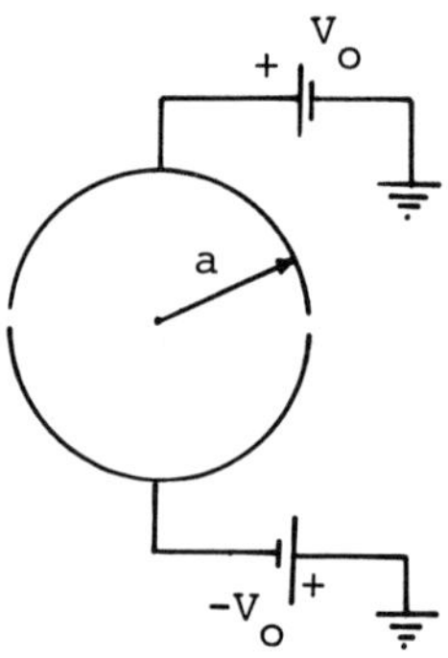

Figure P4-3.2.

[Ans: $V = \frac{4V_o}{\pi} \sum_{n=1}^{\infty} (\frac{r}{a})^n \frac{1}{n} \sin n\phi \qquad n = 1,3,5,\ldots$ and $r < a$

$V = \frac{4V_o}{\pi} \sum_{n=1}^{\infty} (\frac{a}{r})^n \frac{1}{n} \sin n\phi \qquad n = 1,3,5,\ldots$ and $r > a$]

4-3.3. The problem is like that in Ex. 4-3.3 except that the region consists of the space between coaxial cylinders, as shown.

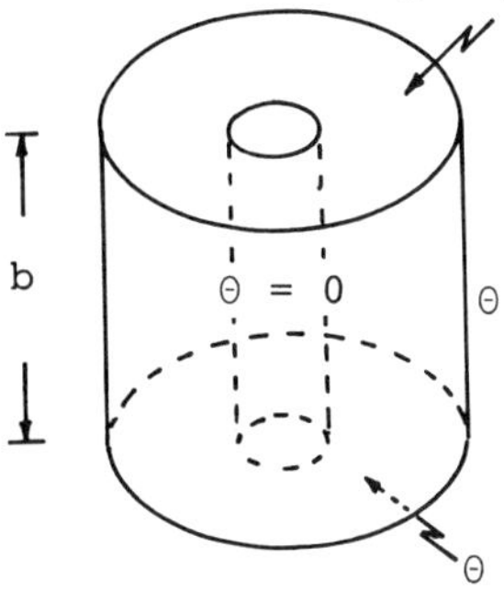

Figure P4-3.3.

4-4.1. Find the solution of Laplace's equation in spherical coordinates if Φ is independent of θ and ϕ. [Ans: $\Phi = A_1 + A_2/r$]

4-4.2. Suppose that the value of Φ is a constant Φ_o at every point on a spherical surface and that there is circular symmetry about any diameter of that surface. From the solution of Laplace's equation in spherical coordinates, show that

$\Phi = \Phi_o$ inside the sphere

$\Phi = \Phi_o \frac{a}{r}$ outside the sphere.

4-4.3. Find the solution of Laplace's equation in spherical coordinates if Φ is independent of r and ϕ. [Ans: $\Phi = A_1 + A_2 \ln(\cot \frac{\theta}{2})$]

4-4.4. Find the potential if a dielectric sphere is placed in a uniform electric field $\overline{E} = \overline{E}_o \overline{a}_z$.

[Hint: $\Phi_{mi} = \sum_{m=0}^{\infty} r^m P_m(\cos\theta)$ $\qquad 0 \le r \le a$

$\Phi_{mo} = -E_o r \cos\theta + \sum_{m=0}^{\infty} B_m P_m(\cos\theta)\, r^{-m-1}$ $\qquad a \le r \le \infty$

$\Phi_{mi} = \Phi_{mo}$ at $r = a$ and $\varepsilon_o \left.\frac{\partial\Phi}{\partial r}\right|_{r=a} = \varepsilon \left.\frac{\partial\Phi}{\partial r}\right|_{r=a}$;

equate terms with the same θ dependence.

[Ans: $\Phi_{mo} = -E_o r \cos\theta + \frac{\varepsilon-\varepsilon_o}{\varepsilon+2\varepsilon_o} E_o \cos\theta \frac{a^3}{r^2}$; $\Phi_{mi} = -\frac{3\varepsilon_o}{\varepsilon+2\varepsilon_o} E_o z$]

4-4.5. A spherical capacitor is formed by two concentric conducting spherical shells separated by two concentric dielectrics as shown in the figure. Find the potential in the two regions.

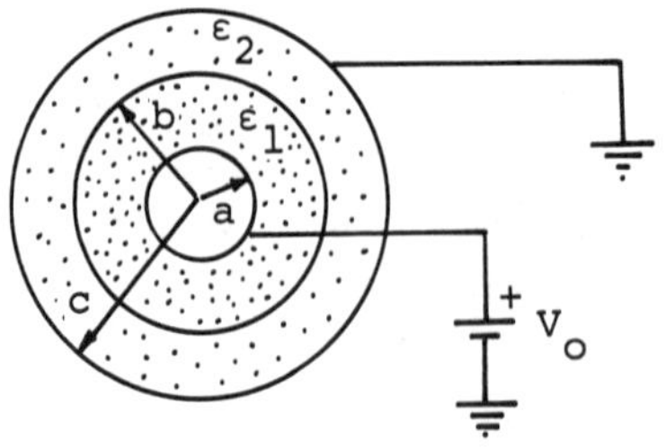

Figure P4-4.5.

4-4.6. Expand the function illustrated in a Legendre series of the form

$$f(x) = \sum_n A_n P_n(x)$$

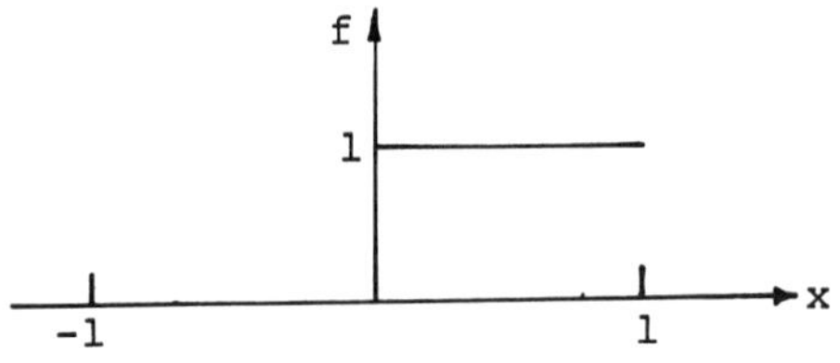

Figure P4-4.6.

The first four orders of $P_n(x)$ are tabulated:

$$P_0(x) = 1$$

$$P_1(x) = x$$

$$P_2(x) = (3x^2-1)/2$$

$$P_3(x) = (5x^3-3x)/2$$

4-5.1. Plot the function $f(x) = \lim_{a\to\infty} \sin a(x-2)/\pi(x-2)$ and show that the area under the main peak is unity.
[Hint: Apprximate the main lobe by an isosceles triangle.]

4-5.2. Show that $\int_{-\infty}^{\infty} \cos xt \, dt = 2\pi \, \delta(x)$. [Hint: Use Eq. (4-5.2c).]

4-5.3. Show that $\int_{-\infty}^{\infty} \cos xt \, \text{cox} \, x_o t \, dt = \pi[\delta(x + x_o) + \delta(x - x_o)]$.

4-6.1. Show that $\nabla^2(1/4\pi R) = 0$ when $R \neq 0$. [Hint: Refer to Eq. (4-6.4).]

4-7.1. Sketch the potential between two grounded plates if (a) $\rho(x) = x$, $0 \leq x \leq 1$; (b) $\rho(x) = x(1-x)$, $0 \leq x \leq 1$; (c) $\rho(x) = \delta(x-0.2)$, $0 \leq x \leq 1$.

4-7.2. Assume that an electronic charge density of 10 Coulomb/m^3 is uniformly distributed between the plates of Fig. 4-7.2. Determine the potential distribution $\Phi(x)$, and sketch this function.

4-7.3. A sheet of charge $a_n \sin n\pi x/a\ \delta(z-z')$ is located at z' in a parallel plate region. The charge layer depends on x according to $\sin n\pi x/a$ and a_n is an amplitude constant. Find a solution for the Green's function such that $G = 0$ at $x = 0, a$ and $G \to 0$ as $|z| \to \infty$.

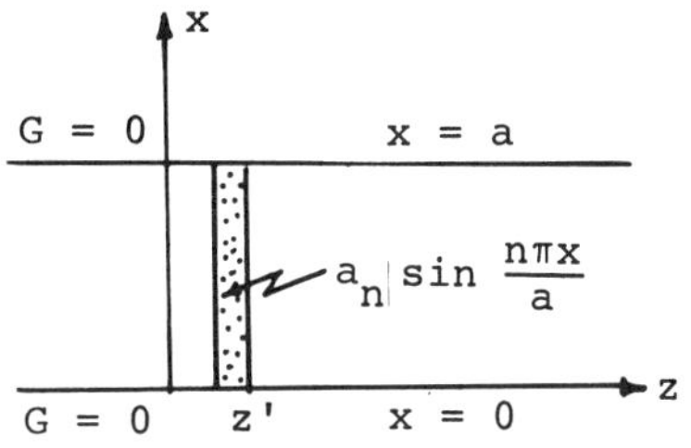

Figure P4-7.3.

The equation to be solved is

$$\frac{\partial^2 G}{\partial x^2} + \frac{\partial^2 G}{\partial z^2} = -a_n \sin \frac{n\pi x}{a}\, \delta(z-z')$$

For $z \neq z'$ we have

$$\frac{\partial^2 G}{\partial x^2} + \frac{\partial^2 G}{\partial z^2} = 0$$

Assume that

$$G = f_n(z) \sin \frac{n\pi x}{a}$$

and show that

$$\left(\frac{\partial^2}{\partial z^2} - \frac{n^2\pi^2}{a^2}\right) f_n = -a_n\, \delta(z-z')$$

Next let

$$f_n = A_n e^{-n\pi z/a} \qquad z > z'$$

and

$$f_n = B_n e^{n\pi z'/a} \qquad z < z'$$

since these are solutions of

$$\left(\frac{\partial^2}{\partial z^2} - \frac{n^2\pi^2}{a^2}\right) f_n = 0$$

and make $f_n \to 0$ as $|z| \to \infty$. Complete the solution by making f_n continuous at z' and adjusting the derivative $\partial f_n/\partial z$ at z' so that the second derivative will generate a discontinuity of $-a_n\ \delta(z-z')$.

4-7.4. Consider a line source $\delta(x-x')\ \delta(z-z')$ in a parallel plate region. Expand this source into a Fourier series to show that

$$\delta(x-x')\ \delta(z-z') = \sum_{n=1}^{\infty} a_n \sin\frac{n\pi x}{a}\ \delta(z-z')$$
$$= \sum_{n=1}^{\infty} \left(\frac{2}{a}\sin\frac{n\pi x'}{a}\right) \sin\frac{n\pi x}{a}\ \delta(z-z')$$

This Fourier series states that the line source can be viewed as the superposition of an infinite number of sheets of charge, the nth one being $a_n \sin n\pi x/a\ \delta(z-z')$. But the solution for one of these was obtained in Pr. 4-7.3; call it $\Phi_n(x,z;x',z')$. By superposition the solution for a line source is then given by

$$G(x,z;x',z') = \sum_{n=1}^{\infty} \Phi_n$$

for this problem. If G is to represent the electric potential, it should be divided by ε_0. Complete the details to obtain the full solution for G as outlined above.

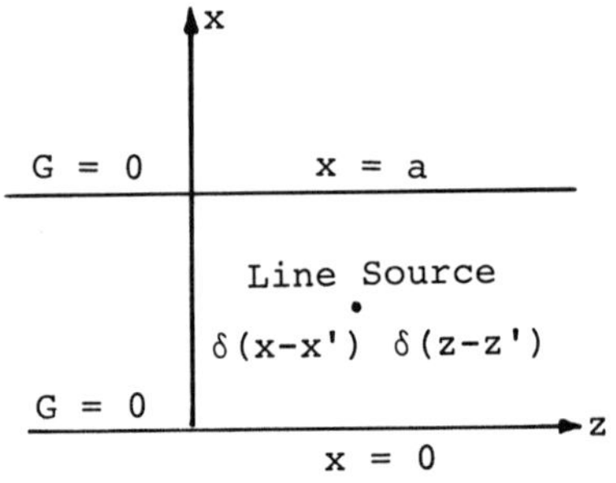

Figure P4-7.4.

4-8.1. Find the electric field around a spherical conductor maintained at zero potential, when there is a charge $+Q_1$ at an outside point T near the sphere.

4-8.2. Show that the total charge distributed over the infinite plane of Ex. 4-8.1 equals to q. [Hint: Use polar coordinates.]

4-8.3. Show that the potential at point P due to $+\Lambda$ charge per unit length of Ex. 4-8.2 is $V^+_{P_0} = (2\Lambda/4\pi\varepsilon_o)\ \ell n(h/r_1)$.

CHAPTER 5

ELECTRIC FIELDS AND CURRENTS

The fundamental equations that describe the electrostatic field in a vacuum were presented in Sec. 2-7. The purpose of this chapter is to extend those results to include the effects produced by dielectric bodies, to examine the energy storage and forces associated with electrostatic fields, and to consider further aspects of electric current fields. For reference purposes, we will repeat the basic equations given in the earlier chapter.

5-1. Electrostatic Field in Vacuum

The electrostatic field is the force field set up by a distribution of electric charges. An initial approach is to consider the force on a test charge $\underline{q}$ placed in an electrostatic field $\overline{E}$. The test charge is small enough so that it does not distort the field $\overline{E}$. The test charge experiences a force given by

$$\overline{F} = q\overline{E} \tag{5-1.1}$$

The electrostatic field is conservative, that is, it has zero curl, and can be expressed in terms of a scalar potential function

$$\overline{E} = -\nabla\Phi \tag{5-1.2}$$

Additionally, the divergence of $\overline{E}$ is related to the charge density in vacuum ρ by

$$\nabla \cdot \overline{E} = \frac{\rho}{\varepsilon_o} \tag{5-1.3}$$

where ε_o is the permittivity of free space or vacuum. Combining Eqs. (5-1.2) and

(5-1.3), we find that the potential function satisfies Poisson's equation

$$\nabla^2\Phi = -\frac{\rho}{\varepsilon_o} \tag{5-1.4}$$

This result shows that the solution of electrostatic field problems will involve solutions of Poisson's equation, or Laplace's equation where $\rho = 0$. This means that all of the techniques discussed in Chaps. 3 and 4 are applicable in the solution of electrostatic field problems.

From prior considerations, we can write the solution for Φ in unbounded space due to a volume distribution of charge

$$\Phi(\bar{r}) = \int_V \frac{\rho(\bar{r}')\, dV'}{4\pi\varepsilon_o|\bar{r}-\bar{r}'|} \tag{5-1.5}$$

For a surface charge distribution, the solution for Φ is

$$\Phi(\bar{r}) = \int_S \frac{\rho_s(\bar{r}')\, dS'}{4\pi\varepsilon_o|\bar{r}-\bar{r}'|} \tag{5-1.6}$$

An integral solution for $\bar{E}$ can be obtained by taking the gradient of Eq. (5-1.5)

$$\bar{E}(\bar{r}) = -\nabla\Phi = -\int_V \frac{\rho(\bar{r}')}{4\pi\varepsilon_o} \nabla\left(\frac{1}{|\bar{r}-\bar{r}'|}\right) dV'$$

where the operator ∇ operates only on $\bar{r}$. Also $|\bar{r}-\bar{r}'| = R$, so that $\nabla \frac{1}{R} = -\bar{a}_R/R^2$ and so

$$\bar{E}(\bar{r}) = \int_V \frac{\rho(\bar{r}')\, \bar{a}_R}{4\pi\varepsilon_o R^2}\, dV' \tag{5-1.7}$$

Similarly, from Eq. (5-1.6) for the surface charge distribution

$$\bar{E}(\bar{r}) = \int_S \frac{\rho_s(\bar{r}')\, \bar{a}_R}{4\pi\varepsilon_o R^2}\, dS' \tag{5-1.8}$$

In practice, it is usually easier to evaluate Φ first and then find $\bar{E}$ from Eq. (5-1.2) than to evaluate Eq. (5-1.7). This conclusion results because Φ involves the solution of an integral with scalar integrand whereas the solution for $\bar{E}$ requires evaluating an integral with a vector integrand.

The scalar potential Φ associated with an electric field has a physical interpretation; it represents the work done in moving a unit charge from a point of zero potential to the point with potential Φ. Consider the work done in moving a charge q from a point P_1 with potential Φ_1 to a point P_2 with potential Φ_2 along an arbitrary path C, as in Fig. 5-1.1. The work done to overcome the force $q\bar{E}$ exerted by the electric field is given by the integral along the path C of the component of the force along the path. This is

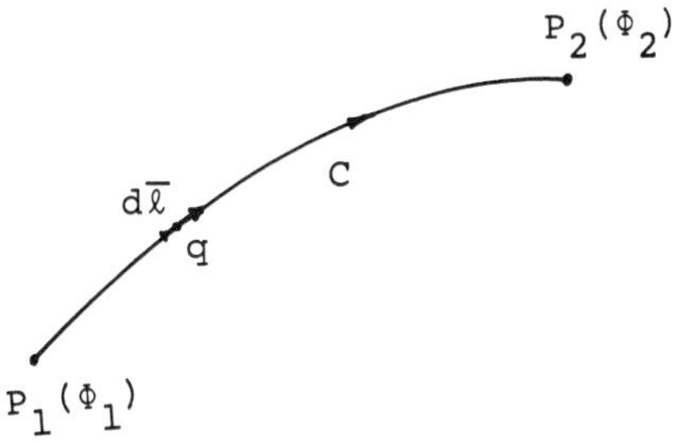

Figure 5-1.1. A point charge moved along a path C.

$$W = \int_{P_1}^{P_2} (-q\bar{E}) \cdot d\bar{\ell}$$

Replace $\bar{E}$ by $-\nabla\Phi$, and noting that $\nabla\Phi \cdot d\bar{\ell} = (d\Phi/d\ell)\, d\ell = d\Phi$ we find that

$$W = \int_{P_1}^{P_2} q\, d\Phi = q(\Phi_2 - \Phi_1) \tag{5-1.9}$$

This result shows that the difference in potential between two points in an electrostatic field is a measure of the work done in moving a unit charge between these two points. Moreover, we see that the final integral in Eq. (5-1.9) is independent of the path C connecting points P_1 and P_2.

If the integral of $d\Phi$ is carried out around a closed path, the net work done is zero. It is this property that establishes that the electrostatic field is a *conservative field*. This property is equivalent to saying that the curl of $\bar{E}$ is zero ($\nabla \times \bar{E} = 0$).

5-2. Electrostatic Field due to Simple Sources

The most elementary source for the electric field is a point charge Q located at some point $\bar{r}'$. Such a point source produces an electric field, as derived from Coulomb's law, or from Eq. (5-1.7),

$$\bar{E} = \frac{Q}{4\pi\varepsilon_o R^2}\bar{a}_R \tag{5-2.1}$$

If the charges are located inside a medium with an associated permittivity ε, then we must substitute ε for ε_o. The relation between ε and ε_o is considered in some detail in Sec. 5-5. For a collection of point charges Q_i at positions specified by position vectors $\bar{r}_i'$ as in Fig. 5-2.1 the field can be found by using the principle of linear superposition, thus

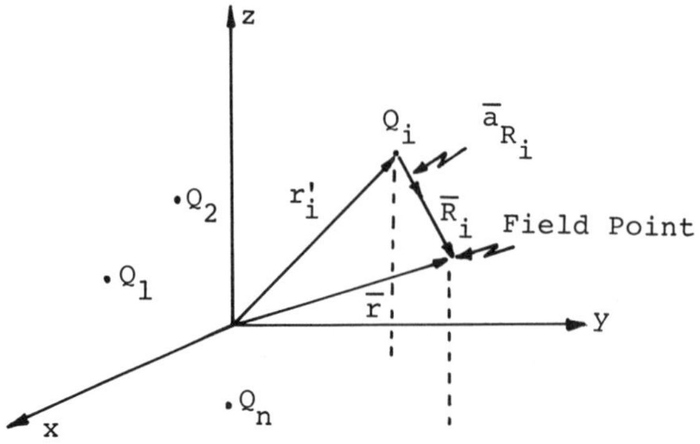

Figure 5-2.1. A collection of N point charges.

$$\bar{E} = \sum_{i=1}^{N} \frac{Q_i \, \bar{a}_{R_i}}{4\pi\varepsilon_o R_i^2} \tag{5-2.2}$$

where $R_i = |\bar{r}-\bar{r}_i'| = [(x-x_i')^2 + (y-y_i')^2 + (z-z_i')^2]^{1/2}$, and $\bar{a}_{R_i}$ is a unit vector directed from the ith charge to the field point. The corresponding scalar potential from a single point charge is given by

$$\Phi = \frac{Q}{4\pi\varepsilon_o R}$$

and for N point charges, as in Fig. 5-2.1, by superposition

$$\Phi = \sum_{i=1}^{N} \frac{Q_i}{4\pi\varepsilon_o R_i} \tag{5-2.3}$$

The negative gradient of this expression yields the result in Eq. (5-2.2).

Another elementary source of importance is the infinitely long line source having a charge density ρ_ℓ per meter, as in Fig. 5-2.2. To find the electric field intensity, we use Gauss' law. The flux through the cylindrical surface shown is

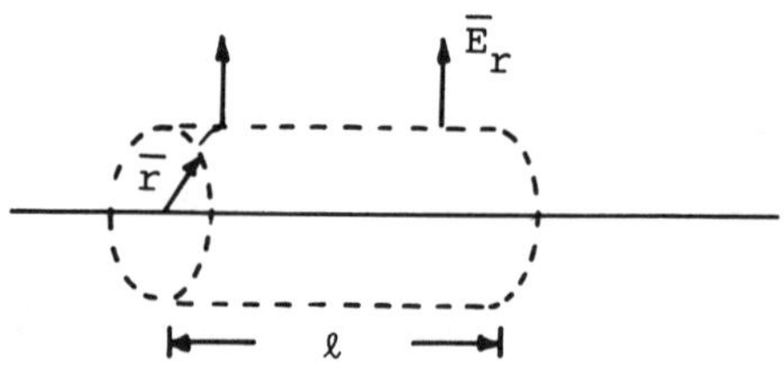

Figure 5-2.2. The infinite line source.

$2\pi r \ell E_r$, and this must equal the enclosed charge $\rho_\ell \ell$ divided by ε_o. Because of symmetry, the field is only a function of the variable r. Thus for the line source

$$E_r = \frac{\rho_\ell}{2\pi r \varepsilon_o} \tag{5-2.4}$$

and the corresponding potential is given by

$$\Phi = -\int_1^r E_r\, dr = -\int_1^r \frac{\rho_\ell dr}{2\pi r \varepsilon_o} = -\frac{\rho_\ell}{2\pi\varepsilon_o} \ln r \tag{5-2.5}$$

since $E_r = -\partial\Phi/\partial r$. The reference or datum of potential in this equation has been arbitrarily chosen as the potential at the surface $r = 1$. The point at infinity cannot be chosen because Φ becomes infinite when $r = \infty$ because of the infinite extent of the line source.

5-3. Conducting Bodies in Electrostatic Fields

X-ray and other studies reveal that most metals are crystalline in structure. This means that they consist of a space array of atoms or molecules (strictly speaking, ions) built up by regular repetition in three dimensions of some fundamental structural unit. Depending upon the metal, at least one, sometimes two, and in a few cases, three electrons per atom are free to move throughout the interior of the metal under the action of applied forces. Thus a metal is visualized as a region containing a periodic three-dimensional array of heavy, tightly bound ions, permeated with a swarm of electrons that may move about quite freely. This is known as the *electron-gas* concept of a metal. However, the space average net charge density is zero in the metal. The electrons are in incessant motion owing to the fact that the ions are in a state of agitation due to the thermal agitation of the atoms, and it is assumed that the electrons share the random velocity of thermal agitation of the ions. The average drift of the electrons is zero under the action of the thermal motion alone.

As has already been noted in Exs. 4-3.4 and 4-4.1, when a conducting body is placed in an electrostatic field, a redistribution of the electrons will occur in such a manner that the resultant induced electric field will cancel the applied electric field everywhere within and also tangent to the surface of the body. The electric field must vanish within the body for static equilibrium. That is, for a static electric field the charge density must be independent of time, and the net force (field) acting must be zero, otherwise the charges will be in motion.

Refer to Fig. 5-3.1 which illustrates an initially uncharged conductor that has been placed in an applied field $\overline{E}_o$. Because of the applied field $\overline{E}_o$ the charge will redistribute itself on the surface of the conductor in the manner shown in Fig. 5-3.1b. In the interior of the conductor, the total field is zero, otherwise there

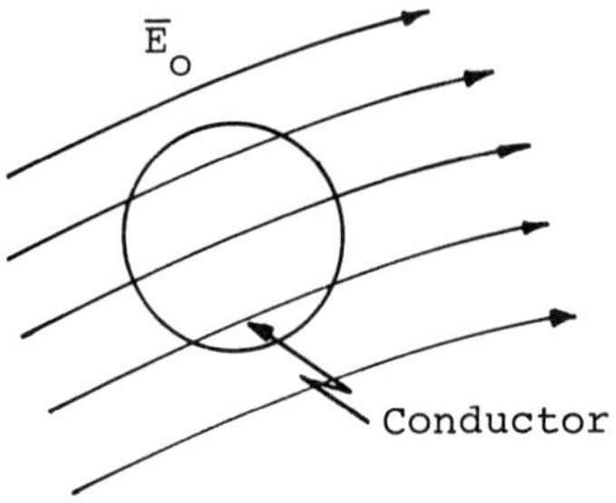

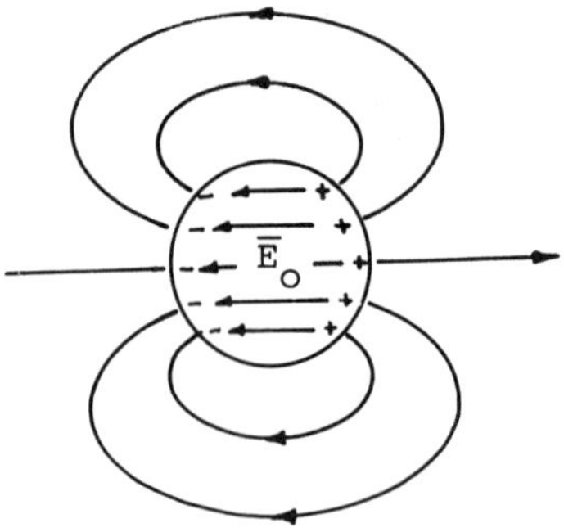

Figure 5-3.1. (a) Conducting body in an applied field $\overline{E}_o$. (b) The resultant induced charge and field.

will be a flow of charge. If the conducting body were originally neutral, it will remain neutral since the charge is only redistributed. There is no free charge density in the interior, i.e., the induced charge is located on the surface only. If the conductor were originally charged with a total charge Q, then the resultant field is that produced by Q acting alone plus the applied field $\overline{E}_o$ and the induced field. This result follows by superposition principle. The redistributed charges alters the external field in the manner illustrated in Figs. 4-3.5 and 4-4.2.

An exception to the foregoing situation occurs in the case of steady state electric currents. In this case the electric field inside the conductor will not be zero, although the charge density will still be zero. However, a nonzero electric field can be maintained only by having some external source, such as a battery, that will continually replace the charge that is flowing out of the body as the current. We will discuss the current field in more detail in a later section. For the present, we will consider only the case where charge flow (current) cannot exist.

Because there can be no flow of charge in an isolated conductor, the total electric field will have a zero tangential component ($\overline{E} \times \overline{n} = 0$) at the surface of the conductor. This means that the potential will also have a zero gradient along the surface, and thus the conductor must be at a constant potential. The normal component of the electric field at the surface is readily related to the surface charge density by Gauss' law. In this connection, refer to Fig. 5-3.2 and let us apply Gauss' law to a small coin-shaped volume with disk-shaped surfaces placed on adjacent sides of the conductor surface. The outward flux of $\overline{E}$ is $E_n \Delta S$ and must equal $\rho_s \Delta S/\varepsilon_o$. From this

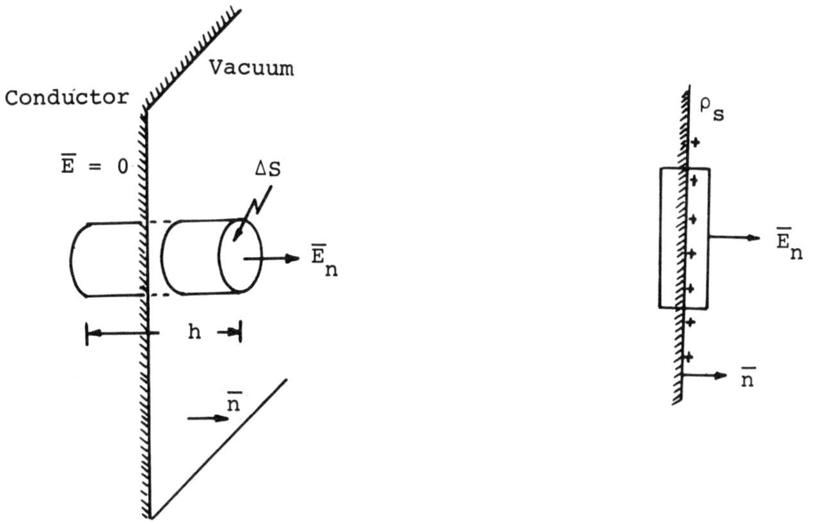

Figure 5-3.2. Electric field normal to a conductor.

$$E_n = \overline{n} \cdot \overline{E} = \frac{\rho_s}{\varepsilon_o} = -\frac{\partial \Phi}{\partial n}$$

where ρ_s is the density of surface charge. Thus the boundary conditions over the surface of the conductor are

$$\overline{E} \times \overline{n} = 0 \qquad \text{a)}$$

$$\overline{E} \cdot \overline{n} = \frac{\rho_s}{\varepsilon_o} = -\frac{\partial \Phi}{\partial n} \qquad \text{b)} \qquad (5\text{-}3.1)$$

The following example will apply the concepts discussed above.

Example 5-3.1. Find the charge induced on the inside surface of a spherical conducting enclosure due to a small electric dipole (two equal and opposite charges

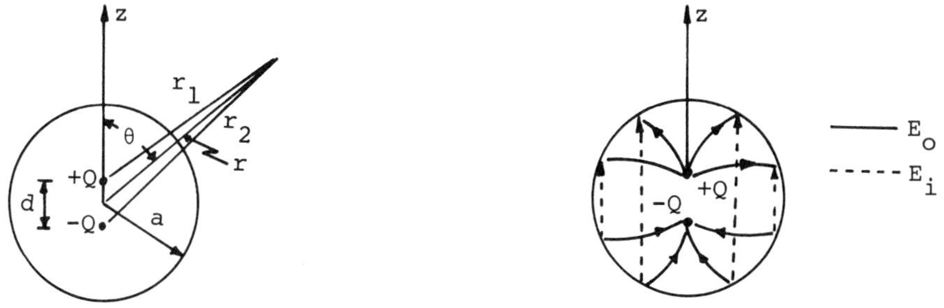

Figure 5-3.3. A dipole inside a conducting sphere.

a very small distance d apart) placed at the origin, as shown in Fig. 5-3.3.

Solution. In the absence of the sphere, the dipole gives rise to a potential

$$\Phi_o = \frac{Q}{4\pi\varepsilon_o}\left(\frac{1}{r_1} - \frac{1}{r_2}\right) = \frac{Q}{4\pi\varepsilon_o}\left(\frac{r_2-r_1}{r_1 r_2}\right) \doteq \frac{Qd\cos\theta}{4\pi\varepsilon_o r^2} \tag{5-3.2}$$

since $r_2-r_1 \doteq d\cos\theta$ for d very small, and also $r_1 r_2$ can be replaced by r^2 with negligible error. The primary field set up by the dipole is [see in Appendix I, Eq. (1-4.9) for the gradient in spherical coordinates]

$$\overline{E}_o = -\nabla\Phi_o = \frac{Qd}{4\pi\varepsilon_o r^3}(2\cos\theta\,\overline{a}_r + \sin\theta\,\overline{a}_\theta) \tag{5-3.3}$$

When the conducting spherical shell surrounds the dipole, the primary electric field will induce a charge distribution on the inner surface of the sphere such that the total resultant electric field tangent to the conducting surface will vanish. The induced field can be expressed as $-\nabla\Phi_i$ where Φ_i is the solution of Laplace's equation. Since Φ_o is independent of the azimuthal angle ϕ, the induced potential will also be independent of ϕ. In addition Φ_i must be finite at the origin. As a result, the general solution for Φ_i can be expressed in the form (see Sec. 4-4)

$$\Phi_i = \sum_{m=0}^{\infty} C_m P_m(\cos\theta)\, r^m$$

where $P_m(\cos\theta)$ is the Legendre polynomial. We shall express Φ_o as

$$\Phi_o = \frac{Qd}{4\pi\varepsilon_o} r^{-2} P_1(\cos\theta)$$

since $P_1(\cos\theta) = \cos\theta$. It is apparent that the boundary conditions at r = a can be taken care of with only the first term in the series for Φ_i; so all C_m except C_1 must be zero (the orthogonality of the P_m functions also establishes this result, as in Ex. 4-3.1). Therefore

$$\Phi_i = C_1 r\cos\theta$$

and the induced field is

$$\overline{E}_i = -\nabla\Phi_i = -C_1\cos\theta\,\overline{a}_r + C_1\sin\theta\,\overline{a}_\theta = -C_1\overline{a}_z \tag{5-3.4}$$

since $\overline{a}_z = \overline{a}_r\cos\theta - \overline{a}_\theta\sin\theta$. The induced field is seen to be uniform and in the Z-direction. To make the total tangential field vanish at r = a, we require that

$$\overline{a}_\theta \cdot (\overline{E}_o + \overline{E}_i) = 0, \qquad r = a$$

which gives

$$C_1 = -\frac{Qd}{4\pi\varepsilon_o a^3}$$

By Eq. 5-3.1b the induced charge on the sphere has a density given by

$$\rho_s = -\varepsilon_o E_r = \varepsilon_o \frac{\partial}{\partial r}(\Phi_o + \Phi_i)\Big|_{r=a} = -\frac{Qd}{4\pi a^3}\cos\theta \tag{5-3.5}$$

The total induced charge is

$$Q_s = -\frac{Qd}{4\pi a^3}\int_0^{2\pi}\int_0^{\pi}\cos\theta\, a^2 \sin\theta\, d\theta\, d\phi = 0$$

Outside of the sphere the induced charge sets up a dipole field equal to the negative of the field produced by the dipole at the origin, but the total field for r = a is zero (see Prob. 5-3.2).

ΔΔΔ

5-4. Electrostatic Shielding

The behavior of conducting bodies in an electrostatic field (Ex. 5-3.1 is an example) is important in connection with electrostatic shielding. Refer to Fig. 5-4.1. Illustrated are two conductors S_1 and S_2 which are maintained at potentials V_1 and V_2 relative to ground. The term ground denotes a common potential reference point and does not necessarily mean a physical ground. It could, for example, be a large conducting plate or simply the laboratory benches, walls, floor, etc. The ground is always considered to represent an infinite source or sink of charge.

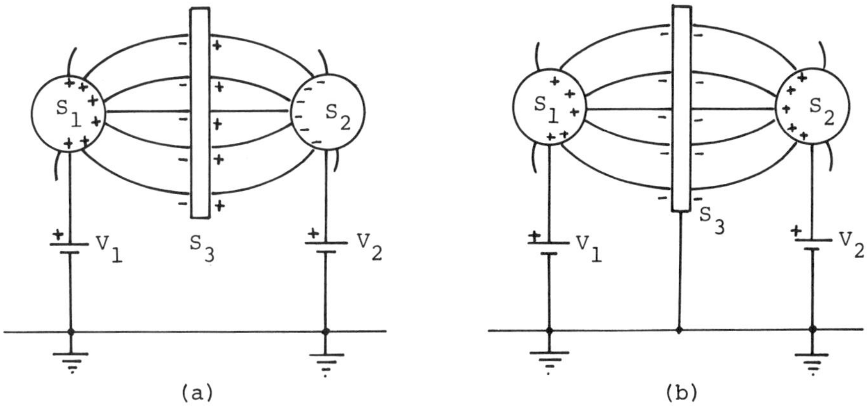

Figure 5-4.1. (a) An ungrounded conductor which is ineffective as a shield. (b) A grounded conductor which shields S_2 from S_1.

We wish to consider means for shielding S_2 from S_1, which means that there should be no electric field lines from S_1 terminating on S_2. If we place a third conducting body S_3, such as a plane, between S_1 and S_2 as in Fig. 5-4.1a but leave S_3 ungrounded, then S_3 is ineffective as a shield. The reason is that the field lines from S_1 will terminate on induced charges on S_3, and will at the same time, induce charges of opposite sign that will give rise to field lines extending from S_3 to S_2. The net effect is as though the field lines from S_1 continued directly to S_2. The potential of S_3 in this case will float at a value intermediate between that of S_1 and S_2. Also S_3 will remain electrically neutral.

To obtain an effective shield, S_3 must be grounded. If all of the field lines from S_1 terminate on S_3 (or infinity or ground) then S_2 is no longer affected by the potential of S_1 since the potential of S_3 is no longer floating. Even if some of the field lines from S_1 still terminate on S_2 a degree of shielding is still obtained. For the case when S_3 is grounded, it will no longer remain neutral since it can receive the required amount of negative charge from the ground reservoir on which to terminate the field lines from S_1 and S_2. Consequently, we see that the essential requirement for an effective shield is that it provide an extension of the ground into a region between the two bodies to be shielded so as to provide a suitable termination for the field lines coming from the two bodies. Precisely these conditions account for the action of the grounded shield grid which surrounds the plate electrode in pentode vacuum tubes. This provides electrostatic isolation between the plate and the other electrodes (control grid, suppressor grid) of the tube.

5-5. Dipoles and Dipole Distributions

As noted in connection with Ex. 5-3.1 two point charges of equal magnitude but opposite sign and separated by a small distance d constitute an electric dipole. The electric dipole is of basic importance in the theory of dielectric material, which is discussed in the next section. Figure 5-5.1 illustrates an electric dipole, for which the resultant potential and electric field are those given in Ex. 5-3.1.

The dipole potential given by Eq. (5-3.2) and repeated here for convenience is

$$\Phi = \frac{Qd \cos \theta}{4\pi\varepsilon_o r^2} \tag{5-5.1}$$

The product Qd is called the *dipole moment*, and is specified by the letter p. Since the dipole has a direction associated with it, the dipole moment is a vector quantity which, by definition, is chosen to have the direction of the line from -Q to +Q. In vector form

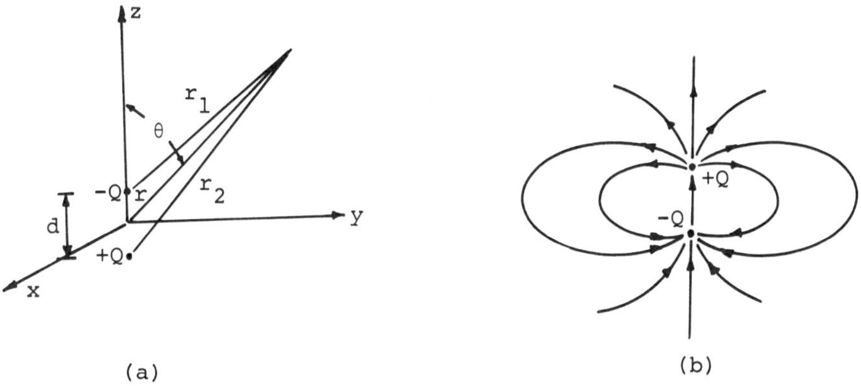

Figure 5-5.1. (a) The electric dipole. (b) The electric field of a dipole.

$$\bar{p} = Qd\,\bar{a}_z \qquad \text{(Coulomb-m)}$$

If we also note that $\bar{a}_z \cdot \bar{a}_r = \cos\theta$, we can express Eq. (5-5.1) in the form

$$\Phi = \frac{\bar{p}\cdot\bar{a}_r}{4\pi\varepsilon_o r^2} = \frac{p\cos\theta}{4\pi\varepsilon_o r^2} \tag{5-5.2}$$

The electric field is given by

$$\bar{E} = -\nabla\Phi = \frac{2p\cos\theta}{4\pi\varepsilon_o r^3}\,\bar{a}_r + \frac{p\sin\theta}{4\pi\varepsilon_o r^2}\,\bar{a}_\theta \tag{5-5.3}$$

and this is the analytic description of the field illustrated in Fig. 5-5.1b.

If we have a dipole $\bar{p}$ located at a point specified by the position vector $\bar{r}'$, then the expression for the potential becomes

$$\Phi = \frac{\bar{p}\cdot\bar{a}_R}{4\pi\varepsilon_o R^2} \tag{5-5.4}$$

where $\bar{a}_R$ is a unit vector pointing from the dipole to the field point, and $R = |\bar{r}-\bar{r}'|$ as usual.

Consider now a volume distribution of dipoles, as shown in Fig. 5-5.2a. Let the number of dipoles in a volume element $\Delta V'$ be so great that the limit

$$\lim_{\Delta V'\to dV'} \frac{\sum_n \bar{p}_n}{\Delta V'} = \bar{P} \qquad \left(\frac{\text{Coulomb-m}}{m^3} = \frac{\text{Coulomb}}{m^2}\right) \tag{5-5.5}$$

is independent of the exact size or shape of the differential volume element dV. The sum $\sum_n p_n$ is the total net dipole moment of all of the dipoles in $\Delta V'$, and $\bar{P}$ is the average *dipole moment per unit volume* or the *dipole density* and it is shown in

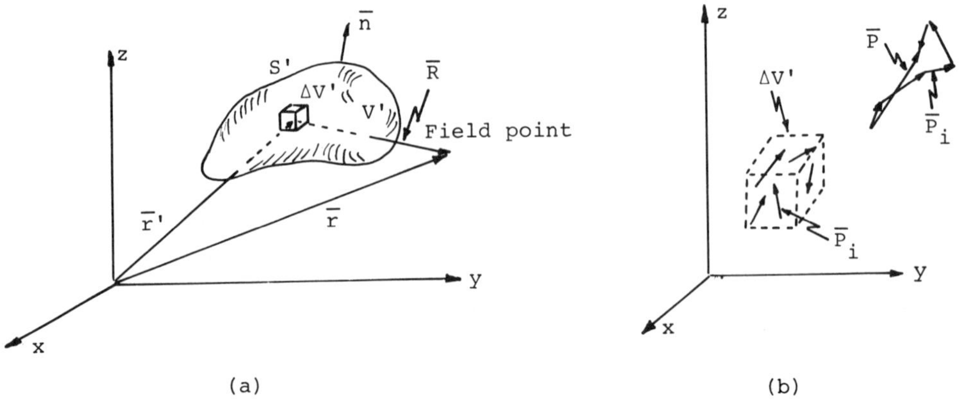

Figure 5-5.2. A volume distribution of dipoles.

Fig. 5-5.2b. When these conditions are valid, we can properly regard the discrete dipoles as equivalent to a smeared-out continuous distribution of dipoles with density $\overline{P}$. Clearly, the dipoles in the volume element dV' will contribute an amount

$$d\Phi = \frac{\overline{P} \cdot \overline{a}_R}{4\pi\varepsilon_o R^2} dV'$$

to the total potential. Therefore, by superposition, from all of the dipoles we get

$$\Phi = \int_V \frac{\overline{P} \cdot \overline{a}_R}{4\pi\varepsilon_o R^2} dV' \tag{5-5.6}$$

The expression for Φ can be recast into a form analogous to that for the potential arising from a volume and a surface distribution of charge. To carry out this transformation, we use the vector expansion

$$\nabla \cdot (u\overline{v}) = u\nabla \cdot \overline{v} + \overline{v} \cdot \nabla u$$

Also, we note that $\overline{a}_R/R^2 = -\nabla(1/R) = \nabla'(1/R)$ $(\nabla' = \overline{a}_x\, \partial/\partial x' + \overline{a}_y\, \partial/\partial y' + \overline{a}_z\, \partial/\partial z')$. Next consider $\nabla' \cdot (\overline{P}/R)$ which can be expanded to give

$$\nabla' \cdot (\frac{\overline{P}}{R}) = \frac{1}{R} \nabla' \cdot \overline{P} + \overline{P} \cdot \nabla'(\frac{1}{R})$$

This expansion is combined with Eq. (5-5.6), with the result

$$\Phi = \int_V \frac{1}{4\pi\varepsilon_o} \nabla' \cdot (\frac{\overline{P}}{R})\, dV' + \int_V \frac{-\nabla' \cdot \overline{P}}{4\pi\varepsilon_o R} dV'$$

which is written

$$\Phi = \oint_S \frac{\overline{P} \cdot \overline{n}}{4\pi\varepsilon_o R} dS' + \int_V \frac{-\nabla' \cdot \overline{P}}{4\pi\varepsilon_o R} dV' \tag{5-5.7}$$

where the first volume integral has been transformed to a surface integral by using the divergence theorem and where $\overline{n}$ is the unit vector perpendicular to the surface S. We now write Eq. (5-5.7) in the form

$$\Phi = \oint_S \frac{\rho_{ps} dS'}{4\pi\varepsilon_o R} + \int_V \frac{\rho_p}{4\pi\varepsilon_o R} dV' \tag{5-5.8}$$

which shows that the final expression for Φ is that due to an effective volume density of charge ρ_p given by

$$\rho_p = -\nabla' \cdot \overline{P} \tag{5-5.9a}$$

and a surface density of charge given by

$$\rho_{ps} = \overline{P} \cdot \overline{n} \tag{5-5.9b}$$

The result expressed by Eqs. (5-5.8) and (5-5.9) can be understood on a physical basis. Refer to Fig. 5-5.3 which shows a distribution of dipoles. It is apparent that in regions where $\overline{P}$ is uniform, the positive charge is effectively cancelled by the negative charge of an adjacent dipole. In regions where P is not uniform, complete cancellation does not take place and a net effective amount of charge with density ρ_p given by Eq. (5-5.9a) remains and produces part of the potential Φ. Likewise at the boundary S' of V', the charges on the ends of the dipoles normal to the surface are not cancelled because there are no dipoles outside S'. An effective surface layer of charge ρ_{ps} given by $\overline{P} \cdot \overline{n}$ is produced and contributes the remaining part of Eq. (5-5.7) for the potential.

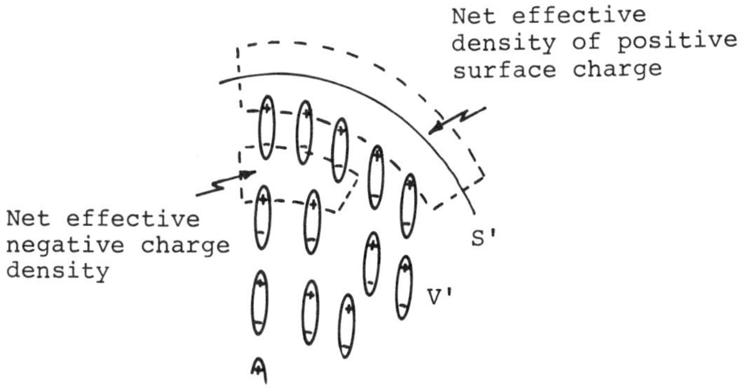

Figure 5-5.3. A distribution of dipoles showing the effective volume and surface charge distributions.

The expression Eq. (5-5.7) and its interpretation in terms of equivalent polarization charge distributions will be used in the next section dealing with the behavior of dielectric mediums.

5-6. Dielectric Materials

A dielectric material is an insulating material which exhibits an electric dipole polarization under the influence of an electric field. Examples of commonly occurring dielectric materials are glass, mica, plastics, paper, wax, gases, etc. The macroscopic (bulk) behavior of dielectric materials acted upon by an electric field can be described in terms of the resultant electric dipole polarization.

For the purpose of this discussion an atom will be regarded as consisting of a positive charged core (nucleus) surrounded by a cloud of electrons. In the absence of an applied electric field, the center of gravity of the negative and positive charges normally coincide so that the atom has a zero dipole moment. When an external electric field is applied the effective centers of the negative and positive charge distributions are displaced and a net dipole moment is induced. This type of polarization mechanism is referred to as *electronic* or *induced* polarization, and is illustrated schematically in Fig. 5-6.1a.

In substances involving ionic bonds, another polarization mechanism comes into effect. A molecule involving an ionic bond is formed when two atoms share one or more valence electrons. In other words, an atom lacking one or more valence electrons constitutes a positive ion which will bind itself to a negative ion, which is an atom having an excess number of valence electrons. Normally, the molecule involving the ionic bond does not have a dipole moment. However, the application of an electric field will cause a separation of the positive and negative ion and thus produce a dipole moment. This kind of polarization is called *ionic* polarization.

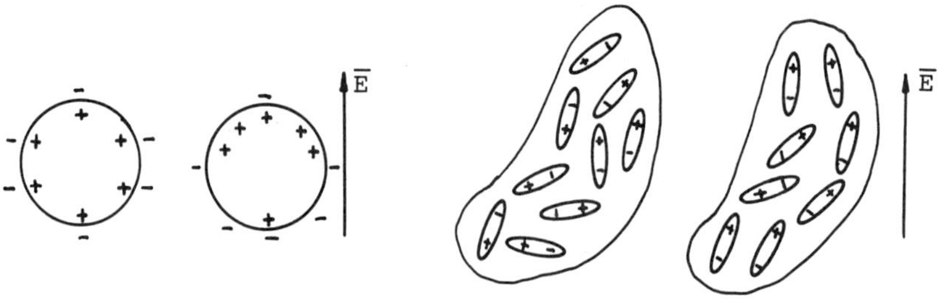

(a) (b)

Figure 5-6.1. (a) Electronic polarization. (b) Orientational polarization.

A third important polarization mechanism is that associated with a class of substances known as *polar* materials; water is a well known example. Polar substances involve molecules which have a permanent dipole moment. These dipoles are randomly oriented in the material so that no net macroscopic dipole polarization is exhibited in the absence of an electric field. When an electric field is applied, the effect is a torque on the dipoles to cause an increase in the number that are aligned in the direction of the field and so produce a net macroscopic dipole polarization in the medium. The alignment of the dipoles is always resisted by the thermal energy (kinetic energy of motion) of the molecules which acts to randomize the dipole polarization. As a result, the degree of polarization in a polar substance shows a strong dependence on temperature. The polarization taking place in polar substances is called *orientational* polarization, and is illustrated in Fig. 5-6.1b. In many materials all three polarizaiton mechanisms are often present.

For electric field strengths that are commonly encountered, it is found experimentally that most materials exhibit a polarization which is directly proportional to the electric field $\overline{E}$. Also, most materials are *isotropic*, which means that the induced dipole polarization is in the same direction as $\overline{E}$. For such materials, the dipole polarization density $\overline{P}$ can be related to $\overline{E}$ by

$$\overline{P} = \varepsilon_o \chi_e \overline{E} \qquad \chi = \frac{NP^2}{3\varepsilon_o kT} \tag{5-6.1}$$

where χ_e is a dimensionless constant called the *electric susceptibility* of the medium. If the material is *homogeneous*, then χ_e is the same at all points in the medium, i.e., it is not a function of x,y,z.

The polarization of the medium constitutes a secondary or induced source for the electric field. The resultant induced field may be determined in terms of the equivalent polarization charges with volume density $\rho_p = -\nabla \cdot \overline{P}$ and surface density $\rho_{ps} = \overline{P} \cdot \overline{n}$ as described in Sec. 5-5. In particular, the divergence of $\overline{E}$ is given by

$$\nabla \cdot \overline{E} = \frac{\rho + \rho_p}{\varepsilon_o} = \frac{\rho}{\varepsilon_o} - \frac{\nabla \cdot \overline{P}}{\varepsilon_o} \tag{5-6.2}$$

in the interior of the dielectric. Note that both the true free charge ρ and the effective polarization charge ρ_p must be included as sources for $\overline{E}$. The polarization charge ρ_p is called bound charge since these are not free to flow through the material, being bound, in fact, to the atoms or molecules involved. We may rewrite Eq. (5-6.2) in the form

$$\nabla \cdot (\varepsilon_o \overline{E} + \overline{P}) = \rho \tag{5-6.3}$$

In practice, it is not convenient to have to take the polarization $\overline{P}$ into account explicitly. This is avoided by introducing the field vector $\overline{D}$ called the *electric displacement* vector and defined by

$$\overline{D} = \varepsilon_o\overline{E} + \overline{P} \qquad (\text{Coulomb/m}^2) \tag{5-6.4}$$

The source for $\overline{D}$ is the true free charge density ρ only, since Eq. (5-6.3) together with (5-6.4) gives

$$\nabla \cdot \overline{D} = \rho \tag{5-6.5}$$

When Eq. (5-6.1) applies, we can also write

$$\overline{D} = \varepsilon_o(1 + \chi_e)\ \overline{E} = \varepsilon_o\varepsilon_r\overline{E} = \varepsilon\overline{E} \tag{5-6.6}$$

where $\varepsilon = \varepsilon_o(1 + \chi_e)$ is called the electric *permittivity* of the medium (units of Farad per meter) and $\varepsilon_r = \varepsilon/\varepsilon_o$ is called the *relative permittivity* or *dielectric constant* (see Table 5-6.1). Since the relative permittivity of a material is a parameter that can easily be measured experimentally, the use of the displacement field $\overline{D}$ and the constitutive relation, Eq. (5-6.6), is a very convenient practical way to take the polarization of a dielectric medium into account.

Table 5-6.1. Relative Permittivity of Selected Materials

Medium	ε_r	Medium	ε_r
Vacuum	1	Liquids	
Gases 1 Atm.		Castor oil	4.67
Air	1.000590	Water 0^oC	88.0
H_2	1.000264	Water 100^oC	48.0
Ne	1.000127	Solids	
0_2	1.000523	Glass	3.8-6.8
		Paraffin	2.1-2.5
		Quartz	3.7-4.1

The observant reader will have noted that although $\overline{D}$ as defined above takes account of the volume polarization charge ρ_p, nothing has been said so far about the surface polarization charge ρ_{ps}. The latter will, of course, also be important in the determination of the total electric field. The way in which the surface polarization charge is brought into the analysis is through a boundary condition on the normal component of the electric field at a dielectric interface. We examine this matter.

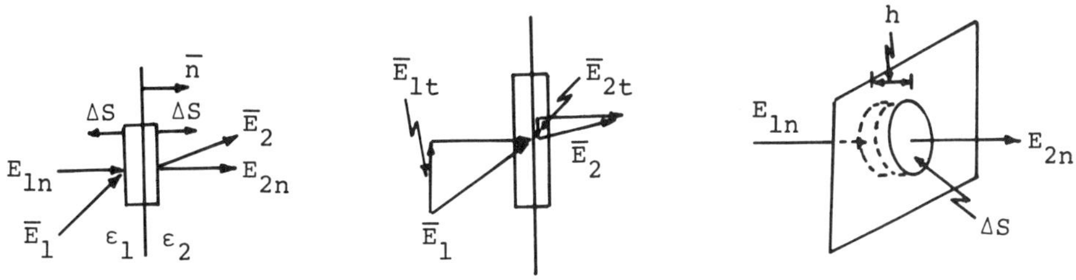

Figure 5-6.2. The boundary between two dielectric materials.

Consider the surface separating two different dielectric materials, as in Fig. 5-6.2. If we construct a coin-shaped box with a face on adjacent sides of the boundary and apply Gauss' law, we see that

$$(E_{2n} - E_{1n})\ \Delta S = \frac{\rho_{ps}\Delta S}{\varepsilon_o}$$

or

$$E_{2n} - E_{1n} = \frac{\rho_{ps}}{\varepsilon_o} \tag{5-6.7}$$

since the flux through the sides of the box is negligible when h is made very small. The polarization surface charge density ρ_{ps} has a contribution $\overline{P}_1 \cdot \overline{n} = P_{1n}$ from the polarization of medium 1, and a contribution $\overline{P}_2 \cdot (-\overline{n}) = -P_{2n}$ from the polarization of medium 2. In place of Eq. (5-6.7) we have the equivalent result

$$E_{2n} - E_{1n} = \frac{P_{1n} - P_{2n}}{\varepsilon_o}$$

or

$$\varepsilon_o E_{2n} + P_{2n} = \varepsilon_2 E_{2n} = \varepsilon_o E_{1n} + P_{1n} = \varepsilon_1 E_{1n}$$

since $P_n = \chi_e \varepsilon_o E_n$ and $(1 + \chi_e)\varepsilon_o = \varepsilon$. This equation states that the normal component of $\overline{D}$ is continuous across the boundary, since $D_n = \varepsilon E_n$. This is an expected result since $\nabla \cdot \overline{D} = \rho$, and if ρ is zero, the flux of D is continuous across the boundary. Thus the surface polarization charge is taken into account by the boundary conditions

$$\overline{n} \cdot \overline{D}_1 = \overline{n} \cdot \overline{D}_2 \quad \text{or} \quad n \cdot (\overline{D}_2 - \overline{D}_1) = 0 \tag{5-6.8}$$

which in turn implies a discontinuity in the normal component of the electric field.

For a field that is normal to the dielectric surface, the dielectric displacement vector is the same in the vacuum and inside the dielectric. Therefore by Eq. (5-6.4) we write

$$\varepsilon_o \overline{E}_o = \varepsilon_o \overline{E} + \overline{P}$$

from which

$$\overline{P} = \varepsilon_o (\overline{E}_o - \overline{E}) \qquad (5\text{-}6.9)$$

where $\overline{E}_o$ is the field in vacuum and $\overline{E}$ is the field in the dielectric slab. This relation shows that the polarization $\overline{P}$ is equal to the difference between the applied field $\overline{E}_o$ and the resultant field $\overline{E}$, multiplied by ε_o. This difference is due to the induced field $\overline{E}_i$ that opposes $\overline{E}_o$, where the induced field is produced by the surface polarization charges on the two sides of the slab. That is, we have that

$$\overline{E}_o - \overline{E} = -\overline{E}_i \quad \text{or} \quad \overline{E} = \overline{E}_o + \overline{E}_i$$

and

$$\overline{P} = -\varepsilon_o \overline{E}_i \qquad (5\text{-}6.10)$$

When we combine Eq. (5-6.4) with Eq. (5-6.6) we obtain

$$\overline{E} = \frac{\overline{P}}{\varepsilon - \varepsilon_o} = \frac{\overline{P}/\varepsilon_o}{\varepsilon_r - 1} = -\frac{E_i}{\varepsilon_r - 1} = E_o + E_i \qquad (5\text{-}6.11)$$

From this result we find that

$$\overline{E}_i = (-1 + \frac{1}{\varepsilon_r})\ \overline{E}_o \qquad (5\text{-}6.12)$$

which shows that $\overline{E}_i$ is always less than the applied field $\overline{E}_o$, and the resultant field $\overline{E}$ is not zero. Only in case of infinite permittivity is the induced field equal to the applied field, and no such dielectric material is known, but this is the approximation for a conductor. Often this permits a useful mathematical procedure for translating dielectric to conducting configurations.

Since $\overline{E}$ can still be derived from the negative gradient of a scalar potential even when dielectric material is present, and moreover, Φ will be a single-valued continuous function, it follows that the tangential component E_{1t} of the electric field in medium 1 must equal the tangential component E_{2t} in medium 2 at the boundary. This equality comes from the equality of the gradient of Φ along the boundary on adjacent sides of the boundary. Thus, in addition to Eq. (5-6.8) the additional boundary condition needed in order to properly join the solution for $\overline{E}$ in the two

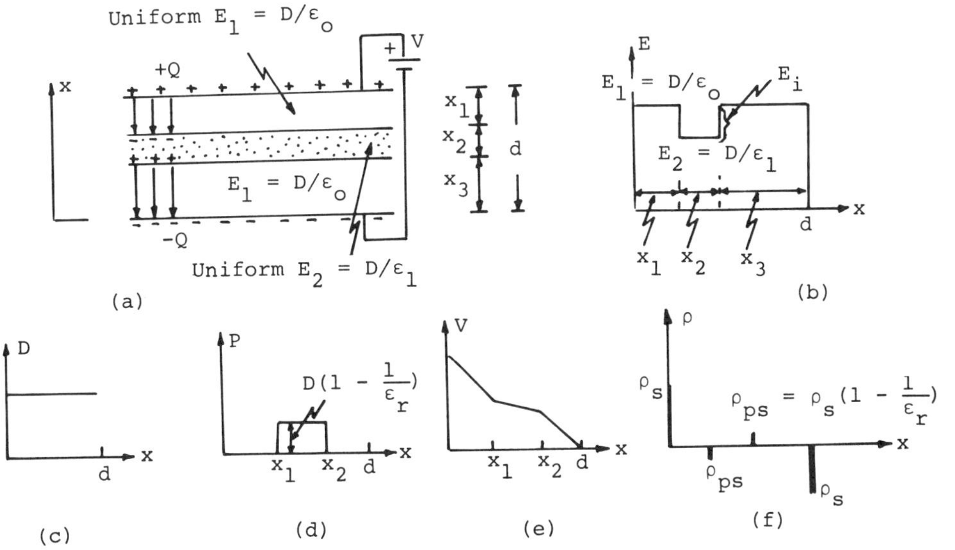

Figure 5-6.3. A dielectric slab in an electric field.

mediums at the common boundary is

$$E_{1t} = E_{2t} \quad \text{or} \quad \overline{n} \times (\overline{E}_2 - \overline{E}_1) = 0 \tag{5-6.13}$$

This is an expected result since $\nabla \times \overline{E} = 0$ for static fields (or equivalently, since $\oint \overline{E} \cdot d\overline{\ell} = 0$ around a closed path as shown in Fig. 5-6.2b) [compare these boundary conditions with those at the surface of a conductor (see Eq. (5-3.1)].

Example 5-6.1. A uniform dielectric slab is contained in a uniform electric field, as shown in Fig. 5-6.3a. Find the polarization charge inside the dielectric and also the surface charge. Specify the electric field distribution.

Solution. It is assumed that the dielectric is totally polarized. Because the dielectric is homogeneous, only the dipoles near the surface are important. That is, the volume distribution $\rho_p = 0$ yields $\nabla \cdot \overline{P} = 0$. This means that for the uniform dielectric $\overline{P}$ is everywhere constant in magnitude and normal to the slab surface.

In the free space region outside of the dielectric the field is $\overline{E}_1$, as shown. Because of the induced surface charges which arise from the alignment of the dipoles of the dielectric, an electric field is produced which is in a direction opposite to the external field. The surface charge density is

$$\rho_{ps} = \overline{P} \cdot \overline{n} = P_n$$

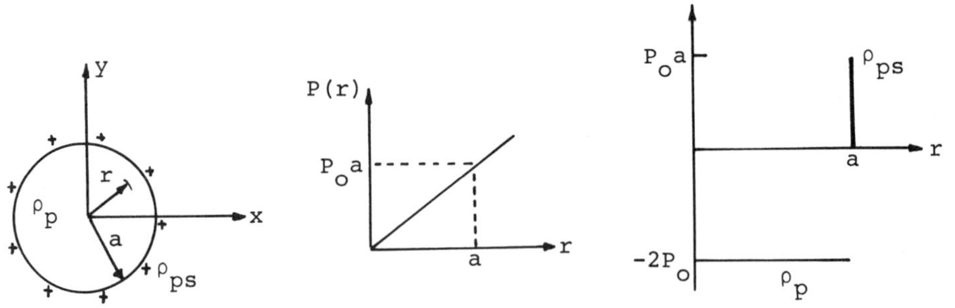

Figure 5-6.4. Polarized cylindrical slab.

As discussed in Eq. (5-6.7), the effect of the surface layer is a reduction in the electric field within the dielectric, with

$$\overline{E}_2 = \overline{E}_1 - \frac{\rho_{ps}}{\varepsilon_o}\overline{n}$$

or

$$\varepsilon_o E_1 = \varepsilon_o E_2 + P = \varepsilon E_2$$

which is simply that

$$\overline{D}_1 = \overline{D}_2$$

A sketch of the electric field distribution is shown in Fig. 5-6.3b. ΔΔΔ

Example 5-6.2. A cylindrical slab as shown in Fig. 5-6.4 possesses a polarization which varies linearly with the r-coordinate

$$\overline{P}(r) = \overline{a}_r P_o r \tag{5-6.14}$$

Find the polarization charge inside the slab and its surface charge.

Solution. Here the point variables are x,y,z, and according to Eq. (5-5.9a) the charge is given by

$$\rho_p = -\nabla \cdot \overline{P} = -\frac{1}{r}\frac{\partial}{\partial r}(rP_o r) = -2\,P_o \tag{5-6.15}$$

which shows that the polarization charge is constant. The polarization surface charge at r = a is found to be, using Eq. (5-5.9b),

$$\rho_{ps} = \overline{a}_r \cdot \overline{P} = P_o a$$

ΔΔΔ

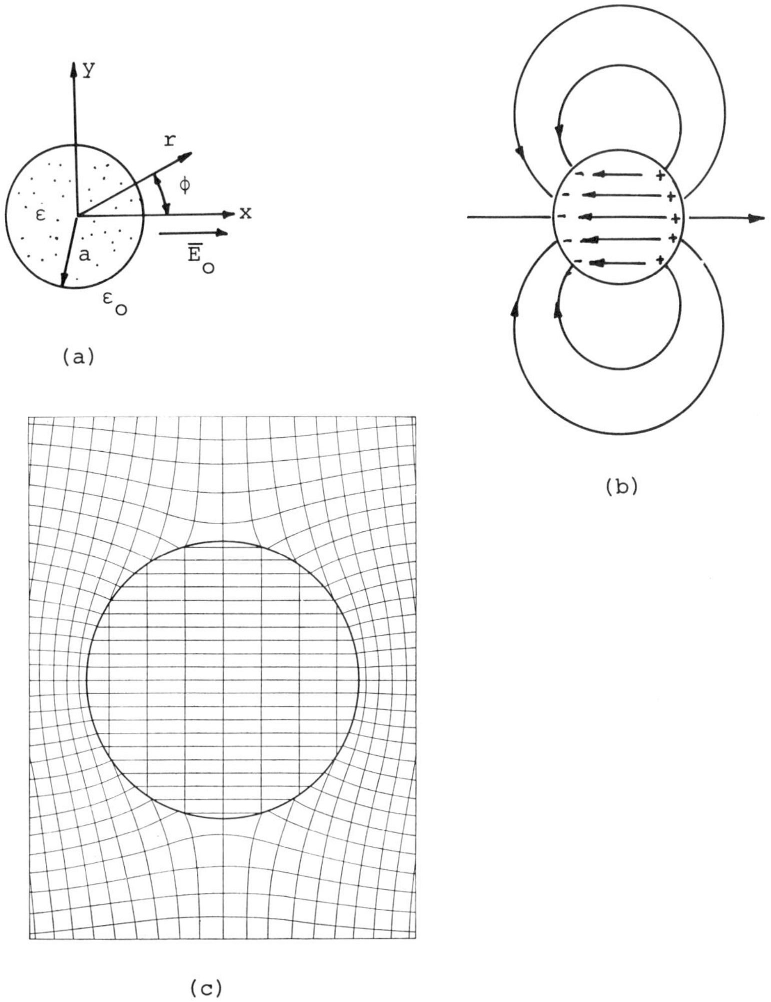

Figure 5-6.5. (a) A dielectric cylinder in a previously uniform applied field. (b) The induced field. (c) Field lines of the dielectric cylinder (from a drawing by Maxwell).

Example 5-6.3. Find the induced field and the induced polarization charge of an infinitely long dielectric cylinder of radius a placed in a previously uniform field $\overline{E}_o = E_o\overline{a}_x$, as shown in Fig. 5-6.5. This is the dielectric counterpart of Example 4-3.4.

Solution. The applied field arises from a potential

$$\Phi_o = -E_o x = -E_o r \cos \phi$$

The induced potential must satisfy Laplace's equation. But as shown in Sec. 4-3 in cylindrical coordinates with no Z-dependence, the appropriate solutions are of the form $r^n \cos n\phi$ and $r^{-n} \cos n\phi$ for any integer n. For the present problem all boundary conditions can be satisfied by the n = 1 solutions. The induced potential in the two regions r < a and r > a that will remain finite at r = 0 and r = ∞ will be

$$\Phi_i = Ar \cos \phi, \qquad r < a$$
$$= B \frac{1}{r} \cos \phi, \qquad r > a$$

But the total potential must be continuous at r = a, hence $B = Aa^2$. The total electric field is given, for r < a, by

$$\overline{E} = -\nabla(\Phi_0 + \Phi_i) = (E_0 - A) \cos \phi \, \overline{a}_r - (E_0 - A) \sin \phi \, \overline{a}_\phi$$

and for r > a, the field is

$$\overline{E} = (E_0 + \frac{Aa^2}{r^2}) \cos \phi \, \overline{a}_r - (E_0 - \frac{Aa^2}{r^2}) \sin \phi \, \overline{a}_\phi$$

At r = a the radial component of $\overline{D}$ must be continuous, and so we must have

$$\varepsilon(E_0 - A) \cos \phi = \varepsilon_0(E_0 + A) \cos \phi$$

which gives

$$A = \frac{\varepsilon - \varepsilon_0}{\varepsilon + \varepsilon_0} E_0$$

Our final solution for Φ_i and E_i is, therefore

$$\Phi_i = \frac{\varepsilon-\varepsilon_0}{\varepsilon+\varepsilon_0} E_0 r \cos \phi \qquad r \leq a$$
$$\Phi_i = \frac{\varepsilon-\varepsilon_0}{\varepsilon+\varepsilon_0} E_0 \frac{a^2}{r} \cos \phi \qquad r \geq a$$
$$\overline{E}_i = -\frac{\varepsilon-\varepsilon_0}{\varepsilon+\varepsilon_0} (\overline{a}_r \cos \phi - \overline{a}_\phi \sin \phi) \qquad r \leq a$$
$$\overline{E}_i = \frac{\varepsilon-\varepsilon_0}{\varepsilon+\varepsilon_0} E_0 \frac{a^2}{r^2} (\overline{a}_r \cos \phi + \overline{a}_\phi \sin \phi) \qquad r \geq a \tag{5-6.16}$$

We note that $\overline{E}_i$ for r < a can also be expressed as

$$\overline{E}_i = -\frac{\varepsilon-\varepsilon_0}{\varepsilon+\varepsilon_0} E_0 \overline{a}_x$$

which is seen to be uniform and acting in a direction to partially cancel the applied field. When ε becomes very large, E_i cancels E_o to give a zero field at the surface; hence the solution becomes identical to that for a conducting cylinder as already noted. [Compare Eqs. (5-6.16) with (4-3.29) and (4-3.30).] The volume polarization charge is zero since $-\nabla \cdot \overline{P} = -\nabla \cdot (\varepsilon_o \chi_e \overline{E}) = 0$ (note that $\overline{P}$ is determined by the total $\overline{E}$ field and not just the induced field, because χ_e was introduced to relate $\overline{P}$ to the total $\overline{E}$ in the medium). At the surface r = a the total radial field E_r is discontinuous by an amount equal to ρ_{ps}/ε_o. Hence

$$\frac{\rho_{ps}}{\varepsilon_o} = E_r\Big|_{a+} - E_r\Big|_{a-} = 2\,\frac{\varepsilon-\varepsilon_o}{\varepsilon+\varepsilon_o} E_o \cos\phi \tag{5-6.17}$$

as obtained from our earlier result for the total field. ΔΔΔ

Example 5-6.4. Find the polarization $\overline{P}$, the polarization charge density ρ_p and the polarization surface charge density ρ_{ps} when a charged cylinder of radius a having charge Q (Coulomb/unit length) is embedded in a dielectric medium.

Solution. Choose the center of the cylinder as the origin of a cylindrical coordinate system. By Gauss' law, the flux density inside the dielectric is readily found to be

$$\overline{D} = \frac{Q}{2\pi r}\,\overline{a}_r \tag{5-6.18}$$

The electric field intensity in the dielectric is then

$$\overline{E} = \frac{Q}{2\pi\varepsilon r}\,\overline{a}_r \tag{5-6.19}$$

and the polarization is, from Eq. (5-6.4)

$$\overline{P} = \overline{D} - \varepsilon_o\overline{E} = (\varepsilon-\varepsilon_o)\,\overline{E} = \left(1 - \frac{1}{\varepsilon_r}\right)\overline{D} \tag{5-6.20}$$

At distances larger than the radius of the cylinder $\rho = 0$ and $\nabla \cdot \overline{D} = 0$. Then by Eq. (5-6.20) $\nabla \cdot \overline{P} = 0$, which indicates that $\rho_p = 0$. However, there does exist a polarization charge density given by

$$\rho_{ps} = -\overline{a}_r \cdot \overline{P} = -\left(1 - \frac{1}{\varepsilon_r}\right)\rho_s \tag{5-6.21}$$

where

$$\rho_s = \frac{Q}{2\pi a}$$

is the surface charge density on the cylinder due to the free charges. ΔΔΔ

5-7. Capacitance

The word capacitance refers to the ability of two separated conducting bodies at different potentials to store electric charge. Refer to Fig. 5-7.1. Let the total charge on body S_1 be -Q and that on S_2 be +Q. If the potential difference between the two bodies is V, the capacitance between the two bodies is given by

$$C = \frac{Q}{V} \tag{5-7.1}$$

The configuration is called a *capacitor* and its capacity to store charge is called *capacitance*, this latter being measured in Farad. From the fact contained in the potential integral Eq. (5-1.5) that the potential is proportional to the charge, then the ratio Q/Φ is a constant that is determined only by the size and shape of the body. That is, the capacitance is a function of the geometry of the system alone.

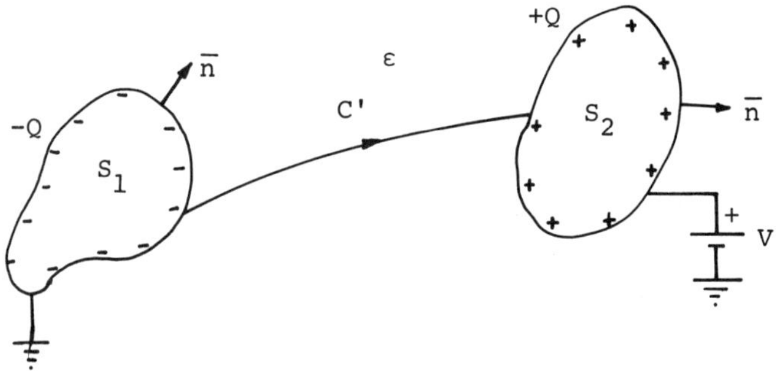

Figure 5-7.1. A capacitor.

In order to determine the capacitance between two bodies, it is necessary to know the electric field existing between the two bodies. When $\overline{E}$ is known, the total charge on S_2 is given by

$$Q = \oint_{S_2} \overline{D} \cdot \overline{n}\, dS = \oint_{S_2} \varepsilon\overline{E} \cdot \overline{n}\, dS \tag{5-7.2}$$

since the surface density of charge is $\rho_s = \overline{D} \cdot \overline{n} = \varepsilon\overline{E} \cdot \overline{n}$. The total charge on S_1 will be -Q since all of the field lines from S_2 will terminate on S_1 when there are no other conducting bodies present. The potential difference between S_1 and S_2 is given by (recall that $\overline{E} \cdot d\overline{\ell} = -\nabla\Phi \cdot d\overline{\ell} = -d\Phi$)

$$V_2 - V_1 = V = \int_{C'} \overline{E} \cdot d\overline{\ell} = \int_2^1 -d\Phi = \int_1^2 d\Phi \tag{5-7.3}$$

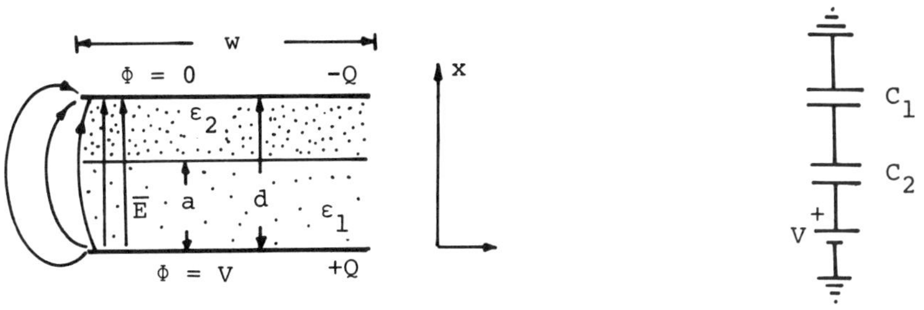

Figure 5-7.2. A parallel plate capacitor.

where C' is an arbitrary path from S_2 to S_1. Hence we can write

$$C = \frac{\oint \rho_s \, dS}{\int \bar{E} \cdot d\ell} = \frac{\int \varepsilon\bar{E} \cdot \bar{n} \, dS}{\int_1^2 \bar{E} \cdot d\bar{\ell}}$$

which relates Eq. (5-7.1) with Eqs. (5-7.2) and (5-7.3). In the case of complicated geometrical field configurations, the methods of Chaps. 3 and 4 for finding the appropriate Φ may be necessary.

Example 5-7.1. Determine the capacitance of a parallel plate capacitor with plate separation d, area A, and maintained at a potential V, as shown. The space between plates is filled with two dielectrics of permittivities ε_1 and ε_2.

Solution. Let the total charge on the power plate be Q. The charge density is then $\rho_s = Q/a$. If we assume that the plate spacing d is very small compared with the plate width, we can consider the electric field to be uniform in the region between the plates. That is, the fringing of the field lines near the edges can be neglected, since this fringing extends over a region of the order d only, and d is small compared with the total width w. Thus the value of the induction D_x will be given by

$$D_x = \rho_s = \frac{Q}{A}$$

The corresponding electric field is

$$E_x = \frac{Q}{A\varepsilon_1} \qquad 0 \le x \le a$$

$$E_x = \frac{Q}{A\varepsilon_2} \qquad a \le x \le d$$

The potential difference V is given by the line integral of the electric field from one plate to the other, i.e., from x = 0 to d, and is

$$V = \int_0^a \frac{Q}{A\varepsilon_1}\,dx + \int_a^d \frac{Q}{A\varepsilon_2}\,dx = \frac{aQ}{\varepsilon_1 A} + \frac{(d-a)Q}{\varepsilon_2 A}$$

Hence the capacitance C is given by

$$C = \frac{Q}{V} = \frac{1}{\dfrac{a}{\varepsilon_1 A} + \dfrac{d-a}{\varepsilon_2 A}} \tag{5-7.4}$$

For the very important case with $\varepsilon_1 = \varepsilon_2 = \varepsilon$, a single dielectric, we find

$$C = \frac{A\varepsilon}{d} \tag{5-7.5}$$

for the capacitance of a simple parallel plate capacitor. Based on this, the composite capacitor can be given an interesting interpretation. From Eq. (5-7.5), and noting that the surface x = a is a constant potential surface, then we may regard the lower plate and the boundary x = a as forming a simple parallel plate capacitor with capacitance $C_1 = \varepsilon_1 A/a$. Similarly, the boundary x = a and the upper plate forms a capacitor, with capacitance $C_2 = \varepsilon_2 A/(d-a)$. The resultant capacitance is that for C_1 and C_2 in a series connection, and is given by Eq. (5-7.4), which can now be expressed in the form

$$C = \frac{1}{\dfrac{1}{C_1} + \dfrac{1}{C_2}} = \frac{C_1 C_2}{C_1 + C_2} \tag{5-7.6}$$

Essentially the same procedure can be followed to show that the capacitance per unit length of a coaxial line with inner radius a and outer radius b is (see Pr. 5-7.1)

$$C = \frac{2\pi\varepsilon}{\ell n \dfrac{b}{a}} \tag{5-7.7}$$

Similarly, the capacitance of two concentric spherical shells is given by (see Pr. 5-7.3)

$$C = 4\pi\varepsilon \frac{ab}{b-a} \tag{5-7.8}$$

ΔΔΔ

Example 5-7.2. Find the capacitance of a spherical capacitor of inner radius a and outer radius b charged with Q Coulombs, and containing a nonhomogeneous dielectric which is assumed to vary according to

$$\varepsilon = \varepsilon_1 + \varepsilon_2 \frac{1}{r^2}$$

where ε_1 and ε_2 are constants and $\varepsilon_1 > \varepsilon_2$.

Solution. By an application of Gauss' law, the electric flux density $\overline{D}$ is given by

$$\overline{D} = \frac{Q}{4\pi r^2}\,\overline{a}_r$$

and the electric field intensity in the dielectric is

$$\overline{E} = \frac{Q}{4\pi\varepsilon r^2}\,\overline{a}_r$$

The potential difference is

$$V = \int_a^b \frac{Q}{4\pi\varepsilon r^2}\,dr = \frac{Q}{4\pi}\frac{1}{\sqrt{\varepsilon_1\varepsilon_2}}\left[\tan^{-1}\left(b\sqrt{\frac{\varepsilon_1}{\varepsilon_2}}\right) - \tan^{-1}\left(a\sqrt{\frac{\varepsilon_1}{\varepsilon_2}}\right)\right]$$

The capacitance of the system is then given by the ratio Q/V. ΔΔΔ

5-8. Energy in an Electric Field

If a system of charges is assembled by bringing the charges from infinity into a finite sized region, expenditure of work is required. As a consequence, the system has energy associated with it and can, in principle, do an amount of work equal to the work done in establishing the charge configuration. The final charge configuration has a unique space distributed electric field associated with it, and consequently, we may anticipate that it will be possible to express the stored energy in terms of a suitable volume integral involving the electric field. In this section we shall show that this is indeed the case.

In order to establish a number of basic ideas, let us first calculate the work done to charge a simple parallel plate capacitor. Refer to Fig. 5-8.1. Let the capacitor have a plate area A, spacing b, and be filled with a dielectric of permittivity ε. We suppose that the battery voltage can be varied from an initial value of zero to a final value V_o. At some instant of time, the charge on the upper plate will be q, the charge density will be q/A, and the corresponding value of D will be q/A. The potential across the plates must then be $Eb = Db/\varepsilon = bq/A\varepsilon$ and

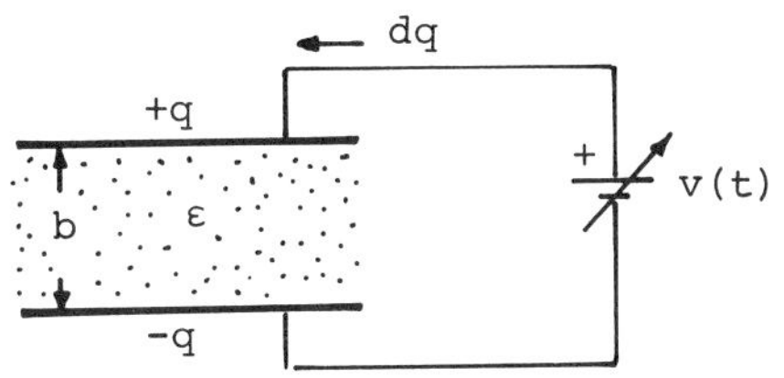

Figure 5-8.1. Charging a parallel plate capacitor.

must be equal to the voltage of the source at this instant of time. If we now transfer an amount of charge dq from the lower plate to the upper plate through the battery, the incremental work done is $V\,dq = bq(dq)/A\varepsilon$. To charge the capacitor from an initial value of zero to a final value of Q requires work of amount

$$W = \int_0^Q V dq = \int_0^Q \frac{bq\,dq}{A\varepsilon} = \frac{bQ^2}{2A\varepsilon} = \frac{Q^2}{2C} \tag{5-8.1}$$

For the linear capacitor for which $C = Q/V$, this also has the form

$$W = \frac{Q^2}{2C} = \frac{CV^2}{2}$$

where $C = A\varepsilon/b$. The work done in charging the capacitor may be regarded as stored in the electric field which, in the absence of fringing, is confined to the region between the plates.

In order for Eq. (5-8.1) to be valid, ε must be a constant independent of the field strength in the material. If ε depends on the field strength (which depends on q) it must then be regarded as a function of q in evaluating the integral in Eq. (5-8.1). This latter condition exists only if the material is nonlinear.

The concept of stored energy has a precise meaning only for systems without dissipation (loss), otherwise the time becomes explicitly involved in the considerations. In other words, the process of building up the electric field in the capacitor must be a reversible process in the sense that no part of the work done must appear as heat or radiation of energy. Radiation will be negligible if the charging process is carried out slowly enough. If dissipative forces are present, it is an inevitable consequence that some heat will be generated in overcoming these forces during the charging process. One also finds in this case that discharging the capacitor will involve some heat generation and not all of the stored energy is recoverable in the form of external work.

To illustrate the above ideas, let the medium in the capacitor of Fig. 5-8.1 be a leaky dielectric with conductivity σ. If an electric field E exists between

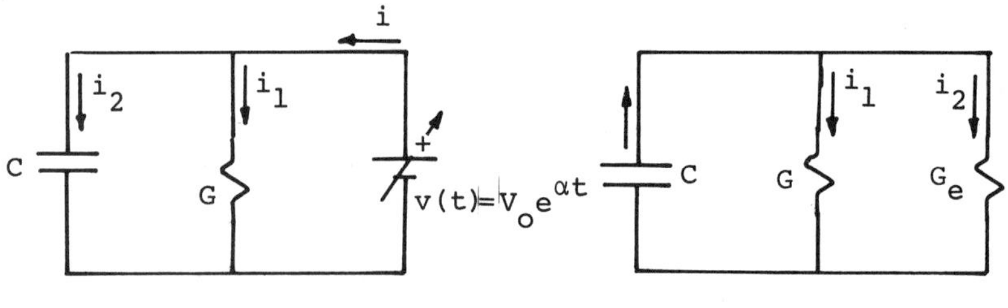

Figure 5-8.2. Equivalent circuit of a lossy capacitor.

the plates, a conduction current $J = \sigma E$ exists. The total current will be $I = AJ = \sigma AE = (\sigma A/b)V = GV$, where G is the equivalent circuit conductance of the lossy capacitor. We can replace the lossy capacitor by an ideal capacitor having capacitance $C = A\epsilon/b$ shunted by a conductance G, as shown in Fig. 5-8.2a. Let a voltage $v(t) = V_0 e^{\alpha t}$ for $-\infty \leq t \leq 0$ be applied to charge the capacitor. The work done is

$$W = \int_{-\infty}^{0} v(t)i(t)dt = \int_{-\infty}^{0} v(t) \frac{dq}{dt} dt$$

since $i = dq/dt$. From circuit considerations

$$i_1 = Gv, \qquad i_2 = C \frac{dv}{dt} = CV_0 e^{\alpha t}\alpha = C\alpha v(t)$$

and $i = i_1 + i_2$ so we have

$$W = \int_{-\infty}^{0} (Gv + C\alpha v)\, v\, dt = \int_{-\infty}^{0} (G + 2C)\, V_0^2\, e^{2\alpha t}\, dt$$

$$= \frac{CV_0^2}{2} + \frac{GV_0^2}{2\alpha} \tag{5-8.2}$$

Note that the work done includes a term $GV_0^2/2\alpha$ which is equal to the heat produced in the lossy material because of the conduction current, and this term depends on the rate α at which the voltage is increased. It is apparent that the stored energy is now less than the work done on the system.

If we now consider the discharge of the capacitor into an external conductance G_e, as illustrated in Fig. 5-8.2b, we find that the energy delivered to G_e is

$$W_1 = \int_0^{\infty} v(t)\, i_2(t)\, dt = \int_0^{\infty} G_e V_0^2\, e^{-2t(G+G_e)/C}\, dt$$

$$= \frac{CV_0^2}{2}\left(\frac{G_e}{G_e+G}\right) = \frac{CV_0^2}{2}\left(\frac{1}{1+\frac{G}{G_e}}\right) \tag{5-8.3}$$

since the voltage across C will decay according to $V_0 e^{-t(G+G_e)/C}$ and $i_2 = G_e v$. During the discharge process an amount of energy equal to $CV_0^2 G_e/2(G + G_e)$ is delivered to G in the form of heat. This shows that because of losses, all of the stored energy in C is not available to do work in the external conductance G_e since the initial stored energy $CV_0^2/2$ is in part dissipated in the internal conductance G of the lossy capacitor. Only if $G = 0$ will $W_1 = 1/2\ CV_0^2$ and all of the stored energy be converted into external work.

The foregoing remarks on energy storage have been made simply to point out that the concept of stored energy and its relation to the work done in bringing a system from an initial state to a final state has a real significance only for reversible processes, i.e., for systems with no loss. In the next section we shall discuss the problem of determining the forces acting on bodies due to the presence of an electric field by using a virtual work process. It will then be important that a unique relation exist between the stored energy and the work done in changing the state of the system.

5-9. Stored Energy as a Field Integral

To establish the relation between the electric field and stored energy, we shall proceed by evaluating the work done in assembling a collection of point charges. This calculation will be rather similar to that carried out for charging a capacitor. We proceed by considering the special case of 3 charges, and we shall then generalize the procedure to a general array of N charges.

We begin, therefore, by establishing the field of 3 charges. We bring a single charge Q_1 from infinity to an arbitrary point; this requires no work since this charge is moved in a field-free region. We now bring a second charge Q_2 from infinity to a point a distance R_{12} from Q_1; this requires the expenditure of work equal to $Q_1Q_2/(4\pi\varepsilon_o R_{12})$ since the potential at the position of Q_2 due to the presence of Q_1 is $Q_1/(4\pi\varepsilon_o R_{12})$ (see Sec. 5-1 for the relation of potential and work). To bring a third charge Q_3 from infinity requires work of amount

$$W_3 = \frac{Q_3Q_1}{4\pi\varepsilon_o R_{13}} + \frac{Q_3Q_2}{4\pi\varepsilon_o R_{23}}$$

because of the potential set up by Q_1 and Q_2. The total work done can be expressed in the form

$$W = W_1 + W_2 + W_3 = 0 + \frac{Q_1Q_2}{4\pi\varepsilon_o R_{12}} + \left[\frac{Q_3Q_1}{4\pi\varepsilon_o R_{13}} + \frac{Q_3Q_2}{4\pi\varepsilon_o R_{23}}\right]$$

which we write

$$W = \frac{1}{2}\left[\frac{Q_1Q_2}{4\pi\varepsilon_o R_{12}} + \frac{Q_1Q_3}{4\pi\varepsilon_o R_{13}} + \frac{Q_2Q_1}{4\pi\varepsilon_o R_{21}} + \frac{Q_2Q_3}{4\pi\varepsilon_o R_{23}} + \frac{Q_3Q_1}{4\pi\varepsilon_o R_{31}} + \frac{Q_3Q_2}{4\pi\varepsilon_o R_{32}}\right]$$

or more conveniently in compact form by including all terms twice and noting that $R_{ij} = R_{ji}$,

$$W = \frac{1}{2}\sum_{i=1}^{3}\sum_{j=1}^{3}{}' \frac{Q_iQ_j}{4\pi\varepsilon_o R_{ij}} \tag{5-9.1}$$

In this expression the prime on the summation sign means that the term i = j for which $R_{ij} = 0$ is to be excluded. We note that this equation can also be expressed in the form

$$W = \frac{1}{2} \sum_{i=1}^{3} Q_i \Phi_i \tag{5-9.2}$$

where

$$\Phi_i = \sum_{j=1}^{3}{}' \frac{Q_j}{4\pi\varepsilon_o R_{ij}} \qquad i \neq j \tag{5-9.3}$$

with Φ_i the potential at the position of the ith charge due to all of the other charges. The total work done to assemble N point charges is written as a logical extension of Eq. (5-9.1) and is

$$W = \frac{1}{2} \sum_{i=1}^{N} \sum_{j=1}^{N}{}' \frac{Q_i Q_j}{4\pi\varepsilon_o R_{ij}} \tag{5-9.4}$$

This expression is also written as

$$W = \frac{1}{2} \sum_{i=1}^{N} Q_i \Phi_i \qquad \text{a)}$$

where (5-9.5)

$$\Phi_i = \sum_{j=1}^{N}{}' \frac{Q_j}{4\pi\varepsilon_o R_{ij}} \qquad \text{b)}$$

with Φ_i the potential at the position of the ith charge due to all other charges.

We now generalize Eq. (5-9.5) to the situation where we have a volume distribution of charge with density ρ, instead of a collection of point charges. This generalization is obtained by treating $\rho\Delta V_i$ as a point charge and taking the limit of the sum as the volume element $\Delta V_i \to 0$. Therefore

$$W = \lim_{\substack{\Delta V_i \to 0 \\ N \to \infty}} \frac{1}{2} \sum_{i=1}^{N} \Phi_i (\rho \Delta V_i) = \frac{1}{2} \int_V \Phi\rho \, dV \tag{5-9.6}$$

since the sum approaches an integral in the limit as $\Delta V_i \to 0$ and $N \to \infty$. We now make use of the relation that $\nabla \cdot \overline{E} = \rho/\varepsilon_o$ and that $\overline{E} = -\nabla\Phi$. As a consequence

$$\begin{aligned} \Phi\rho &= \varepsilon_o \Phi \nabla \cdot \overline{E} = \varepsilon_o \nabla \cdot (\Phi\overline{E}) - \varepsilon_o \overline{E} \cdot \nabla\Phi \\ &= \varepsilon_o \nabla \cdot (\Phi\overline{E}) + \varepsilon_o \overline{E} \cdot \overline{E} \end{aligned}$$

so that

$$W = \frac{\varepsilon_o}{2} \int_V \nabla \cdot (\Phi\overline{E}) \, dV + \frac{\varepsilon_o}{2} \int_V |\overline{E}|^2 \, dV \tag{5-9.7}$$

By using the divergence theorem, the first integral can be replaced by the surface integral, and

$$W = \frac{\varepsilon_o}{2}\int_S \Phi\overline{E} \cdot d\overline{S} + \frac{\varepsilon_o}{2}\int_V |\overline{E}|^2\, dV \tag{5-9.8}$$

Since the original integral must be taken over all of space to include the total field, the surface S is that of a sphere of infinite radius on which Φ decreases as $1/r$ and $\overline{E}$ decreases as $1/r^2$. The surface integral vanishes as $1/r$ since the surface area increases only as r^2. It follows, therefore, that the work done in establishing the field is given by

$$W = W_e = \frac{\varepsilon_o}{2}\int_{\text{space}} |\overline{E}|^2\, dV \tag{5-9.9}$$

Since this is also equal to the stored energy in the field, this integral has been designated by the symbol W_e. The integrand $\varepsilon_o|\overline{E}|^2/2$ is sometimes regarded as the *energy density* in the field. Clearly, this interpretation is not required by Eq. (5-9.9) but it is consistent with it, since only the total energy stored has physical significance. The exact location of the energy in the field cannot be specified.

A question of importance is the form for the stored energy when a dielectric material is present, especially if the possibility of a nonlinear medium is allowed, i.e., a medium for which ε is a function of the field strength. We now consider this problem. Consider a distribution of charge with density ρ in the presence of dielectric material. Let the corresponding potential field be Φ. If we now increase the charge density by an amount $d\rho$ at each point, we shall do an incremental amount of work given by

$$dW = \int_V (\Phi d\rho)\, dV$$

Corresponding to the increment $d\rho$ in ρ is an incremental change $d\overline{D}$ in $\overline{D}$ which is related to d by the divergence equation $\nabla \cdot d\overline{D} = d\rho$. Hence

$$dW = \int_V (\Phi\nabla \cdot d\overline{D})\, dV$$

We now manipulate this integral in the same way as Eq. (5-9.6) in expressing the result in the form Eq. (5-9.9). We then find that

$$dW = \int_{\text{space}} (\overline{E} \cdot d\overline{D})\, dV \tag{5-9.10}$$

To find the total work done, we must integrate this expression with respect to $\overline{D}$ from an initial value of 0 (corresponding to $\rho = 0$) to a final value $\overline{D}$ (corresponding to the final value of ρ). When $\overline{D} = \varepsilon\overline{E}$ and ε is a constant we have

$$W = W_e = \int_{\text{space}} \int_0^D \frac{\bar{D} \cdot d\bar{D}}{\varepsilon} \, dV$$

$$= \frac{1}{2} \int_{\text{space}} \int_0^D \frac{d(\bar{D} \cdot \bar{D})}{\varepsilon} \, dV$$

or finally

$$W = W_e = \frac{1}{2} \int_{\text{space}} \frac{\bar{D} \cdot \bar{D}}{\varepsilon} \, dV = \frac{1}{2} \int_{\text{space}} \varepsilon |\bar{E}|^2 \, dV \tag{5-9.11}$$

In the nonlinear case it is necessary to know the variation of $\bar{E}$ as a function of $\bar{D}$ (that is, ε as a function of $\bar{D}$) in order to evaluate the integral. Fortunately, most materials are linear, and Eq. (5-9.11) is valid. If the medium is homogeneous, ε will be independent of position and can be brought outside of the integral in Eq. (5-9.11).

Example 5-9.1. A conducting sphere of radius a is embedded in a homogeneous linear dielectric medium with permittivity ε, as shown in Fig. 5-9.1. The sphere has a total charge Q. Find the stored energy.

Solution. By Gauss' law we write

$$4\pi r^2 D_r = Q \qquad \text{and so} \qquad E_r = \frac{Q}{4\pi\varepsilon r^2}$$

The stored energy is given by

$$W_e = \frac{\varepsilon}{2} \int_0^{2\pi} \int_0^{\pi} \int_a^{\infty} \frac{Q^2 r^2 \sin\theta \, d\theta \, d\phi \, dr}{(4\pi\varepsilon r^2)^2} = \frac{Q^2}{8\pi\varepsilon a} \tag{5-9.12}$$

If the permittivity ε varies, say according to the form,

$$\varepsilon = \varepsilon_0 \left(1 + \frac{a}{r}\right)^2$$

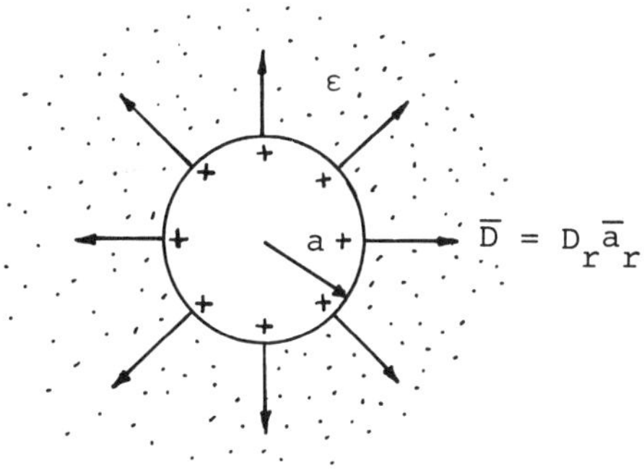

Figure 5-9.1. A charged sphere inside a dielectric.

we will still have $4\pi r^2 D_r = Q$ from Gauss' law. However, in this inhomogeneous case the stored energy is given by

$$W_e = \frac{1}{2}\int_0^{2\pi}\int_0^{\pi}\int_a^{\infty} \frac{Q^2 r^2 \sin\theta\, d\theta\, d\phi\, dr}{(4\pi r^2)^2\, \varepsilon_o\, (1 + \frac{a}{r})^2}$$

where the integrand is $D_r^2/\varepsilon(r)$. After integrating over θ and ϕ, we obtain

$$W_e = \frac{Q^2}{8\pi}\int_a^{\infty} \frac{dr}{\varepsilon_o (r+a)^2} = \frac{Q^2}{8\pi\varepsilon_o}\left(\frac{-1}{r+a}\right)\Bigg|_a^{\infty} = \frac{Q^2}{16\pi\varepsilon_o a} \tag{5-9.13}$$

The reader should explain the difference between Eq. (5-9.12) and (5-9.13) on physical grounds.

ΔΔΔ

5-10. Electric Forces

If we have a lossless system such as a capacitor, then, as already discussed, the energy W_e stored in the electric field is a unique function of the field, and furthermore, is equal to the work done in increasing the field from an initial value of zero to its final value. In addition, the energy function W_e will be independent of how the field was brought to its final value, i.e., independent of the rate at which the field is built up (see Sec. 5-8 for which the stored energy is independent of α when the loss is zero, i.e., $G = 0$). If we now change the configuration of the system, for example, by changing the plate separation in a parallel plate capacitor, the change in stored energy can be uniquely related to the work done on (or the work done by) the field to produce the change in the configuration. But the work done will be given by the force exerted times the displacement, and so it may be anticipated that the electric forces existing in the system can be evaluated in terms of the change in stored energy that takes place in a small incremental displacement of a part of the system. This method of evaluating electric field forces is called the *principle of virtual work*. The energy function W_e must, of course, be uniquely related to the work done on or by the system and must also be a unique function of the final values of the field in (or state of) the system.

In order to illustrate the use of the principle of virtual work for evaluating electric forces, we shall consider the following example.

Example 5-10.1. Find the force between the two charged plates of area A and separation b of the capacitor system illustrated in Fig. 5-10.1.

Solution. The energy stored in the system (neglecting fringing) is

$$W_e = \frac{1}{2}\int_V \varepsilon_o E^2 dV = \frac{\varepsilon_o E^2 Ab}{2} = \frac{\varepsilon_o V^2 A}{2b} = \frac{CV^2}{2}$$

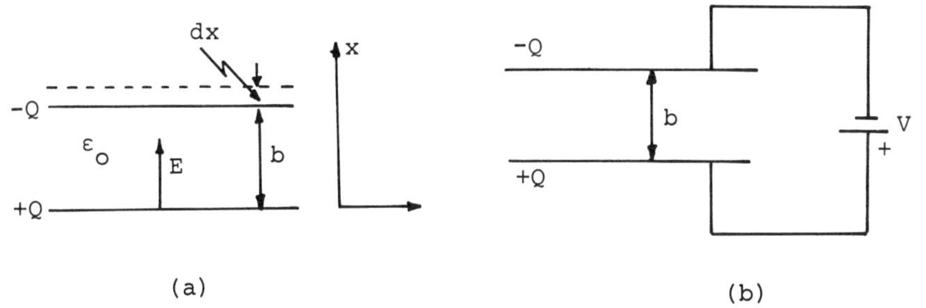

Figure 5-10.1. A parallel plate capacitor (a) with a constant charge constraint (b) with a constant voltage constraint.

where $C = A\varepsilon_0/b$ is the capacitance and the voltage $V = Eb$. If the battery is disconnected as shown in Fig. 5-10.1a and we consider an imaginary (virtual) work process during which we increase the plate separation by an amount dx, the total charge Q is constrained to remain constant. But since $Q = CV$, it follows that if we change C by varying the spacing, the voltage V across the plates must change so as to keep Q constant.

Let the electric field produce a force $\bar{F}_e = -F_e\bar{a}_x$ on the upper plate. If we want to displace the plate, we must apply a force $\bar{F} = -\bar{F}_e$ to overcome the force of the field. In a displacement of amount $\bar{a}_x dx$ we will do work of amount $\bar{F} \cdot \bar{a}_x dx = -F_e dx$ and this work must be equal to the change in stored energy since total energy is conserved. Thus

$$-F_e dx = \left.\frac{\partial W_e}{\partial x}\right|_Q dx$$

where we have indicated that the change in W_e must be evaluated using the constraint that Q is constant. If we express W_e as a function of Q and a general plate separation x, then we can write

$$-F_e dx = \frac{\partial W_e(Q,x)}{\partial x} dx \qquad x = b$$

or (5-10.1)

$$F_e = -\frac{\partial W_e(Q,x)}{\partial x} \qquad x = b$$

since the partial derivative means that Q is to be held constant during a change in x. For $W_e(Q,x)$ we can write

$$W_e(Q,x) = \frac{1}{2}\frac{Q^2}{C(x)} = \frac{Q^2 x}{2A\varepsilon_0}$$

in place of the expression $CV^2/2$, which is in terms of V and x. We now find that

$$F_e = -\frac{\partial W_e(Q,x)}{\partial x} = -\frac{Q^2}{2A\varepsilon_o} = -\frac{Q^2}{2Cb} \tag{5-10.2}$$

The force F_e exerted by the field is, of course, unique for a given configuration of the system. However, in evaluating the force by considering a virtual work process, which is an imaginary change in the system, we are free to consider any arbitrary constraint, such as constant Q or constant V. As long as a correct energy balance equation is written, we will obtain the correct result for the force. Let us, therefore, consider a displacement for which the battery is kept connected so that V is constrained to remain constant. If we change C by an amount dC, then since Q = CV, we have dQ = V dC since V remains constant. Since dC = C(x + dx) - C(x) = (dC/dx) dx an increase of the plate separation by an amount dx causes the battery to do work of amount VdQ on the system. The total work done is

$$\overline{F} \cdot \overline{a}_x dx + VdQ = -F_e dx + VdQ$$

and must equal the change in stored energy with V held constant. We express W_e as a function of V and x and then obtain

$$-F_e dx + VdQ = \frac{\partial W_e(V,x)}{\partial x} dx$$

But $W_e = Q^2/2C = QV/2$, then

$$\frac{\partial W_e(V,x)}{\partial x} dx = \frac{1}{2}\frac{\partial QV}{\partial x} dx = \frac{V}{2}\frac{\partial Q}{\partial x} dx = \frac{VdQ}{2}$$

Under a constant voltage constraint the expression for the force F_e will be

$$F_e dx = VdQ - \frac{\partial W_e(V,x)}{\partial x} dx = \frac{VdQ}{2} = \frac{\partial W_e(V,x)}{\partial x} dx \tag{5-10.3}$$

which differs in sign on the right hand side, when compared with Eq. (5-10.2).

Observe the interesting fact that the energy supplied by the battery, VdQ, divides equally, half doing external work and half being added to the energy storage in the field. However, Eq. (5-10.3) yields the same force as Eq. (5-10.2) which should be the case, of course, since the force is a unique quantity for a given state of the system. For the present problem

$$W_e(V,x) = \frac{CV^2}{2} = \frac{A\varepsilon_o V^2}{2x}$$

and so

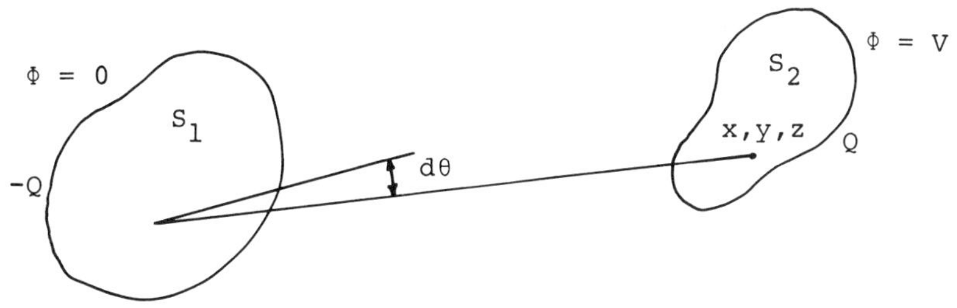

Figure 5-10.2. Two charged bodies.

$$F_e = \frac{\partial(A\varepsilon_o V^2/2x)}{\partial x} = -\frac{A\varepsilon_o V^2}{2b^2} = -\frac{CV^2}{2b} = -\frac{Q^2}{2Cb}$$

when evaluated for x = b. The result is the same as that given by Eq. (5-10.2).ΔΔΔ

We may summarize and generalize the above equations by stating that if the configuration of the system is a function of coordinates x,y,z and a displacement is made in the direction $d\bar{r}$, then

$$\bar{F}_e \cdot d\bar{r} = -\frac{\partial W_e(Q,x,y,z)}{\partial x}dx - \frac{\partial W_e(Q,x,y,z)}{\partial y}dy - \frac{\partial W_e(Q,x,y,z)}{\partial z}dz$$

$$= -\nabla W_e(Q,x,y,z) \cdot d\bar{r}$$

$$= \nabla W_e(V,x,y,z) \cdot d\bar{r}$$

since $d\bar{r} = \bar{a}_x dx + \bar{a}_y dy + \bar{a}_z dz$. But $d\bar{r}$ is arbitrary, so we have

$$\bar{F}_e = -\nabla W_e(Q,x,y,z) = \nabla W_e(V,x,y,z) \tag{5-10.4}$$

For example, if the coordinates of a reference point in body S_2 in Fig. 5-10.2 are x,y,z and S_2 is at a potential V relative to S_1 and carries a charge Q, we can evaluate the stored energy as a function of x,y,z and Q or V. The force of the electric field exerted on S_2 is then given by Eq. (5-10.4).

We can also find the torque exerted by the electric field on S_2 by finding the change in stored energy brought about by rotating S_2 about the center of S_1 (or some other point) by an amount dθ. If we express W_e as a function of θ we will obtain

$$T_e = -\frac{\partial W_e(Q,\theta)}{\partial\theta} = \frac{\partial W_e(V,\theta)}{\partial\theta} \tag{5-10.5}$$

for the torque T_e by the field.

5-11. Electric Currents

Several features of the electric current field have already been studied in Chap. 1 (see also Sec. 2-2). In the present section and in the several to follow, we shall examine some additional topics, such as boundary conditions, resistance, Joule's law, etc.

If an electric field $\overline{E}$ exists in a medium with permittivity ε and conductivity σ, there will be an electric current with density $\overline{J}$ given by Ohm's law

$$\overline{J} = \sigma\overline{E} \qquad (5\text{-}11.1)$$

The electric current density is the rate of flow of charge (Coulomb/sec-m^2). But conservation of charge in a unit volume element requires that the rate of outward charge flow given by $\nabla \cdot \overline{J}$ must be equal to the rate of decrease of the charge density, or

$$\nabla \cdot \overline{J} = -\frac{\partial\rho}{\partial t} \qquad (5\text{-}11.2)$$

This is the continuity equation and was also given earlier in Sec. 2-7 [see Eq. (2-7.12)]. Under steady state conditions ρ does not vary and so $\nabla \cdot \overline{J} = 0$ which requires that all of the current stream lines or flow tubes close upon themselves.

This discussion is limited to what is known as *conduction current*. Other currents exist, including convection current (the movement of charged bodies) and displacement currents (the time changing electric induction). These will be discussed in later chapters.

A given charge distribution sets up an electric field $\overline{E}$ and also a displacement field $\overline{D}$, where $\overline{D} = \varepsilon\overline{E}$ and $\nabla \cdot \overline{D} = \rho$. For this reason, problems involving electric currents must take into account the behavior of both $\overline{E}$ and $\overline{D}$, particularly at boundaries between different mediums. This interrelation among the three fields $\overline{J}$, $\overline{E}$ and $\overline{D}$ is discussed in this and the following sections, in addition to topics already noted.

One important question is the following: suppose that a charge distribution is placed within a conducting body. The charge will move to the surface and distribute itself in such a way that zero field exists within the conductor and such that the field tangent to the conductor surface is zero, as already discussed. A straightforward analysis shows that the charge is distributed in time according to the equation (see Pr. 5-11.2)

$$\rho(xyzt) = \rho_o(xyz)\, e^{-\sigma t/\varepsilon} \qquad (5\text{-}11.3)$$

where the quantity $\tau = \varepsilon/\sigma$ is the *relaxation time*, the time for the initial charge to decay to $1/e^{th}$ of its initial value.

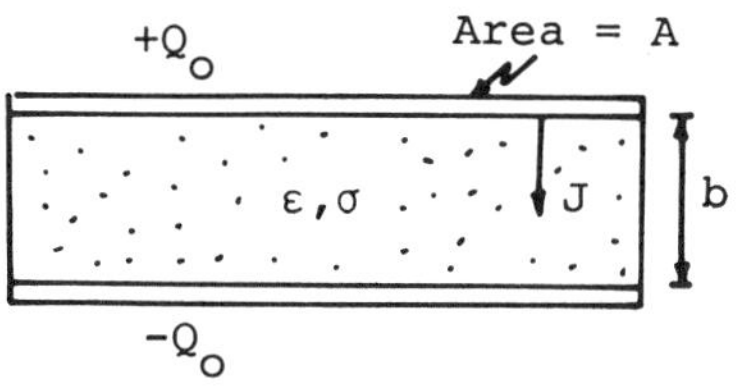

Figure 5-11.1. A lossy capacitor.

Example 5-11.1. Find the relaxation time of a charged capacitor filled with a lossy dielectric.

Solution. Figure 5-11.1 illustrates a parallel plate capacitor with plate spacing b and area A. The medium between the plates is described by parameters ε and σ. Let the charge on the upper plate at time t = 0 be Q_0. The charge density is $\rho_{os} = Q_0/A$, and hence $D = \rho_{os} = Q_0/A$. The electric field and current density will be ρ_{os}/ε and $\sigma\rho_{os}/\varepsilon$, respectively. At time t the charge on the upper plate will have been reduced to a value Q because of the current which carries charge from the upper plate to the lower plate. When the charge is equal to Q, the corresponding fields are given by

$$D = \frac{Q}{A}\ ; \quad E = \frac{Q}{\varepsilon A}\ ; \quad J = \frac{\sigma Q}{\varepsilon A}$$

The rate of decrease of Q must equal the total current from the upper plate which is

$$-\frac{dQ}{dt} = AJ = \frac{\sigma Q}{\varepsilon}$$

This equation may be integrated to give

$$Q = Q_0\, e^{-\sigma t/\varepsilon}$$

which is of the same form as the charge density in Eq. (5-11.3). The quantity ε/σ is known as the *relaxation time*, and is the time constant of the charging process.

The potential difference between the plates at any time is

$$V = bE = \frac{bQ}{\varepsilon A}$$

It follows that the capacitance is equal to $\varepsilon A/b$ since $C = Q/V$. The resistance between the two plates is the ratio of V to the total current, and so we have $R = V/I = V/JA = (bE)/(\sigma AE) = b/\sigma A$. From the expression for R and C, it is seen that $RC = \varepsilon/\sigma$, and Eq. (5-11.3) can be rewritten

$$Q = Q_0 \, e^{-t/RC}$$

which is the usual expression for the discharge of a capacitor through a resistor R. ΔΔΔ

5-12. Boundary Conditions for Current Fields

Consider two different mediums with parameters ε_1, σ_1 and ε_2, σ_2, as shown in Fig. 5-12.1. We wish to examine the conditions to be imposed on the current and the electric fields at the boundary separating the two mediums. If we consider steady state conditions, then just as much current must leave the boundary as enters the boundary. In this case, the normal components of the current must be continuous across the boundary, so that

$$J_{1n} = J_{2n} \tag{5-12.1}$$

If there were zero charge density on the boundary, the normal components of $\overline{D}$ would also be continuous, i.e.,

$$D_{1n} = D_{2n}$$

However, this condition is usually not compatible with Eq. (5-12.1). Under steady state conditions there will usually be a layer of charge on the boundary such that

$$D_{2n} - D_{1n} = \rho_s \tag{5-12.2}$$

If we express $\overline{D}$ in terms of $\overline{J}$ by means of the equations $\overline{D} = \varepsilon\overline{E}$, $\sigma\overline{E} = \overline{J}$, we can write

$$\frac{\varepsilon_2}{\sigma_2} J_{2n} - \frac{\varepsilon_1}{\sigma_1} J_{1n} = \left(\frac{\varepsilon_2}{\sigma_2} - \frac{\varepsilon_1}{\sigma_1}\right) J_{1n} = \rho_s \tag{5-12.3}$$

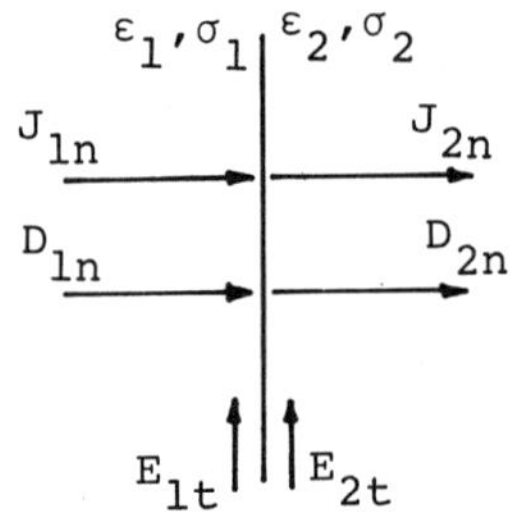

Figure 5-12.1. A boundary between two different conducting mediums.

in place of Eq. (5-12.2). Examination of this expression shows that the boundary charge density ρ_s will vanish only if both mediums have the same relaxation times, i.e., only if $\varepsilon_2/\sigma_2 = \varepsilon_1/\sigma_1$.

Under time varying conditions we do not require the normal component of current to be continuous at the boundary. Instead, we require that the net current directed toward the boundary be equal to the rate at which the charge density builds up, since current is a rate of flow of charge. This requires

$$J_{1n} - J_{2n} = \frac{\partial \rho_s}{\partial t} \tag{5-12.4}$$

for a time dependent situation. In addition, Eq. (5-12.2) will always hold. Equation (5-12.4) can also be found by using the divergence theorem with an appropriate small coin-shaped volume between the interfaces.

As long as the fields vary slowly with time, the electric field can always be expressed in terms of the gradient of a scalar potential (this aspect will be discussed in more detail in a later chapter dealing with general dynamic electromagnetic fields). Since the scalar potential will be a single-valued function, the gradient of the potential along the boundary will be continuous across the boundary, that is, the same on adjacent sides of the boundary. Consequently, the tangential electric field will satisfy the boundary conditions

$$E_{1t} = E_{2t} \qquad \text{a)}$$

from which we obtain

(5-12.5)

$$\frac{1}{\sigma_1} J_{1t} = \frac{1}{\sigma_2} J_{2t} \qquad \text{b)}$$

$$\frac{1}{\varepsilon_1} D_{1t} = \frac{1}{\varepsilon_2} D_{2t} \qquad \text{c)}$$

Example 5-12.1. Find the transient current in a capacitor that is partially filled with a conducting medium.

Solution. Figure 5-12.2 illustrates a parallel plate capacitor that is partially filled with a medium with parameters $\varepsilon;\sigma$ and with the remainder of the intervening space being air with parameters $\varepsilon_o;\sigma = 0$. The plate area is A and at $t = 0$ the plates are charged as shown in Fig. 5-12.2a. The charge will set up an electric field, and a current will exist in the conducting medium. Since the charge cannot flow across the air-filled region, the charge Q_o will flow from the lower plate onto the inner boundary of the conducting slab. Once all of the charge has been transported to this inner surface, the electric and current fields in the conducting region will be zero.

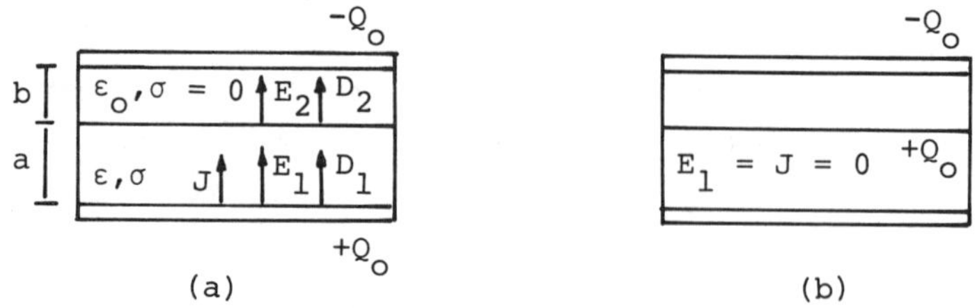

Figure 5-12.2. (a) A capacitor with outer plates initially charged. (b) Final configuration of charge location.

At time t let the charge on the inner boundary be Q. The charge on the lower plate is Q_o-Q, and $D_1 = (Q_o - Q)/A$. The electric field and current in the conducting medium is thus

$$E_1 = \frac{Q_o - Q}{\varepsilon A} \; ; \qquad J = \frac{\sigma}{\varepsilon} \frac{Q_o - Q}{A}$$

The rate of increase of Q must equal the total current to the boundary, so

$$\frac{dQ}{dt} = AJ = \frac{\sigma}{\varepsilon}(Q_o - Q)$$

By integrating this equation we obtain

$$Q = Q_o(1 - e^{-\sigma t/\varepsilon})$$

since at t = 0, Q = 0. We can now find the electric field in the air region since

$$D_2 - D_1 = \frac{Q}{A} = D_2 - \frac{(Q_o - Q)}{A}$$

from the earlier expression for D_1. We then obtain

$$D_2 = \frac{Q_o}{A} \; ; \qquad E_2 = \frac{Q_o}{\varepsilon_o A}$$

which shows that the electric field in the air-filled portion of the capacitor does not change with time while the charge is being transported from the lower plate to the inner boundary. The electric field in the conducting slab will be

$$E_1 = \frac{D_1}{\varepsilon} = \frac{Q_o - Q}{\varepsilon A} = \frac{Q_o e^{-\sigma t/\varepsilon}}{\varepsilon A}$$

and vanishes as t approaches infinity.

ΔΔΔ

5-13. Joule's Law

A charge q placed in an electric field $\overline{E}$ has a force $q\overline{E}$ exerted on it, and consequently will undergo acceleration. From Newton's law we obtain

$$m \frac{d^2\overline{r}}{dt^2} = q\overline{E} \tag{5-13.1}$$

where $\overline{r}$ is the position vector giving the location of the charge, and m is its mass. The phenomenon of conduction (flow of charge) is governed by an equation such as Eq. (5-13.1) only part of the time. In a metal, the electrons cannot move very far before colliding with the atoms of the crystal lattice (refer to the discussion in Sec. 5-3) and when collisions take place the effective velocity is reduced to zero. Thus the electrons progress through the conductor by a series of short bursts of acceleration interrupted by collisions. As a result a low average drift velocity is superimposed on the rather high random motions of the electrons resulting from the collisions. The drift velocity becomes proportional to the applied electric field, as will be described.

Consider an electric field acting in the X-direction on a conductor in which there are N free electrons per unit volume. We focus attention on a free electron which at the instant of collision has zero velocity. Between collisions, the electron is accelerated according to the law

$$\frac{d^2x}{dt^2} = -\frac{e}{m} E_x \tag{5-13.2}$$

where -e is the electronic charge, and m is the mass. If the time before a collision takes place is τ_1 the velocity attained in the X-direction will be

$$-\frac{dx}{dt} = \frac{e}{m} E_x \tau_1 \tag{5-13.3}$$

which is obtained by integrating Eq. (5-13.2) from 0 to τ_1. After the collision the electron will begin with essentially zero velocity and will attain a final velocity of $(e/m)\, E_x\tau_2$ where τ_2 is the interval of time before the next collisions. If the velocity is plotted as a function of time, it consists of a series of sawtooth excursions as in Fig. 5-13.1. The average velocity will be given by $(e/m)\, E_x\tau/2$ where τ is the average time between collisions. The factor of 1/2 enters because the average velocity between each collision is only one-half of the peak velocity attained. The electron current density will be

$$\overline{J}_e = Ne < \frac{dx}{dt} > \overline{a}_x = -\frac{Ne^2\tau}{2m} E_x \overline{a}_x \tag{5-13.4}$$

which is the average velocity multiplied by the charge density Ne. Since

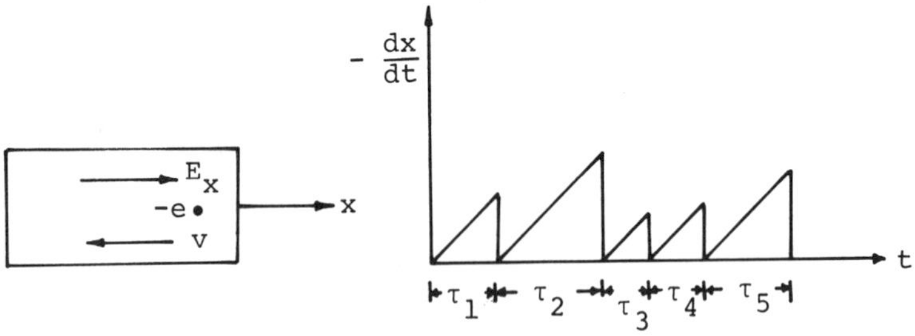

Figure 5-13.1. (a) Electron flow in a conductor. (b) Velocity of electron as a function of time.

conventional current is defined as the flow of positive charge, the conduction current density will be given by

$$\overline{J} = \frac{Ne^2\tau}{2m} E_x \overline{a}_x = \frac{Ne^2\tau}{2m} \overline{E} \qquad (5\text{-}13.5)$$

From this the conductivity σ can be identified to be

$$\sigma = \frac{Ne^2\tau}{2m} \qquad (5\text{-}13.6)$$

This derivation shows that Ohm's law follows from the basic physical mechanisms involved in the flow of electrons in a conductor.

When an electron has gained a velocity v, it has a kinetic energy of $1/2\ mv^2$. When a collision occurs this energy is given up to the atoms of the crystal lattice in the form of heat. To evaluate the rate at which energy is given up, note that for an average velocity of $(e/2m)E_x\tau$ the peak velocity is twice this quantity. Hence each electron gives up an average amount of energy equal to $m(e/m)^2E_x{}^2\tau^2/2$ between each collision. Since there are N electrons per unit volume, and the mean time between collisions is τ, the rate of energy dissipation per unit volume dP is

$$dP = \frac{N\left(\frac{m}{2}\right)\left(\frac{e}{m}E_x\tau\right)^2}{\tau} = \frac{Ne^2\tau E_x{}^2}{2m} \qquad (5\text{-}13.7)$$

But $Ne^2\tau/2m$ is the conductivity, so that

$$dP = \sigma E_x{}^2 \qquad \text{Joule/sec-m}^3 \qquad (5\text{-}13.8)$$

or in general

$$dP = \sigma\overline{E}\cdot\overline{E} = \overline{J}\cdot\overline{E} \qquad \text{Watt/m}^3 \qquad (5\text{-}13.9)$$

Eq. (5-13.9) is known as Joule's law and gives the rate at which heat is generated in a conductor through which a current of density J exists. The total rate of heat generation is obtained by integrating over the volume of the conductor, which yields

$$P = \int_V \overline{E} \cdot \overline{J}\, dV = \int_V \sigma\overline{E} \cdot \overline{E}\, dV = \int_V \frac{\overline{J} \cdot \overline{J}}{\sigma}\, dV \qquad (5\text{-}13.10)$$

which corresponds to the I^2R losses in lumped resistors.

5-14. Resistance

Consider two highly conducting electrodes that make contact with a conducting material, such as shown in Fig. 5-14.1. If the conductivity of the electrodes is infinite, these would be at a constant potential throughout when a battery is connected between them. In a practical situation the electrodes can be assumed to be at a constant potential if they have a conductivity much larger than that of the intervening medium. The resistance R between the electrodes is a macroscopic or terminal parameter defined as the ratio of the potential difference between the electrodes to the total current, thus

$$R = \frac{V}{I} \qquad (5\text{-}14.1)$$

From this expression we have the macroscopic form of Ohm's law

$$I = \frac{V}{R} \qquad (5\text{-}14.2)$$

To determine the resistance R, it is necessary to find the current field $\overline{J}$ first. Under steady state conditions $\overline{J} = \sigma\overline{E} = -\sigma\Delta\Phi$, and $\nabla \cdot \overline{E} = \nabla \cdot \overline{J} = 0$ so that

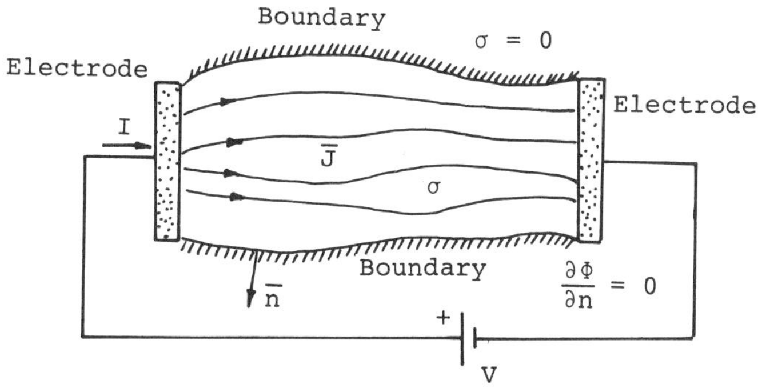

Figure 5-14.1. Electric current between two electrodes.

the potential Φ is a solution of Laplace's equation. The boundary conditions to be imposed on Φ are that Φ is a specified constant on each electrode surface and that $\partial\Phi/\partial n = 0$ along the air-conductor boundary since there can be no normal component of current directed toward the boundary under steady state conditions. The following example will illustrate the technique of evaluating resistance analytically. Of course, flux plotting and other numerical methods may also be used, as discussed in Chap. 3 for the solution of Laplace's equation.

Example 5-14.1. Find the resistance of a conical section.

Solution. Figure 5-14.2 illustrates a cone-shaped resistor with end surfaces that are portions of spherical surfaces. The resistance between the spherical end surfaces is to be found. The conical section can be viewed as a portion of a solid sphere, and so spherical coordinates are appropriate. A suitable solution for Φ is $\Phi = C_1 + C_2/r$, where C_1 and C_2 are constants. At $r = a$, $\Phi = V$, while at $r = b$, $\Phi = 0$. Hence $V = C_1 + C_2/a$ and $0 = C_1 + C_2/b$. These yield

$$C_1 = -\frac{C_2}{b}; \qquad C_2 = \frac{abV}{b-a}$$

Consequently the potential distribution is given by

$$\Phi = \frac{abV}{(b-a)r} - \frac{aV}{b-a}$$

The current field is given by

$$\bar{J} = -\sigma\nabla\Phi = -\sigma\frac{\partial\Phi}{\partial r}\bar{a}_r = \frac{\sigma abV}{(b-a)r^2}\bar{a}_r$$

The total current leaving the surface at $r = a$ is

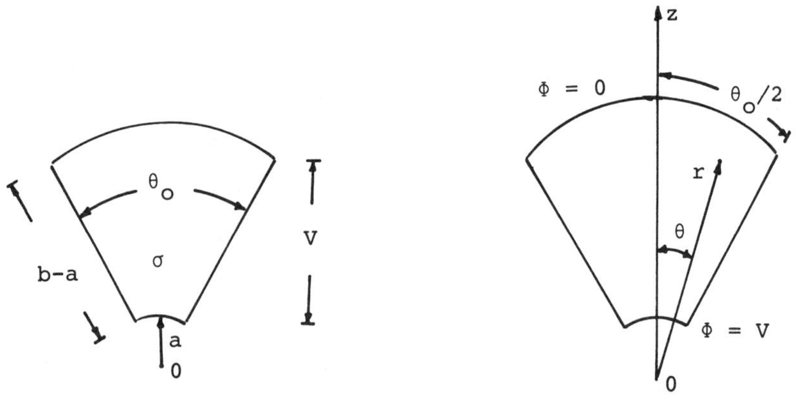

Figure 5-14.2. A conical resistor.

$$I = \int_0^{2\pi}\int_0^{\theta_0/2} \frac{\sigma abV\ a^2}{(b-a)a^2} \sin\theta\ d\theta\ d\phi = \frac{2\pi\sigma abV}{b-a}\left(1 - \cos\frac{\theta_0}{2}\right)$$

Thus the resistance R is given by

$$R = \frac{V}{I} = \frac{b-a}{2\pi\sigma ab(1-\cos\theta_0/2)} \tag{5-14.3}$$

Note that if $\theta_0 = 2\pi$, we obtain the resistance between two concentric spheres, which is $(b-a)/(4\pi ab\sigma)$. This expression differs from that for the capacitance between two concentric spheres (see Pr. 5-7.3) by the presence of conductivity σ instead of ε as a factor, that is

$$C = \frac{4\pi\varepsilon ab}{b-a}\ ; \qquad G = \frac{1}{R} = \frac{4\pi\sigma ab}{b-a}$$

from which it is seen that $G/C = \sigma/\varepsilon$.

ΔΔΔ

The relationship between conductance G and capacitance C noted in the foregoing problem, namely

$$\frac{C}{G} = \frac{\varepsilon}{\sigma} \tag{5-14.4}$$

arises from the similarity between the current field $\overline{J}$ and the displacement field $\overline{D}$. In particular, note that the determination of G and C requires initially a solution of Laplace's equation for the potential Φ. We then have

$$\overline{E} = -\nabla\Phi; \qquad \overline{D} = \varepsilon\overline{E}; \qquad \overline{J} = \sigma\overline{E}$$

so that both $\overline{D}$ and $\overline{J}$ are related to the electric field in a similar manner. The total charge on an electrode surface S is given by

$$Q = \int_S \overline{D}\cdot d\overline{S} = \int_S \varepsilon\overline{E}\cdot d\overline{S}$$

while in a conductance problem, the total current leaving an electrode is

$$I = \int_S \overline{J}\cdot d\overline{S} = \int_S \sigma\overline{E}\cdot d\overline{S}$$

Consequently in those situations involving the same field $\overline{E}$, $Q = (\varepsilon/\sigma)I$ and since the potential difference is the same

$$C = \frac{Q}{V} = \frac{\varepsilon}{\sigma}\frac{I}{V} = \frac{\varepsilon}{\sigma}G$$

Some caution must be expressed in practice in applying this relationship between C and G in those cases where regions of zero conductivity (air or vacuum, etc.)

exist around a conducting medium since the dual problem would require $\varepsilon = 0$, which cannot be obtained. This means that it is not always possible to model exactly a conductance problem by a capacitance problem. However, problems such as the resistance between concentric spheres or between coaxial cylinders, where only a single medium is involved, can be solved by making use of Eq. (5-14.4) and the solution for the capacitance C.

Summary. Upon careful review it will be noted that the entire content of electrostatics is contained in the set of formulas

$$\nabla \times \overline{E} = 0 \qquad \overline{D} = \varepsilon\overline{E} \qquad \overline{F} = \int_V \rho\, \overline{E}\, dV$$

$$\nabla \cdot \overline{D} = \rho \qquad \overline{D} = \varepsilon_o \overline{E} + \overline{P}$$

REVIEW QUESTIONS

1. What is the force on a charge in a static electric field?
2. Write the equation that relates the electrostatic field to its scalar potential.
3. How much work must be done in order to move a charge between two points in an electrostatic field?
4. Given a known charge and an unspecified electrostatic field. Is it possible, using the charge, to ascertain whether the electrostatic field is conservative? If yes, what should we measure?
5. The potential at a point due to many charges is given by $\Phi = \sum_{i=1}^{N} Q_i/(4\pi\varepsilon_o R_i)$ What fundamental property of the field is indicated by this formula?
6. How are the charges in a conductor distributed when the conductor is placed in an electric field?
7. What does the Gauss law tell us?
8. If a conductor having an irregular shape is charged, is the $\overline{E}$ field normal to the conductor at each point of the surface or only on the smooth portions? Explain.
9. Specify the most effective way for electrostatic shielding.
10. What is an electric dipole?
11. Define dipole moment and dipole density.
12. Do dielectric materials exhibit dipole polarization under the influence of an electric field?
13. If the dipole polarization of a dielectric is in the same direction as the field $\overline{E}$, is the material isotropic or anisotropic?
14. What is the name of the proportionality constant which relates the polarization density $\overline{P}$ to the applied electric field $\overline{E}$?
15. What is meant by the phrase, "the dielectric is homogeneous"?

16. Define each term in the formulas given, and give its units: $\overline{D} = \varepsilon_o\overline{E} + \overline{P} = \varepsilon_o(1 + \chi_e)\overline{E} = \varepsilon_o\varepsilon_r\overline{E} = \varepsilon\overline{E}$.
17. What are the boundary conditions for the fields $\overline{D}$ and $\overline{E}$ at the interface between two different dielectric materials?
18. What is the difference between free and polarization charges?
19. What is the definition of capacitance?
20. If a capacitor of 10^{-10}F is charged to 10^3Volt, how much energy is stored in the capacitor?
21. What is the energy density of an electrostatic field.
22. Define Ohm's law in a current carrying medium.

PROBLEMS

5-1.1. Using Eq. (5-1.5) show that Φ is expressed in volts, ρ is in Coulomb/m^3, and ε_o in Farad/m.

5-1.2. Find the electric field which will just keep a proton afloat off the surface of the earth.

5-1.3. Find whether a potential of the form $\Phi = xy + x^2$ can belong to an electrostatic field.

5-2.1. Use Laplace's equation to deduce Eq. (5-2.5).

5-2.2. A charge of +2 microcoulomb is at point (0,1) and a charge of -1 microcoulomb is at point (0,2). Find the electric field $\overline{E}$ (and $|\overline{E}|$) and the electric potential Φ at the points (0,-1) and (1,1).

5-2.3. If a positive charge Q per unit length is distributed over a thin-walled infinitely long cylinder, find $\overline{E},\Phi$ inside and outside the cylinder.

5-2.4. Find the electric field intensity due to an infinite plane sheet of charge of density ρ_s at any height z_o above the plate. [Ans: $\overline{E} = \rho_s/2\varepsilon_o\ \overline{n}$]

5-2.5. Electric charge is distributed with uniform density ρ_o Coulomb/m^3 through the spherical region $r \leq a$.

(a) Use Gauss' law to find the electric field for all values of r.

(b) Use Laplace's and Poisson's equations to find the electric field for all values of r.

[Ans: $\overline{E}_o = \overline{a}_r \dfrac{a^3\rho_o}{3\varepsilon_o r^2}$; $\overline{E}_i = \dfrac{\rho_o r}{3\varepsilon_o}\overline{a}_r$]

5-2.6. Plot the potential Φ and $|\overline{E}|$ versus r for an electric charge that is uniformly distributed with density ρ_o throughout the spherical region $r \leq a$.

5-2.7. Repeat Problems 5-2.5 and 5-2.6 for $\rho = \rho_o r^2$.

5-3.1. Verify Eq. (5-3.3).

5-3.2. (a) Charge with density $\rho_s = -(Qd/4\pi a^3) \cos \theta$ is placed on a spherical surface r = a. Find the resulting potential field Φ for all r. [Hint: Note for r > a and r < a that $\nabla^2\Phi = 0$. Also, Φ must be finite at r = 0 and infinity. At r = a there must be a discontinuity in E_r of amount ρ_s/ε_o, i.e., $E_r\Big|_{a^-}^{a^+} = \rho_s/\varepsilon_o$, where a^+ and a^- signify the value of r exterior and interior to the surface r = a, but infinitesimally close to r = a.]

(b) Prove the boundary condition given in the hint in part (a) by using Gauss' law and a small coin-shaped box with surfaces on adjacent sides of r = a as shown, with h → 0.

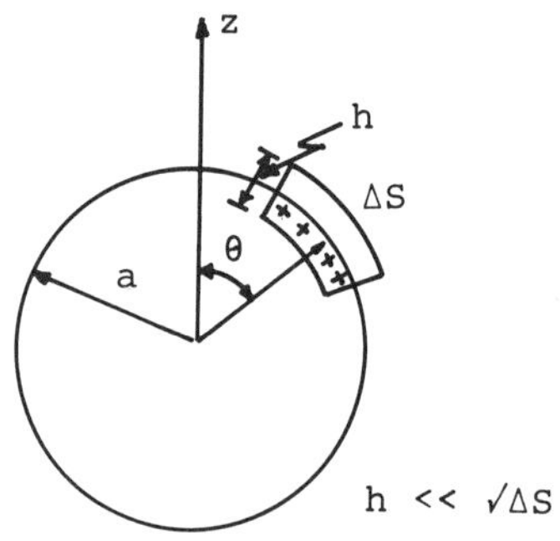

Figure P5-3.2.

5-3.3. For the dipole of Ex. 5-3.1 find the ratio r/r_2 and r/r_1 by expansion and show that if terms containing d^2 and of higher order are neglected Eq. (5-3.2) is correct. [Hint: $r_2 = [r^2 + (d/2)^2 + rd \cos\theta]^{1/2}$; $r_1 = [r^2 + (d/2)^2 - rd \cos\theta]^{1/2}$]

5-3.4. Show that the E-lines of a dipole are given by $r = A \sin^2\theta$, where A is a constant. [Hint: $E_\theta/E_r = r\, d\theta/dr = \sin\theta/2\cos\theta$]

5-5.1. Verify Eq. (5-5.3). [Hint: Use the spherical form for the ∇-operator.]

5-6.1. A charged sphere of radius a having Q Coulomb is embedded in a dielectric medium. Find the polarization $\overline{P}$, the polarization charge density, the polarization surface charge density ρ_{ps}, and the effective total charge Q_e. [Ans: $\rho_{ps} = -(1 - 1/\varepsilon_r)Q/4\pi a^2$; $Q_e = Q/\varepsilon_r$.]

5-6.2. An electric dipole of moment $\overline{p}$ is placed in an electric field $\overline{E}$. Find the torque which is exerted on the dipole.

5-6.3. Consider a medium with permittivity ε which is a function of position. From the relation $\nabla \cdot \overline{D} = \rho$, where ρ is the free charge density, obtain an expression for the equivalent volume polarization charge.
[Hint: Consider $\nabla \cdot \overline{E}$.]

5-6.4. A dielectric sphere of radius a and permittivity ε is placed in a uniform field $\overline{E}_o = E_o \overline{a}_z$. Find the induced field for $r \leq a$ and $r \geq a$. Show that the induced electric field for $r > a$ is a dipole field. What is the equivalent dipole moment of the polarized sphere?

5-7.1. Find the capacitance per unit length of a coaxial line with inner radius a and outer radius b. Q_ℓ is the charge per unit length.
[Hint: $E_r = Q_\ell/2\pi r\varepsilon$.]

5-7.2. Find the capacitance per unit length of a coaxial line containing two dielectrics, as shown in the accompanying figure.

[Ans: $\dfrac{2\pi}{\dfrac{1}{\varepsilon_1}\ln\dfrac{c}{a} + \dfrac{1}{\varepsilon_2}\ln\dfrac{b}{c}}$]

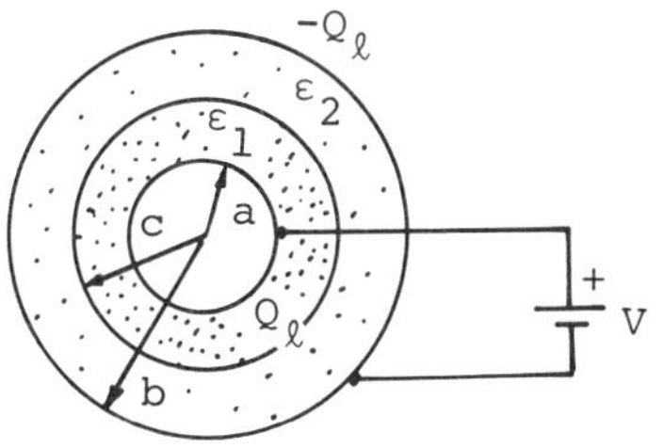

Figure P5-7.2.

5-7.3. Find the capacitance of two concentric spherical shells with inner radius a and outer radius b. [Hint: $E_r = Q/4\pi\varepsilon r^2$.]

5-7.4. Find the capacitance of a parallel plate capacitor of dimensions 2 cm. wide and 1 meter long, and with a spacing of 0.003 m. The plates are separated by a wax impregnated paper insulation of relative permittivity $\varepsilon_r = 2$.
[Ans: 0.0118 μF.]

5-7.5. Find the capacitance per unit length, and the polarization charge density, of a coaxial cable containing a nonhomogeneous dielectric specified by $\varepsilon_r = 1 + (\varepsilon_{r1} - 1)(r-a)/(r+b)$ and charged with Q coulombs per unit length. Denote a and b as the inner and outer radius of the conductors.

5-7.6. The output of a tuned transistor amplifier is connected to the following stage by a shielded wire which consists of a coaxial cable with a = 1 mm, b = 3 mm, and relative permittivity 2.2. The cable is 15 cm. long. Find

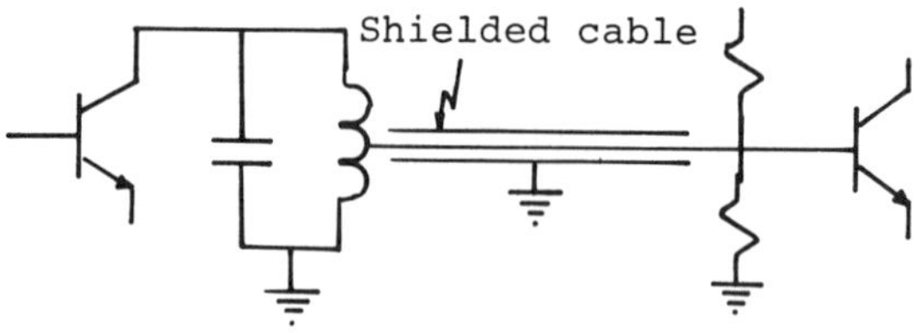

Figure P5-7.6.

the capacitance to ground introduced by this cable. If the input impedance of the transistor stage is 500 Ω, at what frequency does the cable produce a shunting impedance of the same magnitude?

5-8.1. Two concentric spherical shells of radii a and b are kept at a potential difference of V_o, i.e., the inner sphere is at potential V_o. Distilled water with $\varepsilon = 80\ \varepsilon_o$ is pumped into the region between the two conducting spherical shells. Calculate the total work done against the forces due to the electric field.

5-8.2. A parallel plate capacitor is embedded in purified water, $\varepsilon_r = 80$, and is charged to 500 volts, and the potential source is then disconnected. The plates are separated to twice their original spacing. Find the energy stored in the two positions, and discuss the differences, if any.

5-8.3. (a) A parallel plate capacitor of length L, width w, plate separation d, with an air dielectric is initially charged to 600 volts, and the source is then removed. How much energy is stored in the field of the capacitor?

(b) A rubber slab, $\varepsilon_r = 3$, is now inserted between the capacitor plates to fill the space. How much energy is now stored in the field?

5-10.1. A schematic representation of the construction of an absolute voltmeter is given. Circular plates P_1 and P_2 form a parallel-plate capacitor, and GG is a guard ring which surrounds plate P_1 but is very close thereto. The guard ring GG will be maintained at the same potential as P_1 in order that no appreciable distortion of the field exist between P_1 and P_2. Plate P_1

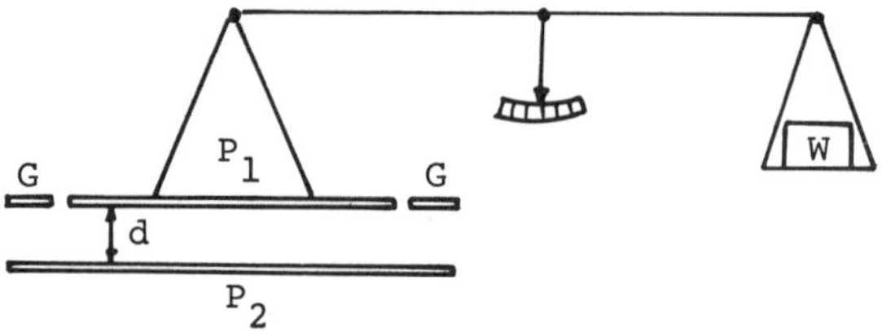

Figure P5-10.1.

is suspended from the beam BB of a precision balance that is to measure the force on P_1 with the application of a potential difference between P_1 and P_2. Under equilibrium the weight in the scale pan just balances the weight of the movable-plate system. Deduce a relation for applied voltage V in terms of the added weight to maintain equilibrium.

5-10.2. Suppose that the movable plate of the absolute voltmeter of Pr. 5-10.1 has an area of 75 cm^2, the space between the fixed and movable plate is 2 mm.

(a) What weight must be added to the balance pan if a potential difference of 800 volts is applied?

(b) What factors limit the potential difference that may be measured with such an instrument?

5-10.3. Suppose that the slab in Pr. 5-8.3 is only t thick, where $t < d$. Deduce an expression for the force acting to pull the slab into the region between the plates, if the voltage remains connected. Neglect edge effects.

5-11.1. Consider a junction of conductors but without sources to the junction. Develop the Kirchhoff current law.
[Hint: Use the relation $\nabla \cdot \overline{J} = 0$ and the divergence theorem.]

5-11.2. Using the relations, $\overline{J} = \sigma\overline{E}$, $\nabla \cdot \overline{J} = -\partial\rho/\partial t$ and $\nabla \cdot \overline{D} = \rho$, show that $\partial\rho/\partial t + (\sigma/\varepsilon)\rho = 0$. From this, show that if initially there is a charge density at any point inside of the conducting medium, the charge density at a later time is given by $\rho = \rho_o e^{-(\sigma/\varepsilon)t} = \rho_o e^{-t/\tau}$. The time constant is the relaxation time, as already discussed. (It is of interest that a wide range of τ-s exist: $\tau = 10^{-19}$ sec. for metals; $\tau = 10^{-6}$ sec. for distilled water; $\tau \doteq 10$ days for fused quartz.)

5-14.1. Show that the resistance of a conductor is given by

$$R = \frac{\int_V \overline{E} \cdot \overline{J}\, dV}{I^2}.$$

[Hint: Use Eq. (5-13.10).]

5-14.2. Show that the resistance between two plates at potentials Φ_1 and Φ_2, respectively, is given by $R = (\Phi_1 - \Phi_2)/I$. [Hint: Use the fact that $\rho = RI^2 = -\int_V \nabla \cdot (\Phi\overline{J})\, dV$ and then employ the divergence theorem.]

5-14.3. Find the resistance between two concentric spheres of radius <u>a</u> and <u>b</u> ($a < b$) respectively. The inner sphere is kept at a potential Φ relative to the outer one. The conductivity of the medium between the spheres is σ.
[Ans: $R = (b-a)/4\pi ab\sigma$.]

5-14.4. Find the resistance between two concentric cylinders per unit length using the same constants as in Pr. 5-14.3.

5-14.5. Compute the current density $\overline{J}$ and the total current in a uniformly thick metal plate shown. [Hint: Use cylindrical coordinates; Φ does not change as a function of r - why?]
[Ans: $\overline{J} = -\overline{a}_\phi \sigma \Phi_o/\pi r$.]

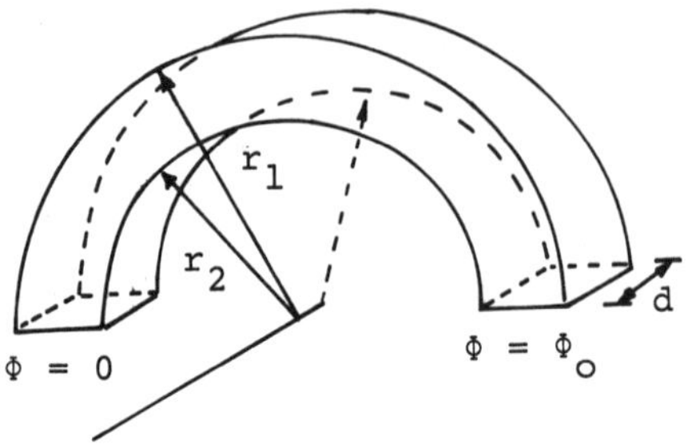

Figure P5-14.5.

CHAPTER 6

STATIC AND QUASI-STATIC MAGNETIC FIELDS

A. Static Magnetic Fields

When electric currents exist in conductors, a force field is set up that causes an interaction between separate conductors and also between the separate parts of a single conducting wire. This force field is identified as the magnetic field, denoted by the symbol $\overline{B}$, and is quite distinct from the Coulomb force field caused by electric charges. The present chapter is devoted to a study of static magnetic fields, and also of magnetic fields that vary slowly with time (quasi-static). A good deal of the theory is methematically similar in structure to that used in describing vortex motion in fluids, and also has features in common with potential theory such as occurs in electrostatics and potential flow in fluids.

The early history of magnetism centered around the curious behavior of naturally occurring magnets, and a theory based on the concepts of north and south seeking poles was developed. This theory was similar to that used in electrostatics in which the north and south poles were analogous to positive and negative charges. With the discovery of the magnetic effects of currents by Oersted in 1820, it became apparent that a more general theory was needed. Subsequent detailed study of the forces acting between current carrying conductors by Ampère, Biot, and Savart and others led to a mathematical formulation of the force law and the concept of the magnetic field $\overline{B}$ as a fundamental force field. This force law now forms a convenient experimental postulate on which to develop the theory of magnetism.

6-1. Ampère's Force Law and the $\overline{B}$ Field

Consider two conductors C_1 and C_2 with very small cross-sections and time varying but space stationary currents I_1 and I_2, as in Fig. 6-1.1. The experimental work of Ampère showed that a force $\overline{F}_{21}$ was exerted on C_2 by C_1 and could be described mathematically by the relation

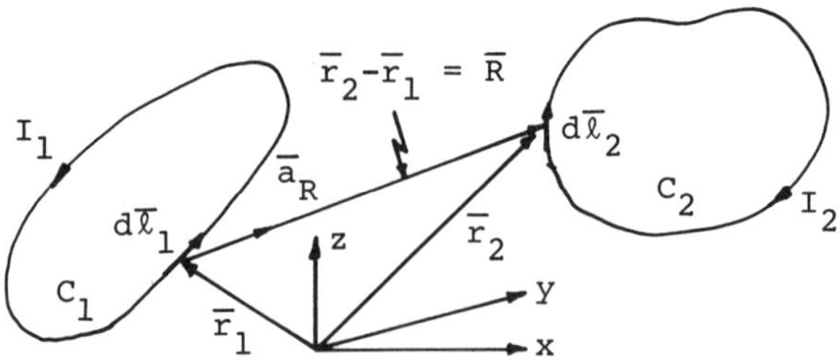

Figure 6-1.1. To study Ampère's Force Law.

$$\bar{F}_{21} = \frac{\mu_o}{4\pi} \oint_{C_2} \oint_{C_1} \frac{I_2 d\bar{\ell}_2 \times [I_1 d\bar{\ell}_1 \times (\bar{r}_2 - \bar{r}_1)]}{|\bar{r}_2 - \bar{r}_1|^3} \; ; \quad \frac{\bar{r}_2 - \bar{r}_1}{|\bar{r}_2 - \bar{r}_1|} = \bar{a}_R \tag{6-1.1}$$

The force is measured in Newton, the current in Ampère, distance in meters, and μ_o is a proportionality constant which has the value $4\pi \times 10^{-7}$ Newton/Amp^2 in the MKS system of units. The constant μ_o is called the *permeability of free space* or vacuum; its units are Henry/m, in honor of Joseph Henry who carried out many pioneering studies on inductance associated with magnetic fields. A careful review will show that the Henry has the dimensions of Newton-m/Amp^2. Note from Eq. (6-1.1) that the force decreases as the square of the distance between the current elements. Equation (6-1.1) is known as the *Ampère Force Law*.

The force acting between the two current loops can be viewed as resulting from a force field set up by the first current loop which pervades all space, and which transmits its effect to the second loop by means of this force field. The $\bar{B}$ field is defined by

$$\bar{B} = \frac{\mu_o}{4\pi} \oint_{C_1} \frac{I_1 d\bar{\ell}_1 \times \bar{a}_R}{R^2} \tag{6-1.2}$$

This result is called the *Biot-Savart* law. The $\bar{B}$ field has the dimensions of Newton/Amp-m, which is also called Weber/m^2 = Tesla. The force acting on loop C_2 may now be expressed as

$$\bar{F}_{21} = \oint_{C_2} I_2 \, d\bar{\ell}_2 \times \bar{B} \tag{6-1.3}$$

The result given in Eq. (6-1.2) is equivalent to postulating that a current distribution sets up a force field in all space surrounding it. Any other conductor in which a current exists when placed in this force field will then experience a force given by Eq. (6-1.3).

We can readily generalize Eq. (6-1.2) to make it applicable to an arbitrary

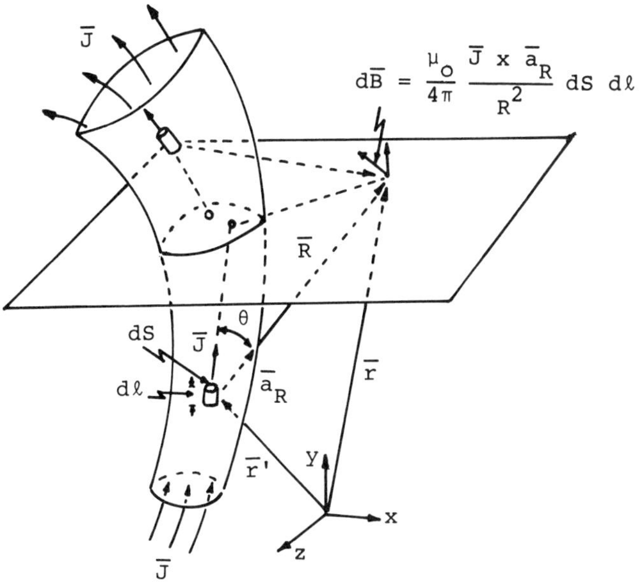

Figure 6-1.2. A differential volume element of current.

current distribution with density $\overline{J}$ Amp/m^2. In a volume element dV = dS dℓ where dℓ is in the direction of $\overline{J}$, we can write

$$I\, d\overline{\ell} = \overline{J}\, dS\, d\ell = \overline{J}\, dV$$

since J dS = I and the direction of $d\overline{\ell}$ is that of $\overline{J}$, as shown in Fig. 6-1.2. Hence, for an arbitrary current distribution

$$\overline{B}(\overline{r}) = \frac{\mu_o}{4\pi} \int_V \frac{\overline{J}(\overline{r}') \times \overline{a}_R}{R^2} dV' \qquad (6\text{-}1.4)$$

As a practical matter, carrying out the integral shown here is generally a difficult task, except in rare cases. For this reason, we shall introduce in the next section an alternative and generally more desirable approach that involves a vector potential.

The force acting on an element of current $\overline{J}$ dV will be given by

$$d\overline{F} = \overline{J} \times \overline{B}\, dV \qquad (6\text{-}1.5a)$$

which follows from Eq. (6-1.3) by replacing $I_2\, d\overline{\ell}_2$ by $J\, dS\, d\overline{\ell}_2 = \overline{J}\, dV$. It follows from this that a point charge q moving with a velocity $\overline{v}$ in a magnetic field $\overline{B}$ will experience a force

$$\overline{F} = q\overline{v} \times \overline{B} \tag{6-1.5b}$$

since $q\overline{v}$ is equivalent to a current element. The force given by Eq. (6-1.5b) is called the *Lorentz force*. If we had a fluid that was charged with a charge density q per unit volume and located in external $\overline{E}$ and $\overline{B}$ fields then a body force (ρ is the fluid density)

$$\overline{F} = \frac{q}{\rho}(\overline{E} + \overline{v} \times \overline{B}) \tag{6-1.6}$$

per unit mass would be exerted on the fluid. This equation is a basic equation in the study of ionized gases and magnetohydrodynamics.

An effect that is closely related to these considerations is the *Hall effect*. To examine this, refer to Fig. 6-1.3 which shows a current in a conductor in the presence of a magnetic field. There is a tendency for the individual charges to move perpendicular to the direction of flow and perpendicular to the magnetic field. The maximum effect occurs when the magnetic field is perpendicular to the current direction. For the situation illustrated, the force per unit volume on the current is given by

$$F_y = J_x B_z \tag{6-1.7}$$

Because of this downward force there will be an accumulation of charge on the conductor surfaces as shown. This charge distribution will give rise to an electric field E_y, the strength of which will be such that the electric force on the charges exactly equals the magnetic force. This requires that $\overline{F} = 0$ in Eq. (6-1.6) so that

$$qE_y = J_x B_z = qv_x B_z \tag{6-1.8}$$

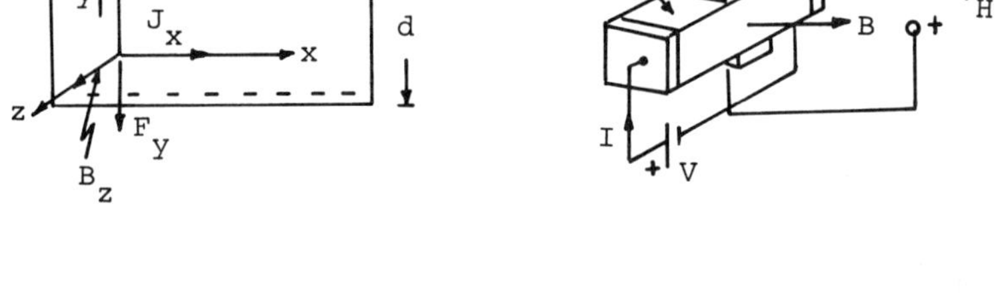

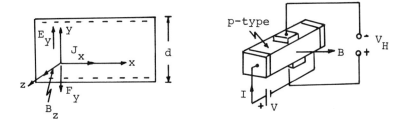

Figure 6-1.3. Hall effect in a conductor.

Because of this electric field, a potential difference exists. The voltage (which is called the *Hall voltage*) develops across the conductor and it is

$$V_h = E_y d = v_x B_z d \tag{6-1.9}$$

If the carriers are positively charged, the bottom edge will be at a higher potential than the top edge, as shown in Fig. 6-1.3. If the carriers are negatively charged, the reverse is true.

In some conductors, the conduction current comprises many electrons with a slow drift velocity; hence the Hall voltage is small. In some semiconductors there are relatively few free electrons, and these must move rapidly to make up even a small current. Thus the Hall voltage in a semiconductor can be relatively large. The Hall effect can be used to measure magnetic field strengths; it may also be used to investigate the number of current carriers in semiconductor materials.

Begin with Eq. (6-1.9) which is multiplied by ne, the free charge density per m^3, so that

$$ne\, E_y = ne\, v_x B_z = J_x B_z$$

from which

$$E_y = \frac{J_x B_z}{ne}$$

For a given material the *Hall constant* is

$$R_H \triangleq \frac{E_y}{J_x B_z} = \frac{1}{ne} = \text{constant, or} \quad Ne\, R_H = 1$$

Actual experimental values approximate this, e.g., for Li $R_H ne = 1.3$, for Na = $R_H ne = 0.9$.

6-2. Vector Potential and Ampere's Circuital Law

If the divergence of $\overline{B}$, i.e., $\nabla \cdot \overline{B}$, is evaluated from the defining relation, Eq. (6-1.4), it will be found to equal zero. This is always so, and

$$\nabla \cdot \overline{B} = 0 \tag{6-2.1}$$

This result expresses the physical fact that there are no free magnetic charges or poles on which the flux lines of $\overline{B}$ can terminate. Thus the flux lines of the $\overline{B}$ field are continuous and will close upon themselves.

We now consider Eq. (6-1.4) and rewrite it in the form

$$\overline{B}(\overline{r}) = -\frac{\mu_o}{4\pi}\int_V \overline{J}(\overline{r}') \times \nabla \frac{1}{R}\, dV'$$

since $-\nabla\, 1/R = -\,\partial/\partial R\,(1/R) = \overline{a}_R/R^2$. Since $\overline{J}(\overline{r}')$ is not a function of $\overline{r}$, we have

$$\overline{J}(\overline{r}') \times \nabla \frac{1}{R} = -\nabla \times \frac{\overline{J}(r')}{R}$$

as may be seen by expanding $\nabla \times \overline{J}/R$. Then

$$\nabla \times \frac{\overline{J}(\overline{r}')}{R} = \frac{1}{R}\nabla \times \overline{J} + (\nabla \frac{1}{R}) \times \overline{J} = -\overline{J} \times (\nabla \frac{1}{R})$$

since $\nabla \times \overline{J}$ is zero. Hence we can write

$$\overline{B}(\overline{r}) = \nabla \times \frac{\mu_o}{4\pi}\int_V \frac{\overline{J}(\overline{r}')}{R}\, dV' \qquad (6\text{-}2.2)$$

This result verifies that $\nabla \cdot \overline{B} = 0$ since the divergence of the curl of any vector is identically zero. Furthermore, it shows that $\overline{B}$ can be expressed as the curl of a *vector potential* $\overline{A}$ which is defined as follows

$$\overline{B}(\overline{r}) = \nabla \times \overline{A}(\overline{r}) \qquad (6\text{-}2.3)$$

where

$$\overline{A}(\overline{r}) = \frac{\mu_o}{4\pi}\int_V \frac{\overline{J}(\overline{r}')}{R}\, dV' \qquad (6\text{-}2.4)$$

These equations are of the same form as those that describe the vortex motion in a fluid. $\overline{A}$ is a vector point function that resembles in form the electrostatic potential Φ [Eq. (5-1.5)].

Further properties of the vector potential $\overline{A}$ can be deduced by taking the curl of Eq. (6-2.3), which yields

$$\nabla \times \overline{B} = \nabla \times (\nabla \times \overline{A}) = \nabla(\nabla \cdot \overline{A}) - \nabla^2\overline{A} \qquad (6\text{-}2.5)$$

However, the divergence of $\overline{A}$ can be found by operating on Eq. (6-2.4) with the divergence operation. This yields

$$\nabla \cdot \overline{A}(\overline{r}) = \frac{\mu_o}{4\pi}\int_V \nabla \cdot \frac{\overline{J}(\overline{r}')}{R}\, dV' \qquad (6\text{-}2.6)$$

But the vector identity, with f a scalar function of space

$$\nabla \cdot (f\overline{A}) = \overline{A} \cdot \nabla f + f\nabla \cdot \overline{A}$$

and so

$$\nabla \cdot \overline{A}(r) = \frac{\mu_o}{4\pi} \int_V [\overline{J}(\overline{r}') \cdot (\nabla \frac{1}{R}) + \frac{1}{R} \nabla \cdot \overline{J}(\overline{r}')] \, dV'$$

The second term of the integrand is zero since ∇ operates on $\overline{r}$ (x,y,z) and not on $\overline{r}'(x',y',z')$. Further, $\nabla(1/R) = -\nabla'(1/R)$, where $\nabla' \equiv \overline{a}_x \, \partial/\partial x' + \overline{a}_y \, \partial/\partial y' + \overline{a}_z \, \partial/\partial z'$. Then

$$\nabla \cdot \overline{A}(\overline{r}) = -\frac{\mu_o}{4\pi} \int_V \overline{J}(\overline{r}') \times \nabla'(1/R) \, dV'$$

or

$$\nabla \cdot \overline{A}(\overline{r}) = \frac{\mu_o}{4\pi} \int_V [\frac{1}{R} \nabla' \cdot \overline{J}(\overline{r}') - \nabla' \cdot (\frac{\overline{J}(\overline{r}')}{R})] \, dV' \tag{6-2.7}$$

We are presently concerned with steady magnetic fields which imposes the constraint that $\nabla' \cdot \overline{J}(\overline{r}') = 0$ as we shall later establish. In these cases Eq. (6-2.7) becomes

$$\nabla \cdot \overline{A}(\overline{r}) = -\frac{\mu_o}{4\pi} \oint_{S'} \frac{\overline{J}(\overline{r}')}{R} \cdot d\overline{S}' \tag{6-2.8}$$

The initial volume integration is over all currents which produce the field. We can always enlarge the surface S' in the last integral so that none of the currents cross the surface. As a consequence the integrand is zero, and

$$\nabla \cdot \overline{A}(\overline{r}) = 0 \tag{6-2.9}$$

Now let us compare Eq. (6-2.4) with Eq. (4-6.6). It is apparent that $\overline{A}(\overline{r})$ is the solution of the vector Poisson equation

$$\nabla^2 \overline{A}(\overline{r}) = -\mu_o \overline{J}(\overline{r}) \tag{6-2.10}$$

Also combining Eqs. (6-2.9), (6-2.10) and (6-2.5) we obtain

$$\nabla \times \overline{B} = \mu_o \overline{J} \tag{6-2.11}$$

If we integrate this equation over a surface S bounded by a contour C, we obtain

$$\int_S \nabla \times \overline{B} \cdot d\overline{S} = \int_S \mu_o \overline{J} \cdot d\overline{S} = \oint_C \overline{B} \cdot d\overline{\ell}$$

or

$$\oint_C \overline{B} \cdot d\overline{\ell} = \int_S \mu_o \overline{J} \cdot d\overline{S} = \mu_o I \qquad (6\text{-}2.12)$$

where the closed line integral was formed by using Stokes' theorem. This equation relates the circulation of $\overline{B}$ to the total enclosed current. This formula is known as *Ampère's circuital law*. This relation may be used to find $\overline{B}$ in certain types of problems having a high order of symmetry. We shall employ this result in some of the examples which follow.

Refer again to Eq. (6-2.3), and now dot-multiply it by $d\overline{S}$. Apply Stokes' theorem, which thus gives

$$\int_S (\nabla \times \overline{A}) \cdot d\overline{S} = \oint_C \overline{A} \cdot d\overline{\ell} = \int_S \overline{B} \cdot d\overline{S} = \psi \qquad (6\text{-}2.13)$$

where S is any surface bounded by the curve C, and ψ is the total *magnetic flux* through the surface S (Weber). We shall find this to be a useful relation between the vector potential $\overline{A}$ and $\overline{B}$. It resembles Eq. (6-2.12).

Example 6-2.1. Find the magnetic field $\overline{B}$ and the magnetic vector potential $\overline{A}$ due to a current in a straight thin wire of length $L_1 + L_2$.

Solution. Figure 6-2.1 illustrates a thin current filament of length $L_1 + L_2$. The equation for $\overline{B}$, Eq. (6-1.4) gives

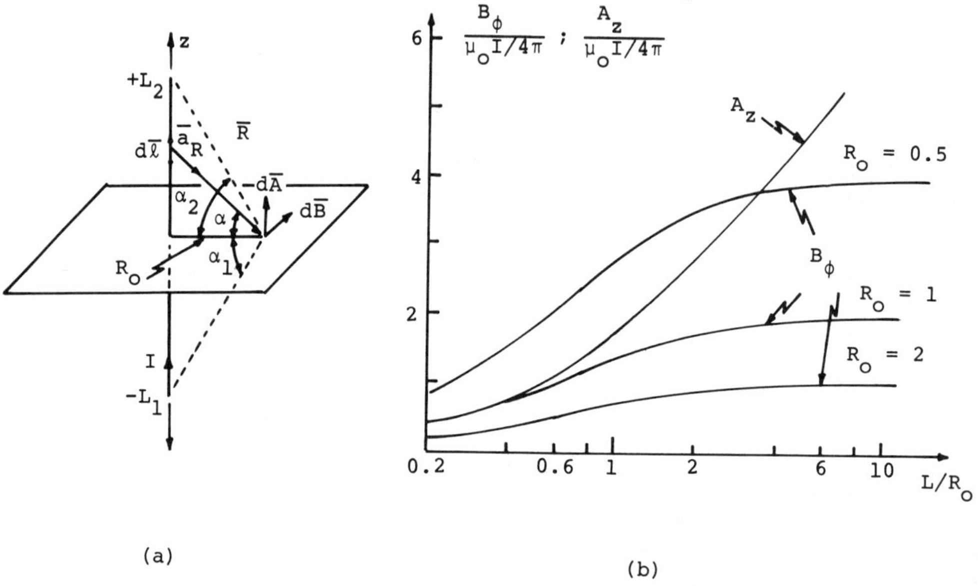

Figure 6-2.1. (a) A rectilinear current filament. (b) The magnetic field and vector potential versus L/R_o.

$$\overline{B} = \frac{\mu_o I}{4\pi}\int_{-L_1}^{L_2} \frac{d\overline{\ell} \times \overline{a}_R}{R^2}$$

Since $d\overline{\ell} \times \overline{a}_R = \sin(\pi/2 + \alpha)\, d\ell\, \overline{a}_\phi$, this equation becomes

$$B_\phi = \frac{\mu_o I}{4\pi}\int_{-L_1}^{L_2} \frac{\sin(\frac{\pi}{2} + \alpha)\, d\ell}{R^2}$$

But from the figure $d\ell \cos\alpha = R\, d\alpha$ and $R \cos\alpha = R_o$. Hence the integral becomes

$$B_\phi = \frac{\mu_o I}{4\pi}\int_{-\alpha_1}^{\alpha_2} \frac{\cos\alpha}{R_o}\, d\alpha = \frac{\mu_o I}{4\pi R_o}[\sin\alpha_2 - \sin(-\alpha_1)] \tag{6-2.14}$$

The field lines are circles with the current filament at the center, and which decrease in strength or concentration as the distance from the filament increases.

When the length of the filament increases to infinity, $L_1 = L_2 \to \infty$, we have the result

$$B_\phi = \frac{\mu_o I}{2\pi R_o} \tag{6-2.15}$$

This expression could be deduced directly using Ampère's circuital law.

Now let us calculate the vector potential using Eq. (6-2.4) for $L_1 = L_2$. We have

$$A_z = \int dA_z = \frac{\mu_o I}{4\pi}\int_{-L}^{L} \frac{dz}{(R_o^2 + z^2)^{1/2}} = \frac{\mu_o I}{4\pi} \ln\left[z + (R_o^2 + z^2)^{1/2}\right]\Big|_{-L}^{L}$$

$$= \frac{\mu_o I}{4\pi} \ln\left[\frac{[1 + (\frac{R_o}{L})^2]^{1/2} + 1}{[1 + (\frac{R_o}{L})^2]^{1/2} - 1}\right] \tag{6-2.16}$$

For $R_o^2 \ll L^2$, we can expand the square roots with respect to the small number $(R_o/L)^2$ and retain terms to the second order. We then have

$$A_z \doteq \frac{\mu_o I}{4\pi} \ln\left(1 + 4\frac{L^2}{R_o^2}\right) \tag{6-2.17}$$

If we use the relation $\overline{B} = \nabla \times (A_z \overline{a}_z)$ in cylindrical coordinates, we obtain

$$B_\phi = \frac{\mu_o I}{4\pi} \frac{8L^2/R_o^3}{1 + 4L^2/R_o^2} \tag{6-2.18}$$

which for $L \to \infty$ becomes

$$B_\phi = \frac{\mu_o I}{2\pi R_o}$$

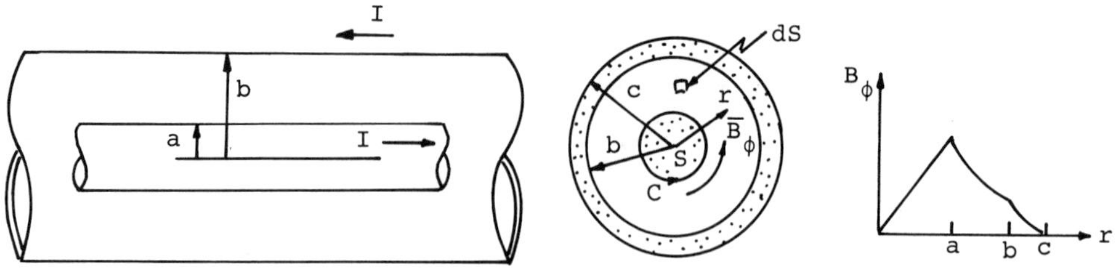

Figure 6-2.2. A coaxial transmission line.

as expected from Eq. (6-2.15). The values of B_ϕ and A_z vs. L/R_0 are shown in Fig. 6-2.1b.

ΔΔΔ

Example 6-2.2. Find the magnetic field in a coaxial line carrying a current I.

Solution. Figure 6-2.2 illustrates a coaxial transmission line on which a uniformly distributed total current I exists on the inner cylinder and -I on the outer cylinder. The magnetic field will be determined using the Ampère circuital law.

Owing to the circular symmetry, $\overline{B}$ possesses only a $\overline{B}_\phi$ component which depends only on r. Equation (6-2.12) becomes in this case

$$\int_0^{2\pi} B_\phi \, r \, d\phi = \mu_0 \int_S \overline{J} \cdot d\overline{S} = \mu_0 I$$

The integral on the left can be evaluated since B_ϕ does not depend on ϕ. We then obtain

$$B_\phi = \frac{\mu_0 I}{2\pi r} \qquad a \leq r \leq b \tag{6-2.19}$$

If the current I is uniformly distributed over the cross section of the center conductor, then for $r < a$ we have

$$2\pi r \, B_\phi = \mu_0 \int_0^r \int_0^{2\pi} \frac{1}{\pi a^2} \, r \, dr \, d\phi$$

since $J = I/(\pi a^2)$. We now obtain

$$B_\phi = \frac{\mu_0 I r}{2\pi a^2} \tag{6-2.20}$$

Finally for $r > b$ the total enclosed current is zero, which shows that $B_\phi = 0$ for $r > b$.

ΔΔΔ

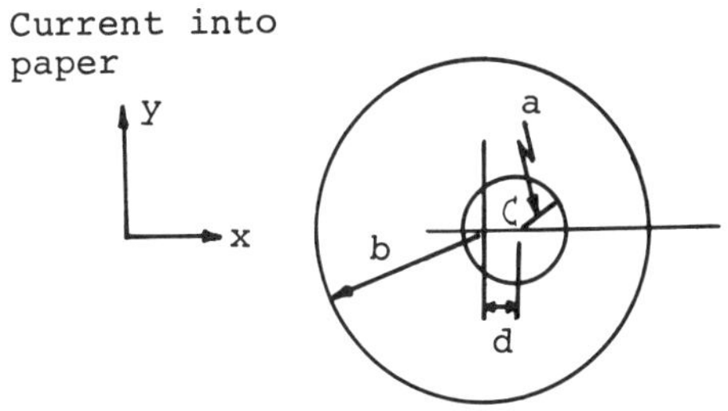

Figure 6-2.3. An off-centered hole in a cylindrical conductor.

Example 6-2.3. Find the magnetic field vector at the center of a cylindrical hole which is displaced from the center of a cylindrical conductor, as shown in Fig. 6-2.3.

Solution. The solution of this problem is readily accomplished if it is first noted that any effect of the hole in the conductor can be accounted for by considering the zero current in the hole as being made up of two equal currents in opposite directions. The problem then becomes the superposition of two problems: (a) to find the field at point C due to a homogeneous conductor carrying a current I', and (b) the field at point C due to a homogeneous conductor of radius a carrying a current of equal current density in the reverse direction to that in (a). The resultant magnetic vector is the vector sum of the effects under (a) and (b). Let I = the actual current in the original conductor; I' = the current in the homogeneous conductor having the same current density. Then

$$\frac{I'}{\pi b^2} = \frac{I}{\pi(b^2 - a^2)}$$

By Eq. (6-2.20), the magnetic vector at C due to an equivalent solid conductor is

$$\overline{B} = \frac{\mu_o Id}{2\pi(b^2 - a^2)}(-\overline{a}_y)$$

The magnetic vector at C due to the equivalent solid conductor of radius a carrying a specified known current opposite to that above is zero, since no current is contained within a path of zero radius. Hence the resultant magnetic vector at point C, which is the summation of the two foregoing factors is then simply

$$\overline{B} = \frac{\mu_o Id}{2\pi(b^2 - a^2)}(-\overline{a}_y)$$

By a straightforward application of the procedure that leads to Eq. (6-2.20) the magnetic vector $\overline{B}$ at any point in the off-centered hole can be found, [see also Eq. (6-9.7)].

ΔΔΔ

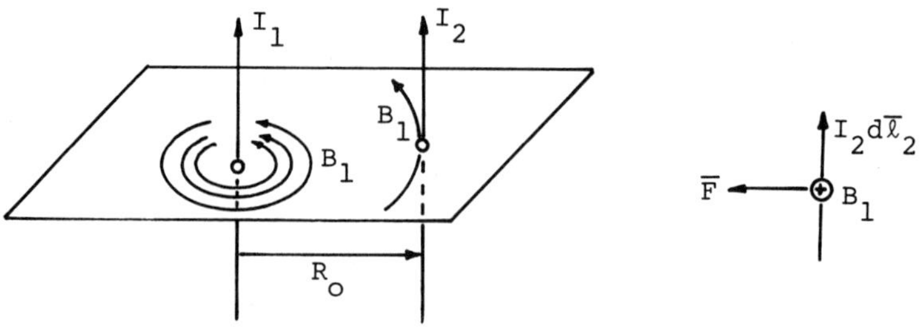

Figure 6-2.4. Two parallel current filaments.

Example 6-2.4. Find the force per unit length between two parallel wires of infinite extent, each carrying current.

Solution. Figure 6-2.4 illustrates the geometry of the system, the infinitely long thin wires carrying currents I_1 and I_2. Let the spacing between the two wires be R_o. The magnetic field at I_2 produced by I_1 is, from Eq. (6-2.15)

$$B_1 = \frac{\mu_o I_1}{2\pi R_o}$$

and in the azimuthal direction. Using the force law Eq. (6-1.3) we find that

$$\overline{F}_{21} = \int I_2 \, d\overline{\ell}_2 \times \overline{B}_1$$

or on a unit length of wire

$$|\overline{F}| = I_2 B_1 = \frac{\mu_o I_1 I_2}{2\pi R_o} \tag{6-2.21}$$

since $d\overline{\ell}_2$ and $\overline{B}_1$ are perpendicular. When the two currents are in the same direction, the force between them is one of attraction. If the currents are in opposite direction, the force is repulsive.

ΔΔΔ

6-3. Magnetic Dipole

A small closed current loop sets up a magnetic field which has the same general structure at large distance from the loop as the electric field produced by an electric dipole. For this reason, the small closed current loop or filament is called a magnetic dipole. The motion of electrons around the nucleus in materials is equivalent to circulating currents or current loops on an atomic scale and the properties of magnetic dipoles are important in describing the magnetic effects of materials, as we shall discuss in the next section.

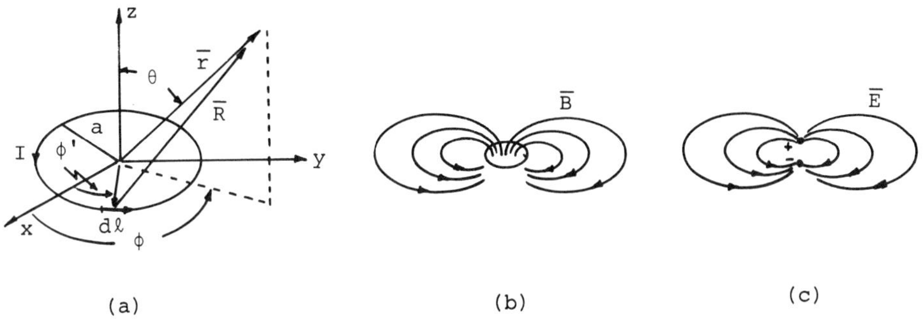

Figure 6-3.1. (a) Current loop. (b) Magnetic dipole. (c) Electric dipole.

Consider a small circular filament as shown in Fig. 6-3.1a. The vector potential $\bar{A}$, given by Eq. (6-2.4), becomes for the current filament

$$\bar{A}(\bar{r}) = \frac{\mu_o}{4\pi}\int_C \frac{I d\bar{\ell}}{R} \tag{6-3.1}$$

We shall evaluate this integral for the case where r is much larger than the loop radius $\underline{a}$. In this case

$$R = |\bar{r}-\bar{a}| = [(\bar{r}-\bar{a})\cdot(\bar{r}-\bar{a})]^{1/2} = (r^2 + a^2 - 2\bar{r}\cdot\bar{a})^{1/2} \doteq r - (\frac{\bar{r}\cdot\bar{a}}{r})$$

and

$$\frac{1}{R} \doteq \frac{1}{r}(1 + \frac{\bar{r}\cdot\bar{a}}{r^2})$$

Also note that

$$d\bar{\ell} = a d\phi' \, \bar{a}_\phi = a(-\bar{a}_x \sin\phi' + \bar{a}_y \cos\phi')\, d\phi'$$

and

$$\bar{r}\cdot\bar{a} = xx' + yy' = ra\sin\theta(\cos\phi\cos\phi' + \sin\phi\sin\phi') = ra\sin\theta\cos(\phi-\phi')$$

since $z' = 0$ and $x' = a \sin\theta' \cos\phi' = a\cos\phi'$, etc. The primed coordinate system which coincides with the unprimed one is introduced so that a distinction can be made between source and observation points. We then obtain

$$\begin{aligned}\bar{A}(\bar{r}) &= \frac{\mu_o I}{4\pi r}\int_0^{2\pi} [1 + \frac{a}{r}\sin\theta\cos(\phi-\phi')]\,[-\bar{a}_x \sin\phi' + \bar{a}_y\cos\phi']\, d\phi' \\ &= \frac{\mu_o I}{4\pi}(\frac{a}{r})^2 \sin\theta(-\bar{a}_x\sin\phi + \bar{a}_y\cos\phi)\pi = \frac{\mu_o I(\pi a^2)}{4\pi r^2}\sin\theta\,\bar{a}_\phi\end{aligned} \tag{6-3.2}$$

But the product of the current I with the area πa^2 of the loop is called the *magnetic dipole strength*, m. In terms of m we can now rewrite Eq. (6-3.2) as

$$\overline{A}(\overline{r}) = \frac{\mu_o \overline{m} \times \overline{a}_r}{4\pi r^2} = \frac{\mu_o}{4\pi}\left(\nabla \frac{1}{r} \times \overline{m}\right) = \frac{\mu_o}{4\pi} \nabla \times \frac{\overline{m}}{r} \tag{6-3.3}$$

since $\overline{m} = m\overline{a}_z = \pi a^2 I\overline{a}_z$; and $\overline{a}_z \times \overline{a}_r = \overline{a}_\phi \sin\theta$.

The magnetic field $\overline{B}$ is given by

$$\overline{B} = \nabla \times \overline{A} = \nabla \times \nabla \times \frac{\mu_o}{4\pi}\frac{\overline{m}}{r}$$

Since $\nabla \times \nabla \times (\overline{m}/r) = \nabla\nabla \cdot (\overline{m}/r) - \nabla^2(\overline{m}/r)$ and $\overline{m}$ is constant and $\nabla^2(1/r) = 0$, for $r \neq 0$ we obtain

$$\overline{B} = \frac{\mu_o}{4\pi} \nabla\nabla \cdot \frac{\overline{m}}{r} = \frac{\mu_o}{4\pi} \nabla\left(\overline{m} \cdot \nabla \frac{1}{r}\right) \tag{6-3.4}$$

which is similar to the expression for the electric potential of an electric dipole [see Eq. (5-5.2)]. This similarity ceases to exist when the details of the sources are observed carefully. Near the magnetic dipole the field lines thread through the current ring, while the electric field lines terminate on the positive and negative charges comprising the electric dipole, as shown in Fig. 6-3.1.

Since $\overline{m} = m\overline{a}_z = m(\overline{a}_r \cos\theta + \overline{a}_\theta \sin\theta)$, Eq. (6-3.4) is readily expanded into spherical coordinates to give

$$\overline{B} = \frac{\mu_o m}{4\pi r^3}(2\overline{a}_r \cos\theta + \overline{a}_\theta \sin\theta) \tag{6-3.5}$$

For an arbitrary shaped current loop the dipole moment is given by

$$\overline{m} = I\overline{S} \tag{6-3.6}$$

where $\overline{S}$ is the vector area enclosed by I. Figure 6-3.2 shows the vector area of the triangle shown shaded, $d\overline{S} = 1/2\ \overline{r} \times d\overline{\ell}$, in view of the definition of the cross product. The total area $\overline{S}$ can be expressed

$$\overline{S} = \frac{1}{2}\oint_C \overline{r} \times d\overline{\ell} \tag{6-3.7}$$

The total vector area with apex at 0 and boundary C is given by Eq. (6-3.7). Because the vector area of a closed surface is zero, Eq. (6-3.7) gives the vector area of any surface with C as its boundary.

The magnetic dipole when placed in a magnetic field $\overline{B}$ will be subjected to a torque. Since the force on a current element $Id\overline{\ell}$

$$d\overline{F} = Id\overline{\ell} \times \overline{B}$$

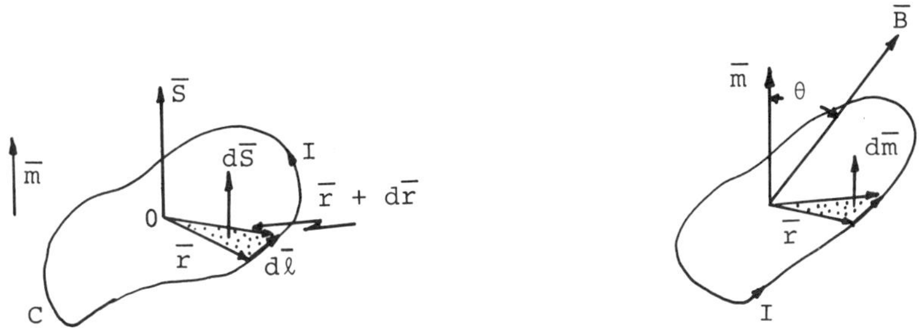

Figure 6-3.2. General magnetic dipole.

the torque acting about an arbitrary origin is given by $d\overline{T} = \overline{r} \times d\overline{F}$, where $\overline{r}$ specifies the location of the current element from the chosen origin. For a current loop the total resultant torque is given by

$$\overline{T} = \oint_C \overline{r} \times (I d\overline{\ell} \times \overline{B})$$

To evaluate this integral, it is noted that

$$\overline{r} \times (d\overline{\ell} \times \overline{B}) = (\overline{r} \cdot \overline{B}) d\overline{\ell} - (\overline{r} \cdot d\overline{\ell})\, \overline{B}$$

Now we rewrite the right hand side in the form

$$\overline{r} \times (d\overline{\ell} \times \overline{B}) = \frac{1}{2} [(\overline{r} \cdot \overline{B}) d\overline{\ell} - (\overline{B} \cdot d\overline{\ell})\overline{r}] + \frac{1}{2}[(\overline{r} \cdot \overline{B}) d\overline{\ell} + (\overline{B} \cdot d\overline{\ell})\overline{r} - 2(\overline{r} \cdot d\overline{\ell})\overline{B})]$$

We note that the first group of terms on the right is equal to $1/2(\overline{r} \times d\overline{\ell}) \times \overline{B}$ and and the second group of terms form a perfect differential $1/2\ d[(\overline{r} \cdot \overline{B})\overline{r} - (\overline{r} \cdot \overline{r})\overline{B}]$ if it is recognized that $d\overline{\ell} = d\overline{r}$, an increment in $\overline{r}$. Thus

$$d(\overline{r} \cdot \overline{B})\overline{r} = (\overline{r} \cdot \overline{B}) d\overline{r} + (\overline{B} \cdot d\overline{r})\overline{r}; \qquad d(\overline{r} \cdot \overline{r})\overline{B} = 2(\overline{r} \cdot d\overline{r})\overline{B}$$

since $\overline{B}$ is assumed constant. The torque integral is then

$$\overline{T} = \oint I\ [\frac{1}{2} (\overline{r} \times d\overline{\ell}) \times \overline{B} + \frac{1}{2} d\ [(\overline{r} \cdot \overline{B})\overline{r} - (\overline{r} \cdot \overline{r})\overline{B}]]$$

But the integral of the perfect differential around a closed path is zero, and so finally

$$\overline{T} = \oint_C \frac{I}{2} (\overline{r} \times d\overline{\ell}) \times \overline{B} = \oint_C d\overline{m} \times \overline{B} = \overline{m} \times \overline{B} \tag{6-3.8}$$

since $\overline{B}$ is constant, and the cross product with $\overline{B}$ can be performed after the integration is completed. The integral gives the magnetic dipole moment as reference to Eqs. (6-3.6) and (6-3.7) shows.

6-4. Magnetization of Materials

The magnetic properties of materials arise from two main effects: (1) the orbital motion of electrons around the nucleus represents circulating currents equivalent to current loops of atomic dimensions. These current loops are equivalent to small magnetic dipoles. (2) The electron has an intrinsic magnetic dipole moment of its own which can give rise to very large magnetic fields. From a macroscopic point of view we may regard a material as being characterized by a volume density of magnetic dipoles $\overline{M}$ called the *magnetization*. In an unmagnetized state the individual dipoles $\overline{m}$ will be randomly oriented so that the net magnetization $\overline{M}$ will be zero. If an external magnetic field is applied, the torque acting on the dipoles will tend to orient them in the direction of the field and this will give rise to a net magnetization $\overline{M}$ per unit volume. The unit of $\overline{m}$ is Ampere-m^2, and so $\overline{M}$ has the units of Amp/m.

Consider that a sample of matter is placed in a region of uniform magnetic induction. This can easily be accomplished by placing a cylinder of matter in an infinite solenoid, as shown in Fig. 6-4.1. As shown, the core is assumed to be divided into regions, supposedly of atomic dimensions, to represent the atomic current loops. Because of the mutual cancellation that occurs in the volume, only a *surface magnetization current* I_{ms} remains. Both the conduction current I_c and the surface magnetization current I_{ms} contribute to the magnetic field. By applying the Ampère circuital law around the circuit C shown in Fig. 6-4.1c we can write

$$\oint_C \overline{B} \cdot d\overline{\ell} = \mu_o(I_c + I_{ms}) \tag{6-4.1}$$

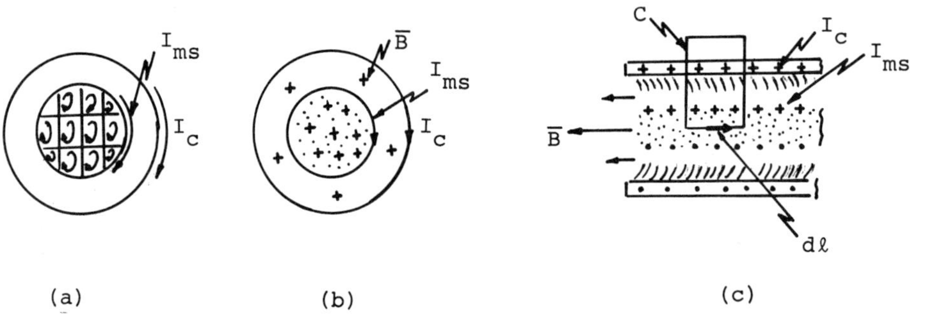

Figure 6-4.1. A cylinder of paramagnetic material in a solenoid.

If there were no core material, then the magnetic field inside of the solenoid would be related to the conduction current by the expression

$$\oint_C \overline{B} \cdot d\overline{\ell} = \mu_o I_c \qquad (6\text{-}4.2)$$

Clearly, the essential difference between the last two equations is the contribution to the line integral by the resulting effect of the core.

To proceed, we employ Eq. (6-2.11) to write Eq. (6-4.1) in point form, thus

$$\nabla \times \overline{B} = \mu_o(\overline{J}_c + \overline{J}_m) \qquad (6\text{-}4.3)$$

indicating that the total source for $\overline{B}$ includes the free and the *magnetization current* I_m which exists in the volume if $\overline{M}$ is nonuniform. The vector $\overline{M}$ is defined by the relation

$$\nabla \times \overline{M} = \overline{J}_m \qquad (6\text{-}4.4)$$

This is combined with Eq. (6-4.3) to yield

$$\nabla \times \left(\frac{\overline{B}}{\mu_o} - \overline{M}\right) = \overline{J}_c \qquad (6\text{-}4.5)$$

In analogy with the electrostatic field study, it is convenient to define a vector $\overline{H}$, usually called *magnetic field intensity*, which depends only on total external currents. Stated another way, the character of the medium does not enter into the definition for $\overline{H}$. $\overline{H}$ is defined by the relation

$$\overline{H} = \frac{\overline{B}}{\mu_o} - \overline{M} \qquad (6\text{-}4.6)$$

from which it follows that

$$\nabla \times \overline{H} = \overline{J}_c \qquad \text{a)}$$

which shows in general the Ampère circuital law is (6-4.7)

$$\oint \overline{H} \cdot d\overline{\ell} = I_c \qquad \text{b)}$$

It is evident from this equation that H has the units Amp/m.

In many materials $\overline{M}$ is proportional to $\overline{B}$, and hence also proportional to $\overline{H}$. By convention it is expressed as

$$\overline{M} = \chi_m \overline{H} \qquad (6\text{-}4.8)$$

where the dimensionless constant χ_m is called the *magnetic susceptibility*. It is a measure of how susceptible the material is to becoming magnetized. If we introduce Eq. (6-4.8) into (6-4.6) we obtain

$$\overline{B} = \mu_0(\overline{H} + \overline{M}) = \mu_0(1 + \chi_m)\overline{H} = \mu\overline{H} \tag{6-4.9}$$

where

$$\mu = \mu_0(1 + \chi_m) = \mu_0\mu_r \tag{6-4.10}$$

is called the *permeability* and μ_r is known as *relative permeability*.

Materials fall into three general categories: diamagnetic, paramagnetic, and ferromagnetic materials. (1) *Diamagnetic materials:* in these, the magnetic effects are due to the electron orbital motion, and χ_m is negative. Thus μ is less than μ_0 but only by a very small amount. The strongest diamagnetic material known is bismuth for which $\mu = 0.99983\ \mu_0$. (2) *Paramagnetic materials:* in these materials, the magnetic effects arise from the magnetic dipole moment of the electron. The exchange forces between the dipoles are very small so that the magnetic polarization is very weak, and μ is only slightly greater than μ_0, e.g., for aluminum $\mu = 1.00002\ \mu_0$. (3) *Ferromagnetic materials:* the magnetic properties of ferromagnetic materials, such as iron, also arise from the electron magnetic dipole moment. However, strong exchange forces exist that help align the dipole so as to produce large magnetization. These exchange forces cannot be explained using our simple model. Ferromagnetic materials also exhibit nonlinear and hysteresis effects. Typical values of μ range up to 10,000 μ_0 or more for special alloys, e.g., for permalloy-78, the value of μ is about $10^5\ \mu_0$.

Ferromagnetic materials are extensively used in magnetic field devices such as motors, relays, generators, galvanometers, etc., where a high magnetic flux density B is required. They are also used for permanent magnets.

6-5. B-H Curves

A nonlinear multivalued relation exists between B and H for ferromagnetic materials. To study this, a practical experimental arrangement as shown in Fig. 6-5.1 is used, since with this the magnetic field in the specimen can be varied. Also shown is a typical hysteresis curve. If the radius R of the toroid is large compared with the cross-section radius r the magnetic field H will be essentially uniform over the cross-section. Since $\nabla \times \overline{H} = \overline{J}$, we have

$$\int_S \nabla \times \overline{H} \cdot d\overline{S} = \oint_C \overline{H} \cdot d\overline{\ell} = \int_S \overline{J} \cdot d\overline{S} \tag{6-5.1}$$

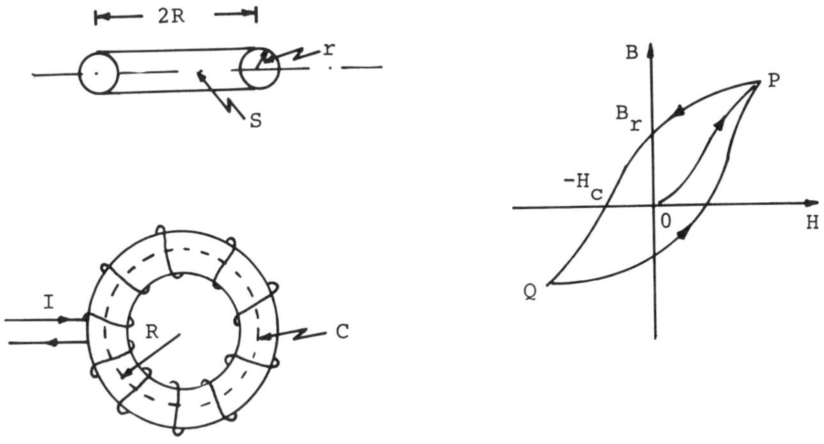

Figure 6-5.1. The experimental setup and a typical hysteresis curve.

which is the Ampère circuital law for H. If we apply this to the contour shown in Fig. 6-5.1 we obtain

$$2\pi RH = NI$$

or

$$H = \frac{NI}{2\pi} \qquad (2\text{-}5.2)$$

This shows that H is directly proportional to the current I and the number of turns N in the coil, and clearly H can be varied by changing I. We have dropped the subscript c on J since it was shown that H is related only to conduction currents. A second winding is often added over the magnetizing winding for measuring B corresponding to each H.

If the specimen is initially unmagnetized, increasing H (by increasing the current I) will cause the magnetic field B to increase along a nonlinear initial *magnetization curve* OP. When H becomes sufficiently large, the material will saturate (χ_m approaches zero) and further increase in B will vary as $\mu_o H$. If the H-field is reduced after reaching the point P, the B-field will decrease also but along a path PQ that lies above OP. When H has been reduced to zero, there will be some *remanent* magnetic flux density B_r in the material. The specimen at this point really constitutes a permanent magnet. Reversal of H (by reversing the current direction) will ultimately reduce B to zero; the value $-H_c$ to reach this point is called the *coercive force*. A further increase in H in the negative direction will bring the value of B to the point Q in the figure. If H is now increased in the positive sense, the flux density B will follow the path QP. In general, the curve of B vs. H will depend on the initial state of magnetization and the manner in which it is varied so that no unique relationship between B and H exists. In a later section we shall show that the area enclosed by a given hysteresis loop is proportional to the energy dissipated in carrying the material around the magnetic loop. The energy dissipated is equal to the work done on the specimen in overcoming the hysteresis forces which act to resist changes in the state of magnetization in the material.

A clear picture of the phenomena that occur in a ferromagnetic material during the process of magnetization is provided by the domain theory of ferromagnetism, a subject that is still the subject of considerable research. According to this theory, ferromagnetic materials are composed of small regions (with physical dimensions of the order of 10^{-3} to 10^{-4} cm) called *domains*, each of which is magnetized to saturation even though no external field is applied. This saturation effect results from the interaction among the electron-spin magnetic moments and interatomic forces in the crystals of the ferromagnetic material to cause the alignment of these spins. In the demagnetized state, the magnetization of the domains is randomly oriented so that the net overall result is zero magnetization. The effect of an applied field is to cause the assemblage of domains making up the material to align themselves with the direction of the applied field.

Refer to Fig. 6-5.2 which illustrates the changes in the domain pattern during magnetization as a gradually increasing external field is applied. In very weak fields, two types of behavior can occur: (a) the magnetization vector in each domain can rotate slightly in the direction of the applied field; (b) there can be a small motion of the domain walls, with those domains which are favorably oriented with respect to the field direction increasing in size at the expense of those less favorably oriented. If the field is sufficiently small, the processes are reversible with the removal of the field. As the applied field becomes stronger, the boundaries continue to change, but now in an irreversible manner. During this irreversible boundary displacement, the movements often take place in large jumps (this gives rise to the Barkhausen jumps, which produce measurable irregularities in the magnetization curve). With further increases in the applied field, the domain walls tend to disappear, but the magnetization is generally close to the direction of easy magnetization. For still stronger fields, the magnetization vector rotates

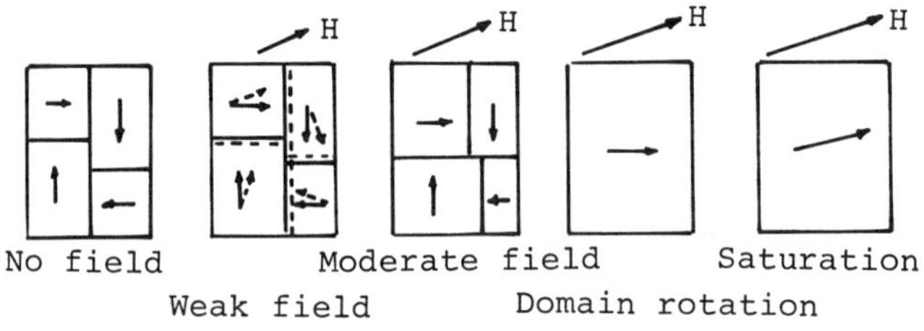

Figure 6-5.2. Changes in domain pattern during magnetization.

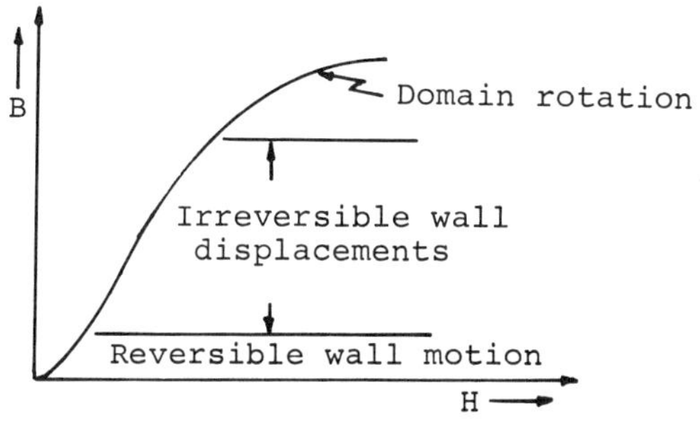

Figure 6-5.3. The magnetization curve, with the various regions identified with the domain behavior.

into the applied field, and saturation occurs. The several important portions of the magnetization curve identified with domain behavior are included in Fig. 6-5.3.

6-6. Boundary Conditions

We now focus on the boundary between a magnetic material with permeability μ and vacuum, as shown in Fig. 6-6.1. We construct a small coin-shaped volume with faces on adjacent sides of the boundary, as shown. We choose the thickness h to be very small. We apply the divergence theorem to the fundamental relation $\nabla \cdot \overline{B} = 0$, to obtain

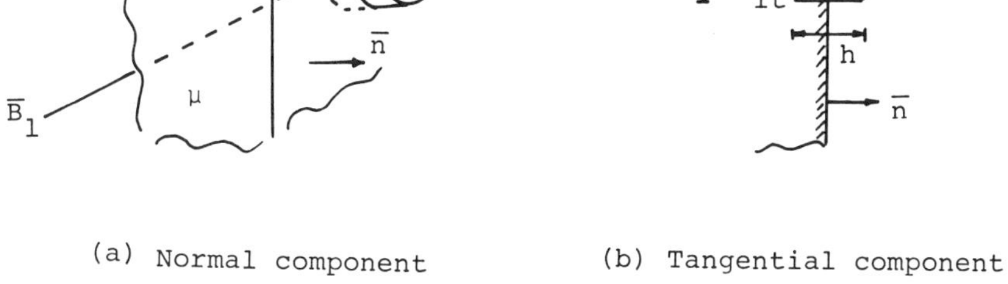

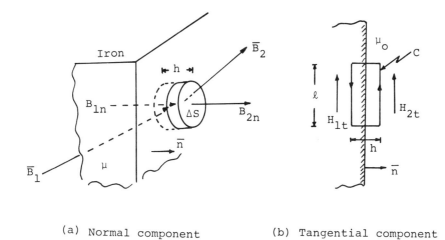

Figure 6-6.1. Boundary between a magnetic material and vacuum.

$$\int_V \nabla \cdot \overline{B}\, dV = \oint_S \overline{B} \cdot d\overline{S} = 0 \tag{6-6.1}$$

Since h can be chosen so small that the flux of $\overline{B}$ through the sides is negligible, Equation (6-6.1) gives

$$B_{1n}\Delta S = B_{2n}\Delta S$$

or in vector form

$$\overline{n} \cdot \overline{B}_1 = \overline{n} \cdot \overline{B}_2 \tag{6-6.2}$$

This states that the normal component of $\overline{B}$ is continuous across a boundary separating two different materials. From this relation we obtain

$$\mu\overline{n} \cdot \overline{H}_1 = \mu_o\overline{n} \cdot \overline{H}_2 \tag{6-6.3}$$

for the boundary condition on the normal component of $\overline{H}$.

To deduce a boundary condition on the tangential component of $\overline{H}$, we begin with the Ampère circuital law. We choose a contour C as in Fig. 6-6.1b and let h be so small that the surface $h\ell$ enclosed becomes negligible. In the limit as h vanishes

$$\int_S \overline{J} \cdot d\overline{S} \to 0$$

as long as $\overline{J}$ is bounded. Thus we get

$$H_{2t}\ell - H_{1t}\ell = 0$$

from which

$$H_{2t} = H_{1t} \qquad \text{a)}$$

In vector form this is (6-6.4)

$$\overline{n} \times \overline{H}_2 = \overline{n} \times \overline{H}_1 \qquad \text{b)}$$

This equation states that the tangential component of $\overline{H}$ is continuous across a boundary.

If a current sheet exists on the surface, the tangential component of $\overline{H}$ will undergo a rapid change as the current sheet is crossed. With reference to Fig. 6-6.2, let there be a winding with n turns per meter placed on the boundary. If a current I exists in each conductor, we will have a surface current sheet with density $J_s = nI$ Amp/m. Application of the Ampère circuit law now gives

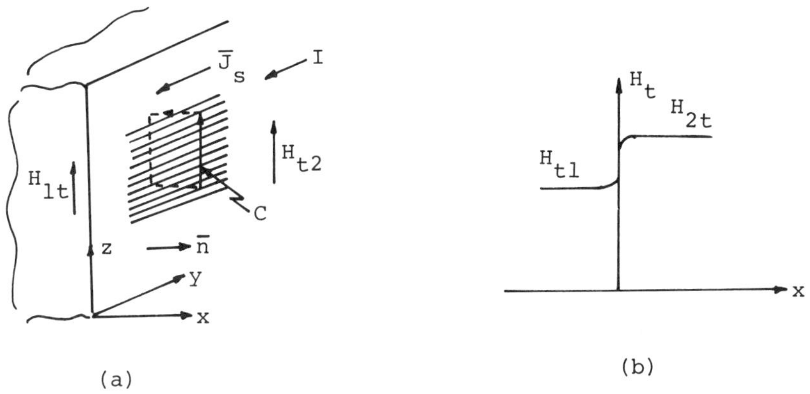

Figure 6-6.2. A boundary with a current sheet.

$$(H_{2t} - H_{1t})\ell = nI\ell$$

from which

$$H_{2t} - H_{1t} = nI = J_s \qquad \text{a)}$$

In vector form, this states that (6-6.5)

$$\overline{n} \times \overline{H}_2 - \overline{n} \times \overline{H}_1 = \overline{n} \times (\overline{H}_2 - \overline{H}_1) = \overline{J}_s \qquad \text{b)}$$

The way in which H_t varies as the current sheet is crossed is shown in Fig. 6-6.2b. If the thickness of the current sheet is made vanishingly small, but with a constant surface current density $\overline{J}s$, then $\overline{H}$ will undergo a step change of amount $\overline{J}_s$ as the current sheet is crossed. It follows that the magnetic field intensity on one side of the current sheet is the negative of that on the other side, because of symmetry. Thus to the right of the sheet

$$H_{2t} = \frac{1}{2} J_s$$

and to the left of the sheet

$$H_{1t} = -\frac{1}{2} J_s$$

If we let $\overline{n}$ denote a unit vector normal to the current sheet, the foregoing two equations can be specified by the single expression

$$\overline{H} = \frac{1}{2}\overline{J}_s \times \overline{n} \qquad \text{a)}$$

or equivalently (6-6.6)

$$\overline{J}_s = 2\overline{n} \times \overline{H} \qquad \text{b)}$$

This equation will be used in later chapters when dealing with wave propagation and radiation.

We shall now apply the above considerations to the tangential component of $\overline{B}$ in order to illustrate how the equivalent magnetization surface current density

$$\overline{J}_{ms} = \overline{M} \times \overline{n} \tag{6-6.7}$$

is taken into account in practice. The magnetization volume current density $\overline{J}_m = \nabla \times \overline{M}$ is taken into account through the introduction of the field $\overline{H}$ and the permeability μ, as reference to Eqs. (6-4.3) through (6-4.9) shows. If we did not introduce $\overline{H}$ and μ, then we would be required to work with the equation $\nabla \times \overline{B} = \mu_o(\overline{J}_c + \overline{J}_m)$ and the surface current density $\overline{J}_{ms}$ in describing the effect of magnetized materials. A surface current $\overline{J}_{ms}$ will cause the tangential component of $\overline{B}$ to undergo a step change at the boundary which, by analogy with Eq. (6-6.5), is given by

$$\overline{n} \times \overline{B}_2 - \overline{n} \times \overline{B}_1 = \mu_o\overline{J}_{ms} \tag{6-6.8}$$

We may rewrite this equation in the form

$$\overline{n} \times \overline{B}_2 - \overline{n} \times \overline{B}_1 = \mu_o\overline{M} \times \overline{n} \quad \text{or} \quad \overline{n} \times \overline{B}_2 = \overline{n} \times (\overline{B}_1 - \mu_o\overline{M})$$

But $\overline{B}_2 = \mu_o\overline{H}_2$ and $\overline{B}_1 - \mu_o\overline{M} = \mu_o\overline{H}_1$, so we obtain

$$\overline{n} \times \overline{H}_2 = \overline{n} \times \overline{H}_1$$

which is Eq. (6-6.4b). Clearly, we see that when we require $\overline{H}$ to satisfy the boundary condition Eq. (6-6.4b) we automatically take care of the boundary condition Eq. (6-6.8) on $\overline{B}$. In practice, it is not necessary to consider the magnetization $\overline{M}$ or the equivalent magnetization currents $\overline{J}_m$ and $\overline{J}_{ms}$ explicitly. These material sources are correctly and completely accounted for through the use of the $\overline{H}$ field, the permeability μ, the constitutive relation $\overline{B} = \mu\overline{H}$, and appropriate boundary conditions on the tangential component of $\overline{H}$ and the normal component of $\overline{B}$, i.e., Eqs. (6-6.2) and (6-6.4) or Eq. (6-6.5) if a free current sheet exists. The procedure used here is similar to that used in the electric field case to take account of the electric polarization $\overline{P}$ in materials by introducing the displacement field $\overline{D}$, the constitutive equation $\overline{D} = \varepsilon\overline{E}$, and appropriate boundary conditions.

6-7. Scalar Potential for the Magnetic Intensity

Boundary value problems involving magnetized materials but no free currents $\overline{J}$ are most conveniently handled by introducing a magnetic scalar potential Φ_m for describing $\overline{H}$. When $\overline{J} = 0$, we have $\nabla \times \overline{H} = 0$, which means that we can express $\overline{H}$ as

$$\overline{H} = -\nabla\Phi_m \tag{6-7.1}$$

since this will make the curl of $\overline{H}$ vanish identically. Since $\nabla \times \overline{H} = 0$ we cannot at the same time have $\nabla \cdot \overline{H} = 0$ everywhere, otherwise $\overline{H}$ will vanish, because there will be no source for this field. However, we will still have $\nabla \cdot \overline{B} = 0$ because the flux lines of $\overline{B}$ are always continuous. But $\overline{B} = \mu_o(\overline{H} + \overline{M})$ so we obtain

$$\nabla \cdot \overline{H} = -\nabla \cdot \overline{M} \tag{6-7.2}$$

and hence

$$\nabla^2\Phi_m = \nabla \cdot \overline{M} = -\rho_m \tag{6-7.3}$$

where ρ_m can be viewed as an equivalent magnetic charge density. $\rho_m = Q_m/V$ has the units = Amp-m/m^3, where Q_m is called the *pole strength* of a short magnet. This means that ρ_m or the divergence of the magnetization $\overline{M}$ is the source for the scalar potential Φ_m. There is also an equivalent magnetization surface charge density $\rho_{ms}(Q_m/S \equiv \text{Amp/m})$ that will contribute to Φ_m. Since the normal component of $\overline{B}$ is continuous across a surface separating a magnetic material and vacuum, the normal component of $\overline{H}$ will be discontinuous. From Eq. (6-6.3) we can write

$$\overline{n} \cdot \overline{B}_1 = \overline{n} \cdot (\mu_o\overline{H}_1 + \mu_o\overline{M}) = \overline{n} \cdot \overline{B}_2 = \overline{n} \cdot \mu_o\overline{H}_2$$

or

$$\overline{n} \cdot (\overline{H}_2 - \overline{H}_1) = \overline{n} \cdot \overline{M} = \rho_{ms} \tag{6-7.4}$$

This shows that the normal component of $\overline{M}$ gives rise to an equivalent surface magnetic charge density ρ_{ms}. By analogy with the electrostatic potential problem, the solution for Φ_m will be

$$\begin{aligned} \Phi_m(\overline{r}) &= \frac{1}{4\pi}\int_V \frac{\rho_m}{R}\,dV' + \frac{1}{4\pi}\oint_S \frac{\rho_{ms}}{R}\,dS' \\ &= \frac{1}{4\pi}\int_V \frac{-\nabla \cdot \overline{M}}{R}\,dV' + \frac{1}{4\pi}\oint_S \frac{\overline{M} \cdot \overline{n}}{R}\,dS' \end{aligned} \tag{6-7.5}$$

When Φ_m has been found, we can find $\overline{H}$ from the relation

$$\overline{H} = -\nabla\Phi_m \qquad \text{a)}$$

and $\overline{B}$ from the relations (6-7.6)

$$\overline{B} = \mu_0\overline{H} \qquad \text{outside the material} \qquad \text{b)}$$

$$\overline{B} = \mu_0(\overline{H} + \overline{M}) \qquad \text{inside the material} \qquad \text{c)}$$

To simplify the concept of the scalar potential for the magnetic intensity, consider the situation of a line current I. We have already seen that the field intensity is given by

$$H_\phi = \frac{I}{2\pi r}$$

and the radial component H_r is zero. In order to calculate a potential function for the field surrounding a line source, it is necessary to exclude a small portion of the field by taking a radial path from infinity to the line of the current, taking a circular path around the current of infinity small radius and then returning to infinity along a radial path adjacent to the original radial path. The path is shown in Fig. 6-7.1, the excluded region being the cross hatched cut in the field.

For the line source the magnetic intensity is entirely tangential and the obvious path of integration is along the circumference of a circle. Thus for the path AB shown, the potential function is

$$\Phi_B - \Phi_A = -\int_A^B \overline{H} \cdot d\overline{\ell} = -\int_0^{\phi_1} H_\phi r \, d\theta$$

which becomes, using Eq. (6-2.15),

$$\Phi_B - \Phi_A = -\int_0^{\phi_1} \frac{Id\phi}{2\pi} = -\frac{I\phi_1}{2\pi}$$

or in the more general case

$$\Phi = -\frac{I\phi}{2\pi}$$

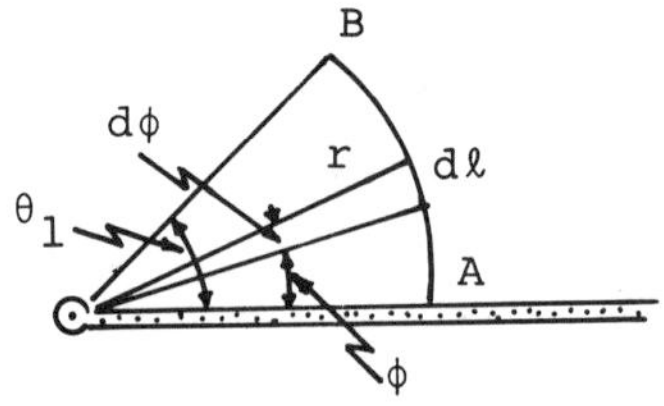

Figure 6-7.1. To calculate the potential function of a line source.

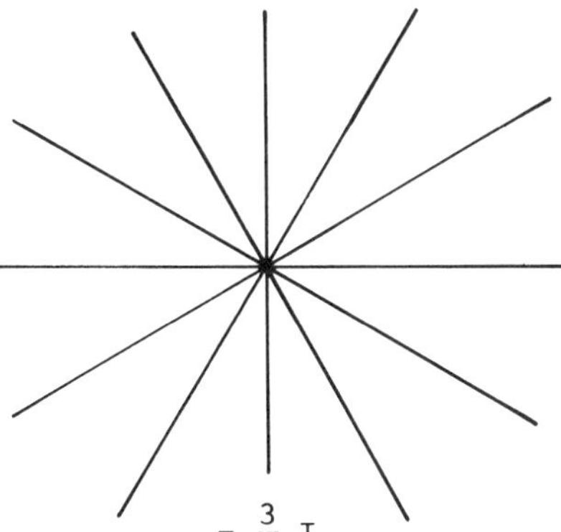

Figure 6-7.2. Equipotential lines for the field surrounding a line vortex of strength I.

The equipotential lines for the field surrounding a current line are shown in Fig. 6-7.2.

From our studies in Chap. 2 we know that the flow lines are perpendicular to the equipotential lines, and the flow lines will then be circles centered on the line which confirms that there is no variation of the flow lines with θ and the only variation of the flow line function is with the radius r. The radial variation of the flux function is then

$$\psi_r - \psi_a = -\int_a^r H_\phi \, dr$$

which integrates, for $\psi = 0$ when $r = a$, to

$$\psi = -\int_a^r \frac{I}{2\pi r} \, dr = -\frac{I}{2\pi} \ln \frac{r}{a}$$

or

$$\psi = \frac{I}{2\pi} \ln \frac{a}{r}$$

Of course, from the nature of our development

$$\overline{H} = -\nabla\Phi$$

or

$$H_\phi = -\frac{1}{r}\frac{\partial\Phi}{\partial\phi} = \frac{I}{2\pi r}$$

Example 6-7.1. Find the field resulting from a cylindrical permanent magnet at a distance r which is very large in comparison with its length L.

Solution. (Case A: using equivalent magnetization current). Refer to Fig. 6-7.3 which illustrates a cylindrical magnet of length L and radius a. The permanent magnet is assumed to be uniformly magnetized with a magnetic polarization density $\overline{M} = M\overline{a}_z$. The point of observation is taken to be at a distance r >>L. The volume density of magnetization current is zero since $\overline{J}_m = \nabla \times \overline{M} = 0$ when M is constant. The surface magnetization current density is $\overline{J}_{ms} = \overline{M} \times \overline{n}$ [see Eq. (6-6.7)]. In a length dz' we have an equivalent current ring source, $I_{m\phi} = M\,dz'$ of radius a. This ring source produces a vector potential, as per Eq. (6-3.2)

$$d\overline{A}_\phi = \mu_o(\pi a^2)M\,dz'\,\overline{a}_\phi \frac{\sin\theta'}{4\pi R^2}$$

The total vector potential will be

$$A_\phi = \frac{\mu_o(\pi a^2)M}{4\pi}\int_{-L/2}^{L/2} \frac{\sin\theta'}{R^2}\,dz' \tag{6-7.7}$$

where $R^2 = [x^2 + y^2 + (z-z')^2]$. We also have that

$$R\sin\theta' = (x^2 + y^2)^{1/2} \doteq r\sin\theta$$

Hence

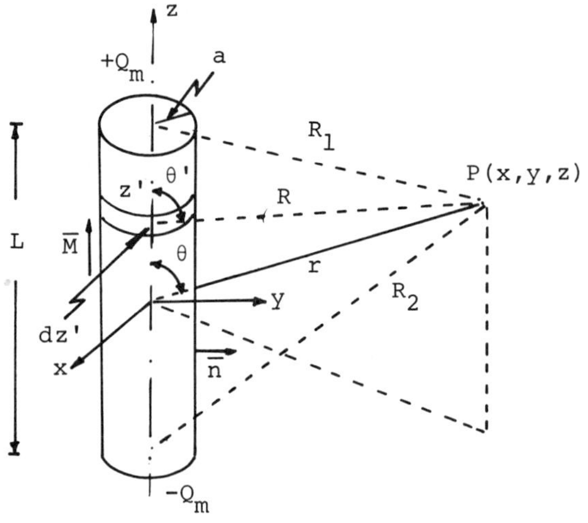

Figure 6-7.3. A cylindrical permanent magnet.

$$A_\phi = \frac{\mu_o(\pi a^2)Mr \sin\theta}{4\pi} \int_{-L/2}^{L/2} \frac{dz'}{[x^2 + y^2 + (z-z')^2]^{3/2}}$$

$$= \frac{\mu_o(\pi a^2)Mr \sin\theta}{4\pi} \left. \frac{z' - z}{(x^2 + y^2)[x^2 + y^2 + (z-z')^2]^{1/2}} \right|_{-L/2}^{L/2}$$

$$= \frac{\mu_o(\pi a^2)M}{4\pi r \sin\theta} [\frac{L-2z}{2R_1} + \frac{L+2z}{2R_2}] \tag{6-7.8}$$

To simplify this expression, we will assume that $r >> L$, and so

$$\frac{1}{R_1} \doteq \frac{1}{r}(1 + \frac{L\cos\theta}{2r}); \qquad \frac{1}{R_2} \doteq \frac{1}{r}(1 - \frac{L\cos\theta}{2r})$$

We now get

$$A_\phi = \frac{\mu_o(\pi a^2)ML \sin\theta}{4\pi r^2} \tag{6-7.9}$$

This expression is the same as that for a magnetic dipole with a total amount $\pi a^2 LM$, as shown in Eq. (6-3.2). The $\overline{B}$ field is specified by Eq. (6-2.3) and specifically becomes

$$\overline{B} = \frac{\mu_o(\pi a^2 LM)}{4\pi r^3} (2\overline{a}_r \cos\theta + \overline{a}_\theta \sin\theta) \tag{6-7.10}$$

If we want the field in the region closer to the magnet but still such that $r >> a$, then Eq. (6-7.8) must be used since this formula is valid as long as $r >> a$ but does not require that $r >> L$. It should be noted that B given by Eq. (6-7.10) is the same as the field produced by a solenoid with an Ampère-turn density $nI = J_{ms} = M$ Amp/m.

Case B: (using scalar potential). To determine the scalar potential, we note that $\nabla \cdot \overline{M} = 0$ and therefore $\rho_m = 0$. At the ends of the magnet we have a total equivalent magnetic charge [see Eq. (6-7.4)]

$$Q_m = \rho_{ms}\pi a^2 = \overline{M} \cdot \overline{a}_z(\pi a^2) = \pi a^2 M \quad \text{at} \quad z = \frac{L}{2}; \quad -Q_m \quad \text{at} \quad z = -\frac{L}{2}$$

If we regard this as a point charge, then Φ_m is given by

$$\Phi_m = \frac{Q_m}{4\pi}(\frac{1}{R_1} - \frac{1}{R_2}) \tag{6-7.11}$$

The magnetic intensity is given by $\overline{H} = -\nabla\Phi_m$ and, therefore, $\overline{B} = -\mu_o\nabla\Phi_m$. Thus

$$\overline{B} = -\frac{\mu_o\pi a^2 M}{4\pi} \nabla (\frac{1}{R_1} - \frac{1}{R_2}) \doteq -\frac{\mu_o\pi a^2 ML}{4\pi} \nabla (\frac{\cos\theta}{r^2}) \tag{6-7.12}$$

upon using the earlier approximations for R_1^{-1} and R_2^{-1}. By carrying out the operation called for in Eq. (6-7.12), the result is that given in Eq. (6-7.10) (prove it!).

ΔΔΔ

Example 6-7.2. Find the magnetic field in a toroid with an air-gap, as shown in Fig. 6-7.4.

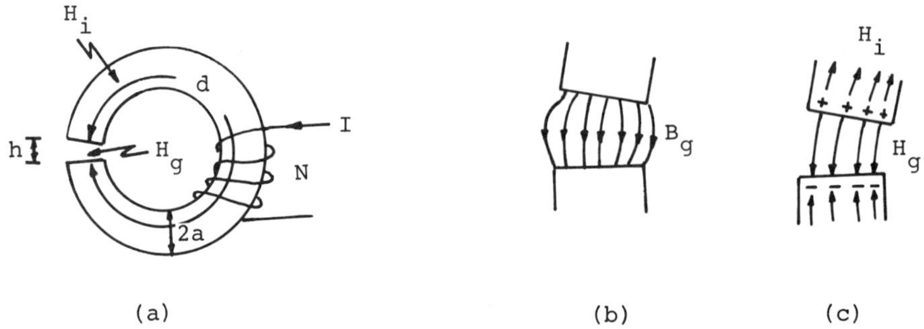

Figure 6-7.4. A toroid with an air gap.

Solution. Also shown in the figure is an enlarged view of the gap. If we assume that h << a and a << d, then the magnetic flux B-lines will be essentially uniform over the cross section and in the air gap. The flux lines will bulge out by a small but negligible amount in the air gap as long as h << a. Let H be denoted by H_i in the iron and by H_g in the air gap. We suppose that the specimen is wound with an N turn coil through which a current I passes. Ampère's circuital law gives

$$\oint_C \overline{H} \cdot d\overline{\ell} = H_i d + H_g h = NI \qquad (6\text{-}7.13)$$

In the air gap $B_g = \mu_o H_g$, and since $\overline{B}$ is continuous, we must have $B_i = B_g = \mu_o H_g$. Combining this result with Eq. (6-7.13), we have

$$H_i d + \frac{B_i}{\mu_o} h = NI$$

or

$$B_i = -\frac{\mu_o d}{h} H_i + \frac{\mu_o NI}{h} \qquad (6\text{-}7.14)$$

This equation is called the *shearing line* (or load line) and gives a relation between B_i and H_i in the iron as specified by the configuration of the toroidal specimen. We also have a relationship between B_i and H_i determined by the hysteresis curve, which is assumed to be that given in Fig. 6-7.5.

The value of B_i and H_i in the iron can be found by plotting the shearing line on the same plane as that on which the hysteresis loop is plotted. The points of

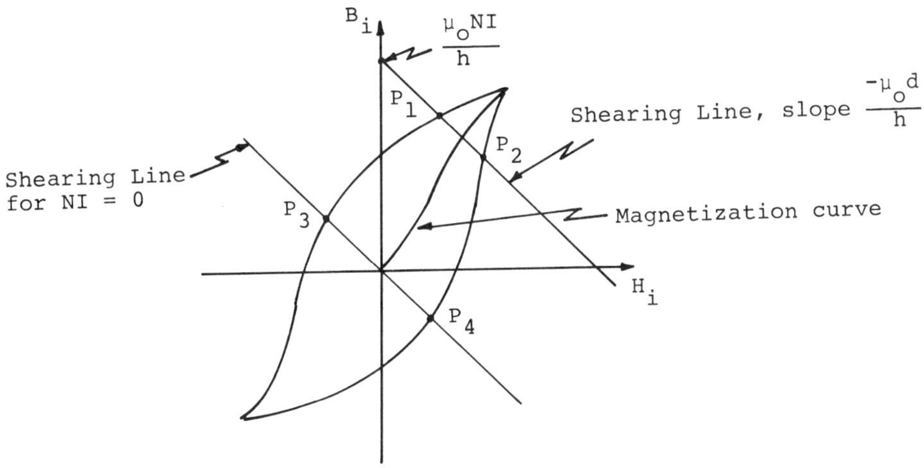

Figure 6-7.5. Determining the magnetic field by plotting the shearing line on the B-H hysteresis plane.

intersection such as P_1 and P_2 indicated in the figure are those which satisfy simultaneously both Eq. (6-7.14) and the equation for the hysteresis loop. We note that the shearing line has a negative slope and that when NI = 0 (the permanent magnet case) that H_i is negative if B_i is positive. This situation may be explained by reference to Fig. 6-7.4c. When NI = 0 but B_i is not zero, then since B is continuous we still have $B_i = B_g$ and also $\mu_o H_g = B_g$. But the Ampère circuital law requires in this case

$$\oint_C \overline{H} \cdot d\overline{\ell} = 0$$

and H_i in the iron must be negative to make the line integral vanish. Thus the normal component of $\overline{H}$ is discontinuous at the pole faces, which of course it should be, since the residual magnetization in the specimen leads to an equivalent magnetic surface charge $\overline{M} \cdot \overline{n}$ at the pole faces, as illustrated. This equivalent magnetic charge can be viewed as the source that maintains $\overline{H}$ and hence produces a flux density $\overline{B}$ in the air gap, even though NI = 0.

If the B_i, H_i hysteresis loop were a straight line given by $B_i = \mu H_i$ with the permeability μ constant, then we would have

$$B_i = -\frac{\mu_o d}{h} H_i + \frac{\mu_o NI}{h} = \mu H_i$$

From this equation we get

$$H_i = \frac{\mu_o}{\mu h + \mu_o d} NI \qquad \text{a)}$$
$$B_i = \frac{\mu\mu_o d}{\mu h + \mu_o d}\frac{NI}{d} \qquad \text{b)} \qquad (6\text{-}7.15)$$

If h = 0 then $B_i = \mu(NI/d)$ so that for $H \neq 0$ and $h \neq 0$ the effective permeability is reduced below μ, and is

$$\mu_e = \frac{\mu_o d}{\mu h + \mu_o d}\mu \qquad (6\text{-}7.16)$$

This reduction in the effective permeability is caused by the demagnetizing effect of the equivalent magnetic charge set up on the pole faces in the air gap. ΔΔΔ

Example 6-7.3. Find the magnetization $\overline{M}$ in an iron sphere placed in a previously uniform magnetic field $\overline{B} = B_o\overline{a}_z$, as shown in Fig. 6-7.6. Refer to Ex. 5-6.3 for the roughly equivalent electric field problem.

Solution. The magnetic field intensity $\overline{H}$ for the specified applied field is

$$\overline{H} = H_o\overline{a}_z = \frac{B_o}{\mu_o}\overline{a}_z = -\nabla\Phi_o$$

where

$$\Phi_o = -H_o z = -H_o r \cos\theta$$

is the applied magnetic potential. The induced magnetic potential Φ_m will satisfy Laplace's equation $\nabla^2\Phi_m = 0$, in spherical coordinates. The solutions, which vary as cos θ and must be finite at r = 0 and vanish at infinity, are

$$\Phi_m = A_1 r \cos\theta\,, \qquad r < a$$
$$= A_2 r^{-2}\cos\theta\,, \qquad r > a$$

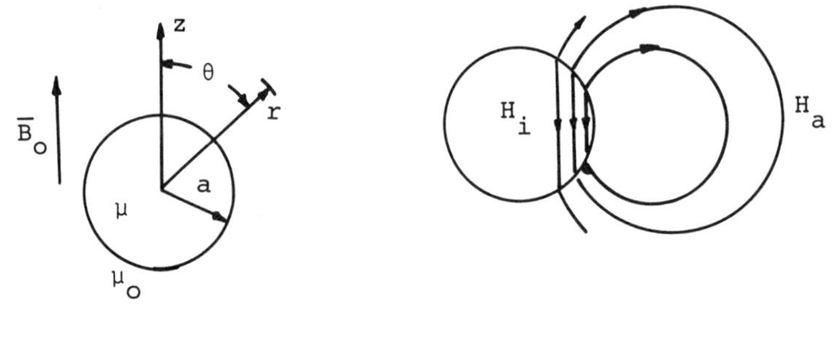

Figure 6-7.6. An iron sphere placed in a uniform B_o field.

The induced magnetic intensity is $-\nabla\Phi_m$, and so

$$\overline{H}_i = -A_1 \cos\theta\, \overline{a}_r + A_1 \sin\theta\, \overline{a}_\theta = -A_1\overline{a}_z, \qquad r < a$$

$$\overline{H}_a = \frac{2A_2}{r^3}\cos\theta\, \overline{a}_r + \frac{A_2}{r^3}\sin\theta\, \overline{a}_\theta, \qquad r > a$$

The total radial component of $\overline{B}$ must be continuous at $r = a$. If the permeability of the iron is a constant μ, then

$$\mu\overline{a}_r \cdot (\overline{H}_0 + \overline{H}_i) = \mu_0\overline{a}_r \cdot (\overline{H}_0 + \overline{H}_a), \qquad r = a$$

or

$$\mu(H_0 - A_1) = \mu_0(H_0 + \frac{2A_2}{a^3})$$

In addition, the tangential component of $\overline{H}$ must be continuous at $r = a$, so

$$\overline{a}_\theta \cdot (\overline{H}_0 + \overline{H}_i) = \overline{a}_\theta \cdot (\overline{H}_0 + \overline{H}_a), \quad r = a$$

These equations give

$$A_1 = \frac{A_2}{a^3}$$

We can now solve for A_1 and A_2 to get

$$A_1 = \frac{\mu - \mu_0}{\mu + 2\mu_0} H_0 \qquad \text{a)}$$

$$A_2 = a^3 A_1 \qquad \text{b)} \qquad (6\text{-}7.17)$$

The total $\overline{H}$ and $\overline{B}$ fields inside of the iron sphere are

$$\overline{H} = \overline{H}_i + \overline{H}_0 = (H_0 - \frac{\mu - \mu_0}{\mu + 2\mu_0} H_0)\overline{a}_z = \frac{3\mu_0}{\mu + 2\mu_0} H_0\overline{a}_z \qquad \text{a)}$$

$$\overline{B} = \mu\,\overline{H} = \frac{3\mu\mu_0}{\mu + 2\mu_0} H_0\overline{a}_z \qquad \text{b)} \qquad (6\text{-}7.18)$$

But $\overline{B} = \mu_0(\overline{H} + \overline{M})$, so $\mu_0\overline{M} = \overline{B} - \mu_0\overline{H}$, and from Eq. (6-7.18) we find that

$$\overline{M} = \frac{3(\mu - \mu_0)}{\mu + 2\mu_0} H_0\overline{a}_z \qquad (6\text{-}7.19)$$

The magnetization in the sphere is uniform and proportional to $\overline{H}_0$. The $\overline{H}$-field is reduced below the applied value $\overline{H}_0$ since, from Eq. (6-7.18a)

$$\overline{H} = \overline{H}_o - \frac{\mu - \mu_o}{\mu + 2\mu_o}\overline{H}_o$$

Using Eq. (6-7.19) we may write this in the form

$$\overline{H} = \overline{H}_o - D\overline{M} = \overline{H}_o - \frac{\overline{M}}{3} \tag{6-7.20}$$

where D is called the *demagnetization factor* (equal to 1/3 for a sphere).

By solving the equations

$$\overline{H} = \overline{H}_o - D\overline{M}$$

$$\overline{B} = \mu\overline{H} = \mu_o(\overline{H} + \overline{M})$$

for $\overline{H}$ and $\overline{M}$ in terms of $\overline{H}_o$ we get

$$\overline{H} = \frac{\overline{H}_o}{1 + D\dfrac{\mu-\mu_o}{\mu_o}} \qquad \text{a)}$$

(6-7.21)

$$\overline{B} = \mu\overline{H} = \frac{\mu\overline{H}_o}{1 + D\dfrac{\mu-\mu_o}{\mu_o}} \qquad \text{b)}$$

The effective permeability is

$$\mu_e = \frac{\mu}{1 + D\dfrac{\mu-\mu_o}{\mu_o}} \tag{6-7.22}$$

since $\overline{B}$ in the iron is increased by a relative amount μ_e/μ_o over the value $\mu_o\overline{H}_o$ of the applied field. To get a large increase in flux density or high μ_e, the demagnetization factor D should be small. This example shows why the use of a powdered iron core in a solenoid coil does not increase the flux density by an amount μ/μ_o.

ΔΔΔ

6-8. Magnetic Circuits

Many magnetic field devices, such as transformers, relays, motors, etc., are so constructed that the magnetic flux is confined almost entirely within high permeability iron regions. For such devices approximate solutions for the magnetic flux in the circuit can be obtained by the resistance net approximation discussed in Sec. 3-4 which will be accurate within a few percent; such an approach is much less complicated than the procedure discussed in Ex. 6-7.2. The analogy is with electric current. If we regard $\overline{B}$ as analogous to $\overline{J}$, then $\overline{B} = \mu\overline{H}$ is considered analogous to $\overline{J} = \sigma\overline{E}$. Thus, the analogs are

$$\overline{B} \rightarrow \overline{J} \qquad \text{a)}$$
$$\mu \rightarrow \sigma \qquad \text{b)} \qquad (6\text{-}8.1)$$
$$\overline{H} \rightarrow \overline{E}$$

In order for there to be an electric current, there must be an applied voltage source such that the line integral of $\overline{E}$ around the circuit equals the source voltage V, i.e.,

$$\oint_C \overline{E} \cdot d\overline{\ell} = V$$

Since the Ampère circuital law gives

$$\oint \overline{H} \cdot d\overline{\ell} = \int_S \overline{J} \cdot d\overline{S} = NI = V_H$$

we see that the line integral of $\overline{H}$, denoted V_H, is analogous to voltage, i.e.,

$$V_H \rightarrow V$$

V_H is often called the *magnetomotive force*, frequently abbreviated *mmf*. We call attention to the name "magnetomotive force" which is a misnomer, since V_H is not a force, it has the units Ampère-turns. Often this is called *magnetomotance*, to avoid this incorrect concept.

The analogy is shown in Fig. 6-8.1. The analogy is not a perfect one since in the electric case $\sigma = 0$ outside of the current conducting structure, while in the magnetic case $\mu = \mu_0$ outside of the iron. However, since $\mu \gg \mu_0$ for iron, there will be very little magnetic flux (leakage flux) outside of the iron. This can be seen by noting that H_t is continuous across the iron-air boundary, but the flux density B_a in the air region is of an order μ_0/μ less than in the iron ($B_a = \mu_0 H_t$; $B_i = \mu H_t$). In addition, there is a difference in the nature of the sources - the battery versus the winding with a current I. The source for the magnetic circuit

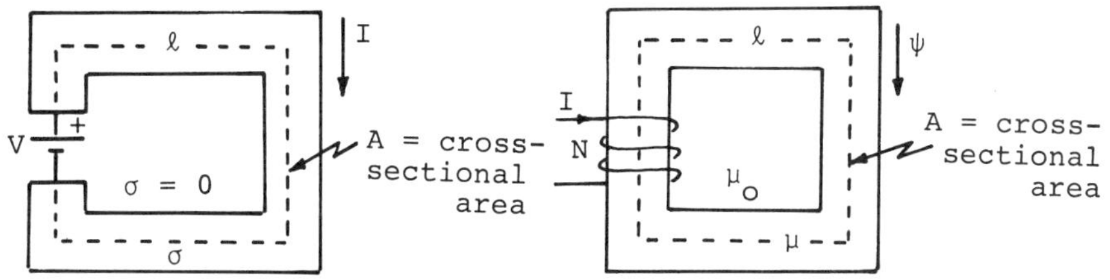

Figure 6-8.1. Analogous electric and magnetic circuits.

may be distributed around the entire circuit, if the winding is so distributed. This would be equivalent to dividing up the battery into many small batteries and inserting them in series with the electric circuit at many points around the circuit. The distributed nature of the magnetic flux sources has very little effect on the total flux, and we may regard the magnetomotance V_H as being localized at a single point in the circuit. The converse for the electric circuit would not necessarily be true, except for short electrical paths.

For the electric circuit, the current is given by

$$I = JA = \frac{V}{R}$$

where A is the cross-sectional area, and the resistance R is given by

$$R = \frac{\ell}{\sigma A} \tag{6-8.2}$$

For the magnetic circuit we have

$$V_H = NI = H\ell \qquad \text{Amp-turns}$$

$$B = \mu H = \frac{\mu NI}{\ell} = \frac{\mu V_H}{\ell} \qquad \text{Weber/m}^2$$

$$\psi = BA = \frac{A\mu V_H}{\ell} = \frac{V_H}{R} \qquad \text{Weber}$$

where ψ is the total magnetic flux (which is analogous to current I) and where R is the *reluctance* (analogous to resistance) and is given by

$$R = \frac{\ell}{\mu A} \tag{6-8.3}$$

Many of the magnetic circuits encountered in practice can be solved by an extension of these ideas. The following example will illustrate some of the needed modifications.

Example 6-8.1. Find the magnetic flux in the air gap of the magnetic circuit illustrated in the accompanying figure. The equivalent electric circuit configuration is also shown.

Solution. The following features of the given magnetic configuration are noted noted:

a. The magnetomotances V_{H1} and V_{H2} act in different directions because of the specified winding directions.
b. The magnetic flux tends to follow the path with least reluctance. Hence essentially all of the flux $\psi_i = B_iA_1$ in the iron is channeled into the smaller air gap

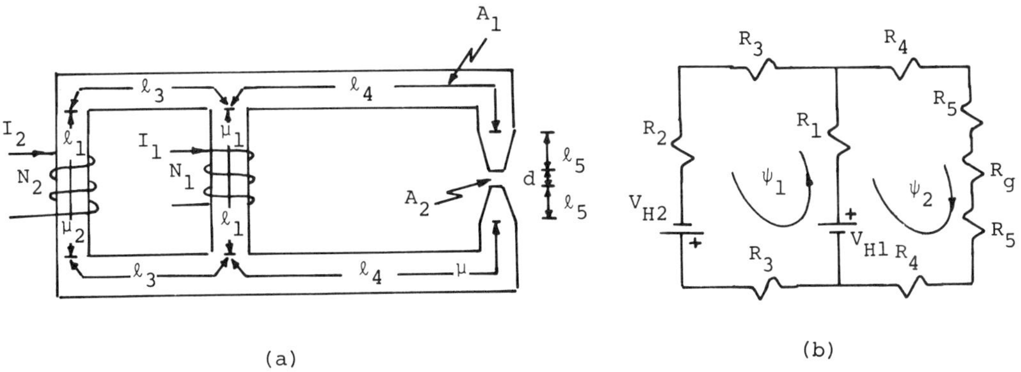

Figure 6-8.2. A magnetic circuit, and its equivalent electric circuit configuration.

of area A_2. Thus $B_iA_1 = B_gA_2$. If the gap spacing is small compared with the gap width, there will be very little fringing of the flux lines in the gap and the effective area of the gap can be approximated by the area A_2 of the pole face (the effective area is always somewhat greater because of fringing or outward bulging of the flux lines).

c. The superposition principle applies if we assume that μ is a constant independent of the magnetic field density (this means that no saturation occurs). Under these conditions, the effects of V_{H1} and V_{H2} can be superimposed.

d. If the length of the path in the iron in which the cross section is reduced from A_1 to A_2 is appreciable, then the reluctance of this part of the circuit is calculated by using the average cross-sectional area for it.

With reference to Fig. 6-8.2a we have

$$V_{H1} = N_1I_1 \qquad V_{H2} = N_2I_2$$

$$R_1 = \frac{\ell_1}{\mu_1A_1} \qquad R_2 = \frac{\ell_1}{\mu_2A_1} \qquad R_3 = \frac{\ell_3}{\mu_1A_1}$$

$$R_4 = \frac{\ell_4}{\mu A_1} \qquad R_5 = \frac{\ell_5}{\mu(A_1+A_2)/2} \qquad R_g = \frac{d}{\mu_0A_2}$$

The magnetic circuit equations are written by using a direct analogy with electric circuit theory (the Kirchhoff voltage law, or equivalently, the line integral)

$$V_{H2} - V_{H1} = \psi_1(R_2 + 2R_3 + R_1) + \psi_2R_1$$

$$V_{H1} = \psi_1R_1 + \psi_2(R_1 + 2R_4 + 2R_5 + R_g)$$

These equations may be solved readily to obtain expressions for the total magnetic flux in any part of the circuit. The solution is straightforward, and so it will not be given here. It might be noted that Thevènin's theorem in electric circuit theory can be applied to magnetic circuits; and the use of this technique is often of value in simplifying the solution.

ΔΔΔ

6-9. Inductance

Refer to Fig. 6-9.1 which illustrates two current carrying circuits with currents I_1 and I_2. We denote the magnetic fields produced by I_1 and I_2 as $\overline{B}_1$ and $\overline{B}_2$. The magnetic flux linking circuit C_2 due to the field $\overline{B}_1$ produced by I_1 is

$$\psi_{21} = \int_{S_2} \overline{B}_1 \cdot d\overline{S} \tag{6-9.1}$$

In the same way, we write the following flux linkages

$$\psi_{12} = \int_{S_1} \overline{B}_2 \cdot d\overline{S} = \text{flux linking } C_1 \text{ due to the current } I_2 \text{ in } C_2$$

$$\psi_{11} = \int_{S_1} \overline{B}_1 \cdot d\overline{S} = \text{self flux linking } C_1 \text{ due to the current } I_1 \text{ in } C_1$$

$$\psi_{22} = \int_{S_2} \overline{B}_2 \cdot d\overline{S} = \text{self flux linking } C_2 \text{ due to the current } I_2 \text{ in } C_2$$

We note that the field $\overline{B}_1$ is proportional to I_1, and so the ratio ψ_{21}/I_1 is independent of the current I_1 and would depend only on the geometry of the circuits. The quantity

$$L_{21} = \frac{\psi_{21}}{I_1} \tag{6-9.2}$$

is defined as the *mutual inductance* L_{21} (mutual inductances are often denoted by the

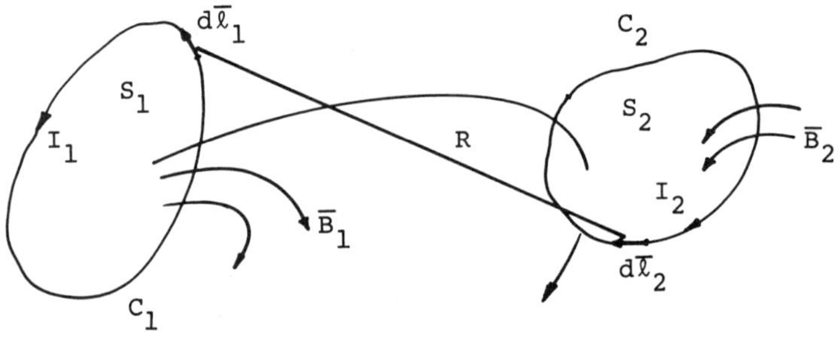

Figure 6-9.1. Two circuits with mutual inductive coupling.

letter M) between circuits C_1 and C_2.

In terms of these flux linkages, the following additional inductance parameters are defined:

$$L_{12} = \frac{\psi_{12}}{I_2}, \quad \text{mutual inductance} \tag{6-9.3}$$

$$L_{11} = \frac{\psi_{11}}{I_1}, \quad \text{self inductance} \tag{6-9.4}$$

$$L_{22} = \frac{\psi_{22}}{I_2}, \quad \text{self inductance} \tag{6-9.5}$$

We shall show later from energy considerations that $L_{12} = L_{21}$. The mutual inductances are taken as positive quantities if the mutual flux and the self flux linkages are in the same direction through the circuit, as shown in Fig. 6-9.1. If the mutual flux links the circuit in a direction opposite to that of the self flux linkages, then the mutual inductance is taken as negative.

The following examples illustrate the calculation of self and mutual inductance.

Example 6-9.1. Find the inductance per unit length of a coaxial line, as illustrated in Fig. 6-9.2.

Solution. Initially we will assume that the inner and outer cylinders are of negligible thickness. By the Ampère circuital law, the magnetic field between the two conductors is given by (see Ex. 6-2.2)

$$B_\phi = \frac{\mu_o I}{2\pi r} \qquad a \leq r \leq b$$

In the space between the inner and outer conductors, the differential flux per meter of length within a differential sheet of thickness dr is

$$d\Phi = B_\phi \, dr = \frac{\mu_o I}{2\pi r} dr$$

and the total flux linking the current I on the inner conductor per unit length is

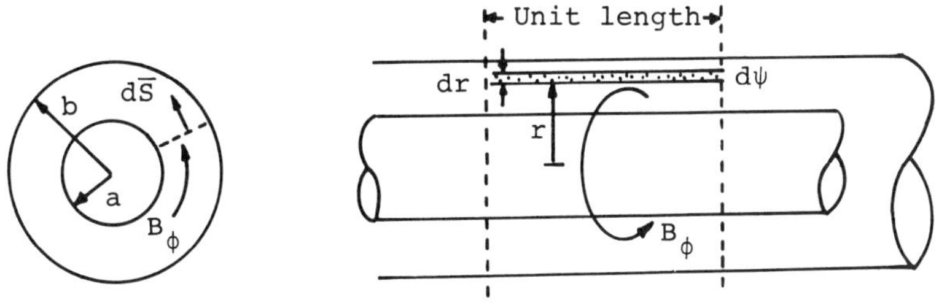

Figure 6-9.2. A coaxial line.

$$\psi_{11} = \int_a^b B_\phi \, dr = \int_a^b \frac{\mu_o I}{2\pi r} dr = \frac{\mu_o I}{2\pi} \ln \frac{b}{a}$$

The self inductance per unit length is

$$L_{11} = \frac{\psi_{11}}{I} = \frac{\mu_o}{2\pi} \ln \frac{b}{a} \tag{6-9.6}$$

If the inner conductor is solid and the current I is uniform over the cross-section, then the field in the coaxial line is given by [see Eq. (6-2.19) and Eq. (6-2.20)]

$$B_\phi = \begin{cases} \dfrac{\mu_o I r}{2\pi a^2} & 0 \le r \le a \\[2ex] \dfrac{\mu_o I}{2\pi r} & a \le r \le b \end{cases} \tag{6-9.7}$$

Now refer to Fig. 6-9.3 for the region within the conductor. The differential flux in the shell of thickness dr per meter of length is

$$d\Phi_1 = B_\phi \, dr = \frac{\mu_o I r}{2\pi a^2} dr$$

The differential flux linkage of this element is the differential flux multiplied by the fraction of the current contained within the path enclosing the flux. The current fraction is

$$\frac{I_r}{I} = \frac{r^2}{a^2}$$

and the total flux linkages within the differential flux element is

$$d\psi = \frac{\mu_o I}{2\pi a^4} r^3 dr$$

The total flux linkages of the inner conductor per unit length is

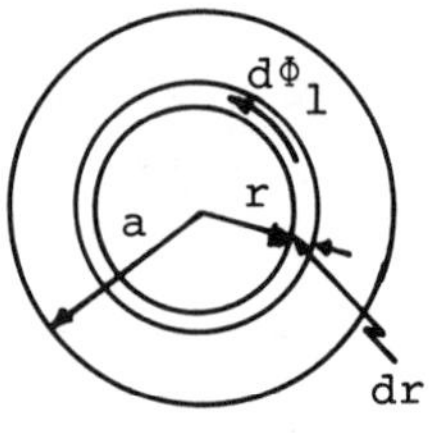

Figure 6-9.3. Flux linkages within the inner conductor.

$$\psi_1 = \int_0^a \frac{\mu_o I}{2\pi a^4} r^3 dr = \frac{\mu_o I}{8\pi}$$

In the space between the inner and outer conductors, the differential flux per meter is

$$d\Phi_2 = \frac{\mu_o I}{2\pi r} dr$$

with all the current linked in this space. Then

$$\psi_2 = \int_a^b \frac{\mu_o I}{2\pi r} dr = \frac{\mu_o I}{2\pi} \ln \frac{b}{a}$$

The total flux linkages are

$$\psi_{11} = \frac{\mu_o I}{8\pi} + \frac{\mu_o I}{2\pi} \ln \frac{b}{a} \tag{6-9.8}$$

and the inductance is then given by

$$L_{11} = \frac{\psi_{11}}{I_1} = \frac{\mu_o}{8\pi} + \frac{\mu_o}{2\pi} \ln \frac{b}{a} \tag{6-9.9}$$

The part given by $\mu_o/8\pi$ is called the *internal inductance* because it arises from flux linkages in the interior of the center conductor. The second term $(\mu_o/2\pi) \ln (b/a)$ is called the *external inductance* since it arises from flux linkages external to the current.

Somewhat different methods of calculating inducatance will be given below, in one case from considerations of induced voltage and in another in terms of energy stored in the magnetic field.

ΔΔΔ

Example 6-9.2. Find the mutual inductance between the coaxial lines shown in Fig. 6-9.4.

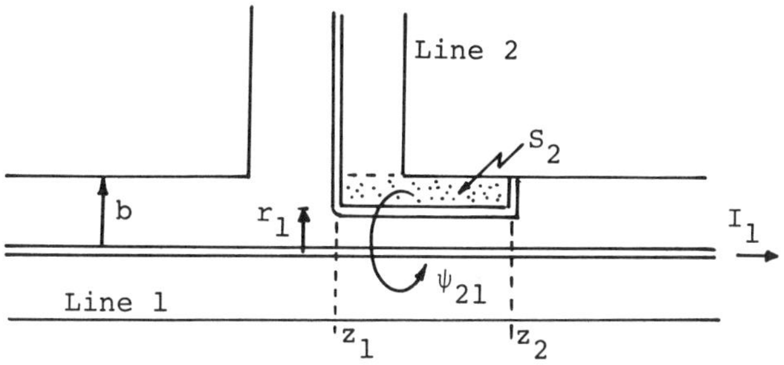

Figure 6-9.4. Two coaxial lines with inductive coupling.

Solution. The two coaxial lines shown are inductively coupled because magnetic flux produced by currents I_1 in line 1 links the center conductor of line 2 in the coupling loop shown. The mutual flux linkage, neglecting flux within the conductors, is given by

$$\psi_{21} = \int_{r_1}^{b} \int_{z_1}^{z_2} \frac{\mu_o I_1}{2\pi r}\, dr\, dz = \frac{\mu_o I_1}{2\pi} (z_2 - z_1) \ln \frac{b}{r_1}$$

Hence the mutual inductance M is given by

$$M = \frac{\psi_{21}}{I_1} = \frac{\mu_o}{2\pi} (z_2 - z_1) \ln \frac{b}{r_1} \tag{6-9.10}$$

ΔΔΔ

B. Quasi-Static Magnetic Fields

The remainder of this chapter will be devoted to a study of quasi-static magnetic fields, that is, magnetic fields that vary slowly with time. Later chapters will consider time-related effects, and it will be shown that when magnetic and electric fields vary with time, they are interrelated and that radiation of electromagnetic energy will take place. However, if the rate of variation with time is small, the radiation effects are negligible and the fields are then said to be quasi-stationary. For effective radiation, we shall find that the dimensions of the current carrying conductors must be of the order of a wavelength or more in size. The wavelength λ_o is given by c/f, where c is the velocity of light ($\doteq 3 \times 10^8$ m/sec) and f is the frequency with which the fields vary. If the size of the circuits to be considered is small compared with λ_o we can neglect radiation. For example, if f = 100 kHz (kilocycle/sec) the wavelength in free space is $\lambda_0 = 3000$ meters. For most laboratory experiments radiation effects at frequencies below 100 kHz would be entirely negligible. Clearly, the quasi-static assumption will be valid for many situations encountered in practice.

6-10. Faraday's Law

The most important aspect of magnetic fields that vary with time is the phenomenon of induced electric fields, and relates a time-varying magnetic field with the electric field that it produces. This effect was discovered by Faraday and is known as the *Faraday law of induction.*

Consider a closed conducting loop of wire C as shown in Fig. 6-10.1. Let a time-varying magnetic field $\overline{B}$ be present. At a given instant of time the magnetic flux passing through or linking C is given by

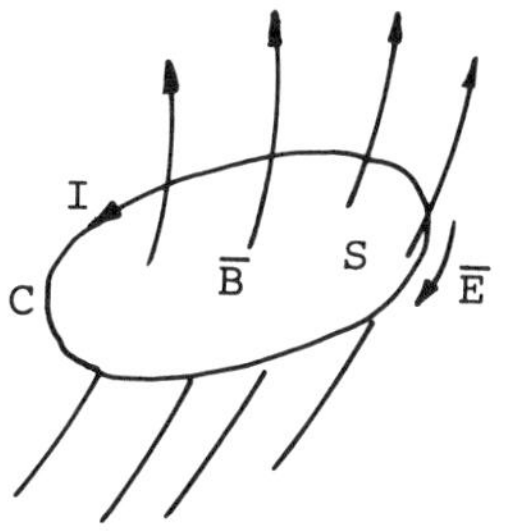

Figure 6-10.1. To illustrate Faraday's law.

$$\psi = \int_S \overline{B} \cdot d\overline{S}$$

where S is any surface with C as the boundary. The Faraday relation obtained for $\overline{E}$ is

$$\oint_C \overline{E} \cdot d\overline{\ell} = -\frac{\partial\psi}{\partial t} = -\int_S \frac{\partial\overline{B}}{\partial t} \cdot d\overline{S} \tag{6-10.1}$$

The induced electric field will give rise to an electric current in the conducting circuit (this is sometimes referred to as an induced current). This physical process is the principle on which electrical generators and electrical transformers operate. The line integral of $\overline{E}$ gives the *induced electromotive force (emf)*. We note the poor choice of name "electromotive force" since it is a voltage that is induced, and voltage is energy, not force. For this reason, the term *electromotance* is preferred, although both terms appear in the literature.

Actually, the induced electric field does not require the presence of a conducting wire for its existence. Equation (6-10.1) is a general law which can be applied to any contour C enclosing a surface S. For many purposes Faraday's law in point form is preferred. By an application of Stokes' theorem, we write

$$\oint_C \overline{E} \cdot d\overline{\ell} = \int_S \nabla \times \overline{E} \cdot d\overline{S} = -\frac{\partial}{\partial t}\int_S \overline{B} \cdot d\overline{S}$$

and since S is arbitrary, then

$$\nabla \times \overline{E} = -\frac{\partial\overline{B}}{\partial t} \tag{6-10.2}$$

This is not the most general formulation of the Faraday law since other effects might contribute to the induced electric field.

Faraday also discovered, in addition to the flux-linking process considered above, that a conductor moving through a magnetic field (which can be a stationary field) will have an induced motional electromotance produced in it. To understand this phenomenon, refer to Fig. 6-10.2 which shows a conductor of length ℓ moving

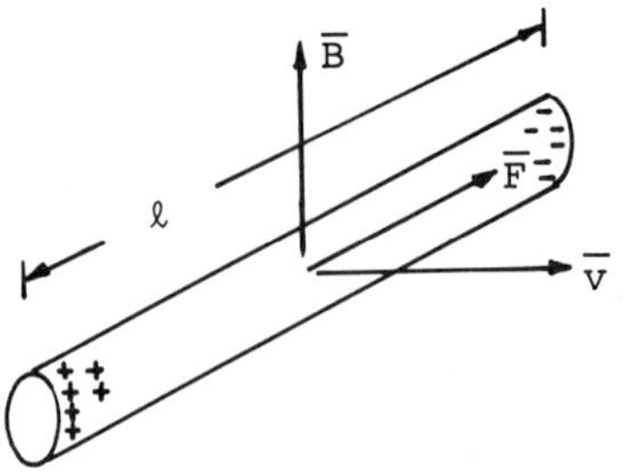

Figure 6-10.2. Motion of a conductor in a magnetic field.

with velocity $\overline{v}$ in a magnetic field $\overline{B}$. The free electrons in the conductor will have a force exerted on them, as given by the Lorentz force law

$$\overline{F} = -e\overline{v} \times \overline{B} \tag{6-10.3}$$

As a result, the electrons will move to one end of the rod, leaving a net positive charge at the other end. Equilibrium will be established when the electric field produced by the charge separation establishes a force equal and opposite to that given by Eq. (6-10.3). Thus the motion of a conductor in a magnetic field can be viewed as resulting in an induced electric field given by

$$\overline{E}_m = \frac{\overline{F}}{-e} = \overline{v} \times \overline{B} \tag{6-10.4}$$

The motional electromotance is given by

$$\int_C \overline{E}_m \cdot d\overline{\ell} = \int_C (\overline{v} \times \overline{B}) \cdot d\overline{\ell} \tag{6-10.5}$$

where C is any path along the conductor. If the conductor forms a closed circuit, the induced electromotance will cause a current.

If a conductor moves in a time-varying magnetic field, the electromotance is the superposition of that due to the time variation in $\overline{B}$ as given by Eq. (6-10.2) and that due to the motion, Eq. (6-10.5). The two effects can be combined into a single law which states that

$$\oint_C \overline{E} \cdot d\overline{\ell} = -\frac{d\psi}{dt} = -\frac{d}{dt}\int_S \overline{B} \cdot d\overline{S} \tag{6-10.6}$$

This equation states that the electromotance is equal to the negative *total* time rate of change of magnetic flux through the circuit. To show the validity of this result, we perform the differentiation indicated in Eq. (6-10.6) to obtain

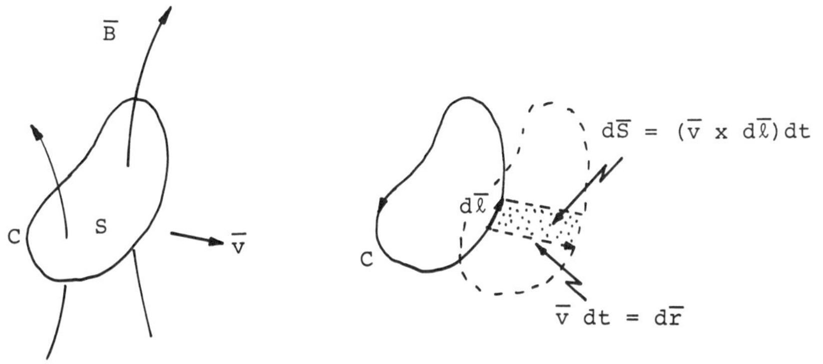

Figure 6-10.3. Motion of a contour C in a magnetic field.

$$\oint_C \bar{E} \cdot d\bar{\ell} = -\int_S \frac{\partial \bar{B}}{\partial t} \cdot d\bar{S} - \int_S \bar{B} \cdot \frac{\partial (d\bar{S})}{\partial t}$$

$$= -\int_S \frac{\partial \bar{B}}{\partial t} \cdot d\bar{S} - \int_S \bar{B} \cdot \frac{\partial}{\partial t}(d\bar{r} \times d\bar{\ell}) = -\int_S \frac{\partial \bar{B}}{\partial t} \cdot d\bar{S} + \oint_C (\bar{v} \times \bar{B}) \cdot d\bar{\ell} \qquad (6\text{-}10.7)$$

where $\bar{v} = \partial(d\bar{r})/\partial t$ and the first vector identity of Appendix I was used. In this expansion we have used results which are made evident by reference to Fig. 6-10.3. This figure shows an arbitrary contour C which may be moving and deforming (changing shape) in a time-varying magnetic field.

Example 6-10.1. Determine the induced electric field and thus the electromotance for the coil shown in Fig. 6-10.4.

Solution. Case A: (stationary coil). Suppose that the current in the winding is periodic of the form $i = I_o \cos \omega_o t$, then the magnetic field will be $\bar{B} = B_o \bar{a}_x \cos \omega_o t$, where we assume that B_o is constant in space over the extent of the rectangular coil. Therefore

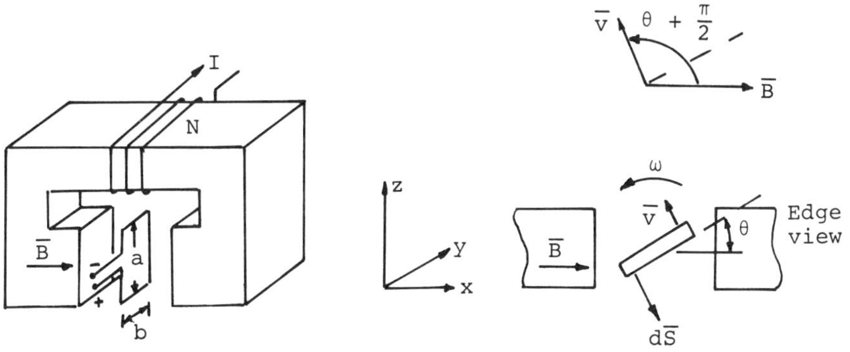

Figure 6-10.4. A simple electric generator.

$$v_i = \oint_C \overline{E} \cdot d\overline{\ell} = -\int_S \frac{\partial \overline{B}}{\partial t} \cdot d\overline{S} = -B_o \int_S \left(\frac{d}{dt} \cos \omega_o t\right)\overline{a}_x \cdot d\overline{S}$$

$$= \omega_o B_o \sin \omega_o t(ab \sin \theta) \qquad (6\text{-}10.8)$$

Case B. (rotating coil, B stationary). Now B is independent of time, $\overline{B} = B_o\overline{a}_x$ but the coil is rotating at an angular rate $\underline{\omega}$. We note that the velocity of the two outer sides of the coil is $a\omega/2$, so that along the upper side $\overline{v} \times \overline{B} =$ $(a/2)\omega B_o \sin (\pi/2 + \theta)\overline{a}_y$ and along the lower side of the coil $\overline{v} \times \overline{B} = (-a/2)\omega B_o \cos \theta \, \overline{a}_y$. Along the two coil ends $\overline{v} \times \overline{B}$ is perpendicular to the conductor, so there will be no contribution to the line integral of $\overline{v} \times \overline{B} \cdot d\overline{\ell}$ around C from these two sides. From Eq. (6-10.5) we get

$$v_i = \oint \overline{E} \cdot d\overline{\ell} = \oint_C (\overline{v} \times \overline{B}) \cdot d\overline{\ell} = -\int_0^b \frac{a}{2} \omega B_o \cos \theta \, dy + \int_b^0 \frac{a}{2} \omega B_o \cos \theta \, dy$$

$$= -ab\, \omega B_o \cos \theta = -ab\, \omega B_o \cos \omega t \qquad (6\text{-}10.9)$$

for the induced voltage, since $\theta = \omega t$ for the rotating coil. This result is possible by using Eq. (6-10.6) since we have that

$$\psi = \int_S \overline{B} \cdot d\overline{S} = B_o ab \sin \theta = B_o ab \sin \omega t$$

and hence

$$v_i = -\frac{d\psi}{dt} = -\omega B_o ab \cos \omega t$$

which agrees with Eq. (6-10.9).

Case C; (B time varying and coil rotating). The induced voltage is now the sum of that given by Eqs. (6-10.8) and (6-10.9) multiplied by $\cos \omega_o t$ since B_o is now replaced by $B_o \cos \omega_o t$; thus

$$v_i = an\, B_o(\omega_o \sin \omega_o t \sin \omega t - \omega \cos \omega t \cos \omega_o t) \qquad (6\text{-}10.10)$$

since $\theta = \omega t$. We can obtain this result from the general statement, Eq. (6-10.6). The flux through the coil is given by

$$\psi = \int_S \overline{B} \cdot d\overline{S} = B_o ab \sin \theta \cos \omega_o t = B_o ab \sin \omega t \cos \omega_o t$$

at the instant of time when $\theta = \omega t$. The induced voltage is

$$-\frac{d\psi}{dt} = -B_o ab(\omega \cos \omega t \cos \omega_o t - \omega_o \sin \omega_o t \sin \omega t)$$

which is Eq. (6-10.10).

ΔΔΔ

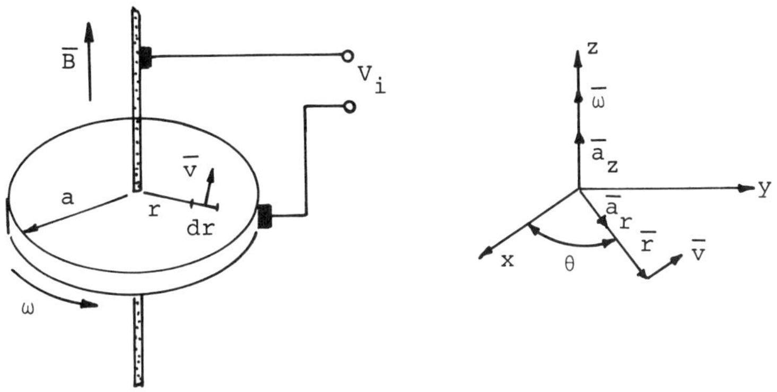

Figure 6-10.5. The Faraday disk generator.

Example 6-10.2. The essential features of the Faraday disk generator (homopolar generator) are illustrated in Fig. 6-10.5. What voltage appears across the terminals?

Solution. We focus on a radial element dr. There are no time changing flux linkages, and the total induced voltage is then

$$v_i = \int_0^a (\bar{v} \times \bar{B}) \cdot d\bar{r}$$

where

$$\bar{B} = B_o \bar{a}_z; \quad \bar{\omega} = \omega \bar{a}_z; \quad \bar{r} = r\bar{a}_r; \quad \text{and} \quad (\bar{v} \times \bar{B}) \cdot d\bar{r} = r\omega B_o \, dr$$

Then

$$v_i = \int_0^a \omega B_o r \, dr = \frac{\omega B_o a^2}{2} \text{ Volt}$$

A practical feature of such machines is that while the induced voltage is low, the current levels can be very high, and such homopolar machines have been produced to provide currents in the thousands of Ampères. ΔΔΔ

Refer again to Fig. 6-9.1 which shows two mutually coupled circuits. In the more general case each circuit may consist of many turns, and these windings may be in air or they may be mounted on an iron core, as in a transformer. If the currents I_1 and I_2 vary with time, the flux linkages will also be time varying, and by Faraday's law, induced electromotances will be produced in the circuits. The induced emf-s always act to oppose the change in current, a result that is usually called *Lenz's* law. The induced voltages v_i are given by

$$v_{i1} = -(\frac{d\psi_{11}}{dt} + \frac{d\psi_{12}}{dt}) = -L_{11}\frac{dI_1}{dt} - L_{12}\frac{dI_2}{dt} \qquad \text{a)}$$

$$v_{i2} = -(\frac{d\psi_{21}}{dt} + \frac{d\psi_{22}}{dt}) = -L_{21}\frac{dI_1}{dt} - L_{22}\frac{dI_2}{dt} \qquad \text{b)} \qquad (6\text{-}10.11)$$

in circuits C_1 and C_2, respectively.

Example 6-10.3. Show from considerations involving the vector potential $\bar{A}$ that the expression for the mutual inductance of two circuits is the Neumann formula

$$M = \frac{\mu_o}{4\pi}\oint_{C_1}\oint_{C_2}\frac{d\bar{\ell}_1 \cdot d\bar{\ell}_2}{R} \qquad (6\text{-}10.12)$$

Solution. Reference is made to Fig. 6-9.1. If the current in circuit 1 is changing with time, there will be a changing magnetic field through circuit 2. As a result, an emf will be induced in circuit 2, as indicated by Eq. (6-10.1)

$$v_{i2} = -\int_{S_2} \bar{n} \cdot \frac{\partial \bar{B}}{\partial t} dS = -\int_{S_2} \bar{n} \cdot \frac{\partial(\nabla \times \bar{A})}{\partial t} dS$$

By interchanging the space (curl) and time derivatives, and by an application of Stokes' theorem, this expression can be written as a line integral as shown

$$v_{i2} = -\int_{S_2} \bar{n} \cdot \nabla \times (\frac{\partial \bar{A}}{\partial t}) dS = -\oint_{C_2} \frac{\partial \bar{A}}{\partial t} \cdot d\bar{\ell}$$

where the line integral is taken along circuit C_2. The known form of the vector potential is now included in this expression [see Eq. (6-2.4)]. This is first written as

$$\bar{A}_1 = \frac{\mu_o}{4\pi}\int_V \frac{\bar{J}_1}{R} dV' = \frac{\mu_o}{4\pi}\oint_{C_1}\frac{I_1}{R} d\bar{\ell}$$

The result by combining the foregoing two formulas is

$$v_{i2} = -\frac{\mu_o}{4\pi}(\oint_{C_2}\frac{\partial}{\partial t}\oint_{C_1}\frac{I_1}{R} d\bar{\ell}_1 \cdot d\bar{\ell}_2)$$

In those cases where the current is constant through the circuit (lumped circuit conditions) the current may be taken out from under the integral sign. Note also in this example that only the current changes with time. Therefore the equation may be written

$$v_{i2} = -\frac{\mu_o}{4\pi}\frac{dI_1}{dt}\oint_{C_2}\oint_{C_1}\frac{d\bar{\ell}_1 \cdot d\bar{\ell}_2}{R}$$

But by definition the coefficient of -dI/dt is the mutual inductance of the two circuits, so that finally

$$M = \frac{\mu_o}{4\pi} \oint_{C_2} \oint_{C_1} \frac{d\overline{\ell}_1 \cdot d\overline{\ell}_2}{R}$$

which is the *Neumann formula*. ΔΔΔ

6-11. Displacement Current

As was pointed out by Maxwell, the Ampère line integral in Eq. (6-4.7b) possesses an inherent weakness. The nature of the problem is made evident by reference to Fig. 6-11.1 which represents a portion of a circuit containing a capacitor, in which a current is assumed to exist. To evaluate the Ampère circuital law, $\oint \overline{H} \cdot d\overline{\ell}$, requires that the line integral taken around the contour of any circuit C be related to the total current through a cap with the contour as its edge. For the cap specified by the surface S_1, the total current is I, and the law is still correct

$$\oint \overline{H} \cdot d\overline{\ell} = I$$

Now consider the cap specified by the surface S_2 which has been so chosen that it passes between the plates of the capacitor. Clearly in this case, assuming a perfect dielectric, no conduction current will pass through the surface S_2, and it appears that

$$\oint \overline{H} \cdot d\overline{\ell} = 0$$

unless the circuital law itself undergoes some change when it goes from the static case to the time-varying case. This is contrary to reason, since if a unique solution exists, it cannot possibly be a function of the choice of the cap with C as the perimeter.

To study this matter in detail, refer to Fig. 6-11.2 which is an enlarged view of Fig. 6-11.1 at the capacitor. We shall study four separate regions in the

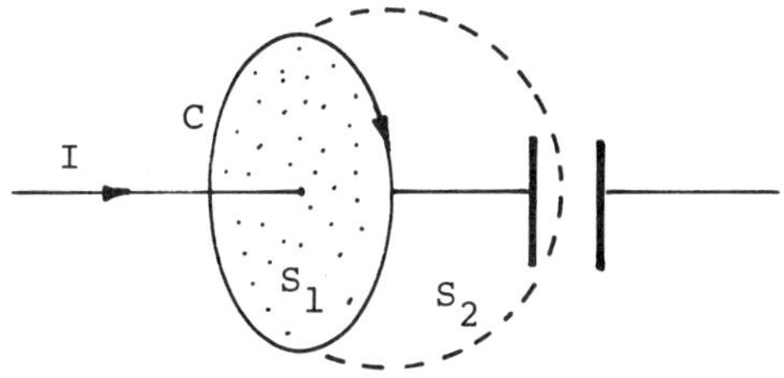

Figure 6-11.1. To demonstrate the incompleteness of Ampère's law.

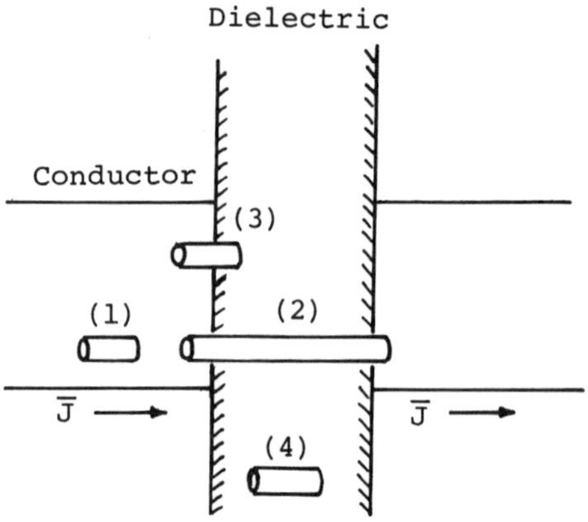

Figure 6-11.2. An enlarged portion of a simple circuit in the neighborhood of a capacitor.

neighborhood of the capacitor as shown. (1) is a Gaussian surface wholly in the conductor; (2) a surface partly in the conductor and partly in the dielectric of the capacitor, but extending through the capacitor; (3) a surface partly in the conductor and partly in the dielectric, but terminating in the dielectric; and (4) a surface wholly in the dielectric. Because the capacitor is assumed large, the currents and field lines are parallel.

1. For surface (1), since the conduction current density is assumed to be uniform, then by conservation of charge (the Kirchhoff current law), written

$$\oint_S \overline{J} \cdot d\overline{S} = 0$$

requires that

$$-J\Delta S\Big|_{\text{left}} + J\Delta S\Big|_{\text{right}} = 0$$

2. For surface (2), regardless of what may happen in the region between the capacitor plates, if conduction current exists through the left-hand face and also through the right-hand face, and assuming that the current lines are normal to the Gaussian faces, then

$$-J\Delta S\Big|_{\text{left}} + J\Delta S\Big|_{\text{right}} = 0$$

3. For surface (3), since a conduction current is assumed to exist through the left-hand face, and since no charged carriers exist in the dielectric to give rise to a conduction current through the right-hand face, it must follow that mobile

charge is collecting on the surface of the conductor lying inside the Gaussian surface. Under equilibrium conditions, it is necessary that

$$J\Delta S\Big|_{\text{left}} = \frac{\partial}{\partial t}(\rho_s\ \Delta S) = \Delta S\ \frac{\partial \rho_s}{\partial t} \qquad (6\text{-}11.1)$$

However, to the right of the surface from Eq. (5-7.2)

$$D = \rho_s \qquad (6\text{-}11.2)$$

from which it follows that

$$-J\Delta S\Big|_{\text{left}} + \frac{\partial D}{\partial t}\Delta S = 0 \qquad (6\text{-}11.3)$$

If now the term $(\partial D/\partial t)\Delta S$ is viewed as a current through the right-hand face of the Gaussian surface to balance the conduction current through the left-hand face, the density of this current would be

$$J_d = \frac{\partial D}{\partial t} \qquad (6\text{-}11.4)$$

This is adopted as the definition of the *displacement current density*. Note that since this current depends on the change of the electric displacement with time, there is no displacement current unless the electric displacement is changing with time. In general, Eq. (6-11.4) is written

$$\overline{J}_d = \frac{\partial \overline{D}}{\partial t} \qquad (6\text{-}11.5)$$

Note from this that the direction of $\overline{J}_d$ is either in the same direction or opposite to $\overline{D}$, depending upon whether the time rate of change of $\overline{D}$ is increasing or decreasing with time.

4. For surface (4), no conduction current exists through either face. However, with the development of the concept of displacement current, this case would be characterized by the expression

$$-\frac{\partial D}{\partial t}\Delta S\Big|_{\text{left}} + \frac{\partial D}{\partial t}\Delta S\Big|_{\text{right}} = 0$$

With the development of the displacement current, the continuity equation Eq. (5-11.2) can be expressed in a very interesting form. Begin with Eq. (5-6.5) for any point in space

$$\nabla \cdot \overline{D} = \rho$$

where ρ is the free charge density. Now differentiate both sides to get

$$\nabla \cdot \frac{\partial \overline{D}}{\partial t} = \frac{\partial \rho}{\partial t}$$

This is combined with Eq. (5-11.2), denoting the conduction current density as $\overline{J}_c$,

$$\nabla \cdot \overline{J}_c + \nabla \cdot \frac{\partial \overline{D}}{\partial t} = \nabla \cdot (\overline{J}_c + \frac{\partial \overline{D}}{\partial t}) = 0$$

It follows from this that

$$\nabla \cdot \overline{J}_t = \nabla \cdot (\overline{J}_c + \overline{J}_d) = 0 \tag{6-11.6}$$

This result shows that the divergence of the total current density $\overline{J}_t$ is zero always, and hence there can be no source or sink of current.

In summary, we can now complete Eq. (6-2.11) to be generally valid. It now reads

$$\nabla \times \overline{H} = \overline{J}_c + \frac{\partial \overline{D}}{\partial t} \tag{6-11.7}$$

which is one of the Maxwell equations. The subscript c is usually omitted in the equation, but it is implied.

6-12. Magnetic Energy

Work is required to establish a magnetic field. The energy supplied in this process can be viewed as stored in the resultant magnetic field. To evaluate the stored energy, we will begin by considering the work required to establish the currents I_1 and I_2 in the two loop circuit shown in Fig. 6-9.1. Suppose that both I_1 and I_2 are zero initially, and we first increase I_1 to its final value. The current I_2 is subsequently increased from zero to its final value. At any arbitrary instant of time the currents in C_1 and C_2 are denoted by i_1 and i_2, respectively.

When the current i_1 is changed by an amount di_1 in a time interval dt, the flux linking C_1 and C_2 changes by amounts

$$d\psi_{11} = L_{11}\, di_1; \qquad d\psi_{21} = L_{21}\, di_1$$

As a result, induced voltages of amounts

$$v_{i1} = -\frac{d\psi_{11}}{dt} = -L_{11}\frac{di_1}{dt}; \qquad v_{i2} = -L_{21}\frac{di_1}{dt}$$

are produced in C_1 and C_2. Since the current i_2 is maintained at zero, the induced voltage v_{i2} does zero work. However, in order to change di_1 we must apply a voltage equal to $-v_{i1}$ to counteract the effect of the induced electromotance. This applied voltage will do an amount of work given by

$$dW_1 = -v_{i1} i_1 \, dt$$

in the time interval dt. Thus the total work done in increasing i_1 from its initial value of zero to the final value I_1 will be

$$W_1 = -\int_0^{I_1} v_{i1} i_1 \, dt = \int_0^{I_1} L_{11} i_1 di_1 = \frac{1}{2} L_{11} I_1^2 \qquad (6\text{-}12.1)$$

upon using the expression for v_{i1} given above.

Let us now increase i_2 from zero to I_2. For a change di_2 the voltages induced in C_1 and C_2 are

$$v_{i1} = -\frac{d\psi_{12}}{dt} = -L_{12} \frac{di_2}{dt}; \qquad v_{i2} = -L_{22} \frac{di_2}{dt}$$

In order to maintain i_1 constant at the value I_1, we must insert a voltage $-v_{i1}$ in C_1. This voltage source will do work of amount

$$dW_{12} = -v_{i1} I_1 \, dt$$

in the time interval dt. Likewise, we must insert a voltage source equal to $-v_{i2}$ in C_2 in order to change i_2 by an amount di_2. This source does work of amount

$$dW_2 = -v_{i2} i_2 \, dt$$

The total work done in increasing i_2 to its final value is

$$W_{12} + W_2 = \int_0^{I_2} L_{12} I_1 di_2 + \int_0^{I_2} L_{22} i_2 di_2$$

$$= L_{12} I_1 I_2 + \frac{1}{2} L_{22} I_2^2 \qquad (6\text{-}12.2)$$

The total work done on the system, which is equal to the energy W_m stored in the magnetic field, is the sum of Eqs. (6-12.1) and (6-12.2) and is given by

$$W_m = W_1 + W_{12} + W_2 = \frac{1}{2} L_{11} I_1^2 + L_{12} I_1 I_2 + \frac{1}{2} L_{22} I_2^2 \qquad (6\text{-}12.3)$$

If we had first brought i_2 up to its final value and then increased i_1, a similar analysis would show that the work done is given by

$$W_m = \frac{1}{2} L_{22} I_2^2 + L_{21} I_1 I_2 + \frac{1}{2} L_{11} I_1^2$$

But the final state of the system is the same in both cases, and so the stored energy is the same, which shows that $L_{12} = L_{21}$.

It should be noted that the work on the system can be identified with the stored energy in the field only if the system can be brought to its final state without energy losses occurring in the process. This is not the case when iron is present, because of hysteresis losses.

Since we are interpreting the work done as energy stored in the $\overline{B}$ field, it must be possible to express W_m as an integral over the field. This is indeed the case, and is demonstrated below. Let a distribution of current $\overline{J}$ exist in a given volume. If we change the current by an amount $\delta\overline{J}(\overline{r})$ in a time interval dt (note that $\delta\overline{J}$ may be different at different points) the $\overline{B}$-field will change and an electric field given by Faraday's law in differential form will be induced. In order to change $\overline{J}$ we must apply an electric field $-\overline{E}$ to overcome the induced field. In a time interval dt this field does work of amount

$$dW = -\int_V \overline{E} \cdot \overline{J}\, dV\, dt$$

We shall write this in a modified form. To do this, we combine Faraday's law $\nabla \times \overline{E} = -\partial B/\partial t$, with $\nabla \times \overline{A} = \overline{B}$, which together require that

$$\nabla \times \overline{E} = \nabla \times \left(-\frac{\partial \overline{A}}{\partial t}\right)$$

or

$$\nabla \times \left(\overline{E} + \frac{\partial \overline{A}}{\partial t}\right) = 0 \qquad (6\text{-}12.4)$$

But when the curl of a field is zero, it can be expressed as the gradient of a scalar potential; thus Eq. (6-12.4) implies that

$$\overline{E} + \frac{\partial \overline{A}}{\partial t} = -\nabla\Phi$$

or

$$\overline{E} = -\frac{\partial \overline{A}}{\partial t} - \nabla\Phi \qquad (6\text{-}12.5)$$

Further, we are considering a solenoidal distribution of current for which $\nabla \cdot \overline{J} = 0$ so that, in accordance with the continuity equation, the electric charge density ρ must be zero. Therefore $\overline{E}$ has no contribution from electric charge and $\nabla\Phi$ must be zero. In view of these considerations, the increment of work done now becomes

$$dW = -\int_V \overline{E} \cdot \overline{J}\, dt\, dV = \int_V \overline{J} \cdot \delta\overline{A}\, dV \qquad (6\text{-}12.6)$$

where $\delta\overline{A}$ is the change $\partial\overline{A}$ in the time interval dt that is produced by the change $\delta\overline{J}$ in $\overline{J}$. Now we make use of the Ampère relation $\nabla \times \overline{H} = \overline{J}$, and note that

$$\delta\overline{A} \cdot (\nabla \times \overline{H}) = (\nabla \times \delta\overline{A}) \cdot \overline{H} - \nabla \cdot (\delta\overline{A} \times \overline{H})$$

and Eq. (6-12.6) becomes

$$dW = \int_V \delta\overline{A} \cdot (\nabla \times \overline{H}) dV = \int_V (\nabla \times \delta\overline{A}) \cdot \overline{H}\, dV - \int_V \nabla \cdot (\delta\overline{A} \times \overline{H})\, dV$$

Furthermore, we note that we can write $\nabla \times \delta\overline{A} = \delta\overline{B}$, the change in $\overline{B}$ caused by $\delta\overline{J}$, and with the use of the divergence theorem, we obtain

$$dW = \int_V \overline{H} \cdot \delta\overline{B}\, dV - \oint_S (\delta\overline{A} \times \overline{H}) \cdot d\overline{S}$$

We observe from Eq. (6-3.1) that $\delta\overline{A}$ decreases as R^{-1}, $\overline{H}$ inside the region of current decreases as R^{-2}, and S increases as R^2; thus the surface integral will vanish when we extend the surface to infinity. Therefore

$$dW = \int_{\text{Space}} \overline{H} \cdot \delta\overline{B}\, dV \tag{6-12.7}$$

In order to integrate this expression, we must know $\overline{H}$ as a function of $\overline{B}$. For a linear medium $\overline{H} = B/\mu$, and the work done in increasing the field from an initial value of zero to the final value $\overline{H}$, $\overline{B}$ at each point in space corresponding to increasing $\overline{J}$ from zero to its final value will be

$$\begin{aligned} W_m = W &= \int_V \int_0^B \frac{\overline{B}}{\mu} \cdot \delta\overline{B}\, dV = \int_V \int_0^B \frac{1}{2\mu} \delta(\overline{B} \cdot \overline{B})\, dV \\ &= \int_B \frac{\overline{B} \cdot \overline{B}}{2\mu} dV = \frac{1}{2} \int_{\text{Space}} \overline{H} \cdot \overline{B}\, dV \end{aligned} \tag{6-12.8}$$

This work equals the energy W_m stored in the field.

It appears from this expression that the total energy in the magnetic field of any system of electric currents may be regarded as distributed throughout the entire field with a density at any point equal to

$$\frac{\Delta W_m}{\Delta V} = \frac{\mu H^2}{2} \qquad \text{Joule/m}^3 \tag{6-12.9}$$

Here, as noted in connection with Eq. (5-9.9) for the corresponding electric field problem, this statement involves the assumption that magnetic energy is, in its nature, something that can be spatially distributed. Clearly, while this expression can suggest such an hypothesis, it in no way demands it.

It is of some interest to write Eq. (6-12.8) in a form that shows the relation to the current sources of the field. To do this we retrace some of the steps in this development by writing Eq. (6-12.8)

$$W_m = \frac{1}{2}\int_{\text{Space}} \overline{H} \cdot (\nabla \times \overline{A})\, dV$$

This expression is expanded to the form

$$W_m = \frac{1}{2}\int_{\text{Space}} \overline{A} \cdot (\nabla \times \overline{H})\, dV + \frac{1}{2}\int_S (\overline{H} \times \overline{A}) \cdot d\overline{S}$$

But the right-hand term in this expression vanishes as 0(1/r) so that finally

$$W_m = \frac{1}{2}\int_{\text{Space}} \overline{A} \cdot \overline{J}\, dV \tag{6-12.10}$$

Now since the currents are confined to the filaments, we may write I = J dS and Eq. (6-12.10) can be written

$$W_m = \frac{1}{2}\sum_k I_k \int \overline{A} \cdot d\overline{\ell} = \frac{1}{2}\sum_k I_k \int_S \overline{B} \cdot d\overline{S}$$

which is the expression

$$W_m = \frac{1}{2}\sum_k I_k \psi_k \tag{6-12.11}$$

where ψ_k denotes the flux linking the kth circuit and produced by all other currents.

If the medium is nonlinear and the relation between H and B is that given in Fig. 6-12.1, then the energy stored in a unit volume is given by

$$U_m = \int_0^B \overline{H} \cdot d\overline{B} \tag{6-12.12}$$

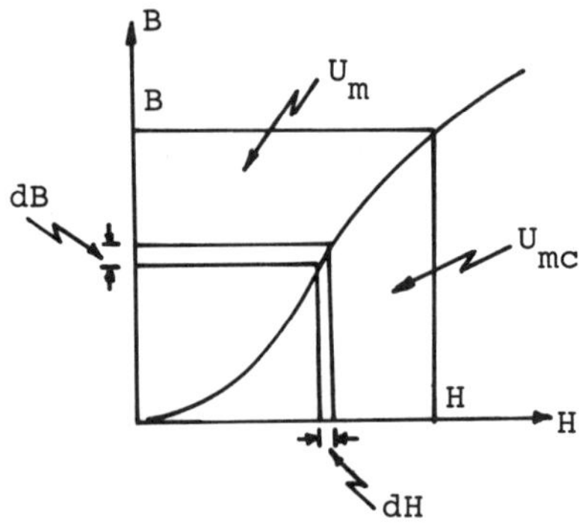

Figure 6-12.1. Illustrating magnetic energy and coenergy.

and is equal to the area above the B,H curve up to the point B. The complementary area is given by

$$U_{mc} = \int_0^H \overline{B} \cdot d\overline{H} \qquad (6\text{-}12.13)$$

Clearly, the magnetic co-energy U_{mc} is related to the magnetic energy per unit volume by the relation

$$U_{mc} = \overline{B} \cdot \overline{H} - U_m$$

as is evident from the figure. In the general case, Eq. (6-12.7) leads to

$$W = \int_V U_m \, dV \qquad (6\text{-}12.14)$$

Example 6-12.1. Derive an expression for the self-inductance per unit length of a coaxial cable of inner radius a and outer radius b, but of negligible thickness. Use is to be made of energy considerations.

Solution. This is an alternate solution to the problem in Ex. 6-9.1. Now the solution begins with the total energy stored in the magnetic field

$$W_m = \frac{1}{2} LI^2 = \frac{\mu_o}{2} \int_V H^2 \, dV$$

where the volume comprises two parts, the space within the inner conductor and the space between the inner and outer conductors. The corresponding values of H for these regions are given in Eq. (6-9.7) and so

$$W_m = \frac{\mu_o}{2} \left[\int_0^a \left(\frac{Ir}{2\pi a^2}\right)^2 2\pi r \, dr + \int_a^b \left(\frac{I}{2\pi r}\right)^2 2\pi r \, dr\right] \qquad \text{per unit length}$$

These reduce to

$$W_m = \frac{\mu_o}{2} \left[\frac{I^2}{8\pi} + \frac{I^2}{2\pi} \ln \frac{b}{a}\right]$$

From this it follows that

$$L = \frac{2W_m}{I^2} = \frac{\mu_o}{I^2} \left[\frac{I^2}{8\pi} + \frac{I^2}{2\pi} \ln \frac{b}{a}\right] \qquad \text{per unit length}$$

$$= \frac{\mu_o}{2\pi} \left[\frac{1}{4} + \ln \frac{b}{a}\right] \qquad \text{per unit length}$$

which is the value given in Eq. (6-9.9).

ΔΔΔ

6-13. Hysteresis Loss

We shall show in this section that when a material such as iron is cycled around the path of the hysteresis loop, the energy loss per unit volume is equal to the area of the hysteresis loop. Refer to Fig. 6-13.1 which shows a toroidal specimen and its hysteresis loop. If the toroid cross sectional area is A and the mean length is ℓ, then

$$H = \frac{NI}{\ell}; \qquad \psi = BA$$

If the current is increased by dI, the induced voltage in the winding will be $-Nd\psi/dt$ since the flux ψ links N turns, and the voltage induced in each turn adds in series. To produce the change in I, a voltage source of strength $Nd\psi/dt$ must be applied. This source will do an amount of work given by

$$dW = NI\frac{d\psi}{dt}\,dt = NI\,d\psi$$

In changing the field from zero to B_1 along the path bc, the work done will be

$$W_1 = \int_0^{B_1} NI\,d\psi = \ell A\int_0^{B_1} H\,dB = V(A_1 + A_2)$$

where $V = \ell A$ is the volume of the toroid and $A_1 + A_2$ is the area between the B axis and the portion bc of the hysteresis loop, as shown in Fig. 6-13.1b. If the current is now reduced in order to decrease B along the path cd, the induced voltage will act to prevent the change in I. The source to be inserted into the winding in order to cancel the induced voltage will then have work done on it since $-Nd\psi/dt$ acts in the direction to increase I. The work done against the external source will be

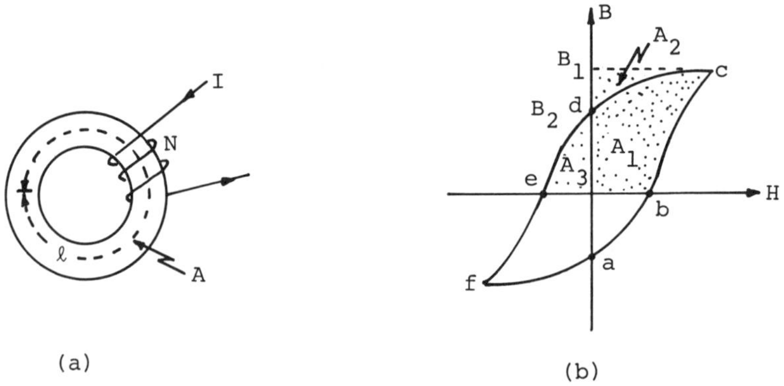

Figure 6-13.1. A toroidal specimen of iron.

$$W_2 = V \int_{B_1}^{B_2} H\, dB = -VA_2$$

where A_2 is the area shown in Fig. 6-13.1b. When B is reduced to zero along the path de, the external source will again do work because the induced voltage still has the same polarity but the direction of the current I has been reversed. As a result, the work done is

$$W_3 = VA_3$$

The total work done to bring the material from the state represented by the point b to the state represented by the point e is given by

$$W = W_1 + W_2 + W_3 = V(A_1 + A_2 - A_2 + A_3) = V(A_1 + A_3)$$

By symmetry, the same amount of work is required to bring the material from state e to state b along the path efab. But $2(A_1 + A_3)$ equals the area of the hysteresis loop. Hence the energy loss in cycling the material around the path of the hysteresis loop once is given by

$$\text{Energy loss/cycle/unit volume} = \text{Area of hysteresis loop} \tag{6-13.1}$$

This energy loss goes into heating the material and is a manifestation of the work required to overcome the forces which resist the change in magnetization of the material.

6-14. Magnetic Forces

The force due to the magnetic field acting on conductors in which currents exist can be calculated from the integral of Eq. (6-1.5a) namely,

$$\overline{F} = \int_V \overline{J} \times \overline{B}\, dV \tag{6-14.1}$$

However, it is often much easier in practice to evaluate the force from $\overline{B}$ by the principle of *virtual work*.

To illustrate the technique, consider two loops of wire in which currents I_1 and I_2 exist, as in Fig. 6-14.1. The energy stored in the field is given by

$$W_m = \frac{1}{2} L_{11} I_1^2 + L_{12} I_1 I_2 + \frac{1}{2} L_{22} I_2^2$$

Suppose that loop C_2 is displaced by an amount $d\overline{r}$ while keeping the currents I_1 and

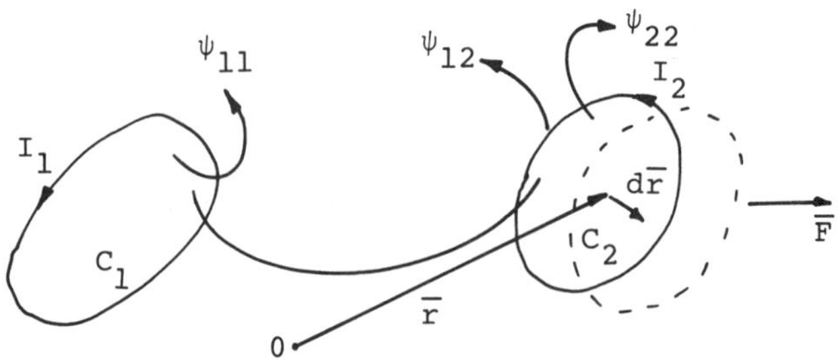

Figure 6-14.1. Two current loops.

I_2 fixed. The displacement will cause a change in the mutual flux linking C_1 by an amount

$$d\psi_{12} = d(L_{12}I_2) = I_2 dL_{12}$$

where dL_{12} is the change in the mutual inductance caused by the displacement. This change in flux results in a voltage being induced in C_1 given by

$$v_{i1} = -\frac{d\psi_{12}}{dt} = -I_2\frac{dL_{12}}{dt}$$

But to keep I_1 constant requires that we must apply an equal and opposite voltage $-v_{i1}$ which will do work of amount

$$dW_1 = -v_{i1}I_1 dt = I_1I_2 dL_{12}$$

The mutual flux ψ_{21} linking C_2 will also change, giving rise to an induced voltage

$$v_{i2} = -\frac{d\psi_{21}}{dt} = -I_1 dL_{12}$$

in C_2. To keep I_2, we must insert a voltage source of strength $-v_{i2}$ which will do an amount of work

$$dW_2 = -v_{i2}I_2 dt = I_1I_2 dL_2$$

during the displacement. If we let $\overline{F}$ denote the force exerted by the field on C_2, then we must apply a force $-\overline{F}$ to produce the displacement. The total work done on the system will then be

$$-\overline{F}\cdot d\overline{r} + dW_1 + dW_2$$

and must equal the change in stored energy. Hence our energy balance equation is

$$-\overline{F} \cdot d\overline{r} + 2\, I_1 I_2 dL_{12} = dW_m = I_1 I_2 dL_{12} \tag{6-14.2}$$

since L_{11}, L_{22}, I_1 and I_2 do not change so that $dW_m = I_1 I_2 dL_{12}$. We can express L_{12} as a function of position coordinates x,y,z relative to a convenient origin. The change in L_{12} due to the displacement is then given by the directional derivative along $d\overline{r}$ multiplied by dr, that is

$$dL_{12} = \nabla L_{12} \cdot d\overline{r}$$

We now obtain

$$-\overline{F} \cdot d\overline{r} = -I_1 I_2 \nabla L_{12} \cdot d\overline{r}$$

and since $d\overline{r}$ is arbitrary, we have

$$\overline{F} = I_1 I_2 \nabla L_{12} \tag{6-14.3}$$

This result may also be expressed as

$$\overline{F} = \nabla W_m(\overline{r}, I_1, I_2) \tag{6-14.4}$$

where the stored energy is expressed as a function of position $\overline{r}$ and the currents. The force in the X-direction will be

$$F_x = \frac{\partial W_m}{\partial x}(x,y,z,I_1,I_2) \tag{6-14.5}$$

where the partial derivative implies that the currents I_1 and I_2 are held constant.

The same force would be obtained, of course, if we assumed some other kind of constraint, as long as the correct energy balance equation is used. If we constrain the flux linkages to remain constant, then we will have to vary the currents during the displacement since L_{12} will change, and $\psi_{12} = I_1 L_{12}$ will remain constant only if $L_{12} dI_1 + I_1 dL_{12} = 0$. Under a constant flux linkage constraint there will be no induced voltages and so no battery work. Consequently the energy balance equation is

$$-\overline{F} \cdot d\overline{r} = dW_m = \nabla W_m(\overline{r}, \psi_{11}, \psi_{22}, \psi_{12}, \psi_{21}) \cdot d\overline{r}$$

or

$$\overline{F} = -\nabla W_m(\overline{r}, \psi_{11}, \psi_{22}, \psi_{12}, \psi_{21}) \tag{6-14.6}$$

where we must now express W_m as a function of the flux linkages, since these will be held constant in forming the partial derivatives in the gradient. The force in the X-direction is

$$F_x = -\left.\frac{\partial W_m}{\partial x}\right|_{\psi = \text{constant}}$$

We can express the energy W_m as

$$W_m = \frac{1}{2L_{11}}\psi_{11}^2 + \frac{1}{L_{12}}\psi_{12}\psi_{21} + \frac{1}{2L_{22}}\psi_{22}^2$$

by using the relations $\psi_{11} = L_{11}I_1$, $\psi_{22} = L_{22}I_2$, $\psi_{12} = L_{12}I_1$, $\psi_{21} = L_{21}I_2 = L_{12}I_2$. Since only L_{12} is a function of $\overline{r}$, Eq. (6-14.6) gives

$$\overline{F} = -\nabla \frac{\psi_{12}\psi_{21}}{L_{12}} = \frac{\psi_{12}\psi_{21}}{L_{12}^2}\nabla L_{12} = I_1 I_2 \nabla L_{12}$$

which is the same result as Eq. (6-14.3) and verifies that Eq. (6-14.6) does indeed give the same force as Eq. (6-14.4). It is important to note that these relations are valid only for linear mediums for which μ is constant.

Example 6-14.1. Calculate the force between coaxial circular coils, as shown, for $R_2 \ll R_1$.

Solution. It is assumed that B_x over R_2 due to I_1 in R_1 is uniform over the smaller coil. But we have found that on the axis at a distance d (see Pr. 6-2.4)

$$B_x = \frac{\mu_o}{2}\frac{N_1 I_1 R_1^2}{(R_1^2+d^2)^{3/2}}$$

The mutual inductance $L_{21} = \psi_{21}/I_2 = M$ is

$$M = \frac{\mu_o}{2}\frac{N_1 N_2 \pi R_2^2 R_1^2}{(R_1^2+d^2)^{3/2}}$$

The force between the coils is

$$F_x = I_1 I_2 \frac{\partial M}{\partial x} = I_1 I_2 \frac{\partial M}{\partial d}$$

from which

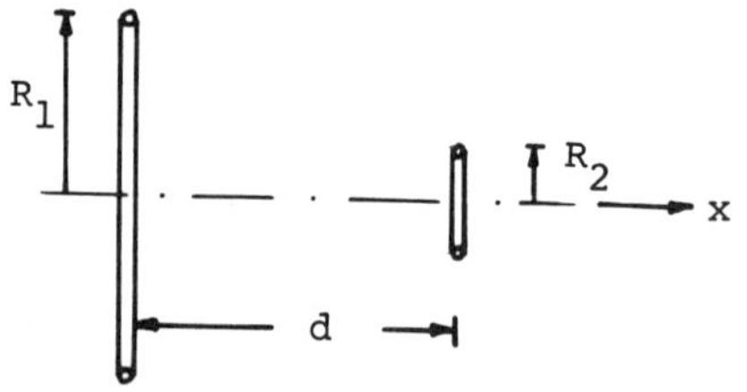

Figure 6-14.2. Two coils a distance d apart.

$$F_x = -\frac{3}{2}\mu_o\pi \frac{N_1N_2I_1I_2R_1^2R_2^2 d}{(R_1^2 + d^2)^{5/2}} = -\frac{3}{2}\frac{\mu_o}{\pi}\frac{(\pi R_1^2N_1I_1)(\pi R_2^2N_2I_2)d}{(R_1^2 + d_1^2)^{5/2}}$$

For the case when R_1 and R_2 are both small compared with d

$$F_x \doteq -\frac{3}{2}\frac{\mu_o}{\pi}\frac{(\pi R_2^2N_2I_2)(\pi R_1^2N_1I_1)}{d^4}$$

The minus sign indicates that the force is one of attraction. ΔΔΔ

Example 6-14.2. Find the lifting force for an electromagnet as illustrated in Fig. 6-14.3.

Solution. Case A: (μ = constant). The flux ψ in the magnetic circuit is readily determined using the techniques discussed in Sec. 6-8. We will find that

$$\psi = \frac{NI}{\frac{\ell_1+\ell_2}{A\mu} + \frac{2x}{A\mu_o}} = \frac{NI}{R} = \frac{V_H}{R} \tag{6-14.7}$$

The stored magnetic energy is

$$W_m = \frac{1}{2}LI^2 = \frac{1}{2}\psi_{11}I = \frac{1}{2}N\psi I = \frac{1}{2}\psi^2 R = \frac{1}{2}\frac{V_H^2}{R} = \frac{N^2I^2A\mu\,\mu_o}{2(\ell_1+\ell_2)\mu_o + 4x\mu} \tag{6-14.8}$$

since the flux ψ links N turns to give a flux linkage $\psi_{11} = N\psi$ for the coil. Since we have W_m expressed as a function of I, we must use Eq. (6-14.4) to evaluate the force. We find

$$F_x = \frac{\partial W_m}{\partial x} = -\frac{N^2I^2A\mu\,\mu_o(4\mu)}{[2(\ell_1+\ell_2)\mu_o + 4x\mu]^2} = \frac{1}{2}\psi^2\left(\frac{\partial R}{\partial x}\right)_{\psi = \text{constant}} \tag{6-14.9}$$

and acts to pull the two pieces of iron together. An equivalent expression is $F_x = (1/2)\psi\,(\partial V_H/\partial x)_\psi$. If we use Eq. (6-14.8) we can express the force in the form

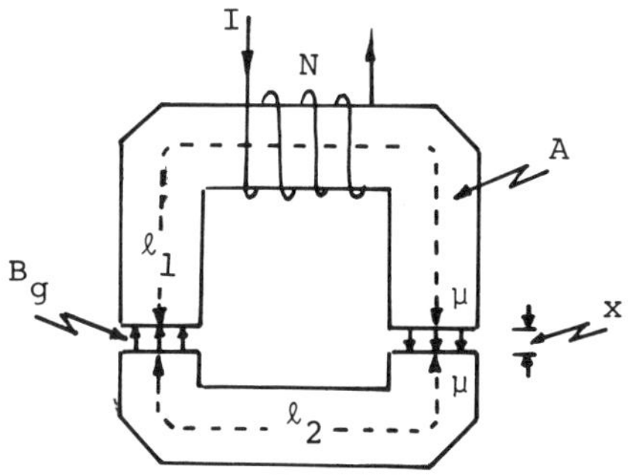

Figure 6-14.3. An electromagnet.

$$F_x = 2\frac{(B_g A)^2}{2\mu_o A} = 2\frac{B_g^{\ 2} A}{2\mu_o} \tag{6-14.10}$$

where $B_g = \psi/A$ is the flux density in the air gap. This equation is interpreted to mean that the magnetic field produces a force with density $B_g^{\ 2}/2\mu_o$ per unit area. Multiplying by the area 2A of the two air gaps then gives the total force. With this interpretation, it is clear that the electromagnet could just as well be a permanent magnet, and as long as the flux density in the air gap is not changed, the lifting force will be the same.

Case B: (μ = variable). In the case of nonlinear mediums μ is not a constant. However, the virtual work principle can still be applied as long as there are no hysteresis losses so that the work done in establishing the magnetic field can be equated to the stored energy. In the case of nonlinear mediums the flux linkages will not be a linear function of the current. In this case if we write $\psi_{11} = LI$ the inductance L will depend on the current. The work done in establishing the magnetic field will be given by

$$W = W_m = \int_0^{\psi_{11}} I \, d\psi_{11} \tag{6-14.11}$$

since the applied voltage required to overcome the induced voltage $-d\psi_{11}/dt$ caused by an increment dI in I will be $d\psi_{11}/dt$. This voltage does work of amount given by Eq. (6-14.11) in building up the field. Note that W_m will be a function of ψ_{11}. Under a constant flux linkage constraint our energy balance equation, Eq. (6-14.7), still holds and may be used to evaluate the force.

In the case of a constant current constraint, we do not have an expression for W_m in terms of I. Refer to Fig. 6-14.4 which introduces the magnetic coenergy W_{mc}, which in this case is given by

$$W_{mc} = \psi_{11} I - W_m = \int_0^I \psi_{11} dI \tag{6-14.12}$$

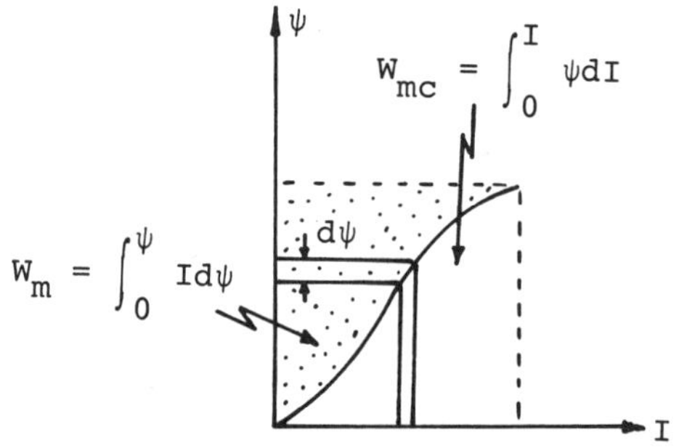

Figure 6-14.4. To specify magnetic coenergy.

We see that

$$dW_m = I\, d\psi_{11} - dW_{mc}, \qquad I = \text{constant} \tag{6-14.13}$$

The energy balance equation in this case will be

$$-\overline{F} \cdot d\overline{r} + I\, d\psi_{11} = dW_m, \qquad I = \text{constant}$$

where $I d\psi_{11}$ is the battery work done against the induced voltage. But from Eq. (6-14.13) we see that we can also write

$$-\overline{F} \cdot d\overline{r} = -dW_{mc}$$

or

$$\overline{F} = \nabla W_{mc}\,(\overline{r}, I) \tag{6-14.14}$$

Hence under a constant current constraint the correct expression for the force is given by the gradient of the magnetic coenergy for nonlinear mediums. The force in the X-direction is

$$F_x = \left.\frac{\partial W_{mc}}{\partial x}\right|_{I\, =\, \text{constant}}$$

When the medium is linear $W_m = W_{mc}$ and Eq. (6-14.14) becomes identical with Eq. (6-14.4).

If there is an actual physical motion resulting from the force, account must be taken of the fact that the force may change during the motion. The work done during such motion can be evaluated by finding the change in energy of the system between the initial and final states. For the electromagnet with constant current the work done will be equal to the change in energy, with

$$\Delta W_m = \frac{1}{2}\,(V_H)^2\left(\frac{1}{R_2} - \frac{1}{R_1}\right)$$

ΔΔΔ

6-15. Summary

In a manner that parallels the discussion relating the entire study of electrostatics in concise mathematical form, a similar compact description is possible of the essential content of magnetostatics, and for the quasi-static field. These descriptions follow.

Magnetostatics is contained in the set of equations:

$$\nabla \times \overline{H} = \overline{J}$$
$$\nabla \cdot \overline{B} = 0$$
$$\overline{B} = \mu\overline{H} \qquad \overline{H} = \overline{B} + \overline{M}$$
$$\overline{F} = \int I\, d\overline{\ell} \times \overline{B}$$

The corresponding set of equations for the quasi-static field is

$$\nabla \times \overline{E} = -\partial\overline{B}/\partial t$$
$$\nabla \cdot \overline{D} = \rho$$
$$\nabla \times \overline{H} = \overline{J} + \partial\overline{D}/\partial t$$
$$\nabla \cdot \overline{B} = 0$$

This latter set is the most general one and constitutes the Maxwell equations. This set will provide the basis for our subsequent studies.

REVIEW QUESTIONS

1. State in words the Ampère force law.
2. State in words the Biot-Savart law.
3. What are the units of the permeability of free space?
4. Define the Lorentz force.
5. When is the Hall effect observed? Can you find use for the Hall voltage?
6. Define the Ampère circuital law.
7. What are the units of magnetic flux?
8. What is the difference between a magnetic dipole and an electric dipole?
9. What happens to a magnetic dipole when it is immersed in a magnetic field?
10. What effects produce the magnetic properties of a material?
11. What is the meaning of magnetization?
12. What does the equation $\overline{H} = \overline{B}/\mu_0 - \overline{M}$ tell us?
13. What is the name and the units of χ_m in the equation $M = \chi_m H$?
14. Identify each term in the given equations and state its units:

$$\overline{B} = \mu_0(\overline{H} + \overline{M}) = \mu_0(1 + \chi_m)\overline{H} = \mu_0\mu_r\overline{H} = \mu\overline{H}$$

15. Describe the differences among: diamagnetic, paramagnetic and ferromagnetic materials.
16. What is meant by coercive force?
17. What are the boundary conditions for the $\overline{B}$ and $\overline{H}$ fields at the interface between two different mediums?
18. What is the analog of resistance in magnetic circuits?
19. Is inductance a function of the geometry of a circuit?

20. What is the difference between self and mutual inductance?
21. Is it possible for a circuit to have both self and mutual inductance?
22. What is meant by internal inductance?
23. State Faraday's law.
24. Given a small magnet and a wire loop. Can one create a high voltage across the ends of the loop?
25. Consider an elastic circular conducting loop that is contained wholly inside of a magnetic field that is shrinking in intensity. Will a voltage be observed across the two ends of the loop? If yes, why?
26. How does a homopolar generator work?
27. What is the significance of Lenz's law?
28. What is meant by displacement current?
29. Do we associate a magnetic energy density with a magnetic field? If yes, how is it defined?

PROBLEMS

6-2.1. Consider two infinitely long wires carrying currents I_1 and I_2. The wires are parallel to the Z-axis and located at $x = \pm d$, $y = 0$ as shown. Find the magnetic field along the Z-axis.
[Hint: Use superposition and the Ampère circuital law.]

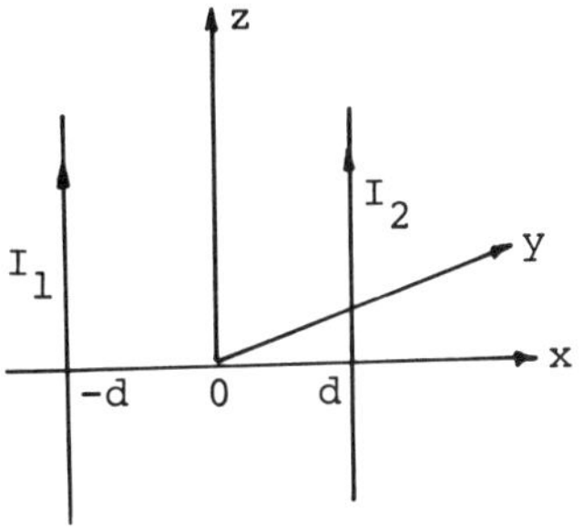

Figure P6-2.1.

6-2.2. Verify Eq. (6-2.18).

6-2.3. (a) Calculate the magnetic field density at the center of a plane circular loop of wire carrying a current I. [Ans: $\mu_o I/2a$]
(b) Calculate the magnetic field density at any point outside, but in the plane of a plane circular loop which carries a current I.
[Ans: B = 0]

6-2.4. Refer to the accompanying figure which shows a current carrying loop of radius a.

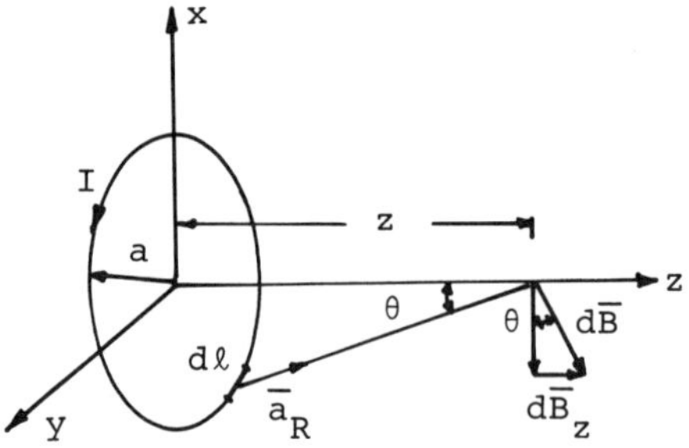

Figure P6-2.4.

(a) Compute the magnetic field at a point on the axis of the circle.

(b) Show that the resulting formula reduces to I/2a when the observation point is shifted to the center of the loop.

[Hint: $d\bar{B} = \frac{\mu_o}{4\pi} \frac{I\,d\ell \sin\frac{\pi}{2}}{R^2} \bar{a}_\phi = \frac{\mu_o}{4\pi} \frac{I\,d\ell}{R^2} \bar{a}_\phi$; $dB_z = \frac{\mu_o}{4\pi} \frac{I\,d\ell}{R^2} \sin\theta$; $\sin\theta = \frac{a}{R}$]

[Ans: $B_z = \frac{\mu_o I a^2}{2(a^2+z^2)^{3/2}}$]

6-2.5. Calculate the magnetic field density on the axis of a solenoid of length L and diameter D with N turns uniformly distributed.

(a) At a remote point on the axis; (b) At the end of the solenoid; (c) At the center of the solenoid.

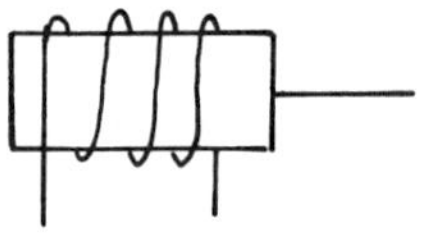

Figure P6-2.5.

6-2.6. A very long solenoid of length L is wound with N turns of wire which carry a current of I Amp. Problem 6-2.5 shows that the B lines are horizontal near the center of the solenoid.

(a) Find the magnetic vectors $\bar{B}_1$, $\bar{B}_2$, $\bar{B}_3$ as indicated in the figure.

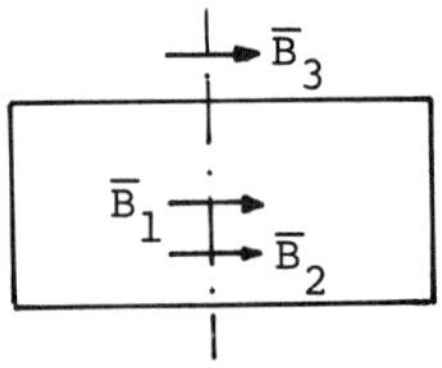

Figure P6-2.6.

(b) The N turns are now replaced by a single turn of aluminum foil of width L. How much current must it carry to produce the same fields as in (a)? Specify the current density in Amp/m. [Hint: Use the Ampère line integral.]

6-2.7. Show that $\nabla \times \overline{B} = \mu_0 \overline{J}$ for the field in each conductor of the cable discussed in Ex. 6-2.2.

6-2.8. Consider two charges moving in paths at right angles to each other at the instant when they are disposed as shown.

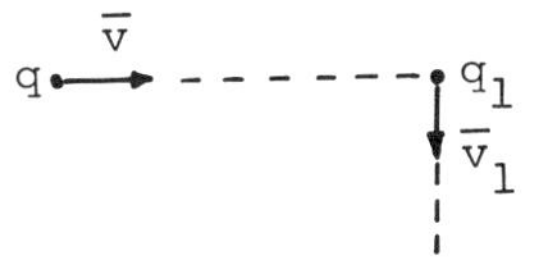

Figure P6-2.8.

(a) It might be expected from Newton's third law that the force on each charge due to the other should be equal. Show that this is not true for the situation shown.

(b) What explanation can you propose for the apparent violation of this basic principle of physics?

6-2.9. By equating the centrifugal force and the $\overline{v} \times \overline{B}$ force, obtain expressions for the frequency of rotation (cyclotron frequency) and the radius of the orbit for a charged particle with charge $\underline{q}$ and mass $\underline{m}$ moving in a uniform field $\overline{B}$ with velocity $\overline{v}$.

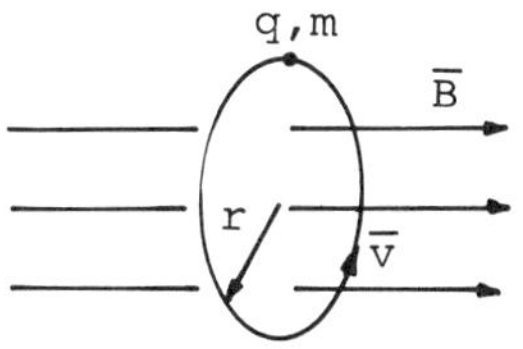

Figure P6-2.9.

6-3.1. Use Eq. (6-3.2) for $\overline{A}(\overline{r})$ and the expression for the curl in spherical coordinates to obtain the components B_r, B_θ, B_ϕ of the magnetic dipole.

[Ans: $B_r = \frac{\mu_0}{4\pi} \frac{2m}{r^3} \cos\theta$; $B_\theta = \frac{\mu_0}{4\pi} \frac{m}{r^3} \sin\theta$; $B_\phi = 0$.]

6-3.2. Show that the magnetic vector potential $\overline{A}$ for a magnetized medium is given by

$$\overline{A} = \frac{\mu_0}{4\pi} \int_V \frac{\overline{J}_c + \overline{J}_m}{R} dV$$

6-4.1. Find $\overline{B}$ and $\overline{H}$ for all values of r for the illustrated coaxial line. The current in the center conductor is I, and is -I in the outer conductor. The current is assumed to be uniformly distributed across the cross-sections.

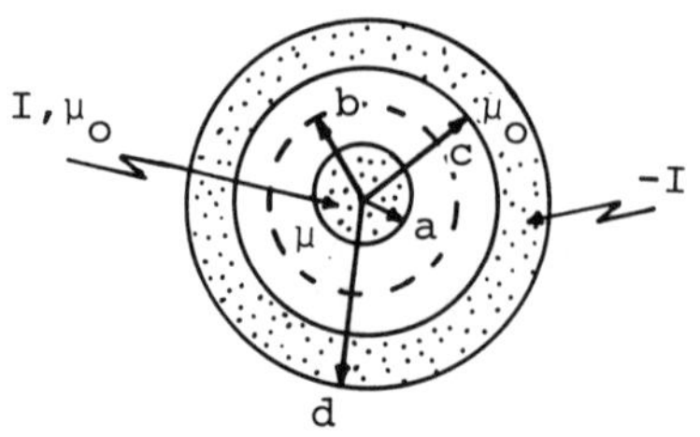

Figure P6-4.1.

[Ans: $B_\phi = \frac{\mu_o I}{2\pi r} - \frac{\mu_o I(r^2 - c^2)}{2\pi r(d^2 - c^2)}$, $c \leq r \leq d$]

6-5.1. Refer to the toroid shown in Fig. 6-5.1 and to Pr. 6-2.4. Is there a magnetic field outside of the toroid? Explain.

6-6.1. Use the boundary conditions for $\overline{B}$ and $\overline{H}$ to obtain a relationship between the angles θ_1 and θ_2 that the $\overline{B}$-field makes with respect to the normal to the interface between iron and air. Show that for θ_1 finite that $\theta_2 \doteq 0$ for high permeability iron, i.e., $\mu >> \mu_o$. Thus, the flux lines leave the iron at right angles to the surface (for practical purposes of flux plotting).

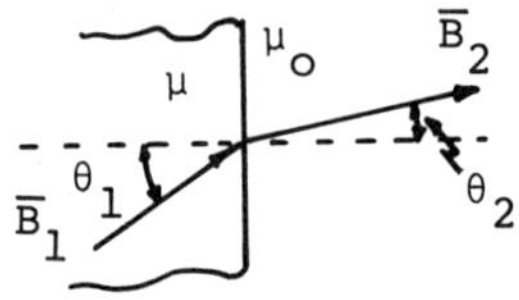

Figure P6-6.1.

6-8.1. A magnetic circuit is shown. Specify the magnetic fluxes ψ_1 and ψ_2 for an exciting coil of N turns with current I. Assume that μ = constant.

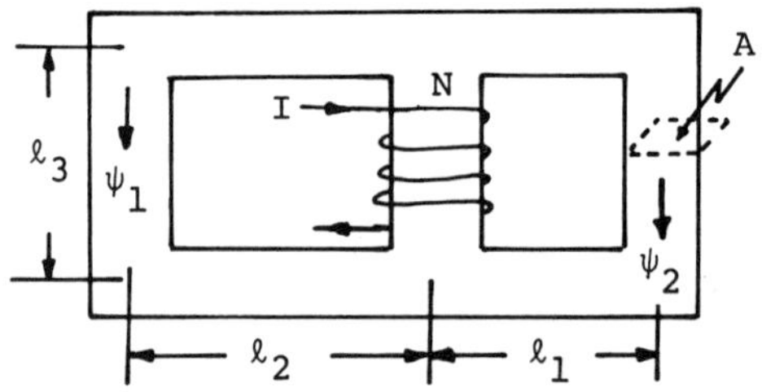

Figure P6-8.1.

6-8.2. Consider the magnetic circuit illustrated. Obtain an equation for the shearing line. When μ is constant, find the flux density B_g in the air gap.

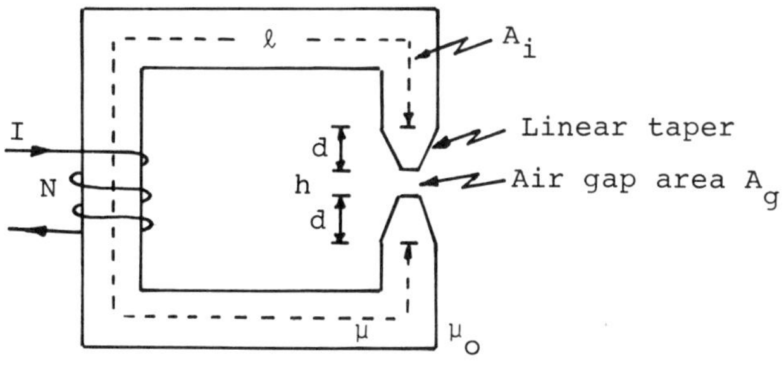

Figure P6-8.2.

6-9.1. Find the mutual inductance between a long wire carrying a current I and (a) a circle, (b) a square, as illustrated.

Figure P6-9.1.

6-9.2. At high frequencies the current in a conductor is confined closely to the surface, with greater confinement at the higher frequencies (this is known as the *skin effect*). Does the self-inductance of a coaxial line increase or decrease with frequency? Explain.

6-9.3. Find the self inductance per unit length of an infinite solenoid of diameter $\underline{d}$ which is wound uniformly with N turns/m.

6-9.4. Obtain an expression for the self inductance of a toroid of circular cross section of diameter $\underline{a}$, with a mean circumference πd, where $d \gg a$, which is wound uniformly with N turns.

6-9.5. Find the mutual inductance between two concentric conducting loops shown in the figure for $d \gg a$ and $d \gg b$.

[Ans: $L_{12} \doteq \dfrac{\mu_o \pi a^2 b^2}{2d^3}$]

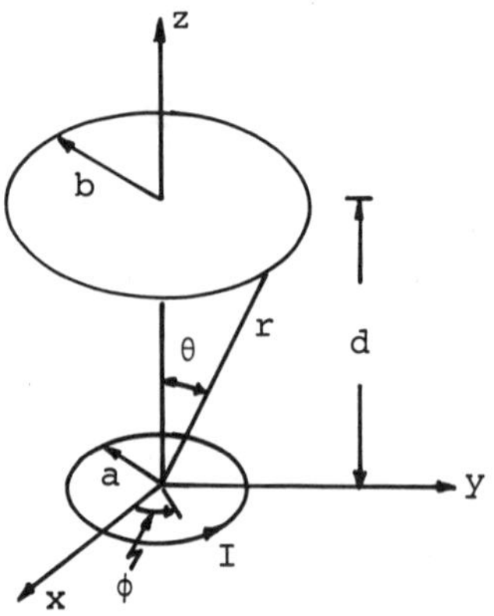

Figure P6-9.5.

6-10.1. A large conducting sheet with conductivity σ and thickness h is moved with velocity v through a uniform field $\overline{B}$, as shown. Show that a force $F = \sigma vhB^2$ per unit area resisting the motion arises from the induced current.

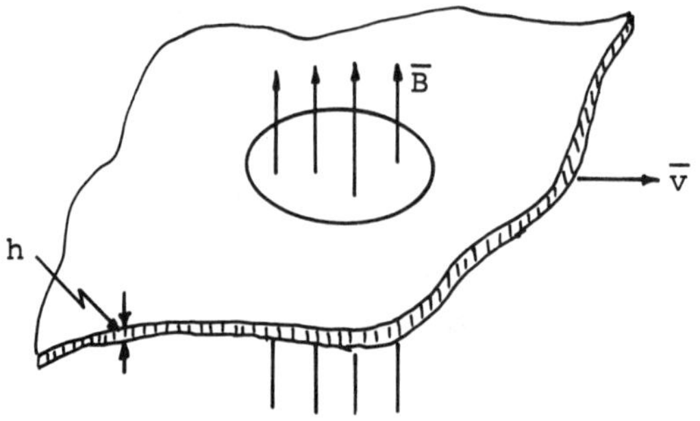

Figure P6-10.1.

6-10.2. A conducting wire is bent in circular form, as shown. It is rotating in a magnetic field $\overline{B}$ at a constant angular velocity $\underline{\omega}$. Find the induced voltage between the center and the rim.

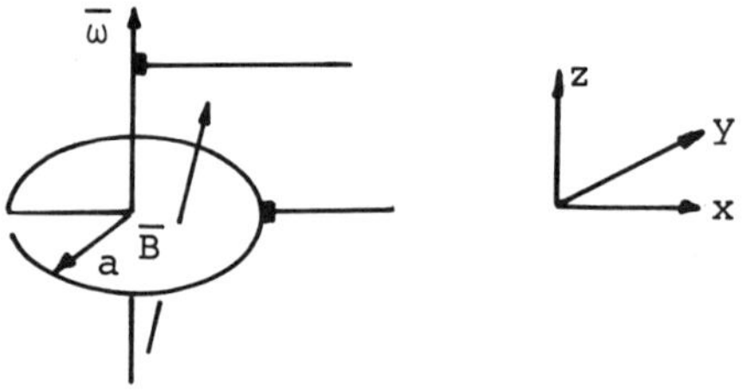

Figure P6-10.2.

6-10.3. A loop antenna consists of 10 turns each of area 0.75 m^2. A radio wave having a frequency of 1 MHz induces a sinusoidally varying emf of 100 μV peak in this antenna. Calculate the magnetic field intensity H of the radio wave.

6-10.4. A sliding bar is moving as illustrated. Find the voltage reading of the voltmeter if $\overline{B} = \overline{a}_z B_z = \overline{a}_z e^{at} e^{-y} x$.

[Ans: $-e^{+at} x_0 (1 - e^{-y_0})(a \frac{x_0}{2} + v)$]

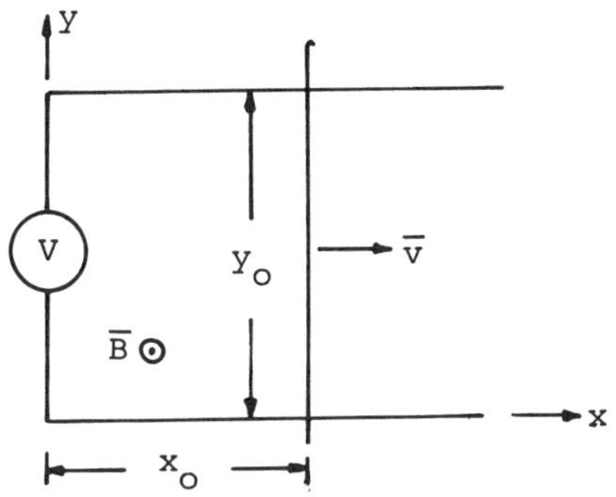

Figure P6-10.4.

6-10.5. As a variant of Pr. 6-10.4, refer to the accompanying diagram which shows a circuit consisting of a number of leads with switches. The switch system is assumed to be such that as one switch closes the prior switch opens. That is, assume that A is closed initially. When B is closed an instant later, A then opens. This process continues with the rest of the switches, thereby causing the area of the resulting loop to change with time. Suppose now that a magnetic field is introduced in the position indicated which produces magnetic flux perpendicular to the plane of the paper. For the spatially limited field distribution specified, as the switch system operates, the amount of flux linking the circuit decreases, with the total flux linkages falling to zero when the final switch H closes. Is there any reading of the voltmeter during the operation of the switch system? Explain.

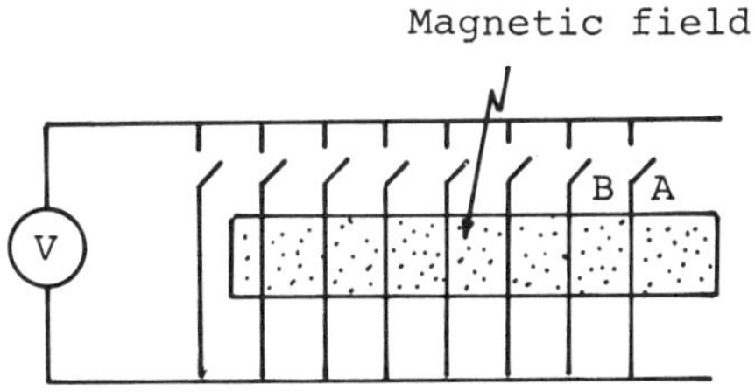

Figure P6-10.5.

6-10.6. Refer to the figure shown which shows an insulating cylinder C which is arranged to rotate so that additional turns are added from the wire spool on drum D. One end of the wire is connected to the slip ring R to which one voltmeter lead is attached. The second voltmeter lead is attached to a sliding contact, as shown. Is there an emf generated? That is, does voltmeter V show any reading when turns are wound on the coil? Carefully explain your results.

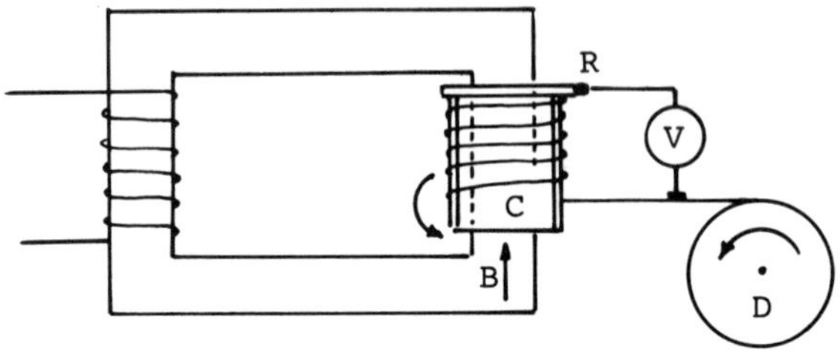

Figure 6-10.6.

6-10.7. Find the voltage induced in a straight wire moving with a velocity $\overline{v}$ over a nonuniform magnetic field B confined to a circular region of space, as shown, with $\overline{B} = \overline{a}_z(a - r)$.

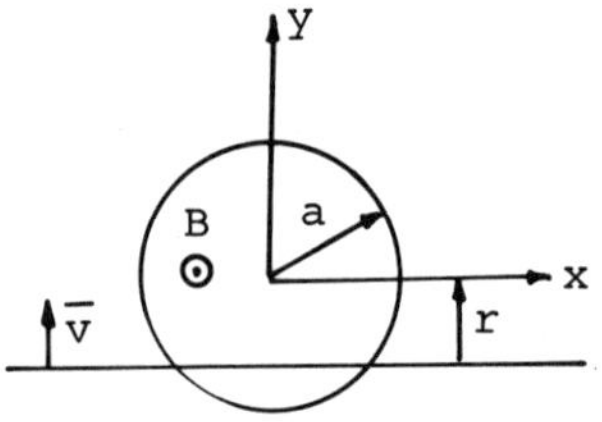

Figure P6-10.7.

6-10.8. The shaded circle of area 1 cm^2 is the cross-section of a long solenoid perpendicular to the plane of the paper. The current in the solenoid is increasing so that the flux density through the shaded area is increasing at the rate of 10^{-2} W/m^2-sec. An ideal voltmeter V can be oriented as either V_1 or V_2.

(a) What will be the readings on V_1 and V_2?

(b) Explain why V_1 is not equal to V_2.

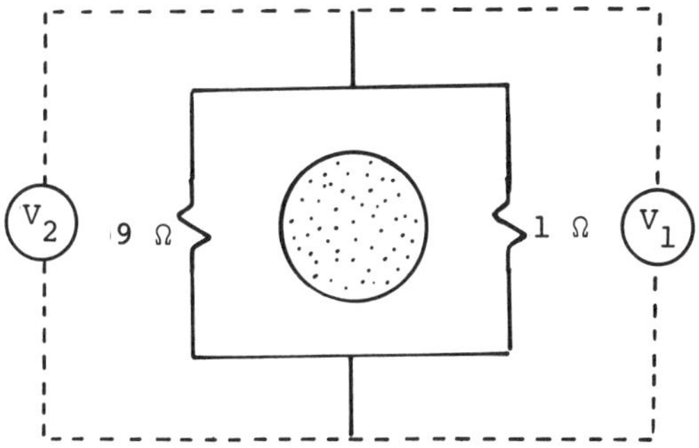

Figure P6-10.8.

6-10.9. Find the emf and sketch its variation versus distance x for the loop shown in the figure. Given: $\bar{v} = \bar{a}_x 4 + \bar{a}_y 4$; $\bar{B} = \bar{a}_z 10$ Weber/m^2.

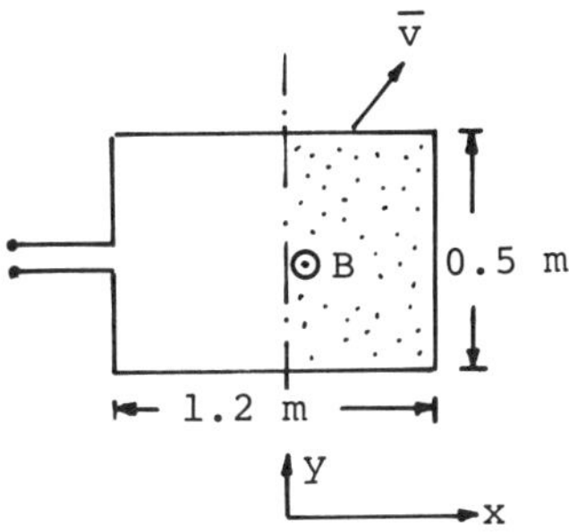

Figure P6-10.9.

6-10.10. A circular coil of wire rotates at a rate ω in a uniform B field normal to the axis of rotation. By using Faraday's law and the definition of self-inductance, show that the current induced in the coil is

$$I = \frac{\pi a^2 \omega B \sin(\omega t - \phi)}{\sqrt{R^2 + (\omega L)^2}} \; ; \; \tan\phi = \frac{\omega L}{R}$$

R coil resistance

L coil self-inductance

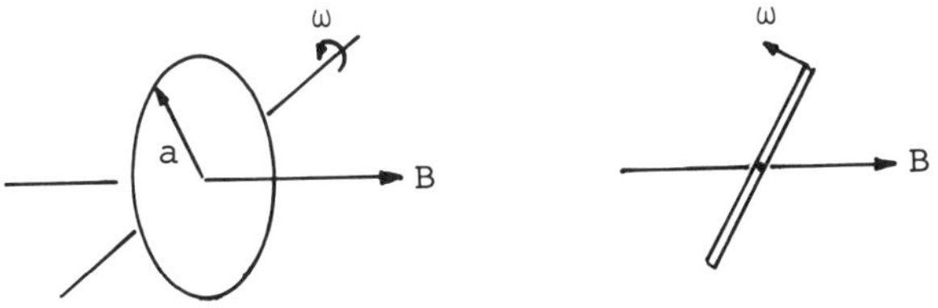

Figure P6-10.10.

6-10.11. Using Neumann's formula, derive an expression for the mutual inductance of two straight filamentary circuits of length L and of infinitesimal cross section which are parallel to each other and a distance D apart.

[Ans: $L_{12} = \frac{\mu_o}{2\pi}\left[L\ \ell n\ \frac{\sqrt{L^2 + D^2} + L}{D} - \left(\sqrt{L^2 + D^2} - D\right)\right]$]

CHAPTER 7

INTERACTIONS OF CHARGED PARTICLES WITH ELECTRIC AND MAGNETIC FIELDS

The motion of charged particles in electric and magnetic fields will be discussed in this chapter, starting with single type particles traversing simple paths, and then proceeding to more complex motions. It will be followed for mediums consisting of mixtures of different type particles, as in plasmas. This study will provide the background for understanding the special field configurations that are used in a variety of important devices.

A. Interactions of Single Type Charged Particles with Fields

7-1. Force on Charged Particles

The force on a charged particle q in combined electric and magnetic fields is given by the Lorentz equation [see Eq. (6-1.6)].

$$\bar{f} = q\ (\bar{E} + \bar{v} \times \bar{B}) \qquad (7\text{-}1.1)$$

This equation is basic to a study of all charged particle ballistics.

In order to calculate the path of a charged particle in a force field Eq. (7-1.1) must be related to the mass and the acceleration of the particle by Newton's second law of motion. Hence the basic differential equation of motion is

$$\bar{f} = m\frac{d\bar{v}}{dt} = q(\bar{E} + \bar{v} \times \bar{B}) \qquad \text{Newton} \qquad (7\text{-}1.2)$$

where m is in kilograms and $d\bar{v}/dt$ is in meters/sec^2. The solution to this differential equation, subject to appropriate initial conditions, will specify the path of the particle in the field. We shall assume in much of our initial study that the charged particle is an electron, and so q = -e, where e is the charge on the electron.

In carrying out the details of a problem, Eq. (7-1.2) will be expressed in a form appropriate to the geometry of the system. In general, Eq. (7-1.2) will be expressed in terms of the three component force terms. For the rectangular system, these equations are

$$m \frac{dv_x}{dt} = q\, [E_x + (\bar{v} \times \bar{B})_x] \qquad \text{a)}$$

$$m \frac{dv_y}{dt} = q\, [E_y + (\bar{v} \times \bar{B})_y] \qquad \text{b)} \qquad (7\text{-}1.3)$$

$$m \frac{dv_z}{dt} = q\, [E_z + (\bar{v} \times \bar{B})_z] \qquad \text{c)}$$

Example 7-1.1. A sinusoidal voltage having a frequency of 1 MHz and a peak value of 10 volts is applied to the plates of a parallel plate capacitor which are 2 cm. apart. If an electron is released from one plate at an instant when the applied voltage is zero, find the position of the electron at any subsequent time t. Assume that the initial velocity of the electron is 10^6 m/sec in the X-direction, which is perpendicular to the plates. No magnetic field is present.

Solution. Neglecting fringing of the electric field, the electric field intensity is

$$E = \frac{10}{0.02} \sin\, (2\pi \times 10^6 t) = 500 \sin\, (2\pi \times 10^6 t) \quad \text{Volt/m}$$

and by Eq. (7-1.3) for one dimension

$$\frac{dv_x}{dt} = \frac{eE}{m} = 1.76 \times 10^{11} \times 500 \sin\, (2\pi \times 10^6 t)$$
$$= 8.80 \times 10^{13} \sin\, (2\pi \times 10^6 t) \qquad \text{m/sec}^2$$

We integrate this differential equation to get

$$v_x = -1.40 \times 10^7 \cos\, (2\pi \times 10^6 t) + A$$

where A = constant of integration. A is determined from the initial condition that

$$v_x(0) = 10^6 \text{ m/sec} \qquad \text{when} \qquad t = 0$$

Thus

$$v_x = 1.50 \times 10^7 - 1.40 \times 10^7 \cos\, (2\pi \times 10^6 t) \qquad \text{m/sec}$$

Integrating this equation with respect to t, subject to the initial condition: t = 0, x = 0, we find

$$x = 1.50 \times 10^7 t - 2.23 \sin (2\pi \times 10^6 t) \qquad \text{m.}$$

ΔΔΔ

7-2. Potential and Energy

We consider Eq. (7-1.3a) in the form

$$-\frac{eE_x}{m} = \frac{dv_x}{dt}$$

Multiply this equation by $dx = v_x dt$ and integrate. This leads to

$$-\frac{e}{m}\int_{x_0}^{x} E_x dx = \int_{v_{ox}}^{v_x} v_x dv_x \tag{7-2.1}$$

But the definite integral

$$\int_{x_0}^{x} E_x dx$$

is an expression for the work done by the field in carrying a unit positive charge from the point x_0 to the point x. Further, as we know, the potential V of point x with respect to point x_0 is the work done against the field in taking a unit positive charge from x_0 to x. Thus

$$V \equiv -\int_{x_0}^{x} E_x dx \tag{7-2.2}$$

The expression Eq. (7-2.1) becomes, therefore,

$$eV = \frac{1}{2} m (v_x^2 - v_{ox}^2) \qquad \text{Joule} \tag{7-2.3}$$

This shows that an electron that has "fallen" through a difference of potential V in going from point x_0 to point x has acquired a specific value of kinetic energy and velocity, independent of the path (a conservative field). Specifically, the increase in kinetic energy of an electron falling through one volt is equal to 1.6×10^{-19} Joule, and this energy is called 1 ev (electron volt). In its more general form, this equation would be written

$$qV_{BA} = \frac{1}{2} m (v_A^2 - v_B^2) \qquad \text{Joule} \tag{7-2.4}$$

Note specifically that this result is not valid if the field varies with time.

If the particle is an electron beginning with zero speed, the speed acquired by falling through a voltage V is

$$v = \left(\frac{2eV}{m}\right)^{1/2} \qquad \text{m/sec} \tag{7-2.5}$$

or

$$v = 5.93 \times 10^5\, V^{1/2} \qquad \text{m/sec} \tag{7-2.6}$$

If we dot multiply Eq. (7-1.2) for an applied electric field $\overline{E}$ by $\overline{v}$, we obtain

$$\frac{d}{dt}\left(\frac{1}{2} mv^2\right) = q\overline{v} \cdot \overline{E} \tag{7-2.7}$$

which, for a stationary field, using the basic relation $\overline{E} = -\nabla V$, takes the form

$$\frac{d}{dt}\left(\frac{1}{2} mv^2\right) = -q\left(\frac{\partial V}{\partial x}\frac{dx}{dt} + \frac{\partial V}{\partial y}\frac{dy}{dt} + \frac{\partial V}{\partial z}\frac{dz}{dt}\right) = -q\,\frac{dV}{dt}$$

or

$$\frac{d}{dt}\left(\frac{1}{2} mv^2 + qV\right) = 0 \tag{7-2.8}$$

This equation shows that the sum of the kinetic and the potential energies stays constant in the motion.

7-3. Relativistic Variation of Mass with Velocity

The accelerating voltage in television tubes and in a number of devices to be considered is such that the particle velocities approach the speed of light. Because of the variation of mass with speed dictated by the theory of relativity, the ballistics situation becomes somewhat more involved in such devices. We wish to examine the effects of this mass variation.

The theory of relativity postulates an equivalence of mass and energy according to the relationship

$$W = mc^2 \tag{7-3.1}$$

where W is the energy in Joule, m is the mass in kilograms, and c is the velocity of light in vacuum, in meters/sec. According to this theory, the mass of a particle will increase with its energy, and thus with its speed. We shall develop the relationship between mass and speed.

If an electron starts at some point with zero velocity and reaches a second point with velocity v, then the increase in energy of the particle is eV Joule, where V is the voltage between the two points. The total energy of the particle will then be

$$mc^2 = m_0 c^2 + eV \qquad \text{Joule} \tag{7-3.2}$$

where $m_0 c^2$ is the energy at the initial point. The quantity m_0 is known as the rest mass of the particle, and is a constant independent of the velocity; m is the total mass of the particle. Suppose now that we differentiate this expression to get

$$c^2 dm = e\, dV = e \frac{dV}{dx} dx = -eE\, dx$$

or

$$c^2 dm = f\, dx \tag{7-3.3}$$

using the relation $\bar{f} = q\bar{E}$ and the basic gradient relationship $E = -\partial V/\partial x$. We combine this with the general form of Newton's second law, namely,

$$\bar{f} = \frac{d}{dt}(m\bar{v})$$

so that Eq. (7-3.3) becomes

$$c^2 dm = \frac{d}{dt}(mv)dx = v\,d(mv) \tag{7-3.4}$$

Upon performing the indicated differentiation, there results

$$c^2 dm = mv\, dv + v^2 dm$$

so that

$$(c^2 - v^2)dm = mv\, dv$$

Now separate variables to write

$$\frac{dm}{m} = \frac{v\, dv}{c^2 - v^2} \tag{7-3.5}$$

By integrating this expression subject to the condition that $m = m_0$ when $v = 0$ we have finally

$$m = \frac{m_0}{\sqrt{1 - v^2/c^2}} \tag{7-3.6}$$

This result was originally derived by Lorentz, and then by Einstein as a consequence of the theory of special relativity. It predicts an increasing mass with increasing velocity; the mass approaches infinity as the velocity of the particle approaches the speed of light.

From Eq. (7-3.2) the increase in kinetic energy due to the applied field is

$$eV = mc^2 - m_0c^2 \tag{7-3.7}$$

or

$$eV = m_0c^2 \left(\frac{1}{\sqrt{1 - v^2/c^2}} - 1\right) \tag{7-3.8}$$

This expression may be used to find the velocity of an electron when it has been accelerated by a voltage V. It is convenient to expand this expression in the following way. Define the quantity v_N as the velocity that would result if the relativistic variation of mass were neglected, i.e.,

$$v_N = \sqrt{\frac{2eV}{m}} \tag{7-3.9}$$

Equation (7-3.8) can be solved for v, the true velocity of the particle, to yield

$$v = c\left[1 - \frac{1}{(1 + v_N^2/2c^2)^2}\right]^{1/2} \tag{7-3.10}$$

It is instructive to expand this expression by the binomial theorem, which becomes

$$v = v_N \left(1 - \frac{3}{8}\frac{v_N^2}{c^2} + \ldots\right) \tag{7-3.11}$$

It is seen from Eq. (7-3.11), that if the speed of the particle is much less than the speed of light, the second and all subsequent terms in the expansion can be neglected, and then $v = v_N$ as it should. It follows from this expansion that if the speed of the electron is 0.1c, then v differs from v_N by only three-eighths of 1 percent. Thus, the relativistic expression must be used only for speeds exceeding 0.1c.

Ordinarily the voltage is known, and the resulting speed is to be determined. The foregoing criterion, when expressed in terms of voltage, shows that relativistic corrections are required if the accelerating voltage is in excess of about 3 kilovolts. Of course, if the particle is an atom or an ion with mass far in excess of that of the electron, a considerably higher voltage will be required. In cases where the speed is not too great, the simplified form in Eq. (7-3.11) can be used.

7-4. Motion in Uniform Magnetic Fields

The force on a charged particle in a magnetic field, in the absence of an electric field, is given by

$$m\frac{d\overline{v}}{dt} = q\,(\overline{v} \times \overline{B}) \tag{7-4.1}$$

where the force due to gravity is assumed to be negligible compared with the electromagnetic force.

For the case of $\bar{v}$ not parallel to the magnetic field lines, we can decompose the particle velocity into two components, one which is parallel to the field and the other which is perpendicular to it. Hence we write

$$\bar{v} = \bar{v}_{\parallel} + \bar{v}_{\perp} \tag{7-4.2}$$

and include this with Eq. (7-4.1). Thus

$$\frac{d\bar{v}_{\parallel}}{dt} + \frac{d\bar{v}_{\perp}}{dt} = \frac{q}{m}(\bar{v}_{\perp} \times \bar{B}) \tag{7-4.3}$$

Upon equating similar vectors on each side of Eq. (7-4.3) we find the set of equations

$$\frac{d\bar{v}_{\parallel}}{dt} = 0 \qquad (\bar{v}_{\parallel} = \text{const}) \qquad \text{a)}$$

$$\frac{d\bar{v}_{\perp}}{dt} = \frac{q}{m}(\bar{v}_{\perp} \times \bar{B}) \qquad \text{b)} \tag{7-4.4}$$

For simplicity and without loss of generality we assume that $\bar{B}$ is parallel to the Z-axis; then $\bar{v}_{\perp} = \bar{v}_{xy}$ and $\bar{v}_{\parallel} = \bar{v}_z$, and the left-hand side of Eq. (7-4.4b) is equal to the centripetal acceleration in the XY plane. If R denotes the radius of curvature of the path, as shown in Fig. 7-4.1, then Eq. (7-4.4b) becomes $(-v_{\perp}^2/R = (q/m)v_{\perp} B)$

$$R = \left|\frac{mv_{xy}}{qB}\right| = \left|\frac{v_{xy}}{qB/m}\right| = \left|\frac{v_{xy}}{\omega_c}\right| \tag{7-4.5}$$

where ω_c is the *gyrofrequency* (or *cyclotron frequency*) and R becomes a constant for uniform magnetic fields.

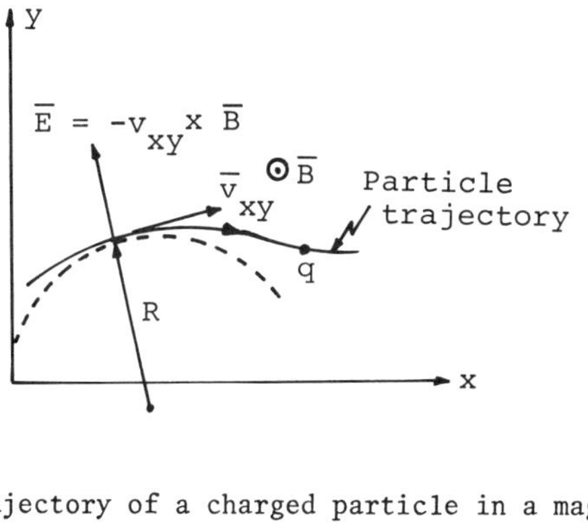

Figure 7-4.1. The trajectory of a charged particle in a magnetic field.

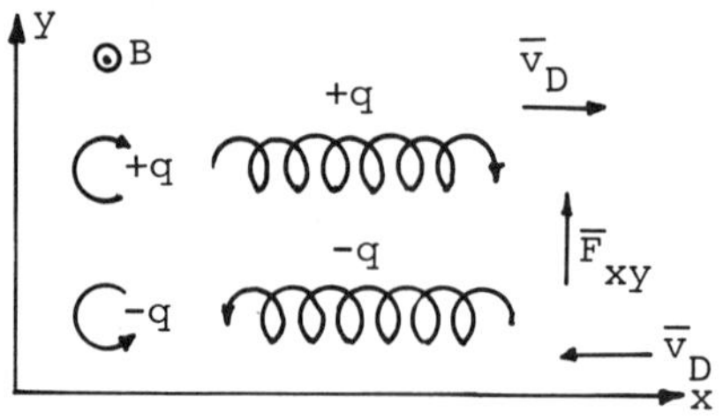

Figure 7-4.2. Orbits of charged particles under the influence of an external force.

We note that as the particle moves on a circular path ($v_z = 0$) it creates its own magnetic field. The equivalent current and its magnetic moment are given by

$$I = \frac{q\omega_c}{2\pi} = \frac{1}{2\pi}\frac{q^2 B}{m} \tag{7-4.6}$$

$$\mu_m = I(\pi R^2) = \frac{1}{2}\frac{q^2 R^2 B}{m} = \frac{1}{2\pi}\frac{q^2}{m}\Psi = \frac{1}{2}\frac{mv_{xy}^2}{B} = \frac{W_{xy}}{B} \tag{7-4.7}$$

where Ψ is the magnetic flux surrounded by the path, and W_{xy} is the kinetic energy of the particle associated with the particle motion perpendicular to the magnetic field.

For those cases where the gravitational force becomes important, Eq. (7-4.1) must be modified to read

$$m\frac{d\bar{v}}{dt} = q(\bar{v} \times \bar{B}) + \bar{F} \qquad (\bar{F} = m\bar{g}) \tag{7-4.8}$$

If, for example, $\bar{F}_{xy}$ is parallel to the XY plane, an additional drift motion appears on the plane, as shown in Fig. 7-4.2. This observation becomes apparent if we write Eq. (7-4.4b) in its modified form which shows the new force explicitly. Thus

$$\frac{d\bar{v}_{xy}}{dt} = \frac{q}{m}(\bar{v}_{xy} \times \bar{B}) + \frac{\bar{F}_{xy}}{m} \tag{7-4.9}$$

We shall now assume that the motion of the particle is composed of a helical motion superimposed upon a constant drift velocity which is perpendicular to both $\bar{B}$ and $\bar{F}_{xy}$ fields. Upon introducing the relation

$$\bar{v}_{xy} = \bar{v}_{oxy} + \frac{\bar{F}_{xy} \times \bar{B}}{qB^2} \tag{7-4.10}$$

into Eq. (7-4.9) we find

$$m \frac{d\bar{v}_{oxy}}{dt} = \bar{F}_{xy} + q\,(\bar{v}_{oxy} \times \bar{B}) + \frac{(\bar{F}_{xy} \times \bar{B}) \times \bar{B}}{B^2} \qquad (7\text{-}4.11)$$

since $\bar{F}_{xy}$ and $\bar{B}$ are perpendicular, then

$$\frac{(\bar{F}_{xy} \times \bar{B}) \times \bar{B}}{B^2} = -\bar{F}_{xy}$$

and Eq. (7-4.11) becomes

$$m \frac{d\bar{v}_{ox}}{dt} = q\,(\bar{v}_{ox} \times \bar{B}) \qquad (7\text{-}4.12)$$

This indicates an orbital motion at $\bar{v}_{ox}$ unaffected by the presence of $\bar{F}_{xy}$. The drift velocity of the equivalent current loop is given by

$$\bar{v}_D = \frac{\bar{F}_{xy} \times \bar{B}}{qB^2} \qquad (7\text{-}4.13)$$

If the force is due to the electric and gravitational fields, we obtain the following two equations

$$\bar{v}_{DE} = \frac{\bar{E} \times \bar{B}}{B^2} \qquad \text{a)}$$

$$\bar{v}_{Dg} = \frac{m\bar{g} \times \bar{B}}{B^2} \qquad \text{b)} \qquad (7\text{-}4.14)$$

Example 7-4.1. Find the velocities and determine the path of a charged particle in constant electric and magnetic fields, as shown in Fig. 7-4.3.

Solution. The force equation for this case reduces to

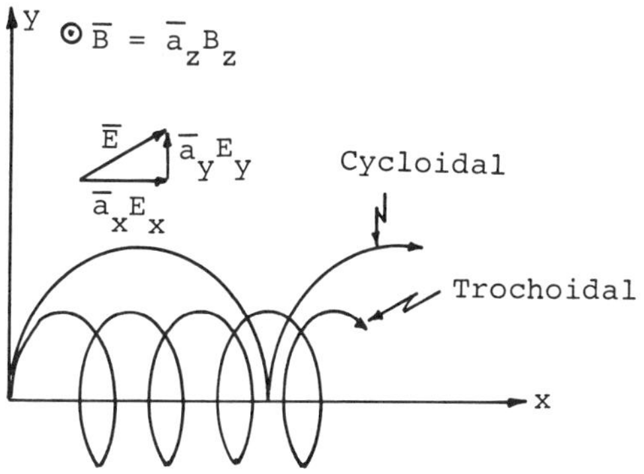

Figure 7-4.3. Trajectories of charged particles in combined fields.

$$\frac{dv_x}{dt} = \frac{q}{m}(E_x + v_y B_z) \qquad \text{a)}$$
$$\frac{dv_y}{dt} = \frac{q}{m}(E_y - v_x B_z) \qquad \text{b)} \qquad (7\text{-}4.15)$$
$$\frac{dv_z}{dt} = 0 \qquad \text{c)}$$

The last equation of this set indicates that the velocity in the Z direction is constant, and it is equal to the initial velocity of the particle in that direction. The solutions of the remaining equations are effected by using Laplace transform techniques. Upon Laplace transforming these equations we obtain

$$s\tilde{v}_x(s) - v_{ox} = \frac{q}{m}\frac{E_x}{s} + \frac{q}{m}B_z\tilde{v}_y(s) = \frac{q}{m}\frac{E_x}{s} + \omega_c\tilde{v}_y(x) \qquad \text{a)}$$
$$s\tilde{v}_y(x) - v_{oy} = \frac{q}{m}\frac{E_y}{s} - \frac{q}{m}B_z\tilde{v}_x(s) = \frac{q}{m}\frac{E_y}{s} - \omega_c\tilde{v}_x(s) \qquad \text{b)} \qquad (7\text{-}4.16)$$

where v_{ox} and v_{oy} are the initial velocities in the corresponding axial directions. Solving these equations, these become

$$\tilde{v}_x(s) = \frac{q}{m}\frac{E_x}{(s^2 + \omega_c^2)} + \frac{v_{ox}s}{s^2 + \omega_c^2} + \frac{q}{m}\frac{\omega_c E_y}{s(s^2 + \omega_c^2)} + \frac{v_{oy}\omega_c}{s^2 + \omega_c^2}$$
$$\tilde{v}_y(s) = \frac{q}{m}\frac{E_y}{(s^2 + \omega_c^2)} + \frac{v_{oy}s}{s^2 + \omega_c^2} - \frac{q}{m}\frac{\omega_c E_x}{s(s^2 + \omega_c^2)} - \frac{v_{ox}\omega_c}{s^2 + \omega_c^2} \qquad (7\text{-}4.17)$$

The inverse Laplace transforms of these are given by

$$v_x(t) = \frac{E_x}{B}\sin\omega_c t + v_{ox}\cos\omega_c t + v_{oy}\sin\omega_c t + \frac{E_y}{B}u_{-1}(t) - \frac{E_y}{B}\cos\omega_c t$$
$$v_y(t) = \frac{E_y}{B}\sin\omega_c t + v_{oy}\cos\omega_c t - v_{ox}\sin\omega_c t - \frac{E_x}{B}u_{-1}(t) + \frac{E_x}{B}\cos\omega_c t \qquad (7\text{-}4.18)$$

For the particular case when $E_x = v_{ox} = v_{oy} = 0$, these equations become for $t > 0$

$$v_x(t) = \frac{E_y}{B}(1 - \cos\omega_c t) \qquad \text{a)}$$
$$v_y(t) = \frac{E_y}{B}\sin\omega_c t \qquad \text{b)} \qquad (7\text{-}4.19)$$

To find the coordinates x and y from these expressions, each equation must be integrated. The Y-coordinate is

$$y = \int v_y\,dt = -\frac{E_y}{B\omega_c}\cos\omega_c t + C$$

Since $y = 0$ when $t = 0$, then $C = E_y/B\omega_c$ and so

$$y = \frac{E_y}{B\omega_c}(1 - \cos \omega_c t) = Q(1 - \cos \omega_c t) \qquad [Q \equiv \frac{E_y}{B\omega_c}] \tag{7-4.20}$$

In a similar way from Eq. (7-14.19a)

$$x = \frac{E_y}{B} t - \frac{E_y}{B\omega_c} \sin \omega_c t = Q(\omega_c t - \sin \omega_c t) \tag{7-4.21}$$

the constant of integration being zero since x = 0 when t = 0. These two equations are the parametric equations for the cycloid, the path traced by a point on the circumference of a circle as the circle rolls on a straight line, with the shape as shown in Fig. 7-4.3. If an initial velocity exists in the Y-direction, $v_{oy} \neq 0$, then the particle will follow a trochoidal path, the path generated by a point within the rolling circle, as shown in the same figure.

The cycloidal curve shows that at each cusp the speed of the electron is zero, since at this point the velocity is reversing its direction. This result also follows from the fact that each cusp is along the X-axis, and hence at the same potential. Therefore the electron has gained no energy from the electric field, and the speed must again be zero.

If an initial velocity exists in the Z-direction, the projection of the path on the XY plane will still be the cycloid, but the electron will now have a constant velocity along the Z axis, resulting in what might be called a "cycloidal helical" motion.

7-5. Motion in Non-Uniform Magnetic Fields

The motion of charged particles in nonuniform magnetic fields can be very complicated. We consider only the simplest cases in this section. We note, however, that the magnetic field configurations and intensity prove to be very important for controlled fusion applications, as will be discussed below. Such applications employ static magnetic fields which are spatially nonuniform to confine high temperature plasmas. The character of the nonuniformities is carefully specified to achieve containment, with deviations from the prescribed configuration causing a degradation of the desired containment.

Consider a magnetic field configuration for which the only important variations of the field are $\partial B_z/\partial z$, $\partial B_y/\partial y$, and $\partial B_x/\partial x$, as shown in Fig. 7-5.1. The field must satisfy the Maxwell equation $\nabla \cdot \overline{B} = 0$, which, in cylindrical coordinates, with circular symmetry, becomes

$$\frac{1}{r}\frac{\partial}{\partial r}(r B_r) + \frac{\partial B_z}{\partial z} = 0 \tag{7-5.1}$$

This equation leads, upon integration, to

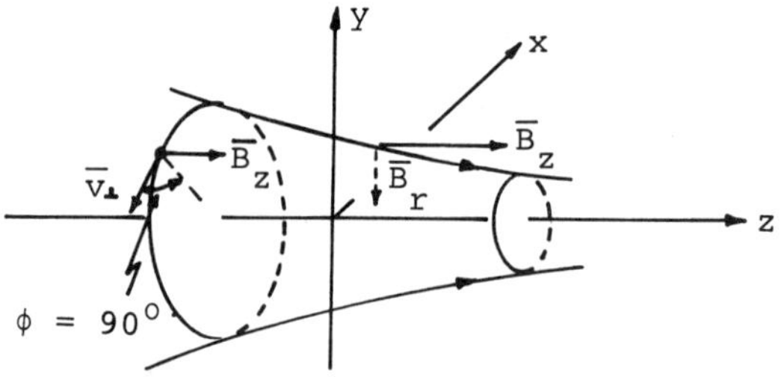

Figure 7-5.1. A magnetic "bottle" configuration.

$$B_r = -\frac{1}{2} r \frac{dB_z}{dz} \tag{7-5.2}$$

assuming that B_z is independent of r. The force on a charged particle along the Z-axis orbiting on a plane perpendicular to the Z-axis is given by

$$F_z = q v_\perp B_r \tag{7-5.3}$$

When this expression is combined with Eq. (7-5.2) then

$$F_z = -\frac{1}{2} q v_\perp r \frac{dB_z}{dz} \tag{7-5.4}$$

This equation shows that the force acts in the direction of the weak part of the field. As a result, the end of the magnetic configuration shown in the figure reflects the particles, and becomes, in effect, a "mirror", thereby keeping the charged particle within the region shown.

Now let us consider the case when the magnetic field has a gradient. This is the case when the partial derivatives $\partial B_z/\partial x$ and $\partial B_z/\partial y$ exist. For simplicity, assume that $\partial B_z/\partial x \neq 0$ and that $\partial B_z/\partial y$ vanishes. This is the situation shown in Fig. 7-5.2. The X-component of the force acting on the particle is

$$F_x = q v_y B_z(x) = q v_y \left[B_z(x_o) + \frac{\partial B_z(x_o)}{\partial x}(x - x_o) + \ldots\right] \tag{7-5.5}$$

The integral of this equation of motion over the time interval required for the particle to move from point 1 to point 2 gives

$$\int_0^t m \frac{dv_x}{dt} dt = \int_0^t F_x dt \tag{7-5.6}$$

However, since $v_x(t) = v_x(0)$, the left hand side of this equation is identically zero, and so

$$\int_0^t F_x dt = 0 \tag{7-5.7}$$

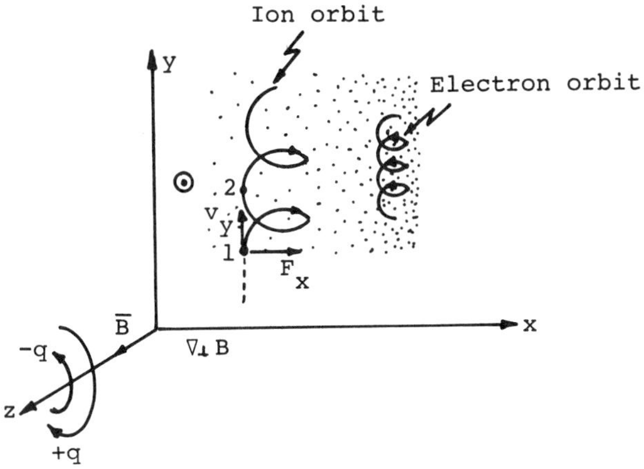

Figure 7-5.2. Moving particles in a magnetic field with a gradient.

By combining Eq. (7-5.5) with this result, the displacement of the particle in the Y direction during one revolution is given by

$$\int_0^t v_y dt = -\int_0^t \frac{(x-x_0)}{B_x(x_0)} \frac{\partial B_z(x_0)}{\partial x} v_y dt = -\int_0^t \frac{(x-x_0)}{B_z(x_0)} \frac{\partial B_z(x_0)}{\partial x} dy \tag{7-5.8}$$

If we assume that the orbits are approximately closed because of the assumed small gradient, the last integral of Eq. (7-5.8) for a positively charged particle is equal to the negative of the area enclosed (observe the clockwise direction) within an orbit of radius R. Hence Eq. (7-5.8) gives

$$\Delta y = \frac{1}{B_z(x_0)} \frac{\partial B_z(x_0)}{\partial x} \pi R^2 \tag{7-5.9}$$

But $\pi R^2 = \mu_m(\tau/q)$ [see Eqs. (7-4.6) and (7-4.7)] where τ is the time spent by the particle in one orbit. Then the last equation takes the form

$$v_y = \frac{\Delta y}{\tau} = \frac{\mu_m}{qB_z(x_0)} \frac{\partial B_z(x_0)}{\partial x} \tag{7-5.10}$$

which in vector form is

$$\overline{v}_{gr} = \frac{\mu_m}{q|\overline{B}|} \overline{a} \times \nabla_\perp B = \frac{\mu_m}{qB^2} \overline{B} \times \nabla_\perp B \tag{7-5.11}$$

where $\overline{a}$ is a unit vector parallel to the magnetic field, $\nabla_\perp$ is the component of the gradient operator perpendicular to $\overline{B}$, and $\overline{v}_{gr}$ is the drift velocity due to the presence of a gradient of the magnetic field. By comparing Eqs. (7-5.11) with Eq. (7-4.13) it is apparent that an effective force exists due to the inhomogeneity of the field which is equal to

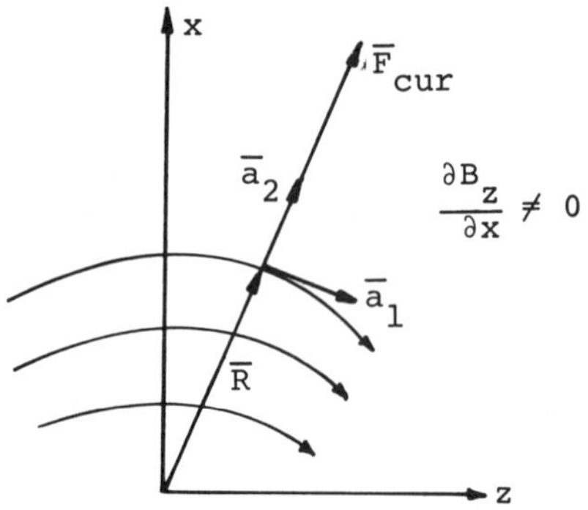

Figure 7-5.3. Particles in a magnetic field with curvature.

$$\bar{F}_{gr} = -\mu_m \nabla_\perp B \tag{7-5.12}$$

When the field has a curvature, the particle tends to follow the field lines, and so experiences a centrifugal force in consequence, given by

$$\bar{F}_{cur} = -\frac{mv_\parallel^2}{R}\bar{a}_2; \qquad \bar{a}_2 = \frac{\bar{R}}{R} \tag{7-5.13}$$

as shown in Fig. 7-5.3. The drift velocity is easily obtained by using Eq. (7-4.13); hence we obtain

$$\bar{v}_{cur} = -\frac{\bar{F}_{cur} \times \bar{B}}{qB^2} = \frac{mv_\parallel^2}{qRB}\bar{a}_2 \times \bar{a}_1 \tag{7-5.14}$$

From the foregoing discussion, we see that because of external applied forces and curvature and gradient of the magnetic field, corresponding currents $\bar{J} = Ne\bar{v}$ are present and in different directions, as dictated by Eqs. (7-5.14), (7-5.11) and (7-4.14).

7-6. Electron Optics

There is a close analogy between the paths of charged particles in electric and magnetic fields and the path of light rays in passing through lenses or mediums of varying index of refraction. To note this analogy, and the lens problem will be considered in some detail in Chap. 11, consider the regions on both sides of an equipotential surface S, as shown in Fig. 7-6.1. Suppose that the electric potential to the left of S is denoted Φ_-, and to the right of S we write Φ_+. Suppose that an electron is moving in the direction PQ with a velocity $\bar{v}_1$. At the surface S a force exists in the direction normal to the equipotential. Because of this force, the velocity of the electron increases to $\bar{v}_2$ after it has passed S. Only the normal

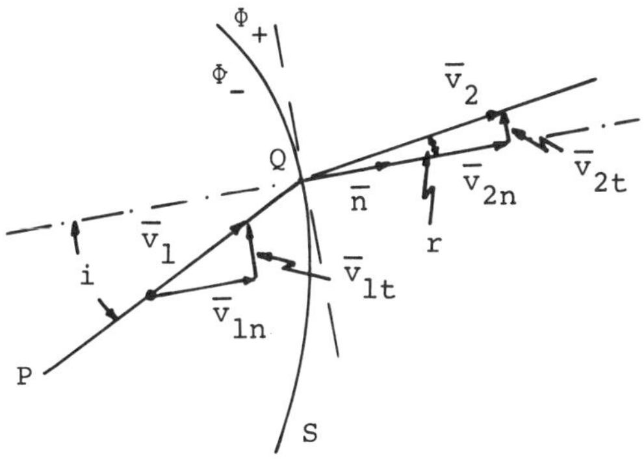

Figure 7-6.1. To show the similarity between geometrical electron optics and geometrical light optics.

component of the velocity of the electron changes, since no work is done by moving the particle along an equipotential. That is, the tangential component of the velocity on both sides of the equipotential remains unchanged. It follows from the figure that

$$v_t = v_1 \sin i = v_2 \sin r$$

where i and r are considered as the angles of incidence and refraction of the electron ray. Then

$$\frac{\sin i}{\sin r} = \frac{v_2}{v_1} \tag{7-6.1}$$

By analogy with geometrical light optics, this ratio might be called the index of refraction, since it is precisely of the form of Snell's law of refraction.

Although the electron lens system and an optical lens system may be considered to be roughly analogous, it must be kept in mind that electron lenses cannot be sharply defined, the region actually being one of continuously varying index of refraction. A very desirable aspect of the electron lens system is that the index of refraction can be varied readily by changing the voltages applied to the electrodes that constitute the lens. Such an arrangement is used for focusing the electron beam in a cathode ray tube. The form of such an electron lens system was discussed in Ex. 4-3.6.

B. Interaction of Positively and Negatively Charged Particles and Field

7-7. Fundamental Characteristics of Plasmas. Microscopic Description

The word *plasma* was first used by Langmuir in 1928 to describe the state of an electrical discharge. Today the word plasma is used to describe phenomena involving strongly or weakly ionized gases. Plasmas are abundant in nature, and the sun, the stars, the ionosphere, the flame, etc., all share the common characteristic of partial or complete ionization of their gaseous state. In our analysis, we shall only consider plasmas which are described by linearized equations, and the induced velocities of the charged particles are smaller than their thermal velocity.

For this type of plasma, the velocity $\overline{v}$ of the electrons when electric and magnetic fields are present is given by Newton's second law, but including Lorentz and Langevin forces. The describing equation is

$$m_e \frac{d^2\overline{r}}{dt^2} = m_e \frac{d\overline{v}}{dt} = e\,(\overline{E} + \overline{v} \times \overline{B}) - m_e \nu \overline{v} \qquad (7\text{-}7.1)$$

where ν sec^{-1} is known as the *electron collision frequency*, and is the average number of collisions that the electron experiences with the heavy gas constituents of the plasma; m_e is the mass of the electron, and $\overline{E}$ and $\overline{B}$ are the applied or self-induced fields by currents in the plasma. A similar equation must be written for the ions. We shall assume, however, that the $\overline{E}$ and $\overline{B}$ fields which exist will vary at such high rates that no movement of ions will take place. In other words, the ions can be considered immobile and to be unaffected by the fields (equivalently, the ions can be thought to have infinite mass - actually $m_i/m_e \sim 10^4$).

When only an electric field is applied, there will be a resulting displacement of an electron from point A to point B. An equivalent viewpoint considers the composite of the electron at its original position plus a dipole, as shown in Fig. 7-7.1. If there are N electrons per unit volume, the total polarization is given by

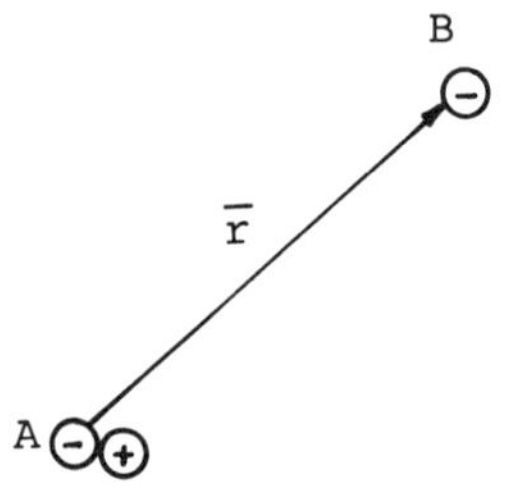

Figure 7-7.1. The polarization effect of plasmas.

$$\overline{P} = Ne\overline{r} \tag{7-7.2}$$

The electric displacement vector is then given by Eq. (5-6.4)

$$\overline{D} = \varepsilon\overline{E} = \varepsilon_o\overline{E} + \overline{P} = \varepsilon_o(1 + \chi_e)\,\overline{E} \tag{7-7.3}$$

where χ_e is the electric susceptibility and is a scalar quantity, since we have assumed that no magnetic field is present.

For a collision-free plasma, and with an applied electric field of the form $\overline{E} = E_o e^{-j\omega t}$, the displacement vector is $\overline{r} = \overline{r}_o e^{-j\omega t}$. Equation (7-7.1) thus becomes

$$\overline{r} = -\frac{e}{m_e\omega^2}\,\overline{E} \tag{7-7.4}$$

Combining Eqs. (7-7.4), (7-7.3), and (7-7.2), we obtain the following plasma characteristic equations

$$\varepsilon = \varepsilon_o\left(1 - \frac{Ne^2/\varepsilon_o m_e}{\omega^2}\right) = \varepsilon_o\left(1 - \frac{\omega_p^2}{\omega^2}\right) \qquad \text{a)}$$

$$\chi_e = \frac{Ne^2}{\varepsilon_o m_e \omega^2} = \frac{\omega_p^2}{\omega^2} \qquad \text{b)} \tag{7-7.5}$$

$$\eta = \sqrt{\varepsilon_o}\left[1 - \frac{\omega_p^2}{\omega^2}\right]^{1/2} \qquad \text{c)}$$

where ω_p^2 is known as the *plasma frequency*, and η is the *index of refraction*. However, when collisions are present, Eq. (7-7.5) is qualitatively the same but with the difference that the electronic mass m_e must be changed to

$$m_e \to m_e\left(1 - j\,\frac{\nu}{\omega}\right) \tag{7-7.6}$$

Consider next a steady electric field which produces a steady state current. In addition, a steady magnetic field $\overline{B}_o$ penetrates the plasma also. Since no time variation exists, Eq. (7-7.1) assumes the form

$$0 = \frac{e}{m_e}\left(\overline{E} + \overline{v} \times \overline{B}_o\right) - \nu\overline{v} \tag{7-7.7}$$

We multiply this equation by $Ne/2\nu$ to obtain the *generalized Ohm's law*

$$\overline{J} = Ne\overline{v} = \sigma_{dc}\left(\overline{E} + \overline{v} \times \overline{B}_o\right) \qquad \text{a)}$$

$$\sigma_{dc} = \frac{Ne^2}{2m_e\nu} \qquad \text{b)} \tag{7-7.8}$$

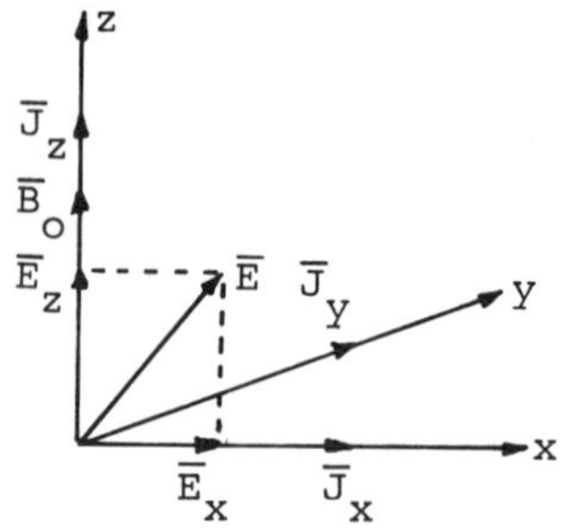

Figure 7-7.2. Steady electric and magnetic fields in a plasma.

where σ_{dc} is the *d-c conductivity of the plasma.*

If we substitute $\bar{v} = \bar{J}/Ne$ in Eq. (7-7.8a) and assume that $\bar{B}_0$ and $\bar{E}$ are applied in the orientation shown in Fig. 7-7.2, we obtain

$$\bar{J} = \sigma_{dc}\bar{E} + \frac{\omega_c}{\nu}\bar{J} \times \bar{a}_z; \qquad \omega_c = \frac{eB_0}{m_e} \tag{7-7.9}$$

where ω_c is the *electron gyrofrequency* or *cyclotron frequency*. Equation (7-7.9) is equivalent to the following set of equations

$$J_x - \frac{\omega_c}{\nu} J_y = \sigma_{dc} E_x \qquad \text{a)}$$

$$\frac{\omega_c}{\nu} J_x + J_y = 0 \qquad \text{b)} \qquad (7\text{-}7.10)$$

$$J_z = \sigma_{dc} E_z \qquad \text{c)}$$

which are found by dot multiplying Eq. (7-7.9) with $\bar{a}_x$, $\bar{a}_y$, and $\bar{a}_z$, respectively. The first two equations of this set give the relations

$$J_x = \sigma_{\perp} E_x \qquad \sigma_{\perp} = \frac{\sigma_{dc}\nu^2}{\omega_c^2 + \nu^2} \qquad \text{a)}$$

$$J_y = -\sigma_H E_x \qquad \sigma_H = \frac{\sigma_{dc}\omega_c\nu}{\omega_c^2 + \nu^2} \qquad \text{b)} \qquad (7\text{-}7.11)$$

where $\sigma_{\perp}$ is called the *perpendicular conductivity*, and σ_H is known as the *Hall conductivity*. Observe that $\sigma_{\perp}$ governs the current perpendicular to $\bar{B}_0$, and σ_H governs the current perpendicular to both $\bar{E}$ and $\bar{B}_0$ fields.

7-8. Macroscopic Description of the One-Fluid Model of Plasmas

In Sec. 7-7 we considered the plasma to be constituted of a uniform gas containing N electrons per unit volume and an equal number of ions which were considered to be immobile. Then the average electron velocity was related through the Newton force law to the Lorentz and Langevin forces. This model is suitable in describing high frequency phenomena. A model that is useful in describing low frequency phenomena is the *hydrodynamic* or *continuous fluid model*. In describing the plasma as a one-fluid model, we must restrict ourselves to those low frequency phenomena which are associated with the movement of massive constituents of the plasma, i.e., the ions and neutral atoms. The electrons play the role of keeping the volume of the plasma electrically neutral.

The study of low frequency phenomena proceeds by neglecting the displacement current $\partial\overline{D}/\partial t$ in Maxwell's equations. Also, the vanishing space average charge density can be taken into consideration by using the equation $\nabla \cdot \overline{E} = 0$. Therefore, for the one-fluid model, the following modified Maxwell's equations must be used:

$$\nabla \times \overline{E} = -\frac{\partial \overline{B}}{\partial t} \qquad \text{a)}$$

$$\nabla \times \overline{B} = \mu \overline{J} \qquad \text{b)}$$

$$\nabla \cdot \overline{B} = 0 \qquad \text{c)} \qquad (7\text{-}8.1)$$

$$\nabla \cdot \overline{E} = 0 \qquad \text{d)}$$

To proceed, we must find the hydrodynamic equations appropriate to a plasma. In this connection, we digress to consider certain fundamental hydrodynamic equations.

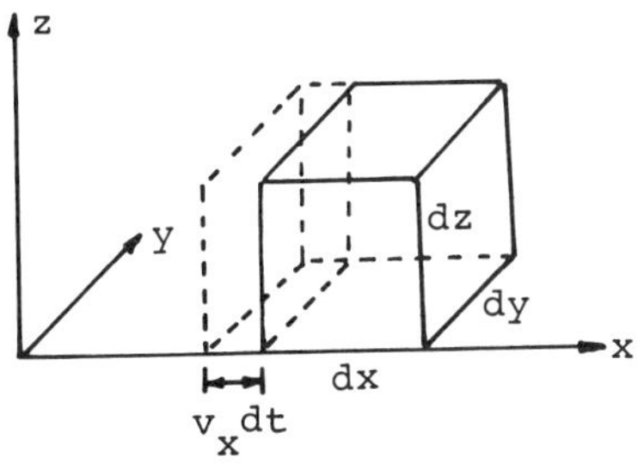

Figure 7-8.1. Ion flow into the elementary volume.

A. Continuity Equation (equation of mass conservation)

Refer to Fig. 7-8.1 which represents an infinitesimal volume within the fluid region, here, a completely ionized plasma. The number of ions which will enter the volume dxdydz through the left-hand face is $Nv_x dtdydz$. It is assumed that all of the ions within the small volume $v_x dtdydz$ have the same average velocity $\bar{v}$ as the ion fluid. The number of ions leaving the right-hand face within the interval dt is

$$Nv_x dtdydz + \frac{\partial(Nv_x)}{\partial x} dxdtdydz$$

as deduced from a Taylor expansion of the number entering the left-hand face. The net increase per unit time is, therefore,

$$\left[\frac{\partial(Ndxdydz)}{\partial t}\right]_x dt = -\frac{\partial(Nv_x)}{\partial x} dtdxdydz$$

from which we find that

$$\left.\frac{\partial N}{\partial t}\right|_x = -\frac{\partial(Nv_x)}{\partial x} \tag{7-8.2}$$

By taking into account the flow through the other two pairs of faces and relating this to the total change in the number of ions per unit time, the result is

$$\frac{\partial N}{\partial t} = -\left[\frac{\partial(Nv_x)}{\partial x} + \frac{\partial(Nv_y)}{\partial y} + \frac{\partial(Nv_z)}{\partial z}\right] = -\nabla \cdot (N\bar{v}) \tag{7-8.3}$$

If Eq. (7-8.3) is multiplied by m, the ion mass, we obtain the well-known mass-conservation equation of fluid mechanics, viz.,

$$\frac{\partial \rho_m}{\partial t} = -\nabla \cdot (\rho_m \bar{v}) \tag{7-8.4}$$

B. Momentum-Conservation Law

Consider that an external force $\bar{F}$ per unit volume acts on a fluid at rest. The volume element dxdydz is acted upon by the force $\bar{F}dxdydz$ and must be balanced by the pressure force. The difference in the pressure force between the two opposite surfaces of the elemental cube dxdydz in the X-direction is given by

$$p(x)dydz - p(x+dx)dydz \doteq p(x)dydz - \left[p(x) + \frac{\partial p(x)}{\partial x}dx\right] dydz = -\frac{\partial p(x)}{\partial x} dxdydz \tag{7-8.5}$$

If an equilibrium state must be maintained, the total force must be identically zero, or

$$-\frac{\partial p(x)}{\partial x} + F_x = 0 \tag{7-8.6}$$

By including the other two sets of faces, Eq. (7-8.6) attains the form

$$\nabla p = \overline{F} \tag{7-8.7}$$

The transition from the static to the dynamic condition can be accomplished by adding the inertial resistance to the external forces. But the inertial resistance of the fluid per unit volume is given by

$$\overline{F}_{in} = -\rho_m \frac{d\overline{v}}{dt} \tag{7-8.8}$$

and Eq. (7-8.7) is modified to the form

$$\rho_m \frac{d\overline{v}}{dt} + \nabla p = \overline{F} \tag{7-8.9}$$

It is very important that we carefully distinguish between the *total* acceleration $d\overline{v}/dt$ and the *local* acceleration $\partial\overline{v}/\partial t$. Let us focus attention on the velocity component in the X-direction, $v_x(t,x,y,z)$. The change in v_x is

$$dv_x = \frac{\partial v_x}{\partial t} dt + \frac{\partial v_x}{\partial x} dx + \frac{\partial v_y}{\partial y} dy + \frac{\partial v_z}{\partial z} dz \tag{7-8.10}$$

and the total acceleration is then

$$\frac{dv_x}{dt} = \frac{\partial v_x}{\partial t} + v_x \frac{\partial v_x}{\partial x} + v_y \frac{\partial v_y}{\partial y} + v_z \frac{\partial v_z}{\partial z} \tag{7-8.11}$$

By including in Eq. (7-8.11) the acceleration components along the Y and Z directions, we easily obtain the general relation

$$\frac{d\overline{v}}{dt} = \frac{\partial\overline{v}}{\partial t} + (\overline{v} \cdot \nabla)\overline{v} \tag{7-8.12}$$

For a better understanding of these two types of accelerations, consider a fluid that is flowing steadily in a tube having a varying diameter, and whose axis coincides with the X-direction. Since the flow does not vary in time $\partial v_x/\partial t = 0$. However, $v_x \, \partial v_x/\partial x \neq 0$ because the flow is higher at those positions where the tube diameter is small and is slower where the diameter is large.

We now combine Eqs. (7-8.12) and (7-8.9) and consider only forces due to electromagnetic fields. We obtain the equations

$$\frac{d\overline{v}}{dt} = \frac{e}{m}(\overline{E} + \overline{v} \times \overline{B}) - \frac{1}{\rho_m} \nabla p \qquad \left[\rho_m = Nm;\ \frac{d}{dt} = \frac{\partial}{\partial t} + \overline{v} \cdot \nabla\right]$$

or

$$\rho_m \frac{d\overline{v}}{dt} = \rho\overline{E} + \overline{J} \times \overline{B} - \nabla p \equiv \overline{J} \times \overline{B} - \nabla p \tag{7-8.13}$$

since no charge can be present at times that are comparable to the characteristic times of the low frequency phenomena.

C. Thermodynamic State Equations

To complete the description of the interacting charged fluids and the fields we must relate the pressure to the density. The usual approximation is the *adiabatic* relation

$$p\rho_m^{-\gamma} = \text{constant} \qquad [p = p(\rho)] \tag{7-8.14}$$

where γ is the ratio of the specific heats of a gas at constant pressure and that at constant volume. For a monatomic gas $\gamma = 5/3$. Upon differentiating this equation we obtain

$$dp = \gamma p\rho_m^{-1} d\rho_m = v_a^2 d\rho_m \qquad v_a = \sqrt{\frac{\gamma P}{\rho_m}} \tag{7-8.15}$$

where v_a is the *adiabatic sound speed* for the charged fluid. This equation indicates that for any change in pressure, there is an instantaneous change in density. This is not always true, and when greater accuracy is required, the adiabatic law must be replaced by a more general energy relation.

For convenience in its later use, we summarize the set of equations which completely describe the one-fluid model of an ionized plasma. These equations are

$$\nabla \times \overline{E} = -\frac{\partial \overline{B}}{\partial t} \qquad \text{Maxwell equations} \qquad \text{a)}$$

$$\nabla \times \overline{B} = \mu \overline{J} \qquad \text{b)}$$

$$\frac{\partial \rho_m}{\partial t} + \nabla \cdot (\rho_m \overline{v}) = 0 \qquad \text{Continuity} \qquad \text{c)}$$

$$\rho_m\left[\frac{\partial \overline{v}}{\partial t} + (\overline{v} \cdot \nabla)\overline{v}\right] = \overline{J} \times \overline{B} - \nabla p \qquad \text{Momentum transport} \qquad \text{d)} \tag{7-8.16}$$

$$\nabla p = v_a \nabla \rho_m \qquad \text{Adiabatic law} \qquad \text{e)}$$

$$\overline{J} = \sigma_{dc}(\overline{E} + \overline{v} \times \overline{B}) \qquad \text{Ohm's law} \qquad \text{f)}$$

where the auxiliary Ohm's law equation was added to make the set of equations complete.

7-9. Some Properties of the Fluid Model of Plasmas

We shall study some important phenomena associated with plasmas, as an application of the set of equations given in the foregoing section. The solution of the generalized equations, Eq. (7-8.16), is very complicated, and it is desirable to introduce appropriate assumptions to make possible an exposition of the essentials of the phenomena. We do this in a series of steps.

A. Diffusion Equation

Consider a conducting fluid at rest, so that $\overline{v} = 0$. In this case Ohm's law assumes the simple form $\overline{E} = \overline{J}/\sigma_{dc}$ or $\nabla \times \overline{E} = \nabla \times (\overline{J}/\sigma_{dc})$ where σ_{dc} is considered to be constant. Introducing this value of $\nabla \times \overline{E}$ into Eq. (7-8.16a) and combining this result with Eq. (7-8.16b), we shall find that

$$\frac{1}{\sigma_{dc}\mu} \nabla \times \nabla \times \overline{B} = -\frac{\partial \overline{B}}{\partial t}$$

or

$$D_m \nabla^2 \overline{B} = \frac{\partial \overline{B}}{\partial t} \tag{7-9.1}$$

where the vector identity $\nabla \times \nabla \times \overline{B} = \nabla(\nabla \cdot \overline{B}) - \nabla^2 \overline{B}$ and the equation $\nabla \cdot \overline{B} = 0$ were used. The quantity D_m is the *diffusivity constant*. This equation, which is known as the diffusion equation for the conducting fluid (see Chap. 9 for a general discussion of the diffusion equation) describes variation of the magnetic field in a uniform stationary conductor. The diffusion time is considered as the longest which one might expect for the magnetic field to confine the plasma or to displace it.

B. Concept of Frozen Field Lines

If we had assumed a finite velocity $\overline{v}$ of the fluid in the foregoing paragraphs, we would have obtained the equation

$$\frac{\partial \overline{B}}{\partial t} = \nabla \times (\overline{v} \times \overline{B}) + \frac{1}{\sigma_{dc}\mu} \nabla^2 \overline{B} \tag{7-9.2}$$

If we further assume that the conductivity is very large so that $\sigma_{dc} \to \infty$, then Eq. (7-9.2) takes the interesting form

$$\frac{\partial \overline{B}}{\partial t} = \nabla \times (\overline{v} \times \overline{B}) \tag{7-9.3}$$

This equation is no longer a diffusion type equation. This indicates that the field lines can be considered to be "frozen" into the conducting fluid and moving with it.

C. Magnetic Reynold's Number

It is possible to distinguish the two extreme cases (diffusion and "frozen" lines) by means of a dimensionless parameter known as the *magnetic Reynold's number*. The Reynold's number is a known constant in fluid mechanics which permits a ready indication of the relative importance of convection and diffusion. In the magnetohydrodynamic case, the conductivity accentuates the convection over the diffusion effects of the magnetic field. The ratio

$$R_m = \frac{v_c L}{D_m} = \mu\sigma_{dc} v_c L \qquad (7\text{-}9.4)$$

is known as the magnetic Reynold's number, where v_c is the velocity of the system and L is its characteristic length. Reynold's number is a measure of the extent to which the convection predominates over the diffusion of the magnetic field lines. For $R_m >> 1$, the magnetic field lines are practically "frozen" in the conducting fluid. For $R_m << 1$, the field lines diffuse easily. For $R_m \doteq 1$, no clear physical picture is possible.

The magnetic Reynold's number R_m is readily ascertained if, in Eq. (7-9.2), we introduce a characteristic velocity v_c and the characteristic length L. In dimensionless form, the resulting relation becomes

$$\frac{\partial \overline{B}}{\partial t_c} = \nabla_c \times \overline{v}_{nc} \times \overline{B} + \frac{1}{R_m} \nabla_c^{\,2}\, \overline{B} \qquad (7\text{-}9.5)$$

where

$$t_c = \frac{t v_c}{L} \qquad v_{nc} = \frac{v}{v_c} \qquad \nabla_c = L\nabla$$

D. Magnetohydrostatics

In the absence of motion, the momentum transport equation becomes

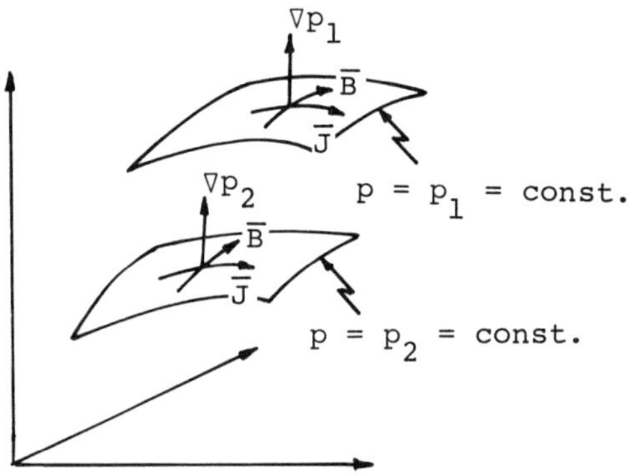

Figure 7-9.1. The constant pressure surfaces in MHD.

$$\nabla p = \overline{J} \times \overline{B} = \frac{1}{\mu} (\overline{\nabla} \times \overline{B}) \times \overline{B} = \frac{1}{\mu} (\overline{B} \cdot \nabla)\overline{B} - \frac{1}{2\mu} \nabla B^2 \tag{7-9.6}$$

where the $\overline{J} \times \overline{B}$ forces are balanced by pressure gradients. From the first part of Eq. (7-9.6) we observe that the current density and the magnetic field are both perpendicular to the pressure gradient, as shown in Fig. 7-9.1. Both, therefore, lie on the surfaces of constant pressure. To confine the plasma with currents and fields distributed through the fluid these surfaces must be multiply connected, somewhat like a torous, rather than simply connected as a sphere. Thus if we evaluate the integral $\oint \overline{B} \cdot d\overline{r}$ on a closed loop lying on a spherical surface of constant pressure, we could find that the value is finite. This means, according to Ampere's law, that the loop must link currents on the other constant pressure surfaces. This is not true, of course, since the loop can shrink to a point while staying on its own constant pressure surface without crossing any of the other currents. Therefore, the constant pressure surfaces must be multiply connected, or of more complicated forms.

E. Magnetic Pressure

We wish to examine the conditions necessary for containing a uniform plasma. Observe first that for the uniform plasma, the pressure must be uniform ($\nabla p = 0$). However, in order to contain the plasma, a pressure difference must exist at the edge of the plasma. This pressure difference is provided by a spatial variation of the magnetic field. To examine this matter, combine the first and last portions of Eq. (7-9.6) to the form

$$\nabla \left(p + \frac{B^2}{2\mu}\right) = \frac{1}{\mu} (\overline{B} \cdot \nabla)\, \overline{B} \tag{7-9.7}$$

where the term $B^2/2\mu$ is known as the *magnetic pressure*. As discussed in Sec. 7-5, electrons and ions tend to move in helical paths along field lines. Also as previously discussed, a field variation perpendicular to the field tends to minimize the particle dispersion. For minimum particle losses, the operator $\overline{B} \cdot \nabla$ is zero, and Eq. (7-9.7) assumes the form

$$\nabla \left(p + \frac{B^2}{2\mu}\right) = 0 \tag{7-9.8}$$

which indicates that the quantity $(p + B^2/2\mu)$ is a constant. In plasma confinement schemes the pressure outside of the plasma is zero. Hence the constant is that corresponding to the external magnetic field B_o, with

$$p + \frac{B^2}{2\mu} = \frac{B_o^2}{2\mu} \tag{7-9.9}$$

We can write from this

$$\beta = \frac{2\mu p}{B_o^2} = 1 - \frac{B^2}{B_o^2} \qquad 0 \leq \beta \leq 1 \tag{7-9.10}$$

which gives the ratio of the plasma pressure to the magnetic pressure of the confining field. The maximum pressure that can exist within the plasma occurs when the internal magnetic field is zero (B = 0), and

$$p_{max} = \frac{1}{2\mu} B_o^{\ 2} \quad \frac{\text{Newton}}{m^2} \tag{7-9.11}$$

Note that the right hand side of this equation is also the energy density of the magnetic field.

The plasma pressure may be determined from the ideal gas law

$$pV = R\Theta \tag{7-9.12}$$

where $R = N_o K$, with N_o = the number of molecules in one kilogram-mole, and K is the Boltzmann constant = 1.38×10^{-23} Joule/^oK. Also, writing $n = N_o/V$, the number density, then the gas law can be written

$$p = nK\Theta \tag{7-9.13}$$

However, a fully ionized plasma contains electrons and ions, and n must be interpreted to reflect the presence of both type particles. For example, a fully ionized deuterium-tritium plasma of importance in proposed plasma fusion devices contains an equal quantity of electrons and ions, and the pressure is, if n is the ion or electron density, twice that for the unionized gas. It is this pressure that must be provided by a magnetic field to contain the plasma. As the pressure and density are linearly related, the pressure achievable by the magnetic pressure tends to set an upper limit for the density.

In particular, for a fusion reaction, the elevated temperature required can result in exceedingly high pressures. Consider a gas at atmospheric pressure and at a temperature of 20° C; this has a number density of 2.5×10^{25} molecules/m^3. A plasma of this density and a temperature of 10^8 ^oK would have a pressure of 7×10^{10} Newton/m^2, or almost 7×10^5 atmospheres. Magnetic fields to achieve this pressure are not possible, and so densities considerably less than this figure must be used. For a density of 10^{21} molecules/m^3, the pressure is 2.76×10^6 Newton/m^2 or 27.3 atmospheres. But for this density, which corresponds to a moderate vacuum (4×10^{-5} atmospheres) and at 20° C, the magnetic field required to confine such a plasma is 2.6 Weber/m^2, which is just barely achievable. Among the important parameters in achieving a fusion reaction are density, confinement time, and temperature. The simultaneous achievement of the conditions on each for fusion has not yet been met. Some consideration of the confinement problem is discussed in the next section.

F. Motion of Conducting Fluids

To study the fluid motion, we complete the momentum transport equation by introducing a viscous drag force. Thus the equation takes the form

$$\rho_m \frac{\partial \overline{v}}{\partial t} + \rho_m(\overline{v} \cdot \nabla)\overline{v} = \overline{J} \times \overline{B} - \nabla p - \rho_m \nu \nabla^2 \overline{v} \tag{7-9.14}$$

where ν is the so-called kinematic viscosity.

The body force $\overline{J} \times \overline{B}$ can provide a large magnetic induction drag on the fluid. To understand this phenomenon, refer to Fig. 7-9.2 which illustrates the fields and forces acting on a fluid filament. When the fluid moves in the indicated direction, the $\overline{v} \times \overline{B}$ field induces a current $\sigma(\overline{v} \times \overline{B})$. This causes the body force $\overline{J} \times \overline{B}$, and for this term we write $\sigma(\overline{v} \times \overline{B}) \times \overline{B} = -\sigma B^2 \overline{v} + \sigma(\overline{B} \cdot \overline{v})\overline{B}$ which indicates a component $-\sigma B^2 \overline{v}$ opposing the motion.

An improved understanding of the phenomenon of magnetohydrodynamics is possible by studying the solutions that apply for the time-independent or steady-state conditions. These steady state solutions are approximately valid for weakly time-dependent phenomena. These solutions are for Eq. (7-8.16) but with time derivative terms set to zero. In this approximation, the continuity equation becomes

$$\nabla \cdot \rho_m \overline{v} = 0 \tag{7-9.15}$$

or equivalently, for an incompressible fluid $\nabla \cdot \overline{v} = 0$. The force equation then assumes the form

$$\nabla p_m = -\rho_m(\overline{v} \cdot \nabla)\overline{v} + \rho_m \nu \nabla^2 \overline{v} \tag{7-9.16}$$

A detailed example will show the procedure and results.

Example 7-9.1. Find the steady state motion of a conducting, incompressible, fluid flowing in the X-direction between two conducting surfaces, as shown in Fig. 7-9.3. A steady magnetic field B_0 is present in the Z-direction, and an electric field E_0 is in the Y-direction.

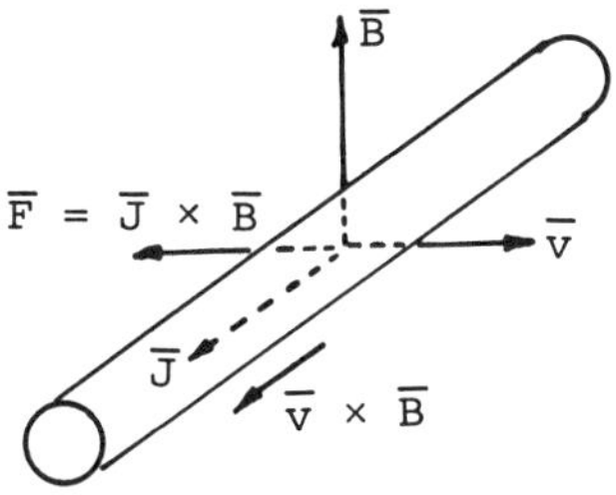

Figure 7-9.2. Inductive drag on a fluid filament.

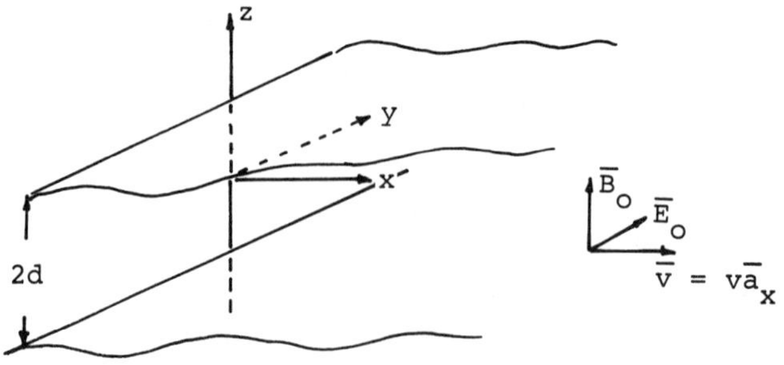

Figure 7-9.3. Conducting fluid between two conducting planes.

Solution. Since the fluid velocity $\overline{v}$ is in the X-direction, the variation in velocity will be in the Z-direction. As a result, the continuity equation, Eq. (7-9.15), is satisfied and the nonlinear term $-\rho_m(\overline{v} \cdot \nabla)\overline{v}$ of the transport equation will vanish. The magnetic lines tend to be pulled forward, with a consequent magnetic field $\overline{B}$ being induced in the X-direction. The fluid velocity is written $\overline{v} = \overline{a}_x v$ and the external electric field is $\overline{E}_o \doteq \overline{a}_y E_o$. It follows from Ohm's law that the current density exists in the Y-direction and is given by

$$J(z)\overline{a}_y = \overline{a}_y \sigma[E_o - v(z)B_o] \tag{7-9.17}$$

The force equation for this particular case becomes

$$\nabla p = \overline{J} \times \overline{B} + \rho_m \nu \nabla^2 \overline{v} \tag{7-9.18}$$

This expression becomes the following set of equations when Eq. (7-9.17) is included

$$\frac{\partial p}{\partial x} = \sigma B_o [E_o - v(z)B_o] + \rho_m \nu \frac{\partial^2 v(z)}{\partial z^2} \qquad \text{a)}$$

$$\frac{\partial p}{\partial y} = 0 \qquad \text{b)} \qquad (7\text{-}9.19)$$

$$\frac{\partial p}{\partial z} = -\sigma B_o [E_o - v(z)B_o] \qquad \text{c)}$$

Because of symmetry, all quantities are independent of the X and Y coordinates, and the first equation of the set becomes

$$\frac{d^2 v}{dz^2} - \left(\frac{M}{d}\right)^2 v = -\left(\frac{M}{d}\right)^2 \frac{E_o}{B_o} \tag{7-9.20}$$

The quantity M is defined as

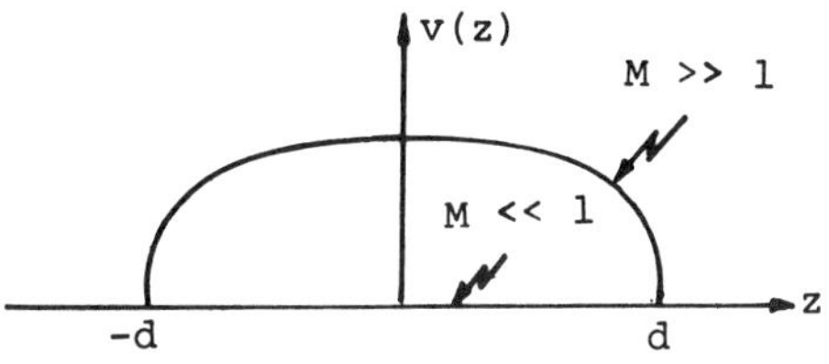

Figure 7-9.4. The velocity profile of a conducting moving fluid.

$$M \equiv \left(\frac{\sigma B_o^2 d^2}{\rho_m \nu}\right)^{1/2} \tag{7-9.21}$$

and is known as the *Hartmann number*, and it is essentially the square root of the ratio of the magnetic to the ordinary viscosity.

Equation (7-9.20) is a relatively simple second order ordinary differential equation, which must be subjected to the boundary conditions $v(-d) = v(+d) = 0$. The solution is written in the form

$$v(z) = \frac{E_o}{B_o}\left[1 - \frac{\cosh \frac{Mz}{d}}{\cosh M}\right] \tag{7-9.22}$$

For small values of the Hartmann number, and this is equivalent to saying that $B_o \to 0$ or $\rho_m \nu \to \infty$, Eq. (7-9.22) is approximately zero since $\cosh(Mz/d) \doteq \cosh M \doteq 1$. For the case when M is very large, the solution for v(z) is

$$v(z) \doteq \frac{E_o}{B_o}\left[1 - \exp\left[\left(\frac{z}{d} - 1\right)M\right]\right] \qquad z > 0 \qquad \text{a)}$$

$$v(z) \doteq \frac{E_o}{B_o}\left[1 - \exp\left[-\left(\frac{z}{d} + 1\right)M\right]\right] \qquad z < 0 \qquad \text{b)} \tag{7-9.23}$$

The features of the solution are shown graphically in Fig. 7-9.4.

7-10. Fusion Reactor Concepts

The major thrust of controlled thermonuclear research has been directed toward the achievement of the plasma conditions of density, confinement, and temperature necessary to produce substantial amounts of power by nuclear fusion. Unlike MHD plasma requirements discussed in Sec. 7-9 which are essentially low temperature, fusion requires a suitably dense plasma at fusion temperatures (10^8 deg K). At these temperatures, the atoms are completely ionized, that is, they consist of electrons and nuclei. Further, the stripped nuclei at these very high temperatures can acquire enormous velocities and their inertial force will carry them over the electric force of repulsion. Thus two nuclei can collide with great violence.

When this happens, the nuclei "fuse" together and form a heavier nucleus. But the mass of this new nucleus is less than the mass of the two original nuclei that collided, and the mass difference appears as energy in accordance with the Einstein equation, Eq. (7-3.1). For example, in the fusion reaction that would involve two deuterium atoms stripped of their electrons, the energy released from 1 gram of deuterium undergoing a fusion reaction is roughly equivalent to that obtained by burning 300 gallons of gasoline.

During the past 20 years, a whole new technology has been developed, not only to heat the plasmas, but also to confine the plasma. Our considerations will be largely concerned with the confinement problem. Clearly, material boundaries are not possible at the fusion temperatures, and magnetic field configurations are used to "bottle" the plasma. We shall discuss some fundamental ideas of plasma confinement, and some of the difference schemes which have been used or proposed for fusion studies.

A. The Stability Question of Plasmas

The question of stability arises in any system that possesses both potential and kinetic energy. Our common experience tells us that a ball on the tip of our fingers is in an unstable equilibrium state since, for any small displacement of the ball, the equilibrium state will be destroyed. The opposite situation is true for a ball in a valley-type configuration. This means that in an equilibrium state the system is *stable* if, due to any small displacement, the system returns to its original state. For the opposite case, the system is in an *unstable* state.

Consider the stability of the plasma-magnetic field configuration shown in Fig. 7-10.1a. In this system, the force of gravity must be balanced by the magnetic pressure. If a perturbation of the field is created, as shown in Fig. 7-10.1b, such that the net area change is zero, then the total magnetic energy and the total pressure of the plasma are unchanged, with no change of stored internal energy. As illustrated, part of the plasma that was originally above the plane y = 0 is now

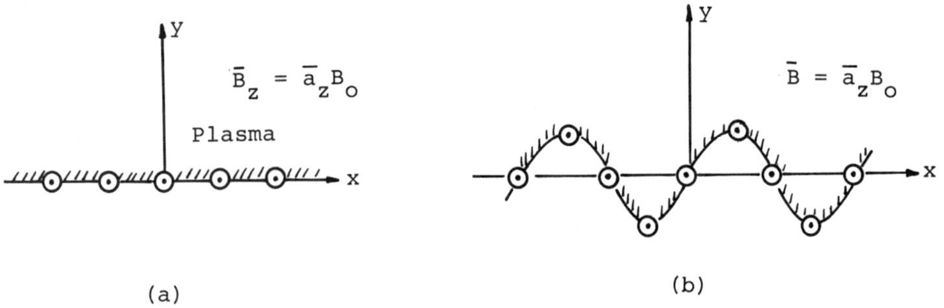

Figure 7-10.1. To illustrate plasma instability.

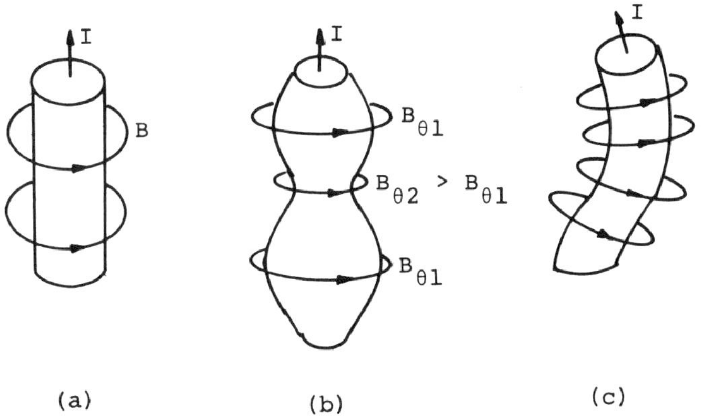

Figure 7-10.2. Column plasma and perturbed configurations.

below it. Since the plasma occupies a lower position, there is a reduction in the potential energy. But since the total energy remains constant, the decrease in potential energy results in an increase in the plasma kinetic energy, and this is an indication of instability of the configuration. This type of instability is called the *Rayleigh-Taylor instability;* the same phenomenon appears when a heavy incompressible fluid is supported by a lighter one. In the present case, the light "fluid" is the magnetic fluid.

Refer now to Fig. 7-10.2 which shows a column plasma and two types of perturbed configurations. In Fig. 7-10.2b, since $B_\theta \propto r^{-1}$, the external magnetic pressure on the plasma surface increases at the compressed portions of the column and decreases where the perturbation causes the diameter of the column to expand. This gradient of the magnetic field causes the perturbations to grow, and a resulting instability ensues. This type of instability is known as *sausage instability.*

If the perturbations cause the plasma column to bend, as shown in Fig. 7-10.2c, the distortion grows because the magnetic pressure on the concave side of the kink is greater than the magnetic pressure on the convex side. This instability is called *kink instability.* In general, when an external confining magnetic field is concave towards the plasma, any perturbation will tend to increase. Contrarywise, when the external magnetic fields are convex towards the plasma, any rippling tends to become smoothed. For this reason, fields of the cusp configuration shown in Fig. 7-10.3 have been proposed for plasma confinement.

B. Field Configurations for Confinement

Magnetic Mirror: The basic idea behind the magnetic mirror follows from the discussion in Sec. 7-5. We consider the motion of an electron in a field which becomes stronger at some point in space, somewhat as shown in Fig. 7-10.4. An electron launched at point P with a velocity that has a component along and normal to the

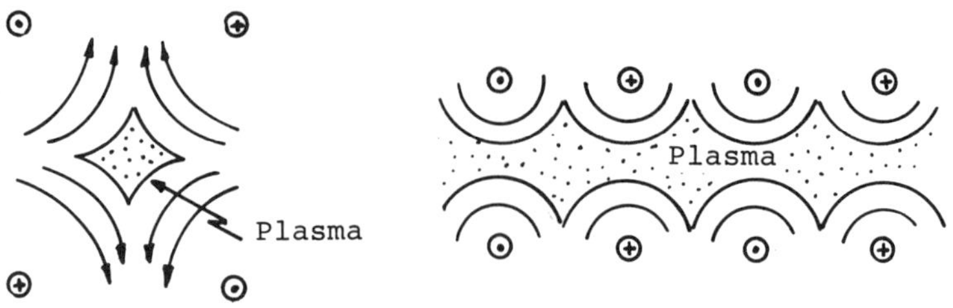

Figure 7-10.3. Cusp field configurations.

field will spiral generally along the magnetic field lines. Because of the increasing magnetic field density in space as the electron moves toward position D, the spiral tightens, and the electron rotates faster. Since no energy is extracted from the magnetic field, as the rotational velocity increases, the velocity parallel to the field must diminish. If the initial electron energy is such that its parallel energy is totally extracted by the time that the electron reaches D, then the electron will stop moving in the CD direction, and will reverse its direction when it reaches D. After doing so it now rotates in the opposite sense. On the other hand, if the electron's parallel energy is not entirely extracted when it is at D, it will continue to move in its original direction and will escape from the region of confinement. Of course, similar arguments apply exactly for the nuclei. The configuration shown is called a magnetic mirror.

We now extend our considerations to a system of two mirrors, as shown in Fig. 7-10.5. In this configuration, as an extension of the discussion above, an electron (or nucleus) that is launched within the region will spiral until it is reflected by one mirror. The electron now retraces its steps until it reaches the second mirror, where it is again reflected. In this configuration the electron will keep bouncing back and forth, but remains confined to the same flux tube, as illustrated in the inset, and such a magnetic system is "tight". Because of the manner in which the electrons (or ions) are trapped between the two magnetic mirrors, the magnetic field configuration of Fig. 7-10.5 is often referred to as a "magnetic bottle".

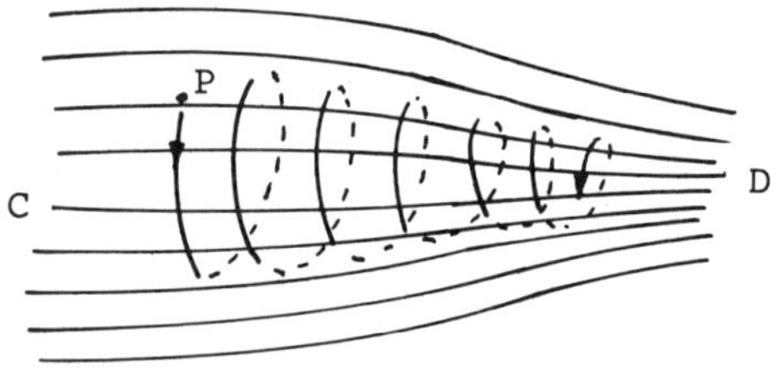

Figure 7-10.4. Reflection of an electron at a "mirror".

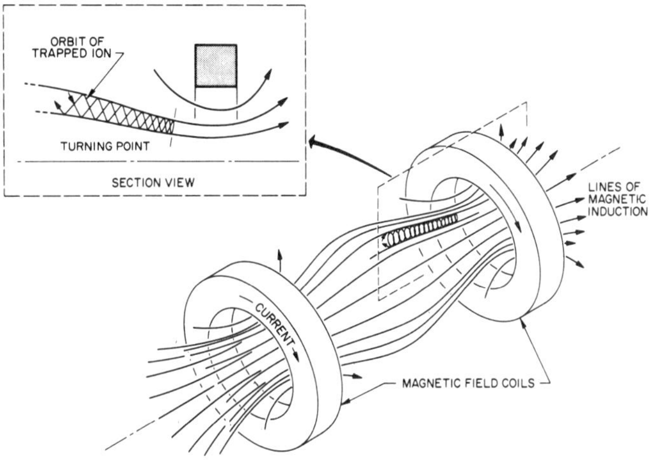

Figure 7-10.5. Principles of the mirror confinement scheme. [Reprinted with permission from IEEE Proc., Vol. 63, p. 1571, Don Steiner "The Technological Requirements for Power by Fusion," 1975.]

To overcome the possibility of a particle leak from the ends of the magnetic bottle, an alternative arrangement has been used, as shown in Fig. 7-10.6. The lines of force are closed loops, and all electrons accelerated in a direction parallel to the magnetic field are trapped since in the ideal case the particles keep spiraling endlessly on the same tubes of force. The particles do not touch the walls where they might get absorbed, and so lost. It appears that this magnetic bottle is "tight".

The Theta Pinch: In the most simple form of this reactor, a hollow long cylinder consisting of an electrically insulating material, is assumed to be filled with a cold plasma. Refer to Fig. 7-10.7 which shows the arrangement for the compression coil in this reactor. A current pulse is now applied to C. The magnetic field associated with this current is directed along the axis of the cylinder. As the

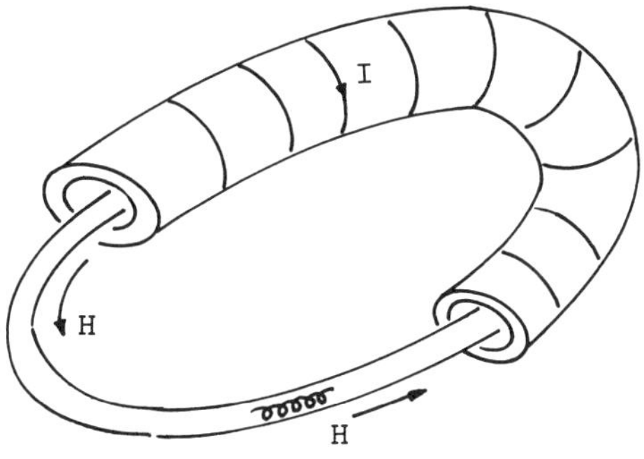

Figure 7-10.6. Method of producing a toroidal field.

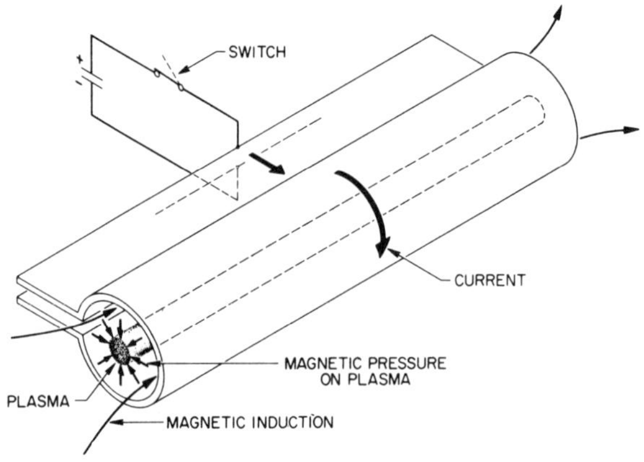

Figure 7-10.7. The principles of the theta-pinch confinement scheme. [Reprinted by permission from IEEE Proc., Vol. 63, p. 1572, Don Steiner "The Technological Requirements for Power Fusion", 1975.]

field changes, a current (which is in the θ direction) is induced in the plasma. As the outermost layers of plasma are accelerated inward, a shock is formed in the plasma, which also travels inward, and appreciably heats up the plasma. The heating of the plasma continues as long as the effect of the magnetic field on I_θ continues to "compress" the plasma. Extremely high temperatures have been registered in such an arrangement.

The scheme shown in Fig. 7-10.7 is not very practical since the plasma will tend to escape from the ends of the cylinder as the plasma is squeezed in the central portion. This shortcoming can be remedied by substituting a toroidal tube for the cylinder, and the coil C is now extended over the whole surface of the torus. In this design, there are no ends from which the plasma can escape, but as the plasma gets hot it becomes unstable and leaks out of the bottle. More elaborate variants of this scheme overcome these deficiencies.

The Tokamak Reactor: The tokamak reactor employs a toroidal magnetic confinement scheme. The principles of this scheme are illustrated in Fig. 7-10.8. An axial current is induced in the plasma by a changing magnetic flux to provide (1) a pulsed poloidal (θ direction) magnetic field which, together with a steady state toroidal field, will confine the plasma, and (2) initial plasma heating which arises from the associated ohmic heating within the plasma ring.

In addition to the poloidal and toroidal fields, a tokamak plasma also requires a pulsed transverse field to provide control on the position of the plasma column. In order to limit Joule heating losses to acceptable levels, the toroidal coil system must be superconducting. But it is generally assumed that the intrinsic ohmic heating process in the plasma will not provide sufficient heating to bring the

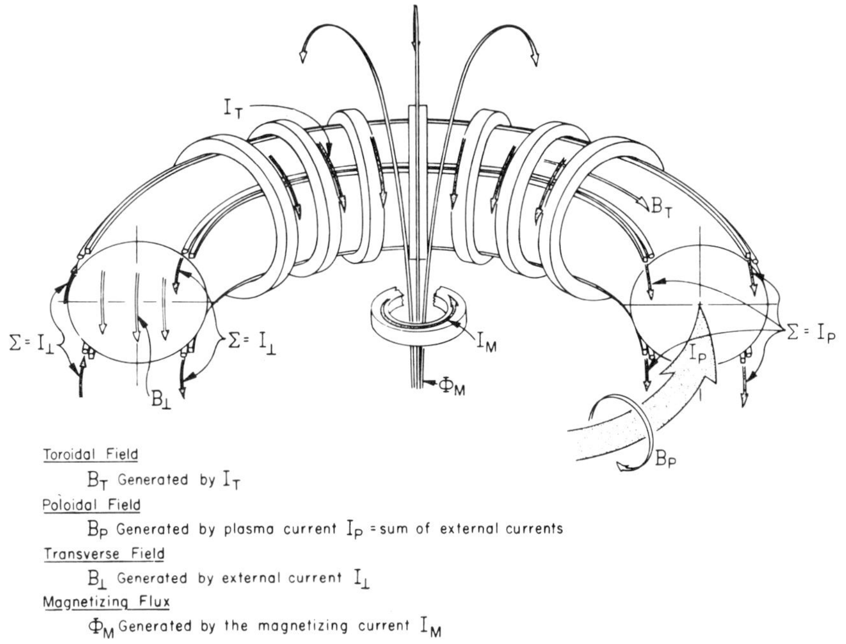

Figure 7-10.8. Principles of the tokamak confinement scheme. [Reprinted with permission from IEEE Proc., Vol. 63, p. 1573, Don Steiner, "The Technological Requirements for Power Fusion", 1975.]

plasma up to the ignition temperature, and auxiliary heating will be required to achieve ignition. A number of such heating techniques are now being investigated.

REVIEW QUESTIONS

1. If a charged particle moves in a combined electric and magnetic field, in what direction is the force on the particle?
2. What is the gyrofrequency of a charged particle? Can you identify one phenomenon in our environment for which this is important?
3. Consider that the magnetic field in which charged particles move to vary spatially and also to have curvature. Do forces appear because of these magnetic field properties?
4. What is meant by plasma frequency?
5. What happens to the index of refraction $\eta = \sqrt{\varepsilon}$ of a plasma if the frequency of a wave f is smaller than the plasma frequency f_p?
6. What is the significance of the magnetic Reynold's number?
7. What is the meaning of the quantity $B^2/2\mu$?
8. Describe some plasma instabilities.
9. How is a theta pinch produced?

PROBLEMS

7-2.1. An electron starts at rest at the negative plate of a plane parallel capacitor across which there is 2,000 volts. The plate separation is 3 cm.

a. How long has the electron been traveling when it acquires a speed of 10^7 m/sec?

b. How far has the electron traveled when it acquires this speed?

c. Through what potential has the electron fallen when it acquires this speed?

7-2.2. An electron is released with zero initial velocity from the lower of a pair of horizontal plates which are 3 cm apart. The accelerating voltage between these plates increases from zero linearly with time at the rate of 10 volts/microsec. When the electron is 2.8 cm from the top plate, a reverse voltage of 50 Volt is applied.

a. What is the instantaneous voltage between the plates at the time of the voltage reversal?

b. With which electrode does the electron collide?

c. What is the time of flight?

d. What is the impact velocity of the electron?

7-2.3. A 100 ev hydrogen ion is released in the center of the plates, as shown in the accompanying figure. The voltage between the plates varies linearly from 0 to 50 Volt in 10^{-7} sec and then drops immediately to zero and remains at zero. The separation between the plates is 2 cm. If the ion enters the region between the plates at time t = 0, how far will it be displaced from the X axis upon emergence from between the plates?

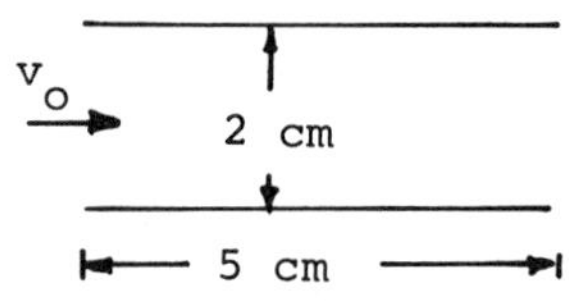

Figure P7-2.3.

7-2.4. 100-Volt electrons are introduced at A into a uniform electric field of 10^4 Volt/m. The electrons are to emerge at point B in time 4.77×10^{-9} sec.

a. What is the distance AB?

b. What angle does the electron gun make with the horizontal?

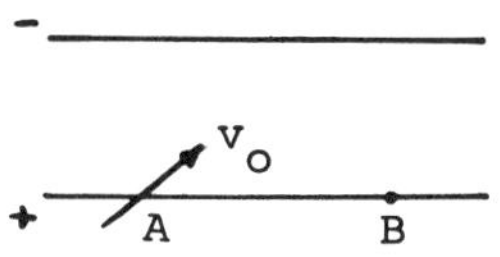

Figure P7-2.4.

7-3.1. Find the rate of mass change of an electron at velocities 0.1 c and 0.999 c.

7-3.2. Find the velocity of an electron for its mass to be equivalent to that of a person, say 70 kg.

7-4.1. Find the velocity of a positron in the X direction if an impulse applied electric field is present. Assume zero initial conditions.

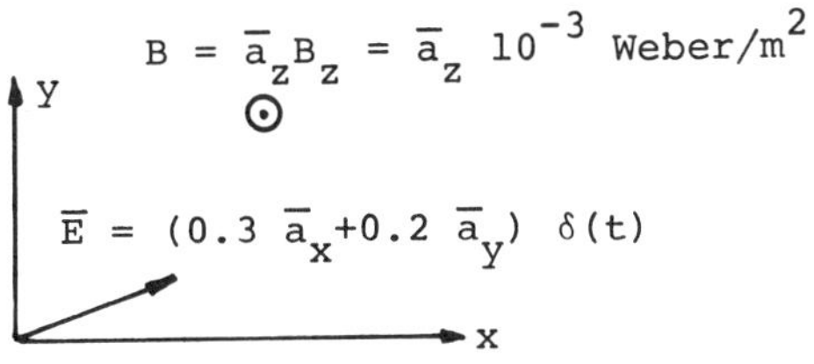

Figure P7-4.1.

7-4.2. Consider perpendicular fields oriented as in Fig. P7-5.6 with $E = 10^5$ V/m and $B = 2$ milliWeber/m^2. Assume that the initial velocity components are $v_{ox} = 10^7$ m/sec, $v_{oy} = 0$, and $v_{oz} = 2 \times 10^7$ m/sec. Plot the path.

7-5.1. What transverse magnetic field acting over the entire length of a cathode ray tube must be applied to cause a deflection of 3 cm on a screen that is 15 cm away from the anode, if the accelerating voltage is 2,000 Volt?

7-5.2. Deuterons (ionized heavy hydrogen atoms - atomic weight 2.015) that are produced in an arc chamber are accelerated by falling through a 100 kV voltage.

a. Through what angle is the direction of the beam deflected if the ions pass through a magnetic field of 800 gauss (1 Weber/$m^2 \triangleq 10^4$ gauss) that is confined to a region 7 cm long?

b. If the particles pass between a pair of plates 7 cm long and 2 cm apart between which there is a voltage of 800 Volt, what is the angle of deflection of the beam?

7-5.3. Lenard's apparatus for measuring e/m for photoelectrons is shown in the sketch. Electrons are released from the cathode K under the influence of the incident illumination. The electrons are accelerated by an accelerating voltage V_a. They pass through the hole in the anode and are deflected by a transverse magnetic field so that they are collected at C. Show that $e/m = 2V_a/R^2B^2$ Coulomb/kg where $R = (D^2 + L^2)/2D$ m is the radius of the path.

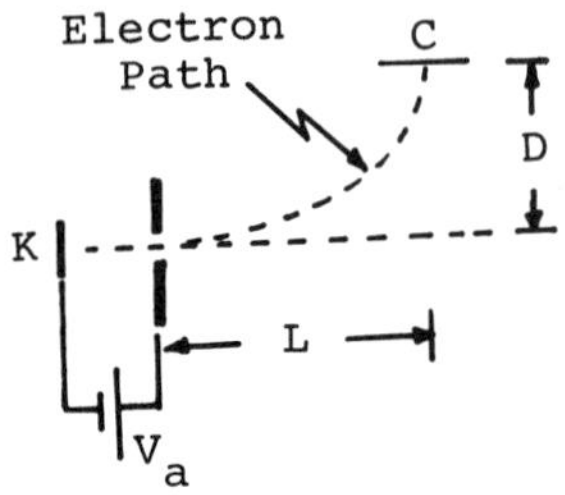

Figure P7-5.3.

7-5.4. A positive hydrogen ion enters a region containing parallel electric and magnetic fields in a direction perpendicular to the lines of force. The electric field strength E is 10^4 Volt/m and the B-field strength is 0.1 Weber/m^2. How far along the direction of the fields will the ion travel during the second revolution of the helical path?

7-5.5. A region includes a uniform electric field E of 2×10^4 Volt, and a uniform magnetic field B of 0.03 Weber/m^2 that are parallel to each other in the same direction. 150-ev hydrogen ions are released into this region in a direction normal to the fields. A photographic plate is placed normal to the initial direction of the ions at a distance of 5 cm from the gun, as shown in the figure.

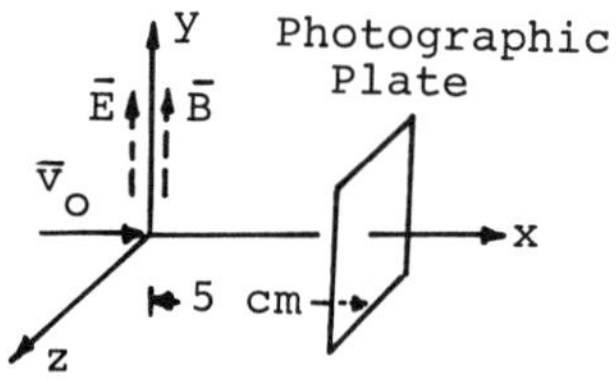

Figure P7-5.5.

a. How long after leaving the gun will the ions hit the plate?
b. What are the coordinates of the point at which the plate is exposed?
c. Repeat for the case where the photographic plate is perpendicular to the Y-axis and 5.0 cm from the origin (instead of perpendicular to the X-axis).

d. Repeat for the case where the photographic plate is perpendicular to the Z-axis and 5.0 cm from the origin.

7-5.6. Consider the configuration of perpendicular electric and magnetic fields shown in the figure. An ion gun fires 100-ev hydrogen ions along the Y-axis. $B = 0.05$ Weber/m^2; $E = 5 \times 10^3$ V/m.

a. What are the coordinates of the point at which the photographic plate is exposed?

b. Repeat for the case where the photographic plate is perpendicular to the X-axis, and at a distance of 14 cm from the origin instead of it being perpendicular to the Y-axis.

c. Repeat for the case where the photographic plate is perpendicular to the negative Z-axis and a distance of 14 cm from the origin.

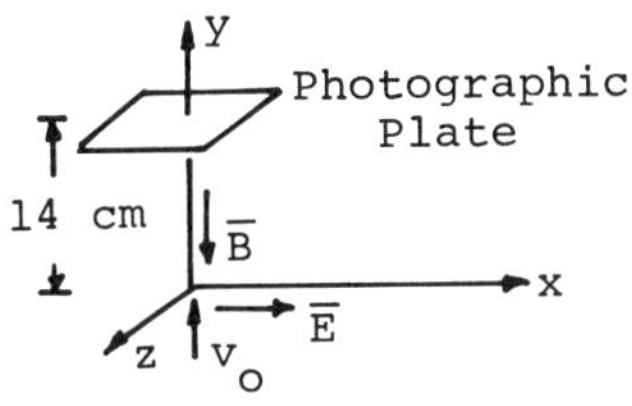

Figure P7-5.6.

7-5.7. A mixture of K^{39}, K^{40}, and K^{41} singly ionized atoms are produced in an ion source. These ions are accelerated by 1,500 volts between the source and an exit probe. The ions pass through a hole in the probe into a uniform transverse magnetic field. If the K^{39} line formed on a photographic plate that is oriented perpendicular to the original direction of the ions is 38.20 cm from the source, calculate the separation of the three lines on the photographic plate.

7-7.1. Find the index of refraction when collisions between charged particles are present.

7-7.2. Find the cyclotron frequency of an electron inside the magnetic field of the earth and in a magnet of 2 Weber/m^2.

7-7.3. What are the conductivities σ_{dc}, $\sigma_{\perp}$, σ_H of the F-region of the ionosphere?

CHAPTER 8

DESCRIPTION OF WAVE PHENOMENA

In this chapter we shall develop equations that govern wave propagation phenomena in physical processes. The problems to be considered are drawn from a variety of different physical areas and include selected problems from mechanical, acoustic, electrical and other systems. To give a better understanding of the procedure in describing certain processes, we shall consider examples that may not initially appear to be related to wave behavior. Further, to aid in an understanding, we shall, wherever possible, consider one-dimensional examples before considering more complex cases. A feature to be found in common for all wave systems is that the description involves a partial differential equation involving second-order partials in both space and time variables. Other terms may also appear depending on the particular features of the problem. Deriving the equations in a particular case requires an understanding of the physics involved, and we shall discuss the fundamental physical considerations as required. We may, in the interest of lucidity and simplicity take some liberties with the mathematics, but the rigor will not be compromised too seriously in our discussions. Details of the solution of particular classes of problems will be deferred until the next and subsequent chapters.

8-1. The Electrical Transmission Line

We first examine the electrical transmission line. We shall employ a circuits viewpoint since our initial objective is to present certain circuit configurations that will be of subsequent interest to us. The field aspects of this problem will be considered later, and this, plus later considerations, will permit a field/circuit viewpoint. We shall find that both concepts have much to recommend them in connection with our later studies. A desirable feature of the present problem is that it is a one-dimensional configuration, but because of its distributed nature,

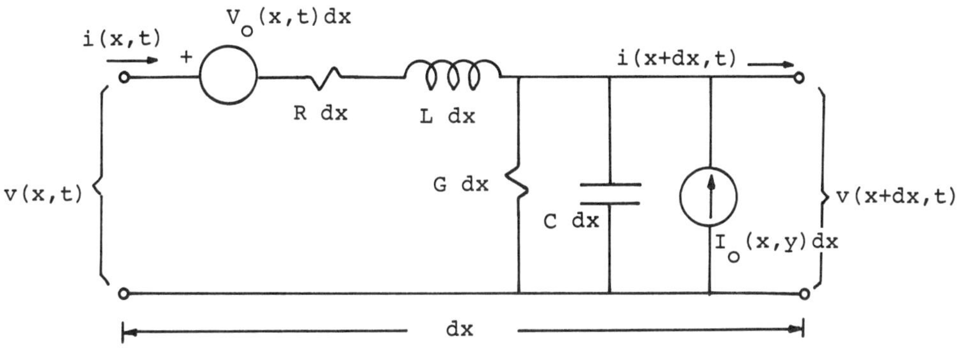

Figure 8-1.1. A typical section of an electrical transmission line.

it must be described explicitly in terms of time and a space variable.

We begin our discussion by replacing the continuous line which is described by the continuous parameters L (Henry /m), C (Farad /m), R (Ohm /m), and G (mho /m) plus distributed sources V_0 and I_0 per unit length by a cascade of repeated sections, in the manner illustrated in Fig. 8-1.1. We apply the Kirchhoff voltage and current laws to describe the network feature of this section. These lead to

$$v(x+dx,t) = v(x,t) - (Rdx)i(x,t) - Ldx\,\frac{\partial i(x,t)}{\partial t} - V_0(x,t)dx \tag{8-1.1}$$

$$i(x+dx,t) = i(x,t) - (Gdx)v(x+dx,t) - (Cdx)\,\frac{\partial v(x+dx,t)}{\partial t} + I_0(x,t)dx \tag{8-1.2}$$

To have this represent the continuous line, we take the limit as $dx \to 0$. We then write

$$\frac{\partial v(x,t)}{\partial x} = \lim_{dx\to 0} \frac{v(x+dx,t) - v(x,t)}{dx} = -Ri(x,t) - L\,\frac{\partial i(x,t)}{\partial t} - V_0(x,t) \tag{8-1.3}$$

$$\frac{\partial i(x,t)}{\partial x} = \lim_{dx\to 0} \frac{i(x+dx,t) - i(x,t)}{dx} = -Gv(x,t) - C\,\frac{\partial v(x,t)}{\partial t} + I_0(x,t) \tag{8-1.4}$$

It is convenient to separate these equations. This is done by differentiating Eqs. (8-1.3) and (8-1.4) with respect to time and the spatial coordinate, and combining the results. The equations that result are the following

$$\begin{aligned}\frac{\partial^2 v(x,t)}{\partial x^2} &= RG\,v(x,t) + (RC+LG)\,\frac{\partial v(x,t)}{\partial t} + LC\,\frac{\partial^2 v(x,t)}{\partial t^2} - \frac{\partial V_0(x,t)}{\partial x}\\ &\quad - RI_0(x,t) - L\,\frac{\partial I_0(x,t)}{\partial t} \qquad \text{a)}\\ \frac{\partial^2 i(x,t)}{\partial x^2} &= RG\,i(x,t) + (RC+LG)\,\frac{\partial i(x,t)}{\partial t} + LC\,\frac{\partial^2 i(x,t)}{\partial t^2} + \frac{\partial I_0(x,t)}{\partial x}\\ &\quad + GV_0(x,t) + C\,\frac{\partial V_0(x,t)}{\partial t} \qquad \text{b)}\end{aligned} \tag{8-1.5}$$

A feature of these equations is their generality since they include series dissipation and energy storage, shunt dissipation and energy storage, and series and shunt distributed sources. The absence of one or more of these terms will reduce the resulting equations, and the equivalent electrical network will be simplified accordingly. The effect of the several terms in the form of the solution will be discussed in Chap. 10 et seq.

8-2. The Vibrating String

As a relatively simple elastic problem, we consider a flexible string under tension, as shown in Fig. 8-2.1. It is supposed that the string is initially distorted by a small amount and it is then released. The system of axes is so chosen that the motion of the string occurs in the X-Y plane. To examine the situation, refer to Fig. 8-2.1b which assumes that the force or tension in the string is a continuous function since no discontinuities in the shape are assumed.

Owing to the curvature of the string which results because the system has been displaced, there will be an effective unbalance in the force component, and this will cause the physical movement of the element of the string. We note that for small displacements that we may approximate the elemental length

$$ds = \left[1 + \left(\frac{dy}{dx}\right)^2\right]^{1/2} dx \doteq dx$$

from which, therefore

$$\frac{dy}{ds} \doteq \frac{dy}{dx} \qquad (8\text{-}2.1)$$

Hence the mass of the element of the string is written

$$\rho_L ds \doteq \rho_L dx \qquad (8\text{-}2.2)$$

where ρ_L is the linear density of the string in kg/m. The perpendicular force acting on the element dx is obtained by taking the algebraic sum of the forces. At the ends of the sample element

$$-f_y(x) = -T \sin \theta \doteq T \frac{dy}{ds} \doteq -T \frac{dy}{dx} \qquad \text{a)}$$

$$f_y(x+dx) = T \frac{\partial y}{\partial x} + T \frac{\partial}{\partial x}\left(\frac{\partial y}{\partial x}\right) dx \qquad \text{b)}$$

(8-2.3)

It is the unbalanced force that causes the motion of the string. This is related to the inertial force through Newton's law, so that

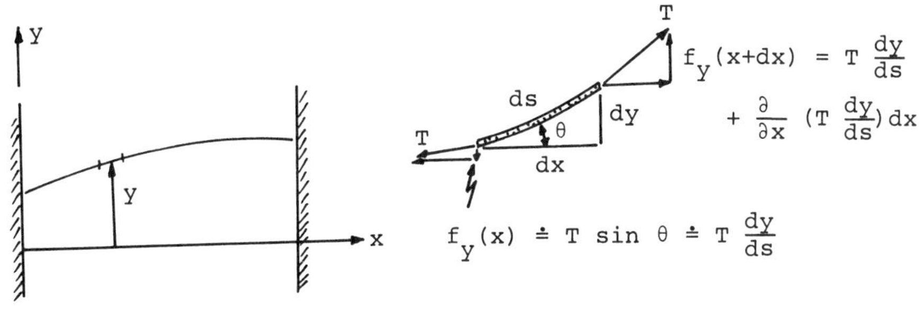

Figure 8-2.1. A flexible string under tension.

$$f_y(x+dx) - f_y(x) = \frac{\partial}{\partial t}(mv_y) = \rho_L dx\,\frac{\partial v_y}{\partial t} \tag{8-2.4}$$

By combining Eqs. (8-2.2) through (8-2.4) the result can be written

$$\frac{\partial^2 y}{\partial x^2} = \frac{1}{c_s^2}\frac{\partial^2 y}{\partial t^2} \tag{8-2.5}$$

where $c_s = \sqrt{T/\rho_L}$

This is the controlling equation from which a description of the motion of the string can be obtained. It is the simplest expression for the wave equation.

Some interesting additional concepts are possible by considering Eq. (8-2.4). From this equation we may write the expression

$$\lim_{dx\to 0}\frac{f_y(x+dx) - f_y(x)}{dx} = \frac{\partial f_y}{\partial x} = \rho_L\,\frac{\partial v_y}{\partial t} \tag{8-2.6}$$

If we differentiate the first of Eq. (8-2.3a) partially with respect to time t, then

$$\frac{\partial v_y}{\partial x} = \frac{1}{T}\frac{\partial f_y}{\partial t} \tag{8-2.7}$$

Eqs. (8-2.6) and (8-2.7) together may be given network representation for the incremental components, as shown in Fig. 8-2.2. Note that this example can be interpreted

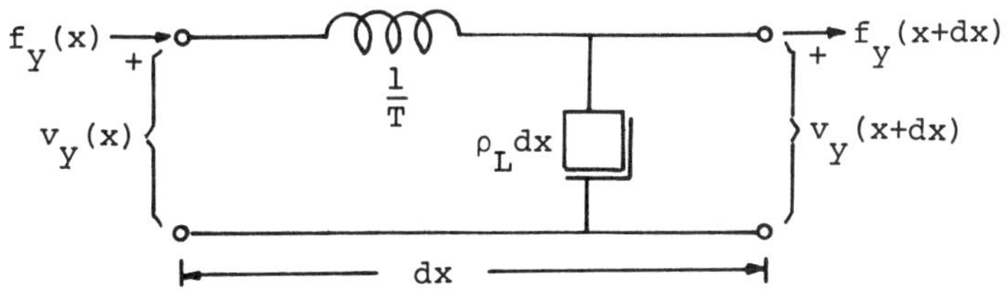

Figure 8-2.2. Transmission line equivalent for the stretched string.

as an analog of the electrical transmission line, and vice versa.

Although the simple wave equation (8-2.5) furnishes the basis for a great deal of analysis in a variety of problems, it does neglect the practical fact that a vibrating string will ultimately damp out owing to frictional losses both in the string and also because of air damping. We shall here consider that only air damping is important. Further, it is assumed that the air friction is of the simple viscous type, and so is proportional to the length of the element ds and also to the velocity. Eq. (8-2.4) can be modified to include the air friction term, say $(2K\,\rho_L dx)v_y$. This additional term when included with Eq. (8-2.5) gives

$$\frac{\partial^2 y}{\partial x^2} = \frac{1}{c_s^2}\left(\frac{\partial^2 y}{\partial t^2} + 2K\,\frac{\partial y}{\partial t}\right) \tag{8-2.8}$$

The effect of the damping term on Eq. (8-2.6) is in the appearance of the term $2K\,\rho_L v_y$, so that

$$\frac{\partial f_y}{\partial x} = \rho_L\,\frac{\partial v_y}{\partial t} + 2K\,\rho_L v_y \tag{8-2.9}$$

However, Eq. (8-2.7) remains unchanged for the air damping, but would be changed were series string losses to be included. The result of the air damping is to change the network representation of Fig. 8-2.2 to that shown in Fig. 8-2.3.

Attention is called to the fact that certain similarities exist between the results of Secs. 8-2 and 8-1. For an LC transmission line and the vibrating string we can draw the following analogies:

Mechanical Quantity	Electrical Quantity
f_y	i
v_y	v
$-\rho_L$	C
$-1/T$	L

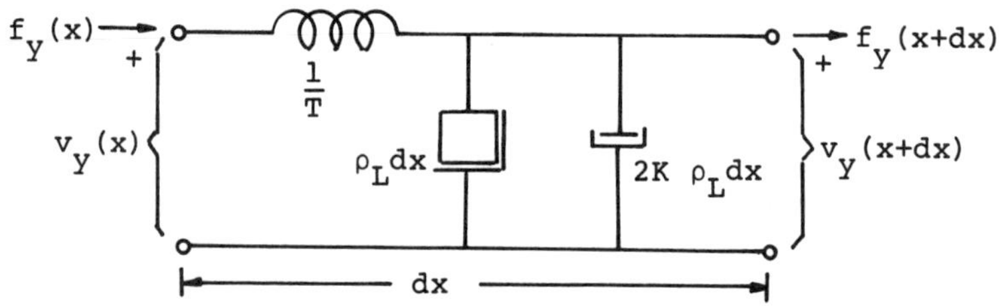

Figure 8-2.3. The transmission line analog of the vibrating string, with air damping.

These analogies are extremely useful because we can study the behavior of mechanical systems using equivalent electrical circuits. This is an approach that is more easily accomplished for persons with backgrounds in electrical technology.

8-3. Transverse and Longitudinal Vibrations of Point Masses

The foregoing ideas can be used as a basis for extending concepts to problems of somewhat different character. Initially, we consider an elastic string having n masses that are equally spaced along its length. We shall later extend this array to a two-dimensional configuration, which will correspond to a plane through a uniform crystal.

a. *The Loaded String*. A light string (assumed to have zero mass) is supporting n equal masses m which are equally spaced to distances d along its length; therefore $\ell = (n+1)d$. We focus our attention initially on three neighboring particles, with particular attention given to the displacement of the rth mass particle and its two adjacent neighbors. Refer to Fig. 8-3.1. As is evident from this figure, the rth mass will experience a force toward the axis equal to

$$F_r = m\frac{d^2y_r}{dt^2} = -\frac{T}{d}[(y_r-y_{r-1}) + (y_r-y_{r+1})]$$

or

$$F_r = m\frac{d^2y_r}{dt^2} = \frac{T}{d}[y_{r-1} + y_{r+1} - 2y_r] \tag{8-3.1}$$

In this expression, any influence due to masses other than the nearest neighbors is neglected.

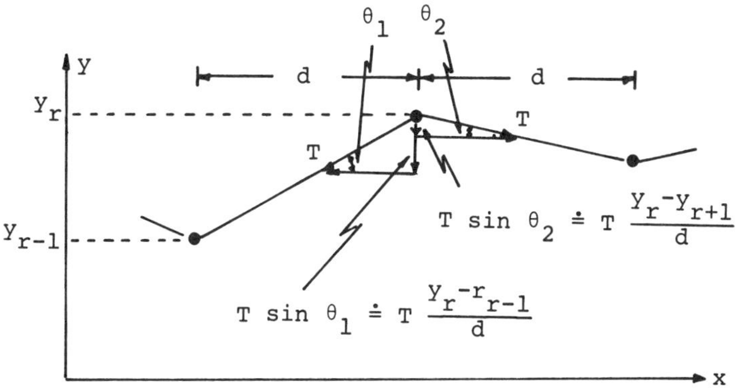

Figure 8-3.1. Three adjacent mass particles on an elastic string.

To take into account the effect of all of the masses, as the more general case, we assume that the force on the rth mass is caused by the displacement of the various mass particles. As an extension of Eq. (8-3.1) we would write for the total force on the rth mass particle, denoting by p the general index,

$$F_r = m\frac{d^2y_r}{dt^2} = \sum_p \frac{T}{d}(y_{r+p} - y_r) \tag{8-3.2}$$

b. *Description for Monatomic and Diatomic Lattices.* We wish to extend the foregoing to an approximate study of elastic waves in crystals. Initially, we assume that the ions are the same and are located at equally spaced points in the crystal lattice. Moreover, it is assumed that displacements of the ions from the normal positions of equilibrium are accompanied by forces that tend to return the ions to the equilibrium center; hence the general situation is quite like that considered above except that a space array now exists. We assume that a disturbance impinges on the crystal in the Y and X directions (here considered to be the transverse and longitudinal directions).

For the transverse wave, the equations are exactly the same as those given in Eq. (8-3.2) and would be the pair

$$F_r = m\frac{d^2y_r}{dt^2} = C_1\,(y_{r-1} + y_{r+1} - 2y_r) \qquad \text{a)}$$

$$F_r = m\frac{d^2y_r}{dt^2} = \sum_p C_{p1}\,(y_{r+p} - y_r) \qquad \text{b)} \tag{8-3.3}$$

for the case of adjacent particle influence and the general case, respectively. C_1 and C_{p1} are the force constants appropriate to the two cases. The equations for the longitudinal waves will have exactly similar forms, and are

$$F_r = m\frac{d^2x_r}{dt^2} = C_2\,(x_{r-1} + x_{r+1} - 2x_r) \qquad \text{a)}$$

$$F_r = m\frac{d^2x_r}{dt^2} = \sum_p C_{p2}(x_{r+p} - x_r) \qquad \text{b)} \tag{8-3.4}$$

for the adjacent particle influence and the general case, respectively, where C_2 and C_{p2} are the appropriate force constants for the two cases. In general C_{p1} and C_{p2} would be different constants.

When the crystals have more than one atom in their primitive cell, for example, we might have alternate ions, say Na and Cℓ, with corresponding different masses, the equations must be appropriately modified. Now we must deduce equations for the motion of the mass particles of masses say m_1 and m_2. If we assume only nearest neighbor influence, with identical force constants, the equations would be

$$m_1 \frac{d^2y_{2r+1}}{dt^2} = C(y_{2r+2} + y_{2r} - 2y_{r+1}) \qquad \text{a)}$$

$$m_2 \frac{d^2y_{2r}}{dt^2} = C\,(y_{2r+1} + y_{2r-1} - 2y_{2r}) \qquad \text{b)} \qquad (8\text{-}3.5)$$

When a longitudinal wave is present, the equations of motion are exactly like these except with a change of coordinate from y to x.

It is instructive to deduce a transmission line analog of the one-dimensional diatomic lattice. For the case of two different masses in the mechanical model, as given in Eqs. (8-3.5), this would suggest the need for two different inductors in the electrical model. However, the coupling coefficients are the same, and the capacitors will have the same capacitance. Refer to Fig. 8-3.2 which is suggested as the electrical equivalent. To check this electrical network equivalent, we write the controlling equations. We find these to be

$$i_{2r} - i_{2r+1} = \frac{dQ_{2r}}{dt}\,; \qquad i_{2r+1} - i_{2r+2} = \frac{dQ_{2r+1}}{dt}$$

$$L_1 \frac{di_{2r+1}}{dt} = v_{2r} - v_{2r+1} = \frac{1}{C}\,(Q_{2r} - Q_{2r+1}) \qquad (8\text{-}3.6)$$

$$L_2 \frac{di_{2r}}{dt} = v_{2r-1} - v_{2r} = \frac{1}{C}\,(Q_{2r-1} - Q_{2r})$$

If we differentiate the second and third of this group and combine with the first, we find the following:

$$L_1 \frac{d^2i_{2r+1}}{dt^2} = \frac{1}{C}\,(i_{2r+2} + i_{2r} - 2i_{2r+1})$$

$$L_2 \frac{d^2i_{2r}}{dt^2} = \frac{1}{C}\,(i_{2r+1} + i_{2r-1} - 2i_{2r}) \qquad (8\text{-}3.7)$$

These equations are seen to be the same form as the equations in Eq. (8-3.5). Hence Fig. 8-3.2 can be considered to represent the crystal structure.

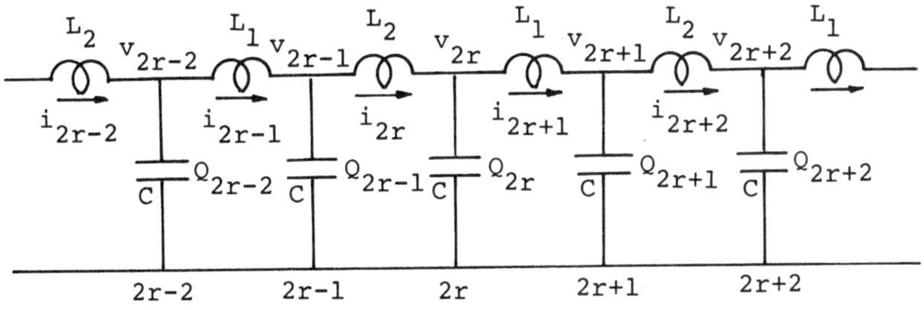

Figure 8-3.2. The electrical analog of the diatomic lattice.

8-4. Rectangular Drumhead

The rectangular drumhead fastened at the edges is essentially an extension of the vibrating string problem of Sec. 8-1. Refer to Fig. 8-4.1 which represents the drumhead. Fig. 8-4.1b is an element along the Y-axis.

Let T denote the tension per unit cut of the membrane. The Z-directed forces for the element along the Y-axis are

$$\begin{aligned} -f_z(y) &= -T\Delta x \sin\theta = -T\Delta x \frac{dz}{ds} \\ f_z(y+\Delta y) &= T\Delta x \frac{dz}{ds} + \frac{\partial}{\partial y}\left(T\Delta x \frac{dz}{ds}\right)\Delta y \end{aligned} \qquad (8\text{-}4.1)$$

But for small displacements, $dz/ds \doteq dz/dy$. The unbalanced force is then

$$f_z(y+\Delta y) - f_z(y) = \frac{\partial}{\partial y}\left(T\Delta x \frac{dz}{dy}\right)\Delta y \qquad (8\text{-}4.2)$$

Correspondingly, the unbalanced forces for the element along the X-axis is

$$f_z(x+\Delta x) - f_z(x) = \frac{\partial}{\partial x}\left(T\Delta y \frac{\partial z}{\partial x}\right)\Delta x \qquad (8\text{-}4.3)$$

The total unbalanced forces which cause the motion of the diaphragm are now related to the inertial force through the Newton equation. We thus have

$$[f_z(y+\Delta y) - f_z(y)] + [f_z(x+\Delta x) - f_z(x)] = \rho_s \Delta x \Delta y \frac{\partial^2 z}{\partial t^2} \qquad (8\text{-}4.4)$$

where ρ_s is the density per unit area of the diaphragm. If we substitute Eq. (8-4.2)

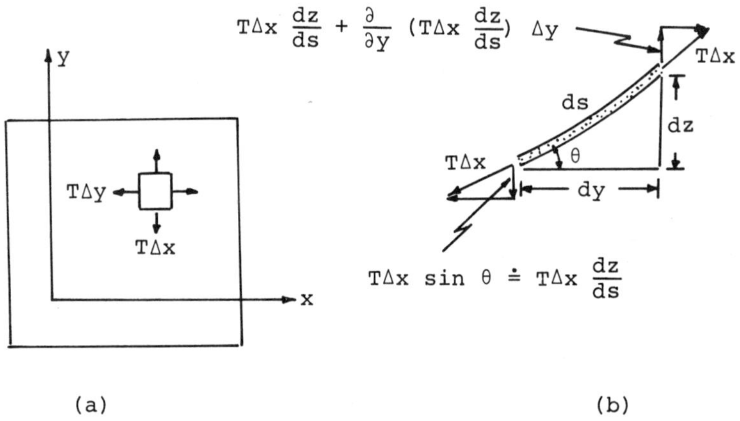

Figure 8-4.1. The rectangular drumhead.

and (8-4.3) into Eq. (8-4.4) and assuming the tension to be constant, we easily obtain the two-dimensional wave equation which describes the present problem

$$\frac{\partial^2 z}{\partial x^2} + \frac{\partial^2 z}{\partial y^2} = \frac{1}{c_d^2}\frac{\partial^2 z}{\partial t^2} \tag{8-4.5}$$

where $c_d = \sqrt{T/\rho_s}$. It is noted that this is a simple two-dimensional extension of the vibrating string discussed in Sec. 8-1.

8-5. Longitudinal Waves

a. Acoustic Waves in Liquids and Gases: In this section we shall consider the propagation of acoustic vibrations in a homogeneous fluid, which may be a liquid or a gas. This is a more complicated problem than those previously considered because a wave passing through a gas will cause gas particle motion resulting in mechanical and thermodynamic effects. In this study, we shall assume that the medium possesses the following properties: homogeneous, continuous, perfect fluidity (the fluid cannot support shear stresses), perfect elasticity, and zero thermal conductivity (compression and expansion is adiabatic - constant energy content). This latter assumption specifies that during expansion and contraction that only local changes in temperature will occur. In consequence, this means that the fluid at each point will experience a disturbance in the following quantities: pressure, density, and fluid particle motion. Note, however, that these are not independent effects.

To proceed in our development, we note that for the adiabatic process the pressure and volume of a gas are related by the expression

$$pV^{\gamma} = \text{constant} \tag{8-5.1}$$

where p is the pressure associated with the volume V, and γ is the ratio

$$\gamma = \frac{c_p}{c_v} = \frac{\text{specific heat at constant pressure}}{\text{specific heat at constant volume}} \tag{8-5.2}$$

By a simple transformation between the volume and the mass of gas contained therein, Eq. (8-5.1) can also be written in the form

$$\frac{p}{\rho^{\gamma}} = \text{constant} \tag{8-5.3}$$

where ρ is the mass density of the fluid. By differentiating Eq. (8-5.1) we can write

$$dpV^{\gamma} + \gamma pV^{\gamma-1}\, dV = 0$$

or

$$\frac{dp}{p} = -\gamma \frac{dV}{V} \tag{8-5.4}$$

This expression is combined with Eq. (8-5.3) differentiated, from which we find that

$$\frac{dp}{p} = \gamma \frac{d\rho}{\rho} \tag{8-5.5}$$

This expression shows that a fractional change in pressure is proportional to the fractional change in volume or density.

Now we proceed by supposing that the disturbances in pressure and in density are denoted by $p_1(x,t)$ and $\rho_1(x,t)$, so that the total pressure and density at a given point and time can be written

$$\begin{aligned} p &= p_o + p_1(x,t) \qquad p_1 \ll p_o \\ \rho &= \rho_o + \rho_1(x,t) \qquad \rho_1 \ll \rho_o \end{aligned} \tag{8-5.6}$$

where p_o and ρ_o are the equilibrium (ambient) pressure and density of the fluid. Moreover, as noted, the changes in p and ρ are assumed to be small compared with these ambient values. Using these expressions we can write

$$\begin{aligned} \frac{dp}{p} &= \frac{p-p_o}{p_o+p_1} \doteq \frac{p_1}{p_o} \\ \frac{d\rho}{\rho} &= \frac{\rho-\rho_o}{\rho_o+\rho_1} \doteq \frac{\rho_1}{\rho_o} \end{aligned} \tag{8-5.7}$$

Using this notation, Eq. (8-5.5) assumes the form

$$\frac{p_1}{p_o} = \gamma \frac{\rho_1}{\rho_o} \tag{8-5.8}$$

The existence of a pressure gradient will give rise to local fluid motion. We must invoke the equation of mass continuity (conservation of mass) in our further considerations, which with provision for effects due to generation ρ_g per unit volume is [see Eq. (7-8.16)]

$$\nabla \cdot \rho\bar{v} = -\frac{\partial\rho}{\partial t} + \rho_g \tag{8-5.9}$$

But from Eq. (8-5.6)

$$\frac{\partial\rho}{\partial t} = \frac{\partial(\rho_o+\rho_1)}{\partial t} \doteq \frac{\partial\rho_1}{\partial t} \tag{8-5.10}$$

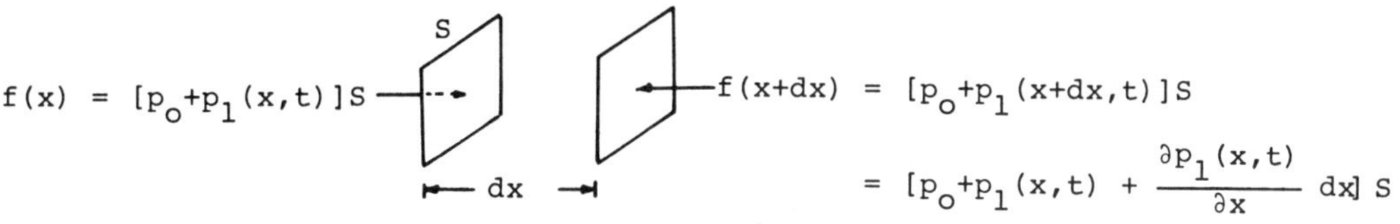

Figure 8-5.1. To deduce the forces on a gas.

Also,

$$\nabla \cdot \rho\overline{v} = \rho\nabla \cdot \overline{v} + \nabla\rho \cdot \overline{v} \tag{8-5.11}$$

We observe that in this case the right hand term $\nabla\rho \cdot \overline{v}$ for a homogeneous medium becomes $\nabla\rho_1 \cdot \overline{v}$. However, since the particle velocity $\overline{v}$ is small and $\nabla\rho_1$ is small, then the term $\nabla\rho_1 \cdot \overline{v}$ is a second-order quantity relative to other quantities in the equation and can therefore be neglected. Additionally, the term $\rho\nabla \cdot \overline{v}$ now becomes $\rho_0\nabla \cdot \overline{v}$. Using these results, the equation of continuity in this case assumes the form

$$\rho_0\nabla \cdot \overline{v} = -\frac{\partial\rho_1}{\partial t} + \rho_g \tag{8-5.12}$$

We now wish to apply the general laws that we have obtained from thermodynamic and conservation of mass considerations to our particular problem. We consider two equal plane surfaces S parallel to the YZ plane, and separated by a distance dx, as shown in Fig. 8-5.1. The net unbalanced force is related to the inertial force by Newton's law, so that

$$f(x) - f(x+dx) = -S\,dx\,\left(\frac{\partial p_1}{\partial x}\right) = \rho_0 S\,dx\,\frac{\partial v_x}{\partial t} \tag{8-5.13}$$

from which we find that

$$\frac{\partial v_x}{\partial t} = -\frac{1}{\rho_0}\frac{\partial p_1}{\partial x} \tag{8-5.14}$$

For the more general case of three dimensions, we need only add the corresponding contributions from the other two directions. The resulting equation is

$$\frac{\partial\overline{v}}{\partial t} = -\frac{\nabla p_1}{\rho_0} \tag{8-5.15}$$

We convert this expression by first operating on it with $\nabla\,\cdot$, which implies space differentiation, and combine the resulting equation with Eq. (8-5.12) without the source term. The result is

$$\frac{\partial^2 \rho_1}{\partial t^2} = \nabla^2 p_1 \tag{8-5.16}$$

Now make use of Eq. (8-5.8) to obtain the result

$$\nabla^2 p_1 = \frac{1}{c_a^2} \frac{\partial^2 p_1}{\partial t^2} \tag{8-5.17}$$

where $c_a = \sqrt{\gamma p_0/\rho_0}$. This equation shows that the pressure disturbance satisfies the wave equation, the pressure disturbance propagating through the gas with wave velocity c_a. For the case of air, $\gamma = 1.41$ and $c_a = 362$ m/sec at 16° C.

Some further properties of the acoustic field are possible from a study of the energy and power associated with the acoustic waves. Consider, therefore, the total energy associated with an elemental volume dV of the acoustic field. This is, of course, the sum of the kinetic and potential energy of the field. We find expressions for both terms. The kinetic energy of the mass ρdV is given by

$$dW_k = \frac{1}{2} \rho dV\, v^2 \doteq \frac{1}{2} \rho_0 v^2 dV \tag{8-5.18}$$

The potential energy is equal to the work done on the fluid to compress the volume element by an amount $V_0 - V$. To deduce this, refer to Fig. 8-5.2. The potential energy is approximately equal to the shaded area of this figure, which we write in the following way

$$dW_p = \text{Area} = \frac{1}{2} p_1 \left(\frac{V_0 - V}{V_0}\right) V_0 = \frac{1}{2} p_1 s V_0 = \frac{1}{2} \frac{p_1^2}{K_a} V_0 = \frac{1}{2} \frac{p_1^2}{c_a^2 \rho_0} V_0 \tag{8-5.19}$$

where:

$$\text{the dilation } s = \left(\frac{V_0 - V}{V_0}\right)$$

$$\text{adiabatic bulk modulus } K_a = \frac{p - p_0}{\left(\frac{V_0 - V}{V_0}\right)} = \frac{p_1}{\left(\frac{V_0 - V}{V_0}\right)} = + \frac{p_1}{s}$$

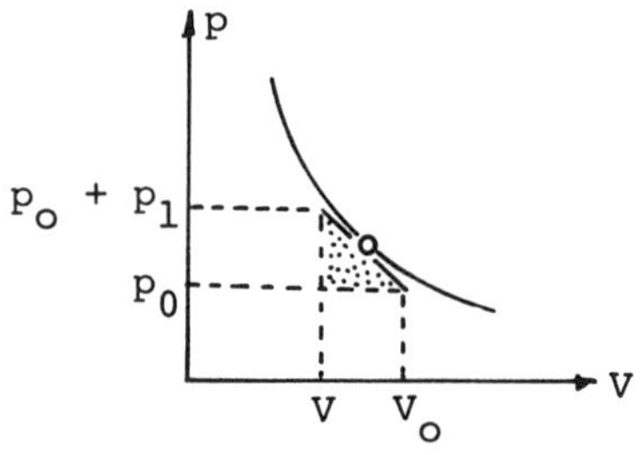

Figure 8-5.2. To evaluate the potential energy.

Also

$$\frac{K_a}{\rho_o} = \frac{\gamma p_1}{\rho_o} = c_a^{\ 2}$$

In Eq. (8-5.19) the potential energy density is given by $p_1^{\ 2}/2c_a^{\ 2}\rho_o$. Thus the total energy existing at a given time in a region occupied by the acoustic field is

$$W = \frac{1}{2}\int_V \left(\rho_o v^2 + \frac{p_1^{\ 2}}{\rho_o c_a^{\ 2}}\right) dV \tag{8-5.20}$$

The *mean energy density* in this same region will be given, of course, by

$$\overline{W} = \frac{W}{V} \tag{8-5.21}$$

The equation of continuity Eq. (8-5.12) less the source term in one dimension is written in the form

$$\frac{\partial \rho_1}{\partial t} = -\rho_o \frac{\partial v_x}{\partial x} \tag{8-5.22}$$

The equation of motion Eq. (8-5.15) in one dimension is of the form

$$\rho_o \frac{\partial v_x}{\partial t} = -\frac{\partial p_1}{\partial x} \tag{8-5.23}$$

Since the dilation

$$s = \frac{V_o - V}{V_o} = \frac{\frac{1}{V} - \frac{1}{V_o}}{\frac{1}{V_o}} = \frac{\rho - \rho_o}{\rho_o} = \frac{\rho_1}{\rho_o} \tag{8-5.24}$$

Eq. (8-5.22) becomes

$$\frac{\partial s}{\partial t} = -\frac{\partial v_x}{\partial x} \tag{8-5.25}$$

Combining Eq. (8-5.25) with the relation $K_a s = p_1$ so that $\partial s/\partial t = (1/K_a)\ \partial p_1/\partial t$, we obtain

$$\frac{1}{K_a}\frac{\partial p_1}{\partial t} = -\frac{\partial v_x}{\partial x} \tag{8-5.26}$$

We shall show in Chap. 10 that the solutions to Eq. (8-5.17) are any function of the form $f(x-c_a t)$, a result that is readily proved by showing that $f(x-c_a t)$ satisfies the wave equation. Let us accept tentatively as a solution the function $p_1 = e^{(x-c_a t)}$. Introducing it into Eq. (8-5.17) we obtain the relation

$$\frac{\partial p_1}{\partial x} = -\frac{1}{c_a}\frac{\partial p_1}{\partial t} \tag{8-5.27}$$

Substituting Eq. (8-5.27) into Eqs. (8-5.26) and (8-5.23) we obtain, respectively,

$$\frac{\partial}{\partial x}(K_a v_x - c_a p_1) = 0 \qquad \text{a)}$$

and (8-5.28)

$$\frac{\partial}{\partial t}(K_a v_x - c_a p_1) = 0 \qquad \text{b)}$$

Equations (8-5.28) state that $K_a v_x - c_a p_1$ is independent of both time and space variables. Thus it must be equal to a constant. The relation, however, is true for $v_x = 0$ and $p_1 = 0$ and therefore the constant must be equal to zero. This requires, therefore, that

$$v_x = \frac{c_a}{K_a} p_1 = \frac{c_a}{\rho_o c_a^2} p_1 = \frac{1}{\rho_o c_a} p_1 \tag{8-5.29}$$

The quantity $(\rho_o c_a)^{-1}$ is the *specific acoustic impedance* Z, the ratio of velocity to pressure. A number of specific acoustic impedances are given in Table 8-5.1.

Table 8-5.1

Acoustic Characteristics of Different Media

Medium	Sound Velocity (m/sec)	Density (kg/m^3)	Impedance (m^2 - sec/kg)	Young's Modulus (Newton/m^2)
Air	331	1.29	2.342 10^{-3}	--
Water	1450	1000	6.896 10^{-7}	--
Mercury	1460	13600	5.036 10^{-8}	--
Copper	4620	8930	2.424 10^{-8}	12.8×10^{10}
Aluminum	6220	2650	6.067 10^{-8}	7.1×10^{10}
Nickel	5600	8900	1.985 10^{-8}	21×10^{10}

The time average of the energy flow per unit time across a unit area perpendicular to the motion defines the *intensity* of the acoustic wave. It is given by

$$I_x = \langle p_1 v_x \rangle = \frac{\langle p_1^2 \rangle}{\rho_o c_a} \tag{8-5.30}$$

where Eq. (8-5.29) was used. The last two equations are true only for plane waves or for spherical waves at large distances from their sources.

It is of interest to note that the controlling differential equation for the particle velocity $\overline{v}$ and the dilation s for a perfect fluid has the wave-equation form given in Eq. (8-5.17). This should not be entirely surprising since we have already seen that most of the properties of the fluid field are intimately related. Because of this, it would seem reasonable to expect that it might be possible to find a unique acoustic potential function Φ_a from which all of these quantities might be derived. This proves to be the case. Specifically, the acoustic potential is defined by the relation

$$\overline{v} = -\nabla\Phi_a \tag{8-5.31}$$

The existence of a unique potential function results from the fact that the velocity field of an acoustic wave in a perfect fluid is an irrotational field, that is, the curl $\nabla \times \overline{v} = 0$.

If we combine Eq. (8-5.31) with Eq. (8-5.15) we find that

$$p_1 = \rho_o \frac{\partial\Phi_a}{\partial t} \tag{8-5.32}$$

which relates the pressure with the acoustic potential. The specific form of the acoustic potential is itself specified by the requirement imposed by the continuity equation Eq. (8-5.12) without the generating term, and the physical requirement imposed by Eq. (8-5.8). Combining these equations, we find that Φ_a is also described by a wave equation given by

$$\nabla^2\Phi_a = \frac{1}{c_a^2}\frac{\partial^2\Phi_a}{\partial t^2} \tag{8-5.33}$$

b. Vibrations in Rods: When a longitudinal wave is present in a rod of cross sectional area S, a small section Δx of the rod will be elongated by an amount $\Delta\xi$, as shown in Fig. 8-5.3. The net force which acts on the element Δx with mass $\rho_o S\Delta x$, is equal to $\partial F/\partial x\ \Delta x$. By Newton's second law, and applying the limiting condition $\Delta\xi \to 0$, we obtain the relation

$$\frac{\partial F}{\partial x} = S\rho_o \frac{\partial^2\xi}{\partial t^2} \tag{8-5.34}$$

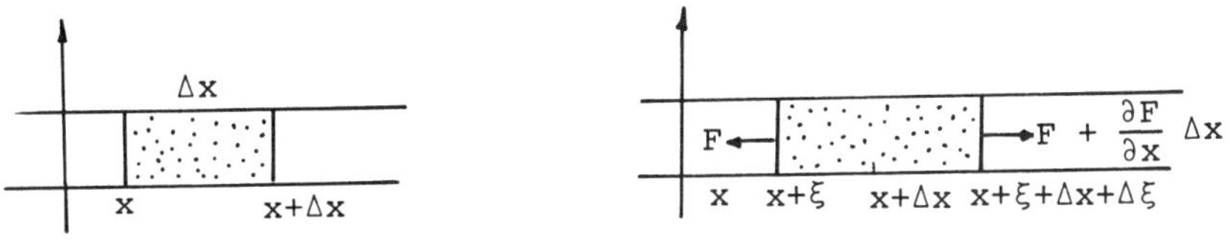

Figure 8-5.3. Longitudinal waves in a rod.

Also we observe from the figure that the average elongation, known as *tension strain*, is given by

$$s = \lim_{\Delta x, \Delta\xi \to 0} \frac{\Delta\xi}{\Delta x} = \frac{\partial\xi}{\partial x} \qquad (8\text{-}5.35)$$

When a linear relation exists between the strain (distortion) and the stress (applied force), Hooke's law yields the relation

$$F = SsY = SY\frac{\partial\xi}{\partial x} \qquad (8\text{-}5.36)$$

where Y is Young's modulus (see Table 8-5.1). Upon introducing Eq. (8-5.36) into Eq. (8-5.34), we obtain the wave equation for the displacement ξ, namely ,

$$\frac{\partial^2\xi}{\partial x^2} = \frac{1}{c_r^2}\frac{\partial^2\xi}{\partial t^2}\,; \qquad c_r = \left(\frac{Y}{\rho_o}\right)^{1/2} \qquad (8\text{-}5.37)$$

The kinetic and potential energy densities per unit length due to the presence of the wave are respectively,

$$W_k = \frac{1}{2}S\rho_o \cdot 1 \cdot \left(\frac{\partial\xi}{\partial t}\right)^2 \qquad \text{a)}$$

$$W_p = \frac{\frac{1}{2}F\ d\xi}{S\ dx} = \frac{1}{2}Y\left(\frac{\partial\xi}{\partial x}\right)^2 \qquad \text{b)} \qquad (8\text{-}5.38)$$

The power transported by the wave can be found from the relation

$$P = -F\frac{\partial\xi}{\partial t} = -SY\frac{\partial\xi}{\partial x}\frac{\partial\xi}{\partial t} \qquad (8\text{-}5.39)$$

The specific impedance Z is given by the relation

$$Z = \frac{\partial\xi/\partial t}{F/S}$$

from which we can write

$$Z = \frac{1}{\rho_o c_r} = (\rho_o Y)^{-1/2} \qquad (8\text{-}5.40)$$

8-6. The Electromagnetic Field - Maxwell's Equations

The description of problems relating to the propagation or radiation of electromagnetic fields begins with the Maxwell equations. These are the set of key equations that have been developed in the foregoing chapters. These equations describe the source and the field vectors in the broad fields of electrostatics, magnetostatics, and electromagnetic induction. It was through these equations that Maxwell was able to describe a wide range of phenomena. Moreover, he developed the theory which enables an examination of the space and time variations of changing fields in the same way that the equations of electrostatics and magnetostatics permits an examination of stationary fields.

The Maxwell equations comprise the following set of four differential equations which express point statements concerning the field quantities. These, with an indication of where they first appear in the text, are:

$$\nabla \cdot \overline{D} = \rho \qquad (5\text{-}6.5) \qquad \text{Gauss} \qquad \text{a)}$$

$$\nabla \cdot \overline{B} = 0 \qquad (6\text{-}2.1) \qquad \text{b)}$$

$$\nabla \times \overline{H} = \overline{J} + \frac{\partial \overline{D}}{\partial t} \qquad (6\text{-}5.7) \qquad \text{Ampère-Maxwell} \qquad \text{c)} \qquad (8\text{-}6.1)$$

$$\nabla \times \overline{E} = -\frac{\partial \overline{B}}{\partial t} \qquad (6\text{-}9.1) \qquad \text{Faraday} \qquad \text{d)}$$

To these are often added several auxiliary equations, including

$$\nabla \cdot \overline{J} + \frac{\partial \rho}{\partial t} = 0 \qquad \text{charge continuity equation} \qquad (8\text{-}6.2)$$

$$\overline{D} = \varepsilon\overline{E} \qquad \overline{B} = \mu\overline{H} \qquad \overline{J} = \sigma\overline{E} \qquad \text{constitutive equations} \qquad (8\text{-}6.3)$$

As known from our previous studies, for each of the equations in Eqs. (8-6.1) which specifies derivatives of the field quantities at a point in space, there is a corresponding statement which applies for a finite region of space. Although the point statement was obtained from considerations of the integral statement, it is not inconsistent to state that the integral statement may be obtained from the point statement. This is done by performing an integration over a surface or volume and then transforming the integrals by an application of the divergence theorem or Stokes' theorem. The integral forms corresponding to the differential equations in Eq. (8-6.1) are the following:

$$\begin{aligned}
&\oint_S \overline{D} \cdot \overline{n}\, dS = \int_V \rho\, dV \\
&\oint_S \overline{B} \cdot \overline{n}\, dS = 0 \\
&\oint \overline{H} \cdot d\overline{\ell} = \int_S \left(\overline{J} + \frac{\partial \overline{D}}{\partial t}\right) \cdot \overline{n}\, dS \\
&\oint \overline{E} \cdot d\overline{\ell} = -\int_S \frac{\partial \overline{B}}{\partial t} \cdot \overline{n}\, dS
\end{aligned} \qquad (8\text{-}6.4)$$

Before extending the Maxwell equations to the general problems of electromagnetic waves, some comments concerning the several equations of Eq. (8-6.1) are in order. Consider Eq. (8-6.1c) which expresses the Ampère-Maxwell law. The divergence of this expression is examined; thus

$$\nabla \cdot (\nabla \times \overline{H}) = \nabla \cdot \overline{J} + \nabla \cdot \left(\frac{\partial \overline{D}}{\partial t}\right)$$

But since div (curl $\overline{A}$) = 0 for any vector, then

$$\nabla \cdot \left(\frac{\partial \overline{D}}{\partial t}\right) + \nabla \cdot \overline{J} = 0 \qquad (8\text{-}6.5)$$

By combining this expression with the continuity equation, Eq. (8-6.2), there results

$$\nabla \cdot \left(\frac{\partial \overline{D}}{\partial t}\right) - \frac{\partial \rho}{\partial t} = 0$$

An interchange of the order of partial differentiation yields the expression

$$\frac{\partial}{\partial t} (\nabla \cdot \overline{D} - \rho) = 0$$

which is always satisfied if, in general

$$\nabla \cdot \overline{D} = \rho \qquad (8\text{-}6.6)$$

This expression is known to hold for static fields, as discussed in Chap. 5. It now appears as a general expression implied by Eqs. (8-6.1c) and Eq. (8-6.2), although Eq. (8-6.5) merely requires that the quantity $\nabla \cdot \overline{D} - \rho$ be independent of time and, in general, be a constant. However, the situation is possible in which both ρ and $\nabla \cdot \overline{D}$ are zero in a region of space so that $\nabla \cdot \overline{D} - \rho = 0$ in the region. Equation (8-6.5) then specifies that this relationship must be independent of time, whence Eq. (8-6.6) follows.

There is no direct proof that the Maxwell generalization of Ampère's law is valid, but there is very convincing indirect proof of its validity. Maxwell showed that it is only through the existence of the displacement current that there should be electromagnetic fields capable of being propagated through space as waves. The velocity and other characteristics of the waves awere predictable from the field equations. Subsequently Hertz, working in Germany in the 1890's, showed the experimental existence of electromagnetic waves which possessed all the properties predicted by Maxwell. It is now known, of course, that radio and light waves are Maxwell electromagnetic waves.

Another interesting feature of the postulate of displacement current is the symmetry that is added to the laws of electromagnetism. The generalized Ampère law indicates that an electric displacement current (a time-changing electric field) produces a magnetic field. Correspondingly, Faraday's law, Eq. (8-6.1d) specifies that a time-changing magnetic field produces an electric field. In fact, by comparing Eqs. (8-6.1c) and (8-6.1d), it is clear that $-\partial\overline{B}/\partial t$ behaves like a magnetic displacement current density. However, magnetic conduction currents do not exist in nature because there are no free magnetic poles. Reference to magnetic currents is a mathematical concept rather than physical reality. Such concepts are useful when one seeks to establish complete duality between electric and magnetic quantities.

It is of some interest to consider Faraday's law specified in Eq. (8-6.1d). We proceed as above, by taking the divergence of both sides of this equation, and again note that div (curl $\overline{A}$) = 0 for any vector. Then it is required that

$$\nabla \cdot (\nabla \times \overline{E}) = -\nabla \cdot \left(\frac{\partial \overline{B}}{\partial t}\right) = 0$$

The order of the partial derivative is changed without affecting the results and yields

$$\frac{\partial}{\partial t} (\nabla \cdot \overline{B}) = 0 \tag{8-6.7}$$

Thie expression states that the quantity $\nabla \cdot \overline{B}$ is a constant, in general, independent of time, but the $\overline{B}$ function may itself be a function of time. Moreover, a nonzero value of the divergence of $\overline{B}$ has never been found in nature, and it is postulated therefore that the constant is zero. Equation (8-6.7) requires that $\nabla \cdot \overline{B}$ remain zero, and, in fact, that it has always been zero. Thus from Eq. (8-6.7) we conclude that everywhere and always

$$\nabla \cdot \overline{B} = 0 \tag{8-6.8}$$

This property was shown to exist for the steady-state case [see Eq. (6-2.1)]. From the present viewpoint, if Eq. (8-6.1d) is postulated, then Eq. (8-6.1b) follows as a deduction. However, Eq. (8-6.1b) is so important that it is usually listed as one of the Maxwell equations.

Summarizing, the two independent equations, Eq. (8-6.1c) and Eq. (8-6.1d), and the *constitutive* equations, Eq. (8-6.3), constitute a complete system for the five unknown vectors, $\overline{E}$, $\overline{B}$, $\overline{D}$, $\overline{H}$, and $\overline{J}$.

8-7. Boundary Condition for Electromagnetic Fields

Electromagnetic boundary value problems often involve regions having materials with different electrical properties. In Chaps. 5 and 6 we discussed some of the relations which describe the fields at the boundaries of the regions. We shall

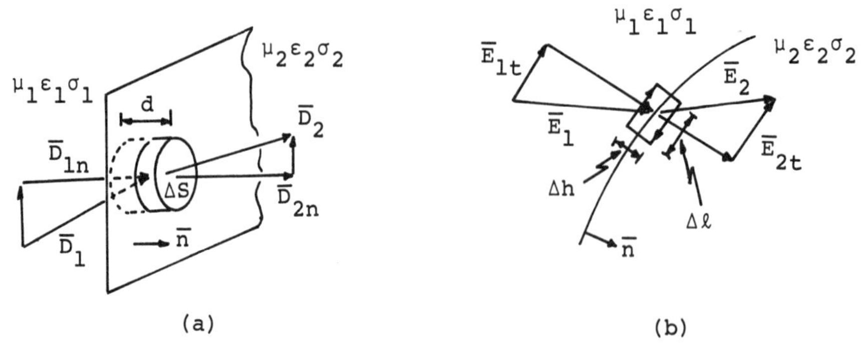

Figure 8-7.1. The electric field properties across a boundary.

briefly review these because some added considerations are necessary.

To each of the field vectors we associate a boundary condition. These are:

$\bar{n} \times (\bar{E}_2 - \bar{E}_1) = 0$	(continuity in tangential component of $\bar{E}$	a)
$\bar{n} \cdot (\bar{D}_2 - \bar{D}_1) = \rho_s$	(discontinuity in normal component of $\bar{D}$)	b)
$\bar{n} \times (\bar{H}_2 - \bar{H}_1) = \bar{J}_s$	(discontinuity in tangential component of $\bar{H}$)	c)
$\bar{n} \cdot (\bar{B}_2 - \bar{B}_1) = 0$	(continuity in normal component of $\bar{B}$)	d)

(8-7.1)

To show the procedure to be used in deducing these equations, we will derive Eqs. (8-7.1a) and (8-7.1b). Refer to Fig. 8-7.1a where V denotes the volume of a small coin-shaped box with faces on adjacent sides of the boundary. The height of the box d will be reduced and will vanish in the limit. As a result, the contribution of the surface integral around the cylindrical surface will be negligibly small. From the divergence theorem applied to Eq. (8-7.1a)

$$\int_V \nabla \cdot \bar{D}\, dV = \oint_S \bar{D} \cdot d\bar{S} = \int_V \rho\, dV \tag{8-7.2}$$

If ΔS is sufficiently small, the normal component of $\bar{D}$ and the surface charge density ρ_s at the boundary are essentially constant over ΔS. Therefore, Eq. (8-7.2) takes the form

$$-D_{1n}\Delta S + D_{2n}\Delta S = \rho\, \Delta V = \rho_s \Delta S$$

or

$$(D_{2n} - D_{1n}) = (\bar{D}_2 - \bar{D}_1) \cdot \bar{n} = \rho_s \tag{8-7.3}$$

where ρ_s is the free charge density.

To determine the boundary condition for $\overline{E}$, we note that

$$\int_S \nabla \times \overline{E} \cdot d\overline{S} = \oint_C \overline{E} \cdot d\overline{\ell} = -\int_S \frac{\partial \overline{B}}{\partial t} \cdot d\overline{S}$$

from Eq. (8-6.1) and Stokes' theorem. Now we choose a small contour, such as that shown in Fig. 8-7.1b. For an incremental region this becomes

$$\lim_{d \to 0} \left(-\frac{\partial \overline{B}}{\partial t} \cdot \Delta\overline{S}\right) = \oint_C \overline{E} \cdot d\overline{\ell} = (E_{2t} - E_{1t})\ell = 0$$

In the limit as $\Delta h \to 0$, the area $\Delta S = \Delta h \Delta \ell \to 0$. But since $\overline{B}$ is finite, the amount of magnetic flux passing through the contour C vanishes. As a result, the tangential component of $\overline{E}$ is continuous across the boundary, and this is expressed in vector form in Eq. (8-7.1a). The derivation of Eqs. (8-7.1c) and (8-7.1d) follows a similar pattern.

8-8. THE WAVE EQUATIONS FOR ELECTROMAGNETIC WAVES

We begin by writing the Maxwell equations in a form that includes the properties of the medium. Hence the modified forms of Eqs. (8-6.1d) and (8-6.1c) that we use are

$$\nabla \times \overline{E} = -\frac{\partial \overline{B}}{\partial t} = -\mu \frac{\partial \overline{H}}{\partial t} \qquad (8\text{-}8.1)$$

$$\nabla \times \overline{H} = \overline{J} + \frac{\partial \overline{D}}{\partial t} = \sigma \overline{E} + \varepsilon \frac{\partial \overline{E}}{\partial t} \qquad (8\text{-}8.2)$$

where ε, μ, σ are assumed to be constants. Taking the curl of Eq. (8-8.1) and combining this expression with Eq. (8-8.2) yields

$$\nabla \times \nabla \times \overline{E} + \mu\sigma \frac{\partial \overline{E}}{\partial t} + \mu\varepsilon \frac{\partial^2 \overline{E}}{\partial t^2} = 0 \qquad (8\text{-}8.3)$$

where the current due to sources are neglected ($\overline{J}_i = 0$). Using the vector identity $\nabla \times \nabla \times \quad = \nabla(\nabla \cdot \quad) - \nabla^2$ in Eq. (8-8.3) and assuming that no charges are present, i.e., $\nabla \cdot \overline{E} = 0$, we obtain the following wave equation

$$\nabla^2 \overline{E} = \mu\sigma \frac{\partial \overline{E}}{\partial t} + \mu\varepsilon \frac{\partial^2 \overline{E}}{\partial t^2} \qquad (8\text{-}8.4)$$

By proceeding in a parallel way, but starting with the curl of Eq. (8-8.2) and combining with Eq. (8-8.1), it will be found that the wave equation for $\overline{H}$ is

$$\nabla^2\overline{H} = \mu\sigma \frac{\partial \overline{H}}{\partial t} + \mu\varepsilon \frac{\partial^2 \overline{H}}{\partial t^2} \tag{8-8.5}$$

It is of some interest to examine the changes that will arise in the wave equations for a spatially inhomogeneous dielectric isotropic medium. Now we begin with Eq. (8-8.3) modified to the form

$$\nabla(\nabla \cdot \overline{E}) - \nabla^2\overline{E} + \mu\varepsilon \frac{\partial^2 \overline{E}}{\partial t^2} = 0 \tag{8-8.6}$$

since we are neglecting conductivity. But

$$\nabla \cdot \overline{D} = \nabla \cdot \varepsilon\overline{E} = \varepsilon\nabla \cdot \overline{E} + \overline{E} \cdot \nabla\varepsilon = \rho = 0$$

For inhomogeneous non-conducting mediums, we must modify Eq. (8-6.1a) to read

$$\nabla \cdot \overline{E} + \frac{\overline{E} \cdot \nabla\varepsilon}{\varepsilon} = \nabla \cdot \overline{E} + \overline{E} \cdot \nabla \ln \varepsilon = 0 \tag{8-8.7}$$

As a result, the wave equation (8-8.6) becomes

$$\nabla^2\overline{E} + \nabla(\overline{E} \cdot \nabla \ln \varepsilon) - \mu\varepsilon \frac{\partial^2 \overline{E}}{\partial t^2} = 0 \tag{8-8.8}$$

Example 8-8.1. A plane wave having a frequency of 1590 MHz is traveling in a medium for which $\mu_r = \varepsilon_r = 1$ and $\sigma = 0.1$ mho/m. If the rms electric field intensity of the wave is 10 Volt/m, determine: (a) the conduction current density, (b) the displacement current density, (c) the total current density.

Solution. Given that $E_o = 10$ Volt/m, then $E = 10\sqrt{2} \sin \omega t$. Then

(a) $J_c = \sigma E = 0.1 \times 10 = 1$ Amp/m^2

(b) Since $\frac{\partial E}{\partial t} = 10\sqrt{2}\ \omega \cos \omega t = 10\sqrt{2}\ \omega \sin(\omega t + \frac{\pi}{2})$

$$J_d = \frac{\partial D}{\partial t} = \varepsilon \frac{\partial E}{\partial t} = \omega\varepsilon E_o \sin\left(\omega t + \frac{\pi}{2}\right)$$

$$= 2\pi \times 1.59 \times 10^9 \times \frac{10^{-9}}{36\pi} \times 10 \sin\left(\omega t + \frac{\pi}{2}\right) = 0.883 \sin\left(\omega t + \frac{\pi}{2}\right) \text{ Amp/m}^2$$

(c) The phasor representation of the total current is given simply as

$$J_t = J_c + J_d = (1 + j0.88) \quad \text{Amp/m}^2$$

This result is suggestive of the situation in a parallel RC circuit. ΔΔΔ

8-9. Electromagnetic Potentials for Homogeneous Isotropic Mediums

Often one introduces auxiliary functions to facilitate the solution of the Maxwell equations. This is readily accomplished if we know the general condition that $\nabla \cdot \overline{B} = 0$. This condition implies the existence of a vector potential $\overline{A}$, as previously shown, such that

$$\overline{B} = \nabla \times \overline{A} \tag{8-9.1}$$

since div (curl $\overline{A}$) of any vector $\overline{A}$ is identically zero. Introduce this expression into Eq. (8-6.1d) with the result that

$$\nabla \times (\overline{E} + \frac{\partial \overline{A}}{\partial t}) = 0 \tag{8-9.2}$$

Now we make use of the vector relation that curl (grad Φ_e) = 0 identically. This suggests that Eq. (8-9.2) implies the existence of a scalar potential, and that

$$\overline{E} = -\nabla\Phi_e - \frac{\partial \overline{A}}{\partial t} \tag{8-9.3}$$

Equations (8-9.1) and (8-9.3) show that $\overline{B}$ and $\overline{E}$ are defined in terms of the vector potential $\overline{A}$ and the scalar potential Φ_e. If we combine this result with Eq. (8-6.1a) in the form $\nabla \cdot \overline{E} = \rho/\varepsilon$, we obtain

$$\nabla^2\Phi_e + \frac{\partial}{\partial t}(\nabla \cdot \overline{A}) = -\frac{\rho}{\varepsilon} \tag{8-9.4}$$

Similarly, by combining Eqs. (8-9.1) and (8-9.3) with Eq. (8-6.1c) we obtain

$$\nabla \times \overline{B} = \nabla \times \nabla \times \overline{A} = \varepsilon\mu \frac{\partial \overline{E}}{\partial t} + \mu\overline{J} = \varepsilon\mu \frac{\partial}{\partial t}(-\nabla\Phi_e - \frac{\partial \overline{A}}{\partial t}) + \mu\overline{J} \tag{8-9.5}$$

Now expand the double curl of $\overline{A}$, and rearrange the equation to the form

$$\nabla^2\overline{A} = \mu\varepsilon\frac{\partial^2\overline{A}}{\partial t^2} + \nabla(\nabla \cdot \overline{A} + \mu\varepsilon\frac{\partial\Phi_e}{\partial t}) - \mu\overline{J} \tag{8-9.6}$$

An important observation must be made with regard to the vector potential $\overline{A}$. The curl of $\overline{A}$ has been chosen by Eq. (8-9.1). Nothing has yet been said about the divergence $\nabla \cdot \overline{A}$, and this is still arbitrary although we found this to be zero for magnetostatic fields [see Eq. (6-2.9)]. Likewise, nothing has been said about $\nabla\Phi_e$ except that it satisfies the basic vector identity. What we seek is a relationship between them so as to simplify the equation for $\overline{A}$. The usual condition that accomplishes this is

$$\nabla \cdot \overline{A} = -\mu\varepsilon \frac{\partial \Phi_e}{\partial t} \tag{8-9.7}$$

which is called the *Lorentz condition.* When this relation is invoked, we obtain the following two equations

$$\nabla^2 \Phi_e - \mu\varepsilon \frac{\partial^2 \Phi_e}{\partial t^2} = -\frac{\rho}{\varepsilon} \qquad \text{a)}$$

$$\nabla^2 \overline{A} - \mu\varepsilon \frac{\partial^2 \overline{A}}{\partial t^2} = -\mu \overline{J} \qquad \text{b)} \tag{8-9.8}$$

where ρ and $\overline{J}$ are the impressed charge and current sources. These equations indicate that the scalar potential Φ_e and the components A_x, A_y, A_z are described by wave equations, and their solutions are thus uniquely specified. When the sources are static, the time-dependent terms become zero, and these equations reduce to a scalar and vector Poisson's equation. In practice we do not need to solve for the scalar potential Φ_e since the field is completely determined by the vector potential $\overline{A}$ through Eq. (8-9.7).

8-10. Energy and Power of the Electromagnetic Field

The notion of energy density and power in linear mediums is best described by Poynting's theorem. Although its physical interpretation is open to some question, we adopt this theorem for two reasons: (a) no other theorem has been found that is a satisfactory substitute, and (b) it has proved to be extremely useful and fruitful, and may be interpreted as the rate flow of energy per unit area in the direction of the vector $\overline{E} \times \overline{H}$, known as the Poynting vector.

Consider that N charged particles each having a charge q are under the influence of an external electromagnetic field. Power is delivered to these particles per unit volume at the rate $Nq\overline{v} \cdot \overline{E} = \overline{J} \cdot \overline{E}$. The magnetic field does no work since $\overline{v}$ is always perpendicular to $\overline{H}$. Let us multiply Eq. (8-6.1d) scalarly with $\overline{H}$, and Eq. (8-6.1c) with $\overline{E}$. Then

$$\overline{H} \cdot \nabla \times \overline{E} + \overline{H} \cdot \frac{\partial \overline{B}}{\partial t} = 0 \qquad \text{a)}$$

$$\overline{E} \cdot \nabla \times \overline{H} - \overline{E} \cdot \frac{\partial \overline{D}}{\partial t} = \overline{E} \cdot \overline{J} \qquad \text{b)} \tag{8-10.1}$$

Subtracting Eq. (8-10.1a) from Eq. (8-10.1b)

$$-\overline{E} \cdot \frac{\partial \overline{D}}{\partial t} - \overline{H} \cdot \frac{\partial \overline{B}}{\partial t} = \overline{E} \cdot \overline{J} - \overline{E} \cdot \nabla \times \overline{H} + \overline{H} \cdot \nabla \times \overline{E}$$

which is written in the form

$$-\bar{E} \cdot \frac{\partial \bar{D}}{\partial t} - \bar{H} \cdot \frac{\partial \bar{B}}{\partial t} = \nabla \cdot (\bar{E} \times \bar{H}) + \bar{E} \cdot \bar{J} \tag{8-10.2}$$

Now consider the integration of this equation over a volume V bounded by a closed surface S. Use is made in this integration of the divergence theorem, with the result

$$\int_V \bar{E} \cdot \bar{J}\, dV = -\int_V [\bar{E} \cdot \frac{\partial \bar{D}}{\partial t} + \bar{H} \cdot \frac{\partial \bar{B}}{\partial t}]\, dV - \int_S \bar{\mathcal{S}} \cdot d\bar{S} \tag{8-10.3}$$

where the Poynting vector $\mathcal{S}$ is defined by

$$\mathcal{S} = \bar{E} \times \bar{H} \tag{8-10.4}$$

Thus the interpretation of $\mathcal{S}$ as the rate of flow of energy per unit area in Watt/m^2 in the direction of the vector $\bar{E} \times \bar{H}$ must be taken as a postulate since other vectors can be formed which would serve as well. That is, if $\bar{N}$ denotes a vector which is defined at every point such that its flux out of any volume is zero, that is, such that div $\bar{N}$ is everywhere zero, then the vector $\mathcal{S} + \bar{N}$ for which div $(\mathcal{S} + \bar{N}) =$ div $\mathcal{S}$ would be an acceptable form to represent the flow of energy. Depending on the choice of $\bar{N}$, a variety of Poynting vectors exist.

For the case of linear homogeneous isotropic mediums, we can denote the total energy density from Eqs. (5-9.11) and (6-12.8) by

$$U = \frac{1}{2} (\bar{E} \cdot \bar{D} + \bar{H} \cdot \bar{B})$$

$$= \frac{1}{2} (\epsilon\bar{E} \cdot \bar{E} + \mu\bar{H} \cdot \bar{H}) = \frac{1}{2}(\epsilon E^2 + \mu H^2) \tag{8-10.5}$$

Equation (8-10.3) becomes, in this case,

$$\int_V \bar{E} \cdot \bar{J}\, dV = -\int_V \frac{\partial U}{\partial t}\, dV - \oint_S \bar{\mathcal{S}} \cdot d\bar{S} = -\int_V [\frac{\partial U}{\partial t} + \nabla \cdot \bar{\mathcal{S}}]\, dV \tag{8-10.6}$$

In differential form, this equation may be written

$$\frac{\partial U}{\partial t} + \nabla \cdot \bar{\mathcal{S}} = -\bar{E} \cdot \bar{J} \tag{8-10.7}$$

For the case when a source field $\bar{E}$ is applied with a consequent current density $\bar{J}_i$, the total current density is the sum of the two currents $\bar{J} = \bar{J}_c + \bar{J}_i$, the conduction current and the impressed current. Under these conditions, Eq. (8-10.3) takes the form

$$\int_V \bar{E} \cdot \bar{J}_i dV = -\int_V \frac{J_c^2}{\sigma}\, dV - \int_V [\bar{E} \cdot \frac{\partial \bar{D}}{\partial t} + \bar{H} \cdot \frac{\partial \bar{B}}{\partial t}]\, dV - \oint_S \bar{\mathcal{S}} \cdot d\bar{S} \tag{8-10.8}$$

This can be interpreted as follows: for any closed volume, the instantaneous power supplied by the source is equal to that leaving the surface $\oint_S \mathscr{S} \cdot d\overline{S}$, plus the rate of increase in stored electric and magnetic densities $\int [\overline{E} \cdot \partial\overline{D}/\partial t + \overline{H} \cdot \partial\overline{B}/\partial t]\, dV$ plus that lost (irreversible transformation) to Joule heating. Clearly, Eq. (8-10.8) is a restatement of conservation of energy applied to the electromagnetic field.

Additional insight into the meaning of these terms is possible by considering the particular case when the field vectors $\overline{E}$ and $\overline{H}$ are sinusoidal functions of time. These are written in the form

$$\overline{E} = \text{Re}\,[\overline{E}_o e^{-j\omega t}] = \text{Re}\,[\underset{\sim}{\overline{E}}] = \frac{1}{2}(\overline{E}_o e^{-j\omega t} + \overline{E}_o^{\,*} e^{j\omega t})$$
$$\overline{H} = \text{Re}\,[\overline{H}_o e^{-j\omega t}] = \text{Re}\,[\underset{\sim}{\overline{H}}] = \frac{1}{2}(\overline{H}_o e^{-j\omega t} + \overline{H}_o^{\,*} e^{j\omega t}) \qquad (8\text{-}10.9)$$

where $\underset{\sim}{\overline{E}}$ and $\underset{\sim}{\overline{H}}$ indicate complex quantities. But $\overline{E}_o$ and $\overline{H}_o$ are complex quantities, in general, and are functions of the spatial coordinates only and may be written as $\overline{E}_o = \overline{E}_r + j\overline{E}_i$ and $\overline{H}_o = \overline{H}_r + j\overline{H}_i$ where $\overline{E}_r$, $\overline{E}_i$, $\overline{H}_r$, $\overline{H}_i$ are real vectors. In these terms, Eq. (8-10.9) can be written

$$\overline{E} = \overline{E}_r \cos\omega t + \overline{E}_i \sin\omega t$$
$$\overline{H} = \overline{H}_r \cos\omega t + \overline{H}_i \sin\omega t \qquad (8\text{-}10.10)$$

Now we combine Eqs. (8-10.10) with (8-10.5) and take the time average over a period $T = 2\pi/\omega$. The result is found to be

$$\langle U\rangle = \frac{1}{4}[\varepsilon(\overline{E}_r \cdot \overline{E}_r + \overline{E}_i \cdot \overline{E}_i) + \mu(\overline{H}_r \cdot \overline{H}_r + \overline{H}_i \cdot \overline{H}_i)]$$
$$= \frac{1}{4}[\varepsilon\underset{\sim}{\overline{E}} \cdot \underset{\sim}{\overline{E}}^* + \mu\underset{\sim}{\overline{H}} \cdot \underset{\sim}{\overline{H}}^*] = \langle U_e\rangle + \langle U_m\rangle = \frac{1}{4}[\varepsilon|\underset{\sim}{E}|^2 + \mu|\underset{\sim}{H}|^2] \qquad (8\text{-}10.11)$$

Similarly, we write for the time average power flow

$$\langle\mathscr{S}_e\rangle = \text{Re}\left[\frac{\underset{\sim}{\overline{E}} \times \underset{\sim}{\overline{H}}^*}{2}\right] = \frac{1}{4}[\underset{\sim}{\overline{E}} \times \underset{\sim}{\overline{H}}^* + \underset{\sim}{\overline{E}}^* \times \underset{\sim}{\overline{H}}] = \frac{1}{4}[(\underset{\sim}{\overline{E}} + \underset{\sim}{\overline{E}}^*) \times (\underset{\sim}{\overline{H}} + \underset{\sim}{\overline{H}}^*)] \qquad (8\text{-}10.12)$$

For complex quantities let us multiply Eq. (8-6.1d) scalarly with $\overline{H}^*$ and the conjugate of Eq. (8-6.1c) with $\overline{E}$. Then

$$\overline{H}^* \cdot \nabla \times \overline{E} = -\overline{H}^* \cdot \frac{\partial\overline{B}}{\partial t} \qquad \text{a)}$$
$$\overline{E} \cdot \nabla \times \overline{H}^* = \overline{E} \cdot \overline{J}_c^{\,*} + \overline{E} \cdot \frac{\partial\overline{D}^*}{\partial t} \qquad \text{b)} \qquad (8\text{-}10.13)$$

Following the same procedure as that at the beginning of this section, we easily obtain the following equation

$$\frac{1}{2}\int_V \bar{E}\cdot\bar{J}^* \, dV = -\frac{1}{2}\int_V \left[\bar{E}\cdot\frac{\partial\bar{D}^*}{\partial t} + \bar{H}^*\cdot\frac{\partial\bar{B}}{\partial t}\right] dV - \frac{1}{2}\int_S \bar{\mathscr{S}}_{co}\cdot d\bar{S} \qquad (8\text{-}10.14)$$

where

$$\bar{\mathscr{S}}_{co} = \bar{E}\times\bar{H}^*$$

is the complex Poynting vector.

Example 8-10.1. Consider a straight wire of radius r_o oriented along the Z-axis carrying a steady current I. Determine the total power entering a unit length of wire.

Solution. We first find the electric and magnetic fields of this configuration. The magnetic field at the surface of the wire is

$$\bar{H} = \frac{I}{2\pi r_o}\bar{a}_\phi$$

The electric field is in the Z-direction and it is equal to

$$\bar{E} = \frac{\bar{J}}{\sigma} = \frac{J\bar{a}_z}{\sigma} = \frac{I}{\pi r_o^2 \sigma}\bar{a}_z$$

Hence the Poynting vector at the surface of the wire is equal to

$$\bar{\mathscr{S}} = \bar{E}_z \times \bar{H}_\phi = -\frac{I^2}{2\pi^2 r_o^3 \sigma}\bar{a}_r$$

The total power entering a unit length of wire is

$$\oint_S \bar{\mathscr{S}}\cdot d\bar{S} = \frac{I^2}{2\pi^2 r_o^3\sigma}\cdot 2\pi r_o = I^2\left(\frac{1}{\pi r_o^2\sigma}\right) = I^2 R$$

which indicates that the field supplies the energy to balance out the I^2R heating losses in the wire. The contribution to the surface integral is only from the cylindrical part of the surface; the contribution from the top and the bottom surfaces is zero since $\bar{E}_z \times \bar{H}_\phi$ is perpendicular to $d\bar{S}$. ΔΔΔ

Example 8-10.2. A 10 MHz plane wave that is traveling in free space has a peak amplitude $E_o = 50\ \mu V/m$. Determine the following: (a) the time average electric energy density of the wave, (b) the peak total energy density, (c) the average Poynting vector, (d) the peak Poynting vector, (e) the energy contained in a cube 10 km on a side.

Solution.

(a) Electric energy density $= \langle \frac{\varepsilon_o E^2}{2} \rangle = \frac{10^{-9}}{36\pi} \frac{(50 \times 10^{-6})^2}{4} = 0.552 \times 10^{-22}$ Joule/m^3

(b) Total peak energy density $= \varepsilon_o E^2 = 2.208 \times 10^{-22}$ Joule/m^3, since $\frac{1}{2} \varepsilon_o E^2 = \frac{1}{2} \mu_o H^2$

(c) $\langle \mathscr{S}_c \rangle = \sqrt{\frac{\varepsilon_o}{\mu_o}} \frac{E^2}{2} = \frac{E^2}{2Z_o} = \frac{(50 \times 10^{-6})^2}{2 \times 120\pi} = 3.66 \times 10^{-14}$ Watt/m^2

($Z_o = \sqrt{\frac{\mu_o}{\varepsilon_o}}$ = characteristic impedance; $H = \sqrt{\frac{\varepsilon_o}{\mu_o}} E$, see Chap. 9)

(d) $\mathscr{S}_{peak} = 2 \langle S_c \rangle = 7.32 \times 10^{-4}$ Watt/m^2

(e) $\langle U \rangle = \frac{\varepsilon_o E^2}{2}$ (vol) $= 1.104 \times 10^{-22} \times (10^4)^3 = 1.104 \times 10^{-10}$ Joule, avg. ΔΔΔ

8-11. The Schrödinger Wave Equation

Consider the following one-dimensional wave equation which is known in particle physics as the DeBroglie wave equation

$$\frac{\partial^2 \psi(x,t)}{\partial x^2} = \frac{1}{v^2} \frac{\partial^2 \psi(x,t)}{\partial t^2} \tag{8-11.1}$$

For a periodic time and space variation, this has the simple solution

$$\psi(x,t) = A \sin \frac{2\pi}{\lambda} x \cos 2\pi ft$$

In the more general case we would expect a solution of the form

$$\psi(x,t) = u(x) \cos 2\pi ft \tag{8-11.2}$$

By introducing Eq. (8-11.2) into Eq. (8-11.1) we obtain

$$\frac{d^2 u(x)}{dx^2} = - \frac{4\pi^2 f^2}{v^2} u(x) \tag{8-11.3}$$

Since $v = \lambda f$, Eq. (8-11.3) assumes the form

$$\frac{d^2 u(x)}{dx^2} + \frac{4\pi^2}{\lambda^2} u(x) = 0 \tag{8-11.4}$$

To apply this equation to particles, we must incorporate the deBroglie relationship

$$\lambda = \frac{h}{mv} = \frac{h}{p} \tag{8-11.5}$$

where h is Planck's constant and p is the momentum of the particle. Eq. (8-11.4) becomes

$$\frac{d^2u(x)}{dx^2} + \frac{4\pi^2m^2v^2}{h^2}u(x) = 0 \tag{8-11.6}$$

The kinetic energy of a particle is $T = (1/2)mv^2$ from which $v^2 = 2T/m$. In addition, the total energy W is equal to the sum of the potential energy V and the kinetic energy T, i.e., $W = T + V$. Therefore we can write the velocity in the form $v^2 = 2(W-V)/m$. This expression is combined to write Eq. (8-11.6) as

$$\frac{d^2u(x)}{dx^2} + \frac{8\pi^2m^2}{h^2}(W - V)u(x) = 0 \tag{8-11.7}$$

This is the time independent Schrödinger equation. The three-dimensional time independent Schrödinger equation is written as an extension of Eq. (8-11.7)

$$\frac{\partial^2u}{\partial x^2} + \frac{\partial^2u}{\partial y^2} + \frac{\partial^2u}{\partial z^2} + \frac{8\pi^2m^2}{h^2}(W - V)u = 0$$

or

$$\left(-\frac{\hbar^2}{2m}\nabla^2 + V\right)u = Wu \tag{8-11.8}$$

This equation is often written

$$Hu = Wu \tag{8-11.9}$$

where $\hbar^2 = (h/2\pi)^2$ and where $H = -\hbar^2/2m\,\nabla^2 + V$ is the so-called *Hamiltonian operator*.

The Schrödinger equation can be solved to determine the function u and so the function ψ. We note that by itself ψ has no physical meaning. However, the product $\psi\psi^*$ is interpreted as being proportional to the probability of finding a particle at a particular point. This interpretation stems from the fact that atomic particles have both particle and wave properties, and as a consequence, they obey the Heisinberg Uncertainty Principle. This principle states that the exact determination simultaneously of the momentum (or energy) of a particle and its position is not possible. Therefore for a particle (e.g., an electron) with a definite energy, its position is uncertain and can only be inferred by probabilistic assertions such as $\psi\psi^*dV$ denotes the probability of finding an electron in the volume dV.

The Schrödinger equation for time varying systems is given by

$$H\psi = j\hbar\frac{\partial\psi}{\partial t} \tag{8-11.10}$$

This equation can be resolved into two equations by writing

$$\psi(x,t) = u(x)\phi(t) \tag{8-11.11}$$

This leads to the separated equations

$$\frac{d\phi(t)}{dt} = -\frac{2\pi j}{h} W\phi(t) = -j\frac{W}{\hbar}\phi(t) \qquad \text{a)}$$

$$-\frac{\hbar^2}{2m}\frac{d^2u(x)}{dx^2} + V(x)u(x) = Wu(x) \qquad \text{b)} \tag{8-11.12}$$

Appropriate to each energy value W_n there corresponds the functions $\phi_n(t)$ and $u_n(x)$. Eq. (8-11.12a) is readily solved by direct integration to yield

$$\phi_n(t) = e^{-j(2\pi W_n t/h)} \tag{8-11.13}$$

The general solution of Eq. (8-11.10) is the sum of all the particular solutions with arbitrary constant coefficients. This can be written

$$\psi(x,t) = \sum_n a_n\psi_n(x,t) = \sum_n a_n u_n(x)e^{-j(2\pi W_n t/h)} \tag{8-11.14}$$

For a continuous range of W, the summation is replaced by an integral.

REVIEW QUESTIONS

1. What are the units of R, L, and C, which appear in the wave equation of a transmission line?
2. What is the name of the equation which describes the vibration of a string?
3. What is the adabatic law of fluids?
4. The velocity of sound is given by $c_a = \sqrt{\gamma p_o/\rho_o}$. Identify each of the constants.
5. Define the specific acoustic impedance and the intensity of plane acoustic waves.
6. Write the four Maxwell equations in differential form and give their physical meaning.
7. What are the three constitutive equations?
8. What are the names and the units of ε, μ, and σ?
9. What are the boundary conditions for the perpendicular components of the magnetic field between a dielectric and a conducting medium?
10. What are the boundary conditions for the perpendicular components of the magnetic field between a dielectric and a conducting medium?
11. Which one of the characteristics of a medium, μ, ε, and σ, introduces a diffusion term into the differential equations of the electromagnetic field?

12. Define the real Poynting vector. What are the units of the Poynting vector $\mathcal{P}$?
13. What is the total energy density of the electromagnetic field in a linear homogeneous and isotropic medium?
14. If a source supplies the power $\int_V \overline{E} \cdot \overline{J}_i \, dV$ in a closed volume, describe the different forms of power that appear in the same volume.
15. If $\psi(x,t)$ is the solution of Schrödinger's equation, what is the meaning of $\psi\psi^*$?

PROBLEMS

8-1.1. Verify Eqs. (8-1.5).

8-1.2. Follow the same procedure as in Sec. 8-1 and show that the voltage equation for an RC line is given by: $\partial^2 v/\partial x^2 = RC\, \partial v/\partial t$. Using Eq. (8-1.5), show your result to be correct.

8-1.3. Introduce the appropriate values for R, G, L, C, I_o, V_o such that Eqs. (8-1.5) take the form of: (a) Poisson-type, (b) Laplace-type, (c) wave-type, and (d) diffusion-type equations.

8-1.4. The velocity of the voltage wave (or current wave) in a lossless transmission line is $v = 1/\sqrt{LC}$. Find the inductance per unit length such that $v = 0.99c$, where c is the speed of light.

8-1.5. If the velocity of the voltage wave (or current wave) in a lossless transmission line is equal to the speed of light and $L = 10^{-12}$ H, what is the value of C, per unit length.

8-1.6. Using equation $v = 1/\sqrt{LC} < c$, specify the constraints on L and C.

8-2.1. If the tension T in a string is 3.5×10^4 dynes its density is 0.5 kg/m^3, what is the speed of the wave in the string?

8-3.1. Show that in the limit as $d \to 0$, $dx \to 0$ and the masses diminish in size, such that $m/d \to \rho_L$, Eq. (8-3.1) becomes the string equation

$$\frac{\partial^2 y}{\partial t^2} = \frac{T}{\rho_L} \frac{\partial^2 y}{\partial x^2} = c_s{}^2 \frac{\partial^2 y}{\partial x^2} .$$

[Hint: $\left.\frac{\partial y}{\partial x}\right|_{r+1} - \left.\frac{\partial y}{\partial x}\right|_r = \left.\frac{\partial^2 y}{\partial x^2}\right|_r dx$]

8-3.2. Find the electrical analog of a monatomic lattice.

8-5.1. What is the ratio of specific heats c_p/c_v for nitrogen; for oxygen?

8-5.2. What is the velocity of sound at a distance of 10 Km above the surface of the earth, given that the density varies according to the so-called barometer equation $\rho = \rho_o e^{-mgh/kT}$.

8-5.3. The bulk modulus of copper is 15×10^{10} Newton/m^2 and its density is 8.9×10^3 kg/m^3. Find the velocity of sound in copper.

8-5.4. The bulk modulus of mercury is 2.9×10^{11} Newton/m^2 and its density is 13.6×10^3 Kg/m^3. Find the specific acoustic impedance of Hg.

8-6.1. Show that the displacement current between two concentric cylindrical conducting shells of radii r_1 and r_2, $r_2 > r_1$, is exactly the same as the conduction current in the external circuit. The applied voltage source is $V = V_o \sin \omega t$.
[Hint: Find V(r) and $C_\ell \equiv$ Farads/unit length and show that $I = C_\ell\, dV/dt$ is equal to $I = \iint_S \partial\overline{D}/\partial t \cdot d\overline{S}$]

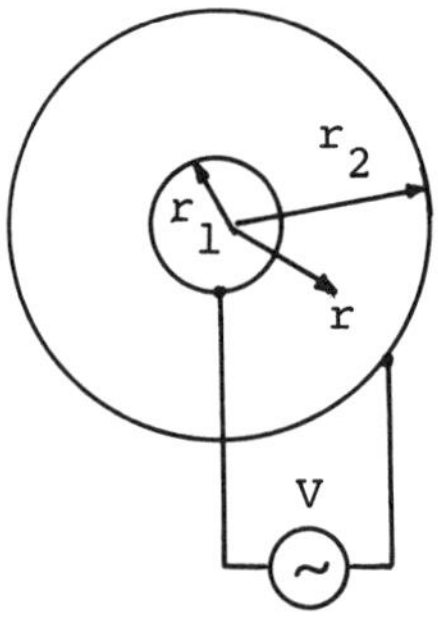

Figure P8-6.1.

8-6.2. Verify Eqs. (8-6.4).

8-6.3. The electric vector of a certain radiowave is vertical and has a magnitude of 30 μV/m and a frequency of 1 MHz. Calculate the maximum value in microamps of the total displacement current through a horizontal area of 1.5 m^2.

8-6.4. Find the magnitude and direction at time t = 0 of the displacement current density in lossless mediums when the magnetic field $\overline{H} = 3 \sin 2x \cos (kz-\omega t)\, \overline{a}_y + 4 \cos 2x \sin (kz-\omega t)\, \overline{a}_z$ is present.

8-6.5. If a field E = 10 cos (500t) is produced across a lossy dielectric having conductivity σ and permittivity ε, show that the ratio (absolute value) of the conduction current to the amplitude of the displacement current is $\sigma/\omega\varepsilon$.

8-7.1. Verify Eq. (8-7.1c) and (8-7.1d).

8-7.2. Two mediums in contact have the following electrical characteristics: $\varepsilon_{r1} = 3$, $\mu_{r1} = 1$; $\varepsilon_{r2} = 0.1$, $\mu_{r2} = 1$. What are the electric field E_2 and the induction D_2, if $E_1 = 10^3$ Volt/m at 30 deg to a perpendicular at the interface and if a surface charge density of 10^3 Coulomb/m^2 exists on the interface surface separating the two mediums.

8-7.3. A plane wave having a frequency of 10 Hz is traveling in the sea. If the electric field intensity of the wave is 100 mV/m, determine: (a) the conduction current; (b) the displacement current; (c) the total current. The relative permittivity of the sea water is 80 and its conductivity is 0.5 mho/m.

8-10.1. The E and H fields of a plane electromagnetic wave in air are related by the relation $E = \sqrt{\mu_o/\varepsilon_o}\, H \doteq 377H$. If the power from the sun falling on the surface of the earth is 150 Watt/m^2, find the electric field E of the sun's rays.

8-10.2. A tungsten wire has a radius of 1 mm and has a conductivity of 1.8×10^7 mho/m. A voltage V = 10 Volt is applied to the ends of a 1.32 m length of this wire. Find the Poynting vector at its surface. Plot the magnitude of the Poynting vector in the range $0 \leq r < \infty$.

8-10.3. Scalarly multiply Eq. (8-6.1d) by $\overline{H}^*$ and the conjugate of Eq. (8-6.1c) by $\overline{E}$ and show that for harmonically time varying fields

$$-\nabla \cdot \mathscr{S}_c = \frac{1}{2}\overline{J}^* \cdot \overline{E} - 2j\omega\left(\frac{1}{4}\mu\overline{H} \cdot \overline{H}^* - \frac{1}{4}\varepsilon\overline{E} \cdot \overline{E}^*\right)$$

8-10.4. Find the power relation for an RLC series circuit and compare it with the relation found in Pr. 8-10.3.

8-10.5. Show that the energy between the plates of a charging capacitor can be considered to come from the space surrounding the capacitor and not through the wires. Find the total amount of flow of energy through the whole surface between edges of the capacitor plates.

8-10.6. Using Eq. (8-10.8) find the energy-balanced equation when polarization and magnetization effects are present. Explain the significance of each term.

8-11.1. Verify Eq. (8-11.11).

CHAPTER 9

DIFFUSION PROCESSES

Diffusion is one of the most prevalent natural processes, and it occurs whenever a concentration gradient exists either within a single substance or when different substances come in contact with each other. Diffusion can occur when gases, liquids or solids come in contact with other gases, liquids or solids.

9-1. Diffusion

The rate of the diffusion process depends on the concentration and the type of mediums involved in the process. It is easy to visualize diffusion in gases and in liquids, but diffusion in solids may seem somewhat less familiar. However, diffusion in solids is basic to the manufacture of semiconductor devices, and discrete transistors and other semiconductor devices and integrated circuits depend on diffusion in solids.

Consider a region in which particles (as, for example, atoms, molecules, electrons, holes, bacteria, etc.) may exist in varying concentrations. Refer to Fig. 9-1.1 which shows two surfaces in a region where a concentration gradient exists.

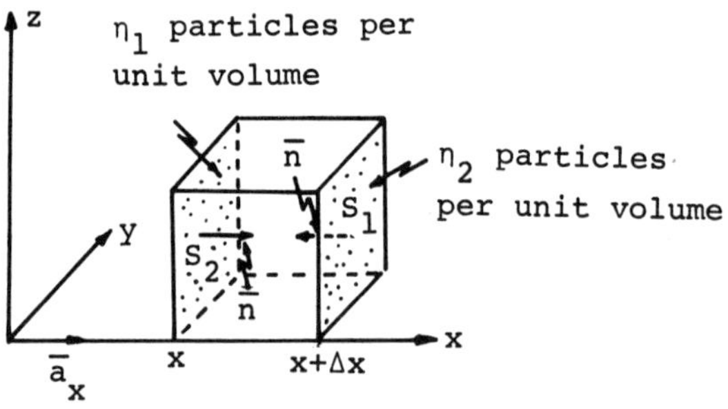

Figure 9-1.1. Two adjacent surfaces in a diffuse medium.

The concentration of particles (particles per unit volume) are η_1 and η_2, respectively, at surfaces S_1 and S_2. We assume that the number of particles leaving surface S_1 per unit time and per unit surface area is proportional to the concentration η_1. The corresponding particle flux density is written

$$\overline{M}_1 = K\eta_1\overline{n} = K\eta_1\overline{a}_x \tag{9-1.1}$$

where K is a proportionality constant with the dimensions m/sec. Correspondingly at the second surface we will have

$$\overline{M}_2 = K\eta_2\overline{n} = -K\eta_2\overline{a}_x \tag{9-1.2}$$

The net particle flux density is equal to the sum of both contributions, and is

$$\overline{M}_x = \overline{M}_1 + \overline{M}_2 = K(\eta_1 - \eta_2)\overline{a}_x \tag{9-1.3}$$

But the difference in particle concentration can be written

$$\eta_2 - \eta_1 = \alpha \lim_{\Delta x \to 0} \frac{\eta_2(x+\Delta x) - \eta_1(x)}{\Delta x} = \alpha \frac{\partial \eta}{\partial x} \tag{9-1.4}$$

where α is another proportionality constant. If we introduce Eq. (9-1.4) into Eq. (9-1.3) we obtain

$$\overline{M}_x = -K\alpha \frac{\partial \eta}{\partial x}\overline{a}_x = -D\frac{\partial \eta}{\partial x}\overline{a}_x \tag{9-1.5}$$

where $D = K\alpha(m^2/sec)$, which is called the *diffusion coefficient*.

If we add the contributions from the other pairs of faces, Eq. (9-1.5) expands to the following form for an isotropic process

$$\overline{M} = -D\left(\frac{\partial \eta}{\partial x}\overline{a}_x + \frac{\partial \eta}{\partial y}\overline{a}_y + \frac{\partial \eta}{\partial z}\overline{a}_z\right) = -D\nabla\eta \tag{9-1.6}$$

This is known as *Fick's law*. In words, this equation states that the diffusion flux density is proportional to the gradient of the concentration. (Refer to Table 1-4.1 for analogous relations.)

A second important relation is found by employing the equation of continuity. This relates the net addition of particles (entering-leaving) in a closed surface to the time rate of change of particles. In symbols, this states that

$$\overline{S} \cdot [\overline{M}(x+\Delta x) - \overline{M}(x)] = -\frac{\partial \eta}{\partial t}(S\Delta x)$$

or

$$\lim_{\Delta x \to 0} \frac{\bar{S}}{S} \cdot \frac{[\bar{M}(x+\Delta x) - \bar{M}(x)]}{\Delta x} = \bar{a}_x \cdot \frac{\partial \bar{M}}{\partial x} = -\frac{\partial \eta}{\partial t} \tag{9-1.7}$$

For the three-dimensional case, we obtain

$$(\bar{a}_x \frac{\partial}{\partial x} + \bar{a}_y \frac{\partial}{\partial y} + \bar{a}_z \frac{\partial}{\partial z}) \cdot \bar{M} = \nabla \cdot \bar{M} = -\frac{\partial \eta}{\partial t} \tag{9-1.8}$$

If we combine Eq. (9-1.8) and (9-1.6) and assume D to be constant, the resulting *diffusion equation* becomes

$$\nabla^2 \eta = \frac{1}{D} \frac{\partial \eta}{\partial t} \tag{9-1.9}$$

When D is a function of spatial coordinates we obtain the equation

$$\nabla \cdot (D \nabla \eta) = \frac{\partial \eta}{\partial t} \tag{9-1.10}$$

instead of Eq. (9-1.9).

The more general case when we include particle sources, ρ_g, and particle sinks, ρ_s, per unit volume Eq. (9-1.10) becomes

$$\nabla \cdot (D \nabla \eta) = \frac{\partial \eta}{\partial t} - \rho_g + \rho_s \tag{9-1.11}$$

Attention is called to the fact that the diffusion equation includes second derivative terms in space, but only a first order time derivative (contrast this with the second order time derivative term in the wave equation).

Example 9-1.1. Consider the case of simple diffusion into a semi-infinite solid, with $\eta(x,t)$ varying sinusoidally with time. Determine the solution, subject to the boundary and initial conditions: $\eta(0,t) = K\, e^{-j\omega t}$.

Solution. For the one-dimensional case, assuming that the solution will be of the form

$$\eta(x,t) = F(x)\, e^{-j\omega t}$$

the diffusion equation, Eq. (9-1.9), yields a differential equation in F(x)

$$\frac{\partial^2 F(x)}{\partial x^2} = -\frac{j\omega}{D_c} F(x)$$

This is an ordinary second order differential equation having a solution of the form

$$F(x) = A\, e^{\sqrt{-j\omega/D_c}\, x} + B\, e^{-\sqrt{-j\omega/D_c}\, x}$$

But since $\sqrt{-j} = (1-j)/\sqrt{2}$, then the function F(x) is

$$F(x) = A\, e^{\sqrt{\omega/2D_c}\, x}\, e^{-j\sqrt{\omega/2D_c}\, x} + B\, e^{-\sqrt{\omega/2D_c}\, x}\, e^{j\sqrt{\omega/2D_c}\, x}$$

The requirement of a bounded solution, $\lim_{x\to\infty} \eta(x,t) = 0$ requires that A = 0 so that

$$F(x) = B\, e^{-\sqrt{\omega/2D_c}\, x}\, e^{j\sqrt{\omega/2D_c}\, x}$$

This expression denotes a simple exponential decay with a linear phase change with x. The distance for which the amplitude falls to $1/e^{th}$ (36.8%) of its initial value

$$x = \delta = \sqrt{\frac{2D_c}{\omega}}$$

is the skin depth, a quantity which denotes the effective field penetration into a conducting medium. Also, the velocity of penetration is

$$v = \frac{\omega}{\sqrt{\frac{\omega}{2D_c}}} = \sqrt{2\,\omega D_c}$$

Now apply boundary conditions to the complete solution

$$\eta(x,t) = B\, e^{-x/\delta}\, e^{-j\omega(t-x/v)}$$

But

$$\eta(0,t) = K\, e^{-j\omega t}$$

and therefore B = K. The solution in real form is

$$\eta(x,t) = K\, e^{-x/\delta} \sin \omega(t-x/v)$$

Some representative diffusion coefficients are given in the tabulation

Typical Diffusion Coefficients

	Temp °C	Diffusion Coefficient D_c (m^2/sec)
Water to Air	8	0.329×10^{-4}
Hydrogen to Air	0	0.634×10^{-4}
HCl to Water	12	2.21×10^{-4}
Sugar to Water	12	0.254×10^{-4}

ΔΔΔ

9-2. Pulses on an RC Transmission Line

It was shown (see Pr. 8-1.2) that an RC transmission line without distributed sources is described by the following limited form of Eq. (8-1.5).

$$\frac{\partial^2 v}{\partial x^2} = RC\frac{\partial v}{\partial t} = \frac{1}{D_\ell}\frac{\partial v}{\partial t} \tag{9-2.1}$$

We shall carry out the solution of this problem using Laplace transform techniques for the case of an applied rectangular pulse to the input. Use is made of the fact that the rectangular pulse is the superposition of two step functions $u_{-1}(t)$ $-u_{-1}(t-T)$. For zero initial conditions, Eq. (9-2.1) Laplace transforms to

$$\frac{d^2\tilde{v}(x,s)}{dx^2} = RCs\tilde{v}(x,s) \tag{9-2.2}$$

This is an ordinary differential equation having as its solution

$$\tilde{v}(x,s) = A\,e^{-x\sqrt{RCs}} + B\,e^{x\sqrt{RCs}} \tag{9-2.3}$$

For simplicity, we shall assume that the line is of semi-infinite length, which requires that B must be zero and thus the value of v becomes zero at infinity. Hence we have as the solution

$$\tilde{v}(x,s) = A\,e^{-x\sqrt{RCs}} \tag{9-2.4}$$

For the case of the applied pulse, we must consider the solution in two parts, that due to the step function at $t = 0$, and that due to the reversed step delayed by time T. For the initial step the boundary condition is: at $x = 0$, $v(0,t) = V_o u_{-1}(t)$, so that

$$\tilde{v}(0,s) = \frac{V_o}{s} \tag{9-2.5}$$

In both cases the initial condition is: $v = 0$ at $t = 0$ and $x > 0$. If we combine this with Eq. (9-2.4), we observe that $A = V_o/s$, and the solution for the initial step is given by the inverse Laplace transform of

$$\tilde{v}(x,s) = \frac{V_o}{s}\,e^{-x\sqrt{RCs}} \tag{9-2.6}$$

The inverse Laplace transform of this expression is the time function

$$v_+(x,t) = \mathscr{L}^{-1}\left[\frac{V_o}{s}\,e^{-x\sqrt{RCs}}\right] = V_o\left[1 - \mathrm{erf}\sqrt{\frac{RC}{t}}\,\frac{x}{2}\right] = V_o\,\mathrm{erfc}\left(\frac{x}{2}\sqrt{\frac{RC}{t}}\right) \tag{9-2.7}$$

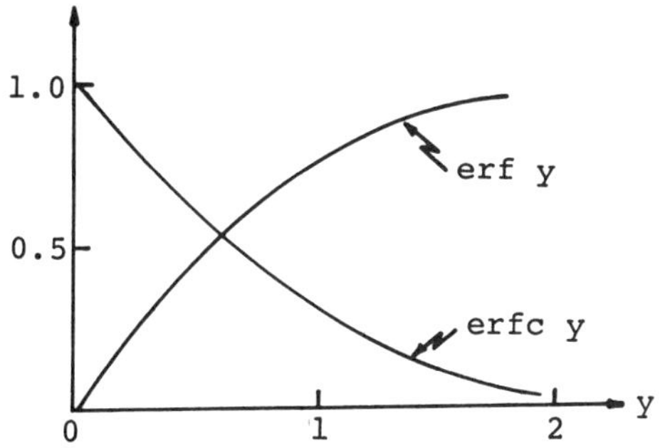

Figure 9-2.1. erf y and erfc y.

where erf denotes the error function and erfc is the complementary error function. These are defined by the formulas

$$\operatorname{erf} y = \frac{2}{\sqrt{\pi}} \int_0^y e^{-\xi^2}\, d\xi$$
$$\operatorname{erfc} y = 1 - \operatorname{erf} y \qquad (9\text{-}2.8)$$

The error function has the properties

$$\operatorname{erf}(-y) = -\operatorname{erf} y, \qquad \operatorname{erf}(0) = 0, \qquad \operatorname{erf}(\infty) = 1 \qquad (9\text{-}2.9)$$

Sketches of erf y and erfc y are given in Fig. 9-2.1.

For the complete solution, we must add to Eq. (9-2.7) the corresponding expression that arises from the excitation function applied at $t = T$. This is the function

$$v_-(x,t-T) = -V_0 \left[1 - \operatorname{erf}\left(\frac{x}{2}\sqrt{\frac{RC}{t-T}}\right)\right] = -V_0 \operatorname{erfc}\left(\frac{x}{2}\sqrt{\frac{RC}{t-T}}\right), \quad t > T \qquad (9\text{-}2.10)$$

The complete solution is given by the equation

$$v(x,t) = \begin{cases} V_0 \operatorname{erfc}\left(\frac{x}{2}\sqrt{\frac{RC}{t}}\right) & 0 \le t \le T \\ V_0 \left[\operatorname{erfc}\left(\frac{x}{2}\sqrt{\frac{RC}{t}}\right) - \operatorname{erfc}\left(\frac{x}{2}\sqrt{\frac{RC}{t-T}}\right)\right] & T \le t < \infty \end{cases} \qquad (9\text{-}2.11)$$

The form of the diffusion pulse along the line may be built up by the proper combination of the time response functions appropriate to each portion of the solution, as shown in Fig. 9-2.2. Clearly, the form of the pulse will depend on the duration of the input pulse.

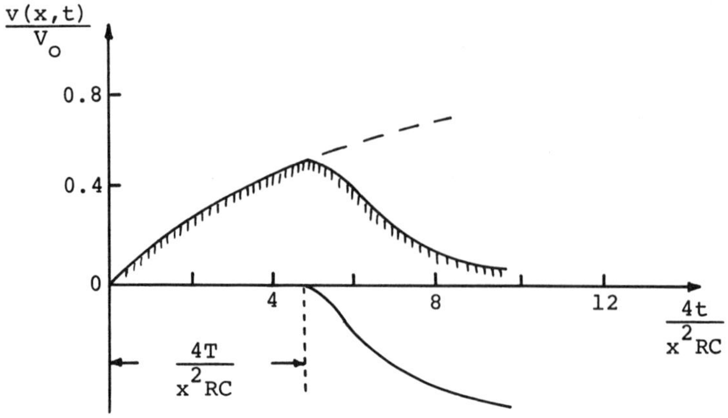

Figure 9-2.2. Diffusion of a pulse on an electrical cable.

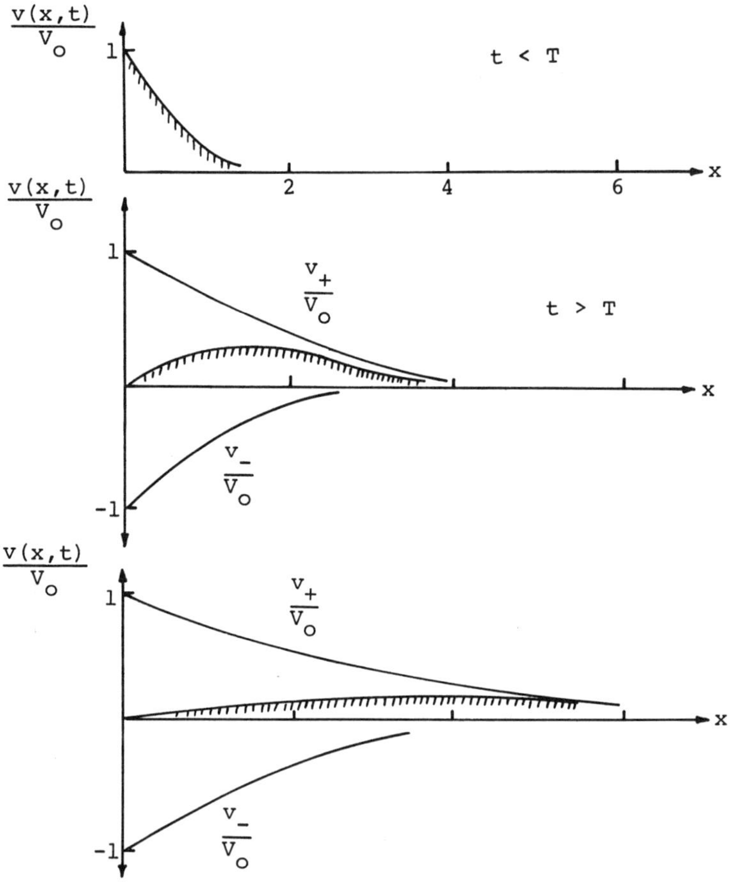

Figure 9-2.3. Time portrait of pulses of different duration.

Other curves of interest are those that show the character of the response at a given instant at various points along the line. Such curves are given in Fig. 9-2.3. These show that the pulse is seriously distorted both with distance along the line and with time. Clearly, such a cable will be a rather poor channel for transmitting electrical signals. However, cables have other desirable attributes and are used extensively. It is necessary to include "repeaters" at periodic intervals to reshape and amplify the signals to approximate the original form.

Example 9-2.1. Find the voltage in an RC finite transmission line subject to the following boundary and initial conditions: $v(x,0) = f(x) \quad 0 \le x \le \ell$; $v(0,t) = 0$; and $v(\ell,t) = 0$.

Solution. Using Eq. (9-2.1) we obtain the separated equation

$$\frac{1}{D_\ell}\frac{dT}{dt}\frac{1}{T} = \frac{d^2X}{dx^2}\frac{1}{X} = -\lambda^2 \qquad (9\text{-}2.12)$$

where $v(x,t) = X(x)\,T(x)$ and λ is a constant. From Eq. (9-2.12) we write the equations

$$\frac{d^2X}{dx^2} + \lambda^2 X = 0 \qquad \text{a)}$$
$$\frac{dT}{dt} + \lambda^2 D_\ell T = 0 \qquad \text{b)} \qquad (9\text{-}2.13)$$

The solutions to the last two equations are given by

$$X = A' \sin \lambda x + B' \cos \lambda x \qquad \text{a)}$$
$$T = C' e^{-\lambda^2 D_\ell t} \qquad \text{b)} \qquad (9\text{-}2.14)$$

The factors A', B' and C' are constants of integration. The solution, therefore, is given by

$$v(x,t) = (A \sin \lambda x + B \cos \lambda x)\, e^{-\lambda^2 D_\ell t} \qquad (A = A'C',\ B = B'C') \qquad (9\text{-}2.15)$$

Further, since our diffusion equation is linear, the most general solution is obtained by summing solutions of the type given by Eq. (9-2.15). Hence we have

$$v(x,t) = \sum_{m=1}^{\infty} (A_m \sin \lambda_m x + B_m \cos \lambda_m x)\, e^{-\lambda_m^2 D_\ell t} \qquad (9\text{-}2.16)$$

where the constants will be determined by imposing the initial and the boundary conditions. The boundary conditions $v(0,t) = 0$ and $v(\ell,t)$ imply that $B_m = 0$ and $\lambda_m = m\pi/\ell$. Equation (9-2.16) thus takes the form

$$v(x,t) = \sum_{m=1}^{\infty} A_m \sin \frac{m\pi}{\ell} x \, e^{-\frac{m^2\pi^2}{\ell^2} D_\ell t} \tag{9-2.17}$$

Apply next the initial condition, which requires that the following relation must be satisfied

$$f(x) = \sum_{m=1}^{\infty} A_m \sin \frac{m\pi}{\ell} x \tag{9-2.18}$$

This represents a Fourier series expansion of the function f(x). Multiply the last equation by sin $n\pi x/\ell$ dx and integrate from 0 to ℓ. Upon using the orthogonality properties of the sine functions we obtain the values of the unknown constants A_m

$$A_m = \frac{2}{\ell} \int_0^{\ell} f(x) \sin \left(\frac{m\pi}{\ell} x\right) dx \tag{9-2.19}$$

Our general solution is given by combining Eqs. (9-2.19) and (9-2.17). ΔΔΔ

9-3. Heat Diffusion

The discussion in Chap. 1 introduced the general aspects of heat diffusion. Thermal conductivity K_t (Watt/m $^\circ$C) was introduced as the proportionality constant that relates the thermal conduction flux density $\overline{q}$ (Watt/m^2) to the thermal gradient

$$\overline{q} = -K_t \nabla\Theta \tag{9-3.1}$$

where Θ is the temperature in deg $^\circ$C. This equation is the Fourier equation of heat conduction. If we proceed as in Sec. 9-1, we will find that

$$\nabla \cdot \overline{q} = -\left\{\begin{matrix}\text{time rate of change of} \\ \text{energy concentration}\end{matrix}\right\} = -\frac{\partial(c_t\rho_v\Theta)}{\partial t} = -c_t\rho_v \frac{\partial\Theta}{\partial t} \tag{9-3.2}$$

where c_t is the specific heat of the material (Joule/kg $^\circ$K) and ρ_v is the mass density (kg/m^3). By combining these two equations there results

$$\nabla^2\Theta = \frac{c_t\rho_v}{K_t}\frac{\partial\Theta}{\partial t} = \frac{1}{D_t}\frac{\partial\Theta}{\partial t} \tag{9-3.3}$$

which is seen to be of the same form as Eq. (9-1.9).

Example 9-3.1. Find the heat in an infinite slab if the following boundary and initial conditions are imposed:

$$\frac{\partial^2\Theta}{\partial x^2} - \frac{1}{D_t}\frac{\partial\Theta}{\partial t} = 0 \qquad \text{for} \quad -\infty < x < \infty, \quad t > 0 \qquad \text{a)}$$

$$\Theta(x,0) = f(x) \qquad \text{b)} \qquad (9\text{-}3.4)$$

$$\Theta(x,t) \quad \text{bounded} \qquad \text{c)}$$

Solution. Since the domain is infinite in both directions we can use the Fourier transform technique in Eq. (9-3.4a). We obtain

$$\frac{\partial\tilde{\Theta}(\omega,t)}{\partial t} + \omega^2 D_t \,\tilde{\Theta}(\omega,t) = 0 \qquad \text{a)}$$

$$\tilde{\Theta}(\omega,0) = \tilde{f}(\omega) \qquad \text{b)} \qquad (9\text{-}3.5)$$

whose solution is

$$\tilde{\Theta}(\omega,t) = \tilde{f}(\omega)\, e^{-\omega^2 D_t t} \qquad (9\text{-}3.6)$$

Assume $\tilde{f}(\omega)$ to be bounded [f(x) must be absolutely integrable] and take the inverse Fourier transform. Using Fourier transform tables, we find that $e^{-\omega^2 D_t t}$ is the Fourier transform of

$$\frac{1}{\sqrt{4\pi D_t t}}\, e^{-x^2/4D_t t}$$

Therefore, the inverse transform of Eq. (9-3.6) is the convolution of the two inverse transform functions $\mathscr{F}^{-1}\{\tilde{f}(\omega)\} = f(x)$ and $\mathscr{F}^{-1}\{e^{-\omega^2 D_t t}\}$. The final result is

$$\Theta(x,t) = \frac{1}{2\pi}\int_{-\infty}^{\infty} e^{+j\omega x}\,\tilde{f}(\omega)e^{-\omega^2 D_t t}\,d\omega = \frac{1}{\sqrt{4\pi D_t t}}\int_{-\infty}^{\infty} f(z')e^{-(x-z')^2/4D_t t}\,dz' \qquad (9\text{-}3.7)$$

ΔΔΔ

Example 9-3.2. Find the diffusion of thermal energy away from a small spherical concentrated region of heat into an infinite space.

Solution. An example of the stated problem is that involving a large spherical region of water at a uniform temperature Θ_1 into which a small steel ball at elevated temperature Θ_b is introduced at the center. We assume that the diameter of the spherical water tank is large compared with the dimension of the steel ball. The situation is also analogous to the introduction of a charge on the inner conductor of a spherical capacitor with a leaky dielectric. It is also analogous to the introduction of a droplet of a chemical dye into still water, and then having the dye diffuse outward spherically.

The basic problem is specified by the diffusion equation, Eq. (9-3.3), which becomes, for the assumed spherical symmetry,

$$\frac{1}{r^2}\frac{\partial}{\partial r}\left(r^2\frac{\partial\Theta}{\partial r}\right) = \frac{1}{D_t}\frac{\partial\Theta}{\Theta t} \qquad (9\text{-}3.8)$$

We proceed by Laplace transform methods, which becomes after transformation

$$\frac{1}{r^2}\frac{d}{dr}\left(r^2\frac{d\tilde{\Theta}(r,s)}{dr}\right) = \frac{s}{D_t}\tilde{\Theta}(r,s) \qquad (9\text{-}3.9)$$

This equation is suggestive of the Helmholtz equation for spherical waves, and so we examine whether a solution of the form

$$\tilde{\Theta}(r,s) = \frac{e^{-\beta r}}{r} \qquad (9\text{-}3.10)$$

will satisfy Eq. (9-3.9). Introducing Eq. (9-3.10) into Eq. (9-3.9) we find that Eq. (9-3.10) is an acceptable solution provided that

$$\beta = \pm\sqrt{\frac{s}{D_t}} \qquad (9\text{-}3.11)$$

Since we must have a decaying function as $r \to \infty$, the solution to the transformed equation is chosen as

$$\tilde{\Theta}(r,s) = A\,\frac{e^{-r\sqrt{s/D_t}}}{r} \qquad (9\text{-}3.12)$$

The time solution, which is the inverse Laplace transform of this function, is given by

$$\Theta(r,t) = \frac{A}{r}\left[\frac{r}{\sqrt{4\pi D_t t^3}}\,e^{-(r^2/4D_t t)}\right] = \frac{A}{\sqrt{4\pi D_t t^3}}\,e^{-(r^2/4D_t t)} \qquad (9\text{-}3.13)$$

To evaluate the constant A in this equation, we use the fact that the total energy to the system is a constant. This condition requires that

$$U = \int_0^\infty c_t\rho_v\Theta\, 4\pi r^2 dr = 4\pi D_t c_t \rho_v A \qquad (9\text{-}3.14)$$

where U denotes this total energy, and with the integral $\int_0^\infty x^2 e^{-ax^2} dx = (1/4a)\sqrt{\pi/a}$. From this we find that

$$A = \frac{U}{4\pi D_t c_t \rho_v} \qquad (9\text{-}3.15)$$

The final solution to this radial diffusion problem is given by the expression

$$\Theta(r,t) = \frac{U}{4\pi D_t c_t \rho_v \sqrt{4\pi D_t t^3}}\,e^{-r^2/4D_t t} \qquad (9\text{-}3.16)$$

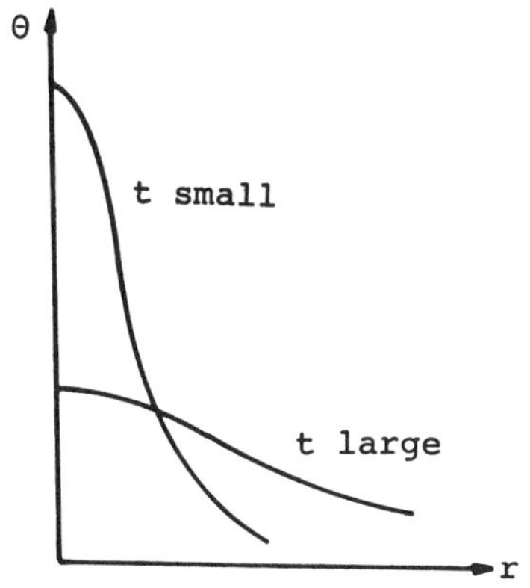

Figure 9-3.1. Diffusion of heat in a spherical system.

Curves showing the form of the variation specified by this equation are given in Fig. 9-3.1. These curves show that the spherical "diffusion cloud" grows uniformly with time. From the equation, the approximate time for the diffusion cloud to reach r = 1 cm for a "point" source in copper is about 0.1 sec. For HCl introduced in water, the corresponding time is about 2 hours.

9-4. Minority Carrier Transport in Semiconductors

Diffusion plays a very important role in semiconductors, and is intimately involved in the theory of semiconductor devices. The process is somewhat complicated and each of the contributing terms must be studied carefully.

Before considering the immediate matter of carrier transport, it is well to discuss semiconductor materials. A doped semiconductor material consists of pure silicon or germanium (valence 4) to which a small amount of trivalent or pentavalent impurity has been added. To be specific, let us suppose that pure silicon has had a small amount of pentavalent impurity (phosphorous, arsenic, or antimony) added to the melt during the refining process. These impurity atoms will replace silicon atoms in their crystal lattice positions. However, since only four electrons are required to complete the silicon covalent bonds, the fifth electron is essentially an excess electron. The doped silicon is then said to be n-type owing to the excess of electrons distributed throughout its volume.

Now suppose that a small dot of indium antimonide is placed on a sample of n-type silicon, and then the combination is properly heat treated. Some trivalent indium will displace silicon atoms. As a result, some of the silicon valence electrons remains without covalent attachment, and this electron is loosely bound to the parent atom. It may move in the semiconductor upon the application of a field.

However, migration of the electron will leave behind a silicon atom lacking one electron. This positively charged atom is called a *hole*. But the hole may migrate by having an electron from one atom recombine with the hole in another silicon atom, thereby neutralizing the positive charge but at the same time producing a hole in the atom from which the electron originates. For the case here discussed in conduction is by holes which are called the *minority* carriers. In thermal equilibrium the carrier densities are uniquely determined.

In general, the hole concentration in the body of the material is a function of both time and distance. To examine the situation, we shall make the following assumptions:

1. The flow is one dimensional;
2. Surface effects are neglected except as they may be involved in the mean lifetime of electrons or holes;
3. The transition layer between the p side of the junction and the n side of the junction is small compared to the diffusion length;
4. Applied voltages appear across the transition region;
5. The x-dimensions of the n and p regions are large compared with the diffusion length in the respective regions.

Now consider a small rectangular control volume in the transition layer. Conservation of charge requires that

$$\overset{(1)}{\left\{\begin{array}{l}\text{Net hole current}\\ \text{flow out of the}\\ \text{volume}\end{array}\right.} + \overset{(2)}{\begin{array}{l}\text{holes lost in}\\ \text{volume due to}\\ \text{recombination}\\ \text{per unit time}\end{array}} - \overset{(3)}{\left.\begin{array}{l}\text{holes generated}\\ \text{in volume per}\\ \text{unit time}\end{array}\right\}} = q \overset{(4)}{\left\{\begin{array}{l}\text{time rate of}\\ \text{decrease in}\\ \text{holes in}\\ \text{volume}\end{array}\right\}}$$

We wish to examine each of these terms in detail.

Term 1. If j_p denotes the hole current density at the left face of the control volume, then we may write

$$\text{Decrease within volume} = [j_p(x+dx)-j_p(x)]\ dy\ dz = (j_p + \frac{\partial j_p}{\partial x} dx - j_p) dy\ dz$$

$$= \frac{\partial j_p}{\partial x} dx\ dy\ dz$$

Term 2. If τ_p denotes the mean lifetime of the holes (the time before recombination will occur) and p denotes the density of holes, then p/τ_p equals the holes per second lost by recombination per unit volume. Then due to recombination, with q denoting the charge per particle,

$$\text{Loss within volume} = q\ dx\ dy\ dz\ \frac{p}{\tau_p}\ \text{Coulomb/sec.}$$

Term 3. If g denotes the thermal rate of generation of hole-electron pairs per unit volume, then

Increase within volume = q dx dy dz g

Term 4. The hole density changes with time because of the three terms.

$$\text{Decrease within volume} = q\,dx\,dy\,dz\,\frac{\partial p}{\partial t}$$

These terms are combined to give the expression

$$\left(\frac{\partial j_p}{\partial x} + \frac{qp}{\tau_p} - qg\right) dx\,dy\,dz = -q\,dx\,dy\,dz\,\frac{\partial p}{\partial t} \tag{9-4.1}$$

It is now noted that the hole current is the sum of the diffusion current and the drift current. The diffusion current density is proportional to the concentration gradient, in accordance with Fick's law. For p-type material this is

$$j_{p1} = -qD_p\,\frac{\partial p}{\partial x} \tag{9-4.2}$$

where D_p is the diffusion constant (m^2/sec). In addition, when holes are in an electric field, they will drift in the field. The directed drift velocity in an electric field is directly proportional to E, the proportionality factor is μ_p, the mobility. Then the drift current density is

$$j_{p2} = (p\mu_p q)E = \sigma_p E \tag{9-4.3}$$

where σ_p is the conductivity due to the holes, and where E is the electric field within the volume in the X-direction. Thus the total hole current density is

$$j_p = j_{p1} + j_{p2} = -qD_p\,\frac{\partial p}{\partial x} + qp\mu_p E \tag{9-4.4}$$

Further, if the semiconductor is in thermal equilibrium with its surroundings and is subject to no applied fields, the hole density will attain a constant value p_0. Under these conditions $j_p = 0$ and $\partial p/\partial t = 0$, so that from the above

$$g = \frac{p_0}{\tau_p} \tag{9-4.5}$$

This expression indicates that the rate at which holes are generated thermally just equals the rate at which holes are lost due to recombination. Representative data for holes and electrons are contained in the following table.

Table 9-4.1. Physical Data on Semiconductors

	Ge	Si
μ_n (cm^2/Volt-sec)	3800	1300
μ_p (cm^2/Volt-sec)	1800	500
D_n (cm^2/sec)	95	33
D_p (cm^2/sec)	45	13
τ_p electrons (microsec)	100-1000	50-500
τ_p holes (microsec)	100-1000	50-500

Equations (9-4.1), (9-4.4) and (9-4.5) are combined to give, as the continuity equation

$$\frac{\partial p}{\partial t} = -\frac{p-p_o}{\tau_p} + D_p \frac{\partial^2 p}{\partial x^2} - \mu_p \frac{\partial(pE)}{\partial x} \tag{9-4.6}$$

Of course, to specify clearly that we are considering holes in the n-type material, we might add the subscripts n to p and p_o, in which case the equation becomes

$$\frac{\partial p_n}{\partial t} = -\frac{p_n-p_{no}}{\tau_p} + D_p \frac{\partial^2 p_n}{\partial x^2} - \mu_p \frac{\partial(p_n E)}{\partial x} \tag{9-4.7}$$

This is a nonlinear equation, with E dependent on p. Two cases prove to be particularly important:

1. For small injection densities of carriers E = 0 and steady state has been reached. Thus $\partial p_n/\partial t = 0$ and Eq. (9-4.7) becomes

$$\frac{\partial^2 p_n}{\partial x^2} = \frac{p_n - p_{no}}{D_p \tau_p} \tag{9-4.8}$$

The acceptable solution of this equation is of the form

$$p_n - p_{no} = A\, e^{-x/\sqrt{\tau_p D_p}} \tag{9-4.9}$$

Further, $p_n - p_{no}\big|_{x=0} = P(0)$, the hole concentration at the boundary, so that

$$p_n - p_{no} = P(0)\, e^{-x/\sqrt{\tau_p D_p}} \tag{9-4.10}$$

The quantity $\sqrt{\tau_p D_p}$ is often called the *diffusion length* of the minority carriers, and is written

$$L_p = \sqrt{\tau_p D_p} \tag{9-4.11}$$

Since τ_p for holes in germanium is on the order of 200 μsec, then L_p for holes in n-type Ge is on the order of $\sqrt{2 \times 10^{-4} \times 5 \times 10^{-3}} \doteq 10^{-3}$ m.

2. We again choose E = 0 but now assume that the concentration is independent of x. This is the situation when radiation falls uniformly over the surface of a semiconductor and raises the concentration above the thermal equilibrium value. At time t = 0 the illumination is removed. How does the concentration vary with time? The controlling equation in this case is

$$\frac{\partial p_n}{\partial t} = -\frac{p_n - p_{no}}{\tau_p} \tag{9-4.12}$$

This equation, which is a measure of the excess hole population is readily solved to give

$$p_n = p_{no} + p(0)\, e^{-t/\tau_p} \tag{9-4.13}$$

where $p(0) = p_n - p_{no}\big|_{t=0}$ is the concentration of holes at t = 0. Thus the excess hole density decays with lifetime τ_p.

9-5. Diffusion of Electrons in Plasmas

A number of different models have been developed to describe the characteristics of plasmas, the model used in a particular case depending on the density of particles making up the plasma. An important model is called the *hydrodynamic* or *continuum model*. In this model, the plasma is treated as an interacting mixture of electrons, ions, and neutral molecules, each with its separate set of mass-, momentum-, and energy-transport equations. We shall assume a simplified model, with the basic assumption that the plasma consists only of electrons and ions and that only the electrons contribute to the fluid characteristics of the mixture. This model is valid if we are interested in studying phenomena whose frequency is characteristically high. For this model the mass-conservation equation (continuity equation) and the momentum-conservation equation for the electron fluid are [see Eqs. (7-8.4) and (7-8.13)]

$$\frac{\partial \rho}{\partial t} + \nabla \cdot (\rho \overline{v}) = 0 \tag{9-5.1}$$

and

$$\frac{d\overline{v}}{dt} = \frac{\partial \overline{v}}{\partial t} + \overline{v} \cdot \nabla \overline{v} = -\frac{e}{m}(\overline{E} + \overline{v} \times \overline{B}) - \frac{1}{\rho}\nabla p - \nu \overline{v} \tag{9-5.2}$$

where $\nu = \Sigma\, \nu_{ep}$ is the total electron collision frequency for momentum transfer with all types of other particles, and where the pressure-gradient term provides a force which tends to smooth out inhomogeneities in the fluid density, and produces either longitudinal waves or a diffusion of particles. If we assume $\overline{E}$ and $\overline{B}$ to be zero, Θ to be constant, and the electron number density n_e to be slightly nonuniform, we have [see Eq. (7-9.13)]

$$\begin{aligned} n_e(\overline{r},t) &= n_o + n(\overline{r},t) \qquad n \ll n_o \\ p(\overline{r},t) &= (n_o+n)K\Theta \end{aligned} \tag{9-5.3}$$

where $K = 1.38 \times 10^{-38}$ Joule/^{o}K is the Boltzmann gas constant. By combining Eq. (9-5.3) with Eqs. (9-5.1) and (9-5.2) and neglecting second and higher order terms, we obtain

$$\frac{\partial n}{\partial t} + n_o \nabla \cdot \overline{v} = 0 \qquad \text{a)}$$

$$\frac{\partial \overline{v}}{\partial t} + \overline{v} \cdot \nabla\overline{v} = -\frac{K\Theta}{mn_o} \nabla n - \nu\overline{v} \qquad \text{b)} \tag{9-5.4}$$

since

$$\rho = mn_e; \qquad p = \frac{K\Theta\rho}{m}$$

To make the second equation linear, we must assume that $\overline{v}$ is a first order quantity. This implies that $\overline{v} \cdot \nabla\overline{v}$ is a second-order quantity, and can therefore be neglected compared to $\partial\overline{v}/\partial t$ and $\overline{v}$. By taking the divergence of Eq. (9-5.4b) without the term $\overline{v} \cdot \nabla\overline{v}$ and using Eq. (9-5.4a), and multiplying by n_o, the result is

$$\frac{\partial n}{\partial t} = D_e \nabla^2 n - \frac{1}{\nu} \frac{\partial^2 n}{\partial t^2} \tag{9-5.5}$$

where

$$D_e = \frac{K\Theta}{m\nu}$$

is the *electron diffusion coefficient*. Now denote by τ and L the characteristic time and length of the system over which n changes. This means that the spatial derivatives are on the order of 1/L and the time derivatives are on the order of $1/\tau$. Subject to these approximations, Eq. (9-5.5) leads to the comparable approximations

$$\frac{\partial n}{\partial t} \cong \frac{n}{\tau} \qquad D_e \nabla^2 n \cong \frac{D_e n}{L^2} \qquad \frac{1}{\nu} \frac{\partial^2 n}{\partial t^2} \cong \frac{n}{\nu\tau^2} \tag{9-5.6}$$

By comparing the first and the last terms, it is observed that if $\nu\tau \gg 1$ the last term in Eq. (9-5.5a) can be neglected, thus leading to the diffusion equation

$$\frac{\partial n}{\partial t} = D_e \nabla^2 n \qquad (9\text{-}5.7)$$

Note that this equation, upon introducing the characteristic lengths, leads to the *diffusion characteristic time constant*

$$\tau_D = \frac{L^2}{D_e} \qquad (9\text{-}5.8)$$

Example 9-5.1. Assuming a plane wave excitation to a medium described by a diffusion equation, find the phase and damping factors.

Solution. Introducing a solution into Eq. (9-5.7) of the form $e^{j(kr-\omega t)}$ we obtain the relation (refer to Ex. 9-1.1)

$$k^2 D_e = -j\omega \qquad (9\text{-}5.9)$$

Setting $k = k' + jk''$ we find the two factors to be, respectively,

$$k' = \sqrt{\frac{\omega}{2D_e}} \qquad \text{a)}$$
$$(9\text{-}5.10)$$
$$k'' = \sqrt{\frac{\omega}{2D_e}} \qquad \text{b)}$$

ΔΔΔ

9-6. ELECTROMAGNETIC FIELDS IN A CYLINDRICAL CONDUCTOR

For a homogeneous isotropic conducting medium, the general wave equation is [see Eq. (8-8.4)]

$$\nabla^2\overline{E} = \mu\varepsilon \frac{\partial^2\overline{E}}{\partial t^2} + \mu\sigma \frac{\partial \overline{E}}{\partial t} \qquad (9\text{-}6.1)$$

The damping effect of the wave motion is due to the term $\mu\sigma\, \partial\overline{E}/\partial t$. In the case of metal conductors the first term on the right side of Eq. (9-6.1) may be neglected in comparison with the dissipative term. Writing $\overline{J}$ for $\sigma\overline{E}$, Eq. (9-6.1) for a harmonic field takes the form

$$\nabla^2\overline{J} = -j\omega\mu\sigma\overline{J} \qquad (9\text{-}6.2)$$

For a symmetric current density in the ϕ direction and uniform in the Z direction, Eq. (9-6.2) expressed in cylindrical coordinates takes the form

$$r^2 \frac{d^2R}{dr^2} + r\frac{dR}{dr} + j\omega\mu\sigma\, r^2 R = 0 \qquad (9\text{-}6.3)$$

where $\bar{a}_z J = R(r)e^{-j\omega t}\,\bar{a}_z$. Equation (9-6.3) is the standard form of Bessel's equation of zero order and its solution is given by

$$R(r) = AJ_o(\sqrt{j}\ kr) \tag{9-6.4}$$

where $k = \sqrt{\omega\mu\sigma}$ and A can be evaluated in terms of the current density at the surface. Expanding the zero-order Bessel function into its series representation we obtain [see Eq. (4-3.7a)]

$$R(r) = A\{1-j\left(\frac{kr}{2}\right)^2 - \frac{1}{(2!)^2}\left(\frac{kr}{2}\right)^4 + j\,\frac{1}{(3!)^3}\left(\frac{kr}{2}\right)^6 + \ldots\} \tag{9-6.5}$$

The real part of $J_o(\sqrt{j}\ kr)$ as given in Eq. (9-6.5) is called $\mathrm{Ber}(\sqrt{j}\ kr)$, and the imaginary part is called $\mathrm{Bei}(\sqrt{j}\ kr)$. Thus Eq. (9-6.5) can be written

$$R(r) = A\ \{\mathrm{Ber}\ kr - j\mathrm{Bei}\ kr\} \tag{9-6.6}$$

The functions Ber (x) and Bei (x) are tabulated in many reference tables. The amplitude of the function R(r) is $R_o = A\ \{\mathrm{Ber}^2 kr + \mathrm{Bei}^2 kr\}^{1/2}$ and its phase is $\Phi = -\tan^{-1}(\mathrm{Bei}\ kr/\mathrm{Ber}\ kr)$. Therefore, the current density in the conductors takes the form

$$J(r,t) = R_o\ e^{j\Phi}\ e^{-j\omega t} \tag{9-6.7}$$

Figure 9-6.1 represents the Ber and Bei functions versus kr.

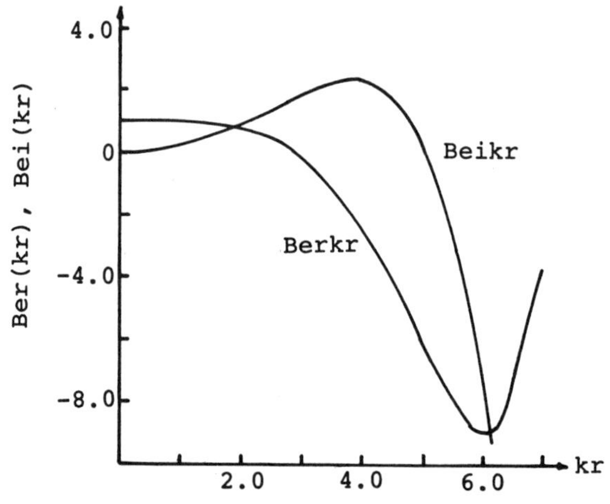

Figure 9-6.1. The functions Ber(kr) and Bei(kr). (Both curves oscillate at higher values of kr.)

REVIEW QUESTIONS

1. What does Fick's law state?
2. What is the main difference between a wave equation and a diffusion equation?
3. What type of transmission line is described by a diffusion equation for its voltage (or current) representation?
4. If we increase the R of a transmission line, is the velocity of a pulse increased or decreased? Justify your answer.
5. Specify the Fourier equation of heat conduction.
6. What are the holes; the minority carriers; in semiconductors?
7. What does the diffusion length of the minority carriers indicate?
8. What is the diffusion characteristic time constant of electrons in plasmas?

PROBLEMS

9-1.1. Find the conditions under which the diffusion equation for electromagnetic fields is given by

$$\nabla^2\bar{E} = \mu\sigma \frac{\partial \bar{E}}{\partial t}.$$

9-1.2. Find the conditions under which the diffusion equation for the transmission line without sources is given by

$$\frac{\partial^2 v}{\partial x^2} = RC \frac{\partial v}{\partial t} = \frac{1}{D_\ell} \frac{\partial v}{\partial t} .$$

9-1.3. Consider that a factory discharges hydrochloric acid onto the shores of a lake at a rate which can be approximated by a sinusoidal function, with a one day cycle. If $\eta(x,0) = 0$ and the peak concentration is 10^3 kg/m^3, when will the hydrochloric acid reach the other side of the lake, a distance of 10 km away? What is the peak concentration?

9-1.4. Repeat Prob. 9-1.3 but assume now that initially the factory dumped 10^4 kg/m^3 into the lake; i.e., $\eta(x,0) = 10^4$.

9-1.5. HCl is discharged sinusoidally in water in a 1/2 day cycle, and sugar is added in a 2.5 day cycle. Both are assumed to have the same peak value. Which of the two pollutants has a greater concentration at a distance of 150 m?

9-2.1. Using the Laplace transform technique, (a) find the voltage on an RC semi-infinite transmission line with boundary and initial conditions: $v(x,0) = 0$, $x > 0$; $v(0,t) = V_0\delta(t)$, and (b) sketch the voltage versus x at different values of t.

[Hint: $\mathscr{L}^{-1}\{e^{-a\sqrt{s}}\} = \frac{a}{2\sqrt{\pi t^3}} e^{-a^2/4t}$]

9-2.2. Discuss how the magnitude of the diffusion coefficient $D_\ell = 1/RC$ affects the propagation of a pulse on a transmission line.

9-2.3. Find: (a) the voltage on an RC line given in Ex. 9-2.1 if $f(x) = 2 \sin \pi x/\ell$; (b) sketch on one sheet the voltage in the line at three different instants of time.

9-2.4. A voltage function $v(0,t) = 10\, u_{-1}(t)$ is applied to an $RC = 10^{-5}$ transmission line. Find and plot the voltage along the line for the times: $t = 10^{-4}$ sec; $t = 10^{-6}$ sec.

9-2.5. A voltage pulse function $v(0,t) = 10[u_{-1}(t) - u_{-1}(t - 10^{-6})]$ is applied to an $RC = 10^{-6}$ transmission line. Find and plot the voltage at x = 10 m versus t, for $t < 10^{-6}$ sec, and $t > 10^{-6}$ sec.

9-2.6. An initial voltage distribution $f(x) = x(1-x)$ exists on an $RC = 10^{-5}$ line one meter long. Plot the voltage across the line at the times: t = 0 sec. and $t = 10^{-7}$ sec.

9-3.1. At time t = 0 the temperature distribution in an infinite slab is

$$\Theta(x,0) = \begin{cases} 1 & -1 \le x \le 1 \\ 0 & \text{otherwise} \end{cases}$$

Find the temperature along the slab at $t = 10^{-6}$ sec, also at $t = 10^{-4}$ sec. The diffusion coefficient is $D_t = 10^{-4}\ m^2 sec^{-1}$.

9-3.2. Find the heat distribution for a situation similar to that described in Pr. 9-3.1 if $f(x) = e^{-x^2}$. Sketch the temperature at three different instants of time.

[Ans: $\sqrt{\frac{\alpha}{1+\alpha}}\, e^{-\frac{\alpha}{1+\alpha}x^2}$, $\alpha = \frac{1}{4D_t t}$]

9-3.3. Find the temperature $\Theta(r,t)$ if the small sphere of Ex. 9-3.2 has a radius R and is kept at a constant temperature $\Theta(R,t) = \Theta_R$ by a chemical reaction.

9-4.1. Find the distance from the boundary of Si material at which the excess hole concentration has decreased by 30%.

9-5.1. Electrons are injected into the F-layer of the ionosphere periodically with a period of 1 msec. Find the phase velocity of the electron wave in the medium. The electron temperature of the ionosphere is 500° K and the collision frequency is $\nu = 10^3\ sec^{-1}$. How much does the wave decay in a distance of 10 km from its source point?

9-5.2. Find the electron density $n(x,t)$ if $n(x,0) = n_0(x) = N\delta(x)$.

[Ans: $e^{-x^2/4D_e t}/N(4\pi D_e t)^{1/2}$]

9-5.3. Sketch the phase and group velocities for a plane wave in a medium which is described by a diffusion equation.

9-6.1. Using Fig. 9-6.1 sketch the amplitude-phase diagram for the current vector $\overline{a}_z J(kr)$ versus kr for two different conductivities σ_1 and σ_2, $\sigma_1 < \sigma_2$.

9-6.2. Find the phase of a sinusoidal current in an aluminum cylinder at a distance of 0.5 cm from the center. The frequency of the current is 10^3 Hz.

CHAPTER 10

WAVES IN UNBOUNDED MEDIUMS

Our discussion of wave problems in Chap. 8 indicated that the basic wave equation is of the form

$$\nabla^2\psi = \frac{1}{c^2}\frac{\partial^2\psi}{\partial t^2}$$

Other terms may appear in the equation, but the presence of second order terms in both space and time will insure that waves are specified. In this equation the function ψ may be a vector or a scalar, the resulting waves being vector or scalar waves, respectively. When ψ denotes mechanical displacement, this equation describes the balance between the net flux of force in a given region and the consequent inertial force. In this case it is a restatement of Newton's law. For electromagnetic waves the equation will specify the propagation of plane waves. This chapter will contain a study of a variety of problems, some of more complex nature, which are described in wave terms.

We shall find that the properties of the region and the medium in which electromagnetic waves propagate will have a marked influence on the waves. When the medium is homogeneous, isotropic and non-conducting, the problem is relatively simple, and the waves are propagated without attenuation, without dispersion, and without changes in polarization (words whose meaning will be clarified in what follows). When the medium is homogeneous, isotropic and conducting, an attenuation of the propagated waves occur, but the wave properties remain otherwise unchanged. If the propagation is in a conducting material medium, then the situation becomes somewhat more complicated since now the effective permittivity is a complex quantity and a function of the frequency. As a result, waves of different frequency are differently propagated, and dispersion results. If the medium is non-conducting but is crystalline, then polarization effects must be taken into account since the permittivity is a tensor quantity and is an explicit function of the frequency. As a result, the polarization properties of the waves will be affected. In nonisotropic and dispersive mediums many types of waves can be present, each of which propagates with different characteristics. The addition of external electromagnetic fields will also influence the propagation properties. If the medium is composed of a series of fixed glass lenses which are uniformly or nonuniformly spaced, a rather different set of results arise.

In short, electromagnetic and also acoustic waves may be propagated in a wide variety of mediums, and many such special mediums are encountered in nature or artificially produced, often for practical devices. The complete description may be quite complicated but the importance warrants the study. A number of such cases will be considered in this chapter.

10-1. Plane Waves

Some useful aspects of the general solutions of the wave equation are possible by considering the simple one-dimensional case in which $\psi(x,t)$ is a function of x and t only. Specifically, we shall consider a simple one-dimensional electromagnetic field $\bar{E} = \bar{a}_y E_y$ in a homogeneous, isotropic, and nonconducting medium. In this case, Eq. (8-8.4) becomes, since $\sigma = 0$,

$$\frac{\partial^2 E_y}{\partial x^2} = \mu\varepsilon \frac{\partial^2 E_y}{\partial t^2} = \frac{1}{c^2} \frac{\partial^2 E_y}{\partial t^2} \tag{10-1.1}$$

where $c = \dfrac{1}{\sqrt{\mu\varepsilon}}$.

A general solution to this partial differential equation is conveniently obtained by Laplace transform methods. Let us, therefore, Laplace transform Eq. (10-1.1) in the time variable, assuming zero initial conditions. The result of this operation is the expression

$$\frac{d^2\tilde{E}_y(x,s)}{dx^2} = \frac{s^2}{c^2} \tilde{E}_y(x,s) \tag{10-1.2}$$

where the tilde ~ over $\tilde{E}_y$ indicates the Laplace transformed field vector. In the Laplace transforming process the time variable has been eliminated, thus yielding an ordinary second order differential equation. The solution of this differential equation is

$$\tilde{E}_y(x,s) = F_1(x)e^{\frac{sx}{c}} + F_2(s)\, e^{-\frac{sx}{c}} \tag{10-1.3}$$

where $F_1(s)$ and $F_2(s)$ are arbitrary functions of s. The corresponding time functions follow from the inversion properties of the Laplace transform. When use is made of the shifting theorem (see Appendix IV) the resulting time solution of Eq.

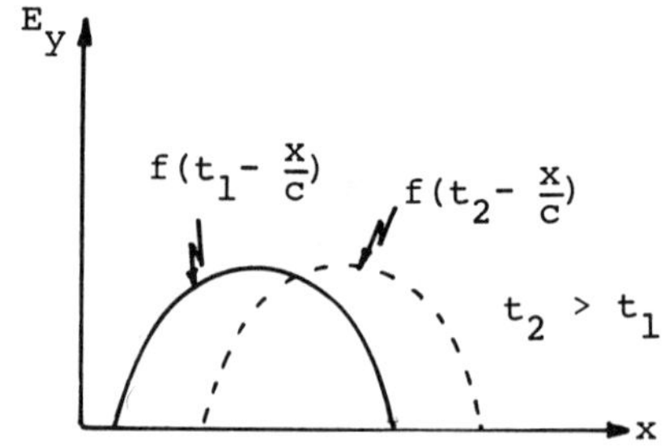

Figure 10-1.1. Properties of the function f(x-ct).

(10-1.3) is

$$E_y(x,t) = f_1(t + \frac{x}{c}) + f_2(t - \frac{x}{c}) \tag{10-1.4}$$

The nature of the solution is clarifed by the sketch in Fig. 10-1.1 which shows a graph of the function f versus x for the function f(x-ct) at two successive times t_1 and t_2, with $t_2 > t_1$. Based on this, the solution given in Eq. (10-1.4) comprises two waves that are moving in opposite directions. More details of such waves will be given in the following section.

10-2. Plane Electromagnetic Waves in a Homogeneous, Isotropic, Nonconducting Medium

As a more detailed example, we shall consider the case appropriate to Eq. (10-1.1) for a nonconducting medium, when $\sigma = 0$. Hence we begin with the vector wave equation (8-8.4)

$$\nabla^2\overline{E}(\overline{r},t) = \mu\varepsilon \frac{\partial^2\overline{E}(\overline{r},t)}{\partial t^2} \tag{10-2.1}$$

where the vector $\overline{r}$ indicates the field point (x,y,z). The field $\overline{E}$ is a function of spatial and time variables. We shall assume that the time variation of the field is harmonic, and of the form

$$\overline{E}(\overline{r},t) = \overline{E}(\overline{r})\, e^{-j\omega t} = \overline{E}\, e^{-j\omega t} \tag{10-2.2}$$

Thus the amplitude of the resulting wave function is specified by the vector wave equation

$$\nabla^2\overline{E} + \mu\varepsilon\omega^2\overline{E} = \nabla^2\overline{E} + k^2\overline{E} = 0 \tag{10-2.3}$$

where the term k, which is known as the *wave number*, is

$$k^2 = \left(\frac{2\pi}{\lambda}\right)^2 = \left(\frac{\omega}{v}\right)^2 = \omega^2\mu\varepsilon = \omega^2\mu_o\varepsilon_o\mu_r\varepsilon_r = \left(\frac{\omega}{c}\right)^2 \mu_r\varepsilon_r = k_o^2\eta^2 \tag{10-2.4}$$

with λ the wavelength of the radiation in the medium, v is the velocity of propagation of the wave, $c = 1/\sqrt{\mu_o\varepsilon_o}$ is the speed of light in vacuum $\doteq 3 \times 10^8$ m/sec, and $\eta = \sqrt{\mu_r\varepsilon_r}$ is the *index of refraction*. Equation (10-2.3) is known as the Helmholtz equation.

To examine the form of the waves that satisfy Eq. (10-2.3), we note from Eq. (10-1.4) that for an harmonic time variation $e^{-j\omega t}$, the resulting plane wave function will be of the form $e^{-j\omega(t-\zeta/v)} = e^{-j\omega t}\, e^{+j\omega\zeta/v}$ where ζ is the distance along the direction of propagation. But the quantity $\omega\zeta/v$ equal to a constant defines a plane perpendicular to the ζ axis, and it can be written in the form

$$\frac{\omega\zeta}{v} = k\bar{n} \cdot \bar{\zeta} = \bar{k} \cdot \bar{\zeta} \tag{10-2.5}$$

where $\bar{n}$ is the unit vector parallel to the direction of propagation, and $\bar{k}$ is the wave vector. The expected form of the solution of Eq. (10-2.3) will then be

$$\bar{E}(\bar{r}) = \bar{a}_1 E_o\, e^{j\bar{k}\cdot\bar{r}} = \bar{a}_1 E(\bar{r}) \tag{10-2.6}$$

where E_o is a complex constant that defines the amplitude and the initial phase of the field, i.e., $E_o = |E_o|\, e^{j\phi}$. In a similar way, had we begun with Eq. (8-8.5) for the magnetic field intensity, the development would have paralleled that above and we would find that the solution to the wave equation in amplitude

$$\nabla^2\bar{H} + k^2\bar{H} = 0$$

would be

$$\bar{H}(\bar{r}) = \bar{a}_2 H_o\, e^{j\bar{k}\cdot\bar{r}} = \bar{a}_2 H(\bar{r}) \tag{10-2.7}$$

In these equations $\bar{a}_1$ and $\bar{a}_2$ are constant unit vectors. Some aspects of these fields are illustrated in Fig. 10-2.1. This figure shows that a surface of constant phase is a plane normal to vector $\bar{k}$.

For the wave that propagates in the negative direction, the time factor will be $e^{-j\omega t}$ and the phase factor will assume the form $e^{-j\bar{k}\cdot\bar{r}}$. The actual fields that specify the wave response are, of course,

$$\bar{E}(\bar{r},t) = \text{Re}\,\{\bar{E}(\bar{r})\, e^{-j\omega t}\} = \frac{1}{2}\,[\bar{E}(\bar{r})\, e^{-j\omega t} + \bar{E}^*(\bar{r})\, e^{j\omega t}] \qquad \text{a)}$$

$$\bar{H}(\bar{r},t) = \text{Re}\,\{\bar{H}(\bar{r})\, e^{-j\omega t}\} = \frac{1}{2}\,[\bar{H}(\bar{r})\, e^{-j\omega t} + \bar{E}^*(\bar{r})\, e^{j\omega t}] \qquad \text{b)}$$

(10-2.8)

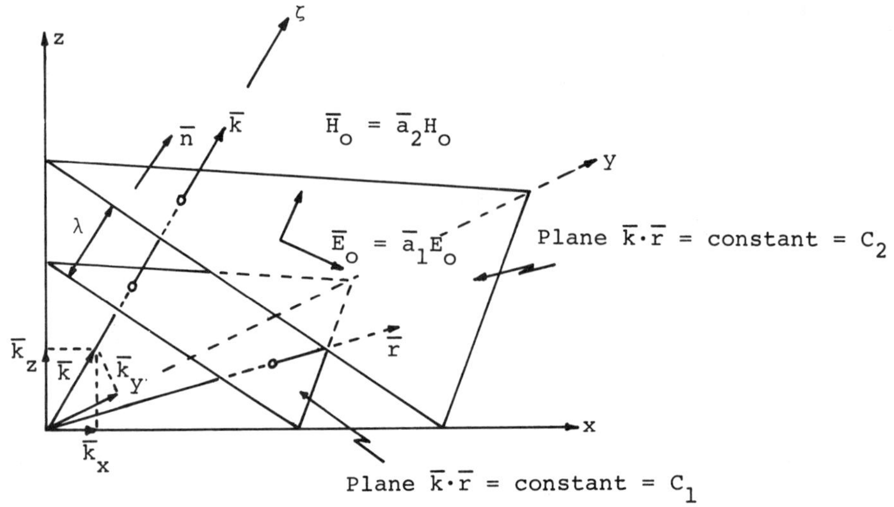

Figure 10-2.1. EM waves in homogeneous, isotropic, nonconducting medium.

We wish to establish other features of the fields. We can show from the designated solutions (10-2.6) and (10-2.7) (see Pr. 10-2.1) that

$$\begin{aligned} &\nabla \cdot \overline{E} = \pm j\,\overline{a}_1 \cdot \overline{k}\,E_o\,e^{j\overline{k}\cdot\overline{r}} \quad a) &&\nabla \cdot \overline{H} = \pm j\,\overline{a}_2 \cdot \overline{k}\,H_o\,e^{j\overline{k}\cdot\overline{r}} \quad c)\\ &\nabla \times \overline{E} = \pm j\,\overline{k} \times \overline{a}_1\,E_o\,e^{j\overline{k}\cdot\overline{r}} \quad b) &&\nabla \times \overline{H} = \pm j\,\overline{k} \times \overline{a}_2\,H_o\,e^{j\overline{k}\cdot\overline{r}} \quad d)\end{aligned} \tag{10-2.9}$$

From these the field conditions, $\nabla \cdot \overline{E} = 0$ and $\nabla \cdot \overline{H} = 0$ ($\nabla = \overline{n}\,\partial/\partial\zeta$), lead respectively to the conditions

$$\begin{aligned}\overline{a}_1 \cdot \overline{k} &= 0\\ \overline{a}_2 \cdot \overline{k} &= 0\end{aligned} \tag{10-2.10}$$

which show that *both* $\overline{E}$ and $\overline{H}$ are perpendicular to the direction of propagation. This type of plane wave is called a *transverse* electromagnetic wave, and is designated as a TEM wave. Furthermore, to find $\overline{H}$ we combine Eq. (10-2.6) with the curl condition on $\overline{E}$ through Maxwell's equations,

$$\nabla \times \overline{E} = j\omega\mu\,\overline{H}$$

then

$$j\overline{k} \times \overline{a}_1\,E = j\omega\mu\,\overline{H} \tag{10-2.11}$$

from which

$$\overline{H} = \frac{k}{\mu\omega}\,\overline{n} \times \overline{E} = \frac{\omega\sqrt{\mu\varepsilon}}{\mu\omega}\,\overline{n} \times \overline{E} = \sqrt{\frac{\mu}{\varepsilon}}\;\overline{n} \times \overline{E} \tag{10-2.12}$$

This shows that the field vector $\overline{E}$ is normal to the direction of propagation $\overline{k}$ and to the magnetic intensity $\overline{H}$. This requires that

$$\overline{n} \times \overline{a}_1 = \overline{a}_2 \tag{10-2.13}$$

Furthermore, since ε and μ are real quantities, then by Eq. (10-2.12) $\overline{H}$ and $\overline{E}$ are in time phase, and the ratio

$$\frac{E_o}{H_o} = \sqrt{\frac{\mu}{\varepsilon}} = \frac{\text{Volt/m}}{\text{Amp/m}} = \text{Ohm} = Z \tag{10-2.14}$$

has the dimensions of Ohm, and is referred to as the *intrinsic impedance* of the medium. For free space, the intrinsic impedance is

$$Z_o = \sqrt{\frac{\mu_o}{\varepsilon_o}} = 376.731 \doteq 120\,\pi\,\Omega \tag{10-2.15}$$

Example 10-2.1. Analyze the properties of a transverse wave that is propagating in such a direction that the fields are

$$\overline{E} = \overline{a}_y E \qquad \overline{H} = \overline{a}_z H$$

The medium is homogeneous, isotropic, and with zero conductance.

Solution. We begin with the general solutions (10-2.6) and (10-2.7) which are, in the present case, since $\overline{k} = \overline{a}_x k$

$$\overline{E}(\overline{r}) = \overline{a}_y E_o\, e^{j[k\overline{a}_x\cdot(\overline{a}_x x+\overline{a}_y y+\overline{a}_z z)]} = \overline{a}_y E_o\, e^{jkx}$$

and

$$\overline{H}(\overline{r}) = \overline{a}_z H_o\, e^{jkx} = \overline{a}_z \sqrt{\frac{\varepsilon}{\mu}}\, E_o\, e^{jkx}$$

From these we write the measurable fields

$$\overline{E}(\overline{r},t) = \text{Re}\,[\overline{E}(\overline{r},t)] = \overline{a}_y\,\text{Re}\,\{E_o\, e^{jkx}\, e^{-j\omega t}\} = \overline{a}_y E_o \cos(kx-\omega t)$$

$$\overline{H}(\overline{r},t) = \text{Re}\,\{\overline{H}(\overline{r},t)\} = \overline{a}_z\,\text{Re}\,\{\sqrt{\frac{\varepsilon}{\mu}}\, E_o\, e^{jkx}\, e^{-j\omega t}\} = \overline{a}_z \sqrt{\frac{\varepsilon}{\mu}}\, E_o \cos(kx-\omega t)$$

where it was assumed that E_o is real (no initial phase). A sketch of the function $\overline{E}(\overline{r},t)$ is given in the Fig. 10-2.2. The sketch indicates that the wave is propagating in the positive X-direction. v_{ph} is known as the *phase velocity*. To find this, we examine the phase factor; particularly, we examine $kx-\omega t$ = constant, which

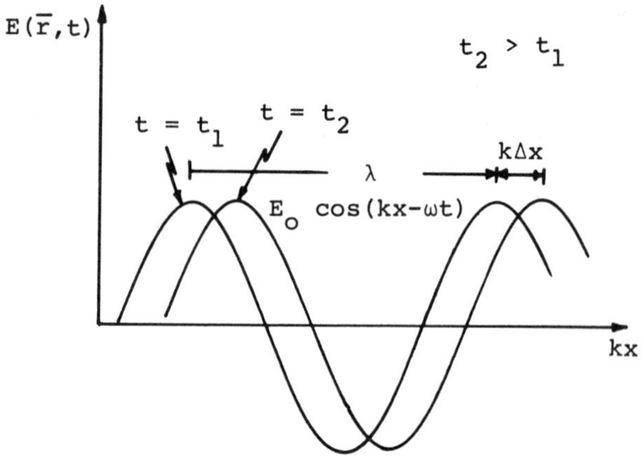

Figure 10-2.2. Illustration of wave propagation.

defines a plane perpendicular to the X axis at each instant of time. The speed of this plane is found by examining the rate of change of the coordinate with respect to time. This gives the relation

$$k\,dx = \omega\,dt$$

and so

$$v_{ph} = \frac{dx}{dt} = \frac{\omega}{k} = \frac{\omega}{\omega\sqrt{\mu_o\varepsilon_o\mu_r\varepsilon_r}} = \frac{c}{\sqrt{\mu_r\varepsilon_r}} = \frac{c}{\eta} \tag{10-2.16}$$

The average power that flows in the X direction is equal to [see Eq. (8-10.12)]

$$<\mathcal{S}_c> = \frac{1}{2}\,\mathrm{Re}\{\bar{a}_y \times \bar{a}_z\, E_o E_o^* \sqrt{\frac{\varepsilon}{\mu}}\} = \frac{1}{2}\,\bar{a}_x |E_o|^2 \sqrt{\frac{\varepsilon}{\mu}} = \frac{\bar{a}_x |E_o|^2}{2\,Z} \tag{10-2.17}$$

ΔΔΔ

Example 10-2.2. Analyze the properties of a transverse wave that is propagating on a string and which is excited by a force $F_o\, e^{-j\omega t}$.

Solution. When a string vibrates at a frequency ω, the tension at each point balances the force which acts perpendicular to the direction at which the string oscillations propagate (see Sec. 8-2). Referring to Fig. 10-2.3, we observe that for small θ the force $F_o e^{-j\omega t}$, which has initiated the transverse wave, is related to the tension by the relation

$$F_o\, e^{-j\omega t} = -T \sin\theta \doteq -T \tan\theta = -T\,(\frac{\partial y}{\partial x}) \tag{10-2.18}$$

The instantaneous displacement of an harmonic transverse wave is represented by the same form as the plane electromagnetic wave. Hence, we set

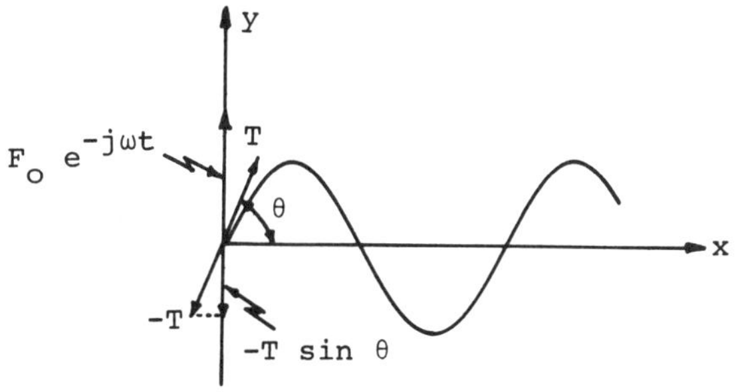

Figure 10-2.3. Equilibrium of forces on a vibrating string.

$$y = A_o e^{j(k_s x - \omega t)} = A_o e^{j\omega(\frac{x}{c_s} - t)} \tag{10-2.19}$$

At the point x = 0, the following relation applies

$$F_o e^{-j\omega t} = -T \left.\frac{\partial y}{\partial x}\right|_{x=0} = -j\omega \frac{TA_o}{c_s} e^{-j\omega t}$$

from which $A_o = -(F_o/j\omega)(c_s/T)$. The complete solution for the wave is given by

$$y = -\frac{F_o}{j\omega}\left(\frac{c_s}{T}\right) e^{j\omega(\frac{x}{c_s} - t)} \tag{10-2.20}$$

Differentiating Eq. (10-2.20) with respect to time we obtain the transverse velocity

$$v_y = \frac{\partial y}{\partial t} = F_o \left(\frac{c_s}{T}\right) e^{j\omega(\frac{x}{c_s} - t)} \tag{10-2.21}$$

The *transfer admittance* of the string is given by

$$Y(x) = \frac{\text{transverse force}}{\text{transverse velocity}} = \frac{T}{c_s} e^{-j\omega \frac{x}{c_s}} = \rho_\ell c_s e^{-j\omega \frac{x}{c_s}}$$

where $T = \rho_\ell c_s^2$ and $(\rho_\ell c_s)^{-1}$ is the input transverse impedance or characteristic impedance of the string (x = 0).

The average power of the string is

$$P_{av} = \langle \frac{1}{2} \text{ force} \times \text{velocity*} \rangle = \frac{1}{2} |F_o|^2 \frac{c_s}{T} e^{-j\omega \frac{x}{c_s}} \tag{10-2.22}$$

where $(1/2)|F_o|^2 c_s/T = (1/2)|F_o|^2 1/\rho_\ell c_s$ is the power input to the string at x = 0. The reader should compare this result with Eq. (10-2.17) for the electromagnetic case.

ΔΔΔ

We have found the general solution of the wave equation for a plane electromagnetic wave E_x that is propagating in the Z-direction to be of the form

$$E = E_o e^{-j\omega t} e^{jkz}$$

In the most general form the field at a point appropriate to Eq. (10-1.4) is the result of two waves that are propagating in opposite directions. The solution in the more general case is

$$\begin{aligned} E &= E_i e^{-j\omega t} e^{+jkz} + E_r e^{-j\omega t} e^{-jkz} \\ &= E_i e^{-j\omega t} e^{jkz} [1 + |\Gamma_o| e^{j\phi} e^{-j2kz}] \end{aligned} \tag{10-2.23}$$

where

$$\Gamma_o = \frac{E_r}{E_i} = \left|\frac{E_r}{E_i}\right| e^{j\phi} = |\Gamma_o| e^{j\phi} \tag{10-2.24}$$

is known as the *reflection coefficient*, and ϕ is the phase difference between E_r and E_i. The second term, which represents a wave that is traveling in the negative Z-direction will be considered as the *reflected wave*. The physical mechanism for the existence of a reflected wave will be discussed in Chap. 11.

It is interesting to note that the combination of the two traveling waves results in a stationary wave, which is known as a *standing wave*. The result follows by finding the value of $\mathscr{E}$, the normalized magnitude of the resulting wave, which is

$$\mathscr{E} = \frac{(EE^*)^{1/2}}{|E_i|} = [1 + |\Gamma_o|^2 + 2|\Gamma_o| \cos(2kz-\phi)]^{1/2} \tag{10-2.25}$$

From this expression we easily obtain $\mathscr{E}_{max} = 1 + |\Gamma_o|$ and $\mathscr{E}_{min} = 1 - |\Gamma_o|$. The ratio of the maximum to the minimum is denoted the *standing wave ratio* SWR, and is

$$\mathrm{SWR} = \frac{\mathscr{E}_{max}}{\mathscr{E}_{min}} = \frac{1 + |\Gamma_o|}{1 - |\Gamma_o|} = \frac{|E_i| + |E_r|}{|E_i| - |E_r|}; \quad |\Gamma_o| = \frac{\mathrm{SWR} - 1}{\mathrm{SWR} + 1} \tag{10-2.26}$$

When the reflected wave is zero ($|E_r| = 0$), the SWR = 1. For all intermediate values

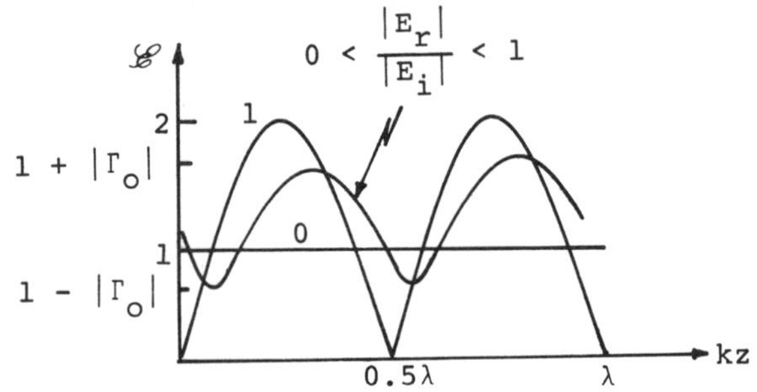

Figure 10-2.4. The standing wave pattern for three values of $|E_r|/|E_i|$.

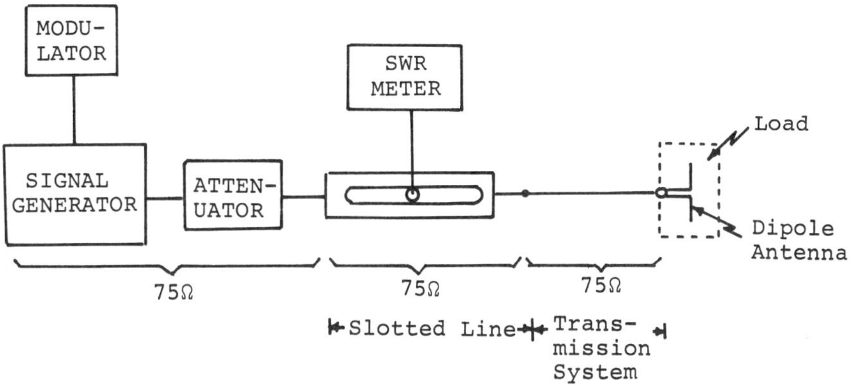

Figure 10-2.5. SWR measuring setup.

of reflected wave the SWR lies between 1 and ∞, an SWR = ∞ occurs when $|E_r| = |E_i|$. The general features of the standing wave pattern for three values of the ratio $|E_r|/|E_i|$ are shown in Fig. 10-2.4.

A typical experimental setup for SWR measurements in the feedline of a microwave antenna is shown in Fig. 10-2.5. As shown, a pickup probe with its associated measuring instruments is mounted on a slotted section which allows movement and measurement of the probe location. The SWR is then noted as the probe is moved over a distance of at least 0.5λ. The antenna radiates most efficiently when the SWR=1.

Standing waves are avoided as much as possible in practice for two reasons: a high SWR indicates a loss of power transmission (some of the energy is reflected away from its destination), and a high SWR indicates a higher total field than transmitted field, with possible extra dielectric stresses in the material through which the energy is propagating. In practice, special circuit elements are incorporated in parallel or in series or both so that the combined impedance of these elements plus the load is equal to the impedance of the transmission system. As is discussed at some length in Sec. 11-1, this reduces (and hopefully eliminates) impedance discontinuities, and the reflection factor is reduced to vanishing.

Example 10-2.3. Find the reflection and transmission coefficients for waves on strings with discontinuities in their mass density, as shown in Fig. 10-2.6.

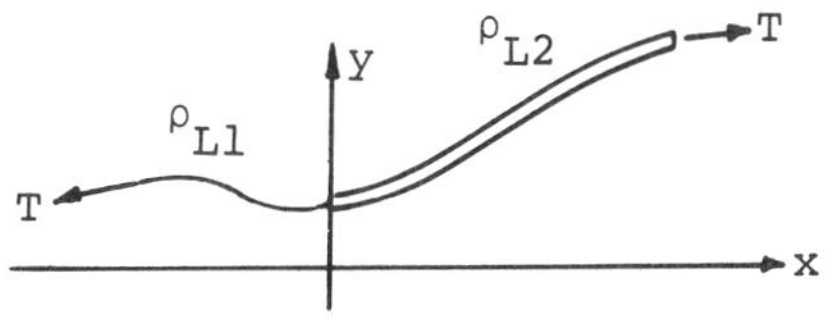

Figure 10-2.6. String with discontinuous mass density.

Solution. At the boundary we have a continuation of the transverse displacement and the continuation of the transverse force. The first condition is obvious, and the second is true since any discontinuity of force will result in a net force at the boundary which will produce an infinite acceleration to an infinitesimal mass at the boundary. Hence in methematical form we have

$$y_1 = y_2 \qquad \text{a)}$$
$$T\frac{\partial y_1}{\partial x} = T\frac{\partial y_2}{\partial x} \qquad \text{b)} \qquad (10\text{-}2.27)$$

Consider an incident wave

$$y_1 = A_1 e^{jk_{s1}x} e^{-j\omega t} \qquad (10\text{-}2.28)$$

which is moving from the left with peak amplitude A_1 and with a speed $c_{s1} = \sqrt{T/\rho_{L1}} = \omega/k_{s1}$. The transmitted wave is y_2 and the reflected wave is y_{1r}. The transmitted wave is written

$$y_2 = A_2 e^{jk_{s2}x} e^{-j\omega t} \qquad (10\text{-}2.29)$$

with a peak amplitude A_2 and a speed $c_{s2} = \sqrt{T/\rho_{L2}} = \omega/k_{s2}$. The reflected wave is written

$$y_{1r} = A_{1r} e^{-jk_{s1}x} e^{-j\omega t} \qquad (10\text{-}2.30)$$

When we apply the boundary conditions, we obtain the relations

$$A_1 + A_{1r} = A_2 \qquad \text{a)}$$
$$k_{s1}A_1 - k_{s1}A_{1r} = k_{s2}A_2 \qquad \text{b)} \qquad (10\text{-}2.31)$$

Upon solving for A_{1r} and A_2 we find that the reflection coefficient and the transmission coefficient are respectively

$$\Gamma_r = \frac{k_{s1} - k_{s2}}{k_{s1} + k_{s2}} = \frac{Z_1 - Z_2}{Z_1 + Z_2} \qquad \text{a)}$$
$$\Gamma_t = \frac{2k_{s1}}{k_{s1} + k_{s2}} = \frac{2Z_1}{Z_1 + Z_2} \qquad \text{b)} \qquad (10\text{-}2.32)$$

where $Z_1 = (\rho_{L1}c_s)^{-1}$ and $Z_2 = (\rho_{L2}c_s)^{-1}$ are the specific impedances. ΔΔΔ

10-3. Plane Electromagnetic Waves in Homogeneous, Isotropic, Conducting Mediums

The presence of a finite conductivity results in interesting changes in the wave behavior. We proceed as before for an assumed harmonic time variation. Equation (8-8.4) now becomes

$$\nabla^2\overline{E} + \omega^2\mu(\varepsilon + j\,\frac{\sigma}{\omega})\,\overline{E} = \nabla^2\overline{E} + \omega^2\mu\varepsilon_e\overline{E} = 0 \tag{10-3.1}$$

where the effective permittivity is a complex quantity

$$\varepsilon_e = \varepsilon_o\varepsilon_{er} = \varepsilon_o(\varepsilon_r + j\,\frac{\sigma}{\omega\varepsilon_o}) = \varepsilon' + j\varepsilon'' \tag{10-3.2}$$

so that

$$k^2 = \omega^2\mu\varepsilon_e = \omega^2\mu\varepsilon + j\omega\mu\sigma \tag{10-3.3}$$

We proceed by taking as the solution of the wave equation for propagation in the positive X-direction

$$\overline{E}(\overline{r}) = \overline{a}_y E_o\, e^{jkx} \tag{10-3.4}$$

Now we express the propagation k as a complex number

$$k = k' + jk'' \tag{10-3.5}$$

and we write $\overline{E}(\overline{r})$ in the form

$$\overline{E}(\overline{r}) = \overline{a}_y E_o\, e^{jk'x} e^{-k''x} \tag{10-3.6}$$

This solution implies, of course, that

$$\overline{E}(\overline{r},t) = \text{Re}\,\{\overline{E}(\overline{r})\, e^{-j\omega t}\} = \overline{a}_y E_o e^{-k''x}\cos\,(k'x - \omega t) \tag{10-3.7}$$

and that the field becomes spatially attenuated in the medium.

It is possible to determine specific expressions for k' and k". These follow by squaring Eq. (10-3.5) and then equating the real and imaginary parts to the real and imaginary parts of Eq. (10-3.3). The equations for the two unknown quantities k' and k" become

$$k' = \omega[\,\frac{\mu\varepsilon}{2}\,[(1 + \frac{\sigma^2}{\varepsilon^2\omega^2})^{1/2} + 1]]^{1/2} \qquad \text{a)}$$

$$k'' = \omega[\,\frac{\mu\varepsilon}{2}\,[(1 + \frac{\sigma^2}{\varepsilon^2\omega^2})^{1/2} - 1]]^{1/2} \qquad \text{b)} \tag{10-3.8}$$

Because k is a function of frequency, the medium is said to be a *dispersive* medium.

The planes of constant phase are propagated with a velocity [see Eq. (10-2.16)]

$$v_{ph} = \frac{\omega}{k'} = [\frac{\mu\varepsilon}{2} [(1 + \frac{\sigma^2}{\varepsilon^2\omega^2})^{1/2} + 1]]^{-1/2} = c/[\frac{\mu_r\varepsilon_r}{2} (1+ \frac{\sigma^2}{\varepsilon^2\omega^2})^{1/2}+1]]^{1/2} \quad (10\text{-}3.9)$$

which decreases with conductivity and increases with frequency as long as σ and ε are independent of frequency.

We can establish other important features of the waves. Refer to Eq. (10-3.1) and examine the terms that contribute to the right hand member. The term $\sigma\overline{E}$ arises from conduction charges, and the component $\omega\varepsilon\overline{E}$ arises from changes in the electric induction vector $\overline{D}$, the displacement current density. The ratio of these terms $\sigma/\omega\varepsilon$ is an important factor, and is often used in analysis as a criterion for distinguishing conductors as *poor* or *good*. We wish to examine this matter.

a. *Poor Conductors.* When the conduction current is much smaller than the displacement current $\sigma/\omega\varepsilon \ll 1$. In this case the values of k' and k" to the first order of approximation are

$$\begin{aligned} k' &\doteq \omega[\frac{\mu\varepsilon}{2} (2 + \frac{1}{2} \frac{\sigma^2}{\varepsilon^2\omega^2})]^{1/2} \doteq \omega \sqrt{\mu\varepsilon}[1 + \frac{1}{8} \frac{\sigma^2}{\varepsilon^2\omega^2}] \\ k'' &\doteq \omega[\frac{\mu\varepsilon}{2} (\frac{1}{2} \frac{\sigma^2}{\varepsilon^2\omega^2})]^{1/2} = \frac{\sigma}{2}\sqrt{\frac{\mu}{\varepsilon}} \end{aligned} \quad (10\text{-}3.10)$$

These govern the phase change of the wave, the attenuation, and the phase shift between the electric and magnetic fields in poor conductors.

b. *Good Conductors.* When the conduction current is much higher than the displacement current, then $\sigma/\omega\varepsilon \gg 1$ and

$$\begin{aligned} k' &= k'' = \sqrt{\frac{\omega\mu\sigma}{2}} \\ Z &= Z_0 \frac{e^{-j\frac{\pi}{4}}}{(\frac{\sigma}{\omega\varepsilon})^{1/2}} = Z_o\sqrt{\frac{\omega\varepsilon_o}{\sigma}} \underline{|- 45^o} \end{aligned} \quad (10\text{-}3.11)$$

and the phase difference between $\overline{E}$ and $\overline{H}$ is 45 deg.

The conduction current in a good conductor is proportional to the electric field intensity in it. At a distance x inside of a good conductor relative to some reference position the fraction of the field is given by

$$\left|\frac{E(x)}{E(o)}\right| = \left|e^{+jk'x} e^{-k''x} e^{-j\omega t}\right| = e^{-\sqrt{\frac{\omega\mu\sigma}{2}}x} = e^{-x/\delta} \quad (10\text{-}3.12)$$

where δ is called the *skin depth.* It measures, for a particular material and a given frequency, the depth in the material at which the current density has decreased to $1/e^{-th}$ of the value of the surface. At high frequencies the skin depth in metals is extremely small, e.g., at 100 MHz in silver $\delta \doteq 10^{-5}$ m; in copper for ultraviolet radiation ($\lambda \doteq 10^{-8}$ m) δ is only 10^{-9} m. However, the radiowaves at 30 KHz in sea water, the skin depth is approximately 1 meter.

Example 10-3.1. Find the average power at any point inside of a good conductor.

Solution. The $\bar{E}$ and $\bar{H}$ fields inside a good conductor are given by

$$\bar{E} = \bar{a}_y E_o \, e^{jk'x} \, e^{-k''x} \, e^{-j\omega t}$$

$$\bar{H} = \bar{a}_z \frac{(k'' + jk'')}{\omega\mu} E_o \, e^{jk'x} \, e^{-k''x} \, e^{-j\omega t}$$

where the magnetic field intensity is out of phase with E by an angle $\phi = \tan^{-1}(k''/k')$. The time average of the complex Poynting vector in the X-direction is found to be

$$\langle \mathcal{S}_c \rangle \doteq \frac{1}{2} \mathrm{Re}[\bar{E} \times \bar{H}^*] = \bar{a}_x \frac{1}{2} \frac{|E_o|^2}{\omega\mu} e^{-2k''x} \, \mathrm{Re}\,\{k' - jk''\}$$

$$= \bar{a}_x \frac{1}{2} \frac{|E_o|^2}{\omega\mu} e^{-2x/\delta} \, \frac{1}{\delta}$$

which shows that the average value of the Poynting vector decreases with penetration into the conductor. ΔΔΔ

It is of some interest to examine the Poynting vector in conducting mediums. We note that it is implicitly assumed that a source of plane electromagnetic waves exists and that the fields are known at some reference surface x = 0 in the medium.

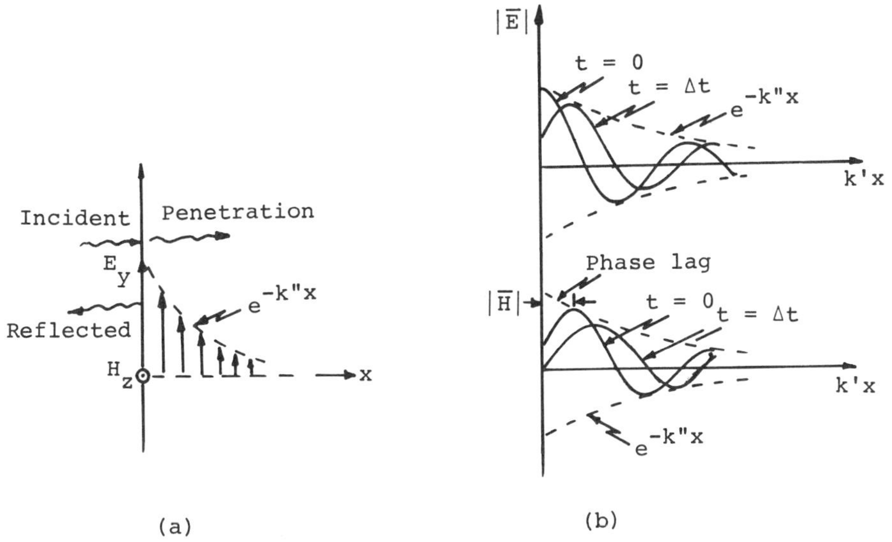

Figure 10-3.1. The field components of the wave in the conducting medium.

We shall assume for convenience that this surface is a boundary surface, as illustrated in Fig. 10-3.1a. As indicated, there are features of this geometry that introduce factors not yet discussed (see Sec. 11-6), namely, that because of the discontinuity at the boundary, there are three component fields - an incident field, a reflected field, and a penetrating or transmitted field. We shall assume that we know the strength of the penetrating field at the surface.

As shown, the net resultant electric field (incident-reflected = penetration) that is assumed to be incident normally on the boundary of the conducting medium which is taken as x = 0, is that specified by Eq. (10-3.12) or Eq. (10-3.6). Therefore, $\overline{E}$ and the associated $\overline{H}$ field are expressed through the relations [see Eq. (10-2.14)]

$$\begin{aligned} \overline{E} &= \overline{a}_y E_o e^{jk'x} e^{-k''x} \\ \overline{H} &= \sqrt{\frac{\varepsilon_e}{\mu}} E_o \overline{a}_z e^{jk'x} e^{-k''x} \end{aligned} \qquad (10\text{-}3.13)$$

Consequently the time average Poynting vector $<\overline{\mathscr{S}}_c>$ given by Eq. (8-10.12) becomes

$$<\overline{\mathscr{S}}_c> = \text{Re}\left(\frac{1}{2}\overline{E}\times\overline{H}^*\right) = \text{Re}\,\frac{1}{2}\left[|E_o|^2 e^{-2k''x}\sqrt{\frac{\varepsilon_e^*}{\mu}}\right]\overline{a}_x \qquad (10\text{-}3.14)$$

which specifies the average power flowing through a closed surface in the medium per unit area. This equation can be written in a form that involves the intrinsic impedance Z of the medium, and is

$$<\mathscr{S}_c> = \frac{1}{2} H_o^2 \text{ Re } Z \qquad (10\text{-}3.15)$$

An equivalent form, for the case of good conductors using Eqs. (10-3.12) and (10-3.13) is

$$<\mathscr{S}_c> = \frac{E_o^2}{2} e^{-2xk''} \text{ Re }\left\{\frac{1}{Z}\right\} = \frac{E_o^2}{2} e^{-2x/\delta} \text{ Re}\left\{\frac{\sqrt{\frac{\omega\mu\sigma}{2}}(1+j)}{\omega\mu}\right\} = \frac{1}{4} E_o^2 \sigma\delta\, e^{-2x/\delta} \qquad (10\text{-}3.16)$$

A physical view is that the power from a wave absorbed by a conducting medium can be written in terms of the I^2R losses in the medium, and this can be expressed in terms of the current induced in the medium. For a plane wave that is incident normally on the conducting medium, as in Fig. 10-3.1a, the current density variation is written

$$\overline{J} = \sigma\overline{E} = \overline{a}_y \sigma E_o e^{jk'x} e^{-k''x} \qquad (10\text{-}3.17)$$

For the case of good conductors this becomes

$$\overline{J}_y = \sigma\overline{E}_y = \overline{a}_y \sigma E_o e^{-(1-j)x/\delta} = J_o e^{-(1-j)x/\delta}\,\overline{a}_y \qquad (10\text{-}3.18)$$

where

$$J_o = \sigma E_o$$

We will assume that the conducting medium extends to infinity in the X-direction, although as a practical matter, this requirement is adequately met if the medium extends about 5δ. The total current per unit width in the Y-direction is

$$J = \int_0^\infty J_y \, dx = \frac{\delta J_o}{1-j} \tag{10-3.19}$$

This expression may be interpreted to show that the total current per unit width is the same as would be obtained if J_y were maintained constant at the surface value J_o to a depth $\delta/\sqrt{2}$ and is zero beyond this point.

Observe that

$$J = \frac{\delta\sigma}{1-j} E_o = \frac{\delta\sigma}{1-j} ZH_o = H_o \qquad \left(Z = \frac{\omega\mu}{k} = \frac{1-j}{\delta\sigma}\right) \tag{10-3.20}$$

Also, if R denotes the resistance of a square sheet of conducting medium of thickness δ, then the equivalent surface resistance per square is

$$R = \frac{1}{\sigma\delta} = \text{Re } Z$$

and Eq. (10-3.15) may be written

$$\langle \mathcal{S}_c \rangle = \frac{1}{2} |J|^2 R \tag{10-3.21}$$

This expression will be found useful later in connection with the attenuation in the walls of waveguides.

The $|\overline{E}|$ and $|\overline{H}|$ fields at two instants of the time are shown in Fig. 10-3.1b.

10-4. Dispersion

When the wave propagation constant k, or equivalently, the permittivity ε or index of refraction η, is a function of frequency, as we have found to be true in conducting mediums, the situation is referred to as dispersion. Dispersion in guided waves propagating in a medium described by the constant μ and ε is called *geometric dispersion*. Dispersion that arises because of the presence of conductivity is called *conductive dispersion;* and *parametric dispersion* exists when the factors σ and ε become complex quantities. Section 10-3 contains a discussion of conductive dispersion and we shall meet geometric dispersion when we discuss waves in bounded mediums. We shall here consider only the parametric dispersion.

a. *Conduction Current.* We wish to study the conductivity physically in order to understand the conditions that lead to complex conductivity. To do this, we must review the electron gas model of electron conduction in metals given in Sec. 5-13. The free electron gas model of the metal has its physical significance since the conduction electrons are moving within the neighborhood of the ion cores.

Another feature of the electron model is the existence and behavior of conduction electrons in matter in a manner dictated by quantum mechanical principles. Of importance is the existence of discrete energy levels which may be occupied by the electrons; in fact, no two electrons will have exactly the same energy. However, the energy levels prove to be so close together in a metal as to constitute an almost continuous distribution, a distribution that is called the Fermi-Dirac distribution. Appropriate to each particular energy level or state, the electron has a unique kinetic energy associated with it. If we associate with each electron a propagating wave, and this is called a matter wave, then we would associate a wavenumber k with each of the states.

In quantum mechanics, the momentum of a free electron is related to its wavenumber by the DeBroglie relation $\lambda = h/mv$, or

$$mv = \hbar k \tag{10-4.1}$$

where $\hbar = h/2\pi$, h is Planck's constant. If an electric field E is applied, there is a change in the electron's momentum given by

$$-eE = F = m\frac{dv}{dt} = \hbar\frac{dk}{dt} \tag{10-4.2}$$

Now, owing to the swarm of electrons moving in the field, they will collide with the ions fixed in the lattice (the collision is not in the mechanical sense of physical contact but owing to the fact that electrical charges mutually repel, the direction and momentum of the electron can change). Let τ denote the mean time during which the electric field acts on an electron before its next collision. The approximate time average change in velocity is obtained from Eq. (10-4.2)

$$\langle\Delta v\rangle = \frac{1}{2}\frac{\tau}{m}F = -\frac{\tau e}{2m}E = -\frac{\mu_e}{2}E \qquad \mu_e = \frac{e\tau}{m} \tag{10-4.3}$$

where μ_e is called *electron mobility.* If there are N electrons of charge -e per unit volume, the electron density in the volume defined by the mean distance between collisions is, in agreement with Eq. (5-13.5),

$$J_c = -Ne\langle v\rangle = \frac{Ne^2\tau}{2m}E = \sigma E \tag{10-4.4}$$

where σ is the *dc conductivity.* Suppose that there is a displacement of the center of the wavenumbers in the k-space due to collisions, which is given by

$$\Delta k = \frac{F\tau}{\hbar} \tag{10-4.5}$$

which shows an incremental momentum change of each electron. To take into consideration both the mean velocity of the electrons between collisions and their acceleration, we modify Eq. (10-4.2) to read

$$-e\bar{E} = \bar{F} = m\frac{\bar{v}}{\tau} + m\frac{d\bar{v}}{dt} \tag{10-4.6}$$

If the electric field is assumed to be of a harmonic time variation $e^{-j\omega t}$, then we obtain for the mean velocity and mean current density the following equations

$$\begin{aligned} \bar{v} &= \frac{-e\bar{E}}{\frac{m}{\tau} - j\omega m} \\ \bar{J}_c &= -Ne\langle\bar{v}\rangle = \frac{1}{2}\frac{(Ne^2/m)\tau}{(1 - j\omega\tau)}\bar{E} = \frac{1}{2}\frac{Ne\,\mu_e}{(1 - j\omega\tau)}\bar{E} = \frac{\sigma}{1 - j\omega\tau}\bar{E} = \sigma_e\bar{E} \end{aligned} \tag{10-4.7}$$

b. *Polarization Current.* Now we consider a dielectric material which is assumed to be without conduction electrons. Our model of matter is as before, but no free conduction electrons exist, and all electrons associated with the atoms of the matter are rigidly bound to a position of equilibrium. When an electric field is applied to a lossless dielectric, the effect will be on the electrons, the ions being considered to be immobile. The equation of motion for bound electrons of the atoms of type i will involve a restoring force $f_i\bar{r}_i$ and a frictional force $m\nu_i d\bar{r}_i/dt$, where ν_i is the collision frequency and f_i is a characteristic constant of the material. Thus the equilibrium equation will be of the form

$$m\frac{d^2\bar{r}_i}{dt^2} + m\nu_i\frac{d\bar{r}_i}{dt} + f_i\bar{r}_i = -e\bar{E}(\bar{r},t) \tag{10-4.8}$$

We assume that the applied field is harmonic in time, so that the displacement from the neutral position will be of the form $\bar{r}_i = \bar{r}_{io}e^{-j\omega t}$. The solution to Eq. (10-4.8) assumes the form

$$\bar{r}_{io} = -\frac{e/m}{(\omega_i^2 - \omega^2) - j\omega\nu_i}\bar{E}(\bar{r}) \tag{10-4.9}$$

where $\omega_i^2 = f_i/m$ denotes the characteristic frequency of the electron belonging to the ith type of atom.

The dipole moment due to the displacement of the ith type electron is

$$\bar{p}_i = -e\bar{r}_i \tag{10-4.10}$$

If there are N electrons per unit volume, there are $\beta_i N$ ($\Sigma_i \beta_i = 1$) electrons of type i, and the total dipole moment per unit volume is

$$\overline{P} = \sum_i N\beta_i \overline{p}_i = \overline{E} \sum_i \frac{N\beta_i e^2/m}{(\omega_i^2 - \omega^2) - j\omega\nu_i} \tag{10-4.11}$$

For simplicity, we shall assume the presence of only one type of atom, $\beta_i = 1$, and Eq. (10-4.11) becomes

$$\overline{P} = \frac{Ne^2/m}{(\omega_o^2 - \omega^2) - j\omega\nu} \overline{E} \tag{10-4.12}$$

where we have set $\omega_i = \omega_o$. The corresponding polarization current ($\overline{J}_p = \frac{\partial \overline{P}}{\partial t}$) is given by

$$\overline{J}_p = -j\omega\overline{P} = -j\omega \frac{Ne^2/m}{(\omega_o^2 - \omega^2) - j\omega\nu} \overline{E} \tag{10-4.13}$$

We wish now to include this expression in the Maxwell equation for curl $\overline{H}$.

We combine our modified $\overline{J}_c$ [Eq. (10-4.7)] and $\overline{J}_p$ [Eq. (10-4.13)] with the Maxwell curl $\overline{H}$ equation. The result becomes

$$\begin{aligned} \nabla \times \overline{H} &= \overline{J}_c - j\omega\varepsilon_o\overline{E} - j\omega\overline{P} \\ &= \left(\frac{\sigma}{1 - j\omega\tau} - j\omega\varepsilon_o - j\omega \frac{Ne^2/m}{(\omega_o^2 - \omega^2) - j\omega\nu}\right) \overline{E} \\ &= \varepsilon_o \left(\frac{1}{\varepsilon_o} \frac{\sigma}{1 - j\omega\tau} - j\omega - j\frac{\omega}{\varepsilon_o} \frac{Ne^2/m}{(\omega_o^2 - \omega^2) - j\omega\nu}\right) \overline{E} \end{aligned} \tag{10-4.14}$$

which can be written

$$\nabla \times \overline{H} = -j\omega\, \varepsilon_e\, \overline{E}$$

This equation shows that the permittivity ε_e, in addition to being a complex quantity, is an explicit function of the frequency ω. Moreover, since we have already found that $k = \omega\sqrt{\mu\varepsilon}$, $\eta = \sqrt{\mu_r\varepsilon_r}$, and $v_{ph} = \omega/k$, this implies that all of these wave characteristics are functions of the frequency in a dispersive medium.

In the case of a plasma, the excitation is such that the electrons are separated from their atoms - hence the restoring force in Eq. (10-4.8) is zero. As a result, the total polarization due to the displacement of the electrons is

$$\overline{P} = -\frac{Ne^2/m}{\omega^2 + j\omega\nu} \overline{E} \tag{10-4.15}$$

The final result for the permittivity of a plasma ($\overline{J}_c = 0$ since the electron and positive ion densities balance each other), is the expression

$$\varepsilon_e = \varepsilon_o \left(1 - \frac{Ne^2/m}{\varepsilon_o(\omega^2 + j\omega\nu)}\right) \tag{10-4.16}$$

This is often written

$$\varepsilon_e = \varepsilon_o \left(1 - \frac{\omega_p^2/\omega^2}{1 + jZ}\right) = \varepsilon_o \left(1 - \frac{X}{1 + jZ}\right) \tag{10-4.17}$$

where

$$\omega_p^2 = \frac{Ne^2}{m\varepsilon_o} = \text{plasma frequency}^2, \quad X = \frac{\omega_p^2}{\omega^2}, \quad Z = \frac{\nu}{\omega}$$

Example 10-4.1. Suppose that the permittivity ε of a crystalline material is due to the host crystal, say a lasing material, $A\ell_2O_3$. Find the wave behavior in such a medium if an impurity Cr^{3+} is added which is supposed to contribute an additional term to the total polarization of the medium. Discuss a condition which might exist for which a negative attenuation is possible, thereby leading to a gain in wave amplitude.

Solution. The electric induction $\overline{D}$ for such materials takes the form

$$\overline{D} = \varepsilon_o\overline{E} + \overline{P}_{host} + \overline{P}_{imp.} = \varepsilon\overline{E} + \overline{P}_{imp.} \tag{10-4.18}$$

In Eq. (10-4.18) we have separated the total polarization into two effects, P_{host} + $P_{imp.}$. $P_{imp.}$ is found to be a weak phenomenon but one which is highly resonant at the laser transition. P_{host} is essentially unchanged under the lasing conditions. Equation (10-4.18) becomes, employing a form for $P_{imp.}$ suggested by Eq. (5-6.1) ($\overline{P}_{imp.} = \varepsilon_o\chi_e E$)

$$\overline{D} = \varepsilon_o\varepsilon_r\overline{E} + \chi_e(\omega)\varepsilon_o\overline{E} = \varepsilon_o[\varepsilon_r + \chi_e(\omega)]\,\overline{E} \tag{10-4.19}$$

where we have explicitly indicated a frequency dependence of the susceptibility which is due to the Cr^{3+} impurities. Using Eq. (10-4.12), the susceptibility $\chi(\omega)$ of the electric-dipole laser transition is found to be

$$\chi_e(\omega) = -\frac{Ne^2/m\varepsilon_o}{(\omega-\omega_o)(\omega+\omega_o)+j\omega\nu} \doteq -\frac{Ne^2/m\varepsilon_o}{2\omega_o[(\omega-\omega_o)+j\,\frac{\nu}{2}]}, \quad (\omega \doteq \omega_o) \tag{10-4.20}$$

From this we can find the real part, $\chi_e'(\omega)$, and imaginary part, $\chi_e''(\omega)$, of the susceptibility. These are, respectively,

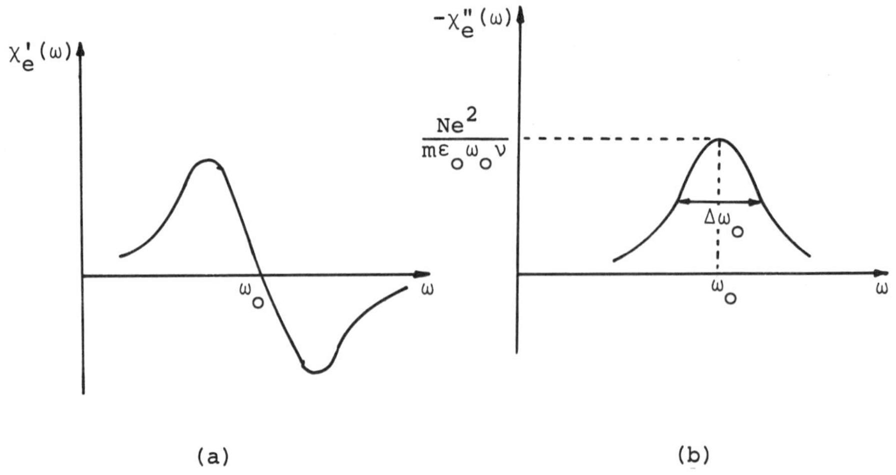

Figure 10-4.1. Frequency variation of the real and imaginary parts of the electric susceptibility.

$$\chi_e'(\omega) = -\frac{(Ne^2/m\varepsilon_o)(\omega-\omega_o)}{2\omega_o[(\omega-\omega_o)^2 + \frac{\nu^2}{4}]} \qquad \text{a)}$$

$$\chi_e''(\omega) = \frac{(Ne^2/m\varepsilon_o)\,\nu}{4\omega_o[(\omega-\omega_o)^2 + \frac{\nu^2}{4}]} \qquad \text{b)} \qquad (10\text{-}4.21)$$

The graphical representation of Eq. (10-4.21) is shown in Fig. 10-4.1a and Fig. 10-4.1b.

Since for plane waves $k = \omega\sqrt{\mu_o\varepsilon} = k_o\sqrt{\varepsilon_{er}}$, the propagation wave constant for a wave in a medium with laser transitions is given by

$$k = k' + jk'' = k_o\sqrt{\varepsilon_r}\left(1 + \frac{\chi_e'(\omega)}{\varepsilon_r} + j\frac{\chi_e''(\omega)}{\varepsilon_r}\right)^{1/2} \doteq k_o\sqrt{\varepsilon_r}\left(1 + \frac{1}{2}\frac{\chi_e'}{\varepsilon_r} + j\frac{1}{2}\frac{\chi_e''}{\varepsilon_r}\right) \qquad (10\text{-}4.22)$$

Hence

$$k' = k_o\sqrt{\varepsilon_r} + \frac{k_o}{2\sqrt{\varepsilon_r}}\chi_e'(\omega) \qquad \text{a)}$$

$$k'' = \frac{k_o}{2\sqrt{\varepsilon_r}}\chi_e''(\omega) \qquad \text{b)} \qquad (10\text{-}4.23)$$

A special feature of lasing materials is that during operation the excitation of the material by an outside source yields the unusual result that population *inversion* takes place, that is, N becomes negative and both $\chi_e'(\omega)$ and $\chi_e''(\omega)$ change signs. The consequence of this is to make k'' in Eq. (10-3.6) a negative number, thereby creating a positive real exponential. This indicates a *gain* for the wave rather than a decay. This example indicates in an elementary way how a laser is capable of amplifying a wave. ΔΔΔ

10-5. Group Velocity

When we are interested in transmitting information, we must resort to a modulation process. This involves the superposition on a continuous wave of the irregularity which constitutes the transmitted signal. For the simple amplitude modulated technique, the low frequency modulating signal m(t), which may denote a voice, and a high frequency carrier wave c(t), are multiplied together. Features of this process are illustrated in Fig. 10-5.1. The resulting amplitude modulated wave comprises many frequency components depending upon both m(t) and c(t). Clearly, of course, if such a modulated wave is transmitted or propagated in a dispersive

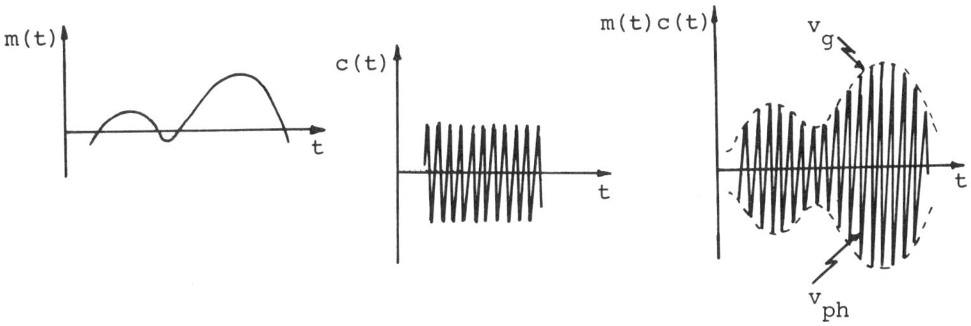

Figure 10-5.1. The amplitude modulation process.

medium, the different frequency components will travel differently, some lagging behind others. As a result, a square pulse transmitted at one end of a dispersive medium might appear as a broadened or dispersed pulse at the receiving end. We wish to study the process in some detail.

Consider a uniform plane modulated wave that is propagating in a dispersive medium. At the sending end (coordinate plane x = 0) the wave is represented as

$$E(x,t)\Big|_{x=0} = E_o m(t)c(t) = E_o m(t) \cos \omega_o t \tag{10-5.1}$$

where $\omega_o/2\pi$ is the carrier frequency, and m(t) is the modulating signal. We assume that m(t) is bandlimited, with a maximum frequency ω_m that is much smaller than $\omega_o/2\pi$. We express m(t) in its Fourier transform representation (see Appendix IV)

$$\mathscr{F}[m(t)] = M(\omega) \qquad -\omega_m \le \omega \le \omega_m \tag{10-5.2}$$

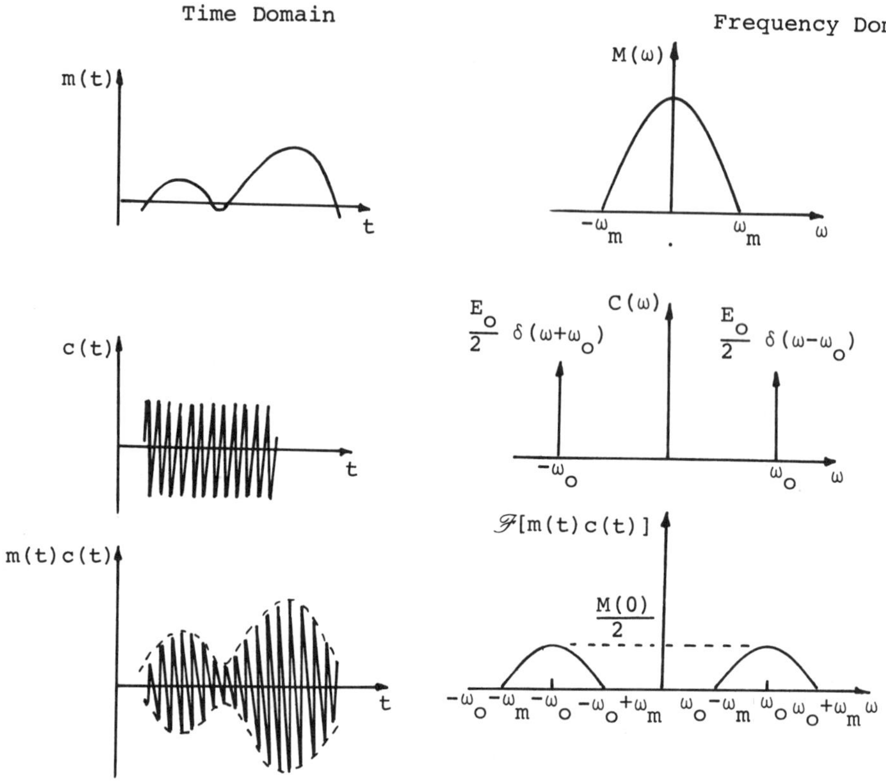

Figure 10-5.2. The modulation process - time and frequency domain.

Further, the transform of the modulated signal at the plane x = 0 is

$$E(x,\omega)\Big|_{x=0} = \mathscr{F}[E_o m(t)c(t)] = \frac{E_o}{2}\,[M(\omega-\omega_o) + M(\omega+\omega_o)] \tag{10-5.3}$$

The situation here being discussed is illustrated graphically in Fig. 10-5.2. If the attenuation is assumed to be negligible, k'' = 0, and the transformed signal at some distance x from the sending end is

$$\begin{aligned} E(x,\omega) &= E_o\, e^{jk'(\omega)x}\mathscr{F}[m(t)\cos\omega_o t] \\ &= \frac{E_o}{2}\,[M(\omega-\omega_o) + M(\omega+\omega_o)]\, e^{jk'(\omega)x} \end{aligned} \tag{10-5.4}$$

The time signal at this distance x is obtained by inversion techniques, and is written

$$E(x,t) = \mathscr{F}^{-1}\,[E(x,\omega)] = \frac{E_o}{4\pi}\,\Big[\int_{-\omega_o-\omega_m}^{-\omega_o+\omega_m} M(\omega+\omega_o)\, e^{jk'(\omega)x}\, e^{j\omega t}\, d\omega + \int_{\omega_o-\omega_m}^{\omega_o+\omega_m} M(\omega-\omega_o)\, e^{jk'(\omega)x}\, e^{j\omega t}\, d\omega\Big] \tag{10-5.5}$$

Now the procedure is to expand $k'(\omega)$ in a Taylor series expansion and retain only the first two terms in the series, namely,

$$k'(\omega) \doteq k'(\omega_o) + (\omega-\omega_o)\left.\frac{dk'(\omega)}{d\omega}\right|_{\omega=\omega_o} = k'(\omega_o) + \frac{\omega-\omega_o}{v_g} \tag{10-5.6}$$

where, we have written

$$v_g = \frac{d\omega}{dk'(\omega)} = \frac{1}{dk'(\omega)/d\omega}$$

which is called the *group velocity*. Combine Eq. (10-5.6) with (10-5.5) to find

$$E(x,t) = \frac{E_o}{2}\,\Big[e^{+jk'(-\omega_o)x}\,\frac{1}{2\pi}\int_{-\omega_o-\omega_m}^{-\omega_o+\omega_m} M(\omega+\omega_o)\, e^{j\frac{\omega+\omega_o}{v_g}}\, e^{j\omega t}\, d\omega + e^{jk'(\omega_o)x}\,\frac{1}{2\pi}\int_{\omega_o-\omega_m}^{\omega_o+\omega_m} M(\omega-\omega_o)\, e^{j\frac{\omega-\omega_o}{v_g}x}\, ee^{j\omega t}\, d\omega\Big] \tag{10-5.7}$$

It is recalled that $k'(\omega)$ is an odd function of ω, i.e., [see Eq. (10-3.8)] and so v_g has the same slope at both $\pm\omega_o$. Also, we write

$$\omega + \omega_o = \Omega \qquad d\omega = d\Omega; \qquad \omega - \omega_o = \Omega' \qquad d\omega = d\Omega'$$

and Eq. (10-5.7) attains the form

$$E(x,t) = \frac{E_o}{2}\,\Big[e^{-j\omega_o t}\, e^{-jk'(\omega_o)x}\,\frac{1}{2\pi}\int_{-\omega_m}^{\omega_m} M(\Omega)\, e^{j\Omega(t+\frac{x}{v_g})}\, d\Omega + e^{j\omega_o t}\, e^{jk'(\omega_o)x}\,\frac{1}{2\pi}\int_{-\omega_m}^{\omega_m} M(\Omega')\, e^{j\Omega'(t+\frac{x}{v_g})}\, d\Omega'\Big]$$

$$= \frac{E_o}{2}\, m\left(t + \frac{x}{v_g}\right)\Big[e^{-j[\omega_o t+k'(\omega_o)x]} + e^{j[\omega_o t+k'(\omega_o)x]}\Big]$$

$$= E_o\, m\left(t + \frac{x}{v_g}\right)\cos\omega_o\left(\frac{x}{\omega_o/k'(\omega_o)} + t\right)$$

$$= E_o m\left(t + \frac{x}{v_g}\right)\cos\omega_o\left(t + \frac{x}{v_{ph}}\right) \tag{10-5.8}$$

This expression indicates that the envelope is propagating with a speed v_g and the carrier propagates with its phase velocity. Moreover, the formula shows that the shape of the signal m(t) does not change. In the more general case of a dissipative medium, not only will the pulse attenuate with distance but the shape of the signal m(t) will also be altered.

Example 10-5.1. Find the phase and group velocity of an electromagnetic wave in a collisionless plasma.

Solution. The dielectric constant of a collisionless plasma is given by Eq. (10-4.17)

$$\varepsilon = \varepsilon_o\left(1 - \frac{\omega_p^2}{\omega^2}\right)$$

Using the definition for k, we obtain the relation

$$k = \omega\sqrt{\mu_o\varepsilon_o\mu_r\varepsilon_r} = \omega\sqrt{\mu_o\varepsilon_o}\ \sqrt{1 - \omega_p^2/\omega^2}$$

or

$$kc = \sqrt{\omega^2 - \omega_p^2}.$$

This is plotted in Fig. 10-5.3a. Also plotted are the phase and group velocities versus frequency. It is observed that the phase velocity is always greater than the speed of light, indicating that no energy transport can be associated with this phase velocity. However, the group velocity remains less than the speed of light for all frequencies. For frequencies below the plasma frequency, the wave constant k becomes imaginary, indicating a decaying and not a propagating character of the wave in the medium.

In very special cases the group velocity is negative, indicating a new phenomenon called *anomalous dispersion*. Group velocity loses its meaning in this case.

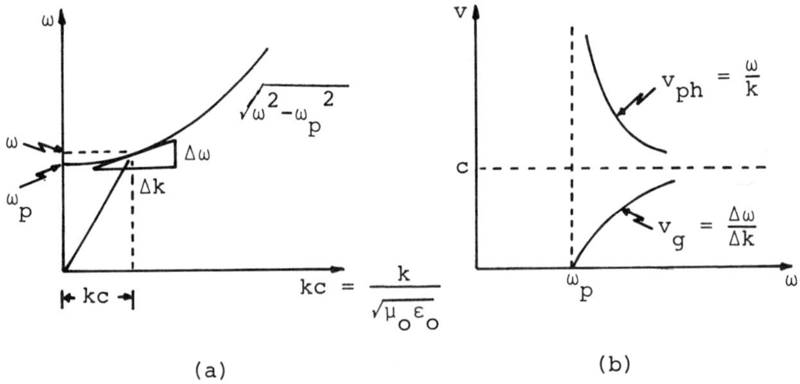

Figure 10-5.3. Dispersion relation for collisionless plasmas.

Under these circumstances there exists another velocity v_e which represents energy transport; its magnitude is always less than the speed of light, and it is positive for all frequencies.

ΔΔΔ

Example 10-5.2. Find the phase and group velocity of waves in crystals whose primitive cell has two different atoms.

Solution. We begin our considerations with Eqs. (8-3.5) which describe the transverse motion for the crystal atoms. We rewrite these equations for convenience.

$$m_1 \frac{d^2 y_{2r+1}}{dt^2} = C(y_{2r+2} + y_{2r} - 2y_{2r+1})$$
$$m_2 \frac{d^2 y_{2r}}{dt^2} = C\,(y_{2r+1} + y_{2r-1} - 2y_{2r}) \tag{10-5.9}$$

where C = T/d = stiffness, T is the eleastic force between the atoms, and d is the separation between atoms (see Fig. 8-3.1). We assume time harmonic solutions of the form

$$y_{2r+1} = M_1\, e^{j(kx-\omega t)} = M_1\, e^{j[k(2r+1)d-\omega t]}$$
$$y_{2r} = M_2\, e^{j(kx-\omega t)} = M_2\, e^{j[k\,2r\,d-\omega t]} \tag{10-5.10}$$

where M_1 and M_2 are the amplitudes for the respective atoms. Combining the assumed solution form with the controlling equations yields

$$-m_1 M_1 \omega^2\, e^{j[k(2r+1)d-\omega t]} = [CM_2(e^{jk(2r+2)d} + e^{jk2rd}) - 2CM_1\, e^{jk(2r+1)d}]e^{-j\omega t}$$
$$-m_2 M_2 \omega^2\, e^{j[k2rd-\omega t]} = [CM_1(e^{jk(2r+1)d} + e^{jk(2r-1)d}) - 2CM_2\, e^{jk2rd}]e^{-j\omega t} \tag{10-5.11}$$

From these, we find that the assumed form is acceptable if

$$(2C - m_1\omega^2)\, M_1 - 2C \cos kd\, M_2 = 0$$
$$-2C \cos kd\, M_1 + (2C - m_2\omega^2)\, M_2 = 0 \tag{10-5.12}$$

This pair of homogeneous linear equations has a non-trivial solution if the determinant of the coefficients of M_1 and M_2 vanishes. From this we find as a necessary condition that

$$\omega^2 = C\left(\frac{1}{m_1} + \frac{1}{m_2}\right) \pm C\left[\left(\frac{1}{m_1} + \frac{1}{m_2}\right)^2 - \frac{4 \sin^2 kd}{m_1 m_2}\right]^{1/2} \tag{10-5.13}$$

The dispersion relation ω vs. k for waves propagating in a diatomic crystal

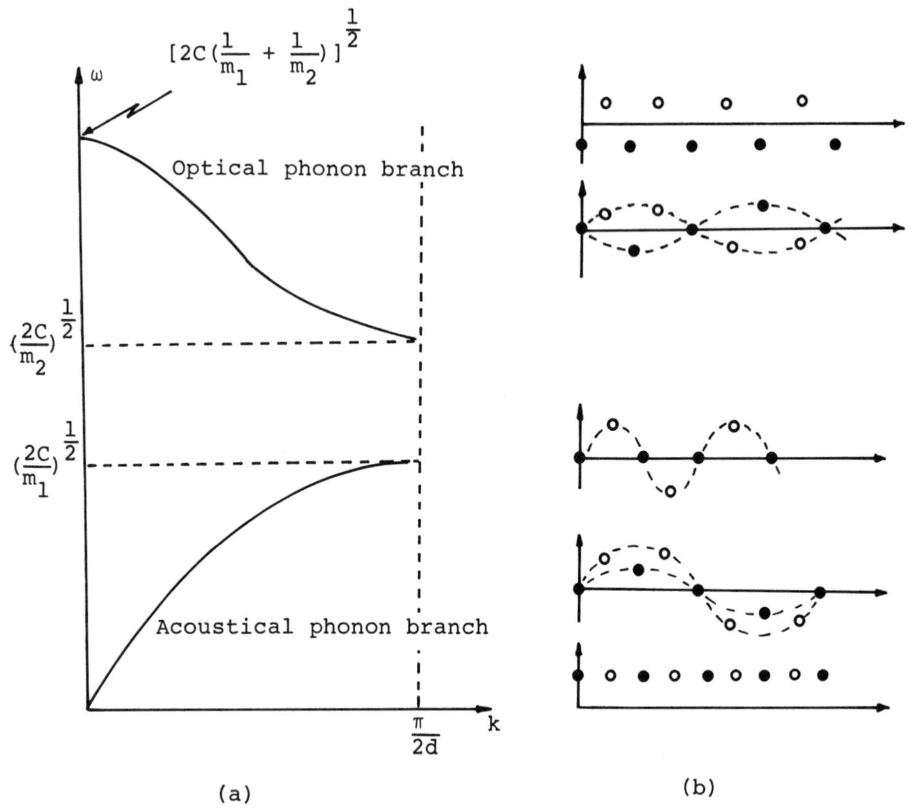

Figure 10-5.4. (a) Dispersion relations for a diatomic crystal, $m_1 > m_2$. (b) Particle displacement.

given by this equation, is shown in Fig. 10-5.4. The positive sign gives the upper curve, with

$$\omega^2 = 2C(\frac{1}{m_1} + \frac{1}{m_2}) \qquad \text{for} \quad k = 0$$

and

$$\omega^2 = \frac{2C}{m_2} \qquad k = k_{max} = \frac{\pi}{2d}$$

Similarly for the lower branch

$$\omega^2 = \frac{2C}{m_1} \qquad k_{max} = \frac{\pi}{2d}$$

Refer to the optical branch: at $k = 0$, $\omega^2 = 2C(1/m_1 + 1/m_2) \neq 0$ and the amplitude ratio $M_1/M_2 = -m_2/m_1$ which shows that the atoms vibrate against each other, with their center of mass fixed. However, for the acoustic branch at $k = 0$, the first of Eq. (10-5.12) yields $M_1 = M_2$. Hence the atoms move together, similar to those of long acoustic vibration - and this accounts for the name.

We observe from the first figure that a *frequency gap* exists $(2C/m_1)^{1/2} < \omega < (2C/m_2)^{1/2}$ at which only attenuated waves exist.

ΔΔΔ

10-6. Polarization Properties of EM Waves

Consider a plane wave propagating in the Z-direction. In this case the phase factor $\overline{k} \cdot \overline{r} = kz$ and the components of $\overline{E}$ on the X and Y axes vary in time and in space. We wish to determine the locus of $|\overline{E}| = \sqrt{E_x^2 + E_y^2}$ on the XY plane. For this, refer to Eq. (10-3.6) for the form of the field expression, but which we now write

$$\overline{E}(\overline{r},t) = \overline{E}_0\, e^{j\phi}\, e^{jk'z}\, e^{-k''z}\, e^{-j\omega t} \tag{10-6.1}$$

where the angle ϕ might denote some initial arbitrary phase and $\overline{E}_0$ is a real vector. Then we have

$$E_x = \text{Re}\,\{\overline{a}_x \cdot \overline{E}\} = \text{Re}\,\{\overline{a}_x \cdot \overline{E}_0\, e^{j\phi_x}\, [e^{jk'z}\, e^{-k''z}\, e^{-j\omega t}]\}$$

and

$$E_y = \text{Re}\,\{\overline{a}_y \cdot \overline{E}\} = \text{Re}\,\{\overline{a}_y \cdot \overline{E}_0\, e^{j\phi_y}\, [e^{jk'z}\, e^{-k''z}\, e^{-j\omega t}]\} \tag{10-6.2}$$

These are conveniently written in the form

$$\begin{aligned} E_x &= a_1 \cos\,(\phi + \phi_x) \\ E_y &= a_2 \cos\,(\phi + \phi_y) \end{aligned} \tag{10-6.3}$$

where

$$\begin{aligned} a_1 &= \overline{a}_x \cdot \overline{E}_0\, e^{-k''z} = E_{ox}\, e^{-k''z} \\ a_2 &= \overline{a}_y \cdot \overline{E}_0\, e^{-k''z} = E_{oy}\, e^{-k''z} \\ \phi &= k'z - \omega t \end{aligned} \tag{10-6.4}$$

Equations (10-6.3) are expanded in trigonometric manner, and sin ϕ and cos ϕ are eliminated; the resulting equation will be

$$\frac{E_x^2}{a_1^2} + \frac{E_y^2}{a_2^2} - \frac{2E_xE_y}{a_1a_2}\cos\Phi = \sin^2\Phi \quad (\Phi = \phi_y - \phi_x) \qquad \text{a)}$$

$$\tan 2a = \frac{2a_1a_2\cos\Phi}{a_1^2 - a_2^2} \qquad \text{b)} \tag{10-6.5}$$

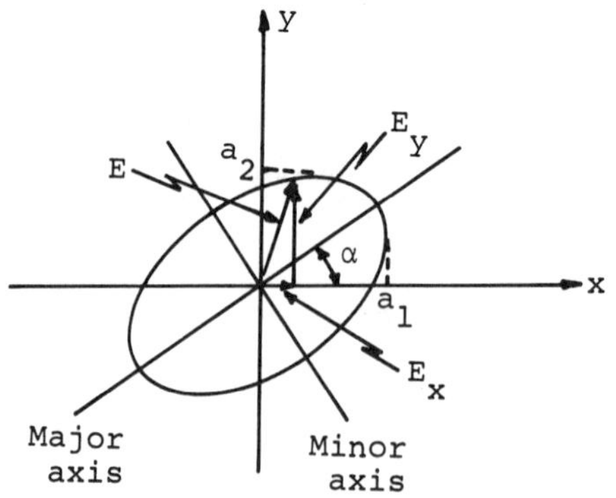

Figure 10-6.1. An elliptically polarized wave.

This equation describes an ellipse, as shown in Fig. 10-6.1. Hence the wave defined by Eq. (10-6.1) is an elliptically polarized wave, since it is described by an ellipse in the XY plane.

A number of important observations follow:

a. If E_{ox} is zero, the wave is linearly polarized in the Y-direction; If E_{oy} is zero, the wave is linearly polarized in the X-direction. If $\Phi = 0$ and $E_{ox} = E_{oy}$, the wave is linearly polarized at 45 deg.
b. If $E_{ox} = E_{oy}$ and $\Phi = \pm m\pi/2$ (m = odd), the wave is circularly polarized. For $\Phi = m\pi/2$, the wave is *right circularly polarized;* For $\Phi = -m\pi/2$, the wave is *left circularly polarized.*

To avoid ambiguity in establishing directions of polarization, the IEEE Standards prescribe that a left circular (or elliptical) polarized wave exists when the rotation of its field vector is clockwise as one views the wave coming toward him.

For the case of propagation in a lossless medium $E_{ox} = E_{oy} = E_o$, $\phi_x = 0$, and $\phi_y = \pi/2$. Equations (10-6.3) become

$$E_x = E_o \cos(kz-\omega t)$$
$$E_y = E_o \cos\left(kz-\omega t + \frac{\pi}{2}\right) = -E_o \sin(kz-\omega t) \qquad (10\text{-}6.6)$$

which represent a right circularly polarized wave. The angle θ that a point on the wave vector $\overline{E}$ makes with respect to the horizontal axis is

$$\theta = \tan^{-1} \frac{E_o \sin(kz-\omega t)}{E_o \cos(kz-\omega t)} = kz-\omega t \qquad (10\text{-}6.7)$$

In case the phase of E_x is changed by π radians, Eq. (10-6.6) and (10-6.7) change to

$$E_x = -E_o \cos(kz-\omega t)$$
$$E_y = -E_o \sin(kz-\omega t) \tag{10-6.8}$$
$$\theta = -(kz-\omega t)$$

which represents a left circularly polarized wave. It is of interest to note that a linear polarized wave can be viewed as the combination of a right circularly polarized wave plus a left circularly polarized wave. To show this we employ Eqs. (10-6.6) and (10-6.8). We add these component waves to find

$$E_x = 0 \qquad E_y = -2\, E_o \sin(kz-\omega t)$$

The absorption of waves in some mediums depends on the sense of rotation of θ with time. A medium that absorbs only right circularly polarized waves traveling in the positive Z-direction will permit right circularly polarized waves to pass when they travel in the negative Z-direction. The construction of microwave *isolators* which are used to permit electromagnetic waves to propagate towards the antenna end of a microwave system but will absorb any wave traveling in the opposite direction is based on this principle.

In certain crystals, two preferable directions exist. One has associated with it a high phase velocity and the other has associated with it a slow phase velocity. Therefore, when a plane linearly polarized wave enters this crystal, its components along the two planes will travel with different phase velocities. As a result, the wave upon traveling a particular distance, say $\lambda/4$, will experience two components which are out of phase, and the wave will be elliptically polarized. When the distance of travel doubles, the sense of rotation will change into the opposite sense. Such crystals are known as *birefringent* mediums, and these can be used to convert linear to elliptical (circular) polarization, with right to left rotations or vice versa.

10-7. EM Waves in Anisotropic Mediums

When an electromagnetic wave is propagating in a medium consisting of equal numbers of electrons and ions (plasma), the wave has an influence on the state of the particles. For simplicity, we shall assume that the wave perturbs the plasma only slightly, so that we avoid nonlinear effects. If the phase velocity of the wave is greater than the thermal velocity of the electrons, and if both are much greater than the induced velocity of the electrons resulting from the electric field of the wave, then we can use linearized equations. In our analysis we shall assume that there are no collisions between electrons and ions so that resonance phenomena are not obscured. All of these assumptions lead to a study of what is known as wave phenomena in a *cold* collisionless plasma. If, in addition, a constant magnetic field penetrates the plasma, then we are studying the propagation of a wave in an *anisotropic* plasma, one of many mediums for which the permittivity has different values in different directions.

Our first objective is to find the dielectric constant of the medium. For simplicity, we assume that a static magnetic field penetrates the plasma and is directed in the Z-direction. We shall assume also that a wave is propagating in the plasma such that its wave vector is located in the XZ plane, as shown in Fig. 10-7.1. Now we make use of the equation of motion for an electron under the influence of the applied fields of the wave, namely

$$m \frac{d\overline{v}}{dt} = e\,(\overline{E} + \overline{v} \times \overline{B}_o) \tag{10-7.1}$$

where $\overline{B}_o = B_o \overline{a}_z$ is the applied magnetic field. The influence of the magnetic field intensity of the wave has been neglected because $|B_o| >> \mu_o|H|$. For the case of an assumed harmonic time variation $e^{-j\omega t}$, this equation now becomes

$$\overline{v} = -\frac{e}{jm\omega}\,(\overline{E} + \overline{v} \times \overline{B}_o) \tag{10-7.2}$$

This vector equation is equivalent to three scalar equations, since Eq. (10-7.2) can be expanded to yield equations along each axis. When this is done and the three equations are arranged into a set of equations, the results can be written in matrix form

$$\overline{v} = \begin{bmatrix} v_x \\ v_y \\ v_z \end{bmatrix} = \left(\frac{e}{m}\right) \begin{bmatrix} -\dfrac{\omega^2}{j\omega(\omega^2-\Omega^2)} & -\dfrac{\Omega}{\omega^2-\Omega^2} & 0 \\ +\dfrac{\Omega}{\omega^2-\Omega^2} & -\dfrac{\omega^2}{j\omega(\omega^2-\Omega^2)} & 0 \\ 0 & 0 & -\dfrac{1}{j\omega} \end{bmatrix} \begin{bmatrix} E_x \\ E_y \\ E_z \end{bmatrix} = \frac{e}{m}\,\hat{v}\,\overline{E} \tag{10-7.3}$$

where $\Omega = eB_o/m$ is the *electron gyrofrequency*, and where $\hat{v}$ specifies the matrix defined in Eq. (10-7.3).

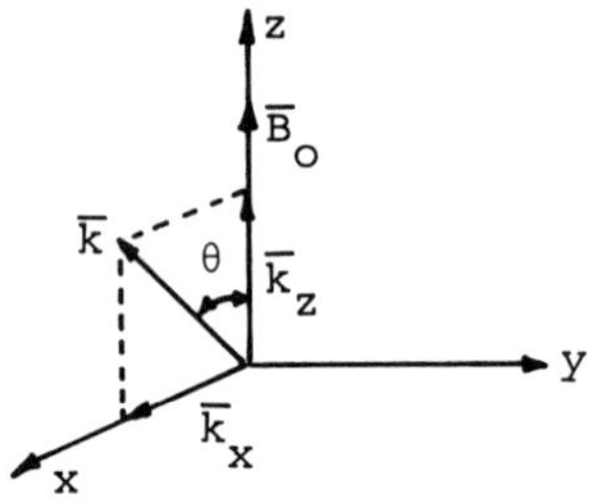

Figure 10-7.1. The geometry employed in this discussion.

The displacement vector $\overline{D}_c$ due to the current in the plasma produced by the passing wave, for harmonic variation, is equal to

$$\overline{D}_c = \frac{\overline{J}}{-j\omega} \tag{10-7.4}$$

The total displacement vector $\overline{D}$ is equal to the displacement vector of free space $\varepsilon_o\overline{E}$ plus the component due to $\overline{J}/(-j\omega)$, so that

$$\overline{D} = \varepsilon_o \hat{\varepsilon}_r \overline{E} = \varepsilon_o \overline{E} + \frac{\overline{J}}{-j\omega} \tag{10-7.5}$$

But the conduction current density is given by

$$\overline{J} = Ne\overline{v} \tag{10-7.6}$$

where N is equal to the number of electrons per unit volume. By combining Eqs. (10-7.6) and (10-7.3) with (10-7.5), the result is found to be

$$\begin{aligned} \overline{D} &= \varepsilon_o \hat{\varepsilon}_r \overline{E} = \varepsilon_o \overline{E} + \varepsilon_o \frac{Ne^2}{m\varepsilon_o} \frac{\hat{v}}{-j\omega} \overline{E} \\ &= \varepsilon_o \left[\hat{I} + \omega_p^2 \frac{\hat{v}}{-j\omega}\right] \overline{E} \end{aligned} \tag{10-7.7}$$

where $\hat{I}$ is the identity matrix (the diagonal elements are 1, and all other terms are zeros), $\omega_p^2 = Ne^2/\varepsilon_o m$ is the *plasma* frequency. This will assume the form

$$\overline{D} = \varepsilon_o \begin{bmatrix} \mathscr{S} & -j\mathscr{D} & 0 \\ j\mathscr{D} & \mathscr{S} & 0 \\ 0 & 0 & \mathscr{P} \end{bmatrix} \begin{bmatrix} E_x \\ E_y \\ E_z \end{bmatrix} = \varepsilon_o \hat{\varepsilon}_r \overline{E} \tag{10-7.8}$$

$\hat{\varepsilon}_r$ is the dielectric matrix defined by Eq. (10-7.8), where

$$\mathscr{S} = \frac{1}{2}(\mathscr{R}+\mathscr{L}) \qquad \text{a)}$$

$$\mathscr{D} = \frac{1}{2}(\mathscr{R}-\mathscr{L}) \qquad \text{b)}$$

$$\mathscr{R} = 1 - \frac{\omega_p^2}{\omega^2}\left(\frac{\omega}{\omega+\Omega}\right) \qquad \text{c)} \qquad (10\text{-}7.9)$$

$$\mathscr{L} = 1 - \frac{\omega_p^2}{\omega^2}\left(\frac{\omega}{\omega-\Omega}\right) \qquad \text{d)}$$

$$\mathscr{P} = 1 - \frac{\omega_p^2}{\omega^2} \qquad \text{e)}$$

For waves in plasmas, the two Maxwell curl equations are written

$$\nabla \times \overline{E} = j\omega\, \mu_o \mu_r \overline{H} \qquad \text{a)}$$

$$\nabla \times \overline{H} = -j\omega\, \left(\frac{\overline{J}}{-j\omega} + \varepsilon_o \overline{E}\right) = -j\omega\, \varepsilon_o \hat{\varepsilon}_r \overline{E} \qquad \text{b)} \qquad (10\text{-}7.10)$$

By taking the curl of the first of these equations and substituting $\nabla \times \overline{H}$ from the second, we find that

$$[\nabla \times \nabla \times -k_o^2 \mu_r \hat{\varepsilon}_r]\, \overline{E} = 0 \qquad (10\text{-}7.11)$$

The complete details of this equation are displayed by writing this expression in matrix form

$$\begin{bmatrix} -\left(\frac{\partial^2}{\partial y^2} + \frac{\partial^2}{\partial z^2}\right) - k_o^2 \mu_r \varepsilon_{r_{11}} & \frac{\partial}{\partial x}\frac{\partial}{\partial y} - k_o^2 \mu_r \varepsilon_{r_{12}} & \frac{\partial}{\partial x}\frac{\partial}{\partial z} - k_o^2 \mu_r \varepsilon_{r_{13}} \\ \frac{\partial}{\partial x}\frac{\partial}{\partial y} - k_o^2 \mu_r \varepsilon_{r_{21}} & -\left(\frac{\partial^2}{\partial x^2} + \frac{\partial^2}{\partial z^2}\right) - k_o^2 \mu_r \varepsilon_{r_{22}} & \frac{\partial}{\partial y}\frac{\partial}{\partial z} - k_o^2 \mu_r \varepsilon_{r_{23}} \\ \frac{\partial}{\partial x}\frac{\partial}{\partial z} - k_o^2 \mu_r \varepsilon_{r_{31}} & \frac{\partial}{\partial y}\frac{\partial}{\partial z} - k_o^2 \mu_r \varepsilon_{r_{32}} & -\left(\frac{\partial^2}{\partial x^2} + \frac{\partial^2}{\partial y^2}\right) - k_o^2 \mu_r \varepsilon_{r_{33}} \end{bmatrix} \cdot \begin{bmatrix} E_x \\ E_y \\ E_z \end{bmatrix} = 0$$

(10-7.12)

This equation was obtained by using the matrix representation of the curl operator

$$\nabla \times = \begin{bmatrix} 0 & -\frac{\partial}{\partial z} & \frac{\partial}{\partial y} \\ \frac{\partial}{\partial z} & 0 & -\frac{\partial}{\partial x} \\ -\frac{\partial}{\partial y} & \frac{\partial}{\partial x} & 0 \end{bmatrix}$$

For an assumed plane wave electric difled of the form $e^{j(\overline{k}\cdot\overline{r}-\omega t)} = e^{j(k_x x + k_y y + k_z z - \omega t)}$ which is introduced into Eq. (10-7.22), and noting the following identities which are applicable to our problem [see Fig. 10-7.1) and Eq. (10-7.8)],

$$\frac{\partial}{\partial x} = jk_x = jk \sin\theta \qquad \text{a)}$$

$$\frac{\partial}{\partial z} = jk_z = jk \cos\theta \qquad \text{b)}$$

$$\frac{\partial}{\partial y} = jk_y = 0 \qquad \text{c)} \qquad (10\text{-}7.13)$$

$$\varepsilon_{r_{13}} = \varepsilon_{r_{23}} = \varepsilon_{r_{31}} = \varepsilon_{r_{32}} = 0, \quad \mu_r = 1$$

$$\eta = \frac{k}{k_o} = \frac{c}{\omega/k} = \frac{c}{v_{ph}}, \quad \left(\overline{\eta} = \frac{\overline{k}c}{\omega}\right) \qquad \text{d)}$$

then Eq. (10-7.12) becomes

$$\begin{bmatrix} \mathcal{S} - \eta^2\cos^2 & -j\mathcal{D} & \eta^2\cos\theta\sin\theta \\ j\mathcal{D} & \mathcal{S} - \eta^2 & 0 \\ \eta^2\cos\theta\sin\theta & 0 & \mathcal{P} - \eta^2\sin^2\theta \end{bmatrix} \cdot \begin{bmatrix} E_x \\ E_y \\ E_z \end{bmatrix} = 0 \qquad (10\text{-}7.14)$$

For a nontrivial solution for the field $\overline{E}$, the determinant of the square matrix of Eq. (10-7.14) must be set equal to zero. The result is the dispersion relation

$$A\eta^4 - B\eta^2 + C = 0 \qquad (10\text{-}7.15)$$

where

$$A = \mathcal{S}\sin^2\theta + \mathcal{P}\cos^2\theta \qquad \text{a)}$$

$$B = \mathcal{R}\mathcal{L}\sin^2\theta + \mathcal{P}\mathcal{S}(1 + \cos^2\theta) \qquad \text{b)}$$

$$C = \mathcal{P}\mathcal{R}\mathcal{L} \qquad \text{c)} \qquad (10\text{-}7.15a)$$

$$\mathcal{S}^2 - \mathcal{D}^2 = \mathcal{R}\mathcal{L} \qquad \text{d)}$$

Solving Eq. (10-7.15) yields

$$\eta^2 = \frac{B \pm \sqrt{B^2 - 4AC}}{2A} \qquad (10\text{-}7.16)$$

For certain values of the plasma parameters, applied magnetic field, and direction of wave propagation, the value of η^2 becomes zero, or infinity. The case when the phase velocity is infinite, which implies $\eta^2 = 0$, is known as the *cutoff* case. The reciprocal case is termed *resonance*. Physically these two states have ready explanation when considered from the point of view of physical optics. When an optical ray passes from a dense to a less-dense medium, it is refracted away from the vertical. This implies that a ray will be totally refracted if it is traversing a medium with decreasing index of refraction, that is, as $\eta \to 0$; the opposite occurs if η increases. Cutoffs and resonances separate values of the plasma parameters for which η^2 is positive or negative, and correspondingly, regions of propagation or no propagation. From Eqs. (10-7.15) and (10-7.15a) these translate to

$\eta^2 = 0 \triangleq$ cutoff at any angle which will make $\mathcal{P} = 0$ or $\mathcal{R} = 0$ or $\mathcal{L} = 0$

$\eta^2 = \infty \triangleq$ resonance at any angle $\triangleq \tan^2\theta = -\dfrac{\mathcal{P}}{\mathcal{S}}$

$\eta^2 = \infty \triangleq$ resonance at $\theta = 0 \triangleq \begin{cases} \mathcal{R} = \pm\infty & \text{electron gyrofrequency} \\ \mathcal{L} = \pm\infty & \text{ion gyrofrequency} \end{cases}$ Principal Resonances

$\eta^2 = \infty \triangleq$ resonance at $\theta = \dfrac{\pi}{2} \triangleq \mathcal{S} = 0$ (10-7.17)

If we add $A\eta^2$ to both sides of Eq. (10-7.15) we obtain

$$\eta^2 = \frac{A\eta^2 - C}{A\eta^2 + A - B}$$

Upon substituting η^2 on the right-hand side from Eq. (10-7.16), this expression takes the form of the Appleton-Hartree formula

$$\eta^2 = 1 - \frac{X}{1 - \frac{\frac{1}{2} Y^2 \sin^2\theta}{1 - X} \pm \sqrt{\frac{1/4\ Y^4 \sin^2\theta}{(1 - X)^2} + Y^2 \cos^2\theta}} \qquad (10\text{-}7.18)$$

where

$$X = \frac{\omega_p^2}{\omega^2}, \qquad Y = \frac{\Omega}{\omega}$$

Some interesting cases for the propagation of VHF waves ($f \simeq 2$ MHz) in a lossless ionosphere follow from these equations. We shall consider three cases which are distinguished by the angle θ at which the wave vector $\overline{k}$ of a plane linearly polarized wave is deviating from the earth's magnetic field $\overline{B}_o$ (see Fig. 10-7.1). When $\overline{k}$ is parallel to $\overline{B}_o$, we are dealing with longitudinal propagation. When $\overline{k}$ is perpendicular to $\overline{B}_o$ the propagation is called transverse propagation.

a. Longitudinal propagation, $\theta = 0^o$ and $Y < 1$. For this condition $\eta^2 = 1 - X/(1 \pm Y)$. These waves are called *extraordinary*, since they are influenced by the applied magnetic field (see Fig. 10-7.2).

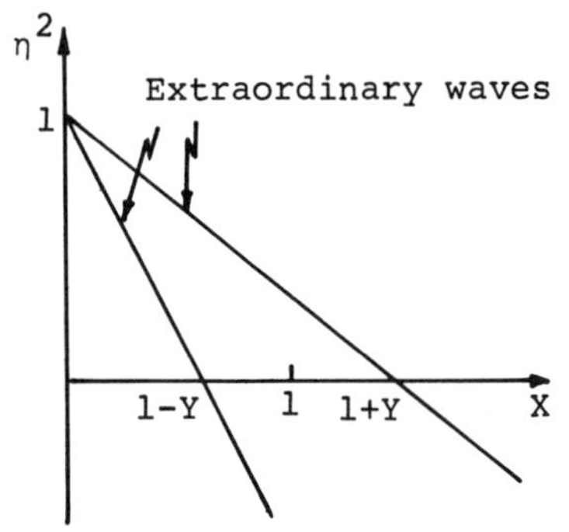

Figure 10-7.2. Longitudinal wave propagation.

b. Transverse propagation, $\theta = \pi/2$, and $Y < 1$. Now

$$\eta^2 = 1 - X \qquad \textit{ordinary wave (no dependence on the magnetic field)}$$

$$\eta^2 = 1 - \frac{X(1-X)}{1 - X - Y^2} \qquad \textit{extraordinary wave}$$

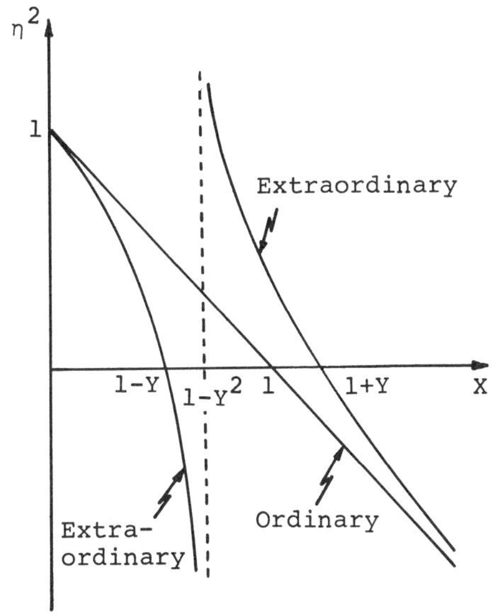

Figure 10-7.3. Transverse wave propagation.

(see Fig. 10-7.3).

c. Intermediate inclination, $0 < \theta < \pi/2$, when $Y < 1$. When the angle between the earth's magnetic field and the wave normal is small, the index of refraction varies between the limits in a. and b. and has a form shown in Fig. 10-7.4. This figure indicates that if an ordinary wave enters a medium of increasing X (increasing electron density) with the additional condition $\theta \doteq 0^{\circ}$, it will lose some of its energy to the extraordinary wave which will be generated near $X = 1$ ($\omega = \omega_p$). In

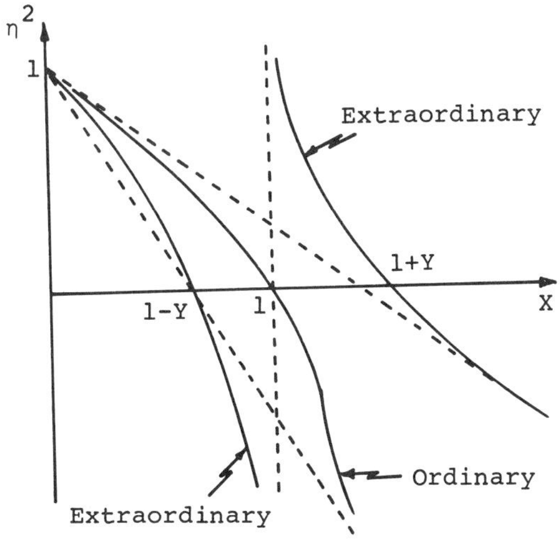

Figure 10-7.4. Intermediate inclination of waves.

the limit when the propagation is entirely longitudinal, the ordinary wave changes completely over to the extraordinary wave at $X = 1$ and thus, for $X > 1$ the only wave present is the extraordinary wave. This phenomenon is called *coupling* since energy is coupled from one mode of propagation to another.

Example 10-7.1. Find the polarization rotation (*Faraday rotation*) of a wave propagating in the ionosphere.

Solution. The presence of a magnetic field in a plasma creates a birefringent medium. As a result the incident radio wave in the ionosphere splits into the ordinary and extraordinary components. These waves do not change their polarization as they propagate through the ionosphere; however, since they have different phase velocities, the plane of polarization of the resultant wave does rotate.

Let λ_1 and λ_2 denote the wavelength of the two waves propagating an incremental distance $d\ell$. The difference of their phase rotations is given by

$$d\Phi = k_1 d\ell - k_2 d\ell = \frac{2\pi}{\lambda_1} d\ell - \frac{2\pi}{\lambda_2} d\ell \tag{10-7.19}$$

However, the wavelength is related to the index of refraction

$$\lambda = \frac{v}{f} = \frac{c}{\eta f} = \frac{2\pi c}{\omega\eta} \tag{10-7.20}$$

Combining these last two equations we obtain

$$d\Phi = \frac{\omega}{c} (\eta_1 - \eta_2) d\ell \tag{10-7.21}$$

The approximate values of the refractive ionospheric index in the longitudinal mode are:

$$\begin{aligned} \eta_1 &= 1 - \frac{X/2}{1 + Y} \\ \eta_2 &= 1 - \frac{X/2}{1 - Y} \end{aligned} \tag{10-7.22}$$

The difference

$$\eta_1 - \eta_2 = \frac{X}{2} \left(\frac{2Y}{1 - Y^2}\right) \doteq XY \qquad \text{for } \omega \gg \Omega_c$$

and thus

$$d\Phi = \frac{\omega}{c} XY\, d\ell = \frac{Ne^3 B_o}{cm^2 \omega^2 \varepsilon_o} d\ell$$

If a radio wave of 136 MHz passes through the ionosphere for a distance of 300 Km with an average electron density of $N = 4 \times 10^{11}$ electrons/m^2 and an average magnetic field $B_o = 50 \times 10^{-6}$ Weber/m^2, the rotation is about 25.6 radians. Since N and B_o may change along the path, the total rotation is proportional to the total quantity $\int N B_o \, d\ell$. For the ionosphere B_o is usually constant in time and, therefore, any change of Φ with respect to time indicates a change of total electron content along the path. This information is extremely important for modern communications networks which employ synchronous satellites.

ΔΔΔ

10-8. Crystal Optics

A number of different crystals exist which are electrically anisotropic. They influence the propagation of electromagnetic (light) waves in ways that are rather similar to the effects of anisotropic plasmas, which we have just studied. The anisotropy in crystals is caused by the nonsymmetric binding of the outermost electrons of the ions making up the crystal. As a result, the displacement of the bound electrons under the action of an applied $\overline{E}$ field will depend on the direction of the field. The resulting polarizability and hence the permittivity $\hat{\varepsilon}$ is a tensor quantity.

Because of the anisotropy present in crystals, generally two possible values of phase velocity exist for a given direction of propagation. Equivalently, the indexes of refraction corresponding to each is different. These two values are associated with orthogonal polarization of the light waves, and it can be shown that this is true for any direction of the wave in the crystal. In other words, the two phase velocities always correspond to two mutually orthogonal polarizations. Hence, two waves exist, and these are called the ordinary and the extraordinary waves. We previously met such waves when we were discussing propagation in the ionosphere. Although the naming of the two waves in crystals and in the ionosphere are the same, it is clear that the phenomenon of anisotropy in these two mediums is produced by completely different physical processes. However, there exists a preferred direction in crystals at which the two phase velocities of the mutually orthogonal polarizations of the wave are equal. Equivalently, the two wave vectors for the ordinary and extraordinary waves in this direction are equal. This preferred direction is called the *optic axis*.

It is possible to rotate the coordinate axes so that the permittivity tensor assumes the diagonal form

$$\hat{\varepsilon} = \varepsilon_o \begin{bmatrix} \varepsilon_{r_{11}} & 0 & 0 \\ 0 & \varepsilon_{r_{22}} & 0 \\ 0 & 0 & \varepsilon_{r_{33}} \end{bmatrix} \tag{10-8.1}$$

These axes are called the *principal axes*, and $\varepsilon_{r_{11}}$, $\varepsilon_{r_{22}}$, $\varepsilon_{r_{33}}$ are called the *principal values* of $\hat{\varepsilon}$ taking specific values for each type of crystal. If we introduce these values into Eq. (10-7.12) which describes the relationships in any anisotropic medium and assume a plane wave solution of the form $e^{j(\bar{k}\cdot\bar{r}-\omega t)} = e^{j(k_x x+k_y y+k_z z-\omega t)}$ we obtain ($\mu_r = 1$)

$$\begin{bmatrix} k_y^2 + k_z^2 - k_o^2\varepsilon_{r_{11}} & -k_x k_y & -k_x k_z \\ -k_x k_y & k_x^2 + k_z^2 - k_o^2\varepsilon_{r_{22}} & -k_y k_z \\ -k_x k_z & -k_y k_z & k_x^2 + k_y^2 - k_o^2\varepsilon_{r_{33}} \end{bmatrix} \begin{bmatrix} E_x \\ E_y \\ E_z \end{bmatrix} = 0 \quad (10\text{-}8.2)$$

We initially examine this equation for crystals for which $\varepsilon_{r_{11}} = \varepsilon_{r_{22}} \neq \varepsilon_{r_{33}}$; and these are known as *uniaxial* crystals. Crystals for which $\varepsilon_{r_{11}} \neq \varepsilon_{r_{22}} \neq \varepsilon_{r_{33}}$ are known as *biaxial* crystals. Further, we suppose that a propagating wave in the uniaxial crystal is oriented as shown in Fig. 10-8.1a. Under these conditions, the following relations hold:

$$k_x = k\sin\theta = kn_x; \qquad k_y = 0; \qquad k_z = k\cos\theta = kn_z$$

and writing

$$\varepsilon_{r_{11}} = \varepsilon_{r_{22}} = \varepsilon_{ro}; \qquad \varepsilon_{r_{33}} = \varepsilon_{re}$$

When these quantities are introduced into Eq. (10-8.2), and remembering that $k_x^2 + k_z^2 = k^2$, we obtain the equation set

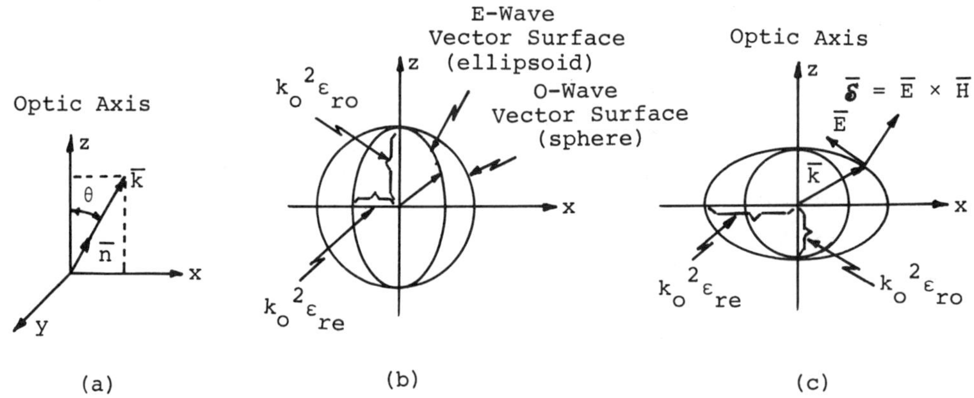

Figure 10-8.1. Propagation characteristics of waves in crystals. (a) Coordinate system. (b) Negative uniaxial crystal $\varepsilon_{re} < \varepsilon_{ro}$. (c) Positive uniaxial crystal $\varepsilon_{re} > \varepsilon_{ro}$.

$$\begin{bmatrix} k^2-k_x^2-k_o^2\varepsilon_{ro} & 0 & -k_xk_z \\ 0 & k^2-k_o^2\varepsilon_{ro} & 0 \\ -k_xk_z & 0 & k^2-k_z^2-k_o^2\varepsilon_{re} \end{bmatrix} \begin{bmatrix} E_x \\ E_y \\ E_z \end{bmatrix} = 0 \qquad (10\text{-}8.3)$$

which is equivalent to the following three equations

$$(k^2-k_o^2\varepsilon_{ro})\,E_x - k^2n_x(n_xE_x + n_zE_z) = 0 \qquad \text{a)}$$

$$(k^2-k_o^2\varepsilon_{ro})\,E_y = 0 \qquad \text{b)} \qquad (10\text{-}8.4)$$

$$(k^2-k_o^2\varepsilon_{re})\,E_z - k^2n_z(n_xE_x + n_zE_z) = 0 \qquad \text{c)}$$

If we set $E_x = E_z = 0$ and $k^2 = k_o^2\varepsilon_{ro}(\eta^2 = \eta_o^2 = \sqrt{\varepsilon_{ro}})$ then $E_y \neq 0$ and we have a solution of our system which corresponds to the *ordinary* wave with $\bar{E} = E_y\bar{a}_y$ perpendicular to both $\bar{k}$ and the optic axis taken in the Z-direction. The corresponding $\bar{D}$ field has the components

$$D_y = \eta_o^2\,E_y \qquad D_x = D_y = 0$$

This shows that $\bar{D}$ and $\bar{E}$ are colinear for the ordinary wave.

A second solution is possible if we set $E_y = 0$ in Eq. (10-8.4b). The two remaining equations have a solution if the determinant of the coefficients of E_x and E_z are zero. Upon setting the determinant to zero, we obtain $(n^2 = 1 - n_x^2)$

$$\frac{1}{k^2} = \frac{n_x^2}{k_o^2\varepsilon_{re}} + \frac{n_z^2}{k_o^2\varepsilon_{ro}} = \frac{\sin^2\theta}{k_o^2\varepsilon_{re}} + \frac{\cos^2\theta}{k_o^2\varepsilon_{ro}} \qquad (10\text{-}8.5)$$

which represents the wave vector surface for the *extraordinary* wave, and it is shown in Figs. 10-8.1b and 10-8.1c for the cases $\varepsilon_{re} < \varepsilon_{ro}$ and $\varepsilon_{re} > \varepsilon_{ro}$, respectively. If the wave propagates in the Z-direction, $n_x = 0$ and $k = k_o\sqrt{\varepsilon_{ro}} = k_o\eta_o$. If the wave propagates in the X-direction, then $k = k_o\sqrt{\varepsilon_{re}} = k_o\eta_e$. Since the velocity is inversely proportional to the wave vector, the wave vector surfaces show the variation of velocity with direction of propagation.

To understand how the wave is behaving in a uniaxial crystal, suppose that the optic axis is directed along an angle with respect to the surface of the crystal as shown in Fig. 10-8.2a. The propagation may be constructed by imaging, assuming that each point along the surface becomes a source which emits waves with wavefronts that are characteristic of the wave-vector surfaces. This approach is known as Huygen's principle, and we shall elaborate on this principle in Chap. 12. From our graphical construction we observe that the crystal of Fig. 10-8.2a will produce double images, whereas that in Fig. 10-8.2b will produce single images. This

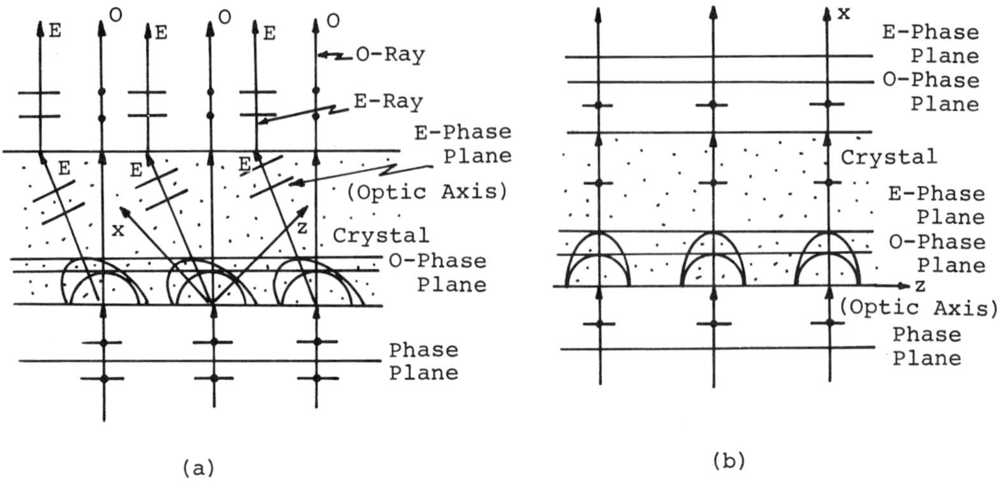

Figure 10-8.2. Rays in uniaxial crystals.

indicates that to observe the double images, which is known as *birefringence*, requires that the crystal must be cut appropriately, as shown above.

In anisotropic crystals (or mediums) the propagation vector $\bar{k}$ defines the direction of the planes of constant phase. However, the energy flow $\bar{E} \times \bar{H}$ is generally not parallel to $\bar{k}$ (see Fig. 10-8.1c) because $\bar{k}$ and $\bar{E}$ are not mutually perpendicular. A schematic representation of this phenomenon is shown in Fig. 10-8.3. The planes of constant phase are perpendicular to the wave vector $\bar{k}$ but they propagate along the ray direction $\mathscr{S}$. If v_{ph} is the phase velocity along $\bar{k}$, then the ray velocity is $v_r = v_{ph}/\cos\theta$ which is always greater than the phase velocity. The two velocities become equal when the direction of propagation is along the optic axis (see Pr. (10-8.1) and both $\bar{k}$ and $\mathscr{S}$ are then in the same direction.

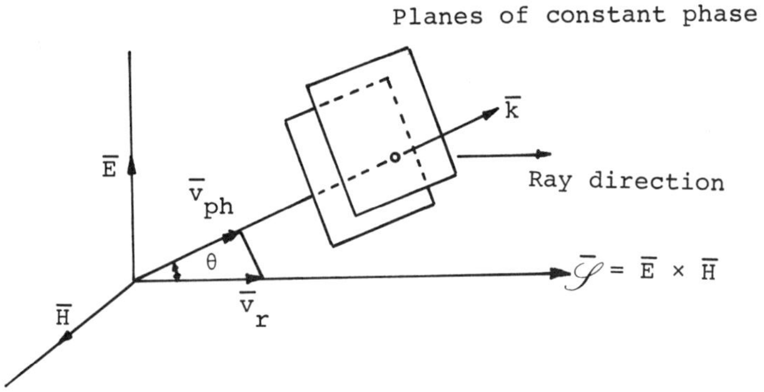

Figure 10-8.3. Illustration of the wave constants in anisotropic crystals.

10-9. Geometrical Optics Approximation for EM Waves

Geometrical optics or ray theory is concerned with the solution of the wave equation in a medium in which the free space wavelength is very small compared with the changes of the medium properties.

One can study ray optics by stratifying the medium and assuming constant properties within each slab, and then employing Snell's law. This approach parallels to some degree the discussion of the transmission line which considers it to be made up of a cascade of incremental sections. This approach has been extensively used in underwater sound tracing techniques. Another approach is to introduce the approximation $\lambda \to 0$ in Maxwell's equations. The approach that we will adopt initially begins with Eq. (8-8.8) assuming an isotropic medium whose permittivity (index of refraction) varies slowly, whence $\nabla \ln \varepsilon = 0$. The wave equation (8-8.8) thus becomes

$$\nabla^2 E + \mu_o \varepsilon_o \mu_r \varepsilon_r \omega^2 E = \nabla^2 E + k_o^2 \eta^2 E = 0 \tag{10-9.1}$$

where the refractive index $\eta = \eta(x,y,z)$, $\mu_r = 1$, ε_r is the relative permittivity, and E is one of the three components of the electric field $\overline{E}$ in an appropriate coordinate space.

Since η varies spatially, we can assume a solution of the form

$$E = E_o(x,y,z)\, e^{jk_o p(x,y,z)} \tag{10-9.2}$$

where p denotes a phase function associated with the medium, and is called an *eikonal*. We differentiate this equation twice with respect to x and obtain

$$\frac{\partial^2 E}{\partial x^2} = \left[\frac{\partial^2 E_o}{\partial x^2} + 2jk_o \frac{\partial E_o}{\partial x}\frac{\partial p}{\partial x} + jk_o E_o \frac{\partial^2 p}{\partial x^2} - k_o^2 E_o \left(\frac{\partial p}{\partial x}\right)^2\right] e^{jk_o p} \tag{10-9.3}$$

In a parallel way, we can find similar expressions for $\partial^2 E/\partial y^2$ and $\partial^2 E/\partial z^2$. By substituting these resulting relations into Eq. (10-9.1), we find

$$\nabla^2 E_o + k_o^2 E_o \left\{\eta^2 - \left[\left(\frac{\partial p}{\partial x}\right)^2 + \left(\frac{\partial p}{\partial y}\right)^2 + \left(\frac{\partial p}{\partial z}\right)^2\right]\right\} + jk_o \left[E_o \nabla^2 p + 2\left(\frac{\partial E_o}{\partial x}\frac{\partial p}{\partial x} + \frac{\partial E_o}{\partial y}\frac{\partial p}{\partial y} + \frac{\partial E_o}{\partial z}\frac{\partial p}{\partial z}\right)\right] = 0$$

This equation may be written in the compact form

$$\nabla^2 E_o + k_o^2 E_o \left[\eta^2 - (\nabla p \cdot \nabla p)\right] = -jk_o \left[E_o \nabla^2 p + 2\nabla E_o \cdot \nabla p\right] \tag{10-9.4}$$

or

$$E_o \left[\eta^2 - (\nabla p)^2\right] = -\frac{j}{k_o}\left[E_o \nabla^2 p + 2\nabla E_o \cdot \nabla p\right] - \frac{1}{k_o^2}\nabla^2 E_o \tag{10-9.5}$$

We now consider the transition from wave optics to geometric optics which occurs when k becomes large; that is, when $\lambda \to 0$. The right side of Eq. (10-9.5) approaches zero, provided, of course, that none of the terms becomes large. Equivalently, this means that we must avoid the neighborhood of sharp edges, source points, focal points and caustic surfaces where there are an infinity of rays passing through a small region. Also, the equations fail in the neighborhood of bodies whose dimensions are in the order of a wavelength. Equation (10-9.5) becomes, for the present case

$$E_o [\eta^2 - (\nabla p)^2] = 0 \tag{10-9.6}$$

Since for a non-trivial solution $E_o \neq 0$, then it is required that

$$\eta^2 = (\nabla p)^2 = \nabla p \cdot \nabla p = \left(\frac{\partial p}{\partial x}\right)^2 + \left(\frac{\partial p}{\partial y}\right)^2 + \left(\frac{\partial p}{\partial z}\right)^2 \tag{10-9.7}$$

This is known as the *eikonal* equation.

We shall limit our considerations to the case of nonhomogeneous lossless and isotropic mediums. We observe that the wavefronts represented by the family $p(x,y,z)$ = constant are the planes of constant phase. Since the energy of the wave propagates in the direction of the wave vector, which is perpendicular to the surfaces of constant phase, then the rays which characterize energy transport are perpendicular to the geometrical wavefronts p = constant, or along ∇p; hence both the surfaces of constant phase and of constant amplitude are perpendicular to the direction of propagation.

To examine this further, refer to Fig. 10-9.1. From this figure, we find the following relations

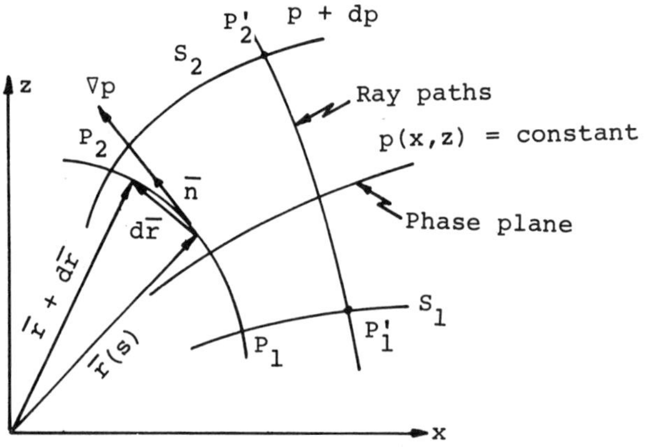

Figure 10-9.1. Wavefronts for ray optics.

$$\bar{n} = \text{unit vector} = \lim_{\Delta s \to 0} \frac{\Delta \bar{r}(s)}{\Delta s} \tag{10-9.8}$$

$$\frac{\nabla p}{|\nabla p|} = \bar{n} = \frac{d\bar{r}(s)}{ds}$$

where s is the distance along the light rays. Equation (10-9.7) requires that $\eta = |\nabla p|$ and thus Eq. (10-9.9) is

$$\eta\bar{n} = \eta \frac{d\bar{r}}{ds} = \nabla p \tag{10-9.10}$$

which is the equation for the *rays*. If we dot multiply this equation with $d\bar{r}/ds$ and use the definition of the gradient, then

$$\nabla p \cdot \frac{d\bar{r}}{ds} = \frac{dp}{ds} = \eta \tag{10-9.11}$$

or

$$p = \int_C \eta \, ds = \text{optical path along the ray} \tag{10-9.12}$$

Integrating from P_1 to P_2 (see Fig. 10-9.1) we find the *optical path length*, O.P.L.,

$$\overline{P_1P_2} = \int_{P_1}^{P_2} \eta \, ds = p(P_1) - p(P_2) \qquad \text{a)}$$

or (10-9.13)

$$\overline{P_1P_2} = \eta \ell s \qquad \text{b)}$$

for constant index of refraction. The integration must be taken along the ray.

10-10. Differential Equations for the Light Rays

To continue with our study of light rays, we differentiate Eq. (10-9.10) with respect to s. This gives

$$\frac{d}{ds}\left(\eta \frac{d\bar{r}}{ds}\right) = \frac{d}{ds}(\nabla p) = \frac{d\bar{r}}{ds} \cdot \nabla(\nabla p); \; \left\{ \frac{d}{ds} = \frac{d}{dx}\frac{dx}{ds} + \frac{d}{dy}\frac{dy}{ds} + \frac{d}{dz}\frac{dz}{ds} = \frac{d\bar{r}}{ds} \cdot \nabla \right\} \tag{10-10.1}$$

Combine this equation with Eqs. (10-9.10) and (10-9.7) with the result that

$$\frac{d}{ds}\left(\eta \frac{d\bar{r}}{ds}\right) = \frac{\nabla p}{\eta} \cdot \nabla(\nabla p) = \frac{1}{2\eta} \nabla[\nabla p \cdot \nabla p] = \frac{1}{2\eta} \nabla \eta^2 = \nabla \eta \tag{10-10.2}$$

The equation for the rays is written as

$$\frac{d}{ds}\left(\eta \frac{d\bar{r}}{ds}\right) = \nabla \eta \tag{10-10.3}$$

which can be written as three equations

$$\frac{d}{ds}\left(\eta \frac{dx}{ds}\right) - \frac{\partial \eta}{\partial x} = 0 \qquad \text{a)}$$

$$\frac{d}{ds}\left(\eta \frac{dy}{ds}\right) - \frac{\partial \eta}{\partial y} = 0 \qquad \text{b)} \qquad (10\text{-}10.4)$$

$$\frac{d}{ds}\left(\eta \frac{dz}{ds}\right) - \frac{\partial \eta}{\partial z} = 0 \qquad \text{c)}$$

a. Rays in One-Dimensional Inhomogeneous Media. The simplest case, and it is the case which is found in nature, has an index of refraction that is a function of only one space coordinate, i.e., z and $\eta = c_o/c(z)$, the ratio of the velocity in free space to that in the medium. Under this assumption, Eqs. (10-10.4) reduce to

$$\eta \frac{dx}{ds} = \text{constant} = C_1 \qquad \text{a)}$$

$$\eta \frac{dy}{ds} = \text{constant} = C_2 \qquad \text{b)} \qquad (10\text{-}10.5)$$

$$\frac{d}{ds}\left(\eta \frac{dz}{ds}\right) = \frac{d\eta}{dz}$$

Because the ratios of the first two equations are equal to constants indicates that the ray path is confined to a plane which is perpendicular to the XY plane. Without loss of generality we shall choose this plane to coincide with the XZ plane.

Referring to Fig. 10-10.1 we obtain the following relation

$$\frac{dx}{ds} = \sin\theta \qquad \text{a)}$$

$$(10\text{-}10.6)$$

$$\frac{dz}{ds} = \cos\theta \qquad \text{b)}$$

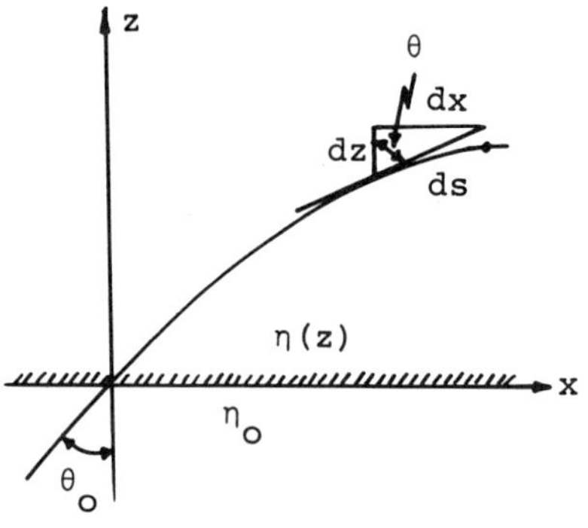

Figure 10-10.1. Ray path in a medium with varying index of refraction.

Combining Eq. (10-10.6a) and (10-10.5a), the resulting equation is $[\eta = c_0/c(z)]$

$$\frac{\sin\theta}{c(z)} = \frac{C_1}{c_0} = q \equiv \text{constant} \qquad (10\text{-}10.7)$$

or

$$\eta(z)\sin\theta = q' = \eta(z_0)\sin\theta_0$$

which is *Snell's law*. The ray parameter q is a constant along any ray path but varies from one ray to another. Equations (10-10.5c) and (10-10.6b) when combined give

$$\frac{d}{ds}(\eta\cos\theta) = \frac{d\eta}{dz} = -\eta\sin\theta\frac{d\theta}{ds} + \cos\theta\frac{d\eta}{dz}\frac{dz}{ds} = -\eta\sin\theta\frac{d\theta}{ds} + \cos^2\theta\frac{d\eta}{dz}$$

or

$$\frac{d\theta}{ds} = -\frac{\sin\theta}{\eta}\frac{d\eta}{dz} \qquad (10\text{-}10.8)$$

Differentiating the index of refraction $\eta = c_0/c(z)$ we obtain the relation

$$\frac{d\eta}{\eta} = -\frac{dc}{c} \qquad (10\text{-}10.9)$$

When this formula is combined with Eq. (10-10.8), the following useful relation results

$$\frac{d\theta}{ds} = q\frac{dc}{dz} \qquad (10\text{-}10.10)$$

Equation (10-10.10) states that the curvature of a ray $d\theta/ds$ is proportional to the velocity gradient. Figure 10-10.2 illustrates two index profiles and the corresponding bending of the rays.

Suppose that a ray is incident at an angle θ_0 at the origin, as shown in Fig. 10-10.1. From Eq. (10-10.7) we obtain the relations

$$\eta(z)\sin\theta = \eta_0\sin\theta_0 \qquad (10\text{-}10.11)$$

and

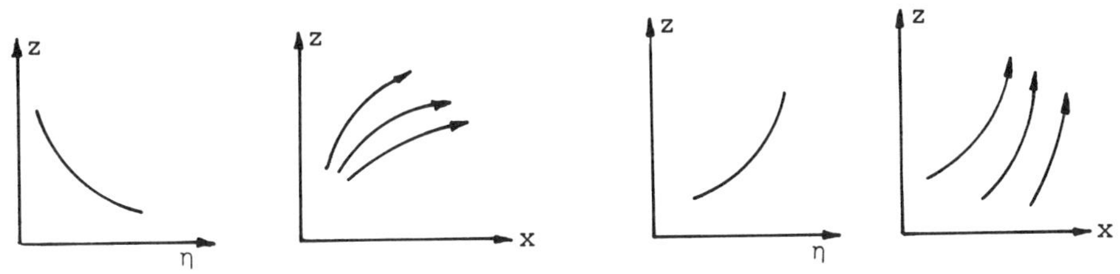

Figure 10-10.2. Intex of refraction profiles and the corresponding rays.

$$\frac{dx}{dz} = \tan\theta = \frac{\sin\theta}{(1 - \sin^2\theta)^{1/2}} \tag{10-10.12}$$

Introducing Eq. (10-10.11) into Eq. (10-10.12) and integrating, we obtain the coordinate x of the ray as a function of height z.

$$x = \eta_o \sin\theta_o \int_0^z \frac{dz'}{(\eta^2(z') - \eta_o^2 \sin^2\theta_o)^{1/2}} \tag{10-10.13}$$

In communication applications an important quantity is the signal strength at different locations relative to a transmitter. Since the rays will ordinarily converge or diverge, it is apparent that the signal strength will increase or decrease correspondingly. To calculate the intensity variation, let us consider a point source at the origin as shown in Fig. 10-10.3. We assume that the source radiates (a total power P_T) uniformly into the upper half space. The area of the band at unit distance away from the origin of the coordinate axis is

$$\Delta S = 2\pi \cdot 1 \cdot \sin\theta_o\, \delta\theta_o$$

The power density at any other point along the ray path will be

$$P = \lim_{\substack{\delta\theta_o \to 0 \\ \delta x \to 0}} \frac{P_T \sin\theta_o\, \delta\theta_o}{2\pi \cdot x \cdot \cos\theta\, \delta x} = \frac{\text{fraction of power through } \Delta S}{\text{area swept by wavefront normal}} = \frac{P_T}{2\pi x} \frac{\sin\theta_o}{\cos\theta} \frac{1}{\frac{\partial x}{\partial\theta_o}} \tag{10-10.14}$$

where $2\pi \cdot x \cdot \cos\theta\, dx$ is the area of the band swept by the wavefront normal to the rays.

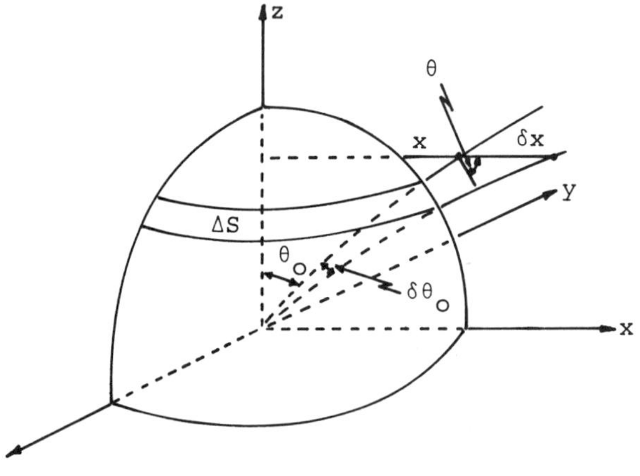

Figure 10-10.3. Illustration of the energy spreading.

Example 10-10.1. Find equations for the horizontal distance x, the height z, and power P in terms of the angle θ if the index of refraction varies linearly in the Z direction.

Solution. Using Eqs. (10-10.12) and (10-10.11) and the relation $\eta(z) = Cz$ (see Fig. 10-10.1) we obtain

$$x = \int_0^z \sin\theta \frac{dz}{\cos\theta} = \int_{\theta_o}^{\theta} \frac{\eta_o \sin\theta_o\, d\theta}{\sin\theta\, (\frac{d\eta}{dz})} = \frac{\eta_o \sin\theta_o}{C} \int_{\theta_o}^{\theta} \frac{d\theta}{\sin\theta}$$

$$= \frac{\eta_o \sin\theta_o}{C} (\log\tan\frac{\theta}{2} - \log\tan\frac{\theta_o}{2}) \tag{10-10.15}$$

and

$$z = \frac{\eta(z)}{C} = \frac{\eta_o \sin\theta_o}{C \sin\theta} \tag{10-10.16}$$

To obtain the power P we must first find the quantity $\partial x/\partial\theta_o$, which can be accomplished from Eq. (10-10.15). We obtain

$$\frac{\partial x}{\partial\theta_o} = \frac{\eta_o}{C} [\cos\theta_o(\log\tan\frac{\theta}{2} - \log\tan\frac{\theta_o}{2}) + \sin\theta_o(\frac{1}{2}\frac{1}{\tan\frac{\theta}{2}} \sec^2\frac{\theta}{2} \cdot \frac{\partial\theta}{\partial\theta_o}$$

$$- \frac{1}{\tan\frac{\theta_o}{2}} \sec^2\frac{\theta_o}{2})] \tag{10-10.17}$$

The quantity $\partial\theta/\partial\theta_o$ can be obtained from Eq. (10-10.11) and it is given by

$$\cos\theta \frac{\partial\theta}{\partial\theta_o} = \frac{\eta_o}{\eta(z)} \cos\theta_o$$

$$\frac{\partial\theta}{\partial\theta_o} = \frac{\cos\theta_o \sin\theta}{\cos\theta \sin\theta_o} \tag{10-10.18}$$

Substituting Eqs. (10-10.17) and (10-10.18) into Eq. (10-10.14) we can obtain an expression for the power P.

ΔΔΔ

b. Rays in Optical Systems. Geometrical optics can also be developed from *Fermat's principle*. This principle states that: "the optical path length difference between an actual ray and another *virtual ray* very close to it is of second order." Figure 10-10.4 shows some typical examples. From the optical path length, OPL, definition given in Eq. (10-9.13a) we write

$$OPL_{virtual} - OPL_{actual} = \delta\, OPL_{actual}$$

or

$$\int_{P_1 (virtual)}^{P_2} \eta\, ds - \int_{P_1 (actual)}^{P_2} \eta\, ds = \delta \int_{P_1 (actual)}^{P_2} \eta\, ds = \text{const. } \varepsilon^2 \tag{10-10.19}$$

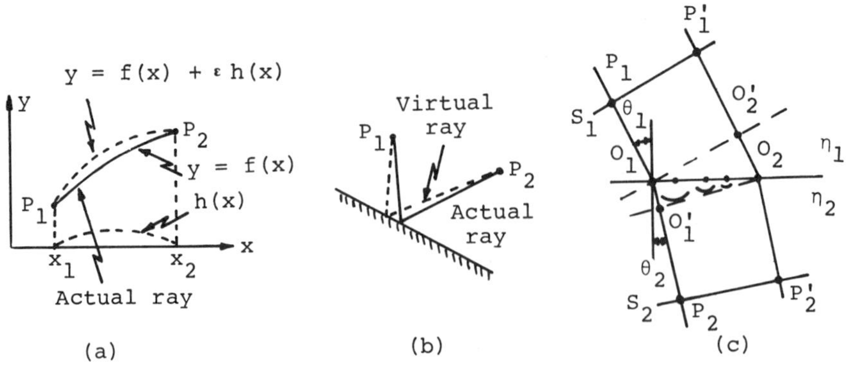

Figure 10-10.4. Representation of Fermat's principle.

where δ implies a small change. Here the change is associated with the entire path and not with a single variable. The quantity ε is a measure of the maximum separation between the actual and the virtual ray. The quantity $\int_{P_1}^{P_2} \eta\, ds_{\text{(actual)}}$ may be a maximum or a minimum depending on the curvatures of the refracting surfaces and the location of the two end points. In the language of the calculus of variation (see Chap. 15) the quantity ε is stationary for small variations of the path.

Refer to Fig. 10-10.4c. We find that the OPL from P_1 to P_2 is

$$\overline{P_1P_2} = \int_{P_1}^{O_1} \eta_1 ds + \int_{O_1}^{P_2} \eta_2 ds = \int_{P_1}^{O_1} \frac{c}{v_1} ds + \int_{O_1}^{P_2} \frac{c}{v_2} ds \qquad \text{a)}$$

$$= \int_{P_1}^{O_1} \frac{c}{ds/dt} ds + \int_{O_1}^{P_2} \frac{c}{ds/dt} ds = \int_{P_1}^{O_1} c dt + \int_{O_1}^{P_2} c dt = c(\Delta t_1 + \Delta t_2)$$

(10-10.20)

The OPL from P_1' to P_2' is

$$\overline{P_1'P_2'} = \int_{P_1'}^{O_1} \eta_1 ds + \int_{O_1'}^{P_2'} \eta_2 ds = c(\Delta t_1 + \Delta t_2) \qquad \text{b)}$$

The OPL-s are the same since the points P_1, P_1' and P_2, P_2' belong to the same wave surfaces S_1 and S_2. The surface S_2 is the same as S_1 but displaced in time $\Delta t_1 + \Delta t_2$ later. This shows that the OPL between two displaced wave surfaces is a constant, independent of the chosen ray.

Fermat's principle predicts rectilinear propagation between two points in a homogeneous medium since the straight line is the shortest distance between the points. The reversibility of light paths is easily deduced from this principle since the OPL is the same in both directions. Furthermore, from Fig. 10-10.4c the equality of the OPL-s O_1O_1' and O_2O_2' gives

$$\eta_2 \overline{O_2O_2'} = \eta_1 \overline{O_1O_1'}$$

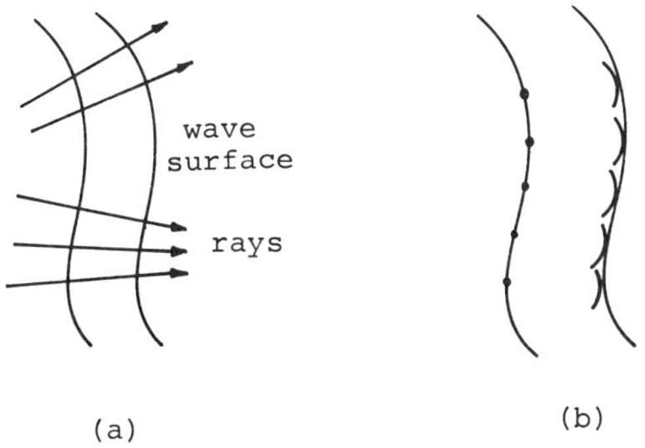

Figure 10-10.5. The relation between the Fermat and Huygens principles.

which becomes, using the angles θ_1 and θ_2,

$$\eta_1 \sin \theta_1 = \eta_2 \sin \theta_2 \tag{10-10.21}$$

which is Snell's law.

Finally, we can construct any waveform as it propagates in a uniform medium by using the equal OPL results. Figure 4-10.5a shows such a construction. As we shall see in Chap. 12, the same surface can be constructed if each point of the waveform can be considered as a point source, as shown in Fig. 10-10.5b. Clearly, the Fermat and the Huygens principles are related, and both describe basic physical laws.

Let us now apply the ideas of virtual ray optics to the optical system shown in Fig. 10-10.6. Let the radius of curvature R be equal to the curvature of a cartesian surface at O which creates an exact image of P_1 at P_2. Cartesian surfaces are hyperboloids and paraboloids, and these perfectly image objects, since any ray from a point object will converge to the same image point. In our example the ray $P_1P_0P_2$ is a virtual ray. We must study the difference

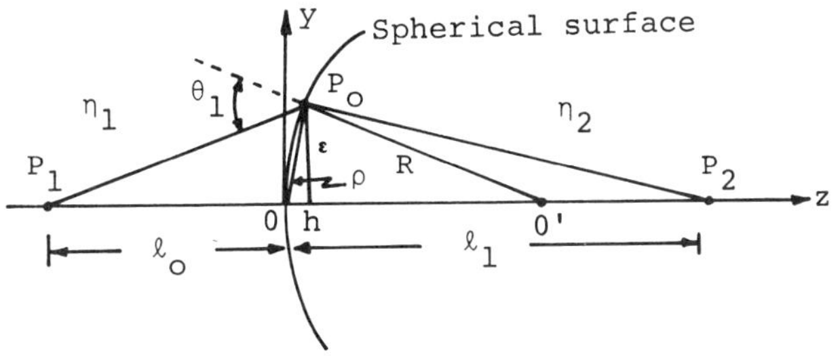

Figure 10-10.6. Imaging in a refracting medium.

$$W(\varepsilon) = OPL(\overline{P_1P_0P_2}) - OPL(\overline{P_1OP_2}) = [\eta_1\overline{P_1P_0} + \eta_2\overline{P_0P_2}] - [\eta_1\overline{P_1O} + \eta_2\overline{OP_2}]$$

$$= \eta_1[\overline{P_1P_0} - \overline{P_1O}] + \eta_2[\overline{P_0P_2} - \overline{OP_2}] \qquad (10\text{-}10.22)$$

From the geometry of Fig. 10-10.6 we obtain the following relations

$$\overline{P_1P_0} = [(\ell_o + h)^2 + \varepsilon^2]^{1/2} \qquad a)$$

$$\overline{P_0P_2} = [(\ell_i - h)^2 + \varepsilon^2]^{1/2} \qquad b) \qquad (10\text{-}10.23)$$

$$R^2 = [(R - h)^2 + \varepsilon^2] \qquad c)$$

From Eq. (10-10.23c) we also obtain the relations

$$h = \frac{\varepsilon^2 + h^2}{2R} = \frac{\rho^2}{2R} \qquad a)$$

$$\varepsilon = \rho\sqrt{1 - \frac{\rho^2}{4R^2}} \doteq \rho \quad \text{for} \quad \rho \ll R \qquad b) \qquad (10\text{-}10.24)$$

As a consequence

$$\overline{P_1P_0} = [(\ell_o + h)^2 + \varepsilon^2]^{1/2} = \ell_o\,[1 + \frac{2h}{\ell_o} + \frac{h^2 + \varepsilon^2}{\ell_o^2}]^{1/2}$$

$$= \ell_o[1 + \frac{\rho^2}{\ell_o}(\frac{1}{\ell_o} + \frac{1}{R})]^{1/2} \doteq \ell_o + \frac{\rho^2}{2}(\frac{1}{\ell_o} + \frac{1}{R}) - \frac{\rho^4}{8\ell_o}(\frac{1}{\ell_o} + \frac{1}{R})^2 + \ldots \qquad (10\text{-}10.25)$$

where the binomial expansion $(1+x)^{1/2} = 1 + x/2 - x^2/8 + \ldots$ was used. Similarly, we also find that

$$\overline{P_0P_2} = \ell_i + \frac{\rho^2}{2}(\frac{1}{\ell_i} - \frac{1}{R}) - \frac{\rho^4}{8\ell_i}(\frac{1}{\ell_i} - \frac{1}{R})^2 + \ldots \qquad (10\text{-}10.26)$$

By combining the last two equations with Eq. (9-10.22) we obtain

$$W(\varepsilon) = \frac{\rho^2}{2}[\frac{\eta_1}{\ell_o} + \frac{\eta_2}{\ell_i} - \frac{(\eta_2-\eta_1)}{R}] - \frac{\rho^4}{8}[\eta_1(\frac{1}{\ell_o} + \frac{1}{R})]^2\frac{1}{\eta_1\ell_o} + [\eta_1(\frac{1}{\ell_i} - \frac{1}{R})^2\frac{1}{\eta_2\ell_i}] + \ldots$$

$$= c_1\rho^2 + c_2\rho^4 + \ldots \qquad (10\text{-}10.27)$$

The quantities c_1, c_2, ... are known as the *aberration* coefficients. Each abberation coefficient characterizes a particular type of abberation of an optical system such as focusing, spherical aberration, astigmatism, coma, etc. The results of Eq. (10-10.27) verify Fermat's principle which dictates that the difference of the two OPL-s between an actual and a virtual ray is of the second order. If we neglect image distortions of the fourth and higher orders, we must set c_1 equal to zero, or equivalently

$$\frac{\eta_2}{\ell_1} + \frac{\eta_1}{\ell_o} = \frac{\eta_2 - \eta_1}{R} \tag{10-10.28}$$

This is exactly the equation we shall develop for imaging when the Gaussian condition is used, $\theta_1 \to 0$. For imaging, the folloinng sign convention must be adopted: (1) rays travel in the positive Z-direction; (2) R is positive if O is to the left of O', and is negative otherwise; (3) ℓ_o is positive if P_1 is to the left of O, and negative otherwise; (4) ℓ_i is positive if P_2 is to the right of O, and is negative otherwise; (5) if the ray direction is obtained by rotating the positive Z-axis counter-clockwise through an acute angle, the angle is positive, and is negative otherwise; (6) the distances y in the positive direction are positive and those in the negative direction are negative.

If we now assume that the object is at infinity, $\ell_o \to \infty$ Eq. (10-10.28) gives

$$\ell_i = \ell_f = \text{focal length} = \frac{\eta_2 R}{\eta_2 - \eta_1} \tag{10-10.29}$$

Equation (10-10.28) takes on the well known form of geometrical imaging in optics, namely,

$$\frac{\eta_1}{\ell_o} + \frac{\eta_2}{\ell_i} = \frac{\eta_2}{\ell_f} \tag{10-10.30}$$

10-11. Magnetohydrodynamic (MHD) Waves

When a conducting fluid interacts with electromagnetic fields, both the electrons and the ionized atoms are influenced by the field. The interactions produce dynamical effects, including bulk motion of the medium. The motion of the fluid, in turn, modifies the electromagnetic fields. This coupling causes the resulting phenomenon to be complicated to analyze. Such phenomena are of importance in important studies. We shall discuss only the most elementary aspects of such coupling, considering only magnetohydrodynamic waves. This discussion supplements that in Sec. 7-9.

In our analysis, we shall consider a neutral conducting fluid (an ionized plasma) that is described by the following functions: density $\rho(\bar{r},t)$, velocity $\bar{v}(\bar{r},t)$, scalar pressure $p(\bar{r},t)$ and a real conductivity σ. For simplicity we shall assume that the ions are immobile and that only the electrons are involved in the interaction. We thus begin our considerations with the continuity and the force equations for a fluid medium,

$$\frac{\partial \rho}{\partial t} + \nabla \cdot (\rho \bar{v}_1) = 0 \tag{10-11.1}$$

from Eq. (2-5.2), and the force equation,

$$\frac{f_{em} + f_p}{m} = \frac{d\overline{v}_1}{dt} = \frac{\partial \overline{v}_1}{\partial t} + \overline{v}_1 \cdot \nabla\overline{v}_1 = \frac{e}{m} (\overline{E} + \overline{v}_1 \times \overline{B}) - \frac{1}{\rho} \nabla p \tag{10-11.2}$$

where f_{em} is the electromagnetic force, and f_p is the pressure force. Gravitational and viscosity forces are neglected and the subscript to the velocity indicates a first order perturbation quantity. Further, in a highly dense conducting fluid, in almost all cases, the density of electrons and ions are in equilibrium. As a result, no localized electric fields will exist for times that are comparable with the characteristic time scale of hydromagnetic phenomena. Therefore, the term $e\overline{E}/m$ in Eq. (10-11.2) and the second order term $\overline{v}_1 \cdot \nabla\overline{v}_1$ can be neglected. Because of this, Eq. (10-11.2) becomes

$$\rho \frac{\partial \overline{v}_1}{\partial t} = \frac{\rho e}{m} \overline{v}_1 \times \overline{B} - \nabla p \tag{10-11.3}$$

which is then written

$$\rho \frac{\partial \overline{v}_1}{\partial t} = \overline{J} \times \overline{B} - \nabla p \tag{10-11.4}$$

since $\overline{J} = (\rho e/m)\overline{v}_1$. The current density is a first order quantity. Ohm's law is written in its *generalized* form

$$\overline{J} = \sigma\overline{E}' = \sigma(\overline{E} + \overline{v}_1 \times \overline{B}) \tag{10-11.5}$$

In addition, the important Maxwell equations become

$$\nabla \times \overline{E} = -\frac{\partial \overline{B}}{\partial t} \qquad \text{a)}$$

$$\nabla \times \overline{B} = \mu\overline{J} \qquad \text{b)} \tag{10-11.6}$$

where we have neglected the displacement current. This approximation is justified since the conductivity of conducting fluids is very high, and the frequencies of magnetohydrodynamic waves are low. Equations (10-11.1) through (10-11.6) constitute a system of equations with the following dependent functions: ρ, $\overline{v}_1$, $\overline{J}$, $\overline{B}$, p, and $\overline{E}$. Here there is one more unknown than the number of equations, and we need an additional relationship. We seek a relationship between p and ρ, and for this we shall use gas thermodynamic considerations. For an adiabatic process, Eq. (8-5.8) applies, which is here written

$$\nabla p = \frac{\gamma p_o}{\rho_o} \nabla \rho = c_a^{\,2} \nabla \rho \tag{10-11.7}$$

where c_a is the electron acoustic velocity and where γ is the ratio of specific heat at constant pressure to specific heat at constant volume.

We now use our equations to develop a number of special expressions relating to MHD waves. First we consider the magnetic pressure.

a. Magnetic Pressure. We combine Eq. (10-11.6b) to replace $\overline{J}$ in the momentum equation (10-11.4). The result is

$$\rho \frac{\partial \overline{v}_1}{\partial t} = \frac{1}{\mu} (\nabla \times \overline{B}) \times \overline{B} - \nabla p = \frac{1}{\mu} (\overline{B} \cdot \nabla) \overline{B} - \nabla (p + \frac{B^2}{2\mu}) \tag{10-11.8}$$

where use has been made of the vector identity

$$(\nabla \times \overline{B}) \times \overline{B} = (\overline{B} \cdot \nabla) \overline{B} - \frac{1}{2} \nabla B^2$$

The term $B^2/2\mu$ is called the *magnetic pressure* (see also Sec. 7-9E). This term gives a rough estimate of the strength of the magnetic field which must be established to confine a plasma in a fusion device.

b. Diffusion of magnetic lines. Using Eq. (10-11.5) to replace $\overline{E}$ in Eq. (10-11.6a), and then using Eq. (10-11.6b) to replace $\overline{J}$ in the new equation, we shall find that

$$\frac{\partial \overline{B}}{\partial t} = - \frac{1}{\mu\sigma} \nabla \times (\nabla \times \overline{B}) + \nabla \times (\overline{v}_1 \times \overline{B}) = \frac{1}{\mu\sigma} \nabla^2 \overline{B} + \nabla \times (\overline{v}_1 \times \overline{B}) \tag{10-11.9}$$

For nonmoving conductors, $\overline{v}_1 = 0$, and this equation assumes the form of a *diffusion equation*

$$\frac{1}{D} \frac{\partial \overline{B}}{\partial t} = \nabla^2 \overline{B} \tag{10-11.10}$$

where $D = 1/\mu\sigma$ is the diffusivity constant. For example, the time for a magnetic field to diffuse through the earth's molten core is of the order of 10 years.

c. London Equations. In superconductors the resistivity is zero, and now the force equation for the electrons becomes

$$m \frac{d\overline{v}}{dt} = e\overline{E} \tag{10-11.11}$$

The drift velocity is known to be $\overline{J} = Ne\overline{v}$ (N electrons per unit volume) and Eq. (10-11.11) becomes

$$\frac{d\overline{J}}{dt} = \frac{Ne^2}{m} \overline{E} \tag{10-11.12}$$

Take the curl of both sides of this equation and combine it with Eq. (10-11.6a) to find

$$\nabla \times \left(\frac{m}{Ne^2}\frac{d\overline{J}}{dt}\right) = -\mu \frac{\partial \overline{H}}{\partial t} \tag{10-11.13}$$

where $\overline{H}$ is the sum of the applied field $\overline{H}_a$, and that due to the magnetic field produced by the current, $\overline{H}_J$. Taking the time derivative of Eq. (10-11.6b) and combining it with Eq. (10-11.13), we obtain

$$\frac{m}{Ne^2}\nabla^2\left(\frac{\partial \overline{H}}{\partial t}\right) = \mu \frac{\partial \overline{H}}{\partial t} \tag{10-11.14}$$

Now suppose that this differential equation is integrated with respect to time. The result can be written

$$\frac{m}{Ne^2}\nabla^2(\overline{H} - \overline{H}_o) = \mu(\overline{H}-\overline{H}_o) \tag{10-11.15}$$

where $\overline{H}_o$ is the field at time $t = 0$.

One of the solutions of Eq. (10-11.15) is $H = H_o$ which indicates that a magnetic field exists inside the superconductor. However, this is contrary to physical observations. London, to overcome this difficulty, postulated the following equation for superconductors

$$\nabla \times \left(\frac{m}{Ne^2}\overline{J}\right) = -\mu\overline{H} \tag{10-11.16}$$

The use of this equation, when combined with the Maxwell-Ampère relation $\nabla \times \overline{H} = \overline{J}$, and $\nabla \cdot \overline{H} = 0$, yields

$$\frac{m}{Ne^2}\nabla^2\overline{H} = \mu\overline{H} \tag{10-11.17}$$

which does not admit a constant field as a solution. We assume a solution of the form

$$\overline{H} = \overline{H}_o e^{-x/\lambda_L}$$

from which it follows that

$$\lambda_L = \left(\frac{m}{\mu Ne^2}\right)^{1/2} = \frac{c}{\omega_p} \tag{10-11.18}$$

This formula gives a measure of the penetration depth of the field in superconductors. In a metal at 0° Kelvin, λ_L is approximately 5×10^{-8} m.

d. Magnetohydrodynamic waves (MHD waves). To study MHD waves of small amplitude, we introduce the following perturbations on the field, i.e., we assume that the fields are slightly disturbed by the waves:

$\overline{B} = \overline{B}_0 + \overline{B}_1(\overline{r},t) \qquad \rho = \rho_0 + \rho_1(\overline{r},t) \qquad p = p_0 + p_1(\overline{r},t)$

Equations (10-11.1), (10-11.4), (10-11.6b), (10-11.7), and (10-11.9) become

$$\frac{\partial \rho_1}{\partial t} + \nabla \cdot (\rho_0 \overline{v}_1 + \rho_1 \overline{v}_1) \doteq \frac{\partial \rho_1}{\partial t} + \rho_0 \nabla \cdot \overline{v}_1 = 0 \tag{10-11.19}$$

$$\rho_0 \frac{\partial \overline{v}_1}{\partial t} = \overline{J} \times \overline{B}_0 - u_a^2 \nabla \rho_1 \tag{10-11.20}$$

$$\nabla \times \overline{B}_1 = \mu \overline{J} \tag{10-11.21}$$

$$\frac{\partial \overline{B}_1}{\partial t} = \frac{1}{\mu\sigma} \nabla^2 \overline{B}_1 + \nabla \times (\overline{v}_1 \times \overline{B}_0) \tag{10-11.22}$$

It is noted that certain second-order quantities have been neglected in these equations. These involve the term $\rho_1 \nabla \cdot \overline{v}_1$ in Eq. (10-11.19), the term $\overline{J} \times \overline{B}_1$ in Eq. (10-11.20) and the term $\nabla \times (\overline{v}_1 \times \overline{B}_1)$ in Eq. (10-11.22). The vector fields in $\overline{v}_1$, $\overline{J}$ and $\overline{E}$ are all first order perturbations produced by the passage of the wave through the medium. Noting that for a spatial and time harmonic plane wave excitation of the form $e^{j(\overline{k}\cdot\overline{r}-\omega t)}$, the operators $\partial/\partial t$ and ∇ are replaced, respectively, by $-j\omega$ and $j\overline{k}$, and Eqs. (10-11.19), (10-11.20), and (10-11.22) become

$$\rho_1 = \frac{\rho_0}{\omega} (\overline{k} \cdot \overline{v}_1) \tag{10-11.23}$$

$$-\omega \rho_0 \overline{v}_1 = \frac{1}{\mu} (\overline{k} \times \overline{B}_1) \times \overline{B}_0 - \overline{k} u_a^2 \rho_1 \tag{10-11.24}$$

$$(-j\omega + \frac{k^2}{\sigma\mu}) \overline{B}_1 = j\overline{k} \times (\overline{v}_1 \times \overline{B}_0) \tag{10-11.25}$$

where we have substituted $\overline{J}$ from Eq. (10-11.21) into Eq. (10-11.20). Now combine ρ_1 from Eq. (10-11.23) and $\overline{B}_1$ from Eq. (10-11.25) with Eq. (10-11.24) and multiply by $j\omega/\rho_0$, to obtain

$$\omega^2 \overline{v}_1 = \frac{[\overline{k} \times [\overline{k} \times (\overline{v}_1 \times \overline{B}_0)]] \times \overline{B}_0}{\mu \rho_0 [1 + j \frac{1}{\mu\sigma\omega} k^2]} + u_a^2 (\overline{k} \cdot \overline{v}_1) \overline{k} \tag{10-11.26}$$

For simplicity, we assume that $\sigma \to \infty$, and the term $k^2/\mu\sigma\omega \ll 1$ and can be neglected. If, in addition, we introduce the vector *Alfvèn velocity*

$$\overline{v}_A = \frac{\overline{B}_0}{\sqrt{\mu \rho_0}} \tag{10-11.27}$$

Eq. (10-11.26) reduces to

$$\omega^2 \overline{v}_1 = [\overline{k} \times [\overline{k} \times (\overline{v}_1 \times \overline{v}_A)]] \times \overline{v}_A + u_a^2 (\overline{k} \cdot \overline{v}_1) \overline{k} \tag{10-11.28}$$

This becomes, after expansion,

$$-\omega^2\overline{v}_1 + (u_a{}^2 + v_A{}^2)(\overline{k}\cdot\overline{v}_1)\overline{k} + (\overline{v}_A\cdot\overline{k})[\overline{v}_1(\overline{k}\cdot\overline{v}_A) - \overline{v}_A(\overline{k}\cdot\overline{v}_1) - \overline{k}(\overline{v}_A\cdot\overline{v}_1)] = 0 \tag{10-11.29}$$

When the wave propagates perpendicular to the applied magnetic field, $\overline{k} \perp \overline{v}_A$, and Eq. (10-11.29) becomes

$$-\omega^2\overline{v}_1 + (u_a{}^2 + v_A{}^2)\ (\overline{k}\cdot\overline{v}_1)\overline{k} = 0 \tag{10-11.30}$$

This is equivalent to the following set of equations

$$\begin{bmatrix} -\omega^2 + (u_a{}^2+v_A{}^2)k^2 & 0 & 0 \\ 0 & -\omega^2 & 0 \\ 0 & 0 & -\omega^2 \end{bmatrix} \cdot \begin{bmatrix} v_{1x} \\ v_{1y} \\ v_{1z} \end{bmatrix} = 0 \tag{10-11.31}$$

where $\overline{k}$ is taken parallel to the X-axis. For a non-trivial solution, the determinant must be zero. This requires that

$$v_{ph} = \frac{\omega}{k} = \sqrt{u_a{}^2+v_A{}^2} \tag{10-11.32}$$

This has the character of a sonic wave with a velocity depending on the sum of the hydrostatic and magnetic pressure. It is observed from Eq. (10-11.31) that v_{1x} is the only velocity component which can have a finite value. This shows, therefore, that the wave is *longitudinal*.

When the wave propagates parallel to the applied magnetic field $\overline{k} \parallel \overline{v}_A$ and Eq. (10-11.29) leads to the following matrix set

$$\begin{bmatrix} \omega^2 - k^2u_a{}^2 & 0 & 0 \\ 0 & \omega^2 - k^2v_A{}^2 & 0 \\ 0 & 0 & \omega^2 - k^2v_A{}^2 \end{bmatrix} \begin{bmatrix} v_{1x} \\ v_{1y} \\ v_{1z} \end{bmatrix} = 0 \tag{10-11.33}$$

where $\overline{k}$ and $\overline{v}_A$ were taken to be parallel to the X-axis. For a non-trivial solution to exist, the following equation must be satisfied:

$$(\omega^2 - k^2v_A{}^2)[\omega^4 - k^2(u_a{}^2 + v_A{}^2)\omega^2 + k^4u_a{}^2v_A{}^2] = 0 \tag{10-11.34}$$

If we set

$$\omega^2 - k^2v_A{}^2 = 0$$

or

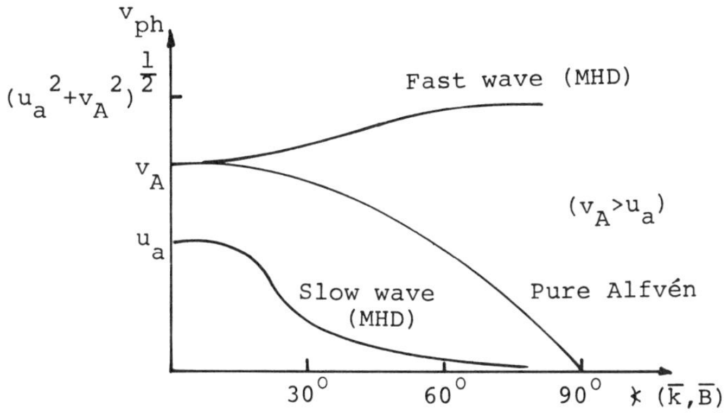

Figure 10-11.1. MHD waves.

$$\left(\frac{\omega}{k}\right)^2 = v_{ph}^2 = v_A^2 \tag{10-11.35}$$

we are describing a *pure Alfvén wave*. If, however, we set the second bracketed term equal to zero, the following dispersion relation is obtained

$$\frac{\omega^2}{k^2} = v_{ph}^2 = \frac{1}{2}\left[(v_A^2 + u_a^2) \pm (v_A^2 - u_a^2)\right] \tag{10-11.36}$$

The solution with the plus sign is called the *fast wave;* that with the minus sign is called the *slow wave*. A plot of the phase velocity as a function of the angle between the applied magnetic field and the propagation vector is shown in Fig. 10-11.1. For mercury at room temperature the Alfvèn velocity is $B_0 \cdot 10^6/13.1$ m/sec compared with the sound speed of 1.45×10^3 m/sec. At the usual laboratory field strengths the Alfvén velocity is much less than the speed of sound, although in astrophysical problems the reverse is true.

10-12. Propagation of Optical Beams

Optical beams have many similarities to plane electromagnetic waves; main difference is that they vary in intensity across their width, with most of the energy concentrated on the beam axis. Additionally, the phase fronts are not planes, but are slightly curved.

The form of optical beam most often used in analysis is one that assumes a Gaussian intensity distribution in all planes normal to the direction of propagation. To derive the form of its propagation function for a harmonic wave ($e^{-j\omega t}$) we start with Eq. (8-8.8). If, in addition, we assume plane polarization, i.e.,

$$\bar{E} = \bar{a}_x E_x(xyz) = \bar{a}_x E \tag{10-12.1}$$

then Eq. (8-8.8) reduces to a scalar equation of the following form

$$\nabla^2 E + \mu\varepsilon\omega^2 E = \nabla^2 E + k^2(x,y,z)\, E = 0 \tag{10-12.2}$$

where we have assumed that $\varepsilon(r)$ varies slowly and thus the term containing $\nabla\, \ell n\, \varepsilon$ can be neglected [Compare with Eq. (10-9.1)].

For light propagating in the Z-direction, we set

$$E(x,y,z) = E_t(x,y,z)\, e^{+jkz} \tag{10-12.3}$$

where the function $E_t(x,y,z)$ must contain the information about the intensity variation and the non-planar wavefront character of the beam. By combining Eq. (10-12.3) with Eq. (10-12.2) we obtain

$$\nabla_t^2 E_t + 2jk \frac{\partial E_t}{\partial z} = \frac{\partial^2 E_t}{\partial x^2} + \frac{\partial^2 E_t}{\partial y^2} + 2jk \frac{\partial E_t}{\partial z} = \frac{\partial^2 E_t}{\partial r^2} + \frac{1}{r}\frac{\partial E_t}{\partial r} + 2jk \frac{\partial E_t}{\partial z} = 0 \tag{10-12.4}$$

where it is assumed that the Z-variation of E_t is very small, so that the term $\partial^2 E_t/\partial z^2$ is neglected when compared with the second term $|2jk\,(\partial E_t/\partial z)|$. This

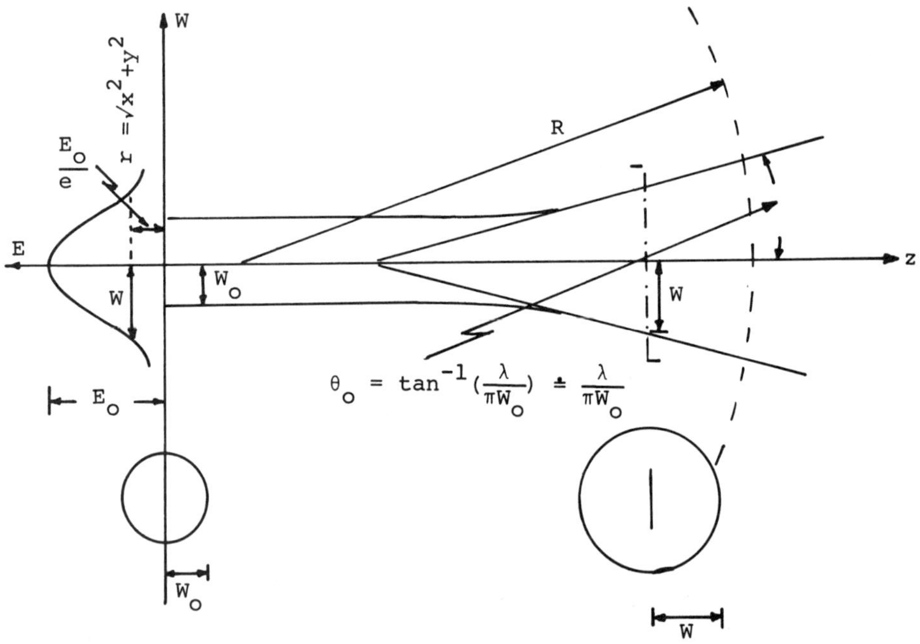

Figure 10-12.1. Properties of the optical beam.

assumption is justified for laser beams since the beam divergence is very small and the field does not vary appreciably along the Z-axis. Some of the physical characteristics of the beam are shown in Fig. 10-12.1.

We assume as a solution to Eq. (10-12.4) the wave function

$$E_t = e^{j\left(p(z) + \frac{k}{2q(z)} r^2\right)} \qquad (10\text{-}12.5)$$

where $r^2 = x^2 + y^2$ (see Fig. 10-12.1). Combine this expression with Eq. (10-12.4) to find

$$2jq - kr^2 - 2q^2 \frac{\partial p}{\partial z} + k \frac{\partial q}{\partial z} r^2 = 0 \qquad (10\text{-}12.6)$$

To satisfy this equation for all values of r, the factors with common powers of r must be identically zero. This requires that

$$\frac{\partial q}{\partial z} = 1 \qquad \text{a)}$$

$$\frac{\partial p}{\partial z} = \frac{j}{q} \qquad \text{b)} \qquad (10\text{-}12.7)$$

The function p(z) represents the complex phase shift which the wave experiences as it propagates, and the complex function q(z) describes the Gaussian intensity variation of the beam and the curvature of its wavefronts.

The solution of Eq. (10-12.7a) is simply

$$q = q_0 + z \qquad (10\text{-}12.8)$$

where q_0 is a constant. We now introduce the relation

$$\frac{1}{q} = \frac{1}{R} + j \frac{\lambda}{\pi W^2} \qquad (10\text{-}12.9)$$

where R(z) is the *complex radius of curvature* of the wavefronts, and W(z) is a measure of the decrease of E from the center. We observe that at the initial plane $z = 0$, $R = \infty$, and thus

$$q_0 = -j \frac{\pi W_0^2}{\lambda} \qquad (10\text{-}12.10)$$

The parameter q at each plane along the beam is then given by

$$q = z - j \frac{\pi W_0^2}{\lambda} \qquad (10\text{-}12.11)$$

The solution of Eq. (10-12.7b) is

$$p = j\,\ell n\left(1 + \frac{z}{q_o}\right) \tag{10-12.12}$$

By combining Eqs. (10-12.11) and (10-12.12) with Eq. (10-12.5) there results

$$E_t = e^{j\left[j\,\ell n\left(1 + \frac{z}{q_o}\right) + \frac{k}{2(q_0+z)} r^2\right]}$$

or

$$E_t = \frac{1}{\left[1 + \left(\frac{z\lambda}{\pi W_o^2}\right)^2\right]^{1/2}} e^{-j\phi} \exp\left[-\frac{r^2}{W_o^2\left[1 + \left(\frac{\lambda z}{\pi W_o^2}\right)^2\right]} + j\frac{kr^2}{2z}\frac{1}{\left[1 + \left(\frac{\pi W_o^2}{\lambda z}\right)^2\right]}\right] \tag{10-12.13}$$

where $\phi = \tan^{-1}(z\lambda/\pi W_o^2)$ (see Pr. 10-12.1). Angle ϕ is the real part of $p(z)$ and it represents a phase shift between the beam and the plane wave. The imaginary part gives the rate of decrease of the beam on the axis.

Let us introduce Eq. (10-12.11) into Eq. (10-12.9) and equate the real and the imaginary parts. We find the following terms [note that these terms appear in Eq. (10-12.13)]:

$$W(z)^2 = W_o^2\left[1 + \left(\frac{\lambda z}{\pi W_o^2}\right)^2\right]$$
$$R(z) = z\left[1 + \left(\frac{\pi W_o^2}{\lambda z}\right)^2\right] \tag{10-12.14}$$

By combining Eqs. (10-12.14) and (10-12.13) with Eq. (10-12.3), we find the fundamental mode of propagation of a Gaussian beam to be

$$E(x,y,z) = \frac{W_o}{W} e^{j(kz-\phi)}\, e^{-r^2\left(\frac{1}{W^2} + \frac{jk}{2R}\right)} \tag{10-12.15}$$

which indicates that the field of the beam is uniquely defined when W_o is given at $z = 0$.

REVIEW QUESTIONS

1. How many waves does the solution of the wave equation represent?
2. What is the name, the units, and its relation to the frequency and electrical characteristics of the medium of the term k?
3. If an electromagnetic wave in a homogeneous and isotropic medium is transverse, what is the geometrical relation of the $\overline{E}$ and $\overline{H}$ vectors?
4. What is meant by the term, intrinsic impedance of the medium?
5. What is the phase velocity of a wave?
6. When do standing waves appear in a field?

7. If the standing wave ratio of an antenna at three different locations has the values 1.001, 10 and 1000, which of these is the most desirable location, and why?
8. If the permittivity of a medium is complex, is the wave number complex or real?
9. What name is used to describe a medium whose permittivity is a function of the frequency?
10. What are the conditions which distinguish between poor and good conductors?
11. Are the $\overline{E}$ and $\overline{H}$ fields in phase or out of phase in a conducting medium?
12. What is the physical significance of the skin depth factor?
13. How many different types of dispersion have we encountered, and what are their physical significance?
14. Under what conditions do we have a polarization current?
15. If $\omega\tau \leq 1$ in a conductor, and the conduction current and the applied field in phase or out of phase?
16. How is the polarization current produced?
17. When does a lasing action take place? It is understood that a feedback mechanism (cavity) and an excitation (pumping) are present.
18. What is group velocity?
19. When are the phase and group velocities the same?
20. What is meant by anomalous dispersion?
21. How many distinct dispersion curves does a crystal have for a primitive cell of two different atoms? Explain their physical characteristics.
22. How many types of polarization can an electromagnetic field have? Give the electric field configuration for each type of polarization.
23. When does the electron gyrofrequency appear?
24. What do we call the phenomenon when $\eta^2 = 0$; when $\eta^2 = \infty$?
25. What is the difference between an ordinary and an extraordinary wave?
26. What do we mean by coupling in radio propagation?
27. What are the characteristics of Faraday rotation?
28. What are the definitions for a uniaxial and a biaxial crystal?
29. From Fig. 10-8.1b indicate which of the two extraordinary waves in the X- and Z-directions respectively is the fastest.
30. Is the path of the energy transmitted in a birefringent medium parallel to the wave vector?
31. What is the definition of the optical path length?
32. State Snell's law.
33. State Fermat's principle.
34. What is meant when we say that an optical system has abberations?
35. What does the magnetic pressure $B^2/2\mu$ indicate?
36. When is an Alfvén wave produced?

PROBLEMS

10-2.1. Show that Eq. (10-2.6) is a solution of Eq. (10-2.3) and verify Eqs. (10-2.9), (10-2.11), and (10-2.13).

10-2.2. A plane wave with a peak value $E_0 = 5\ \mu V\ m^{-1}$ is propagating in a lossless dielectric with $\mu_r = 1$ and $\varepsilon_r = 5$. Find (a) the velocity of the wave, (b) the impedance of the medium, (c) the Poynting vector, and (d) the peak value of H.

10-2.3. A plane wave of 10 MHz has an average Poynting vector of 5 mW m^{-2}. If the medium is lossless with $\mu_r = 1$ and $\varepsilon_r = 5$, find (a) the velocity, (b) the wavelength, and (c) the peak values of the electric and magnetic fields.

10-2.4. Plot the time-instantaneous Poynting vector versus kx for the plane wave given in Ex. 10-2.1 at two different times. Find the difference between the frequency variations of the field components and the instantaneous power flow.

10-2.5. Deduce the wave number of an electromagnetic wave of frequency 10^{14} Hz. in distilled water ($\varepsilon_r = 80$); in vacuum.

10-2.6. If the ratio of the indexes of refraction of two mediums is 3, what is the ratio of the wavelengths of an electromagnetic wave in these mediums?

10-2.7. A plane electromagnetic wave is propagating in a medium with relative permittivity 2.7. If its electric field vector is $\overline{E} = 3.6\overline{a}_x + 1.2\overline{a}_y - 2\overline{a}_z$ Volt/m and its wave number is $\overline{k} = 0.1\overline{a}_x - 0.3\overline{a}_y$ (m^{-1}), find its magnetic field vector $\overline{H}$. The frequency of the wave is 10^6 Hz.

10-2.8. Determine the difference in phase velocity of a HeNe ($\lambda = 632.8 \times 10^{-3}\ \mu m$) laser light in vacuum and in a medium with $\varepsilon_r = 2.1$.

10-2.9. An harmonic electromagnetic wave with $E_0 = 10^{-3}\ \mu V/m$ is propagating in free space. If we double its peak value E_0, by what factor does the average power flow increase?

10-3.1. Plot the instantaneous Poynting vector and its time-average value versus kx for a plane wave in a conducting medium for times t_1 and t_2 ($t_2 > t_1$). Discuss the phenomenon you observe from your plots.

10-3.2. Verify Eqs. (10-3.8), (10-3.9), (10-3.10), and (10-3.11).

10-3.3. Determine the conductance of a poor conductor ($\varepsilon_r = 3$) such that the phase difference between E and H field vectors of a plane wave propagating into the medium is 48° at 30 MHz.

10-3.4. What is the value of the real and imaginary part of the permittivity of sea water at 10 Hz ($\sigma = 0.05$ mho/m; $\varepsilon_r = 80$)?

10-3.5. Determine the phase velocity and skin depth of a 10 Hz electromagnetic wave in sea water.

10-3.6. Plot k' and k" versus ω for poor conductors. The range of ω should be such that $\sigma/\omega\varepsilon \ll 1$. From the plot find graphically the phase and group velocities. Repeat for the case of a good conductor.

10-3.7. Find an expression for the average power of a 10 Hz electromagnetic wave in sea water at a depth of 3.5 m. What is the impedance of the medium?

10-3.8. If one milliwatt of electromagnetic power enters sea water, what is the power present at 1.35 m into the water? The frequency of the wave is 8.5 Mz.

10-4.1. Find the mean time τ between collisions of an electron in copper at room temperature. The d-c conductivity of copper is 5.8×10^7 mho/m. [Hint: the concentration of electrons is equal to Avagadro's number divided by the molar volume.]

10-4.2. The ratio $\varepsilon''/\varepsilon' = \tan\delta$ is called the *loss tangent* and is a measure of power dissipation. For a dielectric medium find the range of frequencies where the loss tangent will have a peak.
[Ans: Near the resonant frequency ω_o.]

10-4.3. Find the real and imaginary parts of the conduction current in copper when the light of a HeNe (λ = 0.6328 μm) laser strikes the conductor. The power of the laser is 50 mW.

10-4.4. Determine the plasma frequency of the F-layer of the ionosphere ($N = 1.5 \times 10^6$ electrons/cm^3). Two local stations broadcast at 136 kHz and 210 kHz. To which of the two stations can an astronaut listen while circling above the F-layer?

10-4.5. If an electromagnetic wave of frequency 0.8 MHz propagates in the F-layer of the ionosphere, by how many dB will it decay if it travels 100 Km? The collision frequency of the electrons is $\nu = 10^4$ sec^{-1}.

10-4.6. Find the gain and the phase shift for a wave propagating 0.5 m in a medium when inverse population takes place. Plot the gain versus ω for values of ω close to ω_o.

10-4.7. Show that the maxima of $\chi_e'(\omega)$ are $\pm\frac{1}{2}\frac{Ne^2}{m\varepsilon_o\omega_o\nu}$.

10-5.1. Determine the frequencies of the modulated signal

$$f(t) = m(t)c(t) = (10 \cos 2\pi 10^3 t)(\cos 2\pi 10^9 t)$$

Show qualitatively that this agrees with Eq. (10-5.3).

10-5.2. A modulated radio wave of the form

$$E(x,t) = 10 \cos 2\pi(10^3 t - \frac{10^{-5}}{3} x) \cos 2\pi(3 \times 10^6 t - 10^{-2} x)$$

is propagating in an ionosphere whose plasma frequency is $f_p = 10^6$ Hz. What is the form of E(x,t) in the ionosphere? Does the modulating signal propagate faster or slower than the carrier signal in the ionosphere?

10-6.1. Verify Eq. (10-6.5).

10-6.2. Describe the state of polarization of the following waves

$$\overline{E} = E_0 \cos(kz-\omega t)\overline{a}_x - E_0 \cos(kz-\omega t)\overline{a}_y$$

$$\overline{E} = E_0 \cos(kz-\omega t-\frac{\pi}{2})\overline{a}_x - E_0 \sin(kz-\omega t)\overline{a}_y$$

$$\overline{E} = (E_{ox}\overline{a}_x - E_{oy}\overline{a}_y) \cos(kz-\omega t)$$

10-6.3. Describe the wave disturbance

$$\overline{E}(x,t) = E_0 [\cos \omega t\, \overline{a}_x + \cos(\omega t + \frac{\pi}{2})\overline{a}_y] \sin kz$$

and sketch it for two instants of time.

10-6.4. Two linear polarized components of a wave, which approaches an observer, are: $E_x = 2.5 \cos \omega t$ and $E_y = \cos(\omega t + \pi/2)$. Find: (a) the axial ratio, (b) the angle between the major axis and the positive X-axis, and (c) define its sense of rotation.

10-7.1. Verify Eqs. (10-7.3) and (10-7.8).

10-7.2. Verify Eqs. (10-7.14), (10-7.15), and (10-7.16).

10-7.3. Verify the diagram shown for transverse propagation when Y > 1.

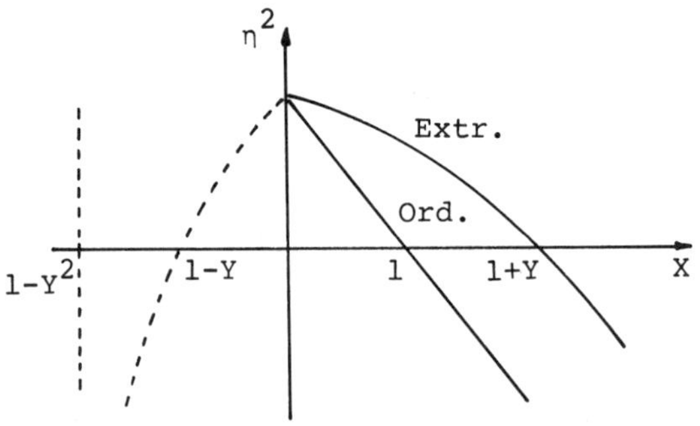

Figure P10-7.3.

10-7.4. Find the value of η^2 using Appleton-Hartree formula for a wave of 1 MHz. that is propagating at an angle $\theta = 45^o$. The magnetic field of the earth is 50×10^{-6} Weber/m^2 and the electron density is $N = 1.5 \times 10^{12}$ electrons/m^3 (daytime value).

10-7.5. Find the Faraday rotation for transverse propagation through the ionosphere. Use the constants given in Ex. 10-7.1.

10-7.6. A 6 MHz wave is propagating in the ionosphere transversely to the earth's magnetic field. Determine the phase change of the ordinary and extraordinary waves if they propagate 1 Km. The magnetic field of the earth is 50×10^{-6} Weber/m^2 and the electron density is $N = 0.5 \times 10^{12}$ electrons/m^3 (night-time).

10-7.7. For values $\theta = 80^o$ and $Y = 0.2$ plot η^2 versus X using the Appleton-Hartree equation. Compare your results with those in Fig. 10-7.4.

10-8.1. Show that if the determinant which defines the three-dimensional surface in the k-space is of the form (*biaxial crystals*) shown

$$\begin{vmatrix} a^2-k^2+k_x^2 & k_xk_y & k_xk_z \\ k_xk_y & b^2-k^2+k_y^2 & k_yk_z \\ k_xk_z & k_yk_z & g^2-k^2+k_z^2 \end{vmatrix}, \quad a = \eta_1k_o,\ b = \eta_2k_o,\ c = \eta_3k_o$$

the two surfaces are intersecting. The lines (directions) along which both waves have the same velocity are called optic axis. Assume the relative magnitude $a < b < g$. [Hint: consider each plane by setting consecutively $k_x = 0$, $k_y = 0$, and $k_z = 0$.]

10-8.2. Light from a HeNe laser ($\lambda = 0.6328\ \mu m$) is incident normally on the surface of a thin quartz crystal, as shown in Fig. 10-8.2b, with components E_z and E_y. If the relative permittivities for the two polarizations are 1.552 and 1.548 respectively, what must be the thickness of the crystal such that the emerging components have a $\pi/2$ phase difference?

10-9.1. The surfaces of constant phase are given by the equation

$$p(x,z) = x^2 + 3x(z^2-1)$$

Find the direction of the rays at the point x = 1,5, z = 3.1.

10-10.1. Sketch the ray for a linear profile of the form $\eta^2(z) = 1 - z/100$ and for $\theta_o = 20^o$ and $\eta_o = 1$.
[Ans: $z_{max} = 100\cos^2\theta_o$, $x = (2z_{max} - 2\sqrt{z_{max}}\sqrt{z_{max} - z})\tan\theta_o$.]

10-10.2. A ray enters at z = 0 from a medium with $\eta_o = 3.1$ to a second medium with $\eta = 2.5z^2 + 5$ at an angle $\theta_o = 35^o$. Find the ordinate x of the ray at the instant at which its height is 1500 m.

10-10.3. Find the aberration function $W(\varepsilon)$ for the reflecting case shown in Fig. P10-10.2.

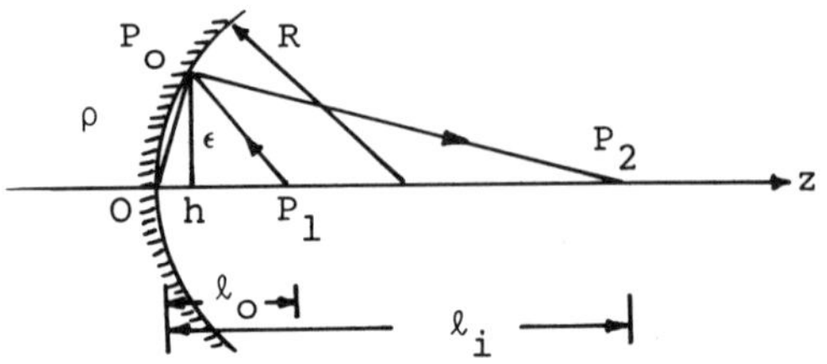

Figure P10-10.2.

[Hint: $W(\varepsilon) = [\overline{P_1P_o} - \overline{P_1O}] + [\overline{P_oP_2} - \overline{OP_2}]$.]

10-11.1. What is the magnetic pressure exerted on a plasma by a 10^5 Gauss magnetic field?

10-11.2. Determine the Alfvèn velocity in mercury, copper and sea water, if the magnetic field is 0.5 Weber/m^2.

10-12.1. Find the angle of the asymptotes of the hyperbola $W(z)$ and verify also Eq. (10-12.13).

[Hint: $\ell n\ (\alpha + j\beta) = (\alpha^2 + \beta^2)^{1/2} + j \tan^{-1} \frac{\beta}{\alpha}$.]

10-12.2. Using Eqs. (10-12.14), show that $\lambda z/\pi W_o^{\ 2} = \pi W^2/\lambda R$ and express W_o and z in terms of W and R.

10-12.3. Find the beam radius and the wavefront radius for a HeNe laser at 0.05 m, 50 m and 500 m if $W_o = 0.005$ m at $z = 0$.

10-12.4. Find the field amplitude at the center of the beam of a HeNe laser (λ = 0.6328 μm) 500 m away, if the diameter of its beam is $2W_o = 5$ mm. What is the field amplitude at 2.2 mm off the axis at this distance.

CHAPTER 11

GUIDED WAVES

The study in Chapter 10 was largely concerned with waves in unbounded mediums. In this chapter we shall study the propagation of waves in mediums that are confined by fixed boundaries. The effect of diffusion type terms will be discussed.

11-1. Transmission Lines

We shall begin this study by considering waves that are guided by transmission line type structures. No distributed sources are assumed to exist. We begin our considerations with Eqs. (8-1.5) which are rewritten for convenience, omitting the distributed source terms:

$$\begin{aligned}\frac{\partial^2 v(x,t)}{\partial x^2} &= RG\, v(x,t) + (RC+LG)\frac{\partial v(x,t)}{\partial t} + LC\frac{\partial^2 v(x,t)}{\partial t^2}\\ \frac{\partial^2 i(x,t)}{\partial x^2} &= RG\, i(x,t) + (RC+LG)\frac{\partial i(x,t)}{\partial t} + LC\frac{\partial^2 i(x,t)}{\partial t^2}\end{aligned} \tag{11-1.1}$$

A discussion of this problem proceeds by first considering the first of these equations. By Laplace transform methods applied to the time variable, and for the initially relaxed case (zero initial conditions), we find

$$\frac{d^2\tilde{V}(x,s)}{dx^2} = [RG+s(RC+LG)+s^2LC]\ \tilde{V}(x,s) \tag{11-1.2}$$

This ordinary differential equation is written in the form

$$\frac{d^2\tilde{V}(x,s)}{dx^2} = \gamma^2\tilde{V}(x,s) \tag{11-1.3}$$

where

$$\gamma^2 = (R+sL)(G+sC) = Z(s)\,Y(s) \tag{11-1.4}$$

with

$$Z(s) = R+sL; \quad Y(s) = G+sC$$

A general solution of this differential equation is

$$\tilde{V}(x,s) = F_1(s)e^{\gamma x} + F_2(s)e^{-\gamma x} \tag{11-1.5}$$

If we substitute Eq. (11-1.5) into Laplace-transformed Eq. (8-1.4) with no sources, we shall find

$$\frac{d\tilde{I}(x,s)}{dx} = -\,(G+sC)\,[F_1(s)e^{\gamma x} + F_2(s)e^{-\gamma x}] \tag{11-1.6}$$

from which

$$\tilde{I}(x,s) = -\frac{(G+sC)}{\gamma}\,[F_1(s)e^{\gamma x} - F_2(s)e^{-\gamma x}] = \sqrt{\frac{Y(s)}{Z(s)}}\,[F_2(s)e^{-\gamma x} - F_1(s)e^{\gamma x}] \tag{11-1.7}$$

Some general properties of the solutions of these equations are easily obtained. We shall consider some important cases.

Case 1. $R = G = 0$. This is the case for the dissipationless line; the general transmission line equation reduced to the simple wave equation. In this case, Eq. (11-1.4) for the propagation function becomes

$$\gamma = s\sqrt{LC} \tag{11-1.8}$$

But for this case, which is precisely that discussed in Sec. 10-1, the solution becomes

$$v(x,t) = F_1(t + x\sqrt{LC}) + F_2(t - x\sqrt{LC}) \tag{11-1.9}$$

The solution comprises the backward and forward traveling waves F_1 and F_2, respectively.

Example 11-1.1. Find the voltage and current in a semi-infinite lossless line having zero initial conditions when a switch is closed at $t = 0$, as shown in Fig. 11-1.1.

Solution. The general solution to this problem is given by Eq. (11-1.5). We note that the voltage must be finite at $x \to \infty$ (why?) and so we must set $F_1(s) = 0$. The solution then becomes

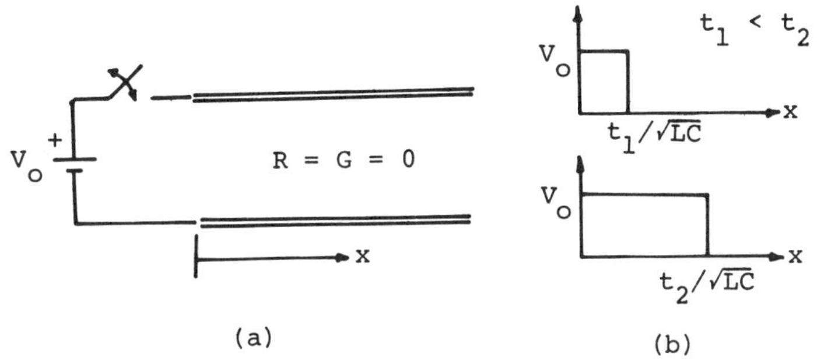

Figure 11-1.1. (a) Semi-infinite lossless transmission line. (b) Voltage distribution on the line times t_1 and t_2 with $t_1 < t_2$.

$$\tilde{V}(x,s) = F_2(s)e^{-\gamma x} = F_2(s)e^{-s\sqrt{LC}\,x} \tag{11-1.10}$$

Since at $t = 0$, $v(0,t) = V_o u_{-1}(t)$, then

$$\mathscr{L}[v(0,t)] = \tilde{V}(0,s) = \frac{1}{s}V_o \tag{11-1.11}$$

This condition, when combined with Eq. (11-1.10) requires that

$$\tilde{V}(0,s) = F_2(s)$$

and Eq. (11-1.10) assumes the form

$$\tilde{V}(x,s) = V_o \frac{e^{-s\sqrt{LC}\,x}}{s} \tag{11-1.12}$$

To find the time variation, we take the inverse Laplace transform of this last equation (see Appendix IV), and the result is

$$v(x,t) = \mathscr{L}^{-1}[\tilde{V}(x,s)] = V_o\mathscr{L}^{-1}\left[\frac{e^{-s\sqrt{Lc}\,x}}{s}\right] = V_o u_{-1}(t - \sqrt{LC}\,x) \tag{11-1.13}$$

which shows a delayed wave front, without distortion, the delay being the time delay for the wave front to reach point x.

ΔΔΔ

Case 2. GL = RC. We shall find that this condition yields attenuated waves but without distortion. To see this, we first examine γ which becomes

$$\gamma = \sqrt{LC\,(s + \frac{R}{L})(s + \frac{G}{C})} = \sqrt{LC}\,(s + \frac{R}{L}) = \sqrt{RG} + s\sqrt{LC} \tag{11-1.14}$$

By combining this expression with the general solution, Eq. (11-1.5), the solution is

$$\tilde{V}(x,s) = e^{\sqrt{RG}\,x}\,F_1(s)e^{s\sqrt{LC}\,x} + e^{-\sqrt{RG}\,x}\,F_2(s)e^{-s\sqrt{LC}\,x} \tag{11-1.15}$$

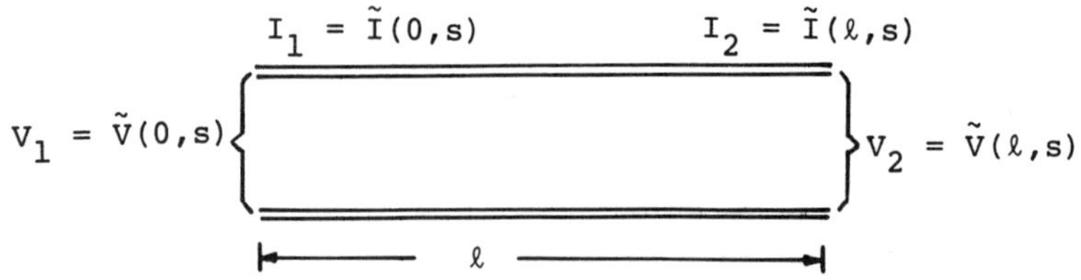

Figure 11-1.2. A transmission line of length ℓ.

Observe that this corresponds exactly to Eq. (11-1.5) except for the presence of the additional amplitude attenuation factors.

Case 3. General Finite Line. Our study begins with the general equations for $\tilde{V}(x,s)$ and $\tilde{I}(x,s)$ given by Eqs. (11-1.5) and (11-1.7). Since two arbitrary functions exist, two boundary conditions are required.

Specifically, we refer to Fig. 11-1.2 which shows a line of length ℓ. We shall suppose that the voltage and current are known at the output end of the line. Thus at $x = \ell$, the controlling equations are

$$V_2 = F_1 e^{\gamma\ell} + F_2 e^{-\gamma\ell} \quad \text{a)}$$

$$I_2\sqrt{\frac{Z(s)}{Y(s)}} = I_2 Z_o(s) = -F_1 e^{\gamma\ell} + F_2 e^{-\gamma\ell} \quad \text{b)} \tag{11-1.16}$$

It is convenient to define the quantity

$$Z_o(s) = \sqrt{\frac{Z(s)}{Y(s)}} \tag{11-1.17}$$

where $Z_o(s)$ is the *characteristic* impedance of the line. The meaning of this impedance will become clear in what follows. The successive addition and subtraction of Eqs. (11-1.16) yields

$$F_2 = \frac{V_2 + I_2 Z_o}{2} e^{\gamma\ell} \tag{11-1.18}$$

and

$$F_1 = \frac{V_2 - I_2 Z_o}{2} e^{-\gamma\ell} \tag{11-1.19}$$

These values are substituted in Eqs. (11-1.5) and (11-1.6) with the result

$$\tilde{V}(x,s) = \frac{V_2 + I_2 Z_o}{2}\left[e^{\gamma(\ell-x)} + \tilde{\Gamma}_L e^{-\gamma(\ell-x)}\right] \tag{11-1.20}$$

$$\tilde{I}(x,s) = \frac{V_2 + I_2 Z_o}{2}\left[e^{\gamma(\ell-x)} - \tilde{\Gamma}_L e^{-\gamma(\ell-x)}\right] \tag{11-1.21}$$

where

$$\tilde{\Gamma}_L = \frac{V_2 - I_2Z_o}{V_2 + I_2Z_o} \tag{11-1.22}$$

For an interpretation of these equations, we focus our attention on the exponentials $e^{\gamma(\ell-x)}$ and $e^{-\gamma(\ell-x)}$. The term $e^{-\gamma(\ell-x)}$ represents a wave travelling in the negative X-direction, and $e^{\gamma(\ell-x)}$ represents a wave traveling in the positive X-direction. The direction is readily recognized if we recall that the direction is specified if the exponential is decreasing with increasing x. The common multiplying factor outside of the parenthesis may be temporarily disregarded. Then the wave traveling to the right has a magnitude of unity, and the wave traveling toward the left has a magnitude $|\tilde{\Gamma}_L|$. The former is called the incident wave; the latter is the reflected wave. $\tilde{\Gamma}_L$ is a complex quantity whose magnitude is the ratio of the magnitudes of the reflected and the incident waves, and whose angle is the phase difference between these waves. Equations (11-1.20) and (11-1.21) show that the steady state voltage (or current) at any given point on the line is the resultant of the incident and the reflected wave at that point.

A particularly important case is that in which the line is terminated in an impedance $Z_L(s)$. For this case $V_2 = Z_L(s)I_2$ and so

$$\Gamma_L = \frac{Z_L(s) - Z_o(s)}{Z_L(s) + Z_o(s)} \tag{11-1.23}$$

which is known as the reflection factor at the load. For the very important case when $Z_L = Z_o$, then $V_2 = I_2Z_o$ and $\Gamma_L = 0$. In this case, Eqs. (11-1.20) and (11-1.21) reduce to

$$\tilde{V}(x,s) = V_2e^{\gamma(\ell-x)} = V_2e^{\gamma\ell}e^{-\gamma x} \tag{11-1.24}$$

$$\tilde{I}(x,s) = \frac{V_2}{Z_o(s)}e^{\gamma(\ell-x)} = \left(\frac{V_2}{Z_o(s)}e^{\gamma\ell}\right)e^{-\gamma x} \tag{11-1.25}$$

These equations indicate that propagation occurs only in the positive X-direction. Hence, the terminated line with $Z_L = Z_o$ becomes equivalent to an infinite line. This result explains the name *characteristic* impedance for Z_o since it shows that by terminating a line in its characteristic impedance, no reflections occur on the line, and the line has been converted, in effect, to an infinite line.

Often in transmission line problems it is assumed that the excitations are periodic functions of time. In this case we would write $s = +j\omega$ in all of the foregoing expressions. The important defined quantities now assume the form

$$Z_o = \sqrt{\frac{R+j\omega L}{G+j\omega C}} \tag{11-1.26}$$

In general, the propagation function γ is complex, which allows it to be written in the form

$$\gamma = \sqrt{(R+j\omega L)(G+j\omega C)} = \alpha + j\beta \tag{11-1.27}$$

By separating the real and imaginary parts, it is possible to show that the amplitude factor α is

$$\alpha = \left[\frac{RG-\omega^2LC+[R^2+\omega^2L^2)(G^2+\omega^2C^2)]^{1/2}}{2}\right]^{1/2} \tag{11-1.28}$$

and the phase factor is

$$\beta = \left[\frac{-(RG-\omega^2LC)+[(R^2+\omega^2L^2)(G^2+\omega^2C^2)]^{1/2}}{2}\right]^{1/2} \tag{11-1.29}$$

These formulas are rather complicated, but they have the following properties. In general α remains bounded and does not vary too markedly with frequency. The phase factor β increases continually with increasing frequency. Limits are readily established for these factors at low and high frequencies. When ω is zero

$$Z_o = \sqrt{\frac{R}{G}} \qquad \alpha = \sqrt{RG} \qquad \beta = 0 \tag{11-1.30}$$

As ω approaches infinity, $R \ll \omega L$ and $G \ll \omega C$, and the term RG in Eq. (11-1.27) can be neglected. A binomial expansion, next, gives

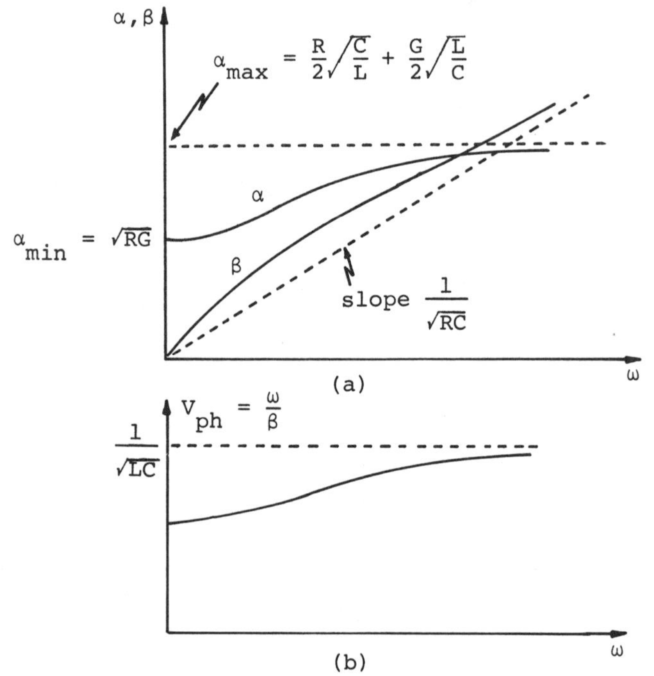

Figure 11-1.3. Frequency characteristics of line properties.

$$Z_o = \sqrt{\frac{L}{C}} \qquad \alpha = \frac{R}{2}\sqrt{\frac{C}{L}} + \frac{G}{2}\sqrt{\frac{L}{C}} \qquad \beta = \omega\sqrt{LC} \tag{11-1.31}$$

A low loss transmission line has amplitude and phase characteristics given by Eq. (11-1.30). Typical sketches of these functions are given in Fig. 11-1.3a. Figure 11-1.3b gives a plot of the phase velocity of the wave as a function of frequency, and so indicates the dispersion characteristics of the transmission line.

Example 11-1.2. Find an expression for the voltage at any point on the transmission line shown in Fig. 11-1.4.

Solution. We may use Eq. (11-1.16) to specify the voltage at the end of the line as a boundary condition

$$\tilde{V}(\ell,s) = F_1(s)e^{\gamma\ell} + F_2(s)e^{-\gamma\ell} = \tilde{I}(\ell,s)Z_L(s) \tag{11-1.32}$$

Now substitute the known form for the current from (11-1.16b) to obtain

$$F_1(s)e^{\gamma\ell} + F_2(s)e^{-\gamma\ell} = \frac{Z_L(s)}{Z_o(s)}[-F_1(s)e^{\gamma\ell} + F_2(s)e^{-\gamma\ell}] \tag{11-1.33}$$

We can find a boundary condition at x = 0 which requires that

$$\tilde{V}_g(s) = Z_g(s)\tilde{I}(0,s) + \tilde{V}(0,s)$$

or

$$\tilde{V}_g(s) = Z_g(s)Y_o(s)\,[-F_1(s) + F_2(s)] + [F_1(s) + F_2(s)] \tag{11-1.34}$$

Solving the system of equations (11-1.33) and (11-1.34) for the unknown functions $F_1(s)$ and $F_2(s)$ and then substituting these values into Eq. (11-1.16) we find that

$$\tilde{V}(x,s) = \frac{\tilde{V}_g(s)Z_o(s)}{Z_o(s)+Z_g(s)}\;\frac{e^{-\gamma x} + \Gamma_L e^{-\gamma(2\ell-x)}}{1 - \Gamma_G\Gamma_L e^{-2\gamma\ell}} \qquad \text{a)}$$

where (11-1.35)

$$\Gamma_G = \frac{Z_g(s) - Z_o(s)}{Z_g(s) + Z_o(s)} \qquad \text{b)}$$

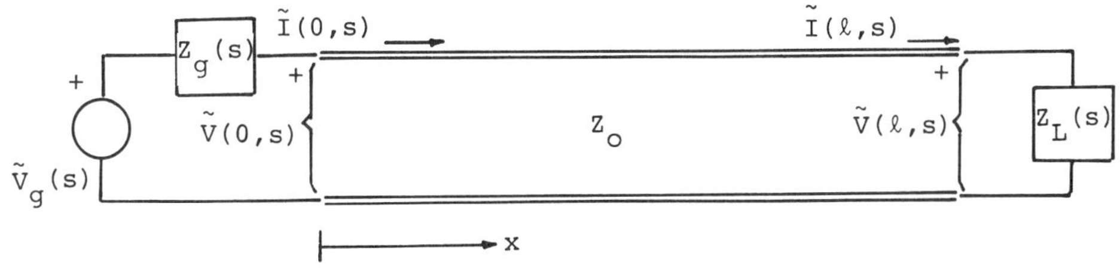

Figure 11-1.4. Finite transmission line.

is the reflection coefficient at the generator side of the transmission line.

An interesting equivalent to Eq. (11-1.35) is deduced by expanding the denominator term using the expansion

$$\frac{1}{1-x} = 1 + x + x^2 + \ldots, \quad x < 1$$

Then

$$\frac{1}{1 - \Gamma_G\Gamma_L e^{-2\gamma\ell}} = 1 + \Gamma_L\Gamma_G e^{-2\gamma\ell} + \Gamma_L{}^2\Gamma_G{}^2 e^{-4\gamma\ell} + \ldots + \Gamma_L{}^n\Gamma_G{}^n e^{-2n\gamma\ell} + \ldots.$$

Equation (11-1.35) can now be written in expanded form

$$\tilde{V}(x,s) = \tilde{V}_g(s) \frac{Z_o(s)}{Z_o(s) + Z_g(s)} [e^{-\gamma x} + \Gamma_L e^{-\gamma(2\ell-x)} + \Gamma_L\Gamma_G e^{-\gamma(2\ell+x)}$$

$$+ \Gamma_L{}^2\Gamma_G e^{-\gamma(4\ell-x)} + \ldots. + \Gamma_L{}^n\Gamma_G{}^n e^{-\gamma(2n\ell+x)} + \ldots.] \qquad (11\text{-}1.36)$$

A physical interpretation of this equation is instructive. It states that under steady state conditions, the voltage at some point x on the line is made up of an infinite number of waves, the components being a wave that had moved in the positive x-direction $e^{-\gamma x}$; plus a component wave that had traveled to the end of the line and had been reflected at $x = \ell$, and so is modified in amplitude and phase, and then propagating in the negative direction $\Gamma_L e^{-\gamma(2\ell-x)}$ to point x; plus another component that had traveled from the input end to the output end, was reflected, and then traveled to the input end where it was again reflected, and then propagated to the point x; thus with form $\Gamma_L\Gamma_G e^{-\gamma(2\ell+x)}$, etc., for successive reflected terms.

Example 11-1.3. Find the voltage in a lossless line at point $x = \ell/2$ for the time spread $2T < t < 3T$, where T is the time that it takes the wave to travel the length ℓ of the line. Given are the following constraints

$$Z_L(s) = sL = \text{inductor};\ Z_g(s) = 0;\ \tilde{V}_g(s) = \mathscr{L}[v_g(t)] = \mathscr{L}[u_{-1}(t)] = \frac{1}{s}$$

Solution. The solution is given by a proper interpretation of Eq. (11-1.36) but now considering a time portrait, which means that only those terms are retained in the expansion that do not exceed t = 3.5 T. First, the specific factors are evaluated

$$\Gamma_L = \frac{sL - Z_o}{sL + Z_o} = \frac{s - Z_o/L}{s + Z_o/L}$$

$$\Gamma_G = -1$$

$$\gamma = \sqrt{LC}\, s = \frac{1}{v} s \qquad \frac{\ell}{v} = T$$

Introducing all the known terms in Eq. (11-1.36) below 3.5 T we have

$$\tilde{V}(\frac{\ell}{2},s) = \frac{1}{s}\left(e^{-0.5sT} + \frac{s - Z_o/L}{S + Z_o/L} e^{-1.5sT} - \frac{s - Z_o/L}{s + Z_o/L} e^{-2.5sT}\right)$$

Taking the inverse Laplace transform of this equation, the result is

$$v(\frac{\ell}{2},t) = u_{-1}(t-0.5T) - u_{-1}(t-1.5T) + 2e^{-\frac{Z_o}{L}(t-1.5T)} u_{-1}(t-1.5T)$$
$$+ u_{-1}(t-2.5T) - 2e^{-\frac{Z_o}{L}(t-2.5T)} u_{-1}(t-2.5T) \quad (11\text{-}1.37)$$

ΔΔΔ

11-2. Transmission Lines Excited by Distributed Sources

In this section we shall study the propagation of a current disturbance that is generated by a spatially distributed voltage source. The situation is illustrated graphically in Fig. 11-2.1. We shall assume a sinusoidal time variation of the form $e^{-j\omega t}$. The lossless transmission line equations (8-1.3) and (8-1.4) become

$$\frac{\partial V(x)}{\partial x} = + j\omega L\ I(x) - V_o(x) \quad \text{a)}$$
$$\frac{\partial I(x)}{\partial x} = + j\omega C\ V(x) \quad \text{b)} \qquad (11\text{-}2.1)$$

By combining these two equations, the result is readily found to be

$$\frac{\partial^2 I(x)}{\partial x^2} + k^2 I(x) = -j\omega C\ V_o(x) \quad (11\text{-}2.2)$$

where $k = \omega\sqrt{LC}$.

To solve this equation, we multiply all terms by $G(x,\xi)dx$ and integrate terms over the domain $[a,b]$, where $G(x,\xi)$ is a Green's function (see Chap. 4). Also, it is assumed that both $I(x)$ and $G(x,\xi)$ are well-behaved functions. A necessary step is, of course, to establish a suitable Green's function for this problem, and this

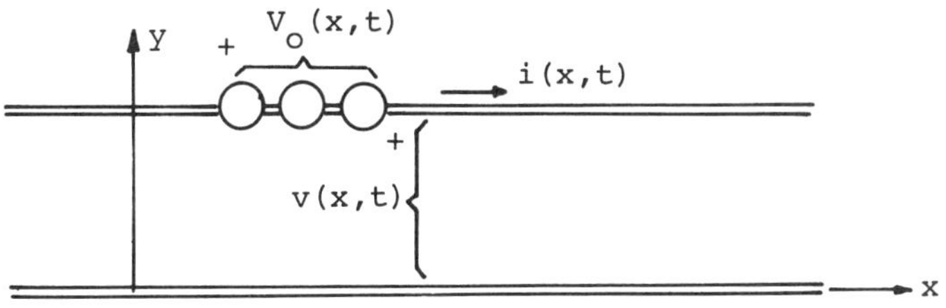

Figure 11-2.1. A line excited by a distributed voltage source.

will be done. Performing the integration by parts twice we obtain

$$[G(x,\xi)\frac{\partial I(x)}{\partial x} - I(x)\frac{\partial G(x,\xi)}{\partial x}]_a^b + \int_a^b [\frac{\partial^2 G(x,\xi)}{\partial x^2} + k^2 G(x,\xi)]\, I(x)dx$$

$$= -j\omega C \int_a^b G(x,\xi)V_o(x)dx \qquad (11\text{-}2.3)$$

We wish to insure that this is a self-adjoint problem (see Appendix II). This is done by choosing identical boundary conditions for both functions $G(x,\xi)$ and $I(x)$, whence the first bracketed terms vanish. Further, in Eq. (11-2.3) we set

$$\frac{\partial^2 G(x,\xi)}{\partial x^2} + k^2 G(x,\xi) = -\delta(x-\xi) \qquad (11\text{-}2.4)$$

Under these circumstances and using the properties of the delta function, Eq. (11-2.3) becomes

$$I(\xi) = j\omega C \int_a^b V_o(x)G(x,\xi)dx \qquad (11\text{-}2.5)$$

We can now proceed to find the explicit form of $G(x,\xi)$. We do this by solving Eq. (11-2.4) and imposing the established boundary conditions, which selects as the domain the entire interval $(-\infty,+\infty)$. The boundary conditions which are

$$\frac{\partial I(x,\xi)}{\partial x} = jkI(x,\xi) \qquad \text{at } x = +\infty \qquad \text{a)}$$

$$\frac{\partial I(x,\xi)}{\partial x} = -jkI(x,\xi) \qquad \text{at } x = -\infty \qquad \text{b)} \qquad (11\text{-}2.6)$$

are known as the *radiation conditions*. As already noted, exactly similar conditions will be selected for $G(x,\xi)$ to insure a self-adjoint equation.

The general solution of Eq. (11-2.4) is written in the two regions as

$$G(x,\xi) = Ae^{jkx} \qquad x > \xi \qquad \text{a)}$$

$$G(x,\xi) = Be^{-jkx} \qquad x < \xi \qquad \text{b)} \qquad (11\text{-}2.7)$$

These solutions automatically satisfy the boundary conditions at the two infinities. Physically Eqs. (11-2.7) indicate that the impulse source $\delta(x-\xi)$ at $x = \xi$ excites two waves which propagate in opposite directions. The unknown amplitudes A and B can be found by employing properties II and V of the Green's function (see Appendix II). These two properties are equivalent to the statement that the current at $x = \xi$ is continuous, and that the voltage difference across the δ-function source that extends from $\xi - \tau$ to $\xi + \tau$ $(\tau \to 0)$ is equal to the strength of the voltage source. Property II for $\tau \to 0$ requires that

$$G(x,\xi)\Big|_{\xi-\tau}^{\xi+\tau} = 0 \tag{11-2.8}$$

or

$$Ae^{jk\xi} - Be^{-jk\xi} = 0 \tag{11-2.9}$$

Integrating Eq. (11-2.4) from $\xi - \tau$ to $\xi + \tau$ and using property II requires that

$$\frac{\partial G(x,\xi)}{\partial x}\Big|_{\xi-\tau}^{\xi+\tau} = -1 \tag{11-2.10}$$

which when combined with Eq. (11-2.7) gives

$$jkAe^{jk\xi} + jkBe^{-jk\xi} = -1 \tag{11-2.11}$$

From Eqs. (11-2.9) and (11-2.11) we can solve for the unknowns A and B. This is done and their values are included in Eq. (11-2.7). The Green's function $G(x,\xi)$ is

$$G(x,\xi) = \begin{cases} \frac{j}{2k}\, e^{jk(x-\xi)} & x \geq \xi \\ \frac{j}{2k}\, e^{-jk(x-\xi)} & x \leq \xi \end{cases} \tag{11-2.12}$$

which can be written in the more compact form

$$G(x,\xi) = \frac{j}{2k}\, e^{+jk|x-\xi|} \tag{11-2.13}$$

Hence the solution for $I(x)$ (by interchanging ξ and x) is given by

$$I(x) = -\frac{\omega C}{2k}\int_{-\infty}^{\infty} V_o(\xi)e^{+jk|x-\xi|}d\xi \tag{11-2.14}$$

For the case of a δ-function source at $x = \xi$, and with a short-circuited input as shown in Fig. 11-2.2 the Green's function would be chosen as

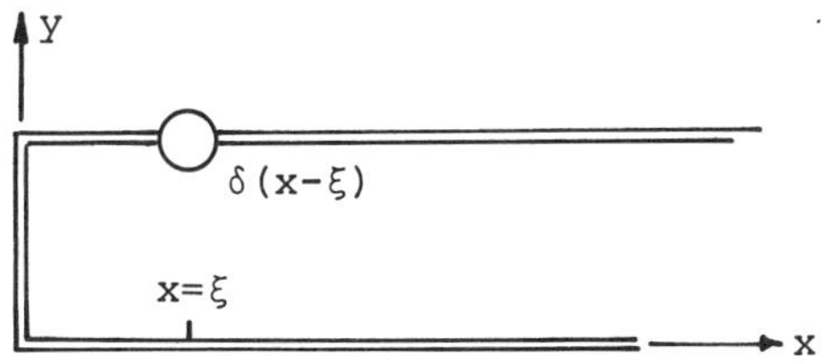

Figure 11-2.2. A function excited line.

$$G(x,\xi) = Ae^{jkx} \qquad x > \xi \qquad \text{a)}$$
$$G(x,\xi) = B\cos kx \qquad 0 \le x < \xi \qquad \text{b)} \tag{11-2.15}$$

The selection of the cosine type solution for the domain $0 \le x < \xi$ is dictated by the requirement that the voltage, with voltage $\propto \partial I/\partial x$, at $x = 0$ is always zero (at the short circuit). Further, since we wish this to be a self-adjoint solution, these same conditions are imposed on the Green's function. By applying the appropriate conditions on $G(x,\xi)$ given by Eqs. (11-2.8) and (11-2.10), we find

$$G(x,\xi) = \begin{cases} \dfrac{j}{k}\cos k\xi \, e^{jkx} & x > \xi \\ \dfrac{j}{k}\cos kx \, e^{jk\xi} & 0 \le x < \xi \end{cases} \tag{11-2.16}$$

This may be expressed in the alternate form

$$G(x,\xi) = \begin{cases} \dfrac{j}{2k}\left[e^{jk(x-\xi)} + e^{jk(x+\xi)}\right] & x > \xi \\ \dfrac{j}{2k}\left[e^{-jk(x-\xi)} + e^{jk(x+\xi)}\right] & 0 \le x < \xi \end{cases} \tag{11-2.17}$$

The second terms in these equations can be interpreted as reflected waves.

11-3. Eigenvalues and Eigenfunctions

Discrete allowable responses of a system are intimately associated with the eigenvalues or characteristic values of the system equations. To study this, let A be a differential operator, e.g., d^2/dx^2 which is defined over a domain D. A regular function in the domain of A is called an *eigenfunction* if there exists a number λ such that

$$Au = \lambda u \tag{11-3.1}$$

The number λ which will ordinarily define a limited set, is called an *eigenvalue*. If we look upon this expression as a vector equation, it requires that the vector u must be in the same direction as Au.

We shall limit our discussion to self-adjoint operators with homogeneous boundary conditions of the form

$$B_1(u) = \alpha_{10}u(a) + \alpha_{11}\frac{\partial u(a)}{\partial x} = 0$$
$$B_2(u) = \beta_{10}u(b) + \beta_{11}\frac{\partial u(b)}{\partial x} = 0 \qquad (11\text{-}3.2)$$

Under these conditions, the following properties exist:

I. The normalized eigenfunctions form a complete orthogonal set, i.e.,

$$\int_a^b u_i(x)u_j(x)dx = M\delta_{ij}$$

where M is a finite constant and δ_{ij} is the Kronecker function; $\delta_{ij} = 1$ for $i = j$; $= 0$ otherwise.

II. The eigenvalues are real.

III. If the operator is positive definite (this requires that $\int_a^b u\, Au\, dx \geq 0$ for all u in D; see Appendix II) then the eigenvalues are nonnegatives (zero or positive).

These properties will be better understood by studying the example below, and the material which follows on waveguides.

Example 11-3.1. With reference to Fig. 11-3.1, find the eigenvalues for this system.

Solution. From Sec. 11-1, the voltage equation for the lossless transmission line, Eq. (11-1.2), with harmonic excitation $e^{-j\omega t}$ can be written

$$\frac{d^2u}{dx^2} + \lambda u = 0 \qquad (11\text{-}3.3)$$

with bondaryy conditions $u(0) = 0$; $u(\ell) = 0$, where u denotes the voltage on the line, and $\lambda = \omega^2 LC$. A non-trivial solution of this equation is the function

$$u(x) = C_1 \sin \sqrt{\lambda}\, x + C_2 \cos \sqrt{\lambda}\, x \qquad (11\text{-}3.4)$$

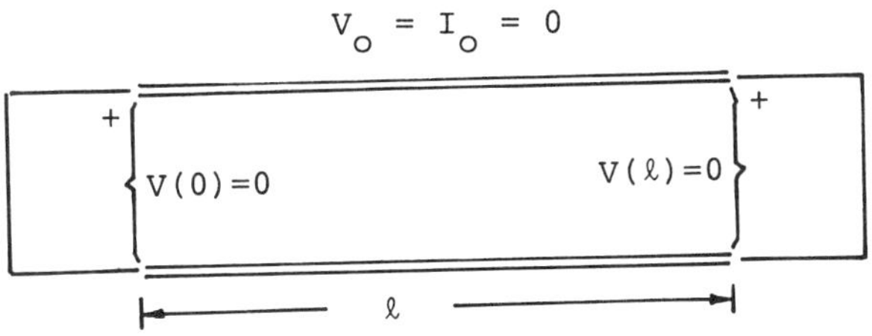

Figure 11-3.1. Finite lossless transmission line.

where C_1 and C_2 are unknown constants. Applying the boundary conditions, we find that $C_2 = 0$ and

$$\lambda_n = \frac{n^2\pi^2}{\ell^2} \qquad (n = 1,2,3,\ldots.) \tag{11-3.5}$$

We continue with several aspects of this example, and wish to show that the operator $A = -d^2/dx^2$ is positive definite. We do this by examining

$$-\int_0^\ell u \frac{d^2u}{dx^2} dx = u(0)\frac{du(0)}{dx} - u(\ell)\frac{du(\ell)}{dx} + \int_0^\ell (\frac{du}{dx})^2 dx = \int_0^\ell (\frac{du}{dx})^2 dx \geq 0 \tag{11-3.6}$$

The eigenvalues are positive, as expected from property III above, and are real, because of property II. Moreover, the integral

$$C_1^2 \int_0^\ell \sin(\sqrt{\lambda_i}\, x)\sin(\sqrt{\lambda_j}\, x)\, dx = \frac{C_1^2\ell}{2}\delta_{ij} \tag{11-3.7}$$

confirms property I.

Equation (11-3.5) indicates that only discrete frequencies can be present in the transmission line of our example, and these frequencies are

$$\omega_n = \sqrt{\frac{n^2\pi^2}{LC\,\ell^2}} \tag{11-3.8}$$

Further, setting $C_1^2\ell/2 = 1$ requires that $C_1 = \sqrt{2/\ell}$ and the *orthonormalized* eigenfunctions of our example are

$$u_n(x) = \sqrt{\frac{2}{\ell}}\sin(\frac{n\pi}{\ell}x) \qquad (n = 1,2,3,\ldots) \tag{11-3.9}$$

This equation indicates that the acceptable solutions are those harmonics which will fit exactly along the length of the line, and Eq. (11-3.5) specifies the corresponding frequencies of these acceptable solutions.

ΔΔΔ

11-4. Waves Reflected by Perfectly Conducting Planes

A. Waves Impinging on Perfectly Conducting Planes

Refer to Fig. 11-4.1 which shows an electric field to be incident obliquely on a perfect conducting metallic surface. As indicated, the incident electric field is chosen along the X-direction only such that $E_i = E_x$; $E_y = E_z = 0$, with

$$\overline{E}_i = \overline{a}_x E_o e^{-j\omega t} e^{j\overline{k}\cdot\overline{r}}$$

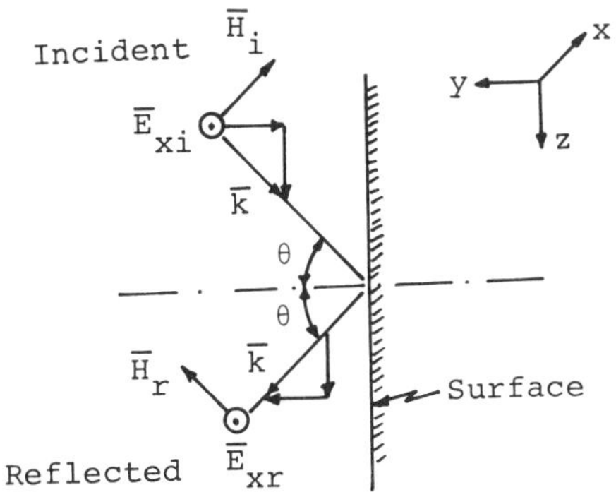

Figure 11-4.1. An electric field impinging on a metallic plane.

or

$$E_{xi} = E_o e^{j(-k_y y + k_z z)} e^{-j\omega t} \tag{11-4.1}$$

The electric field at the surface of the conducting plane must be zero to satisfy the boundary condition, and this requires the presence of a reflected field which must be such that $\overline{E}_i + \overline{E}_r = 0$ at the surface $(y = 0)$. This requires, of course, that $\overline{E}_i = -\overline{E}_r$ at the surface. The reflected field thus has the explicit form

$$E_{xr} = -E_o e^{j(k_y y + k_z z)} e^{-j\omega t} \tag{11-4.2}$$

The total electric field in the left half space is the sum of the incident and reflected fields, and is

$$E_x = E_{xi} + E_{xr} = E_o e^{jk_z z}(e^{-jk_y y} - e^{jk_y y}) e^{-j\omega t}$$

or

$$E_x = -2j E_o e^{jk_z z} \sin k_y y\, e^{-j\omega t} \tag{11-4.3}$$

which clearly satisfies the imposed condition that $\overline{E} = 0$ on the surface. It is observed from the figure that

$$k_y = k \cos \theta \qquad k_z = k \sin \theta \tag{11-4.4}$$

so that

$$k_y^2 + k_z^2 = k^2$$

To find the corresponding H-fields, we begin with the Faraday equation

$$\nabla \times \bar{E} = -\frac{\partial \bar{B}}{\partial t} = -\mu \frac{\partial \bar{H}}{\partial t}$$

which becomes, for the assumed time harmonic form, but omitting the implied time function $e^{-j\omega t}$,

$$\nabla \times \bar{E} = j\,\omega\,\mu\,\bar{H} \tag{11-4.5}$$

In expanded form, this represents the set of equations

$$\frac{\partial E_z}{\partial y} - \frac{\partial E_y}{\partial z} = j\,\omega\,\mu\,H_x \qquad \text{a)}$$

$$\frac{\partial E_x}{\partial z} - \frac{\partial E_z}{\partial x} = j\,\omega\,\mu\,H_y \qquad \text{b)} \qquad (11\text{-}4.6)$$

$$\frac{\partial E_y}{\partial x} - \frac{\partial E_x}{\partial y} = j\,\omega\,\mu\,H_z \qquad \text{c)}$$

The incident H-field components are, using Eq. (11-4.1) and $\omega\mu/k = Z_o$, the intrinsic impedance of free space,

$$H_{xi} = 0 \qquad \text{a)}$$

$$H_{yi} = \left(\frac{E_o}{Z_o}\right) \sin\theta\, e^{j(-k_y y + k_z z)} \qquad \text{b)} \qquad (11\text{-}4.7)$$

$$H_{zi} = \left(\frac{E_o}{Z_o}\right) \cos\theta\, e^{j(-k_y y + k_z z)} \qquad \text{c)}$$

For the reflected wave we also obtain the equations

$$H_{xr} = 0 \qquad \text{a)}$$

$$H_{yr} = -\frac{E_o}{Z_o} \sin\theta\, e^{j(k_y y + k_z z)} \qquad \text{b)} \qquad (11\text{-}4.8)$$

$$H_{zr} = \frac{E_o}{Z_o} \cos\theta\, e^{j(k_y y + k_z z)} \qquad \text{c)}$$

The total fields at all points in the left half-space, which are specified by the sum of the incident and reflected components, are given by

$$E_y = E_z = H_x = 0 \qquad \text{a)}$$

$$E_x = -2j\,E_o\, e^{jk_z z} \sin k_y y \qquad \text{b)}$$

$$H_y = -2j\,\frac{E_o}{Z_o} \sin\theta\, e^{jk_z z} \sin k_y y \qquad \text{c)} \qquad (11\text{-}4.9)$$

$$H_z = 2\,\frac{E_o}{Z_o} \cos\theta\, e^{jk_z z} \cos k_y y \qquad \text{d)}$$

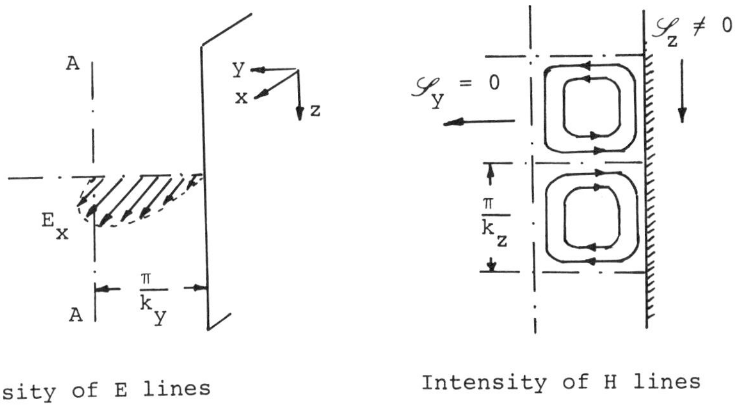

Figure 11-4.2. Intensity patterns of E and H lines.

Sketches showing the intensity patterns of the E-lines and the H-lines are given in Fig. 11-4.2.

Based on the foregoing development, a number of important conclusions are possible:

1. It is observed from Eqs. (11-4.9) that E_x and H_z are 90 deg out of phase. This follows from the factor j in the expression for E_x, and from the fact that these expressions specify the magnitude of the field functions under assumed sinusoidal time excitation. This phase condition specifies that the Y-component of the Poyting vector cannot have a real part. This result is to be expected since no average power is absorbed by the conducting surface or mirror.

2. From the sketches in Fig. 11-4.2 it is observed that $E_x = 0$ whenever $k_y y = -n\pi$, n = 0,1,2,... or when

$$y = \frac{-n\pi}{k_y} = \frac{-n\pi}{k \cos \theta} = \frac{-n\pi\lambda}{2\pi \cos \theta} = -\frac{n}{2}\lambda_y \qquad n = 0,1,2,\ldots$$

This specifies that planes of electric field nodes parallel to the mirror exist at multiples of $(1/2)\lambda_y$ from it. Note also that H_y has nodes on the same planes, but H_z has nodes which are displaced by $(1/4)\lambda_y$ from them.

3. The Z-variation of all field components has a traveling wave character with an effective wavelength λ_z, with propagation in the Z-direction. This condition is consistent with the fact that the Poynting vector $\mathscr{S}_z$ is real and negative, with a real power flow.

The foregoing shows that the electromagnetic waves obliquely incident on a plane reflecting surface result in a standing wave field which extends along the Y-axis and which slides along the Z-axis.

Attention is called to the fact that nodal planes exist which are parallel to the metallic surface. It is entirely possible, therefore, to consider that a second metallic surface can exist at such a nodal surface without disturbing the field configuration. The details of such a limited space are studied in some detail in the following section. The actual presence of a second parallel plane imposes particular constraints on the fields, as will be studied.

B. Waves Between Perfectly Conducting Planes

Consider a homogeneous lossless dielectric to occupy the space between two parallel conducting planes. If we arrange the electric field vector $\overline{E}$ to be parallel to the X-axis, then the magnetic field vector $\overline{H}$ will have a component parallel to the Z-direction. This type of guided wave is called *transverse electric* (TE wave). Similarly, when $\overline{H}$ is parallel to the X-axis, we have a *transverse magnetic* wave (TM wave). We shall discover that TE or TM waves can propagate in hollow conducting pipes (wave guides) with wavelengths that are comparable to the dimensions of the guide, but that TEM cannot propagate in such a geometry.

Refer to Figs. 11-4.3 which define the geometry of the system. The electric vector of the incident wave is represented by the known relation

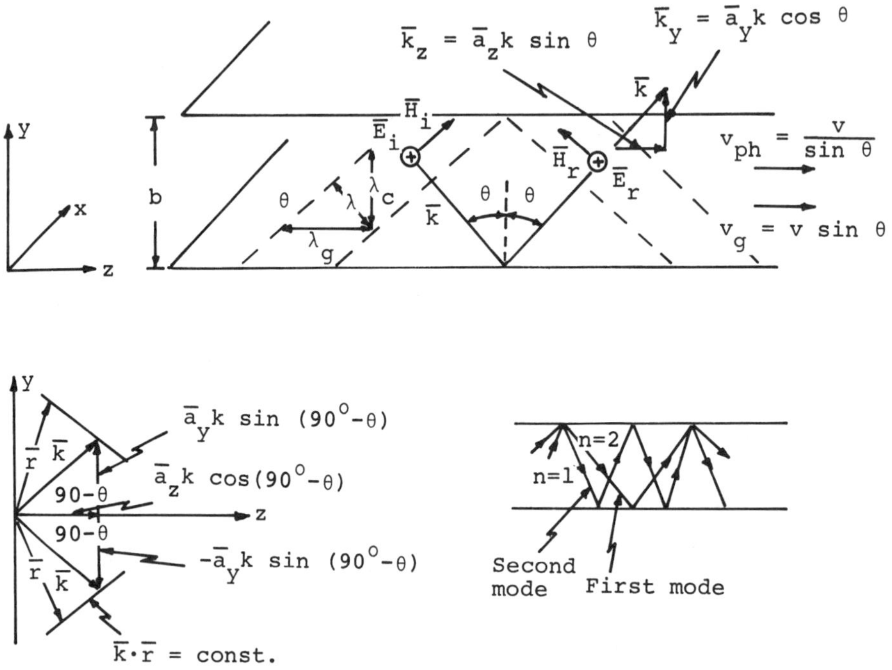

Figure 11-4.3. Field description for propagation between parallel planes.

$$\bar{E}_i = \bar{a}_x E_o e^{-j\omega t} e^{j\bar{k}\cdot\bar{r}} = \bar{a}_x E_o e^{-j\omega t} e^{j(-k_y y + k_z z)}$$
$$= \bar{a}_x E_o e^{-j\omega t} e^{jk(-y \cos\theta + z \sin\theta)} \tag{11-4.10}$$

At the surface $\bar{E}_i + \bar{E}_r = 0$, so that $\bar{E}_r = -\bar{E}_i$. But this relation is valid at any z including z = 0, then this implies that $|\bar{E}_r| = |\bar{E}_i| = E_o$. If the initial phase is assumed zero, then the reflected wave is specified by

$$\bar{E}_r = -\bar{a}_x E_o e^{-j\omega t} e^{jk(y \cos\theta + z \sin\theta)} \tag{11-4.11}$$

The total field at any point between the two planes is then

$$\bar{E} = \bar{E}_i + \bar{E}_r = \bar{a}_x E_o e^{-j\omega t} e^{jk\, z \sin\theta} (e^{-jk\, y \cos\theta} - e^{jk\, y \cos\theta})$$
$$= -2j\bar{a}_x E_o e^{-j\omega t} e^{jk\, z \sin\theta} \sin(ky \cos\theta) \tag{11-4.12}$$

But since the $\bar{E}$ field is entirely transverse, it must satisfy the boundary condition $\bar{E} = 0$ at y = 0 and y = b. The first boundary condition is automatically satisfied; the second condition imposes the requirement that

$$kb \cos\theta = n\pi \qquad (n = 0,1,2,\ldots) \tag{11-4.13}$$

Since the propagation constant in the y direction is $k_c = k \cos\theta$, we obtain the following relation

$$\lambda_c = \frac{\lambda}{\cos\theta} = \frac{2b}{n} \qquad (k_c = k \cos\theta = \frac{n\pi}{b}) \tag{11-4.14}$$

This is a *characteristic wavelength* (effective wavelength) in the Y-direction which is specified by the *mode number* n and the width b. In addition, Eq. (11-4.13) shows that for a particular angle of incidence θ only discrete frequencies

$$\omega_n = \frac{n\pi v}{b \cos\theta} \qquad (k = \frac{\omega}{v}) \tag{11-4.15}$$

are permitted.

The planes of constant phase, from Eq. (11-4.12), for the wave propagating along the guiding structure are given by

$$\omega t - kz \sin\theta = \text{const} \tag{11-4.16}$$

Therefore, they advance with velocity

$$v_{ph} = \frac{dz}{dt} = \frac{\omega}{k \sin \theta} = \frac{v}{\sin \theta} = \frac{f\lambda}{\sin \theta} = f\lambda_g \tag{11-4.17}$$

It follows from this that

$$\lambda_g = \frac{\lambda}{\sin \theta} \tag{11-4.18}$$

We now square and add the inverse of Eqs. (11-4.14) and (11-4.18). This leads to the equation

$$\frac{1}{\lambda_c^{\ 2}} + \frac{1}{\lambda_c^{\ 2}} = \frac{1}{\lambda^2}$$

or (11-4.19)

$$k^2 = k_c^{\ 2} + k_g^{\ 2}$$

Equation (11-4.13) thus leads to

$$\cos \theta = \frac{n\pi}{kb} = \frac{n\lambda}{2b} = \frac{nv}{2fb} = \frac{f_n}{f} \qquad (f_n = \frac{nv}{2b}) \tag{11-4.20}$$

A number of different possibilities exist. If θ is real, $\cos \theta$ must be less than unity, and so $f > f_n$. If $f < f_n$, then the angle θ is complex and the two plane waves forming the TE_n mode are *inhomogeneous waves*. More will be said about this type of wave in Sec. 11-6. When θ is real, we have propagation without attenuation; this mode is called the *propagated mode*. When $f < f_n$, the mode is heavily attenuated, and it is called *evanescent*. The frequency f_n is called the *cutoff frequency*.

For an evanescent mode, $\cos \theta > 1$ and real, which thus requires that $\sin \theta$ is purely imaginary since

$$\sin \theta = j(\cos^2\theta - 1)^{1/2} = j\alpha \tag{11-4.21}$$

where α is real and positive. The electric vector given by Eq. (11-4.12) now assumes the form

$$\overline{E} = -2j\overline{a}_x E_0 \sin(ky \cos \theta)e^{-k\alpha z} \tag{11-4.22}$$

If a study is made of the dependence of the field components E_x, H_y, H_z versus distance y across the guide, it will be found that they have the same form for the evanescent and the propagated modes. For the evanescent modes H_y and H_z are in phase, and both are in quadrature with E_x. This last observation implies that evanescent modes do not transfer energy along the guide (why?).

A diagram of the complex θ plane provides a useful portrayal of the values of representing propagating and evanescent modes. For propagating waves θ is real

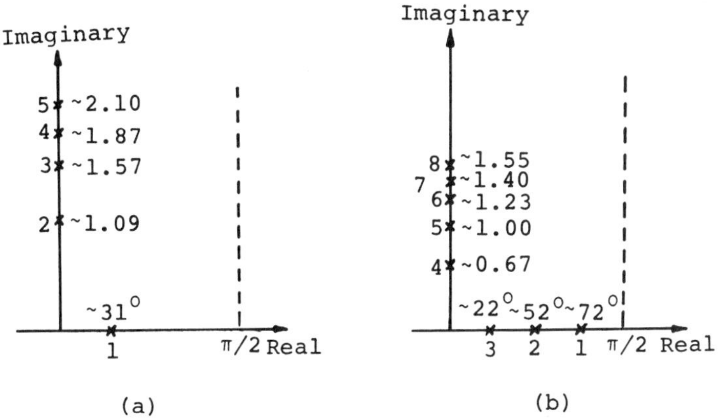

Figure 11-4.4. The propagating and the evanescent modes.

with values from 0 to $\pi/2$. For evanescent waves, $\cos\theta$ is real and greater than unity, and so we write

$$\cos\theta = \cosh\phi \qquad (11\text{-}4.23)$$

where ϕ is real and positive. Since $\cos j\phi = \cosh\phi$, this expression implies that

$$\theta = j\phi \qquad (11\text{-}4.24)$$

and the points which represent evanescent modes lie on the imaginary axis (see Fig. 11-4.4). The positions of the points depend on the applied frequency f.

If we have a wave whose frequency is $f = 1.2\ v/2b$ [see Eq. (11-4.20)] then $f_1/f = 0.85 < 1$, and we have only the TE_1 mode as the propagated mode; $f_2/f = 2/1.2 = 1.66 > 1$, then TE_2 and higher modes are evanescent (as per Fig. 11-4.4a). If we introduce the frequency $f = 3.25\ v/2b$ we have a set of modes shown in Fig. 11-4.4b.

In addition to the purely geometrical factors producing decaying fields we encounter losses if the dielectric constant of the medium between the plates is complex and if the plates are not perfectly conducting.

11-5. Wave Guides

We consider the case of the rectangular waveguide which is an extension of the case discussed in Sec. 11-4 except that now the two parallel planes are assumed to be connected by a second set of parallel planes normal to the original set. This second set of parallel planes imposes certain new constraints on the fields that can be sustained within the hollow pipe that results. We assume, as before, that the dielectric medium within the waveguide is lossless, isotropic, homogeneous and charge free. Then, for a field with sinusoidal excitation $e^{-j\omega t}$ propagating in the positive Z-direction, we have

$$\overline{E}(xyzt) = (E_{ox}\overline{a}_x + E_{oy}\overline{a}_y + E_{oz}\overline{a}_z)e^{j(k_z z-\omega t)} = (\overline{E}_{ot} + \overline{E}_{oz})e^{j(k_z z-\omega t)} \qquad \text{a)}$$

$$\overline{H}(xyzt) = (H_{ox}\overline{a}_x + H_{oy}\overline{a}_y + H_{oz}\overline{a}_z)e^{j(k_z z-\omega t)} = (\overline{H}_{ot} + \overline{H}_{oz})e^{j(k_z z-\omega t)} \qquad \text{b)}$$

(11-5.1)

where k_z is the waveguide wave number which has not yet been specified, and where $\overline{E}_{ot}$, $\overline{E}_{oz}$, $\overline{H}_{ot}$, and $\overline{H}_{oz}$ are functions of the transverse components only. The components of the electric vector are illustrated in Fig. 11-5.1.

Maxwell's two curl equations for this field configuration are

$$(\nabla_t + \overline{a}_z jk_z) \times (\overline{E}_{ot} + \overline{E}_{oz}) = j\omega\mu(\overline{H}_{ot} + \overline{H}_{oz}) \qquad \text{a)}$$

(11-5.2)

$$(\nabla_t + \overline{a}_z jk_z) \times (\overline{H}_{ot} + \overline{H}_{oz}) = -j\omega\varepsilon(\overline{E}_{ot} + \overline{E}_{oz}) \qquad \text{b)}$$

where $\nabla_t = \overline{a}_x\, \partial/\partial x + \overline{a}_y\, \partial/\partial y$, $\overline{E}_{ot}$ and $\overline{H}_{ot}$ are vectors in the XY plane, and $\partial/\partial z = jk_z$. Equating parallel vectors on the two sides of Eq. (11-5.2) we obtain the following sets

$$\nabla_t \times \overline{E}_{oz} + jk_z\overline{a}_z \times \overline{E}_{ot} = j\omega\mu\, \overline{H}_{ot} \qquad \text{a)}$$

$$\nabla_t \times \overline{H}_{oz} + jk_z\overline{a}_z \times \overline{H}_{ot} = -j\omega\varepsilon\, \overline{E}_{ot} \qquad \text{b)}$$

(11-5.3)

$$\nabla_t \times \overline{E}_{ot} = j\omega\mu\, \overline{H}_{oz} \qquad \text{c)}$$

$$\nabla_t \times \overline{H}_{ot} = -j\omega\varepsilon\, \overline{E}_{oz} \qquad \text{d)}$$

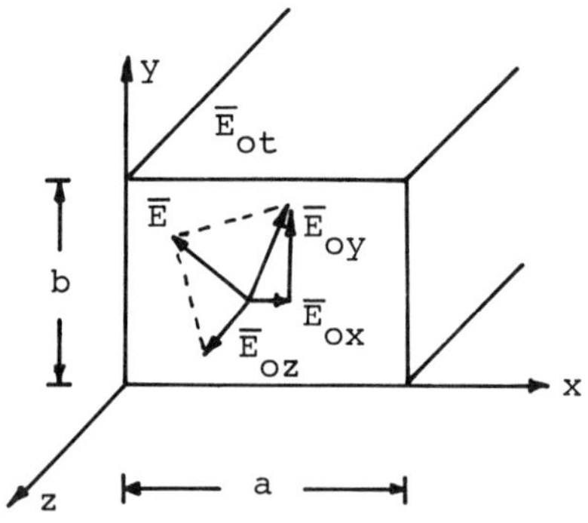

Figure 11-5.1. The simple waveguide.

It can be shown using Eqs. (11-5.3a) and (11-5.3b) that the transverse electric field components ($\overline{E}_{ot}$) and the magnetic field components can be determined if E_{oz} and H_{oz} are known; hence we obtain

$$\overline{E}_{ot} = \frac{j}{k^2-k_z^2}(k_z\nabla_t E_{oz} + \omega\mu\nabla_t \times \overline{H}_{oz}) \qquad \text{a)}$$

$$\overline{H}_{ot} = \frac{j}{k^2-k_z^2}(k_z\nabla_t H_{oz} - \omega\varepsilon\nabla_t \times \overline{E}_{oz}) \qquad \text{b)} \qquad (11\text{-}5.4)$$

where $k^2 = \omega^2\mu\varepsilon$. If we cross multiply Eq. (11-5.3a) by $\overline{a}_z$ we obtain

$$\overline{a}_z \times (\nabla_t \times E_{oz}) + jk_z\overline{a}_z \times (\overline{a}_z \times \overline{E}_{ot}) = j\omega\mu\, \overline{a}_z \times \overline{H}_{ot}$$

With the help of Appendix I this equation becomes

$$\nabla_t(\overline{a}_z\cdot\overline{E}_{oz}) - \overline{E}_{oz}(\overline{a}_z\cdot\nabla_t) + jk_z(\overline{a}_z\cdot\overline{E}_{ot}) - jk_z\overline{E}_{ot}(\overline{a}_z\cdot\overline{a}_z) = j\omega\mu\, \overline{a}_z \times \overline{H}_{ot}$$

or

$$\nabla_t E_{oz} - jk_z\overline{E}_{ot} = j\omega\mu\, \overline{a}_z \times \overline{H}_{ot}$$

If we then substitute $\overline{a}_z \times \overline{H}_{ot}$ from this equation into Eq. (11-5.3b) we obtain Eq. (11-5.4a). We obtain Eq. (11-5.4b) in a similar manner. Since each component of the field must satisfy the wave equation [see Eq. (8-8.4)] then the Z-components of the electric and magnetic field should satisfy the following equations

$$\nabla_t^2 E_{oz} = -(k^2 - k_z^2)\, E_{oz} \qquad \text{a)}$$

$$\nabla_t^2 H_{oz} = -(k^2 - k_z^2)\, H_{oz} \qquad \text{b)} \qquad (11\text{-}5.5)$$

To establish the boundary conditions, we assume that the waveguide walls are perfect conductors. This means, from Sec. 8-8, that at the boundaries

$$\overline{n} \cdot \overline{B} = 0 \qquad \text{a)}$$

$$\overline{n} \times \overline{E} = 0 \qquad \text{b)} \qquad (11\text{-}5.6)$$

where $\overline{E}$ and $\overline{B}$ are fields in the waveguide. Equation (11-5.6b) implies that the tangential component of the electric field must vanish at the boundary. This requires that

$$E_{oz}\Big|_{\text{bound.}} = 0 \qquad (11\text{-}5.7)$$

Furthermore, by dot multiplying Eq. (11-5.3b) by $\overline{a}_x$ and $\overline{a}_y$, respectively, and applying the boundary conditions for the magnetic field ($\overline{n} \cdot \overline{B} = 0$) and the electric field we obtain the relations

$$\left.\frac{\partial H_{oz}}{\partial y}\right|_{y\text{-bound.}} = 0; \qquad \left.\frac{\partial H_{oz}}{\partial x}\right|_{x\text{-bound.}} = 0 \tag{11-5.8}$$

These two boundary conditions in conjunction with Eqs. (11-5.5) specify an eigenvalue problem. However, both types of boundary conditions cannot be satisfied simultaneously, and we proceed by dividing the field into two separate categories: (a) the TM (*transverse magnetic*) case with $H_{oz} = 0$ everywhere and $E_{oz}|_{bound.} = 0$, and (b) the TE (*transverse electric*) case with $E_{oz} = 0$ everywhere and $\left.\frac{\partial H_{oz}}{\partial n}\right|_{bound.} = 0$ where $\partial/\partial n$ denotes the normal derivative at the surface.

The case when only transverse components exist, i.e., for TEM (*transverse electromagnetic*) waves, we must set in Eq. (11-5.4)

$$k_z = k \tag{11-5.9}$$

This creates an indetermine 0/0 form for each of the transverse components. By introducing Eq. (11-5.9) into Eqs. (11-5.5) we obtain Laplace type equations for $\overline{E}_{oz}$ and $\overline{H}_{oz}$. Moreover, each component of the fields also satisfies Laplace's equation, e.g., $\nabla_t^2 E_{ox} = 0$. The consequence of this is that the surface is an equipotential surface and the electric field must therefore vanish inside the waveguide. This shows that no TEM wave can propagate inside a hollow rectangular waveguide. Actually, this observation is true only for waves whose wavelength is comparable with the waveguide dimension, since, for example, a laser light beam (TEM wave) propagates through a hollow pipe.

Example 11-5.1. Refer to Fig. 11-5.2, and discuss the propagation of TM-type waves between the two parallel planes shown.

Solution. The TM waves have no H component in the Z-direction. The nonzero component E_{oz} satisfies Eq. (11-5.5a), but because of the infinite extent there is no Y-variation of the fields, and this equation reduces to the simple form

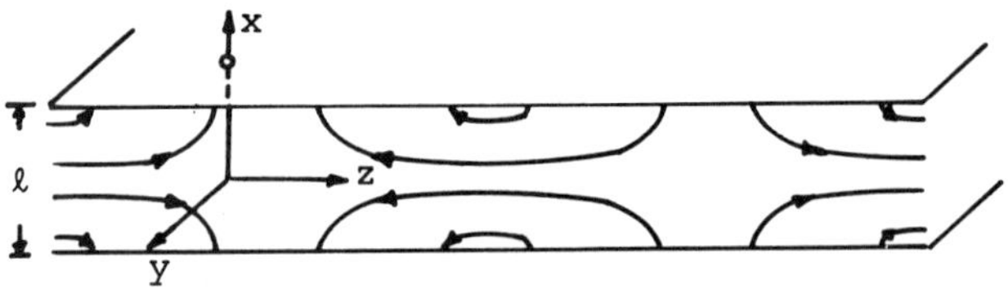

Figure 11-5.2. Electric field lines for TM_{10} waves between parallel planes.

$$\frac{d^2E_{oz}}{dx^2} + (k^2 - k_z^2)E_{oz} = \frac{d^2E_{oz}}{dx^2} + \lambda^2 E_{oz} = 0$$
$$E_{oz}\Big|_{x=0} = E_{oz}\Big|_{x=\ell} = 0 \qquad (11\text{-}5.10)$$

Clearly, this equation constitutes an eigenvalue problem, and our task is to find the eigenvalues and the corresponding eigenfunctions.

The general solution to Eq. (11-5.10) is known to be of the form

$$E_{oz} = a \sin \lambda x + b \cos \lambda x \qquad (11\text{-}5.11)$$

To satisfy the requirement $E_{oz} = 0$ at $x = 0$, we set $b = 0$ which reduces the solution to

$$E_{oz} = a \sin \lambda x \qquad (11\text{-}5.12)$$

Further, since the second boundary condition must also be satisfied, we must write

$$\lambda\ell = n\pi$$

or

$$\lambda_n = \frac{n\pi}{\ell} \qquad (11\text{-}5.13)$$

The solution is the expression

$$E_{ozn} = a_n \sin \frac{n\pi}{\ell} x \qquad n = 0,1,2,\ldots \qquad (11\text{-}5.14)$$

Since $k^2 - k_{zn}^2 = \lambda_n^2 = (n\pi/\ell)^2$, we find that

$$k_{zn} = \pm \left[k^2 - \left(\frac{n\pi}{\ell}\right)^2\right]^{1/2} \qquad (11\text{-}5.15)$$

where the double sign in front of the root indicates the existence of two waves, one propagating in the positive Z-direction, the second propagating in the negative Z-direction.

Now we note that for each value of n, Eq. (11-5.14) defines a particular configuration for the electric field, and as a consequence for the electromagnetic field in the waveguide. Each specific configuration of the field is called a *mode*. For each mode (each value of n) there is a particular frequency at which the mode changes from a propagating to a decaying mode. This particular frequency is called the *cutoff* frequency and is found from Eq. (11-5.15) by setting $k_{zn} = 0$. This requires that

$$f_c = \frac{n}{2\sqrt{\mu\varepsilon}\,\ell} \tag{11-5.16}$$

For $f < f_c$, k_z becomes a pure imaginary which indicates continuous attenuation of the field, and no propagation; when $f > f_c$, k_z is real, wave propagation is present.

Introducing Eq. (11-5.14) into Eqs. (11-5.4) we obtain

$$\begin{aligned}
E_{oxn} &= j\frac{k_{zn}}{\lambda_n} a_n \cos\left(\frac{n\pi}{\ell}x\right) && \text{a)}\\
E_{oyn} &= 0 && \\
E_{ozn} &= a_n \sin\left(\frac{n\pi}{\ell}x\right) && \text{c)}\\
H_{oyn} &= j\frac{\omega\varepsilon}{\lambda_n} a_n \cos\left(\frac{n\pi}{\ell}x\right) && \text{d)}\\
H_{oxn} &= 0 && \text{e)}\\
H_{ozn} &= 0 \text{ by hypothesis} && \text{f)}
\end{aligned} \tag{11-5.17}$$

This shows that the operator $A = -d^2/dx^2$ of Eq. (11-5.10) is positive definite and the eigenvalues λ^2 are non-negative. To observe the physical significance of the orthogonality of the modes, we must determine the power that propagates down the guide due to two superimposed modes, as specified by Eqs. (11-5.17a) and (11-5.17d). We write

$$\begin{aligned}
E_{ox} &= E_{oxn} + E_{oxm} = j\frac{a_n k_{zn}}{\lambda_n} E'_{oxn} + j\frac{a_m k_{zm}}{\lambda_m} E'_{oxm}\\
H_{oy} &= H_{oyn} + H_{oym} = +j\frac{\omega\varepsilon a_n}{\lambda_n} E'_{oxn} + j\frac{\omega\varepsilon a_m}{\lambda_m} E'_{oxm}
\end{aligned} \tag{11-5.18}$$

The total power in the Z-direction over the cross section of unit length in the Y-direction is given by the appropriate Poynting vector. This is

$$\begin{aligned}
P_{total} &= \mathrm{Re}\left\{\int_0^1\int_0^\ell (\overline{E}\times\overline{H}^*)\cdot\overline{a}_z dS\right\} = \mathrm{Re}\left\{\int_0^\ell E_{ox}H_{oy}^* dx\right\}\\
&= \mathrm{Re}\left\{\int_0^\ell \omega\varepsilon\left(\frac{a_n a_n^*}{\lambda_n^2} k_{zn}E'_{oxn}E'^*_{oxn} + \frac{a_m a_n^*}{\lambda_m\lambda_n} k_{zm}E_{oxm}E^*_{oxn} + \frac{a_n a_m^*}{\lambda_n\lambda_m} k_{zn}E'_{oxn}E'^*_{oxn}\right.\right.\\
&\qquad \left.\left. + \frac{a_n a_m^*}{\lambda_m^2} k_{zm}E'_{oxm}E'^*_{oxm}\right) dx\right\}\\
&= \frac{\omega\varepsilon}{\lambda_n^2} k_{zn}\int_0^\ell |a_n|^2|E'_{oxn}|^2 dx + \frac{\omega\varepsilon}{\lambda_m^2} k_{zm}\int_0^\ell |a_m|^2|E'_{oxm}|^2 dx = P_n + P_m
\end{aligned} \tag{11-5.19}$$

since the integrals of the two middle terms are zero (E'_{oxn} and E'_{oxm} are orthogonal functions in $[0,\ell]$).

A. Rectangular Wave Guides. We now wish to consider the detailed solution of the fields in rectangular waveguides. Initially, we consider the case of TE waves in rectangular waveguides, as shown in Fig. 11-5.1. We must find the field components E_{ox}, E_{oy}, H_{ox}, H_{oy}, H_{oz} and the wave number k_z. For transverse electric fields, the starting point is Eq. (11-5.5b) in rectangular coordinates

$$\frac{\partial^2 H_{oz}}{\partial x^2} + \frac{\partial^2 H_{oz}}{\partial y^2} = -k_a^2 H_{oz} \qquad (k_a^2 = k^2 - k_z^2) \tag{11-5.20}$$

We use the method of separation of variables developed in Chap. 4 and set

$$H_{oz} = f(x)\ g(y) \tag{11-5.21}$$

When this is substituted into Eq. (11-5.24) there results

$$\frac{1}{f}\frac{\partial^2 f}{\partial x^2} + \frac{1}{g}\frac{\partial^2 g}{\partial y^2} = -k_a^2 \tag{11-5.22}$$

For there to be a solution to this equation for any x and y, the factors $(1/f)\cdot \partial^2 f/\partial x^2$ and $(1/g)\partial^2 g/\partial y^2$ must be constants as discussed in Chap. 4. Furthermore, as we know, depending on the choice of constants, we can have different forms for the solutions. Here both constants are chosen to be negative such that

$$\frac{1}{f}\frac{d^2 f}{dx^2} = -k_x^2 \qquad \text{a)}$$
$$\frac{1}{g}\frac{d^2 g}{dy^2} = -k_y^2 \qquad \text{b)} \tag{11-5.23}$$

These two ordinary differential equations have sinusoidal forms as their solution, subject to the requirement that

$$k_x^2 + k_y^2 = k_a^2$$

Thus the solution for the TE wave (there will be an identical form for the TM waves) is given by

$$H_{oz} = f(x)\ g(y)$$

where

$$f(x) = A \cos k_x x + B \sin k_x x \qquad \text{a)}$$
$$g(y) = C \cos k_y y + D \sin k_y y \qquad \text{b)} \tag{11-5.24}$$
$$k_x^2 + k_y^2 = k_a^2 \qquad \text{c)}$$

Now apply the boundary conditions, which are

$$\left.\frac{\partial H_{oz}}{\partial x}\right|_{x=0} = 0; \qquad \left.\frac{\partial H_{oz}}{\partial y}\right|_{y=0} = 0$$

[see Eq. (11-5.8)]. Only the cosine terms must be retained, which then specifies Eq. (11-5.21) to be in the form

$$H_{oz} = A_1 \cos k_x x \cos k_y y \tag{11-5.25}$$

Using Eq. (11-5.4) the other components are found to be

$$\begin{aligned}
E_{ox} &= -\frac{j\omega\mu k_y A_1}{k_a^2} \cos k_x x \sin k_y y && \text{a)}\\
E_{oy} &= \frac{j\omega\mu k_x A_1}{k_a^2} \sin k_x x \cos k_y y && \text{b)}\\
H_{ox} &= -\frac{jk_z k_x A_1}{k_a^2} \sin k_x x \cos k_y y && \text{c)}\\
H_{oy} &= -\frac{jk_z k_y A_1}{k_a^2} \cos k_x x \sin k_y y && \text{d)}
\end{aligned} \tag{11-5.26}$$

Further, the same boundary conditions when applied at x = a and y = b require that [see Eq. (11-5.25)]

$$k_x = \frac{m\pi}{a} \qquad k_y = \frac{n\pi}{b} \tag{11-5.27}$$

and therefore

$$k_a = \pm\sqrt{k^2 - k_z^2} = \pm\sqrt{k_x^2 + k_y^2} = \pm\sqrt{\left(\frac{m\pi}{a}\right)^2 + \left(\frac{n\pi}{b}\right)^2} \tag{11-5.28}$$

A transverse electric field is denoted by TE_{mn}, and either m or n may be zero but not both. However, for TM_{mn} waves neither m nor n can be zero. The lowest order of TE is TE_{10} and is of special engineering interest.

Equation (11-5.28) defines the unknown propagation constant k_z and it is given by the relation

$$k_z = \pm\sqrt{k^2 - \left[\left(\frac{m\pi}{a}\right)^2 + \left(\frac{n\pi}{b}\right)^2\right]} \tag{11-5.29}$$

The cutoff frequency is found by setting $k_z = 0$, and thus

$$\sqrt{\mu\varepsilon}\,\omega_c = \left[\left(\frac{m\pi}{a}\right)^2 + \left(\frac{n\pi}{b}\right)^2\right]^{1/2} \tag{11-5.30}$$

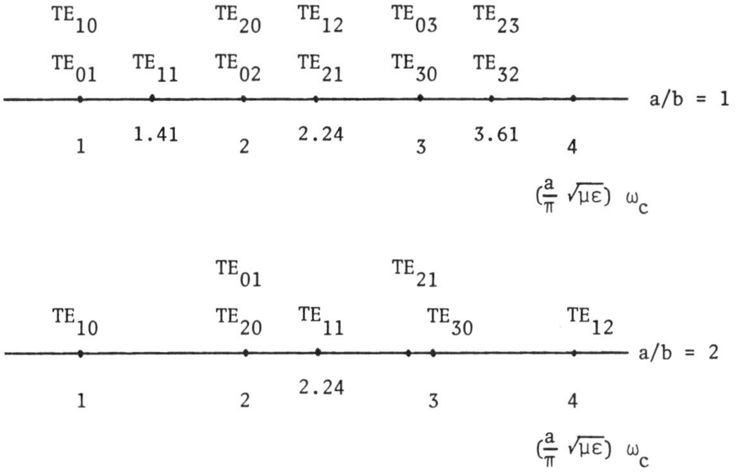

Figure 11-5.3. The cutoff frequencies in rectangular waveguides.

The relative cutoff frequencies of waves in rectangular waveguides are shown in Fig. 11-5.3. It is apparent that the dimensions of the guide play an important role in the separation of modes. If, for example, we select a frequency such that the value of $\omega(a/\pi)\sqrt{\mu\varepsilon}$ is less than two for a guide with sides $a/b = 2$, then only the TE_{10} mode will be propagated. The fields for the TE_{10} mode are shown in Fig. 11-5.4.

The TE_{10} mode is of particular importance in waveguide applications, and we explore this matter in greater detail. By combining Eqs. (11-5.26) with Eq. (11-5.1) with $m = 1$ and $n = 0$, such that $k_x = \pi/a = k_a$, $k_y = 0$, the TE_{10} field configurations are

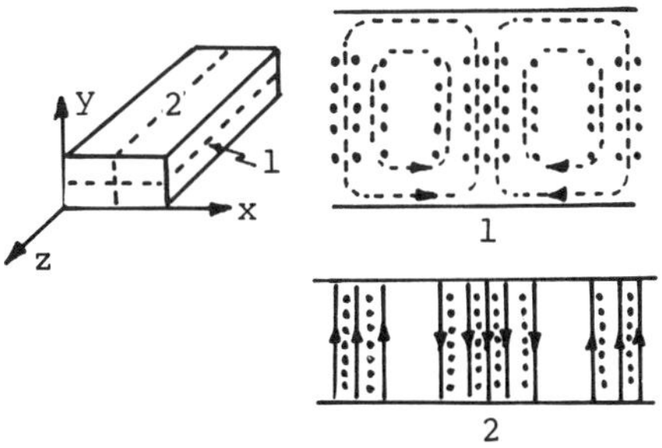

Figure 11-5.4. Fields of TE_{10} mode. (a) Electric fields: solid lines (b) Magnetic fields: dotted lines.

$$E_x = 0 \qquad \text{a)}$$

$$E_y = \frac{j\omega\mu\pi}{k_a^2 a} A_{10} \sin \frac{\pi}{a} x\, e^{jk_z z} \qquad \text{b)}$$

$$H_x = -\frac{jk_z\pi}{k_a^2 a} A_{10} \sin \frac{\pi}{a} x\, e^{jk_z z} \qquad \text{c)} \quad (11\text{-}5.31)$$

$$H_y = 0 \qquad \text{d)}$$

$$H_z = A_{10} \cos \frac{\pi}{a} x\, e^{jk_z z} \qquad \text{e)}$$

A practical consideration is the attenuation characteristics of such a waveguide. This requires an evaluation of the power carried down the guide, and also the losses in the guide walls. The power carried down the guide is given by

$$\mathscr{S}_c = \int_S (\overline{E} \times \overline{H}^*) \cdot d\overline{S} = -\int_0^b\int_0^a E_y H_x^* \, dx\, dy$$

$$= \int_0^a\int_0^b \omega\mu \left(\frac{\pi}{a}\right)^2 \left(\frac{A_1}{k_a^2}\right)^2 k_z \sin^2 \frac{\pi}{a} x\, dx\, dy = \frac{1}{2}\, \omega\mu \left(\frac{\pi}{a}\right)^2 \left(\frac{A_1}{k_a^2}\right)^2 k_z\, ab$$

But $k_a = k_x$ when $k_y = 0$ and so

$$\mathscr{S}_c = \frac{1}{2} \frac{\omega\mu A_1^2 k_z}{k_a^2} ab \qquad (11\text{-}5.32)$$

The time average power is

$$\langle\mathscr{S}_c\rangle = \frac{1}{4} \frac{\omega\mu k_z}{k_a^2} A_1^2\, ab \qquad \text{Joule/sec} \qquad (11\text{-}5.33)$$

To determine the power loss/m^2 in the walls of the guide, we use Eq. (10-3.15) for the time average Poynting vector

$$\langle\mathscr{S}_c\rangle = \frac{1}{2} |H|^2 \,\mathrm{Re}\, Z = \frac{1}{2} |J|^2 R \qquad (11\text{-}5.34)$$

where $R = 1/\sigma\delta$, δ = skin depth [see Eq. (10-3.20)]. Four surfaces are involved - the top, bottom, and two sides. Hence we must evaluate

$$\langle\mathscr{S}_c\rangle = \frac{1}{2}(\mathrm{Re}\ Z) \int HH^* dS = \frac{1}{2}(\mathrm{Re}\ Z) \int_0^1 dz \int_0^{a\ (\text{or } b)} HH^* dx(\text{or } dy) \qquad (\text{Watt/m})$$

over the appropriate surfaces, which yields

$$\langle\mathscr{S}_c\rangle = \frac{1}{2}(\mathrm{Re}\ Z) \left[\int_{\substack{\text{Top +}\\ \text{bottom}}} |H_x|^2 dS + \int_{\substack{\text{top +}\\ \text{bottom}}} |H_z|^2 dS + \int_{\text{sides}} |H_z|^2 dS\right] \qquad (11\text{-}5.35)$$

But the average values over a full cycle of $\cos^2 k_x x$ and $\sin^2 k_x x$ are each 1/2, and also $\cos k_x x = \pm 1$ on the sides so that $\cos^2 k_x x = 1$ in the third integral. The evaluation of these integrals yields

$$\langle \mathscr{S}_c \rangle = \frac{1}{2} R \, [(\frac{k_z k_x}{k_a^2})^2 A_1^2 \cdot \frac{2a}{2} + A_1^2 \cdot \frac{2a}{2} + A_1^2 \cdot 2b]$$

$$= \frac{1}{2} A^2 R \, [a[(\frac{k_z}{k_a})^2 + 1] + 2b] \qquad \text{(Watt/m)} \tag{11-5.36}$$

The attenuation of the guide is defined as

$$2\alpha = \frac{\text{Energy loss/m}}{\text{Energy transmitted}} \qquad \text{neper/m} \tag{11-5.37}$$

Here 2α gives a measure of the fraction of the power that is lost in heating the walls of the waveguide as the energy is transmitted along the waveguide. The factor 2 is introduced because energy is proportional to $\overline{E} \times \overline{H}$ or H^2 and for the field to reduce according to an attenuation α, the energy will decrease according to a 2α law. By including the known expressions for numerator and denominator

$$2\alpha = \frac{\frac{1}{2} R A_1^2 \{a\,[1 + (\frac{k_z}{k_a})^2] + 2b\}}{\frac{1}{4} \frac{\omega\mu k_z}{k_a^2} A_1^2 \, ab} = \frac{2R}{\frac{\omega\mu}{k_z}} \left[\frac{a\,[1 + (\frac{k_z}{k_a})^2 + 2b]}{(\frac{k_z}{k_a})^2 \, ab} \right] \tag{11-5.38}$$

We can write this in more usual form by employing Eqs. (11-5.29) and (11-5.30). For $m = 1$, $n = 0$

$$k_z = \pm \sqrt{k^2 - k_x^2}$$

where $k = 2\pi/\lambda = 2\pi f/v = \omega\sqrt{\mu\varepsilon}$. Note that at cutoff $k_z = 0$ and so

$$\sqrt{\mu\varepsilon}\,\omega_c = \frac{\pi}{a} = k_c \tag{11-5.39}$$

since $\omega_c = 2\pi f_c = (\pi/a)^2 v$. We now write

$$k_z = \sqrt{k^2 - k_c^2}$$

which is

$$k_z = k\sqrt{1 - (k_c/k)^2} = k\sqrt{1 - (f_c/f)^2} \qquad f > f_c \qquad \text{a)}$$

$$k_z = jk_c\sqrt{1 - (k/k_c)^2} = jk_c\sqrt{1 - (f/f_c)^2} \qquad f < f_c \qquad \text{b)} \tag{11-5.40}$$

For $f > f_c$, which is the condition for propagation down the guide, we get

$$2\alpha = \frac{2R}{\frac{\omega\mu}{k_z}} \left[\frac{a\left[1 + \frac{k^2 - k_a^2}{k_a^2}\right] + 2b}{\left(\frac{k^2 - k_a^2}{k_a^2}\right) ab} \right] = \frac{2R}{\frac{\omega\mu}{k_z}} \cdot \frac{1}{b} \left[\frac{1 + \frac{2b}{a}\left(\frac{k_a}{k}\right)^2}{1 - \left(\frac{k_a}{k}\right)^2} \right] \tag{11-5.41}$$

But

$$\frac{\omega\mu}{k_z} = \frac{\omega\mu}{k\sqrt{1 - (f_c/f)^2}} = \frac{Z_o}{\sqrt{1 - (f_c/f)^2}}$$

so that finally

$$\alpha = \frac{2R}{Z_o} \cdot \frac{1}{b} \left[\frac{1 + \frac{2b}{a}\left(\frac{f_c}{f}\right)^2}{\sqrt{1 - (f_c/f)^2}} \right] \quad \text{neper/m} \tag{11-5.42}$$

Often the attenuation is given in units of dB/m rather than in units of neper/m. To convert, we note that since

$$\langle \mathscr{S}_c(z) \rangle = \langle \mathscr{S}_{co} \rangle e^{-2\alpha z}$$

then

$$\log_{10} \frac{\langle \mathscr{S}_c(z) \rangle}{\langle \mathscr{S}_{co} \rangle} = -2\alpha z \log_{10} e = -0.868\ \alpha z$$

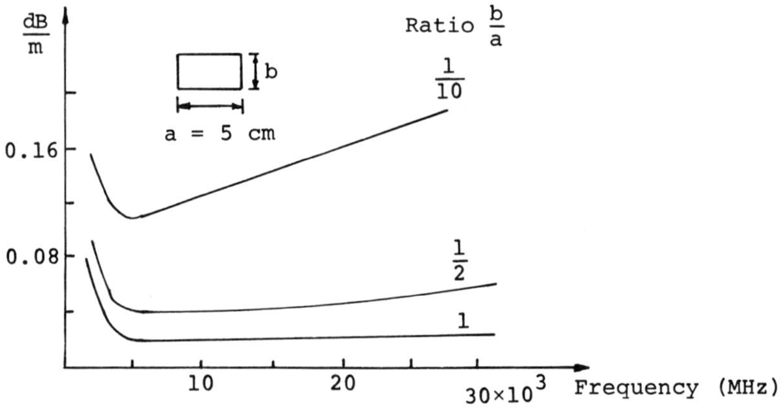

Figure 11-5.5. Attenuation due to Cu losses in rectangular waveguide of fixed width: TE_{10} mode.

Hence we have

$$\alpha = 2 \times 8.68 \frac{R}{Z_o} \cdot \frac{1}{b}\left[\frac{1 + \frac{2b}{a}\left(\frac{f_c}{f}\right)^2}{\sqrt{1 - (f_c/f)^2}}\right] \qquad \text{dB/m} \tag{11-5.43}$$

A sketch of the variation of α specified by this equation for a Cu waveguide of fixed width a is given in Fig. 11-5.5.

B. Cylindrical Wave Guides. For a TM wave Eq. (11-5.5a) in cylindrical coordinates takes the form [see Appendix I]

$$\frac{\partial^2 E_{oz}}{\partial r^2} + \frac{1}{r}\frac{\partial E_{oz}}{\partial r} + \frac{1}{r^2}\frac{\partial^2 E_{oz}}{\partial \phi^2} = -k_a^2 E_{oz} \tag{11-5.44}$$

The same procedure is followed as for the case of rectangular waveguides. This leads, upon setting

$$E_{oz} = f(r)\, g(\phi) \tag{11-5.45}$$

to the expression

$$r^2 \frac{1}{f}\frac{\partial^2 f}{\partial r^2} + r\frac{1}{f}\frac{\partial f}{\partial r} + k_a^2 r^2 = -\frac{1}{g}\frac{\partial^2 g}{\partial \phi^2} \tag{11-5.46}$$

For separation, each of the equations must be equal to a constant, here chosen to be n^2. This leads to the following two ordinary differential equations

$$\frac{d^2 g}{d\phi^2} + n^2 g = 0 \qquad \text{a)} \tag{11-5.47}$$

$$\frac{d^2 f}{dr^2} + \frac{1}{r}\frac{df}{dr} + \left(k_a^2 - \frac{n^2}{r^2}\right) f = 0 \qquad \text{b)} \tag{11-5.48}$$

The solution to Eq. (11-5.47) is given in terms of trigonometric functions and the solution to Eq. (11-5.48) is written in terms of Bessel functions. The solution for TM waves (there will be an identical form for TE waves) specified in Eqs. (11-5.48) and (11-5.47) is

$$f(r) = A\, J_n(k_a r) + B\, Y_n(k_a r) \qquad \text{a)}$$

$$g(\phi) = C \cos n\phi + D \sin n\phi \qquad \text{b)} \tag{11-5.49}$$

For a circular waveguide shown in Fig. 11-5.6 no terms of $Y_n(k_a r)$ can exist since at the origin r = 0 and $Y_n(0) = \infty$. The solution of a TM wave will then be written

$$E_{oz} = J_n(k_a r)(C_1 \cos n\phi + D_1 \sin n\phi) \tag{11-5.50}$$

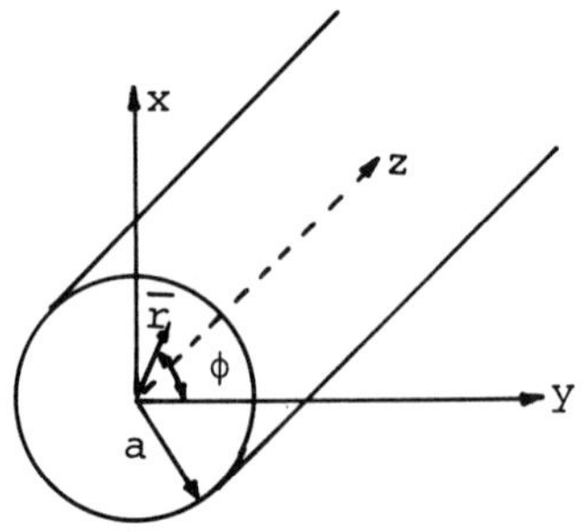

Figure 11-5.6. Cylindrical waveguide.

The constant D_1 can be set equal to zero since, by rotation of the coordinate axes, the harmonic variation of the field versus ϕ can be expressed by a simple cosine function rather than by a combination of sine and cosine terms. The form of E_{oz} reduces to

$$E_{oz} = C_1 J_n(k_a r) \cos n\phi \tag{11-5.51}$$

Finally, the boundary condition $E_{oz}\big|_{r=a} = 0$ must also be satisfied for all values of ϕ. Therefore the relation

$$J_n(k_a r)\bigg|_{r=a} = 0$$

must hold, and this restricts $k_a a$ to discrete values, namely, the roots of $J_n = 0$. Table 4-3.2 gives the lower order roots, where n is associated with the order of the Bessel function, and m with the particular root of J_n. Denoting the roots by p_{nm}, the value of k_a is now given by

$$k_a = \frac{p_{nm}}{a} \tag{11-5.52}$$

The final expression for E_{oz} assumes the form

$$E_{oz} = C_{nm} J_n\left(\frac{p_{nm} r}{a}\right) \cos n\phi \tag{11-5.53}$$

By employing Eq. (11-5.4) in cylindrical coordinates (see Appendix I) we find that

$$E_{or} = \left[\frac{j\omega\mu}{k^2 - k_z^2}\right]\left[\frac{k_z}{\omega\mu}\frac{\partial E_{oz}}{\partial r} + \frac{1}{r}\frac{\partial H_{oz}}{\partial \phi}\right]$$

$$E_{o\phi} = \left[\frac{-j\omega\mu}{k^2 - k_z^2}\right]\left[-\frac{1}{r}\frac{k_z}{\omega\mu}\frac{\partial E_{oz}}{\partial \phi} + \frac{\partial H_{oz}}{\partial r}\right] \tag{11-5.54}$$

$$H_{or} = \left[\frac{-j\omega\varepsilon}{k^2-k_z^2}\right]\left[\frac{1}{r}\frac{\partial E_{oz}}{\partial \phi} - \frac{k_z}{\omega\varepsilon}\frac{\partial H_{oz}}{\partial r}\right]$$

$$H_{o\phi} = \left[\frac{j\omega\varepsilon}{k^2-k_z^2}\right]\left[\frac{\partial E_{oz}}{\partial r} + \frac{k_z}{\omega\varepsilon}\frac{1}{r}\frac{\partial H_{oz}}{\partial \phi}\right] \qquad (11\text{-}5.54)$$

By substituting Eq. (11-5.53) into Eq. (11-5.54) we find that the field inside of a cylindrical waveguide is specified by

$$E_{or} = C_{nm}\frac{jk_z}{k^2-k_z^2}\frac{p_{nm}}{a}J'_n\left(\frac{p_{nm}r}{a}\right)\cos n\phi$$

$$E_{o\phi} = -C_{nm}\frac{jn}{k^2-k_z^2}\frac{k_z}{r}J_n\left(\frac{p_{nm}r}{a}\right)\sin n\phi$$

$$H_{or} = C_{nm}\frac{j\omega\varepsilon}{k^2-k_z^2}\frac{n}{r}J_n\left(\frac{p_{nm}r}{a}\right)\sin n\phi \qquad (11\text{-}5.55)$$

$$H_{o\phi} = C_{nm}\frac{j\omega\varepsilon}{k^2-k_z^2}\frac{p_{nm}}{a}J'_n\left(\frac{p_{nm}r}{a}\right)\cos n\phi$$

where J'_n denotes the derivative of J_n with respect to the variable $(p_{nm}r/a)$. The recurrence formulas for the derivatives of Bessel functions are given in Table 4-3.1. Field distribution of the first few modes are shown in Fig. 11-5.7.

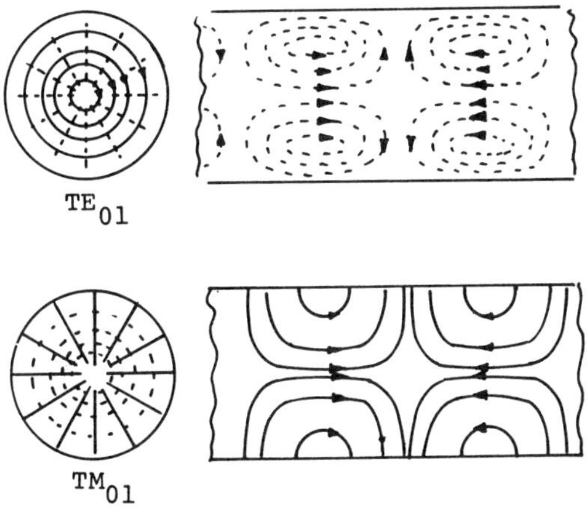

Figure 11-5.7. Two modes for cylindrical hollow waveguides. (Dotted lines indicate the H-field component and the solid lines indicate the E-field component.)

11-6. Reflection and Refraction of EM Waves at Plane Boundaries

Consider a plane wave that is propagating in a homogeneous, isotropic and lossless medium to impinge on a second medium, as shown in Fig. 11-6.1. The simplest solution of the wave equation (10-2.1) in each medium is

$$\overline{E}(\overline{r},t) = \overline{E}_0 e^{j(\overline{k}\cdot\overline{r}-\omega t)} \tag{11-6.1}$$

where $|k| = k = \omega\sqrt{\mu\varepsilon} = k_0\eta = k_0\sqrt{\varepsilon_r}$. The magnetic field is easily found from the Maxwell equation $\nabla \times \overline{E} = j\omega\mu\,\overline{H}$. This has already been found to be [see Eq. (10-2.12)]

$$\overline{H} = \frac{1}{\omega\mu}\,\overline{k} \times \overline{E} \tag{11-6.2}$$

To study the reflection and refraction properties of a plane wave incident on a plane interface between two mediums, we assume initially the case of *perpendicular* polarization (transverse electric, TE, polarization). This means that the electric field vector is directed along the Y-axis and is perpendicular to the *plane of incidence,* in our case the XZ plane. This assumption does not restrict the generality of this problem because we can always decompose the electric field into two components, one component perpendicular to the plane of incidence and the other component parallel to it. The parallel polarization is the transverse magnetic TM

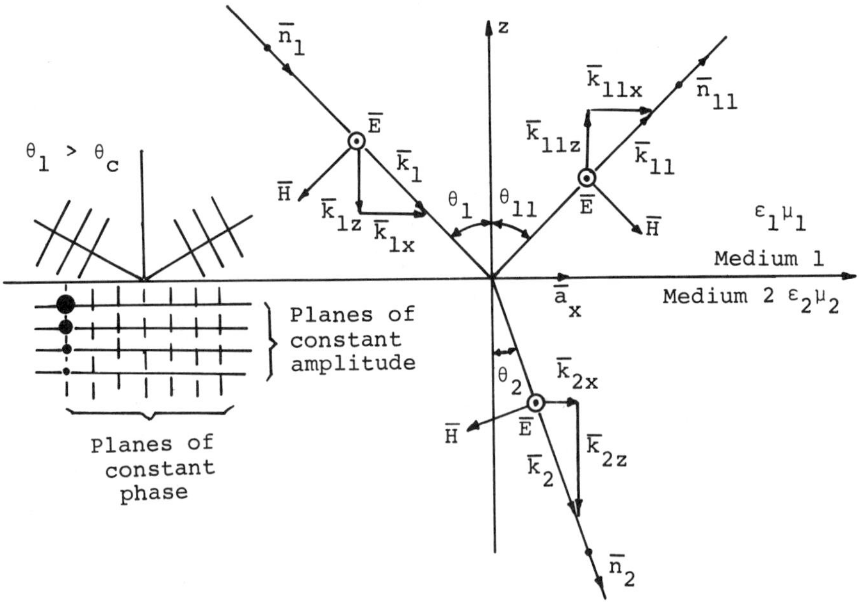

Figure 11-6.1. Refraction at a boundary.

polarization.

The electric field in medium 1 can be written in the form

$$E_{1y} = E_{oy} e^{j(k_{1x}x - k_{1z}z)} + R_{\perp} E_{oy} e^{j(k_{11x}x + k_{11z}z)} \qquad (11\text{-}6.3)$$

where the first term represents the incident wave, the second term represents the reflected wave, and $R_{\perp}$ is the *reflection* coefficient for perpendicular polarization. Substituting Eq. (11-6.3) into Eq. (11-6.2) we find the magnetic field in medium 1 to be:

$$H_{1x} = \frac{k_{1z}E_{oy}}{\mu_1 \omega} [e^{j(k_{1x}x - k_{1z}z)} - R_{\perp} e^{j(k_{11x}x + k_{11z}z)}] \qquad \text{a)}$$

$$H_{1z} = \frac{k_{1x}E_{oy}}{\mu_1 \omega} [e^{j(k_{1x}x - k_{1z}z)} - R_{\perp} e^{j(k_{11x}x + k_{11z}z)}] \qquad \text{b)} \qquad (11\text{-}6.4)$$

We assume a *transmission* coefficient $T_{\perp}$ for the field, and the Y-component of the electric field can be written in the form

$$E_{2y} = E_{oy} T_{\perp} e^{j(k_{2x}x - k_{2z}z)} \qquad (11\text{-}6.5)$$

and the magnetic field is obtained from Eq. (11-6.2)

$$H_{2x} = \frac{T_{\perp} k_{2z}}{\mu_2 \omega} E_{oy} e^{j(k_{2x}x - k_{2z}z)} \qquad \text{a)}$$

$$H_{2z} = \frac{T_{\perp} k_{2x}}{\mu_2 \omega} E_{oy} e^{j(k_{2x}x - k_{2z}z)} \qquad \text{b)} \qquad (11\text{-}6.6)$$

The boundary conditions must be satisfied at each point on the X-axis and at all times. This implies that the spatial and the time variation of the field in both mediums at the interface must be the same. This requires that

$$k_{1x} = k_{11x} = k_{2x}$$

or

$$k_1 \sin \theta_1 = k_{11} \sin \theta_{11} = k_2 \sin \theta_2 \qquad (11\text{-}6.7)$$

and since $k_1 = k_{11}$, then $\theta_1 = \theta_{11}$. Equation (11-6.7) leads to *Snell's law*

$$\frac{\sin \theta_1}{\sin \theta_2} = \frac{k_2}{k_1} = \frac{\sqrt{\mu_2 \varepsilon_2}}{\sqrt{\mu_1 \varepsilon_1}} = \frac{v_1}{v_2} = \frac{\eta_2}{\eta_1} \qquad (11\text{-}6.8)$$

where η is the index of refraction. Now we apply the boundary conditions specified by Eqs. (8-7.1a) and (8-7.1c) (the tangential components of $\overline{E}$ and $\overline{H}$ fields are equal) and the equality (11-6.7) ($k_{1x} = k_{2x}$). We then find that

$$T_\perp = 1 + R_\perp \tag{11-6.9}$$

$$T_\perp = \frac{\mu_2}{\mu_1}\frac{k_{1z}}{k_{2z}}(1 - R_\perp) \tag{11-6.10}$$

If we solve Eqs. (11-6.9) and (11-6.10) simultaneously we find that

$$R_\perp = \frac{\mu_2 k_{1z} - \mu_1 k_{2z}}{\mu_2 k_{1z} + \mu_1 k_{2z}} = \frac{\mu_2 k_1 \cos\theta_1 - \mu_1 k_2 \cos\theta_2}{\mu_2 k_1 \cos\theta_1 + \mu_1 k_2 \cos\theta_2} \tag{11-6.11}$$

$$T_\perp = \frac{2\mu_2 k_{1z}}{\mu_2 k_{1z} + \mu_1 k_{2z}} = \frac{2\mu_2 k_1 \cos\theta_1}{\mu_2 k_1 \cos\theta_1 + \mu_1 k_2 \cos\theta_2} \tag{11-6.12}$$

If we assume that $\mu_1 = \mu_2$ for simplicity, we can distinguish two cases. The first case, for which $\eta_1 < \eta_2$, is called *external* reflection. The second case, for which $\eta_1 > \eta_2$, is called *internal* reflection. For the first case both polarizations have real reflection and transmission coefficients for all values of θ. For the second case, above a certain angle known as the *critical* angle, the reflection coefficients for both polarizations are complex. We observe *total* reflection at these angles.

Since we are dealing with lossless dielectric mediums, the wave number k^2 must be real, and we write

$$k^2 = k_x^2 + k_y^2 + k_z^2 \tag{11-6.13}$$

We can generalize this equation by introducing the following complex numbers:

$$k_x = k_x' + jk_x''; \; k_y = k_y' + jk_y''; \; k_z = k_z' + jk_z'' \quad [\bar{k} = \bar{k}' + j\bar{k}''] \tag{11-6.14}$$

which must also satisfy Eq. (11-6.13). The field now takes the form

$$\bar{E} = \bar{E}_0 e^{j[(k_x'x+k_y'y+k_z'z)-\omega t] - (k_x''x+k_y''y+k_z''z)} \tag{11-6.15}$$

which describes a wave whose amplitude also varies. The equation that describes the family of planes with constant phase is

$$k_x'x + k_y'y + k_z'z = \bar{k}' \cdot \bar{r} = \text{const.} \tag{11-6.16}$$

and the one describing the family of planes of constant amplitude is

$$k_x''x + k_y''y + k_z''z = \bar{k}'' \cdot \bar{r} = \text{const.} \tag{11-6.17}$$

By combining Eqs. (11-6.14) with (11-6.13) and equating the real and imaginary parts (k^2 is real) we obtain

$$\bar{k}'' \cdot \bar{k}'' - \bar{k}' \cdot \bar{k}' = k^2 \qquad \text{a)}$$
$$\bar{k}' \cdot \bar{k}'' = 0 \qquad \text{b)} \qquad (11\text{-}6.18)$$

The last equation shows that the planes of constant phase and constant amplitude are orthogonal to each other. A wave of the form given by Eq. (11-6.15) is called an *inhomogeneous plane wave,* and this has plane equiphase surfaces but its field strength is a function of position over the equiphase planes.

We consider the particular case for which $\mu_1 = \mu_2$ and $k_1 > k_2$ ($\eta_1 > \eta_2$). Then using Snell's law, Eq. (11-6.8), we obtain

$$\cos\theta_2 = \sqrt{1 - \sin^2\theta_2} = \sqrt{1 - \frac{\sin^2\theta_1}{(k_2/k_1)^2}} \qquad (11\text{-}6.19)$$

When the angle of incidence θ_1 is such that $\sin\theta_1 > k_2/k_1$, then $\cos\theta_2$ becomes a pure imaginary. In this case we can write

$$\cos\theta_2 = j\, C_1$$

where

$$C_1 = \sqrt{\frac{\sin^2\theta_1}{(k_2/k_1)^2} - 1} \qquad \theta_1 > \sin^{-1}\left(\frac{k_2}{k_1}\right) \qquad (11\text{-}6.20)$$

At angles of incidence greater than the *critical angle* θ_c [$\theta_c = \sin^{-1}(k_2/k_1)$], the field in the second medium becomes

$$E_{2y} = E_{oy}T_{\perp}e^{j(k_2 \sin\theta_2 x - k_2 \cos\theta_2 z)} = E_{oy}T_{\perp}e^{k_2C_1 z}\, e^{jk_2[(k_1/k_2)\sin\theta_1]x} \qquad (11\text{-}6.21)$$

which shows that the planes of constant amplitude are Z = constant, and the planes of constant phase are X = constant. These are shown in Fig. 11-6.1, and they are perpendicular to each other; this wave is an inhomogeneous one. The dots in the figure are to indicate qualitatively the field intensity, which shows that it decreases away from the interface. The phase velocity of the wave in the X direction and for $\theta_1 > \theta_2$ is given by

$$v_{ph} = \frac{\omega}{k_1 \sin\theta_1} \qquad (11\text{-}6.22)$$

which is a function of the angle of incidence. Note that the amplitude of the penetration field in medium 2 decays very rapidly with depth.

We now turn our attention to medium 2. If medium 2 is conducting, the wave number can take the general form

$$\bar{k}_2 = \bar{k}_2' + j\bar{k}_2'' \qquad (11\text{-}6.23)$$

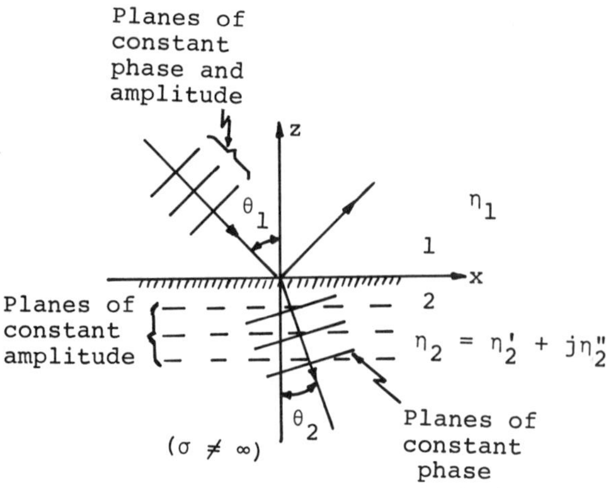

Figure 11-6.2. Planes of constant amplitude and phase in adjacent mediums.

Since the boundary conditions must be satisfied at each point on the X-axis and at all times, it is implied that the spatial and time variations of the field in both mediums at the interface must be the same. This requires that

$$\begin{aligned} \overline{k}_1 \cdot \overline{r} &= \overline{k}_{11} \cdot \overline{r} \\ \overline{k}_1 \cdot \overline{r} &= \overline{k}_2 \cdot \overline{r} = \overline{k}_2' \cdot \overline{r} + j\overline{k}_2'' \cdot \overline{r} \end{aligned} \tag{11-6.24}$$

The first of these equations gives the law of reflection ($k_1 = k_{11}$ and $\theta_1 = \theta_{11}$). From the second, equating the real and imaginary parts, we obtain

$$\begin{aligned} \overline{k}_1 \cdot \overline{r} &= \overline{k}_2' \cdot \overline{r} \\ 0 &= \overline{k}_2'' \cdot \overline{r} \end{aligned} \tag{11-6.25}$$

Observe that since $\overline{k}_2'' \cdot \overline{r} \neq \overline{k}_2' \cdot \overline{r}$ the planes of constant amplitude and constant phase in medium 2 are not parallel. This phenomenon is shown graphically in Fig. 11-6.2. To find the angle between the two characteristic planes in medium 2 we proceed in the same way that we did in discussing the phenomenon of total reflection. We write for the wave number for medium 2

$$k_2 = k_2' + jk_2'' \tag{11-6.26}$$

Also, Snell's law is written in the form

$$\sin \theta_1 = \frac{k_2}{k_1} \sin \theta_2' \tag{11-6.27}$$

where θ_2' cannot be interpreted in the ordinary sense since k_2/k_1 is a complex number and $\sin\theta_1$ is a real number. The electric field in the second medium takes the form

$$E_{2y} = E_{oy}T_{\perp}e^{j(k_2' + jk_2'')(x \sin\theta_2' - z\cos\theta_2')} \tag{11-6.28}$$

From Eq. (11-6.27) we can write

$$\sin\theta_2' = \frac{k_1}{k_2}\sin\theta_1 = \frac{k_1(k_2' - jk_2'')}{(k_2'^2 + k_2''^2)}\sin\theta_1 = \alpha(k_2' - jk_2'')\sin\theta_1 \tag{11-6.29}$$

Therefore

$$\cos\theta_2' = \sqrt{1 - \sin^2\theta_2'} = \sqrt{1 - \alpha^2(k_2'-jk_2'')^2\sin^2\theta_1} = \beta(\cos\phi + j\sin\phi) \tag{11-6.30}$$

If we substitute Eqs. (11-6.30) and (11-6.29) into Eq. (11-6.28) we obtain

$$E_{2y} = E_{oy}T_{\perp}\exp\,[j[x\alpha(k_2'^2 + k_2'^2)\sin\theta_1 - z\beta(k_2'\cos\phi - k_2''\sin\phi] + z\beta(k_2'\sin\phi + k_2''\cos\phi)] \tag{11-6.31}$$

This equation shows that the planes of constant amplitude are parallel to the X-axis while the planes of constant phase make an angle with the X-axis equal to

$$\tan^{-1}\left[\frac{\alpha(k_2'^2 + k_2''^2)\sin\theta_1}{\beta(k_2'\cos\phi - k_2''\sin\phi)}\right]$$

11-7. Reflection and Refraction of Acoustic Waves at Plane Boundaries

We wish to examine the acoustic problem that parallels the situation discussed in Sec. 11-6. Differences arise because the acoustic field is a scalar field, and it is these differences that are to be examined. As discussed in Sec. 8-5, the acoustic field can be characterized by a potential Φ_a in terms of which the velocity and acoustic pressure are, for a harmonic acoustic field $e^{-j\omega t}$,

$$\text{a)}\quad \bar{v} = -\nabla\Phi_a$$
$$\text{b)}\quad p = -j\omega\rho_o\Phi_a \tag{11-7.1}$$

where ρ_o denotes the density of the medium. We suppose that the boundary plane separates medium 1 from medium 2, and these mediums are specified by the characteristic impedances $Z_1 = (\rho_{o1}c_1)^{-1}$ (c_1 is the speed of sound in medium 1) and $Z_2 = (\rho_{o2}c_2)^{-1}$ (c_2 is the speed of sound in medium 2). The incident wave, omitting the implied time factor $e^{-j\omega t}$, is written

$$\Phi_{a_{inc}} = \Phi_{ao} e^{j\bar{k}\cdot\bar{r}} = \Phi_{ao} e^{jk_1(x \sin \theta_1 - z \cos \theta_1)} \tag{11-7.2}$$

The reflected wave will be of the form

$$\Phi_{a_{ref}} = \Phi_{ao} R_a e^{jk_1(x \sin \theta_1 + z \cos \theta_1)} \tag{11-7.3}$$

The transmitted wave will be of the form

$$\Phi_{a2} = \Phi_{ao} T_a e^{jk_2(x \sin \theta_2 - z \cos \theta_2)} \tag{11-7.4}$$

where R_a is the reflection coefficient, T_a is the transmission coefficient, $k_1 = \omega/c_1$, $k_2 = \omega/c_2$, and Φ_{ao} is the magnitude of the incident potential (see Fig. 11-7.1). The total wave in the first medium is given by

$$\Phi_{a1} = \Phi_{a_{inc}} + \Phi_{a_{ref}} \tag{11-7.5}$$

To satisfy the condition of continuity of mass transfer through the interface, we must have the velocity components perpendicular to the interface in the two mediums be continuous. This requires that

$$(\bar{v} \cdot \bar{a}_z)_1 = (\bar{v} \cdot \bar{a}_z)_2 \qquad \text{at} \quad z = 0 \tag{11-7.6}$$

Additionally, the equilibrium of forces at the boundary implies the continuity of the pressure, which is

$$p_1 = p_2 \qquad \text{at} \qquad z = 0 \tag{11-7.7}$$

Equations (11-7.6) and (11-7.7) together with (11-7.1) specify that

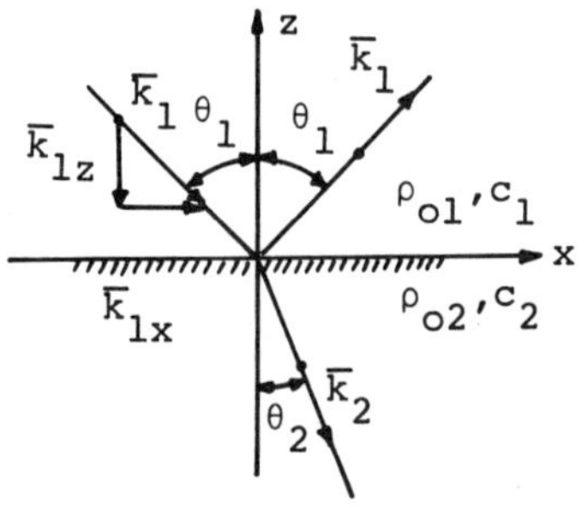

Figure 11-7.1. Acoustic waves at a boundary.

$$\frac{\partial \Phi_{a1}}{\partial z} = \frac{\partial \phi_{a2}}{\partial z} \qquad \text{a)}$$

$$\rho_{o1}\Phi_{a1} = \rho_{o2}\Phi_{a2} \qquad \text{b)} \tag{11-7.8}$$

With these conditions, we can now proceed to obtain explicit expressions for R_a, T_a, and θ_2.

When we combine Eqs. (11-7.4), (11-7.5), and (11-7.8b), we find the following relation

$$\frac{\rho_{o1}}{\rho_{02}}(1 + R_a) = \frac{1 + R_a}{m} = T_a e^{j(k_2 \sin\theta_2 - k_1 \sin\theta_1)x} \tag{11-7.9}$$

with $m = \rho_{o2}/\rho_{o1}$. This implies that

$$k_2 \sin\theta_2 = k_1 \sin\theta_1 \qquad \left[\frac{\sin\theta_1}{\sin\theta_2} = \eta\right] \tag{7-11.10}$$

to insure that the right-hand side of Eq. (11-7.9) is independent of the angle θ. If we had included Eq. (11-7.8a) we would find a second relation

$$(1 - R_a)\cos\theta_1 = T_a \frac{k_2}{k_1}\cos\theta_2 = T_a \frac{c_1}{c_2}\cos\theta_2 = T_a \eta \cos\theta_2 \tag{11-7.11}$$

Now by combining Eqs. (11-7.9), (11-7.10), and (11-7.11) we can deduce explicit expressions for the reflection and transmission coefficients; these are

$$R_a = \frac{m\cos\theta_1 - \eta\cos\theta_2}{m\cos\theta_1 + \eta\cos\theta_2} = \frac{Z_2\cos\theta_1 - Z_1\cos\theta_2}{Z_2\cos\theta_1 + Z_1\cos\theta_2}$$

$$T_a = \frac{2\cos\theta_1}{m\cos\theta_1 + \eta\cos\theta_2} = \frac{\rho_{o1}}{\rho_{o2}} \frac{2 Z_2 \cos\theta_1}{Z_2\cos\theta_1 + Z_2\cos\theta_2} \tag{11-7.12}$$

11-8. EM Waves in Dielectric Slabs (Fiber Optics)

A. Symmetric Substrate

Propagation of laser light in thin films is an interesting and important application of EM waves in dielectric slabs. The introduction of the concept of integrated optics and the development of special optical coupling devices has contributed to the development of optical modulators, frequency converters, and parametric oscillators in planar thin film form.

For simplicity, we assume that the dielectric slab is of thickness 2d, is infinitely wide in the Y-direction, and is embedded in air or some other dielectric medium as a cladding layer as shown in Fig. 11-8.1 ($\partial/\partial y = 0$). For a TE wave, the wave equation (10-2.1) becomes

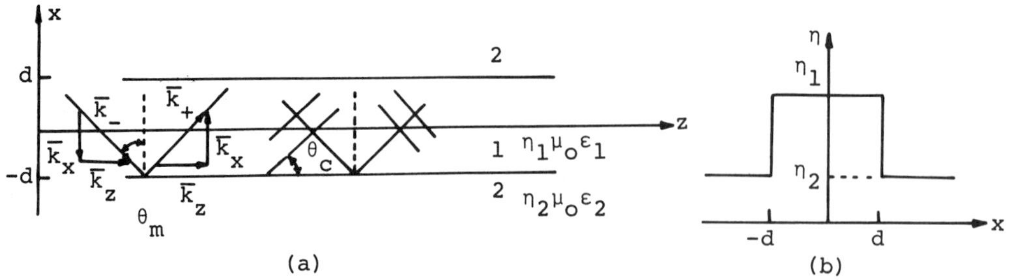

Figure 11-8.1. (a) A dielectric slab. (b) Index of refraction.

$$\frac{\partial^2 E_y}{\partial x^2} + \frac{\partial^2 E_y}{\partial z^2} + \omega^2 \mu\varepsilon E_y = 0 \tag{11-8.1}$$

Upon introducing a solution of the form $e^{jk_z z}$, Eq. (11-8.1) becomes

$$\frac{\partial^2 E_y}{\partial x^2} + (k^2 - k_z^2) E_y = 0 \tag{11-8.2}$$

where the propagation constant k_z is an unknown constant. For simplicity, we study separately the even and the odd modes of the field. The solution for an even mode inside the slab is of the form

$$E_y = E_{y1} \cos k_x x \, e^{jk_z z} \qquad -d \le x \le d \tag{11-8.3}$$

where we assume that $k_x = \sqrt{k_1^2 - k_z^2} > 0$ for non-decaying modes ($k_1 = \omega \sqrt{\mu_1 \varepsilon_1}$). The field outside of the slab must decay to zero at $x = \pm\infty$, and must propagate in the Z-direction. The fields satisfying both the wave equation, Eq. (11-8.1), and also the boundary conditions for E are

$$E_y = E_{y1} e^{-\gamma(x-d)} e^{jk_z z} \cos k_x d, \qquad x \ge d$$

$$E_y = E_{y1} e^{\gamma(x+d)} e^{jk_z z} \cos k_x d, \qquad x \le -d \tag{11-8.4}$$

where $\gamma = \sqrt{k_z^2 - k_2^2} > 0$ for a decaying mode in the x-direction [see Eq. (11-8.2)]. The Z-components for the $\overline{H}$ field can be determined by using the Maxwell curl $\overline{E}$ equation. These are given by the equations

$$H_{z1} = -\frac{E_{y1} k_x}{j\mu\omega} \sin k_x x \, e^{jk_z z} \qquad d \le x \le -d \qquad \text{a)}$$

$$H_{z2} = -\frac{E_{y1}\gamma}{j\omega\mu} e^{-\gamma(x-d)} e^{jk_z z} \cos k_x d, \qquad x \ge d \qquad \text{b)} \tag{11-8.5}$$

$$H_{z2} = \frac{E_{y1}\gamma}{j\omega\mu} e^{\gamma(x+d)} e^{jk_z z} \cos k_x d, \qquad x \leq -d \qquad \text{c)} \qquad (11\text{-}8.5)$$

Upon applying the continuity relations for H_z at $x = -d$ we obtain the *characteristic* equation

$$k_x \tan k_x d = \gamma \qquad (11\text{-}8.6)$$

Equation (11-8.6) is a transcendental equation, and this can be cast into the form

$$\frac{\gamma d}{k_x d} = \frac{\sqrt{(k_1^2 - k_2^2)d^2 - (k_x d)^2}}{k_x d} = \frac{\sqrt{(Kd)^2 - (k_x d)^2}}{k_x d} = \tan k_x d \qquad (11\text{-}8.7)$$

by eliminating k_z in the expressions for γ and k_x. A solution of this equation is obtained graphically (see Fig. 11-8.2). The solution is the intersection of the curves $\gamma d/k_x d$ and the lines of $\tan k_x d$ with Kd as a parameter. Increasing values of Kd imply increasing frequency $[K^2 = d^2\omega^2\mu_o(\varepsilon_1-\varepsilon_2)]$ for a constant width d. This indicates that the number of propagating guided modes increases with K; the reverse is also true. The figure also shows that the lowest order even TE mode can propagate at arbitrarily small frequency. Further the cutoff condition occurs when the end point of $\gamma d/k_x d$ on the $k_x d$ axis coincides with the zero crossing of the tangent function. At these points $\gamma_c d = 0$ and $k_{xc} d = n\pi$ $(n = 1,2,\ldots)$ and so by Eq. (11-8.6)

$$\tan k_x d = 0 \quad \text{or} \quad k_{xc} d = n\pi \quad (n = 0,1,2,\ldots) \qquad (11\text{-}8.8)$$

But $Kd = k_{xc}d$ from Eq. (11-8.7); hence Eq. (11-8.8) becomes

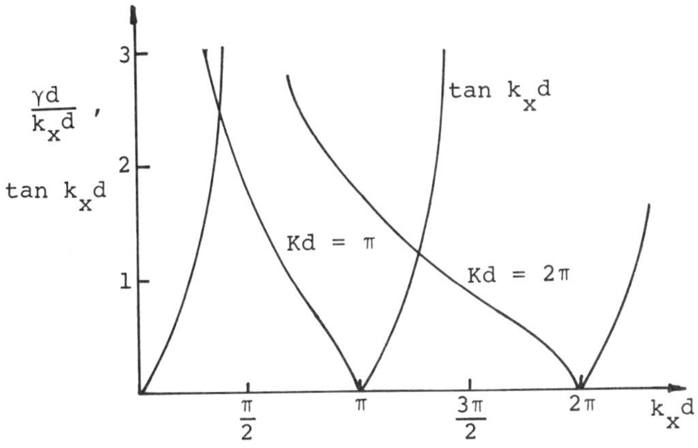

Figure 11-8.2. A graphical portrayal of Eq. (11-8.7).

$$\sqrt{k_1^2 - k_2^2} = \omega_c \sqrt{\mu_o(\varepsilon_1 - \varepsilon_2)} = \frac{n\pi}{d} \tag{11-8.9}$$

and the cutoff frequency is given by

$$f_c = \frac{n}{2d} \frac{1}{\sqrt{\mu(\varepsilon_1 - \varepsilon_2)}} \tag{11-8.10}$$

Also at cutoff $\gamma = 0$, or equivalent ly we have that $k_z = k_2 = k_o\eta_2$. The electric field inside medium 1 is thus given by

$$E_y = \frac{1}{2} E_{y1} [e^{j(k_{xc}x + k_z z)} + e^{-j(k_{xc}x - k_z z)}] e^{-j\omega t} \tag{11-8.11}$$

which indicates the field to be the superposition of two plane waves whose directions are prescribed by

$$\tan \theta_c = \pm \frac{k_2}{k_{xc}} = \pm \frac{k_2}{\sqrt{k_1^2 - k_2^2}} = \frac{\eta_2}{\sqrt{\eta_1^2 - \eta_2^2}} \tag{11-8.12}$$

Physically, the existence of a guided mode is explained in simple terms. Essentially, inside of medium 1 a plane wave is bouncing back and forth between the dielectric interfaces, and is propagating in an angle that is greater than the critical angle. Outside in medium 2 a non-homogeneous wave exists, as was discussed in Sec. 11-6.

A great advantage in using cladding is our ability to control the number of modes. Equation (11-8.9), with $k_o = \omega/\sqrt{\mu_o\varepsilon_o}$, gives the single mode condition in the form

$$k_o d \, (\varepsilon_{r1} - \varepsilon_{r2})^{1/2} \leq 3.14$$

In general, an overmoded fiber with an index difference of one percent could have a time spread of 50 ns/km which limits the bandwidth of a one-kilometer fiber to about 10 MHz. On the other hand, a single mode fiber will not limit the bandwidth below 50 GHz, since a typical 8 psec pulse does not spread more than 4 psecs.

A problem of importance in practice is how to couple the light beam of a laser into a propagating mode inside a thin dielectric film, say of the order of 1 μm. One method that has been used employs prisms, gratings, or tapered sections as couplers. To show that it is not possible to couple energy into the film by merely illuminating the film by a laser light source, consider that a wave is traveling towards the film in a direction that makes an angle θ_2 with the normal to the film surface. The Z-component of the propagation vector in medium 2 is $k_o\eta_2 \sin\theta_2$. For this wave to produce the mth mode in the film with $k_z^{(m)}$ requires that

$$k_z^{(m)} = k_o\eta_1 \sin\theta_m = k_o\eta_2 \sin\theta_2 \tag{11-8.13}$$

where θ_m is the angle shown in Fig. 11-8.1. Since θ_m is larger than the critical angle $\eta_1 \sin \theta_m > \eta_2$, Eq. (11-8.13) cannot be satisfied and no energy can be coupled into the film.

Now consider the situation when a prism is present, with $\eta_p > \eta_1$, as shown in Fig. 11-8.3. If the prism is brought very close to the film surface (~ 1 μm or less) and the condition

$$k_o \eta_p \sin \theta_p = k_z^{(m)} \tag{11-8.14}$$

is satisfied, energy will leak into the film creating the mth mode. By changing θ_p we can produce any mode desired in the film. The input coupler serves equally well as an output coupler. It has been found that prism couplers are about 80 percent efficient. The field distribution in a prism coupler is shown in Fig. 11-8.3b. It is noted that the evanescent fields of the prism and the film overlap in the gap region.

A phase grating coupler as shown in Fig. 11-8.3d can be fabricated on a thin

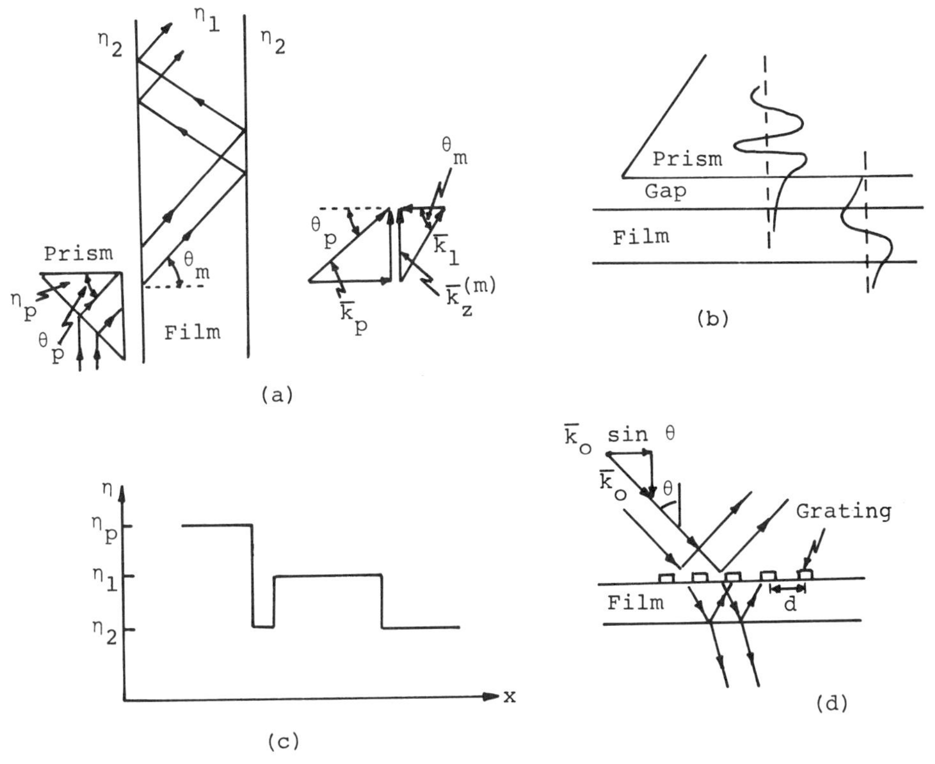

Figure 11-8.3. Prism coupler.

film by means of a photoresist technique like that used in the semiconductor device preparation. A laser beam incident on the grating at an angle θ has a phase variation in the Z-direction equal to $k_o/\sin\theta\, z$, as illustrated. As the beam passes through the grating, it acquires an additional spatial phase modulation $\Delta E \sin(2\pi z/d)$ where ΔE is the amplitude variation due to the phase grating. Since a periodic variation can be analyzed into Fourier components, the light reaching the film will be of the form

$$e^{j[k_o \sin\theta + m(2\pi/d)]z}$$

where m is an integer. Clearly, the grating makes it possible to feed the mth mode in the film provided that

$$k_o \sin\theta + \frac{2\pi}{d} m = k_z^{(m)} \qquad (11\text{-}8.15)$$

By varying θ one can couple energy into all modes in the film. As in the case of the prism, the grating acts as an output coupler also, and its efficiency is about the same as that for the prism.

The tapered film coupler consists of a film with slowly varying thickness. When a light mode reaches the tapered section, it undergoes success reflections with progressively smaller angles θ_m, and when this angle becomes less than the critical value, the light refracts into the substrate.

In broad outline, the foregoing discussion applies equally well to cylindrical fibers. However, the mathematics of cylindrical fibers is rather more involved, and we shall not discuss the matter in detail. We shall discuss some of the important features in a qualitative manner.

Optical fibers are fabricated by using multicomponent glasses which contain a number of oxides and high-silica glasses, which are made of fused silica. The fiber core is contained within a cladding material, and this must have a smaller index of refraction than the core silica. It is made of boron-doped silica.

The optical characteristics of fibers are affected by absorption, scattering, and mode conversion. To achieve low loss, extremely pure and defect-free glasses are required. Absorption and scattering account for approximately equal parts of the total attenuation in the spectral region of about 0.85 μm. The absorption losses are due mainly to impurities, such as Cr, Mn, Fe, etc., water, as well as the intrinsic material absorption. Scattering losses in glasses are caused by microheterogeneities, boundary roughness, and intrinsic material scattering.

The radius of the fibers must be constant to reduce waveguide losses, and to facilitate cabling and connector techniques. In addition, it is important to be able to control precisely the radial distribution of the refractive index in order to minimize mode dispersion. An index profile that is approximately parabolic will

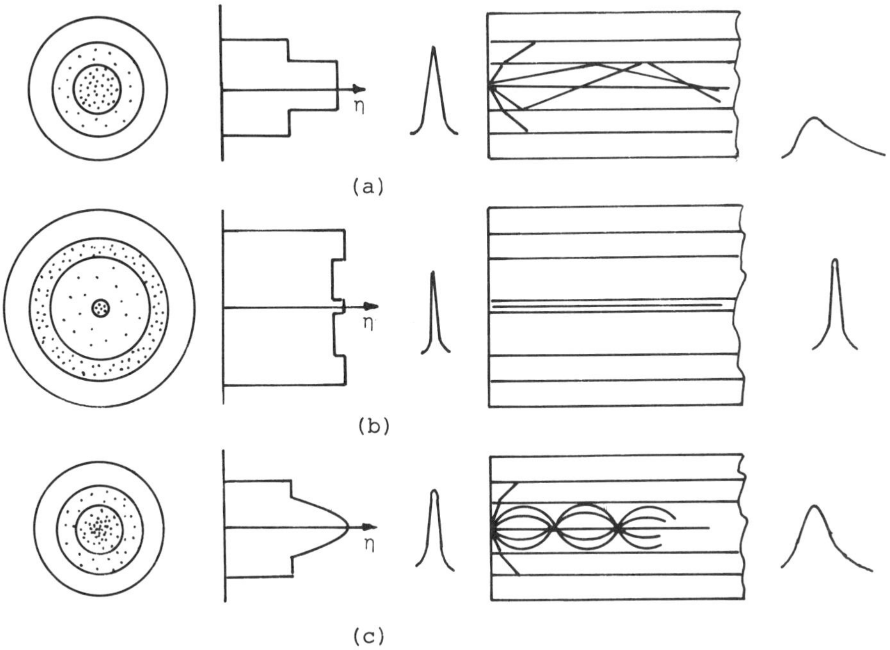

Figure 11-8.4. (a) Multimode fiber, stepped index profile; (b) single mode stepped index profile; (c) multimode fiber, graded index profile. From left to right the columns indicate: cross section; index profiles; input pulses; light paths; output pulses.

eliminate mode dispersion. Also, care must be exercised in fiber bending since, in extreme cases, radiation away from the core will take place.

Bandwidth is limited by pulse broadening, which can result in pulse overlapping. Pulse broadening is caused by dispersion that results from normal waveguide dispersion and the dispersion due to the glasses. A broadening of only 5 picasec/km for single mode fibers has been achieved, and this will allow a large capacity transmission system.

Typical fiber waveguide structures are shown in Fig. 11-8.4. The basic guiding structure is the core, which is surrounded by a cladding layer with a slightly lower refractive index than the core. Each mode is reflected at the core-cladding interface.

Multimode fibers have considerably larger diameters, on the order of 100 μm, than single mode fibers, which have a diameter on the order of a wavelength. The disadvantage of multimode fibers results from the large dispersion which is present because each mode is reflected at a different incident angle. To avoid the large dispersion of multimode fibers, single mode fibers are often used, or fibers with a graded index profile, as shown in Fig. 11-8.4c. In these, a mode (ray) traveling at a large angle with respect to the axis, is propagating in the medium with progressively lower index of refraction. Because of the gradient in the refractive index, the ray is bent back toward the center. Thus the ray spends most of the time in the material with the lower index of refraction, which corresponds to high velocities, than the ray that travels along the axis of the fiber. The near parabolic profile forces the rays to be in phase along the fiber, and this reduces the dispersions.

B. Nonsymmetric Substrate

Refer to the dielectric slab configuration shown in Fig. 11-8.5. The equations appropriate to the three indicated regions, for the TE mode, are

$$\frac{\partial^2 E_y}{\partial x^2} + (k_1^2 - k_z^2)E_y = 0 \qquad k_1 = \sqrt{\omega\mu_o\varepsilon_1} \qquad \text{a)}$$

$$\frac{\partial^2 E_y}{\partial x^2} + (k_2^2 - k_z^2)E_y = 0 \qquad k_2 = \sqrt{\omega\mu_o\varepsilon_2} \qquad \text{b)} \qquad (11\text{-}8.16)$$

$$\frac{\partial^2 E_y}{\partial x^2} + (k_3^2 - k_z^2)E_y = 0 \qquad k_3 = \sqrt{\omega\mu_o\varepsilon_3} \qquad \text{c)}$$

where k_z is the unknown propagation constant in the Z-direction, and which appears in the term $e^{jk_z z}$. The H components of the field are determined by using the Maxwell curl $\overline{E}$ equation and the solution of Eq. (11-8.16). But since we have assumed that $E_y = E_z = 0$, the Maxwell curl $\overline{E}$ equation yields the relations

$$H_x = -\frac{k_z}{\omega\mu_o} E_y \qquad \text{a)}$$

$$H_z = -\frac{j}{\omega\mu_o} \frac{\partial E_y}{\partial x} \qquad \text{b)} \qquad (11\text{-}8.17)$$

The boundary conditions require that the tangential $\overline{E}$ and $\overline{H}$ fields must be continuous across the two interfaces. Hence we must impose the requirement that E_y and H_z are continuous at x = -d and x = +d. The solutions of the E_y component which will satisfy these conditions and which vanish at $x = \pm\infty$ are

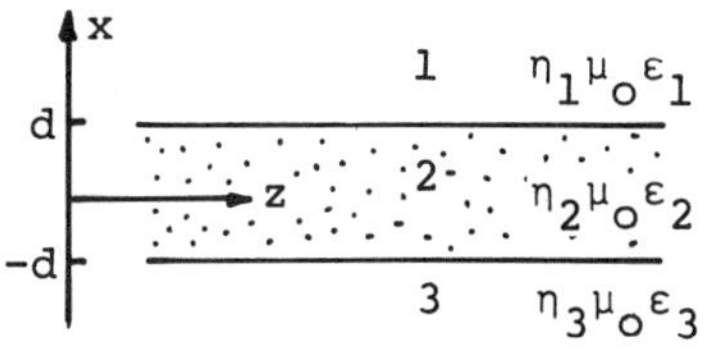

Figure 11-8.5. Asymmetric dielectric slab configuration.

$$E_y = Ae^{-\alpha(x-d)} \qquad x > d \qquad \text{a)}$$

$$E_y = A\cos\beta(x-d) + B\sin\beta(x-d) \qquad -d \le x \le d \qquad \text{b)} \qquad (11\text{-}8.18)$$

$$E_y = (A\cos 2\beta d - B\sin 2\beta d)e^{\gamma(x+d)} \qquad x \le -d \qquad \text{c)}$$

where

$$\alpha = (k_z^2 - k_1^2)^{1/2} = (k_z^2 - \omega^2\mu_o\varepsilon_1)^{1/2} = (k_z^2 - k_o^2\eta_1^2)^{1/2} \qquad \text{a)}$$

$$\beta = (k_2^2 - k_z^2)^{1/2} = (\omega^2\mu_o\varepsilon_2 - k_z^2)^{1/2} = (k_o^2\eta_2^2 - k_z^2)^{1/2} \qquad \text{b)} \qquad (11\text{-}8.19)$$

$$\gamma = (k_z^2 - k_3^2)^{1/2} = (k_z^2 - \omega^2\mu_o\varepsilon_3)^{1/2} = (k_z^2 - k_o^2\eta_3^2)^{1/2} \qquad \text{c)}$$

The H_z component, using Eq. (11-8.17b), become

$$H_z = \left(\frac{j\alpha}{\omega\mu_o}\right) Ae^{-\alpha(x-d)} \qquad \text{a)}$$

$$H_z = \left(\frac{j\beta}{\omega\mu_o}\right)[A\sin\beta(x-d) - B\cos\beta(x-d)] \qquad -d \le x \le d \qquad \text{b)} \qquad (11\text{-}8.20)$$

$$H_z = \left(\frac{-j\gamma}{\omega\mu_o}\right)[A\cos 2\beta d - B\sin 2\beta d\; e^{\gamma(x+d)}] \qquad x \le -d \qquad \text{c)}$$

Now impose the requirements that H_z must be continuous at x = d and x = -d to obtain the following equations

$$\alpha A + \beta B = 0 \qquad \text{a)}$$

$$(\beta\sin 2\beta d - \gamma\cos 2\beta d)A + (\beta\cos 2\beta d + \gamma\sin 2\beta d)B = 0 \qquad \text{b)} \qquad (11\text{-}8.21)$$

The two unknown quantities A and B have nonzero values if the determinant of the equations vanish. This requires that the following equation must be true

$$\alpha(\beta\cos 2\beta d + \gamma\sin 2\beta d) - \beta(\beta\sin 2\beta d - \gamma\cos 2\beta d) = 0 \qquad (11\text{-}8.22)$$

or equivalently that

$$\tan 2\beta d = \frac{\beta(\alpha+\gamma)}{\beta^2 - \alpha\gamma} \qquad (11\text{-}8.23)$$

For the symmetric case where $\eta_1 = \eta_3$, we have $\alpha = \gamma$ and Eq. (11-8.23) becomes

$$\tan 2\beta d = \frac{2\tan\beta d}{1-\tan^2\beta d} = \frac{2(\gamma/\beta)}{1-(\gamma/\beta)^2} \qquad (11\text{-}8.24)$$

This is a second order equation in tan βd, and its solution gives two values

$$\tan \beta d = \gamma/\beta \qquad \text{a)}$$
$$\tan \beta d = -\gamma/\beta \qquad \text{b)} \qquad (11\text{-}8.25)$$

One relation corresponds to the even modes and the other to the odd modes. Equation (11-8.25a) is identical with Eq. (11-8.6), as is to be expected ($k_x = \beta$).

For the nonsymmetric case, Eq. (11-8.23) is written in the form

$$\tan 2\beta d = \frac{2\beta(2\gamma+2\alpha)}{(2\beta)^2-2\alpha\cdot 2\gamma}$$
$$= \frac{(\beta 2d)\left[[(k_2^2-k_3^2)(2d)^2 - (\beta 2d)^2]^{1/2} + [(k_2^2-k_1^2)(2d)^2-(\beta 2d)^2]^{1/2}\right]}{(\beta 2d)^2-[(k_2^2-k_3^2)(2d)^2-(\beta 2d)^2]^{1/2}[(k_2^2-k_1^2)(2d)^2-(\beta 2d)^2]^{1/2}}$$
$$= \frac{(\beta 2d)\left[[(K_{23}2d)^2-(\beta 2d)^2]^{1/2} + [(K_{21}2d)^2-(\beta 2d)^2]^{1/2}\right]}{(\beta 2d)^2-[(K_{23}2d)^2-(\beta 2d)^2]^{1/2}[(K_{21}2d)^2-(\beta 2d)^2]^{1/2}} \qquad \text{a)}$$

where (11-8.26)

$$K_{23}2d = 2d\sqrt{k_2^2-k_3^2} = 2d[\omega^2\mu_o(\varepsilon_2-\varepsilon_3)]^{1/2} = 2dk_o(\eta_2-\eta_3)^{1/2} \qquad \text{b)}$$

$$K_{21}2d = 2d\sqrt{k_2^2-k_1^2} = 2d[\omega^2\mu_o(\varepsilon_2-\varepsilon_1)]^{1/2} = 2dk_o(\eta_2-\eta_1)^{1/2} \qquad \text{c)}$$

This is a transcendental equation, and the two sides of this equation are shown plotted in Fig. 11-8.6 for the following values: (a) $K_{23}2d = 5$, $K_{21}2d = 7$; (b) $K_{23}2d = 10$, $K_{21}2d = 20$.

The β2d coordinates which correspond to the crossing points of the lines represent solutions of Eq. (11-8.23). Each of these solutions corresponds to one TE mode of the slab waveguide. We observe that when $2dk_o(\eta_2-\eta_3)^{1/2}$ decreases, the wave which represents the right hand side of Eq. (11-8.26a) shifts to the left and cuts fewer curves of tan 2βd. In consequence, fewer modes are supported by the structure. Since the quantity $2dk_o(\eta_2-\eta_3)^{1/2}$ is a function of two variables, d and $(\eta_2-\eta_3)$, we can conclude that for specific materials the number of modes decreases by decreasing the width d of the slab.

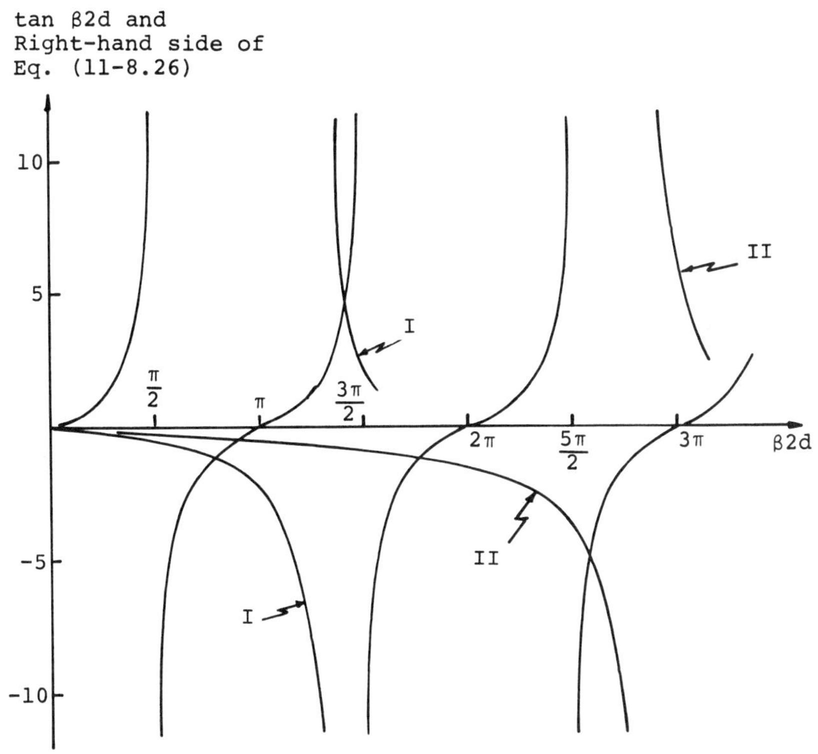

Figure 11-8.6. Solution of Eq. (11-8.26). (a) Case I: $K_{23}2d = 5$, $K_{21}2d = 7$ (b) Case II: $K_{23}2d = 10$, $K_{21}2d = 20$.

11-9. Rays Guided by Lenses

Refer to Fig. 11-9.1 which depicts a ray passing through a converging lens. Let $r(z)$ and $r'(z) = dr/dz$ be the displacement from the Z-axis and the slope of the ray, respectively. At the lens we have the following equalities

$$r_2 = r_1 \qquad \text{a)}$$

$$r_2' = -\left(\frac{r_1 - r_1' f}{f}\right) = r_1' - \frac{r_1}{f} \qquad \text{b)} \qquad (11\text{-}9.1)$$

since it is here assumed that the lenses are thin and the rays have small inclinations - these are known as *paraxial approximations*. These two equations are conveniently written in matrix form

$$\begin{bmatrix} r_2 \\ r_2' \end{bmatrix} = \begin{bmatrix} 1 & 0 \\ -\frac{1}{f} & 1 \end{bmatrix} \begin{bmatrix} r_1 \\ r_1' \end{bmatrix} \qquad (11\text{-}9.2)$$

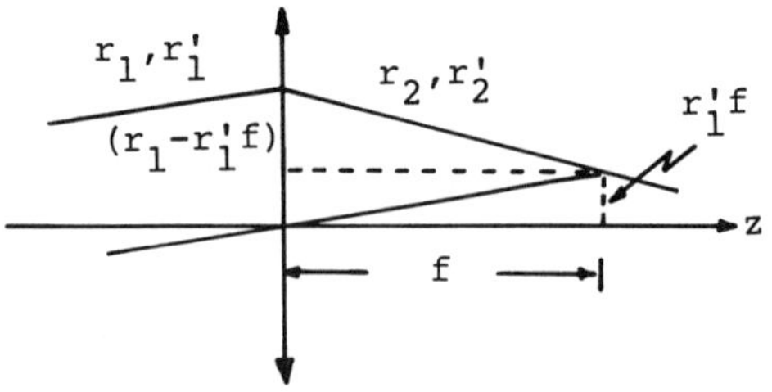

Figure 11-9.1. A ray passing through a converging lens.

where $f > 0$ for converging lenses and $f < 0$ for a diverging one. In general for a lens, the changes in the displacement and slope of a ray as it traverses an optical system can be presented in matrix form, as follows:

$$[r_2] = [0] \quad [r_1] \tag{11-9.3}$$

where

$$\left[r_2\right] = \begin{bmatrix} r_2 \\ r_2' \end{bmatrix}; \quad [0] = \begin{bmatrix} A & B \\ C & D \end{bmatrix}; \quad \left[r_1\right] = \begin{bmatrix} r_1 \\ r_1' \end{bmatrix}$$

where [0] is the optics matrix. Some of the more common optical matrixes are sum-

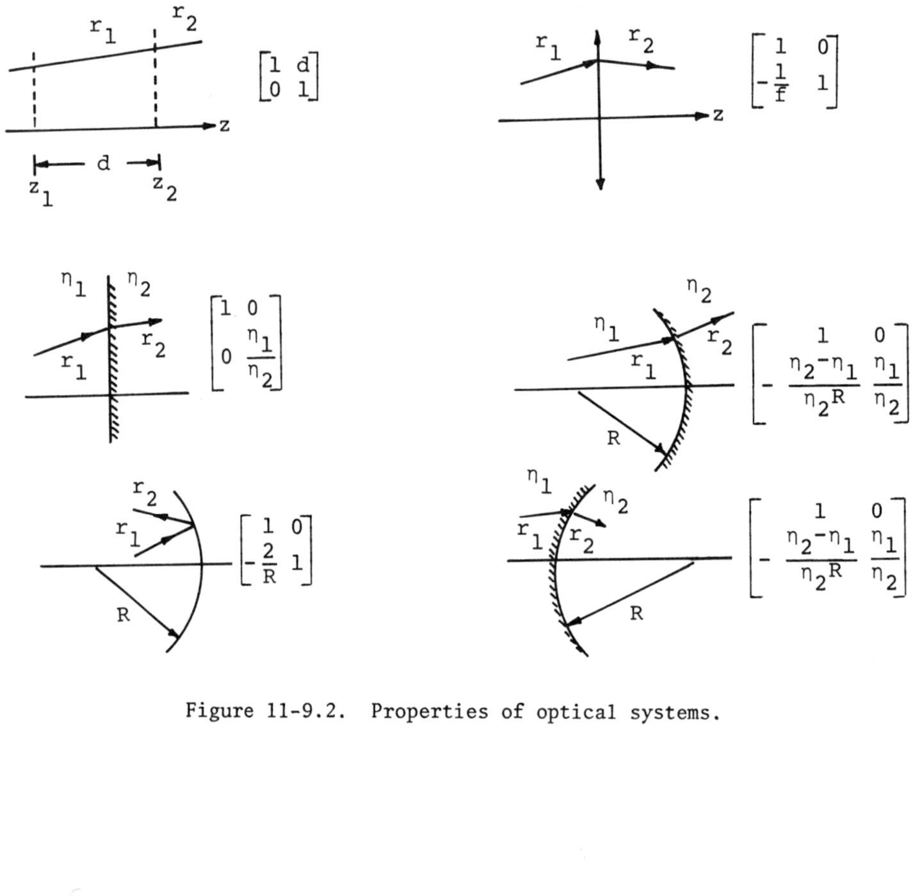

Figure 11-9.2. Properties of optical systems.

marized through the appropriate [0] matrixes given in Fig. 11-9.2. The quantity

$$P = \frac{\eta_2 - \eta_1}{\eta_2 R}$$

is known as the *power* of the surface.

Example 11-9.1. Find the elements of the matrix [0] for a system made up of a straight segment d and a convergent lens of focal length f.

Solution. Refer to Figs. 11-9.3 and 11-9.2. We obtain from these figures the following

$$\begin{bmatrix} r_2 \\ r_2' \end{bmatrix} = \begin{bmatrix} 1 & d \\ 0 & 1 \end{bmatrix} \begin{bmatrix} r_1 \\ r_1' \end{bmatrix} \tag{11-9.4}$$

$$\begin{bmatrix} r_3 \\ r_3' \end{bmatrix} = \begin{bmatrix} 1 & 0 \\ -\frac{1}{f} & 1 \end{bmatrix} \begin{bmatrix} r_2 \\ r_2' \end{bmatrix} = \begin{bmatrix} 1 & 0 \\ -\frac{1}{f} & 1 \end{bmatrix} \begin{bmatrix} 1 & d \\ 0 & 1 \end{bmatrix} \begin{bmatrix} r_1 \\ r_1' \end{bmatrix} = \begin{bmatrix} 1 & d \\ -\frac{1}{f} & -\frac{d}{f} + 1 \end{bmatrix} \begin{bmatrix} r_1 \\ r_1' \end{bmatrix}$$

where we observe that the resultant matrix corresponds to the product of the thin lens matrix times the straight section matrix.

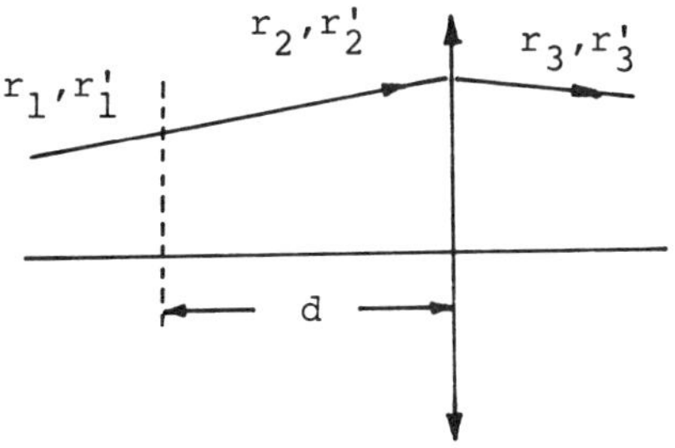

Figure 11-9.3. Straight section plus a lens.

ΔΔΔ

Example 11-9.2. Find the equation for the rays in a system made up of identical lenses, as shown in the accompanying diagram, and discuss the ray trajectories for the cases when d = 4f, d > 4f, d < 4f.

Solution. The unit cell of this system includes only one lens and one distance between lenses, as shown in Fig. 11-9.4b. From the results contained in Fig. 11-9.2 we easily obtain the following relation for successive lenses

$$\begin{bmatrix} r_{n+1} \\ r'_{n+1} \end{bmatrix} = \begin{bmatrix} 1 & d \\ 0 & 1 \end{bmatrix} \begin{bmatrix} 1 & 0 \\ -\frac{1}{f} & 1 \end{bmatrix} \begin{bmatrix} r_n \\ r_n' \end{bmatrix} = \begin{bmatrix} 1 - \frac{d}{f} & d \\ -\frac{1}{f} & 1 \end{bmatrix} \begin{bmatrix} r_n \\ r_n' \end{bmatrix} \tag{11-9.5}$$

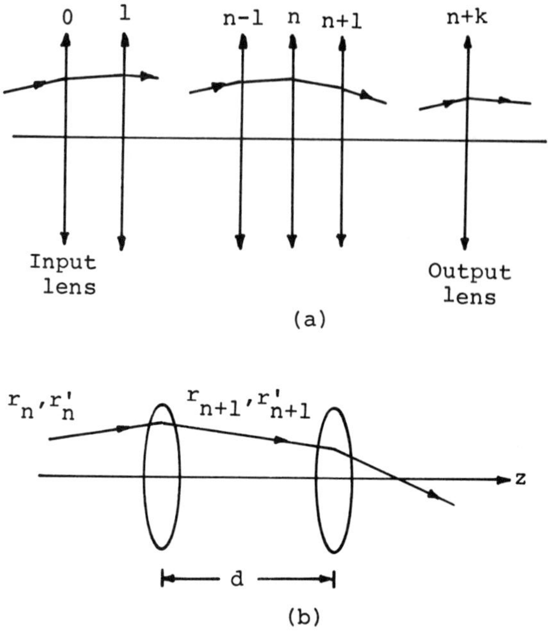

Figure 11-9.4. System of lenses.

In a similar way, we find for the previous cell, the similar relationship

$$\begin{bmatrix} r_n \\ r_n' \end{bmatrix} = \begin{bmatrix} 1 - \frac{d}{f} & d \\ -\frac{1}{f} & 1 \end{bmatrix} \begin{bmatrix} r_{n-1} \\ r'_{n-1} \end{bmatrix} \tag{11-9.6}$$

Now we substitute r'_{n-1} from Eq. (11-9.6) into the first equation in Eq. (11-9.6) with the result

$$r_n = (1 - \frac{d}{f})\, r_{n-1} + dr'_n + \frac{d}{f}\, r_{n-1} = r_{n-1} + dr'_n \tag{11-9.7}$$

Next, eliminate r_n' from Eq. (11-9.7) and the first equation of the system given by Eq. (11-9.5). The result is the second order *difference* equation

$$r_{n+1} - (2 - \frac{d}{f})r_n + r_{n-1} = 0 \tag{11-9.8}$$

or

$$r_{n+1} - ar_n + br_{n-1} = 0 \tag{11-9.9}$$

where a = (2 - d/f) and b = 1. General details of solving difference equations are contained in Appendix V.

To find the ray trajectory specified by Eq. (11-9.9) we first raise the index by 1 and so we now consider the difference equation

$$r_{n+2} - ar_{n+1} + br_n = 0 \qquad (11\text{-}9.10)$$

The auxiliary equation of this difference equation is

$$m^2 - am + b = 0$$

with the roots

$$m_1 = \frac{2 - \frac{d}{f} + \sqrt{\frac{d^2}{f^2} - 4\frac{d}{f}}}{2} \qquad m_2 = \frac{2 - \frac{d}{f} - \sqrt{\frac{d^2}{f^2} - 4\frac{d}{f}}}{2} \qquad (11\text{-}9.11)$$

The form of the results depends on the value of the ratio d/f. We examine each possibility in turn.

Case 1. If d = 4f, then we have $m_1 = m_2 = -1$. The general solution of the homogeneous equation is given by [see Appendix V]

$$r_n^h = (C_1 + C_2 n)(-1)^n \qquad (11\text{-}9.12)$$

Case 2. If d > 4f, then m_1 and m_2 are real and distinct. For the specific case d = 8f the general solution is, [see Appendix V]

$$r_n^h = C_1\left(\frac{-6 + \sqrt{32}}{2}\right)^n + C_2\left(\frac{-6 - \sqrt{32}}{2}\right)^n \qquad (11\text{-}9.13)$$

The value of r_n^h becomes unbounded with increasing n; and this indicates an *unstable* system. Physically this means that the rays will diverge out of the guiding system.

Case 3. If d < 4f then m_1 and m_2 are complex conjugate roots, and the general solution is of the form [see Appendix V]

$$r_n^h = AR^n \cos (n\theta + \phi) \qquad (11\text{-}9.14)$$

where $R = \sqrt{5}/2$, $\theta = \cos^{-1} -1/\sqrt{5}$, and d = 3f. This equation shows that the system is stable and the ray will oscillate about the optical axis as it propagates along the set of lenses.

11-10. Image Formation in Gaussian Optics

Consider the optical system shown in Fig. 11-10.1. With the help of Fig. 11-9.2 the overall transformation matrix from 0 to I with $d \to 0$ (thin lens approximation) is given by

$$[M_{OI}] = \begin{bmatrix} 1 & d_2 \\ 0 & 1 \end{bmatrix} \begin{bmatrix} 1 & 0 \\ -\frac{P_1}{\eta_1} & \frac{\eta_2}{\eta_1} \end{bmatrix} \begin{bmatrix} 1 & 0 \\ 0 & 1 \end{bmatrix} \begin{bmatrix} 1 & 0 \\ -\frac{P_2}{\eta_2} & \frac{\eta_1}{\eta_2} \end{bmatrix} \begin{bmatrix} 1 & d_1 \\ 0 & 1 \end{bmatrix} \tag{11-10.1}$$

where $P_1 = (\eta_1 - \eta_2)/R$ and $P_2 = (\eta_2 - \eta_1)/R$. For the sign conversion in geometric optics the reader should refer to Sec. 10-10. By carrying out the indicated matrix multiplication we obtain

$$[M_{OI}] = \begin{bmatrix} 1 - \frac{d_2}{\eta_1}(P_1 + P_2) & d_1 - \frac{d_1 d_2}{\eta_1}(P_1 + P_2) + d_2 \\ -\frac{1}{\eta_1}(P_1 + P_2) & -\frac{d_1}{\eta_1}(P_1 + P_2) + 1 \end{bmatrix} \tag{11-10.2}$$

which is true for any d_1 and d_2. If we define that the *image* and object are related by $y_i = my_o$, where m is the *magnification* factor, then it is implied that the M_{12} element of the matrix must be equal to zero. This becomes apparent if we write the relation

$$\begin{bmatrix} r_i \\ r_i' \end{bmatrix} = [M_{IO}] \begin{bmatrix} r_o \\ r_o' \end{bmatrix} = \begin{bmatrix} M_{11} & M_{12} \\ M_{21} & M_{22} \end{bmatrix} \begin{bmatrix} r_o \\ r_o' \end{bmatrix} \tag{11-10.3}$$

Setting the M_{12} element equal to zero yields

$$d_1 - \frac{d_1 d_2}{\eta_1}(P_1 + P_2) + d_2 = 0$$

or

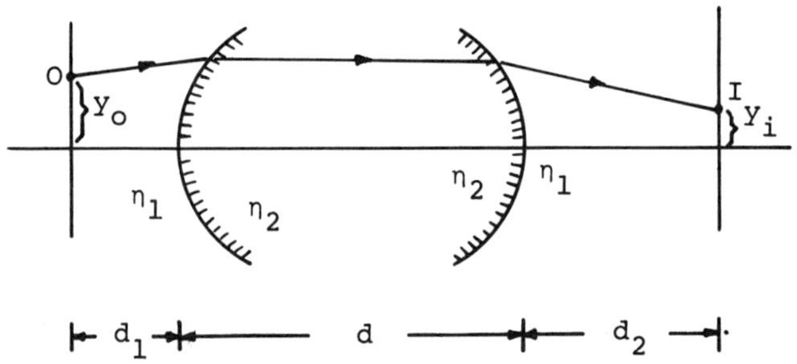

Figure 11-10.1. Imaging forming optical systems.

$$\frac{\eta_1}{d_1} + \frac{\eta_1}{d_2} = P_1 + P_2 = P \tag{11-10.4}$$

Since from Eq. (11-10.4)

$$d_2 = \frac{d_1\eta_1}{d_1P-\eta_1} \tag{11-10.5}$$

the magnification factor for the optical system becomes

$$m = M_{11} = \frac{\eta}{\eta_1-d_1P} \tag{11-10.6}$$

When the image is at + ∞ ($d_2 = \infty$), the object is in the left-hand focal plane at a distance

$$d_1 = \frac{\eta_1}{P} = f_\ell \tag{11-10.7}$$

Similarly, the second focal length is equal to η_1/P. Hence, Eq. (11-10.4) can be written in the form

$$\frac{1}{d_1} + \frac{1}{d_2} = \frac{1}{f_\ell} \tag{11-10.8}$$

This is the well known formula of the geometric optics.

The *principal* planes of an optical system are defined as those conjugate planes with magnification unity. From Eq. (11-10.7) we obtain $d_1 = 0$, which indicates that these planes are tangent to the two surfaces of the lens whose thickness was assumed zero (thin lens).

Let us now consider an optical system as shown in Fig. 11-10.2. If the system consists of a thin lens, the matrix transformation between the two principal planes takes the simple form

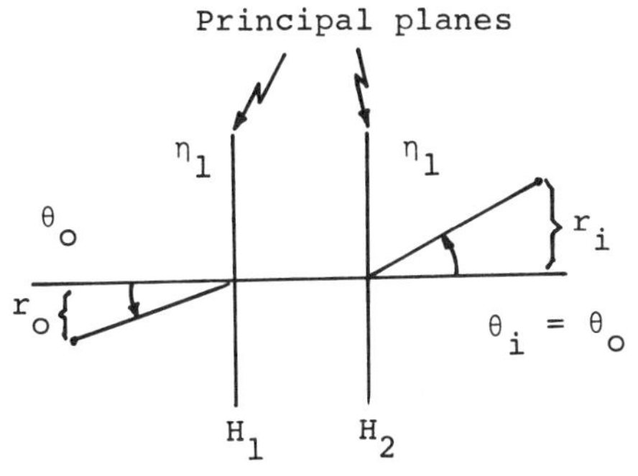

Figure 11-10.2. Simple imaging system.

$$\begin{bmatrix} 1 & 0 \\ -\frac{1}{f_\ell} & 1 \end{bmatrix} \tag{11-10.9}$$

and hence

$$\begin{bmatrix} r_i \\ r_i' \end{bmatrix}_{H_2} = \begin{bmatrix} 1 & 0 \\ -\frac{1}{f_\ell} & 1 \end{bmatrix} \begin{bmatrix} r_o \\ r_o' \end{bmatrix}_{H_1} \tag{11-10.10}$$

The last equation gives

$$r_i = r_o \qquad \text{a)}$$
$$r_i' = -\frac{r_o}{f_\ell} + r_o' \qquad \text{b)} \tag{11-10.11}$$

which indicates that the ray impinging on the plane H_1 at an angle r_o' and at point $r_o = 0$ will leave the principal plane H_2 with the same angle. These two points are called *nodal* points and the planes perpendicular to the optical axis and through them are called *nodal* planes. In our simple system the principal and nodal planes coincide. However, for a general optical system this is not true. The unit and nodal points are called *cardinal* points.

REVIEW QUESTIONS

1. What are the parameters which are missing in a dissipationless transmission line?
2. What is the characteristic impedance of a transmission line?
3. Define the reflection coefficient at the load.
4. What happens to the voltage wave if a transmission line is terminated by a load equal to its characteristic impedance?
5. What do we call the transmission line whose characteristic elements obey the relation GL = RC?
6. If the voltage in a lossless transmission line is $v(t) = A \cos(\omega t - x\sqrt{LC})$, what is its direction of propagation and its velocity?
7. What is the difference in the solution of an infinite lossless transmission line from a short-circuited one?
8. What type of differential equations describe a short-circuited lossless transmission line?
9. What is the difference between a TE and TM wave?
10. If an electromagnetic wave impinges on a conductor at an angle θ, is the energy propagating perpendicular and towards the conductor or parallel to it?

11. What is the mode number and what does it characterize?
12. What is the difference between a propagating wave and an evanescent one?
13. What can we change so that we increase the cutoff frequency of a propagating mode between two conducting planes?
14. What other factors, excluding the geometrical ones, contribute to the losses of a propagating mode?
15. What are the names of the modes which are allowed to propagate in a waveguide?
16. What happens when the frequency of a particular mode becomes less than its cut-off frequency?
17. Do the modes propagate independently? If your answer is yes, can you find a way to attenuate one of the modes without appreciably affecting the others?
18. Do cylindrical waveguides support TM and TE waves? If your answer is yes, are these the only modes supported by cylindrical waveguides?
19. What do we mean by the definition of "transverse electric polarization"?
20. What is the difference between internal and external reflection?
21. What happens if the incident angle becomes equal to the critical angle?
22. Define Snell's law.
23. What is the difference between a homogeneous and inhomogeneous plane wave?
24. What is the significance of cladding?
25. What does the characteristic equation in dielectric guides define?
26. What are the different ways of coupling optical fields into dielectric wave-guides?
27. What do we mean by paraxial approximations in geometric optics?
28. When is an optical system considered stable and when is it considered unstable?
29. When do we use difference equations?
30. Define homogeneous and nonhomogeneous difference equations.
31. Define the principal and cardinal points in Gaussian optics.

PROBLEMS

11-1.1. A transmission line has the following characteristic values: R = 55 Ohm/m, $L = 10^{-3}$ Henry/m, $C = 10^{-6}$ Farad/m, and G = .055 mho/m. Find the velocity of the wave and its amplitude at x = 3.5 m from the start of the line. Assume a pulse of 10 Volt.

11-1.2. If a step voltage $v(0,t) = 10\, u_{-1}(t)$ is applied to the line given in Ex. 11-1.1, plot the voltage along the line at t = 30 msec and at t = 90 msec.

11-1.3. Find and plot the first reflected voltage from the load of a transmission line if the incident voltage is a unit pulse.
Given: $Z_g = 0$, $Z_o = 75$ ohm.
Load: (a) an inductor, L = 100 Henry; (b) a capacitor, $C = 10^{-3}$ Farad;

(c) a resistor of 30 ohm; (d) a resistor of 150 ohm; (e) open-ended line; (f) short-circuited line.

11-1.4. Interpret Eq. (11-1.13) in time and space.

11-1.5. Plot $v(\ell/2, t)$ versus time, using Eq. (11-1.37).

11-1.6. Deduce and plot the voltage on a lossless line at point $x = \ell/2$, and $2T < t < 3T$ if $Z_g = 3Z_o$ and $Z_L = 0.5\, Z_o$ when a unit step function is applied.

11-1.7. Deduce and plot the voltage on a lossless line at point $x = \ell/2$, and $2T < t < 3T$ if $Z_g = Z_o$ and $Z_L(s) = sL$ when a unit step function is applied.

11-2.1. Verify Eq. (11-2.10).

11-2.2. Find the voltage on an infinite lossless transmission line if a distributed current source $I_o(x)$ is present.

11-2.3. Find the current and the voltage on a lossless infinite transmission line if $V_o(x) = 3\delta(x-2)$.

[Ans: $v(x,t) = \text{Re}\, V(x,t) = \frac{3}{2}\frac{\partial|2-x|}{\partial x} \cos(\omega t + k|2-x|)$]

11-2.4. Verify Eqs. (11-2.16) and (11-2.17).

11-2.5. Find the voltage on a semiinfinite lossless transmission line for which a distributed current source is present.

[Hint: Assume solutions of the form Ae^{jkx} and $B \sin kx$]

[Ans: $G(x,\xi) = \frac{1}{k} \sin k\xi e^{jkx}$, $x > \xi$; $G(x,\xi) = \frac{1}{k} \sin kxe^{jk\xi}$, $0 \le x \le \xi$]

11-3.1. A short-circuited transmission line has the following constants: $f = 10^9$ Hz, $L = 2 \times 10^{-3}$ Henry/m, $C = 6 \times 10^{-9}$ Farad/m, $\ell = 10$m. Find: (a) the first three characteristic frequencies, (b) the voltage along the line corresponding to the second characteristic frequency, and (c) sketch the voltage of part (b) along the line versus time.

11-4.1. A plane TE wave, $f = 10^9$ Hz, is impinging on a copper surface at an angle $\theta = 35^o$. Find the effective wavelengths of the TE_2 mode in the Z and Y directions. Find the same wavelength if instead of copper an aluminum surface was present.

11-4.2. Two parallel plates made of copper are 30 cm apart and are filled with plexiglass ($\varepsilon_r = 3$). If a TE_2 wave of 3×10^9 Hz is propagating between the plates, find λ_c, λ_g, and sketch the E field. Find also λ_c, λ_g, and λ if instead of plexiglass distilled water is used.

11-4.3. Find H_y and H_z for the incident and reflected waves in Fig. 11-4.1.

11-4.4. Find the group velocity $v_g = d\omega/dk_g$ of a TE mode between perfectly conducting planes.

[Hint: $k_g = [\frac{\omega^2}{v^2} - (\frac{n\pi}{b})^2]^{1/2}$]

11-4.5. Sketch the phase and group velocities versus frequency for a TE_2 mode between perfectly conducting planes.

11-4.6. Show that an evanescent mode does not transport energy along the guide.

11-4.7. Find the $\overline{E}$ and $\overline{H}$ fields for a TM_n mode of propagation. Does the TM_o mode exist? [Ans: Yes.]

11-4.8. Find the location of the angle θ on the complex θ plane for a TM wave if $f = 1.2\ v/2b$ and $f = 3.25\ v/2b$.

11-5.1. Verify Eqs. (11-5.3), (11-5.4), (11-5.5), and (11-5.17).

11-5.2. Show that the configuration of the $\overline{E}$ field lines shown in Fig. 11-5.2 for the TM_{10} mode are the correct ones.
[Hint: The direction of the $\overline{E}$ field at each point is given by $E_x/E_z = dx/dz = -(k_{zn}\ell/n\pi)\cot(n\pi/\ell\ x)\tan k_{zn}z$; the E's are real quantities.]

11-5.3. In the manner of the last example, develop the propagation of TE waves between two parallel conducting plates and sketch the magnetic and electric field lines.
[Ans: $H_{ox} = -j\frac{k_{zn}}{\lambda_n}a_n \sin\lambda_n x$, $H_{oy} = 0$, $H_{oz} = a_n\cos\lambda_n x$, $E_{ox} = 0$, $E_{oy} = j\frac{\omega\mu}{\lambda_n}a_n\sin\lambda_n x$, $E_{oz} = 0$.]

11-5.4. Plot the dispersion relations for the first three modes of a TM wave in two parallel conducting planes and find explicitly the phase and group velocities for the different modes. Find also the cutoff frequency for the guide and the wave impedance.

[Ans: $v_{phn} = v/\left(1 - \frac{1}{\mu\varepsilon}\left(\frac{n\pi}{\ell}\right)^2\frac{1}{\omega^2}\right)^{1/2}$; $v_{gn} = v\left(1 - \frac{1}{\mu\varepsilon}\left(\frac{n\pi}{\ell}\right)^2\frac{1}{\omega^2}\right)^{1/2}$;
$v = \frac{1}{\sqrt{\mu\varepsilon}}$; $f_{cn} = \frac{1}{2\sqrt{\mu\varepsilon}}\frac{n}{\ell}$.]

11-5.5. Find the average power flowing in a width b in the Y-direction between two parallel plates for the TM modes.

11-5.6. Plot the dispersion relations for TE_{21} mode for rectangular wave guides and find the phase velocity, group velocity, cutoff frequency and wave impedance.

11-5.7. Find all of the field components for TM waves in rectangular wave guides.
[Hint: Begin with $E_{oz} = B_1\sin k_x x\sin k_y y$.]

11-5.8. Plot the magnitude of the field components versus x and y for the following modes: TE_{10}, TE_{11}, TE_{21}, TM_{11}, and TM_{21}.

11-5.9. Plot the dispersion relations for the TM_{11} mode in a cylindrical wave guide, and find the phase velocity, group velocity, cutoff frequency and wave impedance.

11-5.10. Find all the field components for TE waves in cylindrical wave guides. [Hint: $H_{oz} = C_1 J_n(\gamma_c r) \cos n\phi$.]

11-5.11. Plot the magnitude of the field components versus r for angles $\phi = 0^o$, $\phi = 45^o$, and $\phi = 90^o$ for the TE_{11} and TM_{11} modes of a cylindrical wave guide.

11-5.12. A rectangular wave guide has the dimensions a = 3 cm and b = 2 cm. If an oscillator of $f = 0.8 \times 10^{10}$ H_z is exciting the waveguide, find for a TM_{11} mode the following: k_x, k_y, k_z, cutoff frequency, and the power, if the amplitude of the wave is 10 μV/m.

11-5.13. A wave of 9.2 GHz is propagating in a rectangular waveguide of dimensions a = 2.5 cm and b = 0.9 cm. Find the maximum power that can be transmitted in the TE_{10} mode if the air breaks down at 5×10^6 V/m. (This method has been proposed for energy transmission.)

11-6.1. Find the critical angle for a perpendicularly polarized HeNe laser beam propagating from distilled water ($\varepsilon_r = 80$) to air.

11-6.2. Plot the reflection coefficient $R_\perp$ versus the incident angle for the following ratios: (a) $\varepsilon_{r1} = 1$, $\varepsilon_{r2} = 1.1$; (b) $\varepsilon_{r1} = 1$, $\varepsilon_{r2} = 3$; (c) $\varepsilon_{r1} = 1$, $\varepsilon_{r2} = 20$.

11-6.3. Express Eqs. (11-6.11) and (11-6.12) in terms of the incident angle only. [Hint: Use Eq. (11-6.7).]

11-6.4. Show that for parallel polarization

$$R_{\parallel} = \frac{\mu_2 k_1 \cos\theta_2 - \mu_1 k_2 \cos\theta_1}{\mu_2 k_1 \cos\theta_2 + \mu_1 k_2 \cos\theta_1}; \quad T_{\parallel} = 1 + R_{\parallel}$$

11-6.5. Find the angle of the planes of constant phase if the following are given: $\eta_1 = 3$, $\eta_2 = 1 + j\,0.5$, $\theta_1 = 80^o$, $f = 10^6$.

11-7.1. Show that the critical angle θ_c at which no reflection exists is given by

$$\sin\theta_c = \sqrt{\frac{m^2-\eta^2}{m^2-1}}$$

This equation shows that for complete transmission θ_c must be real. Therefore, the quantity under the square root sign must lie in the range from zero to one.

11-7.2. Show that if $\eta < 1$ ($k_1 < k_2$ or $c_1 < c_2$) and $\sin\theta_1 > \eta$

$$R = \exp\left[j(-2mc \tan[\frac{\sqrt{\sin^2\theta-\eta^2}}{m\cos\theta}]) \right]$$

11-7.3. The intensity of the wave is given by $I = |p|^2/2\rho_o c = ((\omega\rho_o)^2/2)|\Phi_{ao}|^2/\rho_o c$. Show that

$$\frac{I_{trans}}{I_{inc}} = \frac{\rho_{01}c_1}{\rho_{02}c_2}|1 + R_a|^2$$

11-7.4. Find the acoustic reflection and transmission coefficients between water and sediment if ρ_w = 1033 kg/m^3, c_w = 1508 m/sec, $\rho_{sed} = 2\,\rho_w$, c_{sed} = 1.15 c_w and the angle of incidence is 35°.

11-8.1. Find the cutoff frequency for the first mode if the following are given: d = 5 μm, ε_{1r} = 1.501, ε_{2r} = 1.499. What is the cutoff frequency if the difference of the dielectric constants changes by 15 percent?

11-8.2. Develop the characteristic equation for the odd TE mode and show that this mode cannot propagate at arbitrarily small frequencies.
[Hint: Set $E_y = E_{y1} \sin k_x x\, e^{jk_z z}$.]
[Ans: $\gamma \tan k_x d = -k_x$.]

11-8.3. Show that for the even TM mode we have

$$H_y = H_{y1} \cos k_x x; \quad E_z = \frac{jk_x}{\eta_1{}^2\omega\varepsilon_o} H_{y1} \sin k_x x; \quad \tan k_x d = \frac{\eta_1{}^2\gamma}{\eta_2{}^2 k_x}$$

11-8.4. Sketch the electric and magnetic fields for the even TE_1 mode.

11-9.1. Verify the matrixes in Fig. 11-9.2.

11-9.2. An optical system of identical converging thin lenses is constructed with d = 5 cm and f = 16 cm. If the ray enters the first lens at height 2 cm and at an angle of 35°, plot the ray for the distance of five lenses.

11-10.1. Verify Eq. (11-10.2).

11-10.2. Find the transformation matrix for the optical signal shown in Fig. 11-10.1 if d ≠ 0.

11-10.3. An optical system is shown in Fig. P11-10.3. Find the focal lengths and its cardinal points.

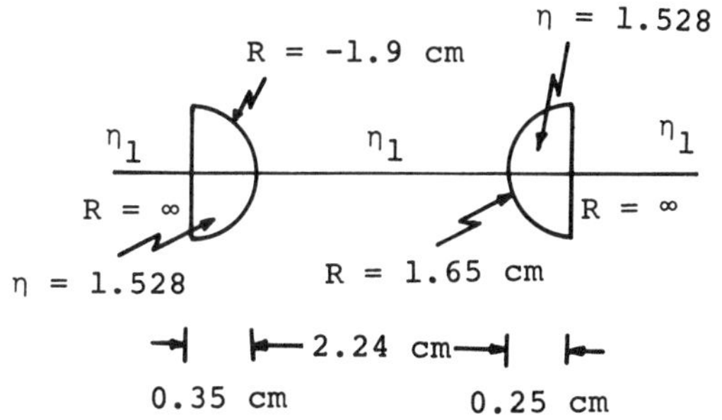

Figure P11-10.3.

CHAPTER 12

ELEMENTS OF DIFFRACTION THEORY

This chapter will be devoted to a study of the basic concepts and formulas that relate to diffraction theory. The study begins with fundamental ideas which were developed by Huygens (1629-1695), and which were subsequently extended by others. The fundamental principle of Huygens may be stated as follows: "each point of a wavefront at a given time can be thought of as the envelope of spherical waves emitted from each point of a previously established wavefront." This means that the secondary spherical waves from points on a wavefront combine to form a new wavefront which is the envelope of the secondary wavelets. Figures 12-0.1 illustrate the application of Huygen's principle. Observe that a plane wave propagates as a plane wave; also a spherical wave propagates as a spherical wave.

Huygens encountered difficulties in applying his principle in a number of cases and was compelled to introduce special ad-hoc hypotheses. To account for the rectilinear propagation of light, for example, he was forced to accept the notion that the secondary waves have effects only at the point where they touch the envelope. In addition, the ambiguity of the direction of propagation had to be resolved by accepting it arbitrarily.

It was almost two centuries later, in 1818, that Fresnel improved on Huygen's ideas. He was able to account for the phenomenon of diffraction by postulating that the secondary wavelets can mutually interfere with each other. The combined principles of Huygens wavelets construction and Fresnel's interference is now known as the Huygens-Fresnel Principle.

Later, in 1882, Kirchhoff succeeded in putting the Huygens-Fresnel principle on a firm mathematical basis. He showed that the Huygens-Fresnel principle is an approximation to the solution of the homogeneous wave equation at a point in terms of the value of the solution and its first derivatives at all points on an arbitrary closed surface surrounding the point. The work of Kirchhoff was criticized by Poincare and Sommerfeld, and Sommerfeld was able to eliminate one of Kirchhoff's

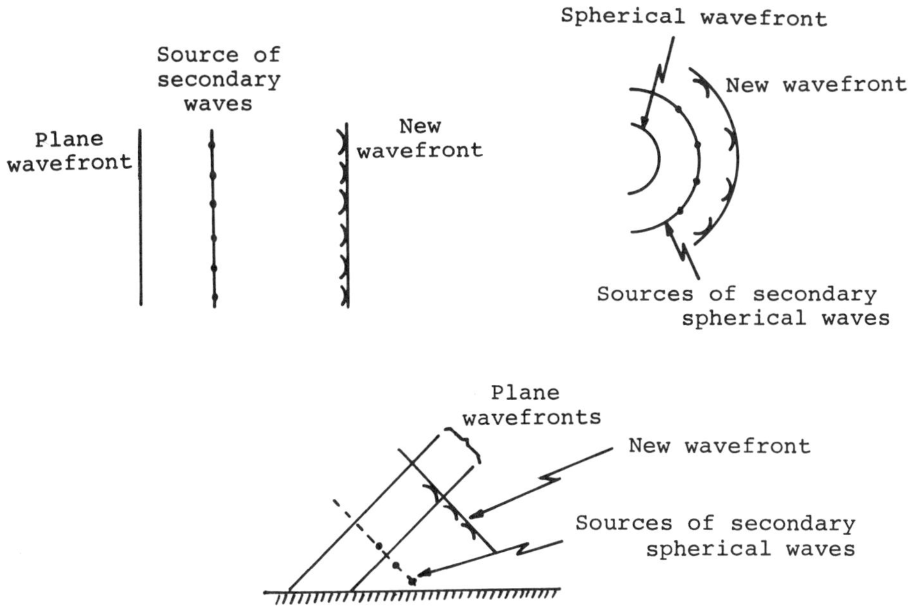

Figure 12-0.1. Illustrations of Huygen's principle.

assumptions. However, it should be pointed out that these theoretical developments are not exact since they treat the propagation of electromagnetic radiation as a scalar phenomenon, rather than as a vector problem. It is remarkable, however, that despite the many simplifying assumptions that were introduced, the experimental observations agree quite well with the approximate theory. In Sec. 14-6 we shall treat related problems from a vector field approach. A comparison of the methods is important.

The first rigorous solution of the diffraction problem was given by Sommerfeld in 1896. He treated the incidence of a plane wave on a thin perfectly conducting half plane. Our studies will build on this prior work.

12-1. Helmholtz-Kirchhoff Integral

Our problem here is to examine the disturbance at a point in a field $\Phi(P_0)$ due to a point source some distance away denoted $\Phi(P_1)$. More precisely, let V be any region within a homogeneous, isotropic medium bounded by a closed regular surface S, and let Φ be any solution of the Helmholtz wave equation

$$\nabla^2\Phi + k^2\Phi = 0 \qquad (12\text{-}1.1)$$

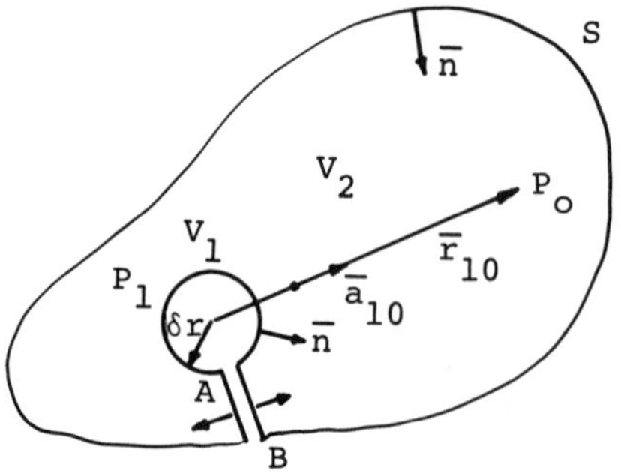

Figure 12-1.1. The geometrical configuration for the diffraction integral.

where $k = 2\pi/\lambda = \omega/v$ and where it is assumed that Φ is continuous and has continuous first derivatives within V and on S. Refer to Fig. 12-1.1. As shown, we suppose that the volume V consists of two parts, the small volume V_1 (a δ-sphere) surrounding point P_1 and the volume V_2 containing the general point P_0. It is required to find the potential at the general point P_0 due to an excitation within the region V.

In continuing, we shall have need for *Green's second identity*. We develop this mathematical form. We begin with the relation for any two scalar functions g and ϕ which are continuous and bounded in a volume V

$$\int_V \nabla \cdot (g\nabla\phi)dV = \int_V [\nabla g \cdot \nabla\phi + g\nabla^2\phi]dV$$

The left-hand side of this expression can be written

$$\oint_S g(\nabla\phi \cdot \bar{n})dS = \oint_S g\,\frac{\partial\phi}{\partial n}\,dS = \oint_S g\nabla\phi \cdot d\bar{S} = \int_V [\nabla g\cdot\nabla\phi + g\nabla^2\phi]dV \tag{12-1.2}$$

where we have used the divergence theorem and the ninth vector identity in Appendix I. Interchanging g and ϕ in the last equation and then subtracting the two equations, we obtain the desired identity

$$\int_V (g\nabla^2\phi - \phi\nabla^2 g)dV = \oint_S (g\,\frac{\partial\phi}{\partial n} - \phi\,\frac{\partial g}{\partial n})dS \tag{12-1.3}$$

where, of course,

$$\bar{n} \cdot \nabla = \frac{\partial}{\partial n} \tag{12-1.4}$$

To help investigate the field, we introduce the Green's function

$$G(P_1,P_o) = \frac{e^{jkr_{10}}}{r_{10}} \tag{12-1.5}$$

This function has no necessary relation to the real sources which produce the field. We shall use the Green second identity in our problem, but this requires that the function $G(P_1,P_o)$ must be continuous throughout the volume V. It is for this reason that we enclose point P_1 inside the small δ-sphere of radius δr, and exclude P_o from entering this volume - this avoids the singularity at P_1. With this modification $G(P_1,P_o)$ possesses the requisite continuous first-order and second-order partial derivatives within the volume V_2, and on the surfaces S, S_{AB}, S_{BA}, $S_{\delta r}$. Also, it satisfies the differential equation (show that this is so)

$$\nabla^2 G + k^2 G = 0 \tag{12-1.6}$$

We now apply Green's second identity specified by Eq. (12-1.3) to the volume V_2 shown in Fig. 12-1.1. We find the following form, writing the total defining closed surface S in terms of the several elements which make up the total surface,

$$\int_{V_2} (\ )dV = \oint_S (\ )dS + \int_{S_{AB}} (\ )dS + \int_{S_{BA}} (\ )dS + \oint_{S_{\delta r}} (\ )dS \tag{12-1.7}$$

We substitute Eqs. (12-1.1) and (12-1.3) into the left-hand side of this equation It is also observed that the two surface integrals $\int_{S_{AB}}$ and $\int_{S_{BA}}$ are equal and opposite. As a result, Eq. (12-1.7) becomes

$$\oint_S \left(G\frac{\partial\Phi}{\partial n} - \Phi\frac{\partial G}{\partial n}\right)dS = -\oint_{S_{\delta r}} \left(G\frac{\partial\Phi}{\partial n} - \Phi\frac{\partial G}{\partial n}\right)dS \tag{12-1.8}$$

where $\partial/\partial n$ signifies a partial derivative in the direction of the inward drawn normal at each point of S.

We now employ the properties of a directional derivative (see Chap. 2) for an arbitrary point P_o on S. We can write

$$\frac{\partial G(P_1,P_o)}{\partial n} = \nabla G \cdot \overline{n} = \frac{\partial G(P_1,P_o)}{\partial r_{10}} \overline{a}_{10}\cdot\overline{n} = \overline{n}\cdot\overline{a}_{10}\left(jk - \frac{1}{r_{10}}\right)\frac{e^{jkr_{10}}}{r_{10}} \tag{12-1.9}$$

For a general point P_o on $S_{\delta r}$, $\overline{n}\cdot\overline{a}_{10} = 1$ and the right-hand side of Eq. (12-1.8) becomes

$$\oint_{S_r} \left[\frac{e^{jk\delta r}}{\delta r}\frac{\partial\Phi}{\partial n} - \Phi\left(jk - \frac{1}{\delta r}\right)\frac{e^{jk\delta r}}{\delta r}\right] dS = \int_\Omega \left[\frac{e^{jk\delta r}}{\delta r}\frac{\partial\Phi}{\partial n} - jk\frac{\Phi}{\delta r} + \frac{1}{(\delta r)^2} e^{jk\delta r}\,\Phi\right](\delta r)^2\, d\Omega \tag{12-1.10}$$

where we have substituted for the surface element $dS = (\delta r)^2 d\Omega$, with $d\Omega$ being an element of solid angle. Since δr is a constant, the integral in Eq. (12-1.10) is independent of δr. The limiting value of the integral is possible by letting δr approach zero. The first and second terms are infinitesimally small as $\delta r \to 0$, and so do not contribute anything to the integral provided that Φ has no singularities inside the volume V_1. Under these circumstances the value of the integral in Eq. (12-1.10) is equal to $+4\pi\Phi(P_1)$ where $\Phi(P_1)$ is the average value of Φ in V_1. This means that the solution of Eq. (12-1.8), and this is the *Helmholtz-Kirchhoff integral*, is

$$\Phi(P_1) = \frac{1}{4\pi}\oint_S [\Phi \frac{\partial}{\partial n} (\frac{e^{jkr_{10}}}{r_{10}}) - \frac{e^{jkr_{10}}}{r_{10}} \frac{\partial \Phi}{\partial n}]dS \qquad (12\text{-}1.11)$$

This equation expresses the value of a function at any point P_1 inside of the closed surface S in terms of its value on S. Since P_1 is an arbitrary point in the volume $V_1 + V_2$, it is implied that the singularities of Φ must be located outside of the closed surface S. It also means that the sources that produce the function Φ are outside of the surface. The distance r_{10} is taken to be from the point P_1 to any point within the surface S.

In the case when the sources are inside of the surface S, and Φ is continuous and differentiable up to the second order outside and on the surface S, we must introduce additional boundary conditions to make the solution applicable to points at infinity. In the present development we shall not be dealing with this problem, nor shall we consider the case of the nonsinusoidal varying excitation.

Example 12-1.1. Find the field behind an aperture S_o when a plane wave is impinging on it as shown in Fig. 12-1.2.

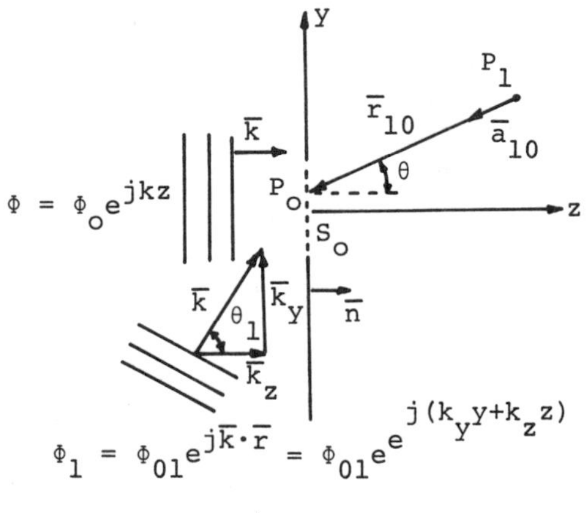

Figure 12-1.2. A plane wave is exicting the aperture.

Solution. For a plane electromagnetic wave, Φ is equal to any one component of the $\overline{E}$ or $\overline{H}$ field. Now following an analysis similar to that in the previous paragraph we obtain

$$\frac{\partial\Phi}{\partial n} = \Phi_o \frac{\partial}{\partial n} e^{jkz} = \Phi_o \cos(\overline{k},\overline{n}) \frac{\partial e^{jkz}}{\partial z} = jk\Phi, \ \overline{k} \text{ parallel to } \overline{n}$$

$$\frac{\partial}{\partial n}\left(\frac{e^{jkr_{10}}}{r_{10}}\right) = \cos(\overline{n},\overline{r}_{10})\left(jk - \frac{1}{r_{10}}\right)\frac{e^{jkr_{10}}}{r_{10}} \doteq -jk\cos\theta\,\frac{e^{jkr_{10}}}{r_{10}}$$

When these are substituted into Eq. (12-1.11) we find the equation

$$\Phi(P_1) = \frac{1}{4\pi}\int_{S_o}\left[\Phi_o e^{jkz}(-)\cos\theta\, jk\,\frac{e^{jkr_{10}}}{r_{10}} - \frac{e^{jkr_{10}}}{r_{10}}\, jk\Phi_o e^{jkz}\right]dS$$

$$= \frac{-jk}{4\pi}\int_{S_o}(1 + \cos\theta)\,\Phi_o\,\frac{e^{jk(z + r_{10})}}{r_{10}}\,dS$$

ΔΔΔ

12-2. Fresnel-Kirchhoff Diffraction Formula

To develop the diffraction formula, we assume the presence of a source P_s in a region V defined by surface S having such a power pattern which illuminates only an area S_o, as shown graphically in Fig. 12-2.1. An equally valid assumption would be to assume a source P_{s1} and a transparent surface S. To avoid any singularity at P_1 due to the source P_s, we enclose it within an infinitesimal (δ-sphere) volume, thus separating it from the volume enclosed by the surface S.

The field at point P_1 due to the sources at S_o can be found using the Helmholtz-Kirchhoff integral. Note first that the closed surface S consists of four parts $S = S_o + S_1 + S_2 + S_3$, but with S_o being the only surface that is illuminated by the source. Therefore the field at point P_1 will be *primarily* due to the field on S_o. The word primarily has been emphasized because we incorporate the following two Kirchhoff mathematically nonrigorous conditions:

1. The field Φ and its normal derivative $\partial\Phi/\partial n$ on S_o are exactly the same as they would be in the absence of the surface $S_1 + S_2 + S_3$.
2. The field Φ and its normal derivative $\partial\Phi/\partial n$ are both zero on the surfaces S_1 and S_3.

What we have done here is to suppose that the contribution to Φ due to the reflected component of the field can be neglected. These conditions simplify the problem considerably since the contribution to the integral occurs only over the surface S_o, and in addition, we can specify the incident disturbance at a given surface by neglecting the presence of its boundaries.

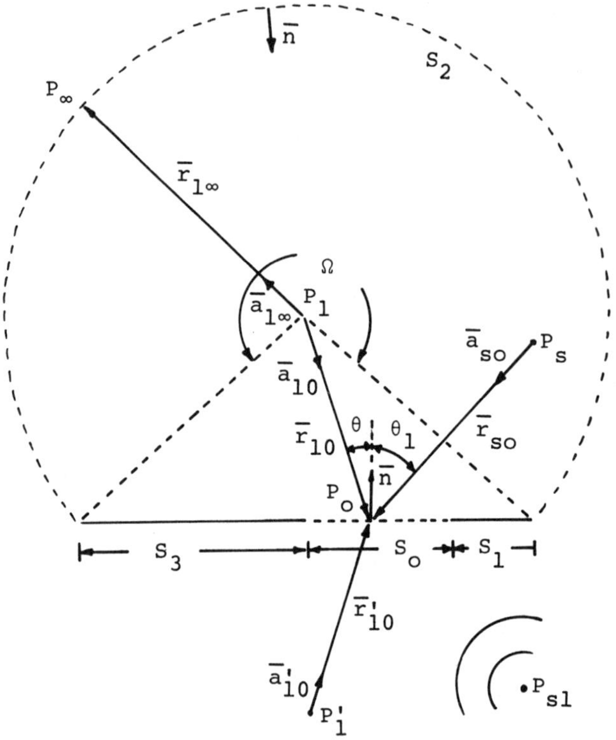

Figure 12-2.1. Illustration for the Fresnel-Kirchhoff diffraction formula. (The source point P_s illuminates only the surface S_o.)

The total field at point P_1 is expressed by the integral in Eq. (12-1.11). Therefore we first write

$$\Phi(P_1) = \frac{1}{4\pi}\left\{\int_{S_o} [\ ]\, dS + \int_{S_1} [\ ]\, dS + \int_{S_2} [\ ]\, dS + \int_{S_3} [\ ]\, dS\right\} \tag{12-2.1}$$

By applying the second Kirchhoff boundary condition on this equation, we find

$$\Phi(P_1) = \frac{1}{4\pi}\int_{S_o} [\ ]\, dS + \frac{1}{4\pi}\int_{S_2} \left[\Phi \frac{\partial}{\partial n}\left(\frac{e^{jkr_{1\infty}}}{r_{1\infty}}\right) - \frac{e^{jkr_{1\infty}}}{r_{1\infty}}\frac{\partial \Phi}{\partial n}\right] dS \tag{12-2.2}$$

However, the normal derivative of $e^{jkr_{1\infty}}/r_{1\infty}$ is

$$\frac{\partial}{\partial n}\left(\frac{e^{jkr_{1\infty}}}{r_{1\infty}}\right) = \bar{a}_{1\infty}\cdot \bar{n}\,\frac{\partial}{\partial r_{1\infty}}\left(\frac{e^{jkr_{1\infty}}}{r_{1\infty}}\right) = -\left(jk - \frac{1}{r_{1\infty}}\right)\frac{e^{jkr_{1\infty}}}{r_{1\infty}} \doteq \frac{-jk}{r_{1\infty}}\, e^{jkr_{1\infty}} \tag{12-2.3}$$

because $1/r_{1\infty} \ll k$ as $r_{1\infty} \to \infty$. Similarly

$$\frac{\partial \Phi}{\partial n} = \bar{a}_{1\infty}\cdot \bar{n}\,\frac{\partial \Phi}{\partial r_{1\infty}} = -\frac{\partial \Phi}{\partial r_{1\infty}} \tag{12-2.4}$$

The second integral of Eq. (12-2.2) reduces to

$$\frac{1}{4\pi}\int_{\Omega} e^{jkr_{1\infty}}\left(\frac{\partial\Phi}{\partial r_{1\infty}} - jk\Phi\right) r_{1\infty} d\Omega$$

where Ω is the solid angle subtended by S_2 at the center of the sphere at P_1 [$dS = r_{1\infty}{}^2 d\Omega$]. Since the quantity $|e^{jkr_{1\infty}}|$ is finite at S_2, the integral over S_2 will vanish if

$$\lim_{r_{1\infty}\to\infty} r_{1\infty}\left(\frac{\partial\Phi}{\partial r_{1\infty}} - jk\Phi\right) \to 0 \tag{12-2.5}$$

uniformly in angle. This last requirement is known as the Sommerfeld *radiation condition*. By applying this condition to Eq. (12-2.2), the field at P_1 is now given by the expression

$$\begin{aligned}\Phi(P_1) &= \frac{1}{4\pi}\int_{S_o} \left[\Phi \frac{\partial}{\partial n}\left(\frac{e^{jkr_{10}}}{r_{10}}\right) - \frac{e^{jkr_{10}}}{r_{10}}\frac{\partial\Phi}{\partial n}\right] dS \\ &= \frac{1}{4\pi}\int_{S_o} \left[\Phi\, \bar{a}_{10}\cdot\bar{n}\left(jk - \frac{1}{r_{10}}\right) - \frac{\partial\Phi}{\partial n}\right] \frac{e^{jkr_{10}}}{r_{10}} dS\end{aligned} \tag{12-2.6}$$

This last equation can be simplified further in the case where $k \gg 1/r_{10}$ [$\lambda \ll r_{10}/2\pi$]. In this case Eq. (12-2.6) assumes the form

$$\begin{aligned}\Phi(P_1) &= \frac{1}{4\pi}\int_{S_o} \left[jk\Phi\, \bar{a}_{10}\cdot\bar{n} + \bar{a}_{so}\cdot\bar{n}\frac{\partial\Phi}{\partial r_{so}}\right]\frac{e^{jkr_{10}}}{r_{10}} dS \\ &= \frac{1}{4\pi}\int_{S_o} \left[\frac{\partial\Phi}{\partial r_{so}}\cos(\bar{r}_{so},\bar{n}) - jk\Phi\cos(\bar{r}_{10},\bar{n})\right] \frac{e^{jkr_{10}}}{r_{10}} dS\end{aligned} \tag{12-2.7}$$

If the source radiates a monochromatic spherical wave of unit amplitude towards the surface S_o, then $\Phi(P_o) = e^{jkr_{so}}/r_{so}$ and for $k \gg 1/r_{so}$ the equation becomes

$$\Phi(P_1) = \frac{jk}{4\pi}\int_{S_o} [-\cos(\bar{r}_{10},\bar{n}) + \cos(\bar{r}_{so},\bar{n})] \frac{e^{jk(r_{10}+r_{so})}}{r_{10}r_{so}} dS \tag{12-2.8}$$

This is known as the *Fresnel-Kirchhoff diffraction formula*. If this equation were to be written in the form

$$\begin{aligned}\Phi(P_1) &= \int_{S_o} \frac{jk}{4\pi}[-\cos(\bar{r}_{10},\bar{n}) + \cos(\bar{r}_{so},\bar{n})] \frac{e^{jkr_{so}}}{r_{so}} \frac{e^{jkr_{10}}}{r_{10}} dS \\ &= \int_{S_o} \Phi_o(P_1,P_o) \frac{e^{jkr_{10}}}{r_{10}} dS\end{aligned} \tag{12-2.9}$$

where

$$\Phi_o(P_1,P_o) = \frac{jk}{4\pi}\,[-\cos\,(\bar{r}_{10},\bar{n}) + \cos(\bar{r}_{so},\bar{n})]\,\frac{e^{jkr_{so}}}{r_{so}}$$

then we can interpret the field at P_1 as the result of secondary fictitious point sources located at S_o and having the following properties:

1. The amplitude is proportional to the incident wave but modified by the factor $1/\lambda$.
2. The amplitude is decreased by the obliquity factor $1/2[-\cos(\bar{r}_{10},\bar{n}) + \cos(\bar{r}_{so},\bar{n})]$ i.e., an anisotropy in directivity of each secondary source.
3. There is a phase advance of $\pi/2$.

These properties are the same as those set forth by Fresnel in an ad-hoc manner to formulate Huygen's principles. Here we find these properties to be a consequence of the Kirchhoff mathematical formulation. The backward wave is lost because it was neglected in the Kirchhoff development and is consistent with the ad-hoc condition imposed in the elementary formulation of Huygen's principle.

12-3. Rayleigh-Sommerfeld Diffraction Formula

When the Kirchhoff approximate boundary conditions are examined critically, a complication arises. This follows from the fact that the requirement that the potential Φ and its normal derivative $\partial\Phi/\partial n$ be zero at an element of surface S leads to zero field at all points enclosed by the surface S. To correct this contradiction, Sommerfeld introduced another type of Green's function which was supposed to be produced not only by a fictitious source at P_1 but also by another source P_1' located symmetrically with respect to the surface S_o (refer to Fig. 12-2.1). If these two equivalent sources are assumed to be oscillating 180 degrees out of phase, the Green's function is then of the form

$$G_1 = \frac{e^{jkr_{10}}}{r_{10}} - \frac{e^{jkr'_{10}}}{r'_{10}} \qquad (12\text{-}3.1)$$

and its normal derivative is

$$\frac{\partial G_1}{\partial n} = \bar{a}_{10}\cdot\bar{n}\,\frac{\partial}{\partial r_{10}}\left(\frac{e^{jkr_{10}}}{r_{10}}\right) - \bar{a}'_{10}\cdot\bar{n}\,\frac{\partial}{\partial r'_{10}}\left(\frac{e^{jkr'_{10}}}{r'_{10}}\right)$$

$$= \cos\,(\bar{r}_{10},\bar{n}_{10})(jk - \frac{1}{r_{10}})\,\frac{e^{jkr_{10}}}{r_{10}} - \cos(\bar{r}'_{10},\bar{n})(jk - \frac{1}{r'_{10}})\,\frac{e^{jkr'_{10}}}{r'_{10}} \qquad (12\text{-}3.2)$$

When the point P_o is located on S_o, $r_{10} = r'_{10}$ and $\cos\,(\bar{r}_{10},\bar{n}) = -\cos\,(\bar{r}'_{10},\bar{n})$. Thus we find that

$$G_1(P_o) = 0 \tag{12-3.3}$$

and

$$\frac{\partial G_1}{\partial n} = 2 \cos (\bar{r}_{10},\bar{n})(jk - \frac{1}{r_{10}}) \frac{e^{jkr_{10}}}{r_{10}} \tag{12-3.4}$$

These latter two equations yield, when substituted into Eq. (12-1.11), and assuming that $k >> 1/r_{10}$,

$$\Phi(P_1) = \frac{jk}{2\pi} \int_{S_o} \Phi(P_o) \frac{e^{jkr_{10}}}{r_{10}} \cos (\bar{r}_{10},\bar{n})\, dS \tag{12-3.5}$$

This is the *Rayleigh-Sommerfeld* diffraction formula.

12-4. Fresnel and Fraunhofer Approximations

Consider a finite plane aperture S_o at a large distance z_{10} from the observation plane x_1y_1 as shown in Fig. 12-4.1. If the observation region S_1 is small and is located around the Z-axis, then $\cos (\bar{n},\bar{r}_{10}) \doteq -1$. In addition, the approximation $|\bar{r}_{10}| \doteq z_{10}$ can be substituted into the factors where only the amplitude is involved (why?). Thus Eq. (12-3.5) assumes the form

$$\Phi(P_1) \doteq - \frac{jk}{2\pi z_{10}} \int_{S_o} \Phi(P_o)\, e^{jkr_{10}}\, dS \tag{12-4.1}$$

Further simplification of the phase factor is possible if we employ the *Fresnel approximation* by retaining the first two terms of its binomial expansion

$$r_{10} = z_{10} \left[1 + \left(\frac{x_o-x_1}{z_{10}}\right)^2 + \left(\frac{y_o-y_1}{z_{10}}\right)^2\right]^{1/2} \doteq z_{10} \left[1 + \frac{1}{2}\left(\frac{x_o-x_1}{z_{10}}\right)^2 + \frac{1}{2}\left(\frac{y_o-y_1}{z_{10}}\right)^2\right] \tag{12-4.2}$$

In this approximation, the spherical wavefront has been replaced by a *quadratic* one. The accuracy of this approximation depends on the aperture size, the observation region size, and the distance z_{10} between the apertures. Substituting Eq. (12-4.2) into Eq. (12-4.1) we find that

$$\Phi(P_1) = - \frac{jk}{2\pi z_{10}} e^{jkz_{10}} \int_{-\infty}^{\infty}\int \Phi(P_o) e^{\frac{jk}{2z_{10}}[(x_o-x_1)^2 + (y_o-y_1)^2]} dx_o\, dy_o \tag{12-4.3}$$

where we have assumed that $\Phi(P_o)$ is identically zero outside of the aperture S_o. This allows us to extend the limits to infinity. Suppose further that we choose our observation point at a distance for which

$$z_{10} >> \frac{k(x_o^2+y_o^2)_{max}}{2} \tag{12-4.4}$$

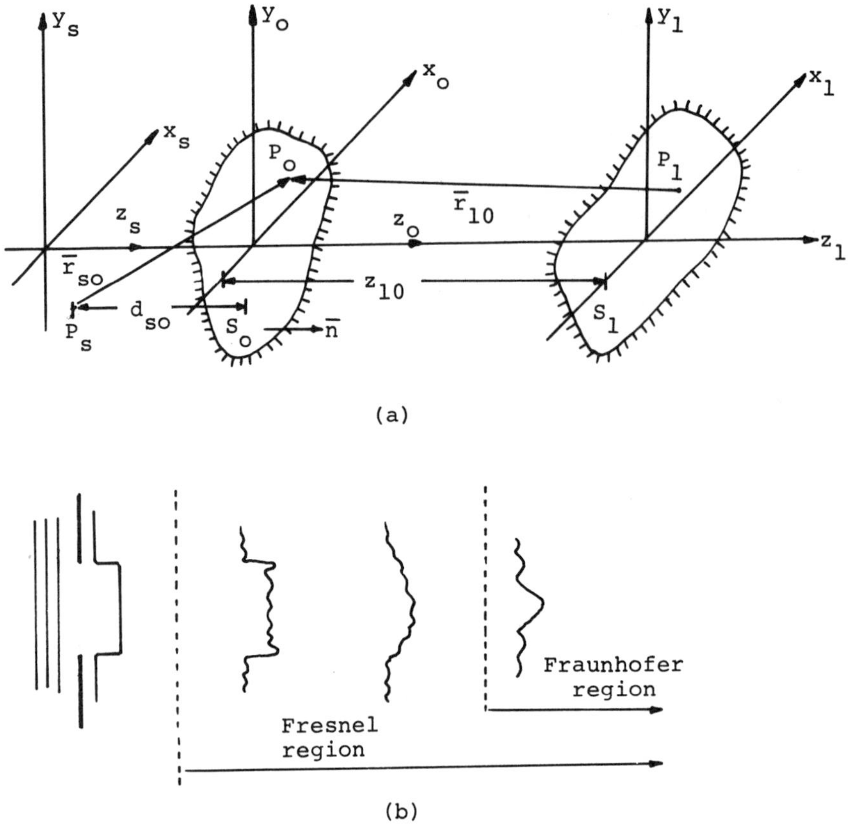

Figure 12-4.1. (a) Diffraction geometry between two planes. (b) Fresnel and Fraunhofer regions.

and this is the *far-field* or *Fraunhofer* region. Equation (12-4.3) becomes

$$\Phi(P_1) = -\frac{jk}{2\pi z_{10}} e^{jkz_{10}} e^{\frac{jk}{2z_{10}}(x_1^2+y_1^2)} \int_{-\infty}^{\infty}\int \Phi(P_o) e^{\frac{-j2\pi}{\lambda z_{10}}(x_o x_1 + y_o y_1)} dx_o\, dy_o \tag{12-4.5}$$

This equation shows that for the Fraunhofer approximation the observation field, apart from a complex constant multiplier, is the *Fourier transform* of the object field $\Phi(P_o)$ evaluated at the spatial frequencies per meter. The two regions where Eqs. (12-4.3) and (12-4.5) are valid are shown in Fig. 12-4.1b.

The inverse one-dimensional Fourier transform discussed in Appendix IV

$$f(t) = \frac{1}{2\pi}\int_{-\infty}^{\infty} F(\omega)\, e^{j\omega t}\, d\omega \tag{12-4.6}$$

expresses the function f(t) as an infinite sum (the integral) of elementary functions

$e^{j\omega t}$ (infinite number of sine and cosine functions each at different frequency) each one weighted (amplitude and phase) by an amount $F(\omega)$. The two-dimensional Fourier transform pair is defined by the relations

$$F(\omega_x,\omega_y) = \int_{-\infty}^{\infty}\int f(x,y)\, e^{-j(\omega_x x+\omega_y y)}\,dx\,dy \tag{12-4.7}$$

$$f(x,y) = \frac{1}{(2\pi)^2}\int_{-\infty}^{\infty}\int F(\omega_x,\omega_y)\, e^{j(\omega_x x+\omega_y y)}\,d\omega_x\,d\omega_y \tag{12-4.8}$$

The function can be interpreted as the addition of an infinite number of elementary functions $e^{j(\omega_x x+\omega_y y)}$ each one weighted by $F(\omega_x,\omega_y)$. Since $e^{j(\omega_x x+\omega_y y)}$ resembles the representation of a wave $e^{j(\bar{k}\cdot\bar{r})} = e^{j(k_x x+k_y y)}$ traveling in the $\bar{k}$ direction, we interpret the function $e^{j(\omega_x x+\omega_y y)}$ at each pair of the spatial frequencies ω_x and ω_y as a sinusoidal amplitude variation in the XY-plane inclined at an angle $\theta = \tan^{-1}(\omega_y/\omega_x)$. Two spatial variations, from an infinite number of variations, are shown in Fig. 12-4.2. The spectrum $F(\omega_x,\omega_y)$ is just a weighting factor for the elementary functions $e^{j(\omega_x x+\omega_y y)}$ such that when all (infinite number) the elementary weighted functions are added together they synthesize the desired function $f(x,y)$.

By comparing Eq. (12-4.5) with Eq. (12-4.8)

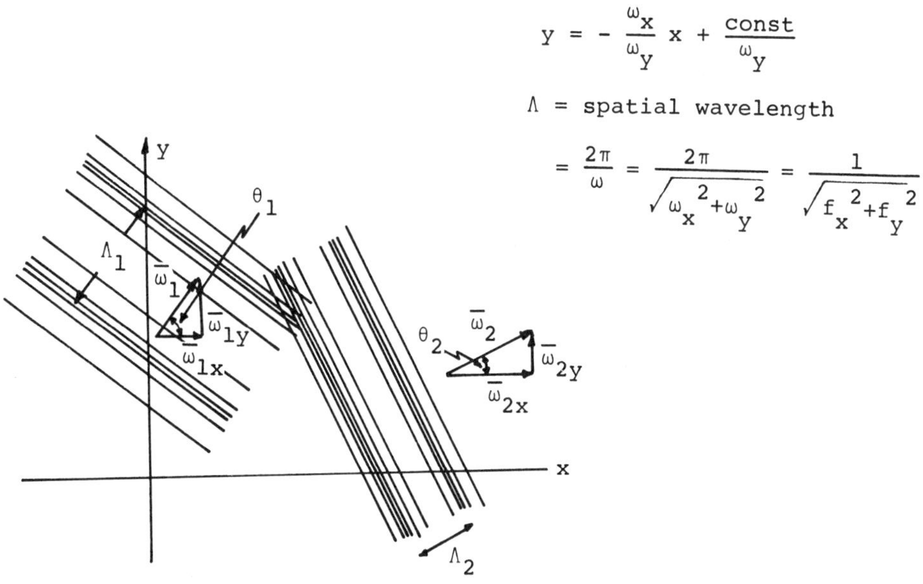

Figure 12-4.2. Illustrating a two-dimensional spatial Fourier transform.

$$f_x = \frac{x_1}{\lambda z_{10}} \qquad \omega_x = \frac{2\pi x_1}{\lambda z_{10}} \qquad (m^{-1}) \tag{12-4.9}$$

$$f_y = \frac{y_1}{\lambda z_{10}} \qquad \omega_y = \frac{2\pi y_1}{\lambda z_{10}} \qquad (m^{-1}) \tag{12-4.10}$$

Example 12-4.1. Find the Fraunhofer diffraction pattern caused by a uniform plane wave falling on a square aperture of dimensions 2a × 2a.

Solution. By an application of Eq. (12-4.5) we obtain

$$\Phi(P_1) = C \int_{-a}^{a} \int 1 \cdot e^{-j(\omega_x x_o + \omega_y y_o)} dx_o\, dy_o = 4Ca^2 \left(\frac{\sin \omega_x a}{\omega_x a}\right)\left(\frac{\sin \omega_y a}{\omega_y a}\right) \tag{12-4.11}$$

and the intensity is given by

$$\Phi(P_1)\, \Phi^*(P_1) = |\Phi(P_1)|^2 = 16|C_1|^2 a^4 \left(\frac{\sin \omega_x a}{\omega_x a}\right)^2 \left(\frac{\sin \omega_y a}{\omega_y a}\right)^2 \tag{12-4.12}$$

Experimental verification of Eq. (12-4.12) is shown in Fig. 12-4.3.

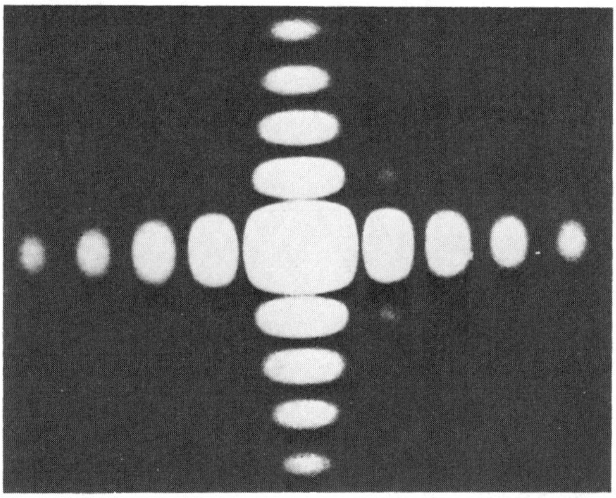

Figure 12-4.3. Fraunhofer diffraction pattern of a rectangular aperture (0.8 × 0.7 cm). [Reprinted with permission from Principles of Optics, Third Edition, by Max Born and Emil Wolf. Pergamon Press, 1965.]

ΔΔΔ

Example 12-4.2. Find the Fraunhofer diffraction pattern when a circular aperture is uniformly illuminated.

Solution. Let (r,θ) be the polar coordinates of a point on the aperture S_o of radius a, and let (ρ,ϕ) be the coordinates at the $f_x f_y$ plane. Then we have

$$
\begin{aligned}
x_o &= r\cos\theta & r &= (x_o^2+y_o^2)^{1/2} \\
y_o &= r\sin\theta & \theta &= \tan^{-1}(y_o/x_o) \\
f_x &= \frac{x_1}{\lambda z_{10}} = \rho\cos\phi & \rho &= (f_x^2+f_y^2)^{1/2} \\
f_y &= \frac{y_1}{\lambda z_{10}} = \rho\sin\phi & \phi &= \tan^{-1}(f_y/f_x)
\end{aligned}
\tag{12-4.13}
$$

Applying these transformations to Eq. (12-4.5) we find

$$
\begin{aligned}
\Phi(P_1) &= C\int_0^\infty\int_0^{2\pi}\Phi(P_o)\,e^{-j2\pi[(\rho\cos\phi)(r\cos\theta)+(\rho\sin\phi)(r\sin\theta)]}\,r\,dr\,d\theta \\
&= C\int_0^\infty r\,\Phi(r)\,dr\int_0^{2\pi}e^{-j2\pi r\rho\cos(\theta-\phi)}\,d\theta
\end{aligned}
\tag{12-4.14}
$$

where it is assumed that the field $\Phi(P_o)$ is independent of θ. We use the known integral form of Bessel's function

$$J_n(x) = \frac{j^{-n}}{2\pi}\int_0^{2\pi} e^{jx\cos\alpha}\,e^{jnx}\,dx \tag{12-4.15}$$

and Eq. (12-4.14) can be written

$$\Phi(P_1) = 2\pi C\int_0^\infty r\,\Phi(r)\,J_o(2\pi r\rho)\,dr \tag{12-4.16}$$

where J_o is the Bessel function of the first kind and zero order. If we also make use of the recursion relation for the Bessel functions

$$\frac{d}{dx}[x^{n+1}J_{n+1}(x)] = x^{n+1}J_n(x) \tag{12-4.17}$$

which translates to the integral

$$\int_0^x \frac{d}{dx'}[x'^{n+1}J_{n+1}(x')]\,dx' = \int_0^x x'^{(n+1)}J_n(x')\,dx' \tag{12-4.18}$$

then for $n = 0$

$$xJ_1(x) = \int_0^x x'\,J_o(x')\,dx' \tag{12-4.19}$$

By Eq. (12-4.19), and Eq. (12-4.16) we see that the field distribution at the observation plane due to a uniform field of unit amplitude $[\Phi(r) = 1]$ across a circular aperture is

$$\Phi(\rho) = \frac{1}{2\pi} C \int_0^a \frac{2\pi r\rho}{\rho^2} \quad J_o(2\pi r\rho)\ d(r2\pi\rho) = \frac{C}{2\pi\rho^2} \int_0^{2\pi\rho a} x'\ J_o(x')\ dx'$$

$$= C \frac{2\pi\rho a}{2\pi\rho^2} J_1(2\pi\rho a) = 2C(\pi a)^2 \left(\frac{J_1(2\pi\rho a)}{2\pi\rho a}\right) \tag{12-4.20}$$

The intensity of the field distribution is then

$$|\Phi(\rho)|^2 = (2C\pi a^2)^2 \left[\frac{J_1(2\pi \frac{a}{\lambda z_{10}} \rho_1)}{2\pi \frac{a}{\lambda z_{10}} \rho_1}\right]^2 \tag{12-4.21}$$

where we have used the relation

$$\rho = \left[\frac{x_1^2}{\lambda^2 z_{10}^2} + \frac{y_1^2}{\lambda^2 z_{10}^2}\right]^{1/2} = \frac{\rho_1}{\lambda z_{10}}$$

and ρ_1 is the radius at the observation plane. Eq. (12-4.21) is of the general form

$$\frac{|\Phi(\rho)|^2}{(C\pi a^2)^2} = \left[2 \frac{J_1(x)}{x}\right]^2$$

which has a form like that shown graphically in Fig. 12-4.4. The dark rings or zeros of this function occur when (see Table 4-3.2)

$$\frac{2\pi a\rho_1}{\lambda z_{10}} = \frac{2\pi a}{\lambda} \tan\theta \doteq \frac{2\pi a}{\lambda} \theta = 3.832,\ 7.016,\ \ldots$$

or for the angles

$$\theta = \frac{3.832\ \lambda}{2\pi a};\ \frac{7.016\ \lambda}{2\pi a};\ \ldots$$

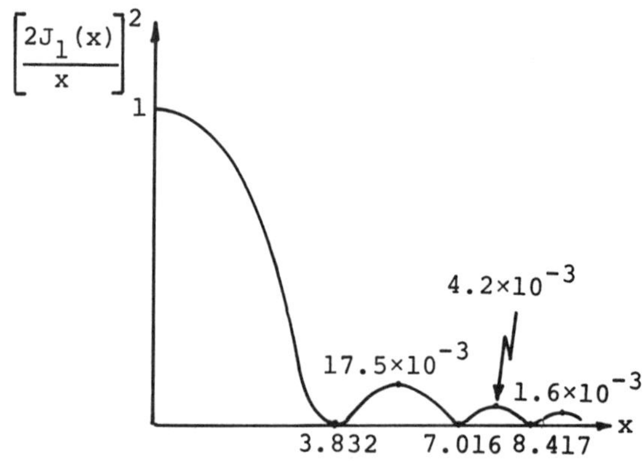

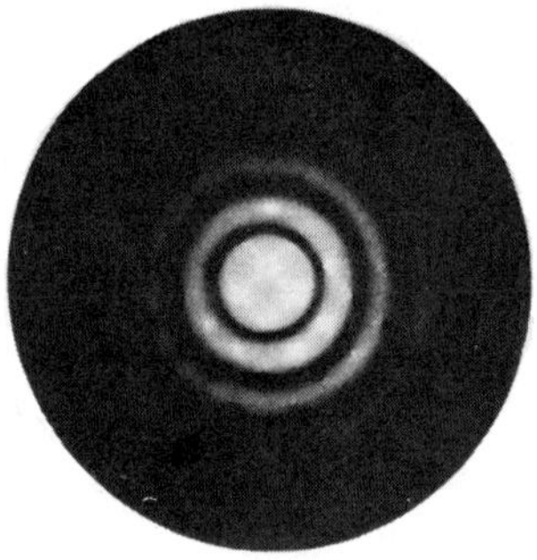

Figure 12-4.4. The intensity variation of a circular apertrue in the Fraunhofer region. [Reprinted with permission from Principles of Optics, Third Edition, by Max Born and Emil Wolf. Pergamon Press, 1965.]

A criterion for resolvability known as the *Rayleigh criterion* follows from these considerations. It may be stated as follows: two point monochromatic sources are said to be resolvable by a circular aperture (say a telescope or microscope) if the maximum intensity of one of the two sources occurs at the position of the first dark ring of the other source. This means that the angular resolution is given by

$$\theta = \frac{3.832\ \lambda}{2\pi a} = \frac{0.61\ \lambda}{a} \tag{12-4.22}$$

which shows that the larger the aperture of a telescope (or an antenna) the easier it is to resolve objects that are close together.

ΔΔΔ

Example 12-4.3. Find the field in the Fraunhofer region from a uniformly illuminated slit of dimensions $\delta(y_o)p_{2a}(x_o)$ where $p_{2a}(x_o)$ is a pulse function of height one and width 2a in the X-direction.

Solution. From Eq. (4-12.5) the field is specified by the integral

$$\Phi(P_1) = C \int_{-\infty}^{\infty} e^{-j\omega_y y_o}\, \delta(y_o)dy_o \int_{-\infty}^{\infty} e^{-j\omega_x x_o}\, p_{2a}(x_o)dx_o = C\cdot 2a\, \frac{\sin \omega_x a}{\omega_x a} \tag{12-4.23}$$

The intensity of the field is then

$$|\Phi(P_1)|^2 = C^2(2a)^2\, \frac{\sin^2\omega_x a}{(\omega_x a)^2} \tag{12-4.24}$$

ΔΔΔ

Example 12-4.4. Find the field in the Fraunhofer region due to two pinholes located at x = -a and x = +a, respectively, which are illuminated by a uniform electric field of unit amplitude.

Solution. In this case, Eq. (12-4.5) for Fraunhofer diffraction assumes the form

$$\begin{aligned}\Phi(P_1) &= C \int_{-\infty}^{\infty}\int [\delta(x_o-a) + \delta(x_o+a)]\, \delta(y_o)\, e^{-j\omega_x x_o}\, e^{-j\omega_y y_o}\, dx_o\, dy_o \\ &= C\, [e^{-j\omega_x a} + e^{j\omega_x a}] = 2C \cos \omega_x a\end{aligned} \tag{12-4.25}$$

The zeros of this function occur at those values of $\omega_x a$ for which

$$\omega_x a = (n + \tfrac{1}{2})\, \pi \qquad n = 0,1,2,\ldots$$

From this, we find that

$$x_1 = (n + \tfrac{1}{2})\, \frac{\lambda z_{10}}{2a} \tag{12-4.26}$$

The function $\Phi^2(P_1)$ is shown in Fig. 13-7.1, where this same problem is examined from a different viewpoint.

ΔΔΔ

Example 12-4.5. Find the field in the Fraunhofer region for a uniformly illuminated rectangular aperture with an aperture transmittance $t(x,y) = (1 + m \sin \omega_o x)$.

Solution. The field crossing the surface of the aperture is

$$\Phi(P_o) = (1 + m \sin \omega_o x_o)\, p_{2a}(x_o)\, p_{2b}(y_o) \tag{12-4.27}$$

and the far field is then given by

$$\Phi(P_1) = C \int_{-\infty}^{\infty}\int (1 + m \sin \omega_o x_o)\, p_{2a}(x_o)\, p_{2b}(y_o)\, e^{-j(\omega_x x_o + \omega_y y_o)}\, dx_o\, dy_o$$

$$= C \int_{-a}^{a}\int_{-b}^{b} e^{-j(\omega_x x_o + \omega_y y_o)}\, dx_o\, dy_o + Cm \int_{-a}^{a}\int_{-b}^{b} \frac{e^{+j\omega_o x_o} - e^{-j\omega x_o}}{2j} \cdot e^{-j(\omega_x x_o + \omega_y y_o)}\, dx_o\, dy_o$$

$$= Cab\, \frac{\sin \omega_y b}{\omega_y b} \cdot \left[\frac{\sin \omega_x a}{\omega_x a} + \frac{m}{j}\, \frac{\sin(\omega_o - \omega_x)a}{(\omega_o - \omega_x)a} - \frac{m}{j}\, \frac{\sin(\omega_o + \omega_x)a}{(\omega_o + \omega_x)a}\right] \tag{12-4.28}$$

The intensity of the diffraction pattern $|\Phi(P_1)|^2$ for $\omega_x > 0$ and $\omega_o \gg 4\pi/a$ and $4\pi/b$ is shown graphically in Fig. 12-4.5. The pattern is symmetric with respect to the y_1-$|\Phi(P_1)|^2$ plane.

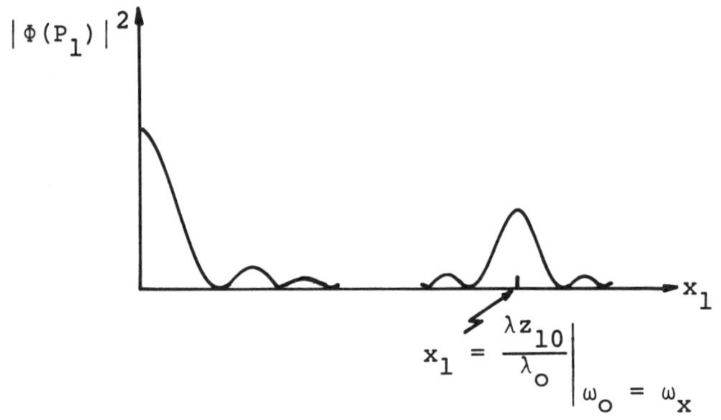

Figure 12-4.5. Diffraction pattern of a modulated rectangular aperture.

ΔΔΔ

Example 12-4.6. Find the Fraunhofer diffraction pattern for an array of N slits which are infinitely narrow in the Y-direction and which have a length 2a in the X-direction, when illuminated uniformly (see Fig. 12-4.6a). This problem is a generalization of Ex. 12-4.3.

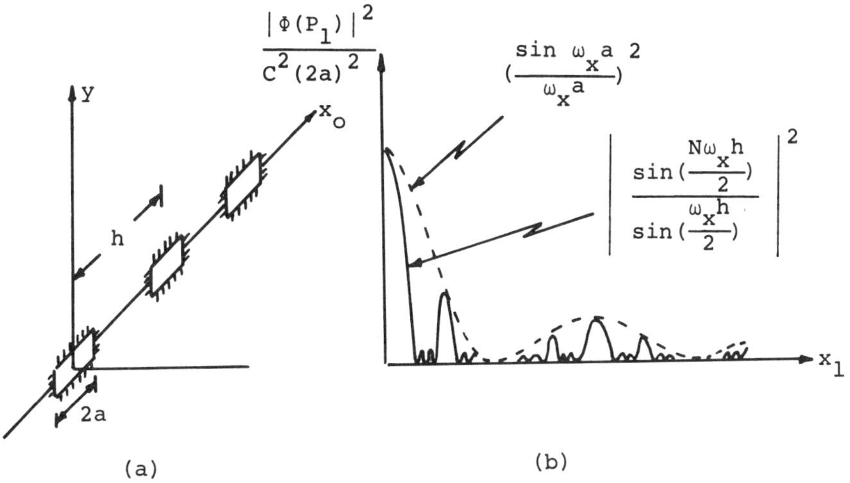

Figure 12-4.6. The cross section of the diffraction pattern due to an array of slits.

Solution. The field intensity across each slit is

$$\Phi(P_o) = [\sum_{n=0}^{N} \int_{-\infty}^{\infty} \delta(x_o - nh)\, p_{2a}(x_o)dx_o]\ \delta(y_o) \tag{12-4.29}$$

and the diffracted field is then given by

$$\Phi(P_1) = C\int_{-\infty}^{\infty}\int [\sum_{n=0}^{N}\int_{-\infty}^{\infty} \delta(nh - x_o)\, p_{2a}(x_o)dx_o]\ \delta(y_o)e^{-j(\omega_x x_o + \omega_y y_o)}\,dx_o\, dy_o$$

The integral may be written

$$\Phi(P_1) = C\sum_{n=0}^{N}\int_{-\infty}^{\infty} [\delta(nh - x_o) * p_{2a}(x_o)]\ e^{-j\omega_x x_o}\, dx_o$$

where * denotes convolution. This becomes

$$\Phi(P_1) = C\sum_{n=0}^{N} (\mathscr{F}[\delta(nh - x_o)])(\mathscr{F}[p_{2a}(x_o)]) = C(\sum_{n=0}^{N} e^{-j\omega_x nh})(2a\,\frac{\sin \omega_x a}{\omega_x a}) \tag{12-4.30}$$

since the Fourier transform of the convolution of two functions is equal to the product of their respective Fourier transforms. The geometric series inside the first parenthesis can readily be added, and the result can be written in the form

$$\Phi(P_1) = C(2a\,\frac{\sin \omega_x a}{\omega_x a})\ \frac{e^{-j\omega_x Nh/2}}{e^{-j\omega_x h/2}}\ \frac{\sin (N\,\frac{\omega_x h}{2})}{\sin \frac{\omega_x h}{2}} \tag{12-4.31}$$

The intensity of the pattern is given by

$$|\Phi(P_1)|^2 = C^2(2a)^2 \left(\frac{\sin \omega_x a}{\omega_x a}\right)^2 \left(\frac{\sin N\omega_x h/2}{\sin \omega_x h/2}\right)^2 \tag{12-4.32}$$

This result is shown in Fig. 12-4.6b.

ΔΔΔ

When a plane wave is incident on a converging or diverging lens, it is transformed into a spherical wave. Since such lenses vary in thickness, the phase of the wave becomes a function of position, with the origin on the optical axis. If the lens does not affect the intensity of the wave, its transmittance function is given by

$$t(x,y) = e^{jk_o\eta_\ell d_o} e^{-j\frac{k}{2f_\ell}(x^2+y^2)} \tag{12-4.33}$$

where η_ℓ is the index of refraction of the lens, d_o is the thickness of the lens at the center, and $\pm f_\ell$ is its focal length, which is positive for a converging lens and negative for a diverging one. The geometry is shown in Fig. 12-4.7. It follows from this figure, using the Pythagorean theorem, that

$$(f_\ell - z)^2 + \rho^2 = f_\ell^2$$

so that approximately

$$z \doteq \frac{\rho^2}{2f_\ell} \tag{12-4.34}$$

where we have neglected the term z^2 as being small in comparison with the term involving z. The total change of the wavefront due to the lens is given by

$$e^{j[k_o\eta_\ell d_o - k\frac{\rho^2}{2f_\ell}]} = e^{jk_o\eta_\ell d_o} e^{-j\frac{k(x^2+y^2)}{2f_\ell}}$$

If, therefore, a lens is located at the $X_oY_o(S_o)$ plane, the field to the right of S_o is equal to

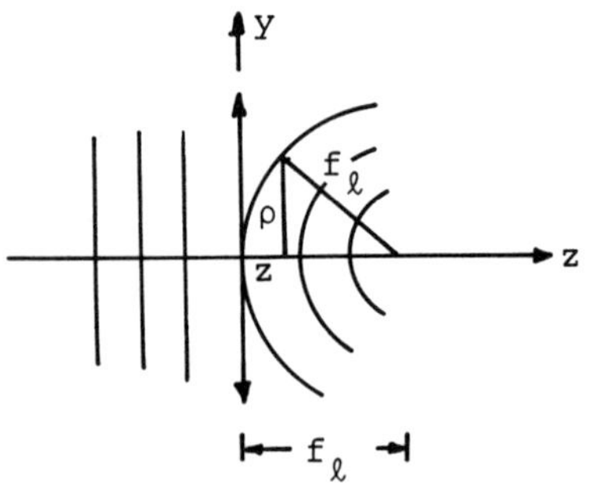

Figure 12-4.7. The refraction properties of a converging lens.

$$\Phi(P_o)e^{jk_o\eta_\ell d_o}\, e^{-j\frac{k}{2f_\ell}(x_o^2+y_o^2)}$$

The corresponding field at a distance z_{10} away is given by

$$\Phi(P_1) = C\int_{-\infty}^{\infty}\int \Phi(P_o)\, e^{-j\frac{k}{2f_\ell}(x_o^2+y_o^2)}\, e^{j\frac{k}{2z_{10}}[(x_o-x_1)^2+(y_o-y_1)^2]}\, dx_o\, dy_o \tag{12-4.35}$$

If we are interested in observing the field at the plane $z_{10} = f_\ell$ (the focal plane), Eq. (12-4.35) becomes

$$\Phi(P_1) = C\int_{-\infty}^{\infty}\int \Phi(P_o)\, e^{-j\frac{k}{f_\ell}(x_1x_o+y_1y_o)}\, dx_o\, dy_o$$

$$= C\int_{-\infty}^{\infty}\int \Phi(P_o)\, e^{-j(\omega_{x\ell}x_o+\omega_{y\ell}y_o)}\, dx_o\, dy_o$$

$$= C\mathscr{F}[\Phi(P_o)] \tag{12-4.36}$$

which shows that the field at the focal plane is the Fourier transform of the field at the input plane multiplied by a constant complex factor.

It can be shown that if the object is at $d_{so} = f_\ell$ (front focal plane), then the field at $z_{10} = f_\ell$ (back focal plane) is the exact Fourier transform of the object field; the complex constant C is not present. This is an important property of lenses that enables us to modify the spatial frequency content of the object at the frequency plane (focal plane) in such a manner that a second lens will permit a reconstruction of the object. This is a very important consideration because it provides the motivation in *spatial filtering* to enhance the signal from the noise in an optical process. This is the same objective as that in other signal filtering processes.

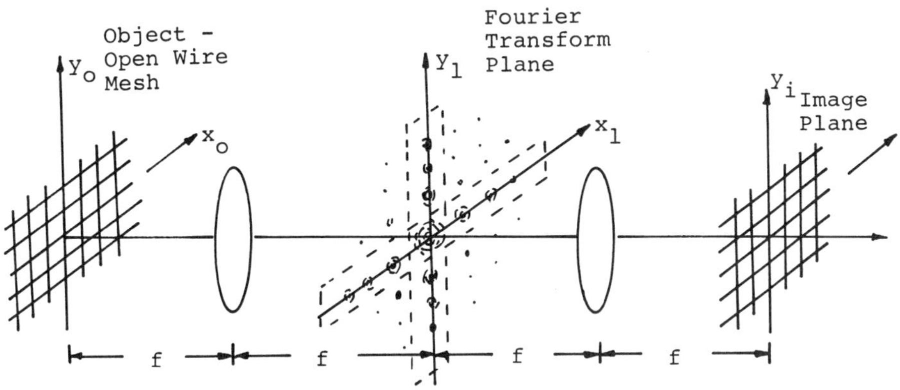

Figure 12-4.8. Optical filtering.

A simple optical filtering process is shown schematically in Fig. 12-4.8. The object is an open-wire mesh. If a slit is placed along the Y_1 axis thereby leaving unobstructed only the light shown by the broken lines, then the image will include only the horizontal lines of the mesh. If the slit is turned through 90 deg along the X_1 axis, then only the vertical lines appear in the image plane. Figure 12-4.9 shows an actual picture of the filtering process. The zero frequency term of the Fourier transform plane is the point (0,0) of the X_1Y_1 plane. The higher frequencies are located around and away from the optical axis, and their values increase with distance from the optical axis.

The light distribution over the Fourier plane as seen on a film is not the amplitude distribution of the optical field, but is its intensity distribution. We have been considering *intensity filters* since they do not affect the phase of the field distribution. A type of filter which does affect the phase as well as the light intensity has been constructed and uses holographic techniques, which will be discussed in Sec. 12-6. These are called *Van der Lugt filters*.

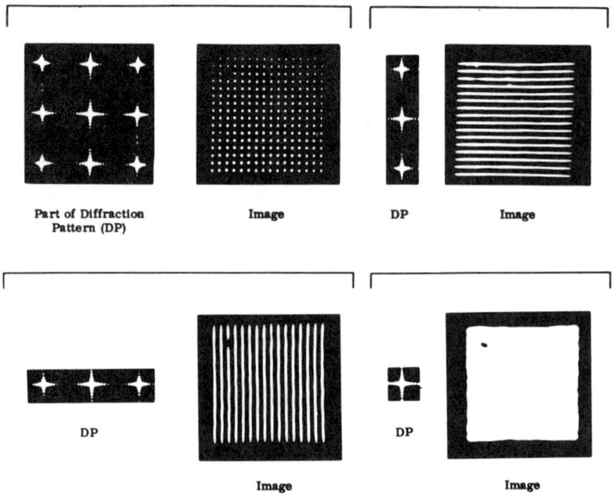

Figure 12-4.9. Intensity filtering process. [Reprinted by permission from Physical Optics Notebook, by George B. Parrent, Jr. and Brian J. Thompson. Society of Photo-optical Instrumentation Engineers, 1969.]

Example 12-4.7. A uniform plane wave is incident on a straight edge. Find the diffracted field in the Fresnel region.

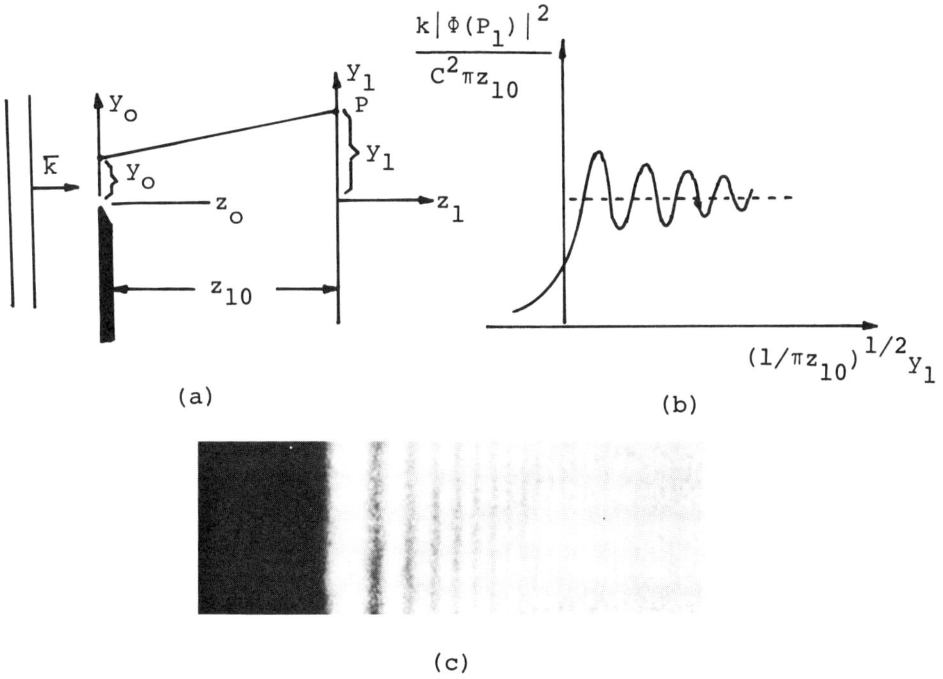

Figure 12-4.10. Diffraction of plane wave by a straight edge. (a) Experimental set up (b) Intensity distribution (c) Experimental results. [Reprinted with permission from Physical Optics Notebook, George B. Parrent, Jr. and Brian Thomson. Socieity of Photo-optical Instrumentation Engineers, 1969.]

Solution. Since the problem is one dimensional, the integration along x_o will give a constant which can be lumped together with the coefficient of the diffraction integral, Eq. (12-4.3), to yield the form

$$\Phi(P_1) = C \int_0^{\infty} e^{j \frac{k}{2z_{10}} (y_o - y_1)^2} dy_o \qquad (12\text{-}4.37)$$

Consider a new variable

$$\frac{k}{2z_{10}} (y_o - y_1)^2 = \frac{\pi}{2} u_1^2 \qquad (12\text{-}4.38)$$

From this

$$y_o - y_1 = \sqrt{\frac{\pi z_{10}}{k}} u_1 \qquad (12\text{-}4.39)$$

and

$$dy_o = \sqrt{\frac{\pi z_{10}}{k}} du_1 \qquad (12\text{-}4.40)$$

u_1 has the values

$$u_1 = -\sqrt{\frac{k}{\pi z_{10}}}\, y_1 \qquad \text{for } y_0 = 0 \qquad \text{a)}$$

and (12-4.41)

$$u_1 = \infty \qquad \text{for } y_0 = \infty \qquad \text{b)}$$

Introducing the new variable into Eq. (12-4.37), the diffraction integral takes the form

$$\Phi(P_1) = C\sqrt{\frac{\pi z_{10}}{k}} \int_{-\sqrt{\frac{k}{\pi z_{10}}}\, y_1}^{\infty} e^{j\frac{\pi}{2}u_1^2}\, du_1$$

Making one more transformation by setting $u_1 = -u$, this integral takes the form

$$\Phi(P_1) = C\sqrt{\frac{\pi z_{10}}{k}} \int_{-\infty}^{\sqrt{\frac{k}{\pi z_{10}}}\, y_1} e^{j\frac{\pi}{2}u^2}\, du \qquad (12\text{-}4.42)$$

The observable quantity is the intensity, which is given by

$$|\Phi(P_1)|^2 = C^2 \frac{\pi z_{10}}{k} \left| \int_{-\infty}^{\sqrt{\frac{k}{\pi z_{10}}}\, y_1} e^{j\frac{\pi}{2}u^2}\, du \right|^2 \qquad (12\text{-}4.43)$$

Equations (12-4.43) is easily solved with the help of the *Fresnel integrals*

$$C(u) = \int_0^u \cos\frac{\pi}{2}u'^2\, du' \qquad \text{a)}$$

(12-4.44)

$$S(u) = \int_0^u \sin\frac{\pi}{2}u'^2\, du' \qquad \text{b)}$$

From integral tables and the definition of integrals, we obtain the following values

$$C(0) = 0 \qquad S(0) = 0 \qquad \text{a)}$$

(12-4.45)

$$C(-u) = -C(u) \qquad S(-u) = -S(u) \qquad \text{b)}$$

Also

$$\int_{-\infty}^{\infty} e^{j\frac{\pi}{2}u'^2}\, du' = 1 + j$$

which is

$$\int_0^{\infty} e^{j\frac{\pi}{2}u'^2}\, du' = \int_0^{\infty} \cos\frac{\pi}{2}u'^2 du' + j\int_0^{\infty} \sin\frac{\pi}{2}u'^2\, du' = \frac{1}{2} + j\,\frac{1}{2} \qquad \text{c)}$$

Equation (12-4.45c) indicates that

$$C(\infty) = \frac{1}{2} \quad \text{and} \quad S(\infty) = \frac{1}{2} \qquad \text{a)}$$

and so (12-4.46)

$$C(-\infty) = -\frac{1}{2} \quad \text{and} \quad S(-\infty) = -\frac{1}{2} \qquad \text{b)}$$

With these results the intensity of the field given in Eq. (12-4.43) can now be written

$$|\Phi(P_1)|^2 = C^2 \frac{\pi z_{10}}{k} \left(\int_{-\infty}^{\sqrt{\frac{k}{\pi z_{10}}} y_1} \cos \frac{\pi}{2} u^2 du + j\int_{-\infty}^{\sqrt{\frac{k}{\pi z_{10}}} y_1} \sin \frac{\pi}{2} u^2 du\right)$$

$$\cdot \left(\int_{-\infty}^{\sqrt{\frac{k}{\pi z_{10}}} y_1} \cos \frac{\pi}{2} u^2 du - j\int_{-\infty}^{\sqrt{\frac{k}{\pi z_{10}}} y_1} \sin \frac{\pi}{2} u^2 du\right)$$

$$= \frac{C^2 \pi z_{10}}{k} \left[\left(\int_0^{\sqrt{\frac{k}{\pi z_{10}}} y_1} \cos \frac{\pi}{2} u^2 du - \int_0^{-\infty} \cos \frac{\pi}{2} u^2 du\right)^2\right.$$

$$\left. + \left(\int_0^{\sqrt{\frac{k}{\pi z_{10}}} y_1} \sin \frac{\pi}{2} u^2 du - \int_0^{-\infty} \sin \frac{\pi}{2} u^2 du\right)^2\right] =$$

$$= \frac{C^2 \pi z_{10}}{k} \left[\left[C\left(\sqrt{\frac{k}{\pi z_{10}}} y_1\right) - C(-\infty)\right]^2 + \left[S\left(\sqrt{\frac{k}{\pi z_{10}}} y_1\right) - S(-\infty)\right]^2\right] \qquad (12\text{-}4.47)$$

The intensity of the field is easily found graphically using the Cornu spiral shown in Fig. 12-4.11. However, tables are also available. The distance between two points on the spiral, u_1 and u_2, is given by

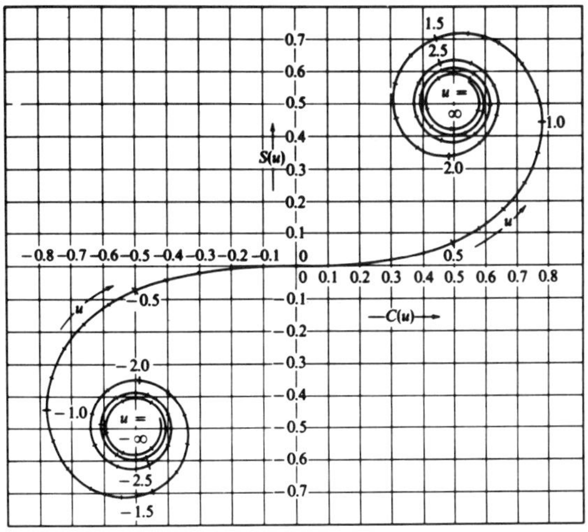

Figure 12-4.11. The Cornu spiral. [Reprinted with permission from Classical Electromagnetic Radiation, by Jerry B. Marion. Academic Press, 1974.]

$$d^2 = [C(u_2) - C(u_1)]^2 + [S(u_2) - S(u_1)]^2 \tag{12-4.48}$$

which is identical with Eq. (12-4.47). The results of Eq. (12-4.47) are shown in Fig. 12-4.10b and the experimental observation in Fig. 12-4.10c.

ΔΔΔ

12-5. Optical Linear Systems

I. Imaging with Optical Systems. The formation of optical images can easily be interpreted if we borrow concepts from circuit and signal theory. As in many electronic systems, optical systems also possess *linearity*, *invariance*, *causality*, and *stability*. The causality condition can, in general, be relaxed in optics since the light distribution exists on both sides of the coordinate axis. The invariance property does not strictly apply in optics unless additional assumptions are made. However, if we consider the working area very close to the optical axis of the system, we can freely invoke the principle of invariance. Since we shall study linear systems we shall accept the linearity principle as being valid here. As far as stability is concerned, optical systems possess this property to a high degree and no further assumptions are needed. For simplicity and without loss of generality, we shall examine the one-dimensional case.

If we symbolically represent the operation of a linear optical system by L{ } then in one dimension the image (output) is related to the object (input) by

$$\phi_i(x_1) = L\{\phi_o(x_o)\} \tag{12-5.1}$$

Note specifically that the operator L operates on the coordinate x_o. Since we can represent any function with the help of the Dirac delta function, Eq. (12-5.1) takes the form

$$\phi_i(x_1) = L\left\{\int_{-\infty}^{\infty} \phi_o(x_o')\delta(x_o'-x_o)dx_o'\right\} = \int_{-\infty}^{\infty} \phi_o(x_o')\ L\ \{\delta(x_o'-x_o)\}\ dx_o' \tag{12-5.2}$$

The quantity

$$L\ \{\delta(x_o'-x_o)\} = h(x_o,x_1) \tag{12-5.3}$$

is the response of the optical system to a point source located at x_o, as shown in Fig. 12-5.1. By the principle of invariance, the impulse response of the optical system, known as the *spread function*, is written in the form $h(x_1-x_o)$ which describes the light distribution at x_1 due to a point source at x_o. Introducing the invariant form of the spread function in Eq. (12-5.2) we obtain

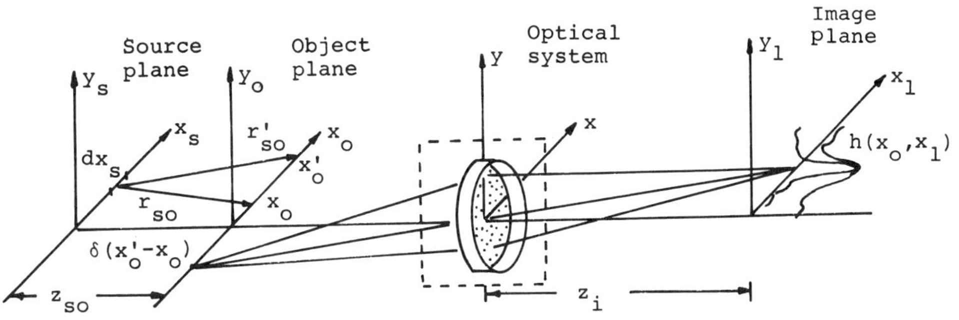

Figure 12-5.1. The impulse response of an optical system.

$$\phi_i(x_1) = \int_{-\infty}^{\infty} \phi_o(x_o)\, h(x_1 - x_o)\, dx_o = \phi_o(x_o) * h(x_o) \tag{12-5.4}$$

where the dummy variable x'_o was changed to x_o and the symbol * indicates convolution. Equation (12-5.4) is important because it relates the output of a system (image) through a convolution integral of its input (object) and its spread function.

If the object has a complex transmittance of the form $\phi_o(x_o)$, then the light distribution just behind the object is $s(x_s)\phi_o(x_o)$ where $s(x_s)$ is the complex amplitude distribution on the object plane due to the incremental light source dx_s. Therefore, the amplitude distribution at the image plane is given by

$$\phi_i(x_1) = [s(x_s)\phi_o(x_o)] * h(x_o) \tag{12-5.5}$$

and the intensity at the same plane due to the total light source is

$$I(x_1) = \int_{\text{source}} \phi_i(x_1)\phi_i^*(x_1)\, dx_s \tag{12-5.6}$$

This can be written explicitly as

$$I(x_1) = \iint_{-\infty}^{\infty} S(x_o, x'_o)\, h(x_1 - x_o)\, h^*(x_1 - x'_o)\, \phi_o(x_o)\, \phi_o^*(x'_o)\, dx_o\, dx'_o \tag{12-5.7}$$

where

$$S(x_o, x'_o) = \int_{\text{source}} s(x_s, x_o)\, s^*(x_s, x'_o)\, dx_s \tag{12-5.8}$$

The amplitude of the field from the source point x_s to a point x_o on the x_o axis is given by

$$s(x_o) = \frac{S^{1/2}(x_s)}{r_{so}}\, e^{jkr_{so}}$$

where $S^{1/2}(x_s)$ is the intensity of the source at x_s. Therefore the intensity at x_o becomes

$$S(x_o) = \int \frac{S(x_s)}{r_{so}r'_{so}} e^{jk(r_{so}-r'_{so})} dx_s \doteq \frac{1}{z_{so}^2} \int S(x_s)\, e^{j\frac{k}{z_{so}} x_s x_o} dx_s$$
$$= C \int S(x_s)\, e^{j\frac{k}{z_{so}} x_s x_o} dx_s \qquad (12\text{-}5.9)$$

since $r_{so} - r'_{so} \doteq 2x_s x_o/(r_{so}+r'_{so}) \doteq x_s x_o/z_{so}$ using the paraxial approximation. If $S(x_s) = C_1$ constant then $S(x_o) = C\,\delta(x_o)$ and the object radiates completely *incoherently*. If $S(x_s) = \delta(x_s)$, then $S(x_o) = C$ and the object radiates *coherently*.

Consider the incoherent case; Eq. (12-5.7) becomes

$$I(x_1) = \int_{-\infty}^{\infty} \int \delta(x'_o - x_o)\, h(x_1 - x_o)\, h^*(x_1 - x'_o)\, \phi_o(x_o)\, \phi_o^*(x'_o)\, dx_o\, dx'_o$$
$$= \int_{-\infty}^{\infty} |h(x_1 - x_o)|^2\, |\phi_o(x_o)|^2 dx_o = |h(x_o)|^2 * |\phi_o(x_o)|^2 \qquad (12\text{-}5.10)$$

where we have set all constants equal to unity, thus avoiding normalization procedures. Equation (12-5.10) indicates that for the incoherent case the optical system is linear in irradiance.

Using the Fourier transform properties (see Appendix IV), Eq. (12-5.10) becomes

$$I(\omega_x) = H_i(\omega_x)\, \Phi_{oi}(\omega_x) \qquad \text{a)}$$

where

$$I(\omega_x) = \int_{-\infty}^{\infty} I(x_1)\, e^{-j\omega_x x_1}\, dx_1 \qquad \text{b)}$$

$$H_i(\omega_x) = \int_{-\infty}^{\infty} h(x_1)\, h^*(x_1)\, e^{-j\omega_x x_1}\, dx_1 \qquad \text{c)} \qquad (12\text{-}5.11)$$

$$\Phi_{oi}(\omega_x) = \int_{-\infty}^{\infty} \phi_o(x_o)\, \phi_o^*(x_o)\, e^{-j\omega_x x_o}\, dx_o \qquad \text{d)}$$

where $\omega_x = 2\pi x/\lambda f_\ell$ and f_ℓ is the focal length of a converging lens.

The function $H_i(\omega_x)$ is known as the *optical transfer function* (OTF) and its modulus $|H_i(\omega_x)|$ is known as the *modulation transfer function* (MTF). Using the properties of the autocorrelation theorem (see Appendix IV), the OTF is written in the form

$$H_i(\omega_x) = \int_{-\infty}^{\infty} H(\omega'_x)\, H^*(\omega'_x + \omega_x)\, d\omega'_x = H(\omega'_x) \otimes H^*(\omega'_x) \qquad (12\text{-}5.12)$$

where $H(\omega_x) = \mathscr{F}\{h(x)\}$ and the symbol $\otimes$ indicates autocorrelation. The reader will notice that we have not developed the spread function explicitly. To do this would take us too far from our intention here to present only basic principles.

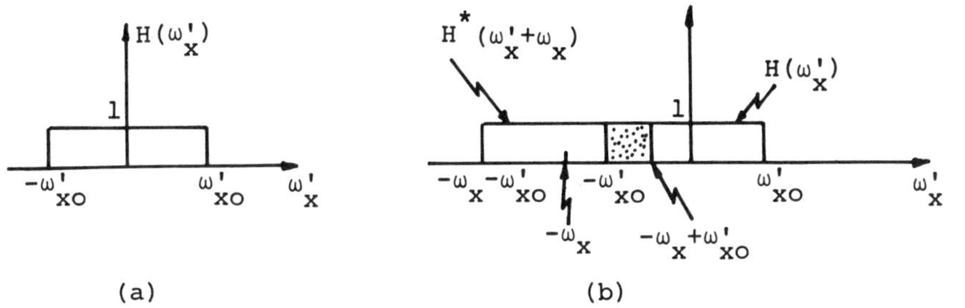

Figure 12-5.2. Frequency response of the spread function.

Example 12-5.1. Find the OTF of an optical system if its $H(\omega'_x)$ is a square pulse as shown in Fig. 12-5.2a.

Solution. Introduce the function which is shown in Fig. 12-5.2a into Eq. (12-5.12). We obtain

$$\frac{H_i(\omega_x)}{2\omega'_{xo}} = \left(1 - \frac{\omega_x}{2\omega'_{xo}}\right) \qquad |\omega_x| \leq 2\omega'_{xo} \qquad \text{a)}$$

$$= 0 \qquad |\omega_x| > 2\omega'_{xo} \qquad \text{b)} \qquad (12\text{-}5.13)$$

The inverse Fourier transform of (12-5.13) normalized is equal to $(\sin \omega_{xo}x_1/\omega_{xo}x_1)^2$ which implies that

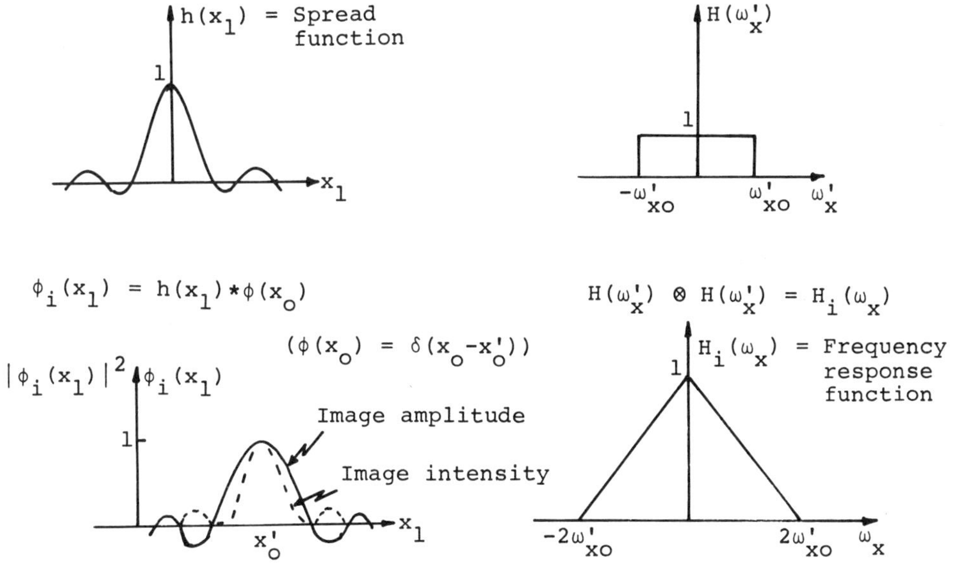

Figure 12-5.3. Optical functions and their relationship.

$$h(x_1) = \frac{\sin \omega_{xo} x_1}{\omega_{xo} x_1} \tag{12-5.14}$$

Figure 12-5.3 presents the different optical functions which are associated with the optical system discussed in the example. Since we integrate over the aperture of diameter a of the system we can assume that the maximum value of $x_1 = a$, or equivalently that the maximum spatial frequency of the system is

$$f'_x = \frac{\omega'_{ox}}{2\pi} = \frac{a}{\lambda z_i} = \frac{2}{\lambda \frac{z_i}{2a}} = \frac{2}{\lambda F^{\#}}, \quad \text{where } F^{\#} \text{ is known}$$

is the "f"-number and z_i is equal to the focal length of the lens. A camera having $F^{\#} = 2.8$ at $\lambda = 0.5$ μm can resolve up to 1428 lines/mm.

ΔΔΔ

When the object radiates coherently, this requires that $S(x_o) = C =$ constant. The intensity integral, Eq. (12-5.7), becomes

$$I(x_1) = \int_{-\infty}^{\infty} h(x_1 - x_o)\, \phi_o(x_o)\, dx_o \int_{-\infty}^{\infty} h^*(x_1 - x'_o)\, \phi^*(x'_o)\, dx'_o \tag{12-5.15}$$

where the constant has been chosen to be unity, for convenience. This equation indicates that the system is linear in the complex field amplitude. In mathematical terms this statement is equivalent to writing

$$\phi_i(x_1) = \int_{-\infty}^{\infty} h(x_1 - x_o)\, \phi_o(x_o)\, dx_o \tag{12-5.16}$$

The Fourier transform of this expression becomes, recalling the convolution property,

$$\Phi_i(\omega_x) = H(\omega_x)\, \Phi_o(\omega_x) \tag{12-5.17}$$

where

$$\Phi_i(\omega_x) = \int_{-\infty}^{\infty} \phi_i(x_1)\, e^{-j\omega_x x_1}\, dx_1 \qquad \text{a)}$$

$$H(\omega_x) = \int_{-\infty}^{\infty} h(x_1)\, e^{-j\omega_x x_1}\, dx_1 \qquad \text{b)} \tag{12-5.18}$$

$$\Phi_o(\omega_x) = \int_{-\infty}^{\infty} \phi_o(x_o)\, e^{-j\omega_x x_o}\, dx_o \qquad \text{c)}$$

$H(\omega_x)$ is known as the *coherent transfer function* (CTF).

Observe that no explicit formula has been given for the impulse function h. As already noted, its development is somewhat involved, but we do note that its form can be established experimentally in a setup as shown in Fig. 12-5.4. The result for a positive lens system as illustrated is found to be given by

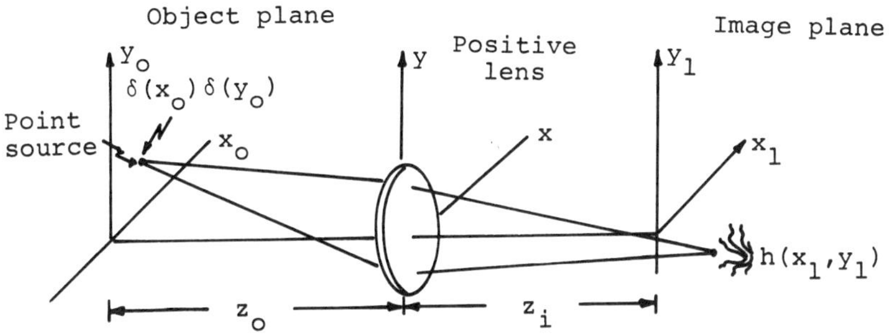

Figure 12-5.4. An imaging system for studying its impulse response.

$$h_M(x_1) = \frac{h(x_1)}{M} = \int_{-\infty}^{\infty} P(\frac{z_i}{k}\omega_x)e^{-j\omega_x x_1}\, d\omega_x \qquad \text{a)}$$

For the two-dimensional case, this expression extends to (12-5.19)

$$h_M(x_1,y_1) = \frac{h(x_1,y_1)}{M} = \iint_{-\infty}^{\infty} P(\frac{z_i}{k}\omega_x, \frac{z_i}{k}\omega_y)e^{-j\omega_x x_1}e^{-j\omega_y y_1}\, d\omega_x\, d\omega_y \qquad \text{b)}$$

where $\omega_x = 2\pi x/\lambda z_i$, $\omega_y = 2\pi y/\lambda z_i$, M = magnification factor = z_i/z_o, and P(x,y) is the *pupil* function, sometimes also called the *window* function. On the assumption that we know the impulse function from Eq. (12-5.19), two interesting cases can be studied.

A. Frequency Response of a Coherent Imaging System

For a positive lens, Eq. (12-5.18b) gives the CTF as the Fourier transform of the space invariant impulse function. But Eq. (12-5.19) indicates that the impulse function is the Fourier transform of the pupil function. Then we can write

$$H(\omega_x) = \mathcal{F}^{-1}\{h_M(x_1)\} = \mathcal{F}^{-1}\{\mathcal{F}\{P(\frac{z_i}{k}\omega_x)\}\} = P(-\frac{z_i}{k}\omega_x) \qquad (12\text{-}5.20)$$

The optical system whose pupil function is zero or one and which creates a converging spherical wave at its exit pupil when a diverging spherical wave is impinging on its entrance pupil, is known as the *diffraction limited system.* When the same system operates under coherent conditions, the CTF, $H(\omega_x)$, of the system is also zero or one. This is equivalent to saying that the system will pass a finite band of spatial frequencies without amplitude or phase distortion. The minus sign that appears in the pupil function arises from the repetition of the Fourier transform rather than using its inverse. That is, in optics, positive lenses take the Fourier transforms only of the objects, and this results in imaging inversion. The minus sign can be ignored by defining the pupil function P to be in a reflected coordinate system, and this we shall do in our subsequent analysis.

B. Frequency Response of an Incoherent Imaging System

Upon substituting $H(\omega_x)$ from Eq. (12-5.20) into Eq. (12-5.12), and ignoring the minus sign, we obtain the OTF in the form

$$H_i(\omega_x) = \int_{-\infty}^{\infty} P(\frac{z_i}{k}\omega_x')\, P^*(\frac{z_i}{k}\omega_x' + \frac{z_i}{k}\omega_x)\, d(\frac{z_i}{k}\omega_x')$$

$$= \int_{-\infty}^{\infty} P(x')\, P^*(x' + \frac{z_i}{k}\omega_x)dx' \qquad (12\text{-}5.21)$$

We note than an extension of Eq. (12-5.12) to a two-dimensional case would be of the form

$$H_i(\omega_x,\omega_y) = \iint_{-\infty}^{\infty} H(\omega_x',\omega_y')\, H^*(\omega_x'+\omega_x,\omega_y'+\omega_y)\, d\omega_x'\, d\omega_y' \qquad (12\text{-}5.22)$$

Thus by considering Eq. (12-5.21) we can write it in the extended form

$$H_i(\omega_x,\omega_y) = \iint_{-\infty}^{\infty} P(x',y')\, P^*(x' + \frac{z_i}{k}\omega_x,\ y' + \frac{z_i}{k}\omega_y)\, dx'\, dy' \qquad (12\text{-}5.23)$$

We can symmetrize these equations by introducing a change of variables,

$$\xi = x' + \frac{z_i}{2k}\omega_x, \qquad \eta = y' + \frac{z_i}{k}\omega_y$$

These, when included in Eq. (12-5.21) and (12-5.23), give

$$H_i(\omega_x) = \int_{-\infty}^{\infty} P(\xi - \frac{z_i\omega_x}{2k})\, P^*(\xi + \frac{z_i\omega_x}{2k})d\xi \qquad \text{a)}$$

$$H_i(\omega_x,\omega_y) = \iint_{-\infty}^{\infty} P(\xi - \frac{z_i\omega_x}{2k},\ \eta - \frac{z_i\omega_y}{2k})\, P^*(\xi + \frac{z_i\omega_x}{2k},\ \eta + \frac{z_i\omega_y}{2k})d\xi d\eta \qquad \text{b)} \qquad (12\text{-}5.24)$$

Eq. (12-5.24b) has an interesting geometrical interpretation. For aberration-free

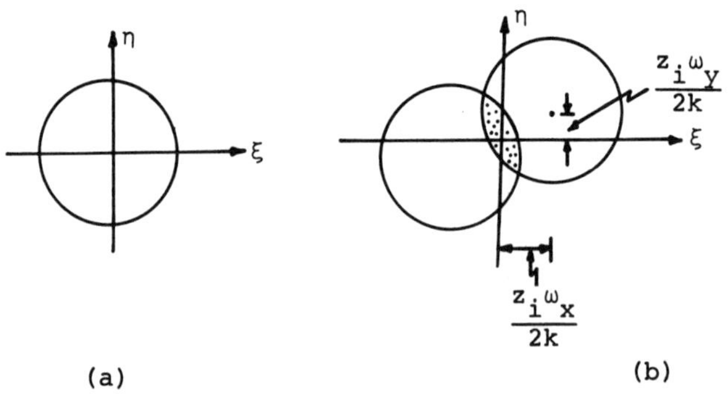

Figure 12-5.5. Geometrical interpretation of the optical transfer function. (a) Exit pupil. (b) Two displaced pupils. The shaded area is equal to Eq. (12-5.24b).

systems of a diffraction-limited incoherent system, it represents the area of overlap of two displaced pupil functions which are centered at $(z_i\omega_x/2k,\ z_i\omega_y/2k)$ and at $(-\ z_i\omega_x/2k,\ -\ z_i\omega_y/2k)$ as shown in Fig. 12-5.5. To consider the normalized OTF, we would divide Eqs. (12-5.24a) and (12-5.24b) by

$$\int_{-\infty}^{\infty} P(\xi)P^*(\xi)d\xi \qquad \text{a)}$$

$$\iint_{-\infty}^{\infty} P(\xi,\eta)P^*(\xi,\eta)d\xi\, d\eta \qquad \text{b)} \qquad (12\text{-}5.25)$$

respectively. Note that Eq. (12-5.25b) represents the total area of the pupil. The reader should remember that for a diffraction-limited and abberation-free system, $P(\xi,\eta) = 1$ at any point (ξ,η) within the perimeter of the pupil.

Example 12-5.2. Find the OTF of an optical system whose pupil function is that shown in Fig. 12-5.6a and which is diffraction limited, abberation-free and has no attenuation.

Solution. Using Eq. (12-5.21) and Fig. 12-5.6b, we easily find that

$$H_i(\omega_x) = \int_{-\infty}^{\infty} P(x')\ P^*(x' + \frac{z_i\omega_x}{k})dx' = \int_{-a}^{a-\frac{z_i\omega_x}{k}} dx' = 2a - \frac{z_i\omega_x}{k}$$

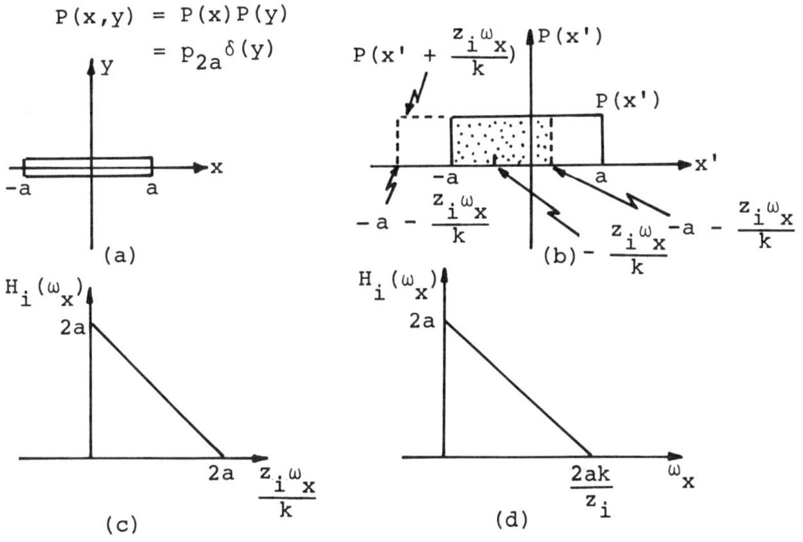

Figure 12-5.6. OTF of a diffraction-limited system with slit-type pupil (a) Geometry of pupil; (b) Two pupil function, one unshifted; (c) OTF versus $z_i\omega_x/k$; (d) OTF versus ω_x. ΔΔΔ

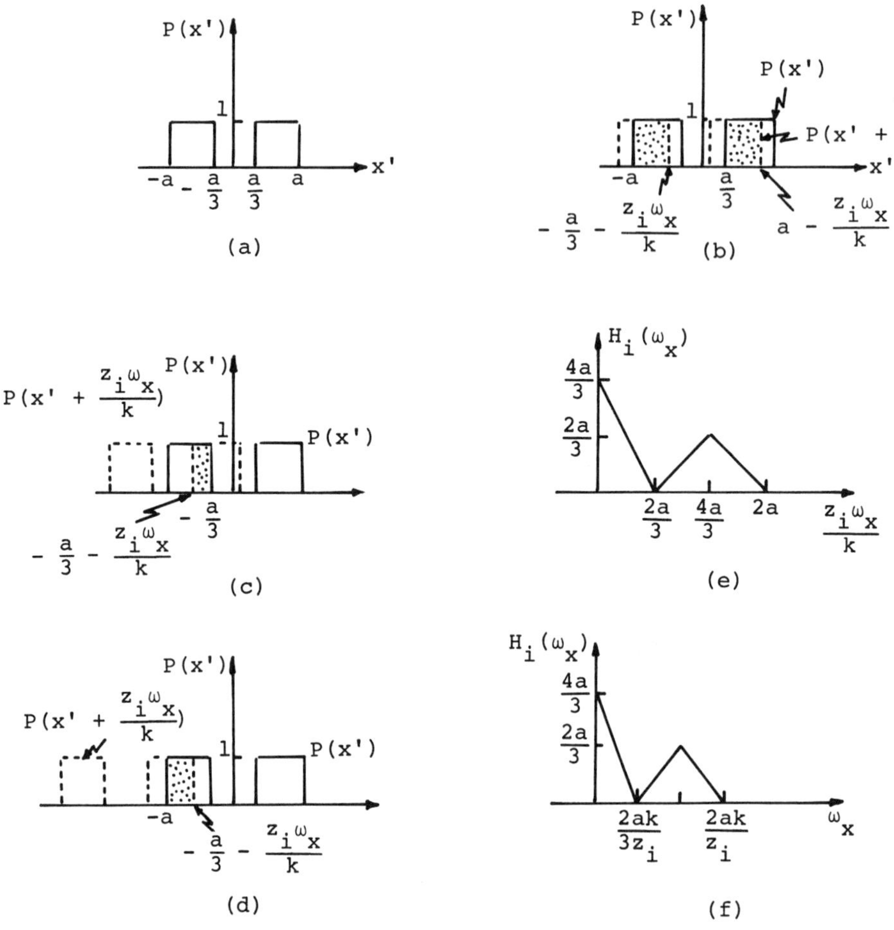

Figure 12-5.7. OTF of a diffraction-limited system with slit-type pupil and attenuation present. (a) Pupil function where blocking of light at the center is present; (b), (c), (d) The process in deriving the OTF; (e) OTF versus $z_i\omega_x/k$; (f) OTF versus ω_x.

Example 12-5.3. Repeat Ex. 12-5.2 but now for the pupil function, which has an absorption band, as shown in Fig. 12-5.7a.

Solution. We follow the well known procedure of finding the correlation of two functions. This involves the steps:

a. For $0 < z_i\omega_x/k < 2a/3$ (see Fig. 12-5.7b)

$$H_i(\omega_x) = \int_{-a}^{a/3 - \frac{z_i\omega_x}{k}} dx' + \int_{a/3}^{a - \frac{z_i\omega_x}{k}} dx' = \frac{4a}{3} - \frac{2z_i\omega_x}{k}$$

b. For $2a/3 < z_i\omega/k < 4a/3$ (see Fig. 12-5.7c)

$$H_i(\omega_x) = \int_{-a/3 - \frac{\omega_x z_i}{k}}^{-a/3} dx' = \frac{z_i\omega_x}{k}$$

and thus

$$H_i(\omega_x) = \frac{z_i\omega_x}{k} - \frac{2}{3}a$$

c. For $4a/3 < z_i\omega_x/k < 2a$ (see Fig. 12-5.7d)

$$H_i(\omega_x) = \int_{-a}^{-\frac{a}{3} - \frac{z_i\omega_x}{k}} dx' = \frac{2a}{3} - \frac{z_i\omega_x}{k}$$

The result is

$$H_i(\omega_x) = \frac{2a}{3} - \left(\frac{\omega_x z_i}{k} - \frac{4a}{3}\right)$$

The OTF of Figs. 12-5.7e and 12-5.7f were constructed from the above steps. Fig. 12-5.7f vividly shows the effect of pupil function on the frequency response of the optical system. ΔΔΔ

Example 12-5.4. Find the OTF of a diffraction limited optical system when its pupil function is a circle, as shown in Fig. 12-5.8a.

Solution. The OTF of a circular pupil is important because of the widespread use of circular lenses. The area of overlap is 4 (Area ABD - area ABO). But we can write

$$\text{area ABD} = \frac{1}{2} R^2\theta = \frac{1}{2} R^2 \cos^{-1}\left(\frac{z_i\omega_x}{2kR}\right)$$

$$\text{area ABO} = \frac{1}{2}\frac{z_i\omega_x}{2k}\left[R^2 - \left(\frac{z_i\omega_x}{2k}\right)^2\right]^{1/2}$$

It then follows that

$$H_i(\omega_x) = 2R^2\left[\cos^{-1}\left(\frac{z_i\omega_x}{2kR}\right) - \frac{z_i\omega_x}{2kR}\left[1 - \left(\frac{z_i\omega_x}{2kR}\right)^2\right]^{1/2}\right] \qquad (12\text{-}5.26)$$

This has been plotted in Fig. 12-5.8c. Because of symmetry considerations, the three dimensional OTF is easily obtained by rotating the curve given in Fig. 12-5.8c, and this is shown in Fig. 12-5.8d.

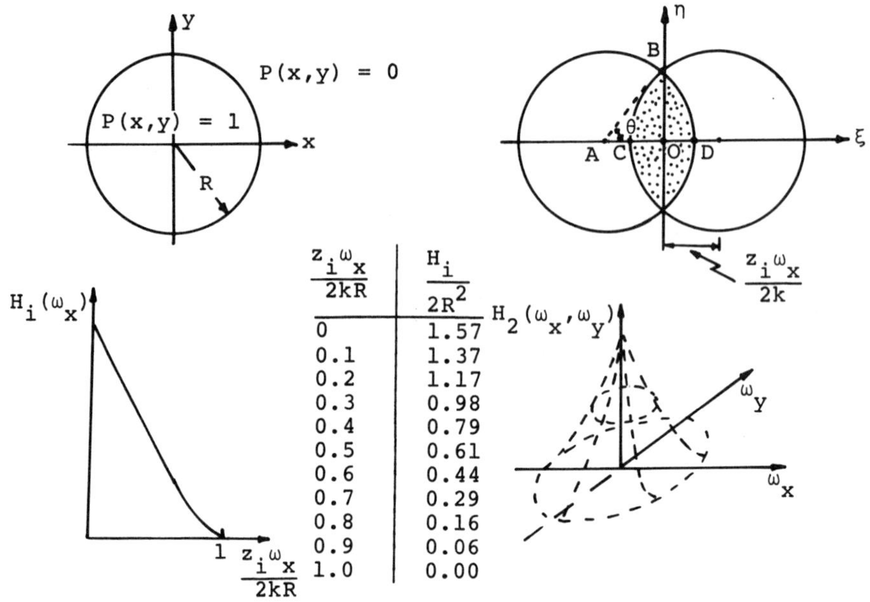

$\frac{z_i\omega_x}{2kR}$	$\frac{H_i}{2R^2}$
0	1.57
0.1	1.37
0.2	1.17
0.3	0.98
0.4	0.79
0.5	0.61
0.6	0.44
0.7	0.29
0.8	0.16
0.9	0.06
1.0	0.00

Figure 12-5.8. OTF of an optical system with circular pupil. (a) Optical function; (b) Area of overlap; (c) OTF; (d) Three dimensional OTF. ΔΔΔ

For those cases when the phase effects are to be included in the optical system, generalized pupil functions can be defined, and these will be of the form

$$P = P(x)\, e^{jkW(x)} \qquad \text{a)}$$

$$P = P(x,y)\, e^{jkW(x,y)} \qquad \text{b)} \qquad (12\text{-}5.27)$$

for the one and two-dimensional systems, respectively. Also, Eqs. (12-5.20) when appropriately modified, become

$$H(\omega_x) = P\left(-\frac{z_i\omega_x}{k}\right) e^{jkW\left(-\frac{z_i\omega_x}{k}\right)} \qquad \text{a)}$$

$$H(\omega_x,\omega_y) = P\left(-\frac{z_i\omega_x}{k}, -\frac{z_i\omega_y}{k}\right) e^{jkW\left(-\frac{z_i\omega_x}{k}, -\frac{z_i\omega_y}{k}\right)} \qquad \text{b)} \qquad (12\text{-}5.28)$$

$W(x,y)$ is an effective path-length error, and $kW(x,y)$ is the phase error. The phase error function $kW(x,y)$ makes it possible to study the different abberations that can be of importance, such as: focusing errors, spherical abberation, coma, etc.

Let us examine specifically the one-dimensional incoherent case. We introduce Eq. (12-5.27a) into Eq. (12-5.21). This leads to

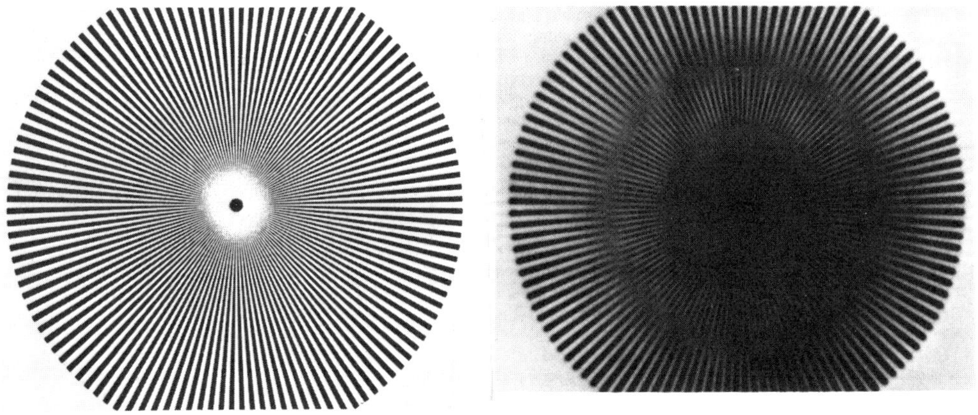

Figure 12-5.9. The effect of OTF on the image with negative spatial frequencies. [Reprinted with permission from Introduction to Fourier Optics, by Joseph W. Goodman, McGraw-Hill, 1968.]

$$\begin{aligned} H_i(\omega) &= \int_{-\infty}^{\infty} P(x')P^*(x' + \frac{z_i\omega_x}{k})dx' = \\ &= \int_{\infty}^{\infty} P(x')e^{jkW(x')}P^*(x' + \frac{z_i\omega_x}{k})e^{-jkW(x' + \frac{z_i\omega}{k})}dx' \end{aligned} \tag{12-5.29}$$

This expression shows that the phase errors introduce further deterioration of the MTF, and it is possible that these errors might even cause the OTF to acquire negative values. Image components having spatial frequencies that correspond to the negative frequencies of the OTF function undergo a contrast reversal, that is, the dark peaks become light, and vice versa. This phenomenon is shown in Fig. 12-5.9.

ΔΔΔ

Example 12-5.5. Find the OTF for a one-dimensional incoherent system when the pupil function is of the form

$$P = 1\cdot e^{jkbx^2} \qquad -a \leq x \leq a$$

where b is a constant. This type of abberation is known as focusing error.

Solution. We obtain, using Eq. (12-5.29),

$$\begin{aligned} H_i(\omega_x) &= \int_{-a}^{a-\frac{z_i\omega}{k}} e^{jbkx'^2} e^{-jkb(x'+\frac{z_i\omega_x}{k})^2} dx' \\ &= e^{-jbk(\frac{z_i\omega}{k})^2} \int_{-a}^{a-\frac{z_i\omega_x}{k}} e^{-j2bz_i\omega_x x'} dx' \end{aligned}$$

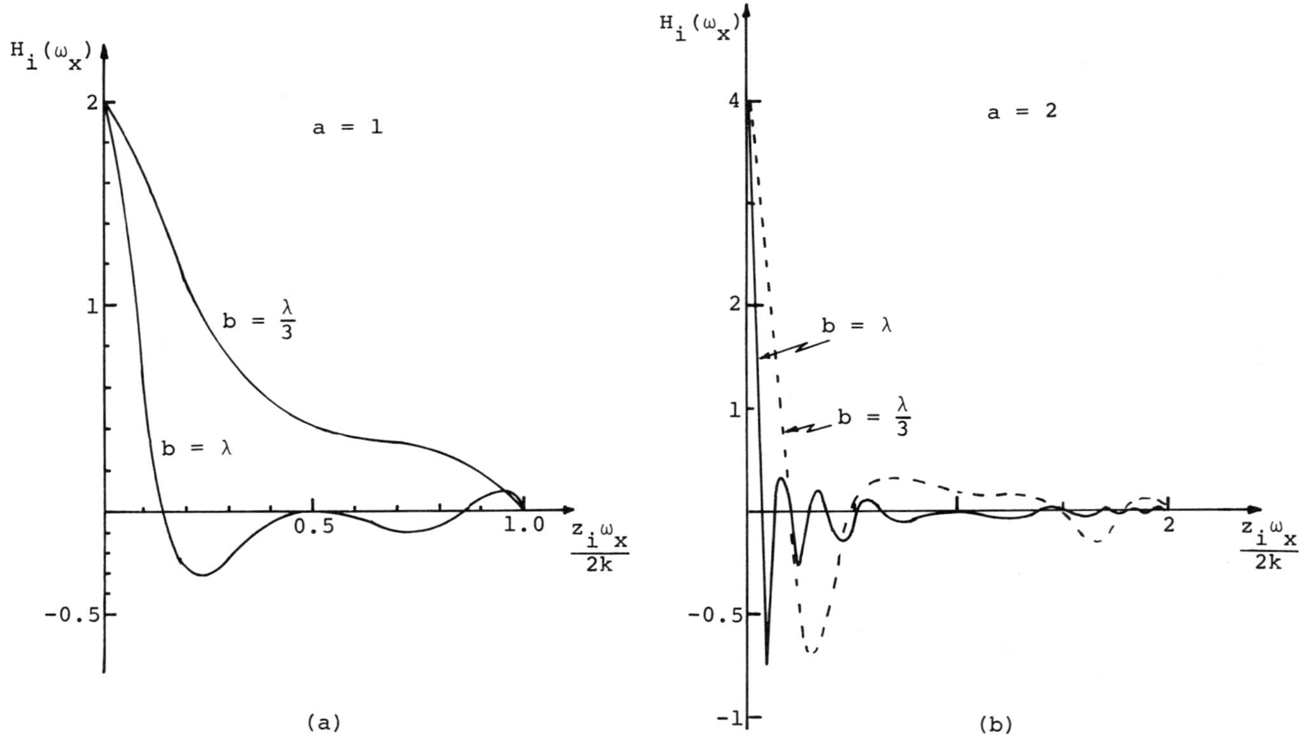

Figure 12-5.10. One-dimensional OTF with focusing error. (a) Optical system with aperture a = 1; (b) Optical system with aperture a = 2.

Introduce next a shifting of the coordinate axis which will succeed in centering the function. By setting

$$\xi = x' + \frac{z_i\omega_x}{2k}; \quad d\xi = dx'$$

the last integral becomes

$$H_i(\omega_x) = \int_{-a+\frac{z_i\omega}{2k}}^{a-\frac{z_i\omega}{2k}} e^{-j2bz_i\omega_x\xi}\, d\xi = 2\int_0^{a-\frac{z_i\omega_x}{2k}} \cos(2bz_i\omega_x)\xi\, d\xi$$

since the sine is an odd function. Upon performing the integration, we obtain finally

$$H_i(\omega_x) = \frac{\sin[(2bz_i\omega_x)(a-\frac{z_i\omega}{2k})]}{bz_i\omega_x} = \frac{\sin[4bk\frac{z_i\omega_x}{2k}(a-\frac{z_i\omega_x}{2k})]}{2bk\cdot\frac{z_i\omega_x}{2k}} \tag{12-5.30}$$

This equation is plotted in Figs. 12-5.10. The effect of phase error and aperture are easily identified from the plots.

ΔΔΔ

II. Information Processing and Filtering. The ability of lenses to analyze optical fields through the use of Fourier transforms relating object and image fields has been used extensively since the early 1950's when the communication theory aspects of optical processing techniques became evident. The discovery by Van der Lugt of the phase and amplitude filtering process introduced a new dimension into optical information processing, and this has been shown to have many interesting applications, such as signal detection, character recognition, and others. We examine certain of these processes.

a. Correlation and Convolution

For simplicity, we assume only one-dimensional cases. Consider the optical system shown in Fig. 12-5.11. In this figure we show an optical system that is imaging an object onto a second transparency $\phi_2(y_1)$. If the signal transparency $\phi_1(y_0)$ is illuminated by an incoherent source of irradiance I_0, then the light

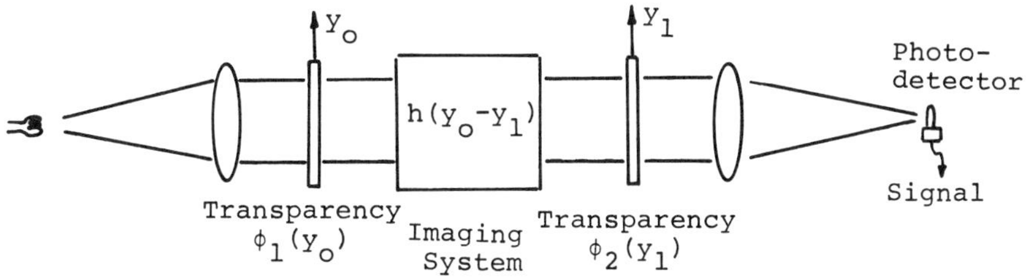

Figure 12-5.11. Incoherent optical processing apparatus.

intensity immediately next to the film is

$$I(y_o) = I_o \phi_1(y_o)$$

The irradiance behind the second transparency will be given by

$$I(y_1) = I_o\ [\phi_1(y_o) * h(y_o)]\ \phi_2(y_1)$$

For a perfect imaging system for which $h(y_1 - y_o) = \delta(y_1 - y_o)$, this assumes the form

$$I(y_1) = I_o\ \phi_1(y_1)\ \phi_2(y_1)$$

The total response of the photodetector will be proportional to the integral

$$I = \int I(y_1)\ dy_1 = I_o \int \phi_1(y_1)\ \phi_2(y_1)\ dy_1 \tag{12-5.31}$$

If the optical imaging system contains only one positive lens, then $\phi_1(y_1) = \phi_1(-y_1)$ and the output I represents the convolution between the two signals ϕ_1 and ϕ_2 when either of the two signals is translated along the Y-axis. However, if the optical system does not invert the object, a similar translation will produce a cross-correlation between the signals.

b. Spectrum Analyzer

If a laser source is used to illuminate a transparency, as shown in Fig. 12-5.12, the complex amplitude of the signal $\phi(y_o)$ at the transform plane is written [see Eq. (12-4.36)]

$$\phi(y_1) = \int \phi(y_o)\ e^{-j\omega_y y_o}\ dy_o\ , \qquad \omega_y = \frac{2\pi y_1}{\lambda f} \tag{12-5.32}$$

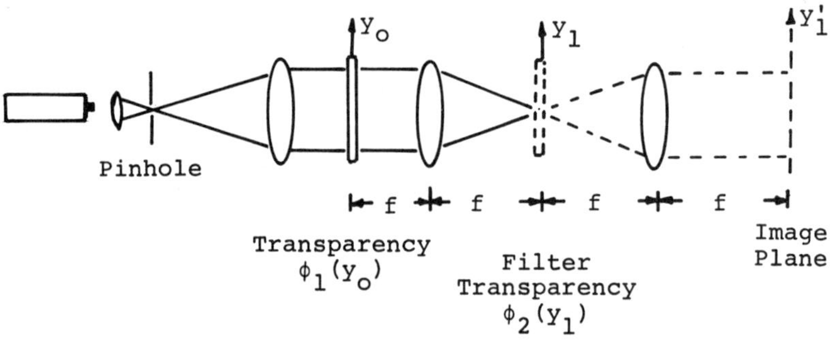

Figure 12-5.12. Optical spectrum analyzer.

Here the complex constant amplitude factor of the plane wave has been set equal to unity, for convenience. The signal $\phi(y_1)$ is the Fourier transform of the input signal $\phi(y_o)$ and the observable photographed irradiance is given by $\phi(y_1)\ \phi^*(y_1) = |\phi(y_1)|^2$ which is proportional to the power spectrum of the signal being processed.

c. Ambiguity Function

An optical cross-correlator using a coherent light source is shown in Fig. 12-5.13. The amplitude of signal just behind the second transparency is equal to $\phi_1(y_1)\ \phi_2(y_1)$. Therefore the amplitude at the Y_1' plane is given by

$$\phi(y_1') = \int \phi_1(y_1)\ \phi_2(y_1)\ e^{-\frac{2\pi}{\lambda f} y_1' y_1}\ dy_1$$

This is known as the *ambiguity function.* If we restrict our light pick-up system to the light falling on the optical axis $y_1' = 0$, then the current in the photodetector is proportional to $\phi^2(y_1')\big|_{y_1'=0}$. If, in addition, $\phi_2(y_1)$ is being displaced continuously, the output signal will be proportional to the cross-correlation of the two signals.

d. Filtering with Coherent Optical Systems

We extend the optical system shown in Fig. 12-5.12 by adding an extra lens, as shown dotted in this figure. We obtain thereby a coherent optical system that is capable of performing linear filtering operations. For example, if a filter transparency is inserted on the Y_1 plane, the complex amplitude distribution adjacent to the transparency will be given by

$$\phi(y_1) = \phi_1(y_1)\ \phi_2(y_1) = \mathscr{F}\{\phi_1(y_o)\}\ \phi_2(y_1) \tag{12-5.33}$$

Here, as before, we have assumed that the proportionality factor is unity.

The filter function in its most general form can be written

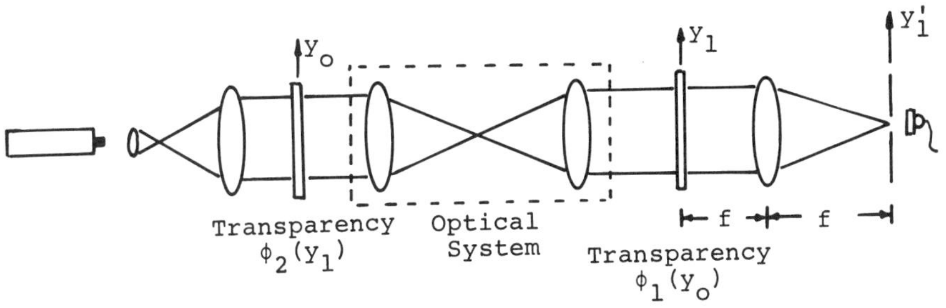

Figure 12-5.13. Coherent cross-correlator.

$$\phi_2(y_1) = |\phi_2(y_1)|\, e^{j\theta(y_1)} \tag{12-5.34}$$

where the variation of transparency of the emulsion of the film is described by $|\phi_2(y_1)|$ and its thickness variation which affects the phase is described by $e^{j\theta(y_1)}$.

Since the second lens takes the Fourier transform of $\phi(y_1)$, the image on the Y_1' plane is given by

$$\phi(y_1') = \int \phi_1(y_1)\, \phi_2(y_1)\, e^{j\omega_{y'} y_1}\, dy_1 \qquad \omega_{y'} = \frac{2\pi}{f} y_1' \tag{12-5.35}$$

By the Fourier transform property (see Appendix II), we can also write

$$\phi(y_1') = \frac{1}{2\pi} \int \phi_1(\omega_{y'} - \xi)\, \phi_2(\xi) d\xi = \phi_1(\omega_{y'}) * \phi_2(\omega_{y'}) \tag{12-5.36}$$

which is the convolution of the Fourier transforms of the complex amplitude of the signal at the plane Y_1 and the filter signal.

It follows from Eq. (12-5.34) that the following types of optical filters are possible: (a) amplitude filters $\phi_2(y_1) = |\phi_2(y_1)|$; (b) phase filters $\phi_2(y_1) = e^{j\theta(y_1)}$; (c) complex filters $\phi_2(y_1) = |\phi_2(y_1)| e^{j\theta(y_1)}$; and (d) simple blocking filters.

12-6. Reconstruction of a Wavefront by Diffraction Holography

The experimental verification and the theory of wavefront reconstruction was first introduced by D. Gabor in 1948. Since that time, a number of wavefront reconstruction techniques have been developed - these are known as holographic techniques. These same general techniques have been applied to microwaves, to acoustic waves, and to laser light. To understand this new and very important imaging technique, we shall present it as it is applied to a point object.

Consider a point source located at a distance z_{so} from a photographic plate and a plane reference wave to exist simultaneously as shown in Fig. 12-6.1. The wave amplitude due to the point source at a distance r (or scattered wave from a point object) is expressed as [see Eq. (10-13.4)]

$$\Phi = \frac{\Phi_o}{r} e^{j(kr - \omega t)} \tag{12-6.1}$$

where Φ_o is a complex constant. If the *reference wave* is a monochromatic plane wave, its amplitude is given by

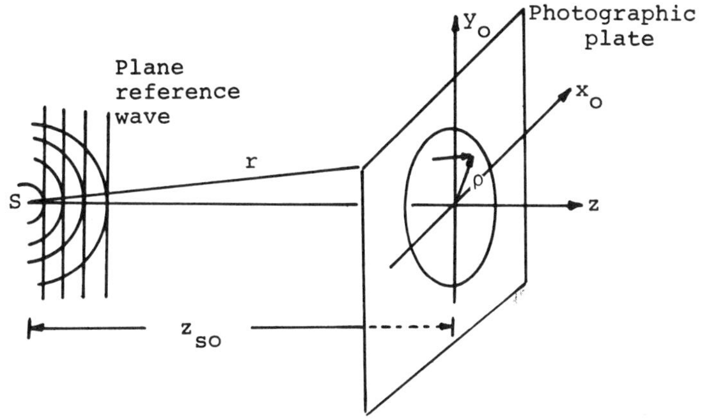

Figure 12-6.1. Recording of spherical and plane wavefronts.

$$\psi = \psi_o e^{j(\bar{k}\cdot\bar{r}-\omega t)} = \psi_o e^{j[\bar{a}_z k \cdot (\bar{a}_x x_o + \bar{a}_y y_o + (z_{so}+z)\bar{a}_z - \omega t]}$$
$$= \psi_o e^{j[(z_{so}+z)k-\omega t]} \tag{12-6.2}$$

where ψ_o is another complex constant. At the photographic plate (z = 0) these equations become, respectively,

$$\Phi(x_o,y_o) = \frac{\Phi_o}{\sqrt{z_{so}^2+\rho^2}} e^{jk\sqrt{z_{so}^2+\rho^2}}$$
$$\psi(x_o,y_o) = \psi_o e^{jkz_{so}} \tag{12-6.3}$$

where the time factor $e^{-j\omega t}$ is not shown but is implicitly assumed. The total amplitude on the plate is equal to $\Phi(x_o,y_o) + \psi(x_o,y_o)$. If the distance z_{so} is large in comparison with the aperture of the recording medium, we can write the first of Eq. (12-6.3)

$$\Phi(x_o,y_o) = \frac{\Phi_o}{z_{so}\sqrt{1+(\frac{\rho}{z_{so}})^2}} e^{jkz_{so}\sqrt{1+(\frac{\rho}{z_{so}})^2}} \doteq \frac{\Phi_o}{z_{so}} e^{jkz_{so}(1+\frac{1}{2}\frac{\rho^2}{z_{so}^2})} \tag{12-6.4}$$

Thus the total field on the plane z = 0 is

$$\Phi(x_o y_o) + \psi(x_o y_o) = e^{jkz_{so}}[\frac{\Phi_o}{z_{so}} e^{jk\frac{\rho^2}{2z_{so}}} + \psi_o] \tag{12-6.5}$$

and its intensity, recorded on the film is given by

$$I(x_o,y_o) = \{e^{jkz_{so}}[\frac{\Phi_o}{z_{so}} e^{jk\frac{\rho^2}{2z_{so}}} + \psi_o]\}\{e^{-jkz_{so}}[\frac{\Phi_o^*}{z_{so}} e^{-jk\frac{\rho^2}{2z_{so}}} + \psi_o^*]\}$$

$$I(x_o y_o) = \frac{|\Phi_o|^2}{z_{so}^2} + |\psi_o|^2 + \frac{2|\psi_o||\Phi_o|}{z_{so}} \cos(\frac{k\rho^2}{2z_{so}} + \phi) \tag{12-6.6}$$

where ϕ is the phase angle between the complex numbers Φ_o and ψ_o. When the film is developed properly, its transmittance is proportional to the intensity which had fallen on the film. This has the form

$$T(\rho,k) = C_1 + C_2 \cos(\frac{k\rho^2}{2z_{so}} + \phi) \tag{12-6.7}$$

where C_1 and C_2 are proportionality constants.

Suppose now that the field on a plane (the hologram) due to a point source at infinity is a plane wave. Then the field at a plane parallel to the hologram at a distance $z_{so} = z_{10}$ is, by Eq. (12-4.3),

$$\Phi(x_1 y_1) = C \int_{-\infty}^{\infty}\int [C_1 + C_3 e^{j\frac{k\rho^2}{2z_{so}}} + C_4 e^{-j\frac{k\rho^2}{2z_{so}}}]$$

$$\cdot e^{j\frac{k}{2z_{so}}[(x_o-x_1)^2 + (y_o-y_1)^2]} dx_o\, dy_o \tag{12-6.8}$$

where $C_3 = \frac{1}{2} C_2 e^{j\phi}$ and $C_4 = \frac{1}{2} C_2 e^{-j\phi}$ are new complex constants. This expression is expanded to the form

$$\Phi(x_1 y_1) = CC_1 \int_{-\infty}^{\infty} e^{j\frac{k}{2z_{so}}(x_o-x_1)^2} dx_o \int_{-\infty}^{\infty} e^{j\frac{k}{2z_{so}}(y_o-y_1)^2} dy_o$$

$$+ CC_3 e^{j\frac{k(x_1^2+y_1^2)}{4z_{so}}} \int_{-\infty}^{\infty} e^{j\frac{k}{z_{so}}(x_o-\frac{1}{2}x_1)^2} dx_o$$

$$\cdot \int_{-\infty}^{\infty} e^{j\frac{k}{z_{so}}(y_o-\frac{1}{2}y_1)^2} dy_o + C_1C_4 \int_{-\infty}^{\infty} e^{-j\frac{k}{z_{so}}x_1x_o} dx_o$$

$$\cdot \int_{-\infty}^{\infty} e^{-j\frac{k}{z_{so}}y_1y_o} dy_o$$

which is written in the form

$$\Phi(x_1,y_1) = K_1 + K_2 e^{j\frac{k}{4z_{so}}(x_1^2+y_1^2)} + K_3\, \delta(x_1)\, \delta(y_1) \tag{12-6.9}$$

where K_1, K_2 and K_3 are complex constants. The first four integrals are of the form

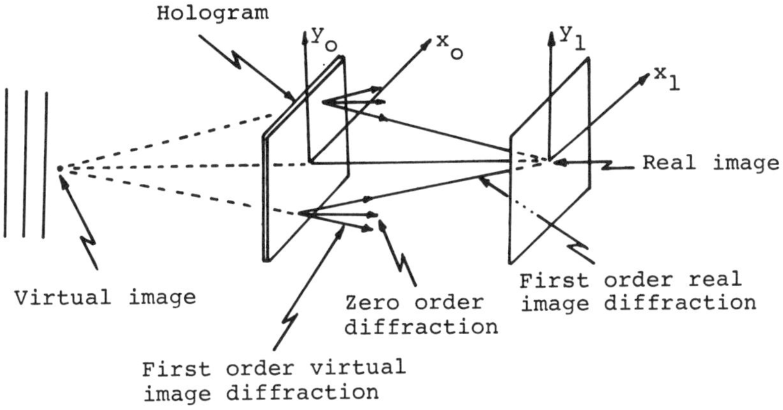

Figure 12-6.2. Wavefront reconstruction of a point object.

$$\int_{\infty}^{\infty} e^{ja(x_0-bx_1)^2}\,dx_0 \int_{-\infty}^{\infty} e^{ja(y_0-by_1)^2}\,dy_0$$

$$= \left(\sqrt{\frac{\pi}{2a}} + j\sqrt{\frac{\pi}{2a}}\right)\left(\sqrt{\frac{\pi}{2a}} + j\sqrt{\frac{\pi}{2a}}\right) = j\,\frac{\pi}{a} = \frac{\pi}{a}\,e^{j\frac{\pi}{2}} \qquad (12\text{-}6.10)$$

where we have used the standard form integrals

$$\int_0^{\infty} \cos ax^2\,dx = \int_0^{\infty} \sin ax^2\,dx = \frac{1}{2}\sqrt{\frac{\pi}{2a}}$$

These are thus seen to be complex numbers. The last two integrals are recognized as the two dimensional delta function $\delta(x,y) = \delta(x_1)\delta(y_1)$.

Now refer to Fig. 12-6.2 which shows the geometry involved. The three terms of Eq. (12-6.9) can now be identified on this figure. The term K_1 corresponds to the undiffracted light (zero order diffraction). The term $K_2 e^{j(k/2z_{so})(x_1^2+y_1^2)}$ corresponds to a spherical wave (quadratic approximation) starting at a virtual point, since the "eye" has to extrapolate the first order diffracted light. The term $K_3\delta(x_1)\delta(y_1)$ corresponds to the first order real image. Since each object is the sum of an infinite number of points, it follows that we can use the holographic technique to reconstruct images of objects with different dimensions.

It is apparent from Fig. 12-6.2 that both the real and virtual images are colinear. Leith and Upatnieks have considered a setup shown in Fig. 12-6.3 to alleviate this problem and thus improve the contrast and clarity of the reproduced image. When the plane incident wave falls on the object-prism combination, part of it still remains plane but it is deflected by an angle θ. The other portion passes through an object of varying transmissivity and falls at the film. Therefore the total amplitude distribution across the film is

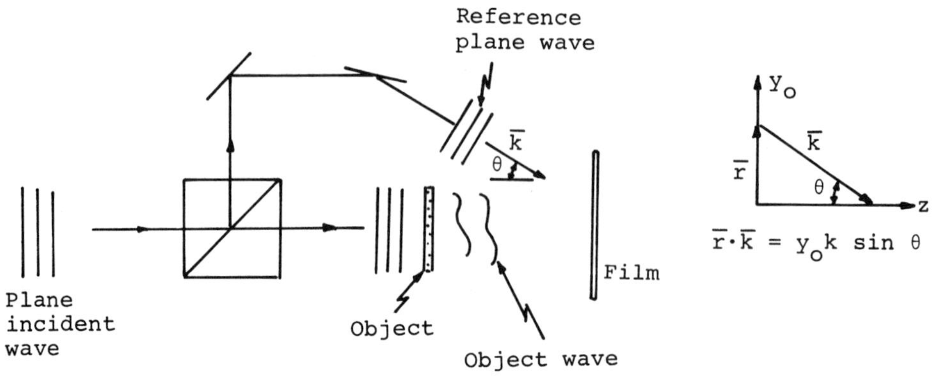

Figure 12-6.3. Recording of Leith-Upatnieks hologram.

$$\Phi(x_o,y_o) = A\,e^{j\frac{2\pi \sin\theta}{\lambda}y_o} + \underset{\sim}{a}(x_o,y_o) \tag{12-6.11}$$

where $\underset{\sim}{a}(x_o,y_o) = a(x_o,y_o)\,e^{+j\phi(x_o,y_o)}$ is the object complex wavefront to be recorded and $A \exp[j(2\pi \sin\theta/\lambda)y_o]$ is the reference wave.

The intensity distribution on the film is then

$$I(x_o,y_o) = \Phi\Phi^* = A^2 + |\underset{\sim}{a}(x_o,y_o)|^2 + (\underset{\sim}{a}^* A\,e^{jk\sin\theta\, y_o})^* + \underset{\sim}{a}^* A\,e^{jk\sin\theta\, y_o}$$

$$= A^2 + |\underset{\sim}{a}(x_o,y_o)|^2 + aA\cos\left[2\pi\frac{\sin\theta}{\lambda}y_o - \phi(x_o,y_o)\right] \tag{12-6.12}$$

Let us assume that an ideal film development took place such that its transmittance is proportional to the intensity of the field which exposed the film. If next we irradiate the developed film with a plane wave A, as shown in Fig. 12-6.4, we shall observe the separation of the two images. The equation which governs the phenomenon

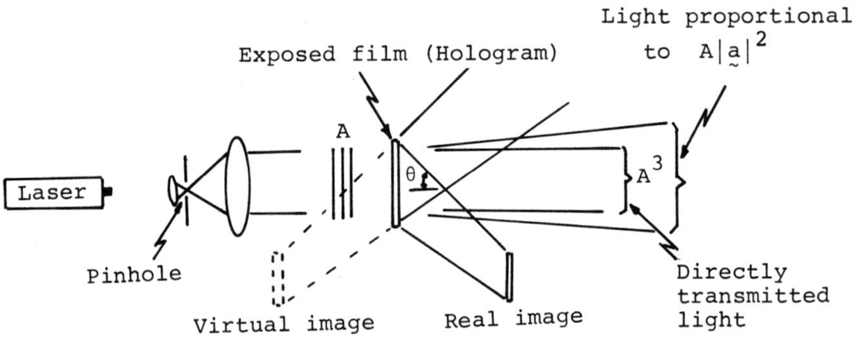

Figure 12-6.4. Holographic reconstruction of images.

shown in Fig. 12-6.4 is

$$\underset{\sim}{\Phi} = A\, I(x_o,y_o) = A^3 + A|\underset{\sim}{a}|^2 + A^2\underset{\sim}{a}\, e^{-jk \sin\theta\, y_o} + A^2\underset{\sim}{a}^* e^{jk\sin\theta\, y_o} \tag{12-6.13}$$

The last two terms are the virtual and real images, respectively.

It is interesting to look at the spatial frequencies of the various terms of an optical field transmitted through a hologram. From Eq. (12-6.9) we obtain

$$\mathscr{F}\{\Phi(x_1,y_1)\} = K_1\delta(\omega_x,\omega_y) + K_2\frac{4\pi z_{so}}{k}\, e^{j\left(\frac{\pi}{2} - \frac{\omega_x^2}{k/4z_{so}} - \frac{\omega_y^2}{k/4z_{so}}\right)} + K_3 \tag{12-6.14}$$

The amplitude of the different terms of Eq. (12-6.14) are shown in Fig. 12-6.5a. However, if we take the Fourier transform of Eq. (12-6.3) we obtain the expression (see Appendix IV)

$$\mathscr{F}\{\underset{\sim}{\Phi}(x_o,y_o)\} = A^3\delta(\omega_x,\omega_y) + AO(\omega_x,\omega_y) * O^*(-\omega_x,-\omega_y) + A^2O(\omega_x,\omega_y + k\sin\theta\, y_o)$$

$$+ A^2O^*(-\omega_x,-\omega_y + y_o\, k\sin\theta) \qquad \text{a)}$$

where

$$\mathscr{F}\{a(x,y)\} = O(\omega_x,\omega_y) \qquad \text{b)} \qquad (12\text{-}6.15)$$

$$\mathscr{F}\{a^*(x,y)\} = O^*(-\omega_x,-\omega_y) \qquad \text{c)}$$

and the second term indicates convolution.

The amplitudes of the spectra from Eq. (12-6.15) are shown schematically in Fig. 12-6.5b. From these two figures it is apparent that when the reference wave impinges at an angle, a shifting of the object spectra is created. This makes it

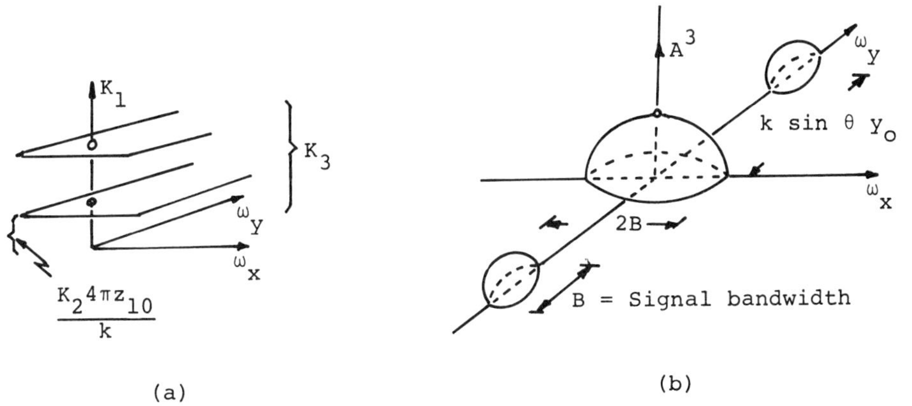

Figure 12-6.5. Fourier spectra of holograms.

easy to separate the virtual and real images as well as the background noise.

The unique properties of laser holography have resulted in its use in testing of materials, in biological research, in medical research and diagnosis, in art, and many other fields.

12-7. Gaussian Light Beam

Consider a source at a point S that radiates spherical waves with Gaussian amplitude distribution, as shown in Fig. 12-7.1a. The phase of the spherical wave at any point (x,y) on the plane is given by

$$\Phi_p(P) = e^{jkr} = e^{jk[R^2 + x^2 + y^2]^{1/2}} \doteq e^{jkR} e^{jk\frac{(x^2 + y^2)}{2R}} \tag{12-7.1}$$

From Eq. (12-7.1) any wave that has a phase variation of the form $k(x^2+y^2)/2R = (\pi/R\lambda)(x^2+y^2)$ will be recognized as a spherical wave with radius of curvature R. Therefore the field of a Gaussian beam can be written in the form

$$\Phi(P) = \sqrt{\frac{2}{\pi}}\frac{1}{W} e^{-\frac{x^2+y^2}{W^2}} e^{j\frac{\pi}{\lambda}(\frac{x^2+y^2}{R})} = \sqrt{\frac{2}{\pi}}\frac{1}{W} e^{j\frac{\pi}{\lambda}\frac{x^2+y^2}{q}} \tag{12-7.2}$$

where the factor

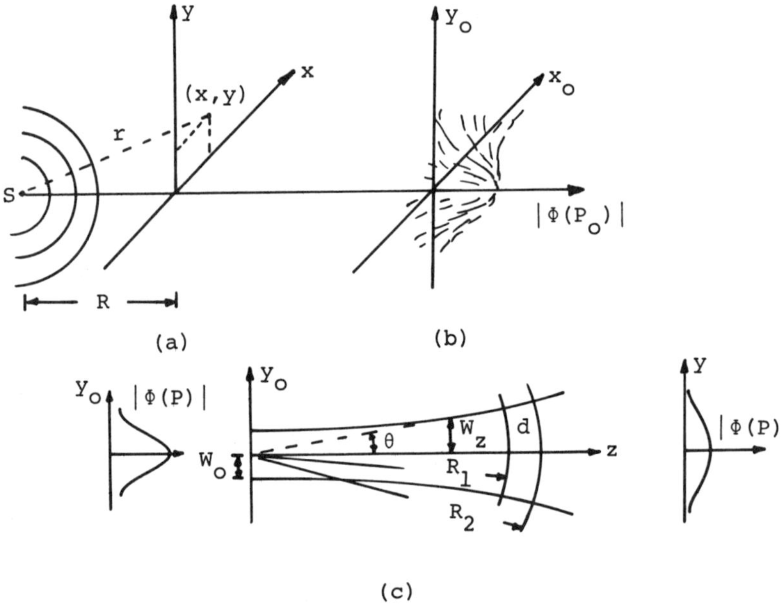

Figure 12-7.1. Features of a Gaussian light beam.

$$|\Phi(P)| = \sqrt{\frac{2}{\pi}}\,\frac{1}{W}\,e^{-\frac{x^2+y^2}{W^2}} \tag{12-7.3}$$

defines the amplitude variation of the beam, normalized to unit power, i.e.,

$$\int_{-\infty}^{\infty}\!\!\int |\Phi(P)|^2 dx\, dy = 1$$

The complex radius of curvature [see Eq. (10-12.9)] which is written

$$\frac{1}{q} = \frac{1}{R} + j\,\frac{\lambda}{\pi W^2} \tag{12-7.4}$$

is a very important factor since it contains both the radius of the beam R and the spot size W.

Let us consider a laser beam at an input plane z = 0 to be a plane wave with Gaussian amplitude distribution (see Fig. 12-7.1c). Then

$$\Phi(P_o) = \sqrt{\frac{2}{\pi}}\,\frac{1}{W_o}\,e^{j\frac{k}{2}\frac{x_o^2+y_o^2}{q_o}}$$

where

$$\frac{1}{q_o} = \frac{1}{\infty} + j\,\frac{\lambda}{\pi W_o^2} = j\,\frac{\lambda}{\pi W_o^2} \tag{12-7.5}$$

To find the field at any other plane $z \neq 0$, we must use Eq. (12-4.3) in the form

$$\Phi(P_1) = -\frac{jk}{2\pi}\sqrt{\frac{2}{\pi}}\,\frac{e^{jkz_{10}}}{z_{10}W_o}\int_{-\infty}^{\infty}\!\!\int e^{j\frac{k}{2q_o}(x_o^2+y_o^2)}\,e^{j\frac{k}{2z_{10}}[(x_o-x_1)^2+(y_o-y_1)^2]}\,dx_o dy_o \tag{12-7.6}$$

But it is noted that

$$\frac{1}{z_{10}}(x_o-x_1)^2 + \frac{x_o^2}{q_o} = \frac{1}{q_o+z_{10}}x_1^2 + \left(\frac{1}{q_o}+\frac{1}{z_{10}}\right)(x_o-bx_1)^2 \tag{12-7.7}$$

where

$$b = \frac{q_o}{q_o+z_{10}}$$

then Eq. (12-7.6) becomes

$$\Phi(P_1) = -\frac{j}{\lambda}\sqrt{\frac{2}{\pi}}\,\frac{1}{W_o}\,\frac{e^{jkz_{10}}}{z_{10}}\,e^{j\frac{k}{2}\frac{x_1^2+y_1^2}{q_o+z_{10}}}\int_{-\infty}^{\infty}\!\!\int e^{j\frac{k}{2}\left(\frac{1}{q_o}+\frac{1}{z_{10}}\right)[(x_o-bx_1)^2+(y_o-by_1)^2]}\cdot dx_o\, dy_o \tag{12-7.8}$$

The integration involved here are identical with those given in Eq. (12-6.10). After integration, we obtain

$$\Phi(P_1) = \sqrt{\frac{2}{\pi}}\, e^{jkz_{10}}\, e^{j\frac{k}{2}\frac{x_1^2+y_1^2}{q}}\, \frac{e^{-j\phi(z_{10})}}{W(z_{10})} \qquad \text{a)}$$

where

$$q = q_0 + z_{10} = z_{10} - j\,\frac{\pi W_o^2}{\lambda} \qquad \text{b)}$$

$$\frac{1}{q} = \frac{1}{R(z_{10})} + j\,\frac{\lambda}{\pi W^2(z_{10})} = \frac{1}{z_{10} - j\frac{\pi W_o^2}{\lambda}} \qquad \text{c)} \qquad (12\text{-}7.9)$$

$$R(z_{10}) = z_{10} + \left(\frac{\pi W_o^2}{\lambda}\right)^2 \frac{1}{z_{10}} \qquad \text{d)}$$

$$W(z_{10}) = W_o\left[1 + \left(\frac{\lambda z_{10}}{\pi W_o^2}\right)^2\right]^{1/2} \qquad \text{e)}$$

$$\phi(z_{10}) = \tan^{-1}\left(\frac{\lambda z_{10}}{\pi W_o^2}\right) \qquad \text{f)}$$

Eq. (12-7.9) indicates that a beam starting as a Gaussian plane wave at $z = 0$ will retain its Gaussian amplitude distribution.

Next consider a laser beam with a complex radius of curvature q which represents a wavefront of curvature R_1 and a spot size W_1. Since for this case the relation that applies is

$$q_1 = \left(\frac{1}{R_1} + j\,\frac{\lambda}{\pi W_1^2}\right)^{-1} = q_0 + z_{10} = z_{10} - j\,\frac{\pi W_o^2}{\lambda}$$

we get, by equating the real and imaginary parts,

$$z_{10} = \frac{R_1}{1 + \left(\frac{\lambda R_1}{\pi W_1^2}\right)^2} \qquad \text{a)} \qquad (12\text{-}7.10)$$

$$W_o = \frac{W_1}{\left[1 + \left(\frac{\pi W_1^2}{\lambda R_1}\right)^2\right]^{1/2}} \qquad \text{b)}$$

which shows that we can trace the beam backwards to the initial plane $z = 0$ and spot size W_o.

The distance z_R at which the beam is $\sqrt{2}\,W_o$ wide from its initial width W_o is called the *Rayleigh range* and it is found by using the equality [see Eq. (12-7.9e)]

$$\sqrt{2}\,W_o = W_o\left[1 + \left(\frac{\lambda z_R}{\pi W_o^2}\right)^2\right]^{1/2}$$

or

$$z_R = \frac{\pi W_o^2}{\lambda} \qquad (12\text{-}7.11)$$

REVIEW QUESTIONS

1. Define Huygen's principle.
2. In what way did Fresnel improve Huygen's principle?
3. What was Kirchhoff's contribution to the same principle?
4. What are the functions which the Helmholtz-Kirchhoff integral relates?
5. What were the ad-hoc conditions defined by Fresnel which can be identified in the Fresnel-Kirchhoff diffraction formula?
6. What do we mean by Sommerfeld radiation condition?
7. Which one of the nonrigorous assumptions made by Kirchhoff was eliminated by Sommerfeld?
8. Does the Fresnel approximation change the phase front from quadratic to spherical or from spherical to quadratic surface?
9. Is the paraxial approximation for the rays used in the Fresnel approximation?
10. How is the field at the Fraunhofer region related to that in the input surface?
11. Is the field at the Fraunhofer region an exact Fourier transform of the field in the input surface?
12. Illustrate the two-dimensional spatial Fourier transform.
13. Is the picture we observe on a film at the Fraunhofer region the Fourier transform of the amplitude of the field at the input plane?
14. What is the Rayleigh criterion?
15. What is the significance of the Fourier transform properties of converging lenses?
16. What is a Van der Lugt filter?
17. Discuss linearity, invariance, causality and stability for optical systems.
18. What is the spread function in optical systems?
19. What is the difference between the optical transfer function (OTF) and the coherent transfer function (CTF)?
20. Why is the knowledge of the modulation transfer function (MTF) important for optical systems?
21. What is a diffraction limited optical system?
22. How is a focusing error produced in optical systems?
23. How does one proceed to do filtering of optical signals?
24. Is the hologram a picture of an object? If your answer is no, then what is it?
25. What type of wave is needed to shine a hologram plate so that we can be able to see the object?
26. Which of the two images, the virtual or real, will expose a film so that the image may be recognized?
27. What is the Rayleigh range?

PROBLEMS

12-1.1. Find the field at P_1 if a plane wave is incident on the surface S_0 at an angle θ_1 as shown in Fig. 12-1.2.

12-1.2. A HeNe laser beam falls perpendicularly on a slit of $s_0 = 25\ \mu m$ wide (see Fig. 12-1.2). If the amplitude of the beam is constant, $\Phi_0 = 10\ \mu Volt/m$, find the field at the point $(z,y) = (10m, 1m)$. Approximate your integral as a sum of five terms. Compare your result with the "exact" value using a computer.

12-3.1. Develop an equation similar to Eq. (12-3.5) but for the case when the two equivalent sources oscillate in phase.

12-3.2. If the source P_s radiates a spherical wave of unit strength, show that

$$\Phi(P_1) = \frac{jk}{2\pi}\int_{S_0} \frac{e^{jk(r_{10}+r_{so})}}{r_{10}r_{so}} \cos(\bar{r}_{10},\bar{n})dS$$

when the Sommerfeld assumption on source oscillation is used.

12-4.1. Show that the third order term of the expansion in Eq. (12-4.2) contributes less than one radian to the phase if $z_{10}^3 \gg \frac{k}{8}[(x_1-x_0)^2+(y_1-y_0)^2]^2_{max}$.

12-4.2. A triangular field distribution

$$\Phi(x,y) = \frac{1}{a}(a - |x|) \qquad -a \le x \le a$$

$$\Phi(x,y) = 0 \qquad x < -a,\quad x > a$$

exists across an infinitely narrow slit in the Y-direction with a finite width in the X-direction. Find the field distribution in the Fraunhofer region.

[Ans: $\Phi(P_1) = 4C \dfrac{\sin^2(\omega_x a/2)}{\omega_x^2 a}$]

12-4.3. Find the Fraunhofer diffraction field for a rectangular aperture a × b that is illuminated by a uniform plane wave.

12-4.4. An infinitely narrow slit in the X-direction runs along the Y-axis. If the field intensity is given by $e^{-a|y|}$, find the field in the Fraunhofer region.

12-4.5. Find the field in the Fraunhofer region due to N pinholes located along the Y-axis which are illuminated by a uniform electric field of unit intensity.

12-4.6. A uniform plane wave of frequency 10 GHz and amplitude 100 μVolt/m falls on a rectangular aperture with dimensions 3 cm by 0.5 cm. Find the field at 5 m away and at the point $x_1 = 0.5$ m, $y_1 = 0.75$ m.

12-4.7. A wave, $\lambda = 0.6328\ \mu m$, falls on a converging lens whose focal length is 55 mm. What type of an aperture is it and what must its dimensions be so that only frequencies from 100 mm^{-1} to 600 mm^{-1} are passed?

12-4.8. Using Fig. 12-4.11 find the Fresnel diffraction intensity pattern of a straight edge if the diffracted wave has 0.5 μm wavelength and the distance of recording is $z_{10} = 2.5$ m. Plot the value $|\Phi(P_1)|^2 k/C^2 \pi z_{10}$ versus y_1 and compare your result with Fig. 12-4.10b.

12-4.9. Four pinholes are located as follows: $\delta(x-a)$, $\delta(x+a)$, $\delta(y-b)$, $\delta(y+b)$. If these are uniformly illuminated, find the field in the Fraunhofer region.

12-4.10. Find the diffraction pattern in the Fraunhofer region from two infinitely long slits each having a width 2a in the Y-direction and located symmetrically with respect to the X-axis. The distance of their centers is d and the slits are uniformly illuminated with coherent light.

[Ans: $\Phi(P_1) = 4C \sin \omega_y a \cos \frac{\omega_y d}{\omega_y}$]

12-5.1. Find the convolution between two square pulses.

12-5.2. Find the convolution between a square pulse and the function $\delta(x-x') - \delta(x+x')$.

12-5.3. Show that for a coherent source the intensity distribution of light is given by

$$I(x_1) = \left|\int_{-\infty}^{\infty} h(x_1-x_0)\ \phi(x_0)dx_0\right|^2.$$

12-5.4. Find the OTF if the one-dimensional pupil function is that shown in Fig. P12-5.4. Compare your result with Fig. 12-5.7e and 12-5.7f.

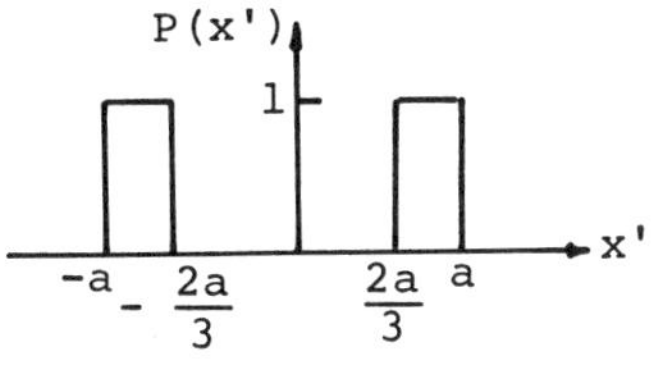

Figure P12-5.4.

12-5.5. Find the OTF if the one-dimensional pupil function is that shown in Fig. P12-5.5.

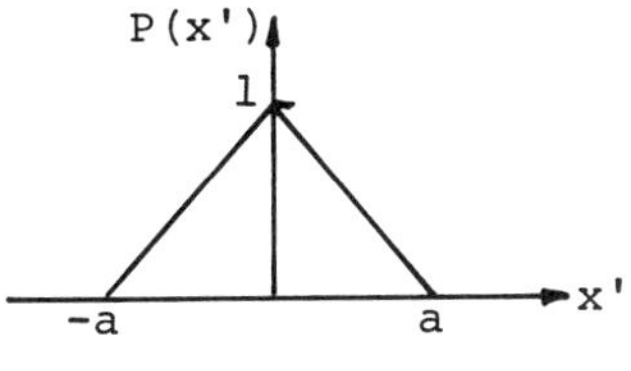

Figure P12-5.5.

12-6.1. Using Fig. 12-6.5, find the minimum angle θ for a HeNe laser constructing a hologram of an object whose greatest frequency is $f_x = 600\ \text{mm}^{-1}$.

12-7.1. Find W_2 and R_2 of a Gaussian beam in terms of W_1 and R_1, if $z_{20} > z_{10}$ and $z_{20} - z_{10} = d$. [Hint: $q_2 = q_1 + d$.]

12-7.2. Verify Eq. (12-7.9).

12-7.3. Show that at distance $z_{10} >> \pi W_o^2/\lambda$ the beam wave is spherical with its center of curvature located essentially at the plane $z_{10} \doteq 0$.

12-7.4. Find the beam diameter at $z_{10} >> \pi W_o^2/\lambda$.

[Ans: $\sim \dfrac{\lambda z_{10}}{\pi W_o}$.]

CHAPTER 13

RESONANCE, RESONATORS AND COHERENCE

Resonance and interference, two important phenomena, will be discussed in this chapter, and we shall review the physical properties associated with them. Both of these physical processes occur frequently in a variety of systems. For example, the resonance phenomenon is associated with the natural frequency, and is the process in which energy changes continuously between potential and kinetic form. It is usually associated with systems with low losses. For the phenomenon of *coherence* to exist, a specific phase relation must exist between two or more independent waves. We shall examine these phenomena in various systems.

13-1. Free Oscillations in Second-Order Systems

Systems without any applied force (energy) can oscillate freely under certain circumstances. The character of the oscillations characterize the system, since a decaying oscillation corresponds to a system with damping. A system which oscillates without decay is free of damping effects. In general, any second-order dynamical system of lumped elements is represented by an ordinary differential equation of the form

$$\frac{d^2x}{dt^2} + \alpha\frac{dx}{dt} + \omega_o{}^2x = f(t) \qquad (13\text{-}1.1)$$

where α is a factor indicating losses and ω_o is the *natural frequency* of oscillation. Such an equation will arise in a variety of physical disciplines. We consider specifically the cases of electrical and mechanical systems.

a. Lossless free oscillating system: Shown are typical examples of a mechanical and an electrical system. We give the equilibrium equations and their solutions without derivation

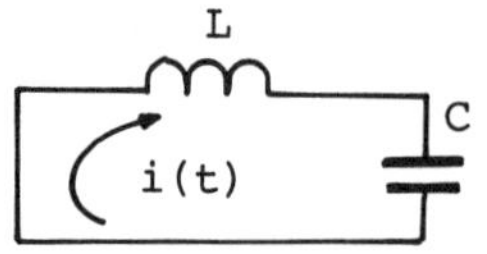

$$\frac{d^2i}{dt^2} + \frac{1}{LC}\,i = 0 \qquad \omega_0^{\,2} = \frac{1}{LC} \tag{13-1.2}$$

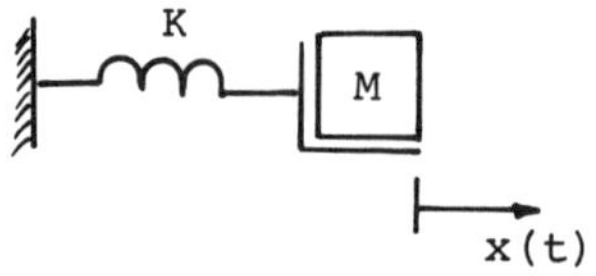

$$\frac{d^2x}{dt^2} + \frac{K}{M}\,x = 0 \qquad \omega_0^{\,2} = \frac{K}{M} \tag{13-1.3}$$

where K is the *stiffness constant* and $C_m = 1/K$ is the compliance of the spring.

b. Lossy free oscillating systems: When losses are present, the following two examples take the form

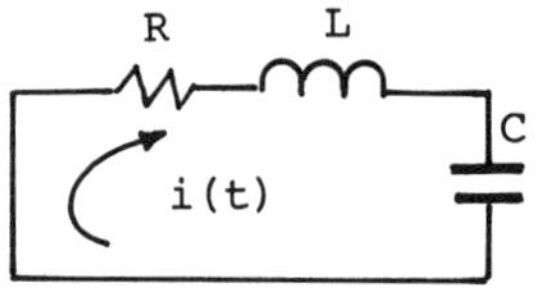

$$\frac{d^2i}{dt^2} + \frac{R}{L}\frac{di}{dt} + \frac{1}{LC} = 0; \; \alpha = \frac{R}{L}, \quad \omega_0^{\,2} = \frac{1}{LC} \tag{13-1.4}$$

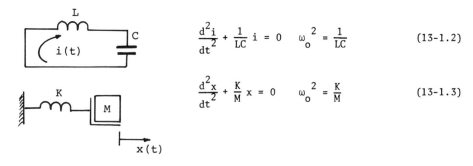

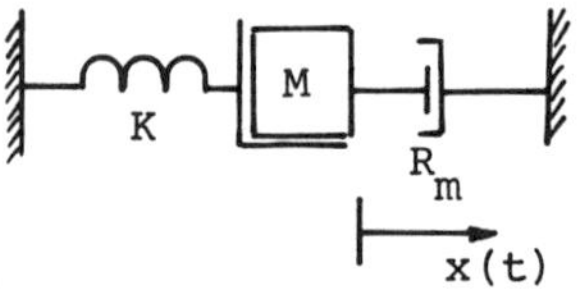

$$\frac{d^2x}{dt^2} + \frac{R_m}{M}\frac{dx}{dt} + \frac{K}{M}\,x = 0; \; \alpha = \frac{R_m}{M}, \quad \omega_0^{\,2} = \frac{K}{M} \tag{13-1.5}$$

The general solution to Eq. (13-1.1) in the absence of the driving source f(t) is given by

$$x(t) = e^{-\frac{\alpha}{2}t}\left[C_1 e^{\sqrt{(\frac{\alpha}{2})^2 - \omega_0^2}\,t} + C_2 e^{-\sqrt{(\frac{\alpha}{2})^2 - \omega_0^2}\,t}\right] \tag{13-1.6}$$

where C_1 and C_2 are constants which are prescribed in any given situation by the initial conditions. When there is no friction (resistance) the oscillation is a pure periodic response. When α is present and $\alpha/2 < \omega_0$, the solution is no longer a pure sinusoidal function; it is a damped oscillatory response whose amplitude decreases by a factor of 1/e in the time $1/(\alpha/2)$ sec. which is known as the *modulus of decay* of the oscillations. The rate of decrease is sometimes expressed in terms of the "Q" of the system, where $Q \equiv \omega_0/\alpha$. For the two systems considered, we tabulate the important factors in terms of the constants of the two systems. If there is friction in the system and $\alpha/2 > \omega_0$ the solution is not oscillatory. For the critically damped case which occurs when $\alpha/2 = \omega_0$, the solution is not oscillatory, with the decay being at its optimal rate without overshoot.

Table 13-1.1. System Factors of Oscillatory Systems

	System Factors			
	α	$\omega_0 = 2\pi f_0$	$\tau = \frac{1}{\alpha/2}$	$Q = \frac{\omega_0}{\alpha}$
Electrical	$\frac{R}{L}$	$\frac{1}{\sqrt{LC}}$	$\frac{2L}{R}$	$\frac{\omega_0 L}{R}$
Mechanical	$\frac{R_m}{M}$	$\sqrt{\frac{K}{M}}$	$\frac{2M}{R_m}$	$\frac{\omega_0 M}{R_m}$

13-2. Forced Oscillations

The general solution to Eq. (13-1.1) for a specified forcing function f(t) is readily found using Laplace transform methods (see Appendix IV). The transformed equation for zero initial conditions x(0) = 0 and dx(0)/dt = 0 is

$$s^2X(s) + \alpha s\, X(s) + \omega_0^2X(s) = F(s) \tag{13-2.1}$$

where $s = \sigma + j\omega$ is the Laplace variable. The ratio of the Laplace output to the Laplace input for a unit impulse (Dirac delta function) input $[\mathcal{L}\{f(t)\} = 1]$ is

$$H(s) = \frac{X(s)}{F(s)}$$

H(s) is the *transfer function*, and for the second order system. H(s) is given by

$$H(s)\Big|_{s=-j\omega} = \frac{1}{s^2+\alpha s+\omega_0^2}\Big|_{s=-j\omega} = \frac{1}{-\omega^2+\omega_0^2-j\omega\alpha} \tag{13-2.2}$$

The absolute value of H(s) for small $\alpha \ll 1$ is shown in Fig. 13-2.1. The quality factor Q of the system is defined by a number of equivalent forms. One form is the relation

$$Q = \frac{\omega_0}{2\Delta\omega} \tag{13-2.3}$$

where $2\Delta\omega$ is known as the *bandwidth* (BW) of the system. We recall that Q was defined in the previous section as the ratio ω_0/α, which means therefore that $\Delta\omega = \alpha/2$. For the function $|H(-j\omega)|$ to fall to $1/\sqrt{2}$ of its peak value, we must have, from Eq. (13-2.2) that

$$\omega_0^2 - \omega^2 = \omega\alpha = (\omega_0 + \omega)\ (\omega_0 - \omega)$$

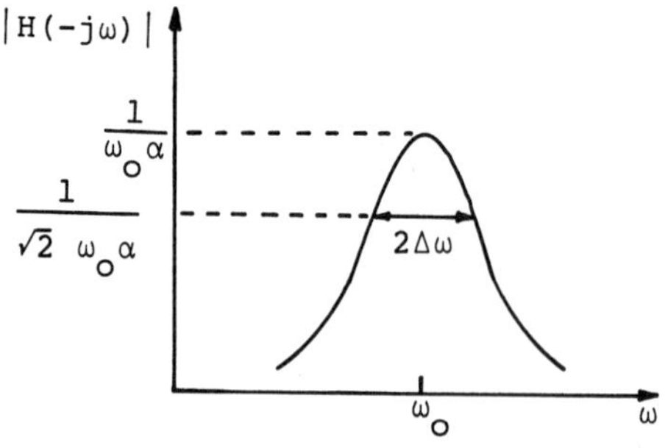

Figure 13-2.1. The response of a second order system.

For high Q systems, $\omega \doteq \omega_0$, and this expression becomes

$$(\omega_0 + \omega)\ (\omega_0 - \omega) \doteq 2\omega_0 \Delta\omega = \omega_0 \alpha \tag{13-2.3}$$

which is identical with the relation $\alpha = 2\Delta\omega$ previously defined.

If we assume a driving source of the form $F_0 e^{-j\omega t}$ for the mechanical system, where F_0 is a constant, the complete solution of Eq. (13-1.5) is given by

$$x(t) = C\, e^{-\frac{R_m}{M}t}\, e^{-j\omega_n t} + j\,\frac{F_0}{\omega Z_m}\, e^{-j\omega t}$$

or

$$x(t) = e^{-\frac{R_m t}{M}}\,[C_1 \cos \omega_n t + C_2 \sin \omega_n t] + \frac{F_0}{\omega |Z_m|} \cos(\omega t - \theta) \tag{13-2.4}$$

where C_1 and C_2 are constants to be determined from the specified initial conditions, and where

$$Z_m = R_m - j\,(\omega M - \frac{K}{\omega}) = R_m - j\,X_m = |Z_m|\, e^{-j\phi} \qquad \text{a)}$$

$$\theta = \frac{\pi}{2} + \tan^{-1}\left[\frac{\omega M - K/\omega}{R_m}\right] \qquad \text{b)} \tag{13-2.5}$$

$$\phi = \theta - \frac{\pi}{2} \qquad \text{c)}$$

$$\omega_n = \sqrt{\omega_0^2 - (\frac{R_m}{2M})^2} \qquad \text{d)}$$

A sketch of the amplitude of the displacement versus frequency for different values of R_m is shown in Fig. 13-2.2a. Figure 13-2.2b shows the phase angle between displacement and driving force.

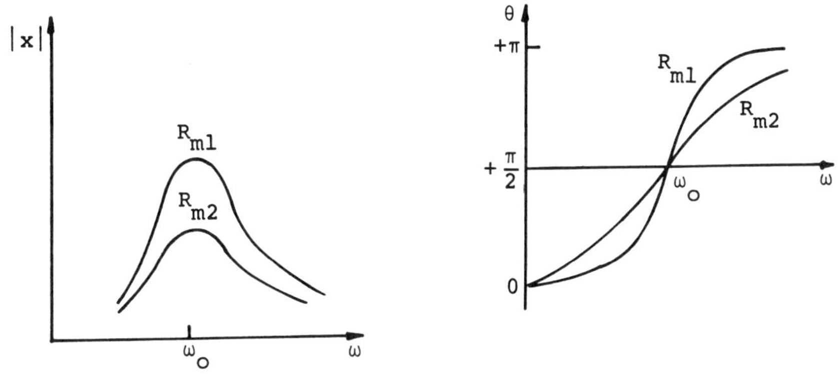

Figure 13-2.2. Amplitude and phase of a dissipative second-order mechanical system.

13-3. Transmission Line as a Resonator

We wish to consider a number of important resonator assemblies. We consider first the transmission line as a resonator.

We assume an electrical transmission line, but with no voltage or current sources present. However, we shall assume a sinusoidal time variation of the form $e^{-j\omega t}$.* For this case, Eqs. (8-1.3) and (8-1.4) becomes

$$\frac{dV}{dx} = -(R-j\omega L)\ I \qquad \text{a)}$$

$$\frac{dI}{dx} = -(G-\ j\omega C)\ V \qquad \text{b)} \qquad (13\text{-}3.1)$$

By differentiating the first with respect to x and combining with the second we develop the equation

$$\frac{d^2V}{dx^2} = \gamma^2 V \qquad (13\text{-}3.2)$$

where

$$\gamma^2 = (\alpha + j\beta)^2 = (R - j\omega L)\ (G - j\omega C) \qquad (13\text{-}3.3)$$

The solution to Eq. (13-3.2) is written in terms of hyperbolic functions of the form

*Throughout this text we have used the time function $e^{-j\omega t}$. Because of this certain functional forms may appear different from the forms which result when the time function $e^{j\omega t}$ is used.

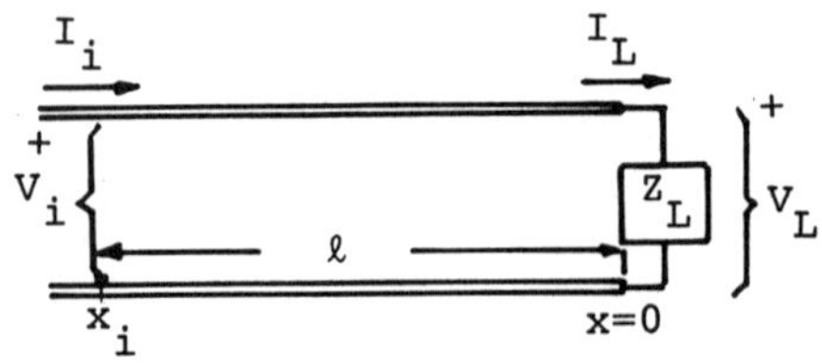

Figure 13-3.1. A terminated transmission line.

$$V = V_1 \cosh \gamma x + V_2 \sinh \gamma x \tag{13-3.4}$$

We substitute this equation into Eq. (13-3.1a) which yields for the current distribution on the line

$$I = -\sqrt{\frac{G - j\omega C}{R - j\omega L}}\,(V_1 \sinh \gamma x + V_2 \cosh \gamma x) \tag{13-3.5}$$

We shall relate the foregoing result to Fig. 13-3.1. Using the last two equations, we see that for x = 0

$$V_L = V_1 \qquad I_L = -Y_o V_2 \qquad Y_o = \sqrt{\frac{G - j\omega C}{R - j\omega L}} \tag{13-3.6}$$

so that at any position x_i relative to the output end of the line

$$\begin{aligned} V_i &= V_L \cosh \gamma x_i - Z_o I_L \sinh \gamma x_i \\ I_i &= I_L \cosh \gamma x_i - \frac{V_L}{Z_o} \sinh \gamma x_i \end{aligned} \tag{13-3.7}$$

Let us take the ratio of these equations, and let $x_i = -\ell$. This gives the input impedance of the transmission line at any distance ℓ from its output end to be

$$Z_i = \frac{V_i}{I_i} = Z_o \frac{Z_L \cosh \gamma\ell + Z_o \sinh \gamma\ell}{Z_o \cosh \gamma\ell + Z_L \sinh \gamma\ell} \tag{13-3.8}$$

We use this equation to find the input impedance to a lossless and lossy line with open and short circuited conditions. These results are contained in Table 13-3.1.

Table 13-3.1. Input Impedance to Transmission Lines of Length ℓ.

	Open Line	Shorted Line
Lossless line	$jZ_o \cot \beta\ell$	$-jZ_o \tan \beta\ell$
Lossy line	$Z_o \coth \gamma\ell$	$Z_o \tanh \gamma\ell$

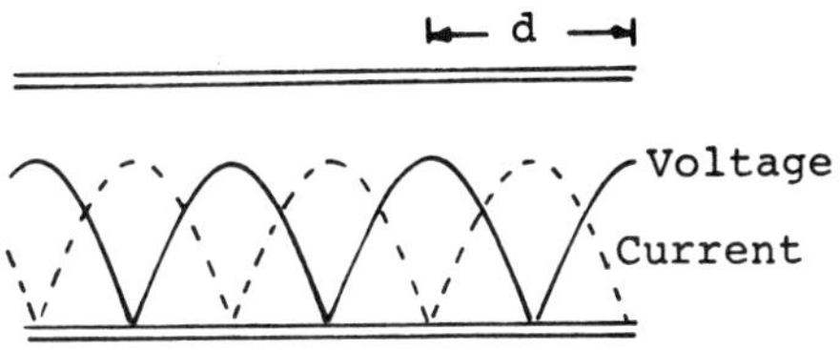

Figure 13-3.2. The voltage and current wave pattern on an open transmission line.

Figure 13-3.2 shows the resonant condition for the lossless transmission line with an open end.

For a low-loss short-circuited line, the input impedance assumes the form

$$Z_{in} = Z_o \tanh \gamma \ell = Z_o \frac{\sinh \alpha\ell \cos \beta\ell - j \cosh \alpha\ell \sin \beta\ell}{\cosh \alpha\ell \cos \beta\ell - j \sinh \alpha\ell \sin \beta\ell} \qquad (13\text{-}3.9)$$

where $Z_o \doteq \sqrt{L/C}$ and $\gamma \doteq R/2 \ \sqrt{L/C} + G \sqrt{L/C}/2 - j\omega \sqrt{LC}$. We examine this equation in some detail. When the input frequency corresponds to the resonant frequency, we have

$$\beta\ell = \frac{\omega_o}{v} \ell = \frac{n\pi}{2} \qquad n = 1,3,5,\ldots$$

When the frequency is shifted a small amount, that is, for $f = f_o + \Delta f$, then

$$\beta_f \ell = \frac{\omega\ell}{v} = \frac{2\pi(f_o+\Delta f)\ell}{v} = \frac{n\pi}{2} + \frac{2\pi\Delta f}{v} \ell$$

and Eq. (13-3.9) becomes

$$Z_{in} = \frac{Z_o}{\alpha\ell - j\left(\frac{2\pi\Delta f\ell}{v}\right)} = \frac{Z_o/\alpha\ell}{1 - j \frac{\omega_o}{v} \frac{\Delta f}{f_o\alpha}} = \frac{Z_o/\alpha\ell}{1 - j\beta \frac{\Delta\omega}{\omega_o} \frac{1}{\alpha}} \qquad (13\text{-}3.10)$$

where we have set

$$\cosh \alpha\ell \doteq 1; \quad \sinh \alpha\ell \doteq \alpha\ell; \quad \cos\left(\frac{2\pi\Delta f\ell}{v}\right) \doteq 1; \quad \sin\left(\frac{2\pi\Delta f\ell}{v}\right) \doteq \frac{2\pi\Delta f\ell}{v}$$

and we have neglected the term $-\sinh \alpha\ell \sin(2\pi\Delta f\ell/v)$ in the numerator as a second order quantity. A plot of Z_{in} expressed by Eq. (13-3.10) as a function of $\Delta\omega/\omega_o$ is given in Fig. 13-3.3. When $|Z_{in}|$ falls to 0.707 of its maximum value, its phase angle is ± 45 deg. The corresponding frequency spread is the bandwidth BW and is given by Eq. (13-3.10),

$$\frac{\beta}{\alpha} \frac{BW}{2\omega_o} = 1$$

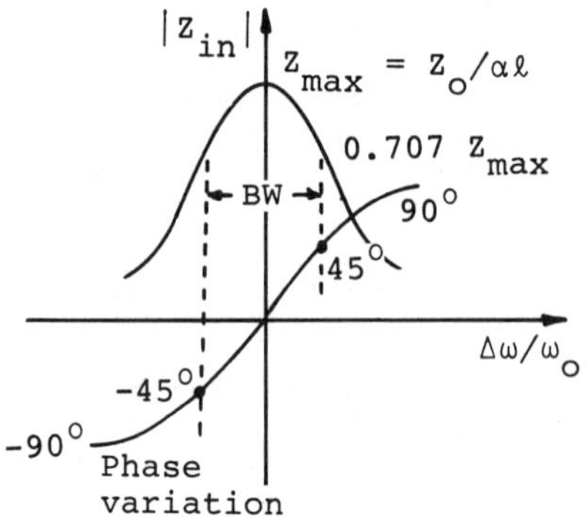

Figure 13-3.3. Z_{in} to a lossy transmission line.

or

$$BW = \frac{2\alpha\omega_o}{\beta}$$

But by definition $Q = \omega_o/BW$, and the Q for the low-loss short-circuited line is given by

$$Q = \frac{\beta}{2\alpha} \tag{13-3.11}$$

13-4. Resonant Phenomenon of Vibrating Strings

We discussed the vibrating string in Chap. 8 where we found that the motion of the string was expressed by the wave equation. For a periodic time variation of the form $e^{-j\omega t}$, Eq. (8-2.5) becomes

$$\frac{d^2y}{dx^2} + \frac{\omega^2}{c_s^2}\, y = 0 \tag{13-4.1}$$

The general solution to this equation is given by

$$y = C_1\, e^{-j\omega\left(t - \frac{x}{c_s}\right)} + C_2\, e^{-j\omega\left(t + \frac{x}{c_s}\right)} \tag{13-4.2}$$

where C_1 and C_2 are constants to be determined from the boundary conditions. If the string of length ℓ is rigidly clamped at its two ends, the boundary condition for all times are:

$$y = 0 \quad \text{at} \quad x = 0; \quad x = \ell \tag{13-4.3}$$

The condition $y = 0$ at $x = 0$ gives

$$0 = (C_1 + C_2)\, e^{-j\omega t}$$

for all t, which implies that $C_1 = -C_2$. This means that the two oppositely moving waves are reflected with a phase change of π degrees. Using this condition, we obtain

$$y = C_1\, e^{-j\omega t}\,(e^{j\omega \frac{x}{c_s}} - e^{-j\omega \frac{x}{c_s}}) = 2jC_1\, e^{-j\omega t} \sin \omega \frac{x}{c_s} \tag{13-4.4}$$

The second condition $y = 0$ at $x = \ell$ requires that

$$\sin \frac{\omega\ell}{c_s} = 0 \qquad \text{or} \qquad \frac{\omega\ell}{c_s} = n\pi$$

which imposes a limit on the allowed frequencies of vibration. The allowed frequencies are specified by

$$\omega_n = \frac{n\pi c_s}{\ell} \qquad n = 1,2,3,\ldots \tag{13-4.5}$$

Sketches showing the first three allowed vibrations of a fixed string are shown in Fig. 13-4.1. The allowable frequencies are the *eigenfunctions, normal frequencies* or *modes*. The points which remain fixed in time are called *nodes* (except for the end-points).

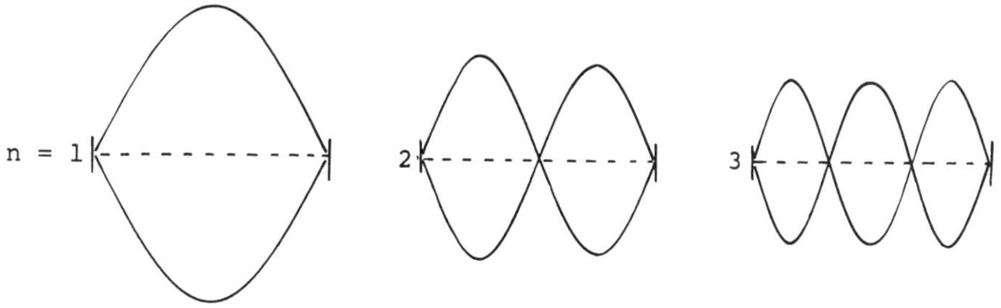

Figure 13-4.1. The first three resonant vibrations of a string.

13-5. Resonances of Membranes

A rectangular membrane of dimensions a, b can be considered as the equivalent of two independent sets of strings along the two directions. To apply the previous analysis, we must have a standing wave with nodal lines parallel to the X- and the Y-axes. In a more formal way, we must begin our discussion with the two-dimensional wave equation [see Eq. (8-4.5)]

$$\frac{\partial^2 z}{\partial x^2} + \frac{\partial^2 z}{\partial y^2} + \frac{\omega^2}{c_d^2} z = 0$$

where z is the upward displacement. To solve this equation, we employ the method of separation of variables. The solution is sought of the form

$$z(x,y,t) = X(x)\ Y(y)\ e^{-j\omega t} \tag{13-5.1}$$

When combined with the controlling differential equation, we find

$$\frac{1}{X}\frac{d^2X}{dx^2} + [\frac{1}{Y}(\frac{\omega^2}{c_d^2} Y + \frac{d^2Y}{dy^2})] = 0 \tag{13-5.2}$$

The sum of the two bracketed terms to be zero requires that each must be equal to a constant, which allows us to write

$$\frac{1}{X}\frac{d^2X}{dx^2} = k_x'^2 \qquad \text{a)}$$

$$\frac{1}{Y}(\frac{\omega^2}{c_d^2}Y + \frac{d^2Y}{dy^2}) = k_y'^2 \qquad \text{b)} \tag{13-5.3}$$

$$k_x'^2 + k_y'^2 = 0 \quad \text{or} \quad k_x'^2 = -k_y'^2 \qquad \text{c)}$$

We assume $k_x' = jk_y'$ to be the imaginary constant, so that the solutions to the two separated equations are

$$X(x) = C_1 \sin k_y'x + C_2 \cos k_y'x$$
$$Y(y) = D_1 \sinh k_y y + D_2 \cosh k_y y \tag{13-5.4}$$

where

$$k_y = (k_y'^2 - \frac{\omega^2}{c_d^2})^{1/2}$$

The resulting solution, with the time factor implied, takes the form

$$z(x,y) = (C_1 \sin k_y'x + C_2 \cos k_y'x)(D_1 \sinh k_y y + D_2 \cosh k_y y) \tag{13-5.5}$$

We apply the boundary conditions which requires that the membrane is rigidly secured at the edges. Thus z = 0 along the diaphragm edges, when x = 0, x = a, y = 0, y = b. For z = 0 at x = 0, Eq. (13-5.5) for any y becomes

$$0 = C_2\ (C_1 \sinh k_y y + D_2 \cosh k_y y)$$

For this equation to become zero, C_2 must be set equal to zero. We do not use the alternate suggested solution with $D_1 = D_2 = 0$ because the resulting function z(x,y) would be independent of y. Thus, the solution which satisfies the first stated boundary condition, z = 0 at x = 0 is

$$z(x,y) = C_1 \sin k_y' x\ (D_1 \sinh k_y y + D_2 \cosh k_y y)$$

We now impose a second boundary condition which requires that z(x,y) = 0 when x = a, independent of y. This requires that either $C_1 = 0$ or $\sin k_y' a = 0$. For a non-trivial solution, the requirement demands that

$$k_y' = \frac{n\pi}{a} \qquad n = 1,2,3,\ldots \tag{13-5.6}$$

Thus the solution that satisfies the two imposed boundary conditions is

$$z_n(x,y) = C_n' \sin \frac{n\pi x}{a}\ [D_n' \sinh k_y y + \cosh k_y y]$$

where we have replaced the arbitrary coefficients C_1, D_1 and D_2 by new coefficients C_n' and D_n'. Hence

$$k_y = \left(\frac{n^2\pi^2}{a^2} - \frac{\omega^2}{c_d^2}\right)^{1/2} = j\left[\frac{\omega^2}{c_d^2} - \frac{n^2\pi^2}{a^2}\right]^{1/2} = j\tau$$

and the solution has now been specialized to

$$z_n(x,y) = C_n' \sin \frac{n\pi x}{a}\ [j \sin \tau y + D_n \cos \tau y] \tag{13-5.7}$$

A third boundary condition requires that z(x,y) = 0 when y = 0. Equation (13-5.7) will meet this condition if $D_n = 0$. The solution now becomes

$$z_n(x,y) = C_n \sin \frac{n\pi}{a} x \sin \tau y \tag{13-5.8}$$

Application of the final boundary condition $z_n(x,y) = 0$ at y = b, requires that the following relationship must hold

$$\tau = \left[\frac{\omega^2}{c_d^2} - \left(\frac{n\pi}{a}\right)^2\right]^{1/2} = \frac{m\pi}{b} \qquad m = 1,2,3,\ldots \tag{13-5.9}$$

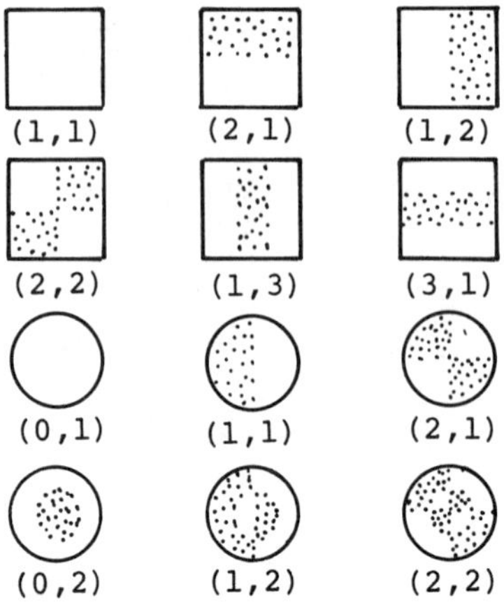

Figure 13-5.1. The first few modes of vibration of a rectangular and a circular membrane.

This equation defines the distinct frequencies (eigenfrequencies) ω_{mn} given by the equation

$$\omega_{mn} = c_d \left[\left(\frac{n\pi}{a}\right)^2 + \left(\frac{m\pi}{b}\right)^2\right]^{1/2} \tag{13-5.10}$$

By combining these results, the real part of Eq. (13-5.1) gives finally

$$z_n(x,y,t) = C_n \sin\frac{n\pi x}{a} \sin\frac{n\pi y}{b} \cos\left(c_d \left[\left(\frac{n\pi}{a}\right)^2 + \left(\frac{m\pi}{b}\right)^2\right]^{1/2} t\right) \tag{13-5.11}$$

The first four modes and the degenerate first and third harmonics are shown in Fig. 13-5.1.

If the membrane is circular, the development will be carried out in cylindrical coordinates in a way that parallels the development for the rectangular membrane. Without including the details several modes of a circular membrane are also shown in Fig. 13-5.1.

13-6. Microwave Resonators

At frequencies greater than 1 or 2 GHz, transmission line resonators have relatively low Q-values. It is preferable to use metallic enclosures. The energy stored in these structures results from the standing-wave electric and magnetic fields. The currents in the walls of the resonator contribute to the power loss. The cavities can be excited by small openings in their walls or by small coaxial-

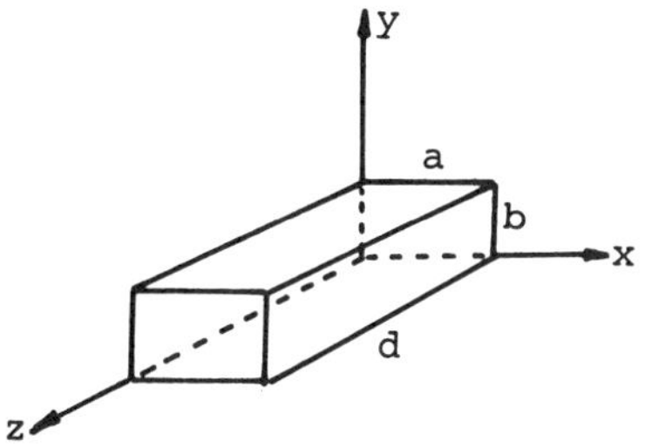

Figure 13-6.1. Rectangular cavity resonator.

line probes or loops. We shall explore such resonators in some detail.

a. Rectangular cavity resonators. Refer to Fig. 13-6.1 which shows a rectangular waveguide resonator. We shall consider that only the lowest TE-mode (namely TE_{10}) is present in this resonator. From Eqs. (11-5.4) and (11-5.20) we find that the wave-field vectors $\overline{E}$ and $\overline{H}$ that propagate in the positive Z-direction are [see Eq. (11-5.26)]

$$\begin{aligned} E_{oy} &= j\frac{\omega\mu k_x A_1}{k_a^2}\sin k_x x\, e^{jk_z z} = j\frac{A_1\omega\mu a}{\pi}\sin\frac{\pi x}{a}\, e^{jk_z z} \\ H_{ox} &= -j\frac{k_z k_x A_1}{k_a^2}\sin k_x x\, e^{jk_z z} = -j\frac{A_1 k_z a}{\pi}\sin\frac{\pi x}{a}\, e^{jk_z z} \\ H_{oz} &= A_1\cos k_x x\, e^{jk_z z} = A_1\cos\frac{\pi x}{a}\, e^{jk_z z} \end{aligned} \tag{13-6.1}$$

To obtain the fields in the interior of the resonator, we must add the waves that propagate in both the positive and the negative directions. This leads to the following expressions

$$E_{oy} = j\frac{\omega\mu a}{\pi}(A_1^+ e^{jk_z z} + A_1^- e^{-jk_z z})\sin\frac{\pi x}{a} = -2A_1^+\frac{\omega\mu a}{\pi}\sin\frac{\pi x}{a}\sin k_z z$$

$$H_{ox} = -jk_z\frac{a}{\pi}(A_1^+ e^{jk_z z} - A_1^- e^{-jk_z z})\sin\frac{\pi x}{a} = -j\frac{2ak_z}{\pi}A_1^+\sin\frac{\pi x}{a}\cos k_z z$$

$$H_{oz} = (A_1^+ e^{jk_z z} + A_1^- e^{-jk_z z})\cos\frac{\pi x}{a} = 2jA_1^+\cos\frac{\pi x}{a}\sin k_z z \tag{13-6.2}$$

In these expressions we have set $A_1^- = -A_1^+$ in order to take into account the 180 degree phase change in the reflected E field. The minus sign in the second equation takes into account the reversal of the H field after reflection, noting that the E field remains unchanged in sign.

In order to satisfy the boundary condition that $E_{oy} = 0$ at $z = d$, we must set

$$k_z = \frac{\pi\ell}{d} \qquad \ell = 1,2,3,\ldots$$

For $\ell = 1$, $k_z = \pi/d$, and the set of equations (13-6.2) now become

$$E_{oy} = -2A_1^+ \omega\mu \frac{a}{\pi} \sin\frac{\pi x}{a} \sin\frac{\pi}{d} z = -2A_1^+ kZ \frac{a}{\pi} \sin\frac{\pi x}{a} \sin\frac{\pi}{d} z; \; Z = \sqrt{\frac{\mu}{\varepsilon}}$$

$$H_{ox} = -j\, 2A_1^+ \frac{a}{d} \sin\frac{\pi x}{a} \cos\frac{\pi}{d} z \qquad (13\text{-}6.3)$$

$$H_{oz} = 2j\, A_1^+ \cos\frac{\pi x}{a} \sin\frac{\pi}{d} z$$

where [see Eq. (11-5.28)] for consistency only discrete values of k are allowed. Hence $k = k_{mn\ell}$, and for our case we have

$$k = k_{101} = [(\frac{\pi}{a})^2 + (\frac{\pi}{d})^2]^{1/2} = [(\frac{\pi}{a})^2 + k_z^2]^{1/2} \qquad (13\text{-}6.4)$$

It follows from this that the resonant frequency is

$$\omega = \frac{k}{\sqrt{\mu\varepsilon}} = \frac{[(\frac{\pi}{a})^2 + (\frac{\pi}{d})^2]^{1/2}}{\sqrt{\mu\varepsilon}}$$

This particular excitation mode is known as the TE_{101} mode and it is shown in Fig. 13-6.2.

The time averaged electric and magnetic energy stored in the cavity is [see Eq. (8-10.11)]

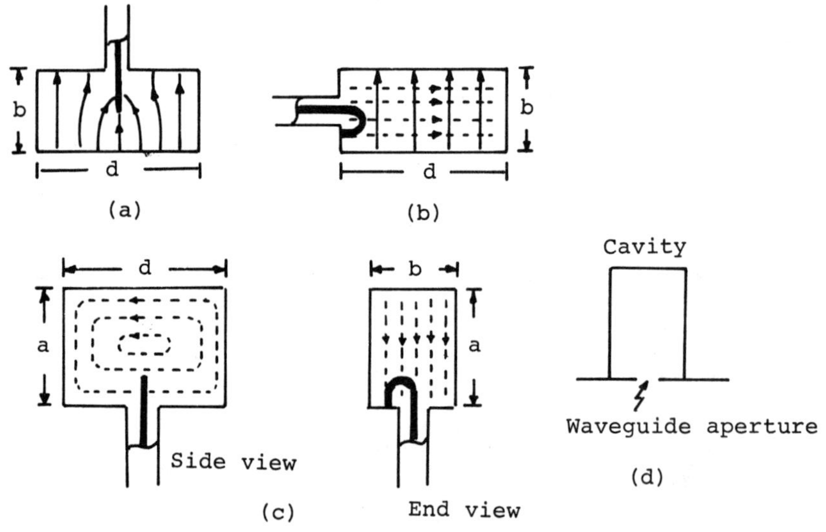

Figure 13-6.2. Methods of exciting the TE_{101} mode from a coaxial line. (a) Probe coupling with E_y; (b) Loop coupling with H_z; (c) Loop coupling with H_z; (d) Aperture coupling.

$$\langle W_e \rangle = \frac{\varepsilon}{4} \int_0^a \int_0^b \int_0^d E_{oy} E_{oy}^* dx\, dy\, dz = \frac{\varepsilon}{4\pi^2} a^3 bd\, k^2 Z^2 |A_1^+|^2 = \langle W_m \rangle \tag{13-6.5}$$

For a low-loss cavity, the currents induced on the six surfaces are nearly equal to those found in the lossless cavity. This means that the magnetic field intensity at the surfaces are not significantly altered by the currents in the walls. By Eq. (10-3.20) the ratio of transmitted fields of a good conductor is

$$\frac{E}{H} = \frac{1-j}{\sigma\delta} = \frac{\sqrt{2}}{\sigma\delta} e^{-j\frac{\pi}{4}} \tag{13-6.6}$$

where δ is the skin depth. As the wave enters the conductor, currents result and this produces power dissipation in the walls. The time-averaged power loss per unit area is computed from the transverse fields E_t and H_t [see Eq. (8-10.12)]. The result is

$$\langle \mathscr{S}_c \rangle = \frac{1}{2} \operatorname{Re} [E_t H_t^*] = \frac{1}{2} \frac{1}{\sigma\delta} |H_t|^2 \tag{13-6.7}$$

Therefore the power dissipated over the area S is

$$P_\ell = \int_S \langle \mathscr{S}_c \rangle \, dS = \int_S \frac{|H_t|^2}{2\sigma\delta} dS = \frac{R}{2} \int_S |H_t|^2 \, dS \tag{13-6.8}$$

where $R = 1/\sigma\delta$ is the surface resistance. For our specified cavity, Eq. (13-6.8) becomes

$$P_\ell = \frac{R}{2} \Big[2 \int_0^a \int_0^d |H_{oz}|^2 dx\, dz + 2 \int_0^b \int_0^d |H_{oz}|^2 dy\, dz + 2 \int_0^a \int_0^d |H_{ox}|^2 dx\, dz + 2 \int_0^b \int_0^d |H_{ox}|^2 dy\, dz\Big] \tag{13-6.9}$$

Using the values for the H-components given in Eq. (13-6.3) in this equation leads to the following expression for the power loss results

$$P_\ell = |A_1^+|^2 R \frac{2a^3 b + 2d^3 b + ad^3 + da^3}{d^2} \tag{13-6.10}$$

The Q-value of this rectangular cavity containing a lossless dielectric becomes, using Eq. (13-8.5),

$$Q = \frac{\omega(\langle W_e \rangle + \langle W_m \rangle)}{P_\ell} = \frac{\omega k_{101}^2 Z^2 a^3 d^3 b\varepsilon}{2\pi^2 R\, (2a^3 b + 2d^3 b + a^3 d + d^3 a)} ; \quad k = k_{101} \tag{13-6.11}$$

b. Number of modes in a rectangular cavity: The number of modes in a given frequency range for a specified cavity is of considerable importance in the theory of radiation. In free space where no boundary conditions exist, electro-magnetic waves can propagate with any wavelength. This is not the case for enclosed spaces for which boundary conditions restrict the allowable field configurations, with only particular modes being permitted. From our previous discussion, we have found that each component of the propagation vector $\overline{k}$ must be of the form

$$k_{x,m} = \frac{m\pi}{a}; \quad k_{y,n} = \frac{n\pi}{b}; \quad k_{z,\ell} = \frac{\ell\pi}{d} \; (n,m,\ell = 1,2,3,\ldots) \tag{13-6.12}$$

which is equivalent to limiting the possible wavelengths that are permitted to

$$\frac{\lambda_x}{2} = \frac{a}{m}; \quad \frac{\lambda_y}{2} = \frac{b}{n}; \quad \frac{\lambda_z}{2} = \frac{d}{\ell}$$

Each set of values (m,n,ℓ) corresponds to a possible mode inside the cavity. Moreover, since it is also required that

$$k^2 = \frac{\omega^2}{c^2} = \pi^2 \left(\frac{m^2}{a^2} + \frac{n^2}{b^2} + \frac{\ell^2}{d^2}\right) \tag{13-6.13}$$

it is evident that for a given frequency (or k) only certain values of m, n, and ℓ are allowed. We wish to examine the allowable modes in some detail.

To study the mode structure, we use a coordinate system that defines the k-space. In this space for a specified frequency, the magnitudes of k_x, k_y and k_z are recorded. This can be done relatively easily if we plot the ellipsoid corresponding to Eq. (13-6.13) which is shown in Fig. 13-6.3. Also graphed in this figure is a cube whose corners represent a particular mode. The distance between modes will be represented as

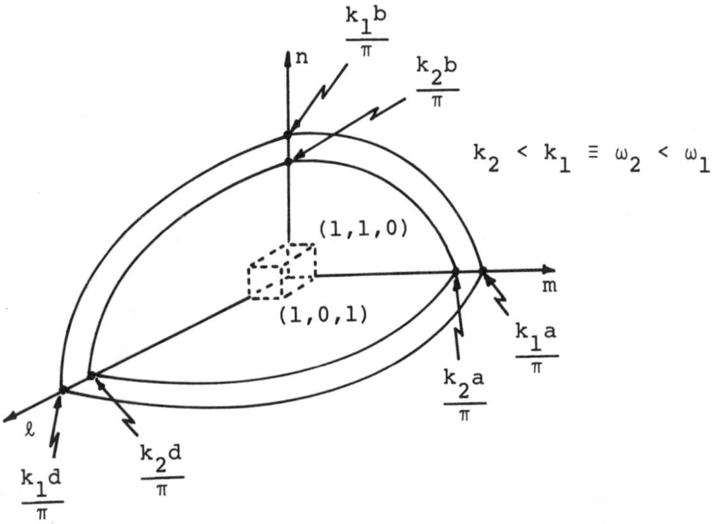

Figure 13-6.3. The k-space ellipsoid whose points correspond to different modes.

$$\Delta k_{x,m} = k_{x,m+1} - k_{x,m} = \frac{2\pi}{2a}\ ;\quad \Delta k_{y,n} = \frac{2\pi}{2b}\ ;\quad \Delta k_{z,\ell} = \frac{2\pi}{2d}$$

which shows that each mode in k-space has an associated volume $(2\pi)^3/8abd$. Hence the mode density is $(8abd)/(2\pi)^3 = 8\ (\text{volume})/(2\pi)^3$. If the frequencies which exist in the cavity range from zero to f, it implies that there exist wave vectors which lie in the range from 0 to ω/c. Hence in k-space the oscillation modes are within the volume of the octant of the ellipsoid. The number of modes is thus seen to be

$$N_{mode} = \left(\frac{\text{volume of ellipsoid}}{8}\right)(\text{mode density})$$

$$= \frac{1}{8}\cdot\frac{4\pi}{3}\left(\frac{\omega}{c}\right)^3 \times \frac{8(abd)}{(2\pi)^3} = \frac{4\pi}{3}\frac{f^3}{c^3}V \tag{13-6.14}$$

where V is the volume of the cavity. Since the propagation of electromagnetic waves can support two orthogonal polarizations, the total number of modes is twice the value given by Eq. (13-6.14). The number of modes N_m per unit volume and per unit frequency range is

$$N_m = \left(\frac{2N_{mode}}{V}\right) = \frac{d}{df}\left(2\cdot\frac{4\pi}{3}\frac{f^3}{c^3}\right) = \frac{8\pi}{c^3}f^2 \tag{13-6.15}$$

In fact, it can be shown that this number applies for cavities of any shape provided that the cavity dimensions are large compared with the wavelengths present.

Using Eq. (13-6.15) we find that the number of modes of a laser cavity of volume V and resonant frequencies lying within the full atomic linewidth Δf of the atomic transition is given by

$$p = \frac{8\pi f^2}{c^3} V\,\Delta f$$

The mode number for a He-Ne ($\lambda = 0.6328\ \mu$) laser cavity of dimensions 35 cm long by 3 mm diameter and atomic linewidth of 1.5 GHz is approximately 5×10^8. In case the cavity contains a dielectric, we must substitute c/η for c in the above equation.

c. Cylindrical cavity: Cylindrical cavities are used extensively in practice as wavemeters because of the high Q-values and the wide frequency ranges possible. Owing to the high Q-values, the resolution is also very high.

In cylindrical waveguides when $d/a < 2$, the TM_{01} mode is the dominant one. The field distribution at points of minimum transverse electric field is shown in Fig. 13-6.4. For the mode numbers n = 0, m = 1, Eqs. (11-5.53) and (11-5.55) will attain the form, using the relation $J_0'(ax) = -aJ_1(ax)$ from Eq. (4-3.14b)

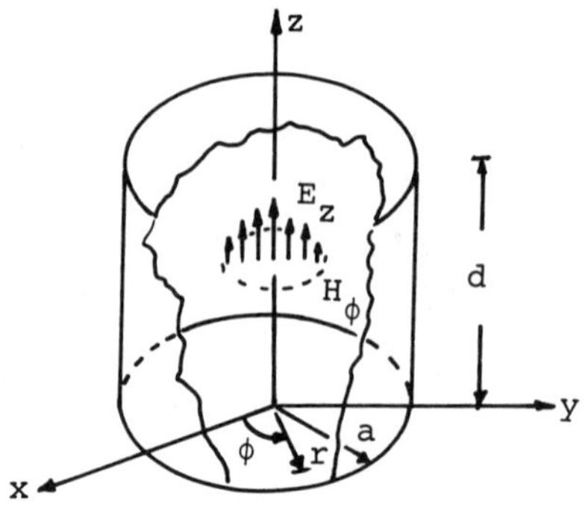

Figure 13-6.4. A cylindrical cavity.

$$E_{oz} = A_1 J_o\left(\frac{p_{01} r}{a}\right)$$

$$E_{or} = j\,\frac{A_1 k_z}{k^2 - k_z^2}\,\frac{p_{01}}{a}\,J_o'\left(\frac{p_{01} r}{a}\right) = -j\,\frac{A_1 k_z}{k^2 - k_z^2}\left(\frac{p_{01}}{a}\right)^2 J_1\left(\frac{p_{01} r}{a}\right) \qquad (13\text{-}6.16)$$

$$H_{o\phi} = -A_1\,\frac{j\omega\varepsilon}{k^2 - k_z^2}\left(\frac{p_{01}}{a}\right)^2 J_1\left(\frac{p_{01} r}{a}\right)$$

where [see Eq. (11-5.52)]

$$k^2 - k_z^2 = k_a^2 = \left(\frac{p_{01}}{a}\right)^2$$

Taking into account that two propagating wave modes travel in opposite directions inside the cavity, we obtain for the total field

$$E_{oz} = J_o\left(\frac{p_{01} r}{a}\right)\left(A_1^+ e^{jk_z z} - A_1^- e^{-jk_z z}\right) = A_1^+\,2j\,J_o\left(\frac{p_{01} r}{a}\right)\cos k_z z$$

$$E_{or} = -j\,\frac{k_z}{k^2 - k_z^2}\left(\frac{p_{01}}{a}\right)^2 J_1\left(\frac{p_{01} r}{a}\right)\left(A_1^+ e^{jk_z z} + A_1^- e^{-jk_z z}\right)$$

$$= 2k_z A_1^+\,J_1\left(\frac{p_{01} r}{a}\right)\sin k_z z$$

$$H_{o\phi} = -\,\frac{j\omega\varepsilon}{k^2 - k_z^2}\left(\frac{p_{01}}{a}\right)^2 J_1\left(\frac{p_{01} r}{a}\right)\left(A_1^+ e^{jk_z z} - A_1^- e^{-jk_z z}\right)$$

$$= -2j\omega\varepsilon\,A_1^+\,J_1\left(\frac{p_{01} r}{a}\right)\cos k_z z \qquad (13\text{-}6.17)$$

where we have set $A_1^+ = -A_1^-$ in order to take the 180° phase change in the reflected field. The component E_{or} vanishes at the boundary $z = 0$. For E_{or} to be zero at $z = d$, we must set

$$k_z = \frac{\pi}{d}\,\ell \qquad \ell = 0,1,2,\ldots \qquad (13\text{-}6.18)$$

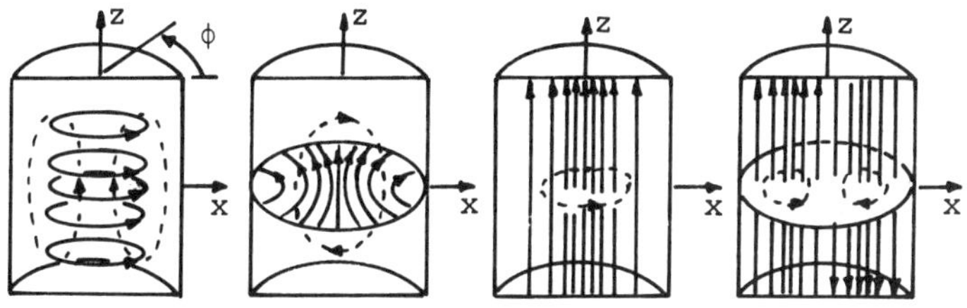

Figure 13-6.5. Fundamental modes in a cylindrical cavity. (Solid line indicate the $\overline{E}$ field, and dotted lines indicate the $\overline{H}$ field.)

and so for the TM_{010} mode

$$k = k_{010} = (k_a^2 + k_z^2)^{1/2} = [(\frac{p_{01}}{a})^2 + (\frac{\pi}{d} \cdot 0)^2]^{1/2} = \frac{p_{01}}{a} = \frac{\omega_{010}}{v} \qquad (13\text{-}6.19)$$

where $v = 1/\sqrt{\mu\epsilon}$; $k_{010} = \omega_{010}/v$. It is evident that for this mode only the fields E_{oz} and $H_{o\phi}$ are present. The lowest resonant frequency of the cavity is specified by the value $p_{01} = 2.405$ given in Table 4-3.1. The value of Q of this cavity follows from Eqs. (8-11.11), (13-6.8), and (13-6.11). Field configurations of different modes in a cylindrical cavity are shown in Fig. 13-6.5.

d. Q-values and shunt resistance of resonators: When cavity resonators are used as wavemeters, as filters, as integral portions of microwave tubes (magnetrons, klystrons) the Q-value and the shunt resistance are of critical importance. We shall discuss these matters.

To discuss the Q-value, we note that the damping of fields in resonators results from energy loss due to the conductivity of the walls and dielectric. Where low damping is required dielectric loss can be minimized in comparision with conductor loss by using air as the dielectric. Where both sources of loss are present, the resultant damping is the sum of the separate dampings. If the conductivity of a uniform dielectric completely filling the resonator is σ and its permittivity is ϵ, then the damping is simply $\sigma/\omega\epsilon$ for any shape or mode. In the more important case of conductor loss, the shape and mode are very important, since the allowable fields are controlled thereby. To explore this matter, we begin with the definition of Q in the more general form

$$Q = \omega \frac{\text{time average energy stored}}{\text{power loss}}$$

To determine the value of Q of the resonator, we must determine the fields inside it and then find by integration the energy of the field and the flow into the walls.

In our previous work we have established that the energy stored in the magnetic field of a resonator (or of any field configuration) is

$$W_m = \frac{1}{2}\int_V \mu H^2 dV = \frac{1}{2}\int_V \mu\overline{H}\cdot\overline{H}^* \, dV \tag{13-6.20}$$

The mean flow of energy into the walls is the real part of the Poynting vector directed toward the walls and the area, thus this is $(1/2)\int_S E_t H_t^* dS$ where E_t is the tangential component of the electric field, and dS is an element of area of the wall. But we found in Sec. 10-3 that for a good conductor [see Eq. (10-3.20)]

$$E_t = R(1-j)\, H_t \tag{13-6.21}$$

where $R = 1/\sigma\delta$ is the equivalent surface resistance per square. The energy lost per second is

$$\mathscr{S}_c = \frac{R}{2}\int H_t H_t^* dS = \frac{R}{2}\int \overline{H}\cdot\overline{H}^* \, dS \tag{13-6.22}$$

We assume that the energy loss is too small to appreciably affect the field distribution, and the expression for Q becomes

$$Q = \frac{\omega\langle W_m\rangle}{\langle\mathscr{S}_c\rangle} = \frac{\mu\omega}{R}\,\frac{\int_V \overline{H}\cdot\overline{H}^* \, dV}{\int_S \overline{H}\cdot\overline{H}^* \, dS}$$

We assume that the dielectric and the conductor have equal permeabilities and we write

$$Q = \frac{2}{\delta}\,\frac{\int_V \overline{H}\cdot\overline{H}^* \, dV}{\int_S \overline{H}\cdot\overline{H}^* \, dS} = \frac{2}{\lambda}\,\frac{\int_V \overline{H}\cdot\overline{H}^* \, dV}{\int_S \overline{H}\cdot\overline{H}^* \, dS}\cdot\frac{\lambda}{\delta} \tag{13-6.23}$$

where δ is the skin depth and λ is the wavelength.

An idea of the order of magnitude of Q can be obtained by assuming a uniform distribution of magnetic energy. A better approximation will result by halving the value obtained as the magnetic fields tend to be strongest near the conducting surface. Approximately, therefore

$$Q \doteq \frac{1}{\delta}\,\frac{V}{S} \tag{13-6.24}$$

where V is the volume and S is the surface area. This indicates the need, for achieving the highest possible Q, that the volume to surface area should be as high as possible. Owing to the approximations concerning the field distribution, one cannot conclude that the spherical resonator has the highest Q, although generally the sphere is better than the cylinder or the cube.

The behavior of a resonant cavity in the neighborhood of a resonance is reminiscent of the parallel resonant circuit with small losses and suggests the existence of a parallel combination of L, C and R_s, where R_s is the resistance across the resonant circuit at resonance, and is called the *shunt resistance.* The suitability of the cavity for producing a high gap voltage from a given input power is measured by the shunt resistance which is defined so that

$$\frac{V^2}{2R_s} = \frac{VV^*}{2R_s} = \mathscr{L}_c \tag{13-6.25}$$

This is so written that if the gap voltage were applied across the shunt resistance, the dissipation would equal that in the cavity. In general terms

$$R_s = \frac{\text{voltage across poles}}{\text{energy loss/cycle}} \tag{13-6.26}$$

If A and B are two points on the wall of a cavity at opposite ends of an electric field line, then for the path AB

$$R_s = \frac{\left|\int_A^B \overline{E} \cdot d\overline{\ell}\right|^2}{R \int_S \overline{H} \cdot \overline{H}^* \, dS} \tag{13-6.27}$$

Transforming the line integral into a surface integral using Stokes' theorem, and using the Faraday law expression for harmonic excitation, $\nabla \times \overline{E} = +j\omega\mu \, \overline{H}$, the result is a formula that involves the magnetic field only

$$R_s = \frac{\omega^2\mu^2}{R} \; \frac{\left|\int_{S_1} \overline{H} \cdot d\overline{S}_1\right|^2}{\int_S \overline{H} \cdot \overline{H}^* \, dS} \tag{13-6.28}$$

For the case of relative permeabilities of dielectric and conductor both unity the factor $\omega^2\mu^2/R$ equals $2\omega\mu_o/\delta$ or $4\pi Z_o/\lambda\delta$ and

$$R_s = \frac{4\pi Z_o}{\lambda^2} \left[\frac{\left|\int \overline{H} \cdot d\overline{S}_1\right|^2}{\int_S \overline{H} \cdot \overline{H}^* \, dS} \right] \frac{\lambda}{\delta} \tag{13-6.29}$$

Here dS_1 denotes an element of the surface having AB as one boundary or path and the rest of the contour being within the wall.

13-7. Coherence of Fields

We shall describe the notion of coherence and fringe formation at optical frequencies by first reviewing the classical experiment by Young. Consider that a source is illuminating two pinholes, as shown in Fig. 13-7.1. We consider the two waves arriving at a point P on a screen at a distance z_{10} from the pinholes as sources. They will arrive at point P with different phases. To simplify the notation, we shall assume that the waves are linearly polarized in the same direction. Two basic cases can be differentiated in our discussion. One case deals with the ideal situation where the optical fields are completely *coherent* and *monochromatic*. The second case refers to partially coherent and incoherent fields. We shall examine both cases.

a. Coherent optical fields: Assume that the screen is at a sufficiently

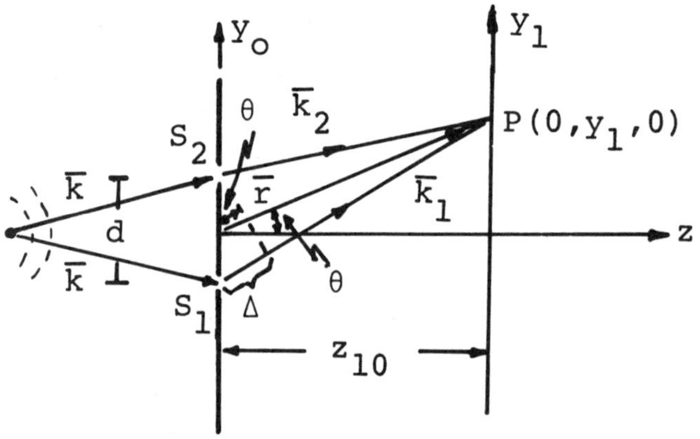

(a)

(b)

Figure 13-7.1. (a) The essentials of Young's experiment; (b) Actual picture of Young's fringes. [Reprinted with permission from Principles of Optics, Third Edition, by Max Born and Emil Wolf. Pergamon Press, 1965.]

large distance so that we can regard the waves produced by the two sources as plane waves. The intensity at the point P is given by

$$I = (E_1+E_2)(E_1+E_2)^* = [E_{10}e^{j\bar{k}_1\cdot\bar{r}}e^{-j\omega t}e^{j\phi_1} + E_{20}e^{j\bar{k}_2\cdot\bar{r}}e^{-j\omega t}e^{j\phi_2}]$$
$$\cdot\ [E_{10}e^{-j\bar{k}_1\cdot\bar{r}}e^{j\omega t}e^{-j\phi_1} + E_{20}e^{-j\bar{k}_2\cdot\bar{r}}e^{j\omega t}e^{-j\phi_2}]$$
$$= E_{10}^2 + E_{20}^2 + 2E_{10}E_{20}\cos[(\bar{k}_1-\bar{k}_2)\cdot\bar{r} + \phi] \tag{13-7.1}$$

where ϕ_1 and ϕ_2 are the initial phases of the wavefronts, and $\phi = \phi_1 - \phi_2$. From Fig. 13-7.1 we can find that $(\bar{k}_1-\bar{k}_2)\cdot\bar{r} = k(\bar{a}_1-\bar{a}_2)\cdot\bar{r} = k\Delta = kd\sin\theta \doteq k\theta d \doteq kdy_1/z_{10}$ and therefore

$$I = E_{10}^2 + E_{20}^2 + 2E_{10}E_{20}\cos\left(\frac{ky_1d}{z_{10}} + \phi\right) \tag{13-7.2}$$

For identical pinholes $E_{10} = E_{20} = E_0$, and for zero initial phases, we have a coherent field with intensity

$$I = 2E_0^2\left[1 + \cos\left(\frac{ky_1d}{z_{10}}\right)\right] = 2I_0\left[1 + \cos\left(\frac{ky_1d}{z_{10}}\right)\right] \tag{13-7.3}$$

This expression shows that the intensity can vary between zero and $4E_0^2$, there being bright fringes when $ky_1d/z_{10} = 0, 2\pi, 4\pi, \ldots$, or equivalently, the fringes occur at the positions

$$y_1 = \frac{n\lambda z_{10}}{d} \qquad (n = 0,1,2,\ldots) \tag{13-7.4}$$

b. Quasi-monochromatic sources: We now assume that the source S of Fig. 13-7.1 radiates two different wavelengths, say $k = k_0 \pm \delta$. Each component will produce its own interferences fringes. Under these conditions, the intensity variation on the screen will be equal to the sum of the intensities

$$I\left(\frac{y_1d}{z_{10}}\right) = I_1 + I_2 = 4E_0^2 + 2E_0^2\left[\cos\left((k_0-\delta)\frac{y_1d}{z_{10}}\right) + \cos\left((k_0+\delta)\frac{y_1d}{z_{10}}\right)\right]$$
$$= 4E_0^2\left[1 + \cos\frac{k_0y_1d}{z_{10}}\cos\delta\frac{y_1d}{z_{10}}\right] \tag{13-7.5}$$

where $\delta \ll k_0$. This formula is well known to the communication engineer, and is exactly of the form of amplitude modulation signals which are transmitted from an AM radio station (see Sec. 10-5). The graphical representation of this equation is shown in Fig. 13-7.2. The dotted line is known as the *visibility curve* and its shape depends on the spectral distribution of the source.

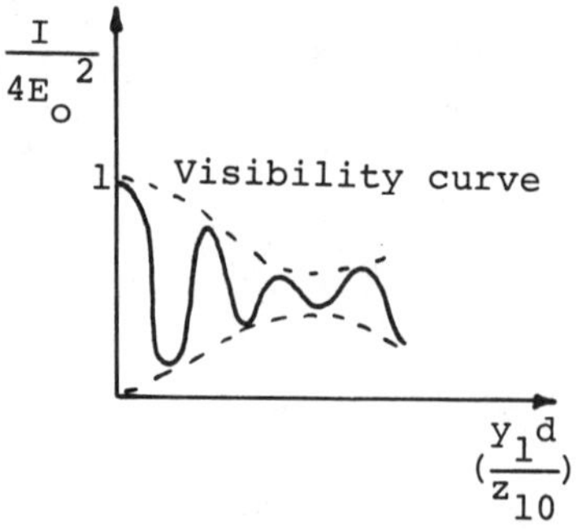

Figure 13-7.2. Visibility curve for a source with two different frequencies.

Suppose, now, that the source spectral distribution is specified in the range from ω to $\omega + d\omega$. The intensity of two interfering beams from the source in the range ω to $\omega + d\omega$ have the following functional form [see Eq. (13-7.3)]

$$I(\omega, \frac{y_1 d}{cz_{10}})d\omega = 2I_o(\omega)\ [1 + \cos(\frac{\omega y_1 d}{z_{10}c})]d\omega = 2I_o(\omega)\ [1 + \cos \omega T]d\omega \qquad (13\text{-}7.6)$$

where $T = y_1 d/cz_{10}$ and c is the speed of light. Upon integrating this formula, we find that the total intensity over the wave frequencies is given by

$$I_t(T) = 2\int I_o(\omega)\ [1 + \cos \omega T]\ d\omega \qquad (13\text{-}7.7)$$

Further, if we assume a symmetrical spectral distribution with a small deviation around the middle frequency ω_o, then we can set $\omega = \omega_o + \Omega$ $(d\omega = d\Omega)$ in the integral with the result that

$$I_t(T) = P + C(T)\cos \omega_o T - S(T)\sin \omega_o T$$

where (13-7.8)

$$P = 2\int I_o(\Omega)d\Omega;\quad C(T) = 2\int I_o(\Omega)\cos \Omega T\ d\Omega;\quad S(T) = 2\int I_o(\Omega)\sin \Omega T\ d\Omega$$

For a band-limited distribution with $\Omega << \omega_o$ we can obtain the variation of I_t with respect to T by assuming that the variations of C(T) and S(T) are slowly varying in comparison to the variations of $\sin \omega_o T$ and $\cos \omega_o T$. Hence we can write

$$\frac{\partial I_t(T)}{\partial T} = -\omega_o[C \sin \omega_o T + S \cos \omega_o T] = 0$$

from which we find that

$$\tan \omega_o T = -\frac{S}{C} \qquad (13\text{-}7.9)$$

The maximums and minimums of I_t are given by

$$\begin{aligned} I_{t,max} &= P + \sqrt{C^2 + S^2} \\ I_{t,min} &= P - \sqrt{C^2 + S^2} \end{aligned} \tag{13-7.10}$$

We now define the *visibility function* by

$$V(T) = \frac{I_{t,max} - I_{t,min}}{I_{t,max} + I_{t,min}} = \frac{\sqrt{C^2 + S^2}}{P} \tag{13-7.11}$$

This equation is of great value because we can determine analytically V(T) if we know the intensity distribution $I_o(\omega)$ of the source. For a spectral distribution with symmetric intensity S = 0 the function $I_o(\omega)$ can be found by a Fourier inversion, if V(T) = C/P is known.

Example 13-7.1. Find the visibility function if the spectral distribution of the source is described by an intensity function of the form shown in Fig. 13-7.3a.

Solution. Since the intensity is a symmetric function, S = 0, and V(T) = C/P. The visibility function, writing $\Omega = \omega - \omega_o$, is then expressed by

$$V(T) = \frac{\int_{-\infty}^{\infty} e^{-|\Omega|/\alpha} \cos \Omega T \, d\Omega}{\int_{-\infty}^{\infty} e^{-|\Omega|/\alpha} \, d\Omega} = \frac{\alpha^2}{(1+T^2\alpha^2)}$$

This function is plotted in Fig. 13-7.3b for two different widths.

c. Monochromatic source and partial coherence: In the foregoing discussion we neglected the influence of the phase of the wave. In actual cases the phase is a function of time, and it should be taken into account. Because the phase is time dependent, the intensity of light at a point will fluctuate rapidly. Since

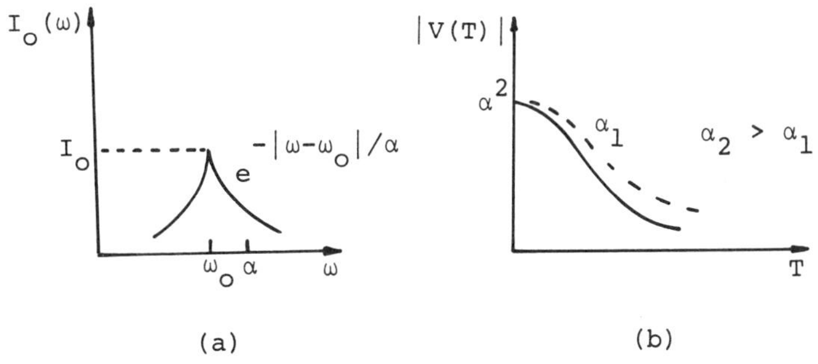

Figure 13-7.3. The intensity distribution and the visibility function of a quasi-monochromatic source.

any detector (e.g., photographic film) responds only to the intensity of the field, we must take the time average of the field at the point of observation. This is

$$I = <(E_1+E_2)(E_1+E_2)^*> = <|E_1|^2 + |E_2|^2 + 2\mathrm{Re}(E_1E_2^*)>$$
$$= I_1 + I_2 + 2\mathrm{Re}\, <E_1E_2^*> \qquad (13\text{-}7.12)$$

where, the brackets indicate the time average over a time interval T_0 that is very large in comparison to the time 1/f of oscillation of the wave.

If the time it takes for the wave to travel the path s_1P is $t_1 = r_1/c$ and the path time s_2P is $t_2 = r_2/c$ (see Fig. 13-7.1) then the interference term of Eq. (13-7.12) is given by the expression

$$\Gamma_{12}(t_1,t_2) = <E_1(t - \frac{r_1}{c})\, E_2^*(t - \frac{r_2}{c})> \qquad (13\text{-}7.13)$$

where $t_1 = t - r_1/c$; $t_2 = t - r_2/c$; and t denotes some initial time. The function $\Gamma_{12}(t_1,t_2)$ is known as the *mutual coherence function.* We shall assume that a *stationary* condition in time exists; this means that the time average is independent of the choice of the origin of time. Setting $t - r_1/c = 0$, Eq. (13-7.13) becomes

$$\Gamma_{12}(\tau) = <E_1(0)E_2^*(\frac{r_1}{c} - \frac{r_2}{c})> = <E_1(0)E_2^*(\tau)> = <E_1(t)E_2^*(t+\tau)> \qquad (13\text{-}7.14)$$

where the term inside the bracket depends only on the difference $(r_1-r_2)/c = \tau$ and not on the times r_1/c and r_2/c explicitly. The time-average of the function $E_1(t)E_2^*(t + \tau)$ is the *correlation* function. From the definition given, we also have the following two identities

$$\Gamma_{11}(0) = I_1; \qquad \Gamma_{22}(0) = I_2$$

The mutual coherence function is usually normalized as follows:

$$\gamma_{12}(\tau) = \frac{\Gamma_{12}(\tau)}{\sqrt{\Gamma_{11}(0)\Gamma_{22}(0)}} = \frac{\Gamma_{12}(\tau)}{\sqrt{I_1I_2}} \qquad (13\text{-}7.15)$$

By combining Eqs. (13-7.15) and (13-7.12) we find that

$$I = I_1 + I_2 + 2\sqrt{I_1I_2}\,\mathrm{Re}\,\gamma_{12}(\tau) = I_1 + I_2 + 2\sqrt{I_1I_2}\,|\gamma_{12}(\tau)|\cos\phi_{12}(\tau) \qquad (13\text{-}7.16)$$

where $\phi_{12}(\tau) = \arg\gamma_{12}(\tau)$. This equation may be written in the form

$$I = |\gamma_{12}(\tau)|\,[I_1 + I_2 + 2\sqrt{I_1I_2}\cos\phi_{12}(\tau)] + [1 - |\gamma_{12}(\tau)|]\,(I_1 + I_2) \qquad (13\text{-}7.17)$$

The first term can be considered the result of the superposition of the coherent parts of the two beams. The second term is the result of the non-coherent parts. Depending on the value of $|\gamma_{12}(\tau)|$, we observe the following cases: (a) $|\gamma_{12}(\tau)| = 1$, complete coherence; (b) $0 < |\gamma_{12}| < 1$, partial coherence; (c) $|\gamma_{12}| = 0$, complete incoherence. The visibility function is easily found to be

$$V = \frac{I_{max} - I_{min}}{I_{max} + I_{min}} = \frac{2\sqrt{I_1 I_2}\,|\gamma_{12}(\tau)|}{I_1 + I_2} \qquad (13\text{-}7.18)$$

and in the particular case for $I_1 = I_2$,

$$V = |\gamma_{12}(\tau)|$$

which shows that the fringe visibility is equal to the *degree of coherence*.

d. Quasi-monochromatic sources: Coherence time and coherence length: It is known as a practical matter that no source of light can radiate strictly monochromatic waves, that is, every spectral line has a certain line width. This follows since in any source, the light is made up of wave-trains of finite length, as shown in Fig. 13-7.4a. Since the wavetrain is finite in time, we may find its spectral components by taking its Fourier transform. We obtain

$$F(\omega) = \int_{-\tau_o}^{\tau_o} (\cos \omega_o t)\, e^{-j\omega t}\, dt = \frac{\sin[(\omega-\omega_o)\tau_o]}{(\omega-\omega_o)} + \frac{\sin[(\omega+\omega_o)\tau_o]}{(\omega+\omega_o)} \qquad (13\text{-}7.19)$$

The spectral function $F(\omega)$ for positive frequencies is plotted in Fig. 13-7.4b. However, since most of the energy associated with the spectral components is contained in the region between $\omega_o - 2\pi/2\tau_o$ and $\omega_o + 2\pi/2\tau_o$, the width of the frequency distribution is given by

$$\Delta\omega = \frac{\pi}{\tau_o} \qquad \text{or} \qquad \Delta f = \frac{1}{2\tau_o} \qquad (13\text{-}7.20)$$

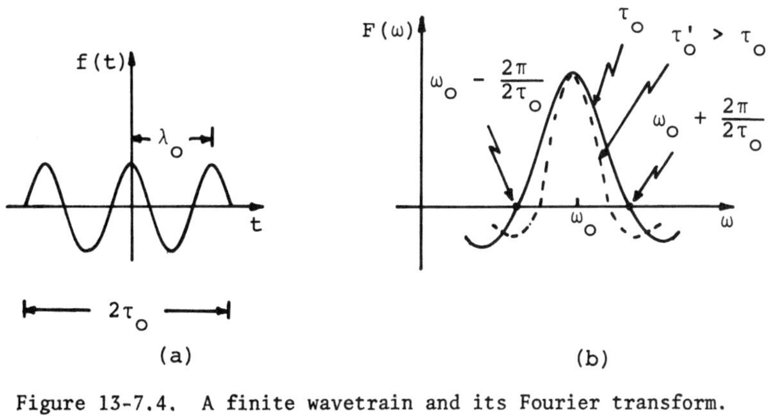

Figure 13-7.4. A finite wavetrain and its Fourier transform.

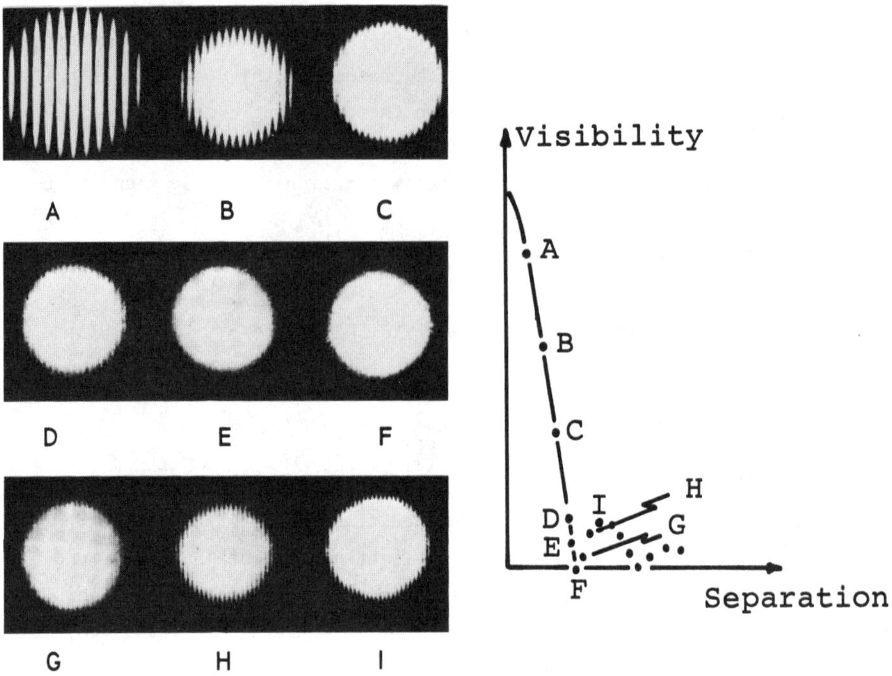

Figure 13-7.5. Visibility versus separation of pinholes. [Reprinted with permission from Physical Optics Notebook, by George B. Parrent, Jr., and Brian J. Thomson, Society of Photo-Optical Instrumentation Engineers, 1969.]

This shows that for wavetrains of different time duration, say of average value $\langle 2\tau_0 \rangle$, there will be a corresponding frequency width Δf. The average time duration $\langle 2\tau_0 \rangle$ is called the *coherence time,* and it is the reciprocal of the line width of the source. Thus the *coherence length* is given by

$$\ell_c = c\,\langle 2\tau_0 \rangle = \frac{c}{\Delta f} = \frac{\lambda^2}{\Delta\lambda} \tag{13-7.21}$$

For example, the line width of an ordinary light source in the visible region is on the order of 10^{-10} m, and so $\ell_c = (.5 \times 10^{-6})^2/10^{-10} = 2.5$ mm. The frequency line width for the laser is about 10^4 which gives a coherence length of the order of 30 km.

Our analysis has been restricted to point sources. If the source is finite the degree of coherence decreases. This can readily be demonstrated if we examine the change of the visibility function with the change in the size of the source. Further, if we keep the size of the source constant and vary the pinhole separation, the visibility of the fringes vary. For a circular source the change of the visibility function has the form shown in Fig. 13-7.5b. However, varying the source size while holding the separation of the pinholes constant produces the same effect.

13-8. Fabry-Perot Resonator

When we are concerned with extremely high frequencies, it becomes impractical to construct simple transmission line or cavity resonators because their dimensions become extremely small. In addition, their Q-values also become very small, owing to the fact that the shunt-Q is inversely proportional to the frequency. The Fabry-Perot resonator is a practical alternative form that has achieved universal acceptance for work in the millimeter and shorter wavelength region, as well as in optics. We shall first examine a simple electromagnetic version, and then we shall examine its form in optics.

a. Simple Fabry-Perot resonator: Refer to Fig. 13-8.1 which illustrates a resonator which comprises two parallel plates separated a distance d apart. If a TEM standing wave exists inside of this resonator, the electric and magnetic fields will be specified by [see Sec. 11-4]

$$E_z = E_o e^{-jkx} e^{-j\omega t} - E_o e^{jkx} e^{-j\omega t} = -2j\, E_o \sin kx\, e^{-j\omega t} \qquad \text{a)}$$

$$H_y = \bar{a}_y \cdot \left(\frac{1}{j\omega\mu} \nabla \times (\bar{a}_z E_z)\right) = 2E_o Y_o \cos kx\, e^{-j\omega t} \qquad \text{b)} \qquad (13\text{-}8.1)$$

Observe that there is a $\pi/2$ spatial phase difference between the two field distributions, and also there is a $\pi/2$ phase difference in time. For the field E_z to be zero at both plates requires that we set

$$kd = n\pi \qquad n = 1,2,3,\ldots$$

or

$$f = \frac{nv}{2d} \qquad (13\text{-}8.2)$$

which determines the resonant frequencies. Also included in Fig. 13-8.1 are the

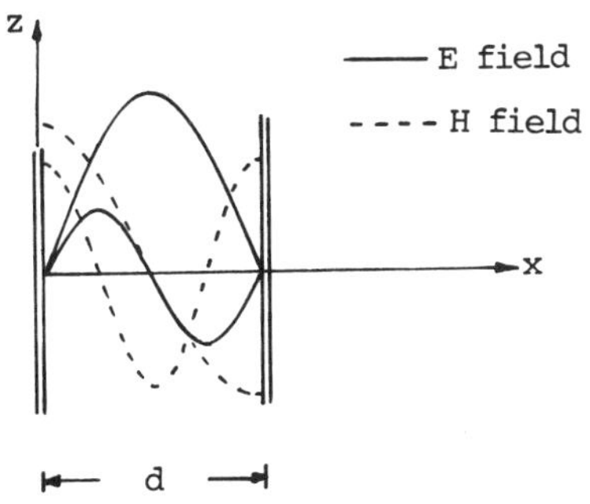

Figure 13-8.1. An ideal Fabry-Perot resonator.

distribution of the two fields for the first and second modes.

To evaluate the Q of this resonator requires that we must evaluate the stored energy and the energy losses. For the parallel plate configuration per unit area, the time-average electric and magnetic energy stored in the field is

$$<W_e> = \frac{1}{4}\varepsilon \int_0^1 \int_0^1 \int_0^d \bar{E} \cdot \bar{E}^* \, dy\, dz\, dx = \varepsilon |E_0|^2 \int_0^d \sin^2 \frac{n\pi x}{d}\, dx$$

$$= \frac{\varepsilon |E_0|^2 d}{2} = <W_m> \tag{13-8.3}$$

Further, the power dissipated in the two plate surfaces is RI^2, where R is the surface resistance of the plates. Now, since $J_{sy} = H_y$, then the power loss per unit area for both plates is

$$P_\ell = 2|J_{sy}|^2 R = 2|2E_0Y_0|^2 R = 8|E_0|^2 Y_0^2 R \tag{13-8.4}$$

The Q of the cavity is, therefore,

$$Q = \frac{\omega_0(<W_e> + <W_m>)}{P_\ell} = \frac{\omega_0 \varepsilon |E_0|^2 d}{8|E_0|^2 Y_0^2 R} = \frac{n\pi Z_0}{8R} \tag{13-8.5}$$

Because n can be chosen to be large, high Q values are possible with this configuration.

Example 13-8.1. Find the Q-value of a Fabry-Perot cavity with dimension d = 6 cm, with an excitation frequency of 100 GHz. The space between the plates is assumed to be a vacuum.

Solution. By Eq. (13-8.2) we find the mode index to be

$$n = \frac{f\ 2d}{c} = \frac{100 \times 10^9 \times 2 \times 0.06}{3 \times 10^8} = 40$$

If we suppose a typical value of 0.1 Ohm for the surface resistance, the Q of this cavity is found to be 59,219. ΔΔΔ

We shall discuss below some of the advantages of this type of resonator.

b. Fabry-Perot resonator in optics: Interference phenomena in optics is essentially the same as that resulting from an array of antennas that radiate coherently with a specified phase difference among the several sources (input currents in this case). The antenna problem will be discussed in Chap. 14, but some important features of the problem will be discussed below. One method for producing a large number of optical beams with a constant phase difference between successive components is by employing multiple reflections between two plane parallel plates which are partially transmitting. For microwave resonators, perforated conducting plates are usually used. Refer to Fig. 13-8.2 which shows a parallel plate

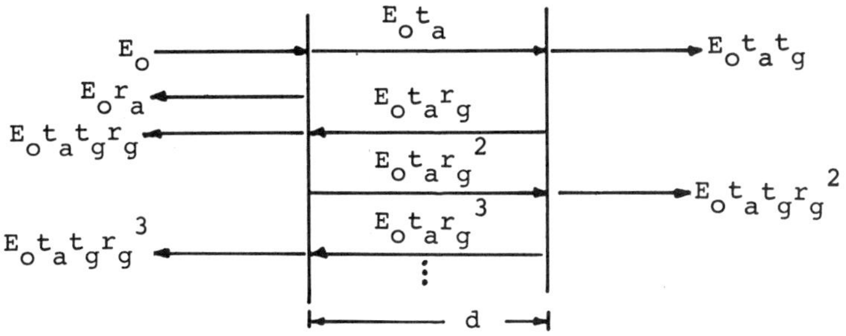

Figure 13-8.2. Fabry-Perot resonator.

configuration with both transmitted and reflected waves. In this figure the factors t denote transmissions and the r's denote reflections. A careful study of the components will show the specific transmission and reflected components by and through the glass surfaces. The amplitudes for the successive internally reflected and transmitted rays are, respectively,

$$E_o t_a,\ E_o t_a r_g,\ E_o t_a r_g^2,\ E_o t_a r_g^3,\ \ldots \quad \text{internal reflected} \qquad \text{a)}$$
$$E_o t_a t_g,\ E_o t_a t_g r_g^2,\ E_o t_a t_g r_g^4,\ \ldots \quad \text{transmitted} \qquad \text{b)} \qquad (13\text{-}8.6)$$

where t_a and t_g are the transmission coefficients from air-to-glass and glass-to-air, respectively, and r_a abd r_g are reflection coefficients from air-to-glass and glass-to-air, respectively. We observe that $r_a = -r_g$, $r_a^2 = r_g^2$, and since $t_a = 1 + r_a$ we obtain (from Eq. (11-8.11))

$$t_a t_g = (1 + r_a)(1 + r_g) = 1 - r_a^2 = 1 - \Gamma_r = \Gamma_t \qquad (13\text{-}8.7)$$

where Γ_r and Γ_t are the *reflectance* and *transmittance factors* of one surface. Furthermore, the phase difference between two successive transmitted rays is $\phi = 2kd$, and this must be taken into account by introducing an exponential phase term $e^{j\phi}$. Equation (13-8.6b) thus assumes the form

$$E_T = E_o\Gamma_t\,(1 + \Gamma_r e^{j\phi} + \Gamma_r^2\, e^{j2\phi} + \ldots) = \frac{E_o\Gamma_t}{1 - \Gamma_r e^{j\phi}} \qquad (13\text{-}8.8)$$

where the geometric series summation was used. If, in addition, we also include any phase change that may occur during reflection, such that $r = |r|e^{j\phi_r/2}$, Eq. (13-8.8) becomes

$$E_T = E_o\,\frac{\Gamma_t}{1 - \Gamma_r e^{j\Phi}} \qquad (13\text{-}8.9)$$

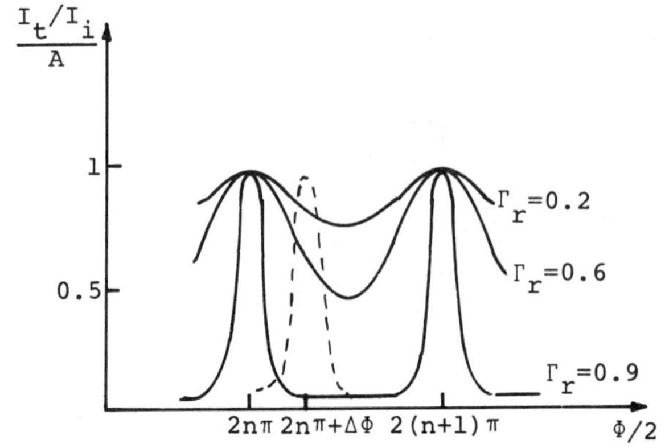

Figure 13-8.3. The Airy function properties.

where $\Phi = \phi + \phi_r$. The transmitted intensity is found to be

$$|E_T|^2 = \frac{\Gamma_t^2}{(1 - \Gamma_r e^{j\Phi})(1 - \Gamma_r e^{-j\Phi})} E_o^2 = \frac{\Gamma_t^2}{1 + \Gamma_r^2 - 2\Gamma_r \cos \Phi} E_o^2$$

and so

$$\frac{I_t}{I_i} = \frac{|E_T|^2}{E_o^2} = \frac{\Gamma_t^2}{(1 - \Gamma_r)^2 + 4\Gamma_r \sin^2 \frac{\Phi}{2}} = \frac{\Gamma_t^2}{(1 - \Gamma_r)^2} \frac{1}{1 + \dfrac{4\Gamma_r \sin^2(\Phi/2)}{(1 - \Gamma_r)^2}}$$

$$= A \frac{1}{1 + B \sin^2 \frac{\Phi}{2}} \qquad (13\text{-}8.10)$$

where

$$A = \frac{\Gamma_t^2}{(1 - \Gamma_r)^2} \quad \text{and} \quad B = \frac{4\Gamma_r}{(1 - \Gamma_r)^2}$$

The second term of Eq. (13-8.10) is known as the Airy function and the factor A is a measure of the sharpness of the interfering fringes. The general behavior of this function is shown in Fig. 13-8.3 for different values of reflectance Γ_r. For a point monochromatic source illuminating a Fabry-Perot interferometer the image is comprised of a set of concentric circles, as shown in Fig. 13-8.4a. If the source radiates two different wavelengths, then the image is like that shown in Fig. 13-8.4b.

This characteristic property of the Fabry-Perot resonator has been successfully used to find the spectrum of sources whose frequencies are too close together to be resolved by any other method, that is, by the use of prisms. If we assume that two frequencies can be resolved when the half-values of their maximums coincide, then from the Airy function [Eq. (13-8.10)] we require that

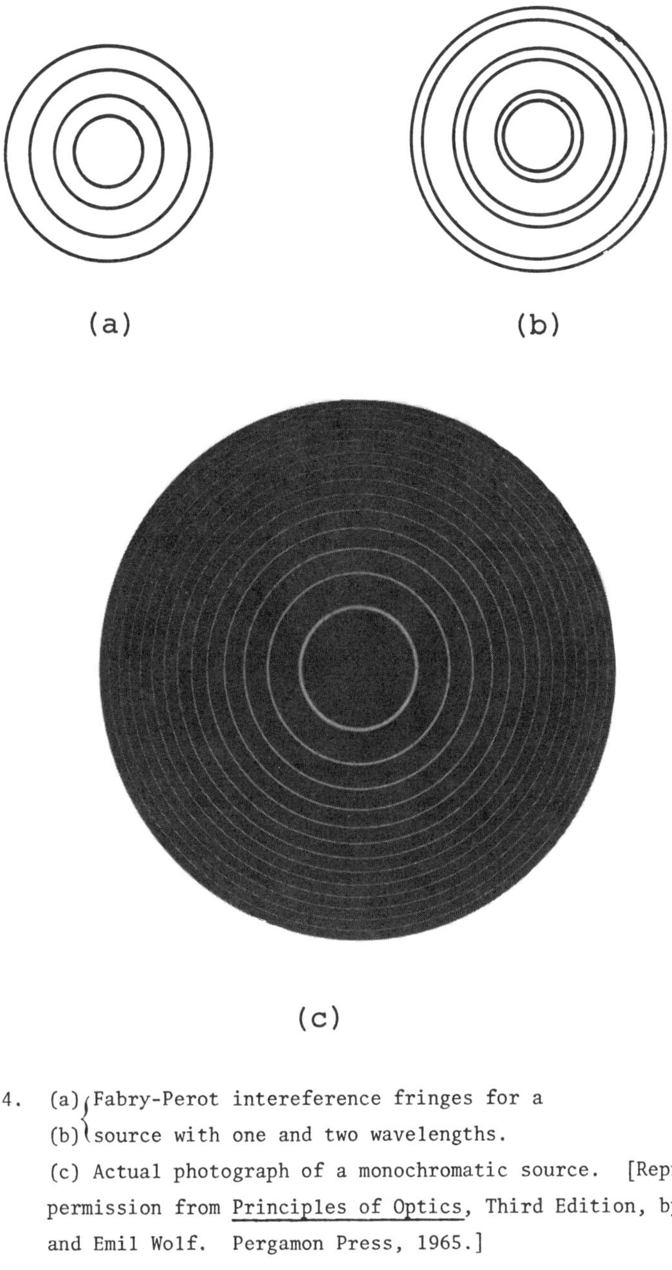

Figure 13-8.4. (a), (b) Fabry-Perot intereference fringes for a source with one and two wavelengths.
(c) Actual photograph of a monochromatic source. [Reprinted with permission from Principles of Optics, Third Edition, by Max Born and Emil Wolf. Pergamon Press, 1965.]

$$\frac{1}{1 + B \sin^2(2n\pi + \frac{\Delta\Phi}{2})} = \frac{1}{2}$$

or

$$\Delta\Phi \doteq \frac{2}{\sqrt{B}} \tag{13-8.11}$$

where we have substituted $(\Delta\Phi/2)^2$ for $\sin^2(2n\pi + \Delta\Phi/2)$. Since the maximum transmitted intensity occurs for phase difference $\Phi = 2n\pi$, then

$$\Phi(2n\pi) = \phi_r + 2kd$$

and for a new wavelength λ'

$$\Phi'(2n\pi) = \phi_r + 2k'd$$

The difference is, for $\lambda \doteq \lambda'$,

$$\Delta\Phi = \Phi - \Phi' = 2\pi d \frac{\lambda'-\lambda}{\lambda\lambda'} \doteq 2\pi d \frac{\Delta\lambda}{\lambda^2} \tag{13-8.12}$$

Combining Eqs. (13-8.11) and (13-8.12) we deduce the *resolving power* of the resonator to be

$$\mathscr{R} = \left(\frac{\lambda}{\Delta\lambda}\right) \doteq \frac{\pi d \sqrt{B}}{\lambda} \tag{13-8.13}$$

For a reflecting surface having $\Gamma_r = 0.9$ with a plate distance $d \doteq 0.85$ cm two spectral lines of approximately $.5 \times 10^{-6}$ microns can be resolved if their wavelengths differ by $\Delta\lambda \doteq 5 \times 10^{-13}$ m which is about one thousand times smaller than the diameter of the hydrogen atom.

13-9. Optical Resonators

A number of different aspects of optical resonators will be examined in this section.

a. Geometrical optics approach: We developed the difference equation that governs the ray propagation in a periodic lens waveguide in Chap. 11. To study the resonance problem, which is equivalent to finding the stability of the system, we

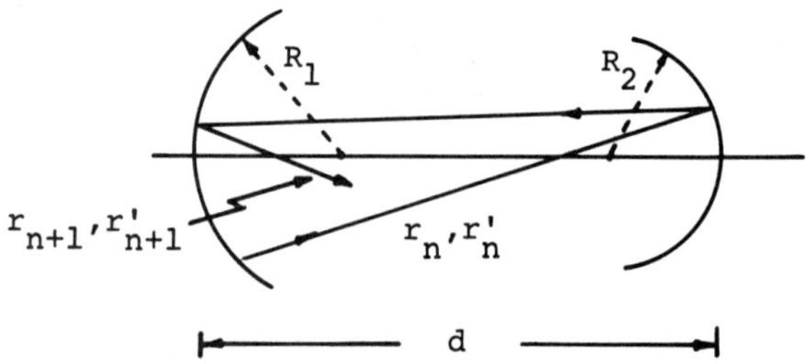

Figure 13-9.1. Optical resonator with two curved mirrors.

shall consider the case involving two mirrors, as shown in Fig. 13-9.1. To develop the equations that govern the rays in this system, we must find the net transformation of a ray in one complete round trip; this is equivalent to one full period of a lens waveguide. We begin with Eq. (11-9.2) where the transformation due to the distance $\underline{d}$ between mirrors is included. Hence

$$\bar{r}_{n+1} = \begin{bmatrix} r_{n+1} \\ r'_{n+1} \end{bmatrix} = \begin{bmatrix} 1 & d \\ -\frac{2}{R_1} & (1-\frac{2d}{R_1}) \end{bmatrix} \begin{bmatrix} 1 & d \\ -\frac{2}{R_2} & (1-\frac{2d}{R_2}) \end{bmatrix} \begin{bmatrix} r_n \\ r'_n \end{bmatrix}$$

which expands to

$$\bar{r}_{n+1} = \begin{bmatrix} r_{n+1} \\ r'_{n+1} \end{bmatrix} = \begin{bmatrix} (1 - q_2) & d(2 - q_2) \\ -\frac{1}{d}[q_2(1-q_1)+q_1] & -q_1+(1-q_1)(1-q_2) \end{bmatrix} \begin{bmatrix} r_n \\ r'_n \end{bmatrix} = [A]\,\bar{r}_n \tag{13-9.1}$$

where $\bar{r}_{n+1}$ and $\bar{r}_n$ are the vector representations of the two column matrixes, and $q_1 = 2d/R_1$ and $q_2 = 2d/R_2$.

To find the eigenvalues of the system and thus to find the normal modes, we require that the output vector $\bar{r}_{n+1}$ is equal to the input vector $\bar{r}_n$ multiplied by a constant λ. [See Appendix VI.] We thus obtain

$$\bar{r}_{n+1} = [A]\bar{r}_n = \lambda\bar{r}_n \tag{13-9.2}$$

We now solve this eigenvalue problem by examining

$$|[A] - \lambda[I]| = \begin{vmatrix} \zeta_2 - \lambda & d(1 + \zeta_2) \\ -\frac{1}{d}(1 - \zeta_1\zeta_2) & (\zeta_1 + \zeta_1\zeta_2 - 1) - \lambda \end{vmatrix} = 0 \tag{13-9.3}$$

where we have written $\zeta_1 = 1 - q_1$ and $\zeta_2 = 1 - q_2$. We find from this that

$$\lambda = \lambda_1,\lambda_2 = \frac{\zeta_1 + \zeta_2 + \zeta_1\zeta_2 - 1}{2} \pm \sqrt{\left(\frac{\zeta_1 + \zeta_2 + \zeta_1\zeta_2 - 1}{2}\right)^2 - 1} \tag{13-9.4}$$

Associated with these two eigenvalues are the two eigenvectors that satisfy the equations

$$[A]\bar{r}^{(1)} = \lambda_1\bar{r}^{(1)}; \qquad [A]\bar{r}^{(2)} = \lambda_2\bar{r}^{(2)} \tag{13-9.5}$$

From matrix algebra considerations we know that the eigenvectors are independent for distinct eigenvalues. We can use these eigenvectors as a basis so that any vector may be written as a sum of $\bar{r}^{(1)}$ and $\bar{r}^{(2)}$ in the form

$$\bar{r}_0 = C_1\bar{r}^{(1)} + C_2\bar{r}^{(2)} \tag{13-9.6}$$

Since with each complete passage each eigenvector is multiplied by its eigenvalue, then after n such passages, the output vector takes the form

$$\bar{r}_n = C_1\lambda_1^{\,n}\,\bar{r}^{(1)} + C_2\lambda_2^{\,n}\,\bar{r}^{(2)} \tag{13-9.7}$$

For this system to be stable, that is, for $\bar{r}_n$ to be bounded, the values which the eigenvalues take must be complex. Therefore for a stable system [see Eq. (13-9.4)] we must have that

$$0 \leq \frac{\zeta_1 + \zeta_2 + \zeta_1\zeta_2 - 1}{2} \leq 1$$

or

$$0 \leq \left(1 - \frac{d}{R_1}\right)\left(1 - \frac{d}{R_2}\right) \leq 1 \tag{13-9.8}$$

The eigenvalues then become

$$\lambda_1, \lambda_2 = (2s_1s_2 - 1) \pm j\sqrt{4s_1s_2(s_1s_2 - 1)} \tag{13-9.9}$$

where $s_1 = 1 - d/R_1$ and $s_2 = 1 - d/R_2$. If we set

$$\lambda_1, \lambda_2 = \cos\theta \pm j\sin\theta = e^{\pm j\theta} \qquad (\cos\theta = 2s_1s_2 - 1) \tag{13-9.10}$$

then Eq. (19-9.7) takes the form

$$\begin{bmatrix} r_n \\ r'_n \end{bmatrix} = C_1 e^{jn\theta}\begin{bmatrix} r^{(1)} \\ r'^{(1)} \end{bmatrix} + C_2 e^{-jn\theta}\begin{bmatrix} r^{(2)} \\ r'^{(2)} \end{bmatrix} \tag{13-9.11}$$

Since r_n and r'_n must be real numbers, then $C_1r^{(1)}$ and $C_2r^{(2)}$ must be complex conjugates. The same reasoning applies to the other two terms $C_1r'^{(1)}$ and $C_2r'^{(2)}$. We set, for convenience,

$$C_1r^{(1)} = \frac{C}{2}\,e^{j\phi}$$

$$C_2r^{(2)} = \frac{C}{2}\,e^{-j\phi}$$

and the displacement after n passages is given by

$$r_n = C\cos(n\theta + \phi) \tag{13-9.12}$$

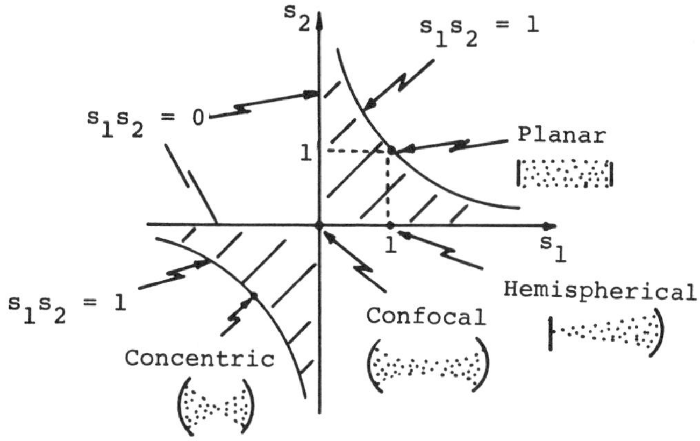

Figure 13-9.2. The stability diagram for optical resonators.

This indicates that the ray oscillates about the axis and remains within a bounded maximum.

The system is unstable if either of the following inequalities exist

$$s_1 s_2 < 0, \quad \text{or} \quad s_1 s_2 > 1 \tag{13-9.13}$$

To find the regions of stability, we graph the relation $s_1 s_2 = 1$, which is shown in Fig. 13-9.2. The shaded region gives the values of s_1 and s_2 which correspond to stable systems.

b. Gaussian beams in resonators: If two curved mirrors are provided such that their curvatures coincide with the curvature of the wavefront of the beam, as shown in Fig. 13-9.3, then the beam will bounce back and forth between the two mirrors, preserving the spot size. This trapped beam will form a standing-wave resonant mode of the lowest order. For large mirrors and small diameter beams, the resonant

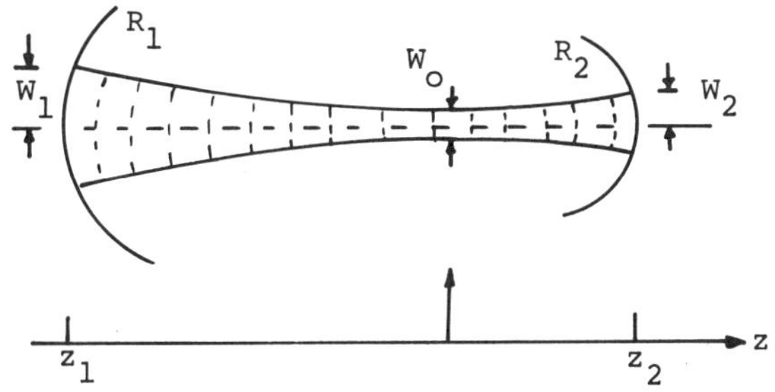

Figure 13-9.3. Optical resonator.

mode depends on the mirror curvatures and their spacing $d = z_2 - z_1$.

We wish to find the appropriate beam dimension for two mirrors, given the spacing and the mirror characteristics. We apply the Gaussian beam formula, Eq. (12-7.9d), so that

$$z_1 + \frac{(\pi W_o^2/\lambda)^2}{z_1} = -R_1; \quad z_2 + \frac{(\pi W_o^2/\lambda)^2}{z_2} = R_2; \quad z_2 - z_1 = d \tag{13-9.14}$$

Now eliminate $(\pi W_o^2/\lambda)^2$ from the first two equations, and substitute $z_2 = d + z_1$ from the third expression, to find

$$z_1 = -\frac{R_2 d - d^2}{R_1 + R_2 - 2d} = -\frac{R_1R_2d(\frac{d}{R_1} - \frac{d^2}{R_1R_2})}{R_1R_2(\frac{d}{R_1} + \frac{d}{R_2} - \frac{2d^2}{R_1R_2})} = -d\,\frac{s_2(1 - s_1)}{s_1 + s_2 - 2s_1s_2} \qquad \text{a)}$$

where $s_1 = 1 - d/R_1$ and $s_2 = 1 - d/R_2$. By substituting Eq. (13-9.15a) into (13-9.14) the other two unknowns can be specified; thus

$$z_2 = d\,\frac{s_2(1 - s_2)}{s_1 + s_2 - 2s_1s_2} \qquad \text{b)} \tag{13-9.15}$$

$$\left(\frac{\pi W_o^2}{\lambda}\right)^2 = d^2\,\frac{s_1s_2(1 - s_1s_2)}{(s_1 + s_2 - 2s_1s_2)^2} \qquad \text{c)}$$

The spot size at the distance z_2 is found by using Eq. (12-7.9e) and (13-9.15c). The result is

$$W_2(z_2) = W_o\left[1 + \frac{z_2}{\left(\frac{\pi W_o^2}{\lambda}\right)^2}\right]^{1/2} = W_o\left[1 + \frac{(1 - s_1)(s_1 + s_2 - 2s_1s_2)}{s_1(1 - s_1s_2)}\right]^{1/2} \tag{13-9.16}$$

We observe from this equation that the spot size will remain finite except when $s_1 = 0$ or when $s_1s_2 = 1$. It is observed that the stability relation $s_1s_2 = 1$ is identical with that found in Eq. (13-9.13). Hence the stability diagram of Fig. 13-9.2 applies equally well for the Gaussian resonator mode solutions.

Modes higher than the fundamental are also observed. A schematic representation of some of these modes is shown in Fig. 13-9.4.

c. Multielement resonator: When the resonator is composed of many elements, it often is desired to find the wave profile of the Gaussian beam such that the total system resonates. To proceed in this analysis, we must refer to the factor q (complex radius) given in Eq. (12-7.9c) in the form (setting $z_1 = z$)

$$\frac{1}{q(z)} = \frac{1}{q_o + z} = \frac{1}{R(z)} + j\,\frac{\lambda}{\pi W^2(z)} \tag{13-9.17}$$

where $q_o = -j(\pi W_o^2/\lambda)$. From the first part of Eq. (13-9.17) we see that with a

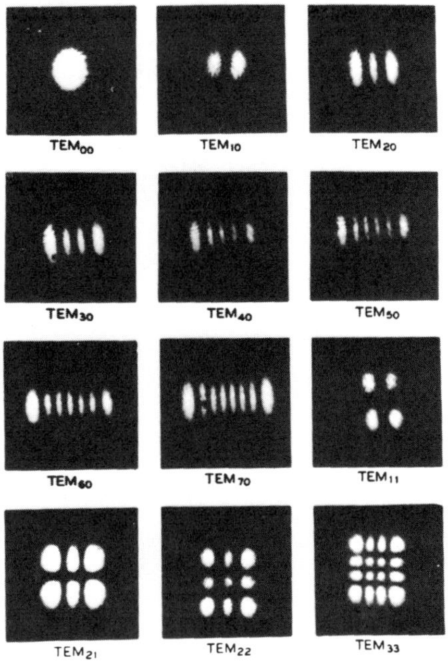

Figure 13-9.4. Mode patterns of a gas laser oscillator. [Reprinted with permission from IEEE Proc., Vol. 54, p. 1317, H. Kogelnik and T. Li, "Laser Beams and Resonators," 1966.]

knowledge of q(z) at some plane $z = z_1$, then its value at any other plane $z = z_2$ is readily determined, since

$$q(z_2) = q(z_1) + (z_2 - z_1) \tag{13-9.18}$$

For a spherical wave shown in Fig. 13-9.5, the radius at z_2 is related to that at z_1 by

$$R(z_2) = R(z_1) + (z_2 - z_1) \tag{13-9.19}$$

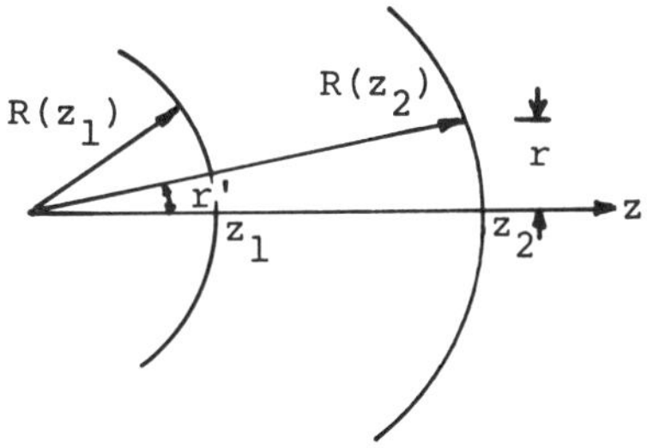

Figure 13-9.5. A spherical wavefront.

which is identical in form to Eq. (13-9.18). But from the figure we also find a relation between the wavefront curvature R and the ray parameters r and r'; this is

$$R = \frac{r}{r'} \tag{13-9.20}$$

But using Eq. (13-9.1) we find that the wavefront curvatures between the input and output ray is given by

$$R = \frac{r_2}{r_2'} = \frac{Ar_1 + Br_1'}{Cr_1 + Dr_1'} = \frac{AR_1 + B}{CR_1 + D} \tag{13-9.21}$$

where

$$A = (1 - \frac{d}{f_{\ell 2}}); \qquad B = d(2 - \frac{d}{f_{\ell 2}})$$

$$C = -\frac{1}{d}[\frac{d}{f_{\ell 1}}(1 - \frac{d}{f_{\ell 2}}) + \frac{d}{f_{\ell 1}}]; \quad D = -\frac{d}{f_{\ell 1}} + (1 - \frac{d}{f_{\ell 1}})(1 - \frac{d}{f_{\ell 2}}) \tag{13-9.22}$$

We have here set $R/2 = f_\ell$ which means that we are considering the wavefront transformation in a system of lenses as shown in Fig. 13-9.6. This configuration is described by an expression having the same form for the A,B,C,D factors as given for the system of two reflecting mirrors. Equation (13-9.21) is important because it relates the curvature of the wavefront in two different planes. We note that if a spherical wave passes through a thin lens, its curvature before and after its emergence is given by [see Eq. (11-9.2)]

$$\frac{1}{R_2} = \frac{1}{R_1} - \frac{1}{f} \tag{13-9.23}$$

Also, comparing Eqs. (13-9.19) and (13-9.18) we see that in passing through a homogeneous medium, the parameter q transforms identically as the wavefront curvature of R of a spherical wave. Moreover, when a Gaussian beam passes through a thin lens, its width W does not change even though 1/R changes as -1/f, as shown in Eq. (13-9.23). We thus observe from Eq. (13-9.17) that

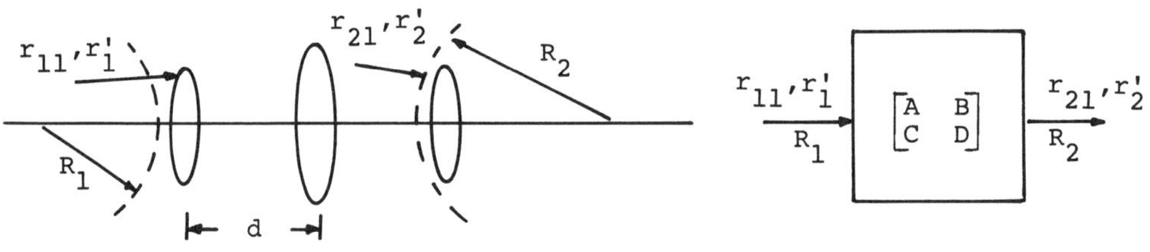

Figure 13-9.6. Propagation in period resonator.

$$\frac{1}{q_2(z_2)} = \frac{1}{q_1(z_1)} - \frac{1}{f} \tag{13-9.24}$$

The similarity between Eqs. (13-9.19) and (13-9.23) and Eqs. (13-9.18) and (13-9.24) leads us to the conclusion that q is also transformed by a relation of the form

$$q_2 = \frac{Aq_1 + B}{Cq_1 + D} \tag{13-9.25}$$

For a stable Gaussian mode, we must have a repetition of its wavefront at the beginning of its spatial period. This requires that

$$q_2 = \frac{Aq_1 + B}{Cq_1 + D} = q_1 \qquad \text{or} \qquad B\left(\frac{1}{q_1}\right)^2 - (D-A)\frac{1}{q_1} - C = 0$$

which has the solution

$$\frac{1}{q_1} = \frac{D-A \pm \sqrt{(D-A)^2 + 4BC}}{2B} \tag{13-9.26}$$

We obtain from this expression, using the property of ray matrixes $AD - BC = 1$ (see Eq. 13-9.22)

$$\frac{1}{q_1} = \frac{D-A}{2B} + j\,\frac{1}{2B}\sqrt{4-(A+D)^2} = \frac{1}{R_1} + j\,\frac{\lambda}{\pi W_1{}^2} \tag{13-9.27}$$

Since the Gaussian beam must have a finite real spot size, the constants of the matrix must obey the condition

$$(A-D)^2 \leq 4BC \tag{13-9.28}$$

Equation (13-9.27) permits us to find the wavefront curvature for the resonant mode and its spot size W_1 at a selected starting point.

Optical resonators have losses associated with them, the most important of which are:

a. Nonperfect reflection (transmission, surface irregularities, etc.)
b. Absorption (in the medium between the reflectors)
c. Scattering (in the medium between the reflectors)
d. Diffraction (the wavefield distribution extends outside of the reflecting areas; higher modes tend to spread the field away from the optic axis).

To investigate the Q of an optical resonator, we shall consider a simple parallel plane resonator, shown in Fig. 13-9.7. In this cavity, the number of half-

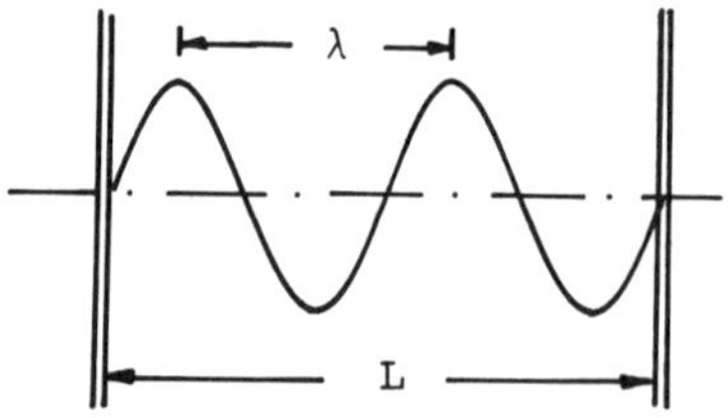

Figure 13-9.7. Optical cavity with parallel mirrors.

wavelengths which can be present are

$$\frac{n\lambda}{2} = L \tag{13-9.29}$$

The number n is an integer and defines the mode number that may exist. In addition to purely geometrical considerations which must be satisfied for a mode to exist, the net gain of the cavity at the resonant wavelength must exceed unity. Suppose that the cavity resonates at wavelengths λ_1 and λ_2 which are quite close together. We write the following relations for two different modes

$$\begin{aligned} n\lambda_1 &= 2L \\ (n+1)\lambda_2 &= 2L \end{aligned} \tag{13-9.30}$$

We combine the two relations to find that

$$\Delta\lambda = \frac{\lambda^2}{2L} \tag{13-9.31}$$

where it has been assumed that $\lambda_1\lambda_2 \doteq \lambda^2$ and $\lambda_1 - \lambda_2 = \Delta\lambda$. Equation (13-9.31) indicates that the wavelength separation between modes is a function of the wavelength itself and the length of the cavity.

The quality factor Q of the resonator can be expressed in terms of the loss per reflection at each mirror and the energy stored in the cavity. If α is the loss per reflection due to all causes noted above, then we can write

$$Q = \omega\left(\frac{\text{time-average energy stored}}{\text{energy lost per second}}\right) = \omega\left(\frac{Nh\nu AL}{\alpha Nh\nu Ac}\right) = \frac{2\pi L}{\alpha\lambda} \tag{13-9.32}$$

where N = density of quanta in the cavity, A = the cross-sectional area, $h\nu$ = energy per photon. If the diffraction, absorption and scattering losses are small in comparison with reflection losses, then the Q of the cavity can increase by increasing the spacing between the reflecting mirrors. However, a separation is reached when the diffraction losses start to predominate and it becomes impractical to increase further the mirror spacing.

REVIEW QUESTIONS

1. What determines the natural frequency of a system?
2. Do dissipative systems have natural frequencies?
3. What do the Q of systems indicate?
4. What does the transfer function define?
5. What do modes and what do nodes specify in a system?
6. Are the modes of a string different from those of a rectangular membrane?
7. Why always does the field inside a resonator decay?
8. What is the shunt resistance of a resonator?
9. What conclusions may we reach by observing the results of Young's experiment?
10. What type of sources produce the visibility curve?
11. Define the mutual coherence function.
12. Can we ever find a source with completely monochromatic light?
13. What is coherence length and coherence time?
14. What happens to the visibility curve when we increase the dimensions of the source?
15. What is one of the many uses of the optical Fabry-Perot resonator?
16. What factors increase the resolving power of the optical Fabry-Perot resonator?
17. What do we mean by stable or unstable optical systems?
18. Which are the most important losses in an optical resonator?

PROBLEMS

13-1.1. Is there any difference in frequency between a damped and an undamped oscillator operating at presumably the same frequency? If there is, find this difference for $\delta/2\omega \ll 1$, where δ is the decrement, and show that for all practical purposes the difference can be ignored.

13-1.2. Find the Q of a low loss RLC parallel circuit.
[Ans: $Q = R/\omega L$]

13-3.1. Find the Q of an open line resonator.
[Ans: $Q = \beta/2\alpha$]

13-3.2. Find the Q of a line with low losses and $G = 0$.
[Ans: $Q = \omega L/R$]

13-5.1. Sketch the normal modes of a rectangular membrane for $n = 2$, $m = 3$.

13-6.1. Sketch the E and H fields on the plane $y = b/2$ of the rectangular resonator.

13-6.2. Verify Eqs. (13-7.5), (13-7.6), and (13-7.11), and find the Q of the cube.

13-6.3. Find the Q of a rectangular cavity whose dimensions are the following: $a = 3$ cm, $b = 2$ cm, $d = 5$ cm. The cavity is being excited by an X-band microwave source (range 8.5 - 12.5 GHz). The conductivity of the walls is $\sigma = 6 \times 10^7$ mhos/m.

13-6.4. Find the Q value of the TM_{010} in a cylindrical cavity.

13-7.1. Find the amount of shift of an interference pattern in Young's experiment if $\phi = \pi/4$.

13-7.2. Verify Eqs. (13-7.5), (13-7.10), and (13-7.11).

13-7.3. Show the proof of the relation $I_t(T)/A = 1 + V(T) \cos(\theta + \omega_0 T)$ where $\theta = \tan^{-1}(S/C)$. This relation shows that the visibility function is the envelope of the intensity variation.

[Hint: From Eq. (13-7.7a) $\frac{I_t}{A} = 1 + \frac{C}{A}(\cos \omega_0 T - \frac{S}{C} \sin \omega_0 T)$. Set $S/C = \tan \theta$ and compare with Eq. (13-7.10).]

13-7.4. Find the visibility function if the spectral distribution is a pulse of height I_0 and width $\Delta\Omega$.

[Ans: $V(T) = \sin(\frac{\Delta\Omega}{2} T)/(\frac{\Delta\Omega}{2} T)$]

13-7.5. A plane wave that is polarized in the X-direction is reflected from a perfect conducting plane, as shown in the figure. Show that when a photographic film is exposed to the field it will be darkened at the positions shown.

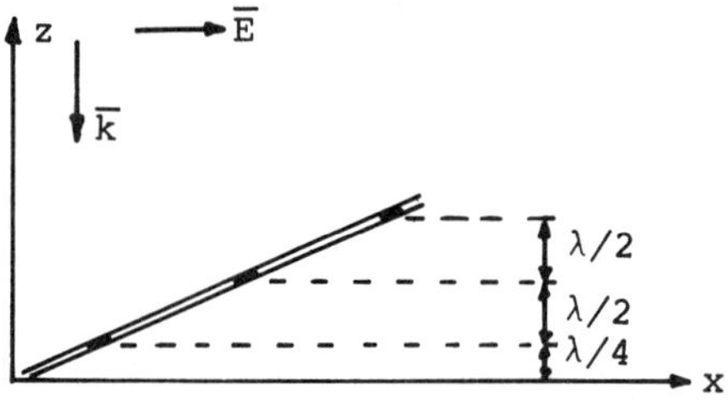

Figure P13-7.5.

13-7.6. Deduce the visibility function, if the spectral intensity distribution is given by $I_0(\omega) = I_0 e^{-(\omega-\omega_0)^2/\alpha^2}$ where $\Delta\Omega$ is the width of the distribution function at $I_0(\omega) = (1/2)I_0$.

[Ans: $V(T) = e^{-\alpha^2 T^2/4}$]

13-8.1. Find the ratio I_r/I_i of the reflectances in a multiple beam reflection experiment.

[Hint: $I_r = I_i - I_t$] [Ans: $\frac{I_r}{I_i} = \frac{4\Gamma_r \sin^2 \frac{\Phi}{2}}{(1 - \Gamma_r)^2 + 4\Gamma_r \sin^2 \frac{\Phi}{2}}$]

13-8.2. Find the phase difference between two adjacent transmitted rays if the angle of incidence is θ_o.
[Ans: $\phi = 2kd \cos \theta_o$]

13-9.1. A lens transmission system is made up of a series of converging lenses, the lenses coming from groups with two different focal lengths. The lenses are placed a distance d apart, with the lenses being alternated from the two groups. Find the eigenvalues of this coaxial lens waveguide.

13-9.2. Find the difference equation for the system of lenses described in Pr. 13-9.1.
[Ans: $r_{n+2} - 2br_{n+1} + r_n = 0$, where $b = (1 - \frac{d}{f_2} - \frac{d}{f_1} + \frac{d^2}{2f_1f_2})$]

13-9.3. Verify Eq. (13-9.8).
[Hint: $\zeta_1 + \zeta_2 + \zeta_1\zeta_2 - 1 = (1 + \zeta_1)(1 + \zeta_2) - 2$]

13-9.4. Show that the value of θ in Eq. (13-9.10) is $\theta = \cos^{-1}(2s_1s_2 - 1)$.

13-9.5. Sketch the type of optical resonators that correspond to the points shown in the given stability diagram.

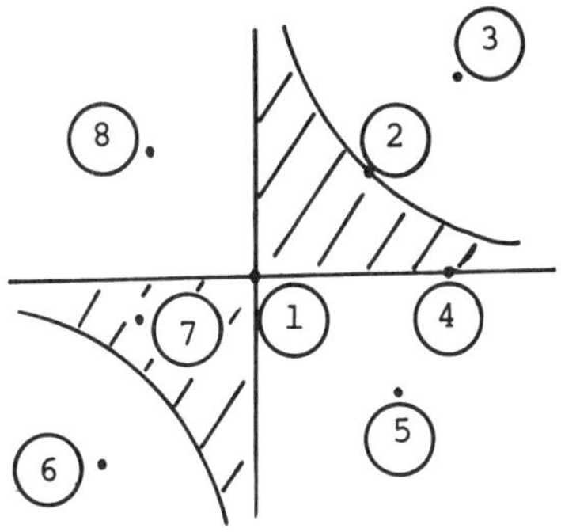

Figure P13-9.5.

13-9.6. Find the spot size for a HeNe laser resonator $\lambda = 0.6328\mu$ having the following dimensions: (a) $d = 1$ m, $R_1 = R_2 = 100$ m; (b) $d = 1$ m, $R_1 = R_2 = 2$ m.

13-9.7. Find the spot size for a HeNe laser resonator $\lambda = 0.6328\mu$ with the following dimensions: $d = 1$ m, $R_1 = \infty$, $R_2 = 2$ m.

CHAPTER 14

RADIATION

In Chapter 11 we discussed the phenomenon of wave propagation but without discussing how these waves are produced. In this chapter we shall develop the basic ideas of radiation due to localized sources. That part of a system which radiates energy is called an antenna. This means that antennas are connected to nonradiating power sources through nonradiating connecting devices. That is, it is supposed that the radiation occurs only from the radiator, and that leakage is assumed to be negligible.

The study of radiation systems is important since it permits evaluating (a) the field strength at a specified distance from the source, (b) the input impedance or load on the source, (c) the efficiency of the radiating element, (d) the power radiated in different directions, etc. Unfortunately, the exact solution of Maxwell's equations with boundary conditions at the antenna is not an easy task. However, adequate approximate solutions are ordinarily used except for the very few simple cases where exact solutions are possible. In our studies we shall restrict ourselves to simple radiating systems, since our objectives are essentially the elucidation of the phenomenon of radiation and an introduction to the general approach to the solution of such problems.

14-1. Field of an Infinitesimal Dipole

The discussion in Sec. 8-9 relates to the solution of Maxwell's equations in the description of electromagnetic phenomena in terms of a scalar potential Φ_e and a vector potential $\overline{A}$. These potential functions satisfy the differential equation

$$\nabla^2\Phi_e + \mu\epsilon\omega^2 \Phi_e = -\frac{\rho}{\epsilon} \tag{14-1.1}$$

$$\nabla^2\overline{A} + \mu\varepsilon\omega^2\,\overline{A} = -\mu\overline{J} \tag{14-1.2}$$

for an assumed harmonic time variation of the form $e^{-j\omega t}$. In addition, we recall the following identities

$$\overline{B} = \nabla \times \overline{A} \tag{14-1.3}$$

$$\overline{E} = -\nabla\Phi_e + j\omega\overline{A} \tag{14-1.4}$$

$$\nabla \cdot \overline{A} = j\omega\varepsilon\Phi_e \tag{14-1.5}$$

where the last equation is the Lorentz condition. These equations, plus Eqs. (14-1.1) and (14-1.2) would seem to imply the need for solving both differential equations in order to obtain Φ_e and $\overline{A}$. Actually, this is not required since by operating on Eq. (14-1.5) by ∇ and substituting the value of $\nabla\Phi_e$ into Eq. (14-1.4) we obtain the relation

$$\overline{E} = \frac{j}{\omega\mu\varepsilon}\nabla(\nabla \cdot \overline{A}) + j\omega\overline{A} \tag{14-1.6}$$

This shows that we can find the $\overline{E}$ and $\overline{B}$ fields by solving only Eq. (14-1.2). We undertake this solution for the infinitesimal dipole, a theoretical device that has the merit of suggesting further extensions.

In order to solve Eq. (14-1.2), we proceed in a manner that parallels that in Sec. 4-6 for static fields. We now consider the equation

$$\nabla^2 G + k^2 G = 0 \tag{14-1.7}$$

where $G = G(R) = G(|\overline{r}-\overline{r}'|)$. The vectors $\overline{r}$ and $\overline{r}'$ are defined in Fig. 14-1.1. To

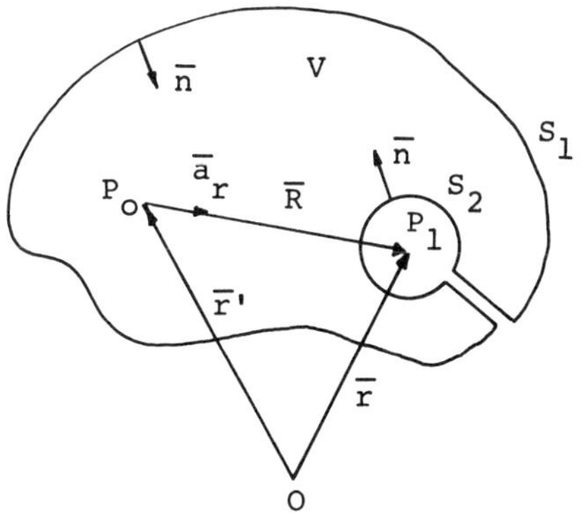

Figure 14-1.1. The configuration for the Green's function for the infinitesimal dipole.

proceed, we note that by direct substitution that

$$G(R) = \frac{e^{jkR}}{R} = \frac{e^{jk|\bar{r}-\bar{r}'|}}{|\bar{r}-\bar{r}'|} \tag{14-1.8}$$

is a solution to the equation

$$\frac{1}{R^2}\frac{\partial}{\partial R}\left(R^2 \frac{\partial G}{\partial R}\right) + k^2 G = 0$$

Now suppose that we multiply Eq. (14-1.7) by A_x and the X-component of Eq. (14-1.2) by G and then subtract the two resulting equations. This yields the relation

$$A_x \nabla^2 G - G\nabla^2 A_x = \mu J_x G \tag{14-1.9}$$

This equation is to be integrated over a volume V from which the point P_1 has been excluded, so that

$$\int_V (A_x \nabla^2 G - G\nabla^2 A_x)\, dV = \mu \int_V J_x G\, dV \tag{14-1.10}$$

By an application of Green's theorem [see Eq. (12-1.5)] to the left hand side of this equation, with the result that

$$\int_{S_1} \left(A_x \frac{\partial G}{\partial n} - G\frac{\partial A_x}{\partial n}\right) dS_1 + \int_{S_2} \left(A_x \frac{\partial G}{\partial n} - G\frac{\partial A_x}{\partial n}\right) dS_2 = \mu \int_V J_x G\, dV \tag{14-1.11}$$

The first integral reduces to zero as the surface recedes to infinity provided that $\lim_{R\to\infty} R(\partial A_x/\partial R - jkA_x) \to 0$ [see Eq. (12-2.5)]. The second surface integral becomes, as $S_2 \to 0$ ($e^{jkR} \doteq 1$)

$$\lim_{S_2\to 0} \int_{S_2} (A_x \bar{n}\cdot\nabla G - G\bar{n}\cdot\nabla A_x) dS_2 \doteq A_x(\bar{r}) \int_{S_2} \bar{n}\cdot\nabla G\, dS_2 = -A_x(\bar{r}) \int_{S_2} \frac{\partial}{\partial R}\left(\frac{1}{R}\right) dS_2$$
$$= 4\pi A_x(\bar{r})$$

since $\bar{n}$ and $\bar{a}_R$ are oppositely directed and A_x becomes independent of the point $\bar{r}$. The derivative of A_x was assumed to have a finite value. By these reductions Eq. (14-1.10) becomes

$$A_x(\bar{r}) = \frac{\mu}{4\pi} \int_V J_x(\bar{r}')\, G(\bar{r},\bar{r}')\, dV' \tag{14-1.12}$$

Similar relations will be found for the other two components of $\bar{A}$. The combination of the three relations combined vectorially leads to

$$\bar{A}(\bar{r}) = A_x\bar{a}_x + A_y\bar{a}_y + A_z\bar{a}_z = \frac{\mu}{4\pi}\int_V G(J_x\bar{a}_x + J_y\bar{a}_y + J_z\bar{a}_z)dV'$$

$$= \frac{\mu}{4\pi}\int_V \bar{J}(\bar{r}')G(\bar{r},\bar{r}')dV'$$

or

$$\bar{A}(\bar{r}) = \frac{\mu}{4\pi}\int_V \bar{J}(\bar{r}')\, G(\bar{r},\bar{r}')dV' = \frac{\mu}{4\pi}\int_V \bar{J}(\bar{r}')\,\frac{e^{jk|\bar{r}-\bar{r}'|}}{|\bar{r}-\bar{r}'|}\,dV' \tag{14-1.13}$$

where $\bar{r}$ is the point of observation (the field point). Since G is symmetrical with respect to $\bar{r}$ and $\bar{r}'$, sometimes we write Eq. (14-1.13) in the form

$$\bar{A}(\bar{r}') = \frac{\mu}{4\pi}\int_V \bar{J}(\bar{r})\,\frac{e^{jk|\bar{r}-\bar{r}'|}}{|\bar{r}-\bar{r}'|}\,dV \tag{14-1.14}$$

where the field point and the source point have been interchanged. For specific geometry shown in Figs. 14-1.2a and b, with the corresponding equations, we have

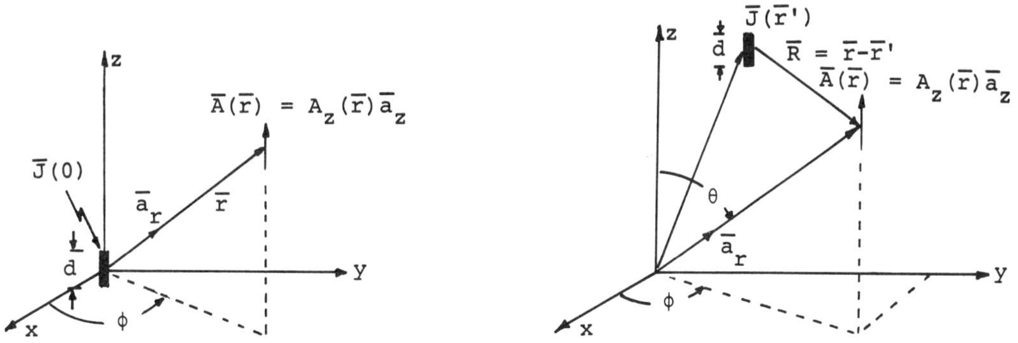

$$\bar{A}(\bar{r}) = \frac{\mu}{4\pi}\int_V \bar{J}(0)G(\bar{r},0)dV'$$

(a)

$$\bar{A}(\bar{r}) = \frac{\mu}{4\pi}\int_V \bar{J}(\bar{r}')G(\bar{r},\bar{r}')dV'$$

(b)

Figure 14-1.2. To illustrate the field point and the source point.

Equation (14-1.13) is the general expression for the vector potential $\bar{A}$ for a radiating current element. Observe that this expression is similar to Eq. (6-2.4) for a static configuration, except for the presence of the phase factor $e^{jk|\bar{r}-\bar{r}'|}$. Equation (14-1.13) is often referred to as the *retarded* vector potential because the phase factor takes account of the time delay or phase delay caused by the finite propagation time for the field originating at $\bar{r}$ to reach point $\bar{r}'$. This situation is made more evident if we include the implied time factor $e^{-j\omega t}$ with the phase factor $e^{jk|\bar{r}-\bar{r}'|}$ and write the result $e^{-j\omega(t-(k/\omega)|\bar{r}-\bar{r}'|)}$. In essence therefore, if we consider the field at $\overline{r}'$ at time t, this must be related to the vector potential at $\overline{r}$ at the earlier time $(t - |\overline{r}-\overline{r}'|/c)$, thereby accounting for the propagation delay.

As a specific example of the use of this expression, we shall evaluate the fields set up by an infinitesimal radiating dipole which is located at the origin ($\overline{r}' = 0$), and for which $\overline{r}$, the field point, is at a large distance from the origin (the source point). Now, since $\overline{r}$, which is the distance between each point of the infinitesimal antenna and the field point, the factor e^{+jkr}/kr in Eq. (14-1.13) is assumed to be substantially constant, and may be removed from behind the integral sign. This assumes that the fields from each portion of the dipole are in phase. In the more general case this would not be a valid assumption. Now the resulting integral attains the form

$$\overline{A} = \frac{\mu_o}{4\pi}\frac{e^{+jkr}}{kr}\{k\int \overline{J}(\overline{r}')dV'\} = \overline{C}\,\frac{e^{+jkr}}{kr} \tag{14-1.15}$$

where $\overline{C}$ is the amplitude factor

$$\overline{C} = \frac{\mu_o k}{4\pi}\int_V \overline{J}(\overline{r}')\, dV' \tag{14-1.16}$$

Suppose that the dipole is oriented along the Z-axis; then

$$A_x = A_y = 0$$

$$A_z = C\,\frac{e^{+jkr}}{kr} \tag{14-1.17}$$

This equation and particularly the factor e^{+jkr}/kr represents a diverging spherical wave, and characterizes a field whose amplitude decreases inversely with the distance from the source. We shall show in Sec. 14-2 that this equation is precisely of the form for the scalar potential of an oscillating acoustic sphere.

It is of some interest to note that Eq. (14-1.17) is a solution of the wave equation

$$\nabla^2 A_z + k^2 A_z = 0$$

in which A_z is independent of coordinates θ and ϕ.

To find the magnetic field intensity $\overline{H}$, it is required to find the curl of $\overline{A}$, as specified by Eq. (14-1.3). The vector $\overline{A}$ can be expressed in the form

$$\overline{A}_z = C\left[\frac{e^{+jkr}}{kr}\cos\theta\,\overline{a}_r - \frac{e^{+jkr}}{kr}\sin\theta\,\overline{a}_\theta\right] \tag{14-1.18}$$

But from the expression for the curl of a vector in spherical coordinates (see Appendix I), it will be seen that only the ϕ-component exists in the expression for

$\overline{H}$. This leads to

$$\overline{H} = \frac{1}{\mu_0} \nabla \times \overline{A}_z = \frac{C}{\mu_0 r} [-j\, e^{+jkr} \sin\theta + \frac{e^{+jkr}}{kr} \sin\theta]\, \overline{a}_\phi$$

or finally

$$\overline{H}_\phi = -\frac{jkC \sin\theta}{\mu_0} \frac{e^{jkr}}{kr} (1 + \frac{j}{kr})\, \overline{a}_\phi \qquad (14\text{-}1.19)$$

We obtain an expression for the electric field for the infinitesimal dipole by combining $\overline{A}_z$ from Eq. (14-1.18) with Eq. (14-1.6). It is

$$\overline{E} = \omega C\, e^{jkr} [(\frac{2}{k^2r^2} + \frac{2j}{k^3r^3}) \cos\theta\, \overline{a}_r + (\frac{j}{k^3r^3} + \frac{1}{k^2r^2} - \frac{j}{kr}) \sin\theta\, \overline{a}_\theta] \qquad (14\text{-}1.20)$$

Several features of the $\overline{H}$ and $\overline{E}$ fields are important, and should be noted carefully. These are:

1. The magnetic field lines are concentric circles about the dipole, and these are strong near the equator but weak near the poles.
2. Two terms are involved: one is the *radiation field*, and this varies as $1/r$; the second is an *induction field*, and this varies as $1/r^2$.
3. At large distances from the dipole, when $kr \to \infty$, Eqs. (14-1.19) and (14-1.20) become approximately

$$\overline{H}_\phi \doteq -j \frac{Ck}{\mu_0} \frac{e^{jkr}}{kr} \sin\theta\, \overline{a}_\phi \qquad (14\text{-}1.21)$$

   and

$$\overline{E}_\theta \doteq -j\omega C \frac{e^{jkr}}{kr} \sin\theta\, \overline{a}_\theta \qquad (14\text{-}1.22)$$

   At these large distances the $\overline{H}$ and $\overline{E}$ lines are orthogonal circles having their maximum amplitudes at the equator and zero amplitudes at the poles. Furthermore, the amplitude decreases as $1/r$. The ratio E_θ/H_ϕ (units, Volt/m × m/Amp-turns = Ohm) becomes $E_\theta/H_\phi = \omega\mu_0/k = Z_0 = 377.6\ \Omega$, with Z_0 denoting the characteristic impedance of free space.
4. When $kr \to 0$, the factor $e^{jkr} \doteq 1$, and the electric field reduces to the expression

$$\overline{E} = \omega C [\frac{2j}{k^3r^3} \cos\theta\, \overline{a}_r + \frac{j}{k^3r^3} \sin\theta\, \overline{a}_\theta] \qquad (14\text{-}1.23)$$

which is eactly the field that results from the infinitesimal electric dipole. This expression is sometimes called the *electrostatic field term* [see Eq. (5-5.3)]. The corresponding expression for the magnetic field is

$$\overline{H}_\phi = \frac{Ck}{\mu_o} \frac{\sin\theta}{k^2 r^2} \overline{a}_\phi \tag{14-1.24}$$

This formula is precisely of the form of the magnetic field intensity due to an infinitesimal current element as specified by a direct application of the Biot-Savart law.

Figure 14-1.3 shows the electric field near a dipole for four different instants of time. At t = 0, the field is just that of a static dipole. As time progresses, the field lines are pinched off, and these bundles of field lines propagate outward.

A number of different quantities are associated with electromagnetic radiation. We consider these for the infinitesimal dipole radiator.

a. Radiated power: In order to calculate the power radiated by an infinitesimal dipole, we must evaluate the Poynting vector. The only power radiating away from the infinitesimal dipole antenna is that due to the fields $\overline{E}_\theta$ and $\overline{H}_\phi$ (why?). Thus the complex radiated power density [see Eq. (8-10.12)]

$$\overline{\mathscr{S}}_c = \frac{1}{2}\overline{E}_\theta \times \overline{H}_\phi^* = \frac{1}{2}\frac{k\omega|C|^2 \sin^2\theta}{\mu_o}\left[\frac{1}{k^2r^2} - \frac{1}{jk^5r^5}\right]\overline{a}_r \tag{14-1.25}$$

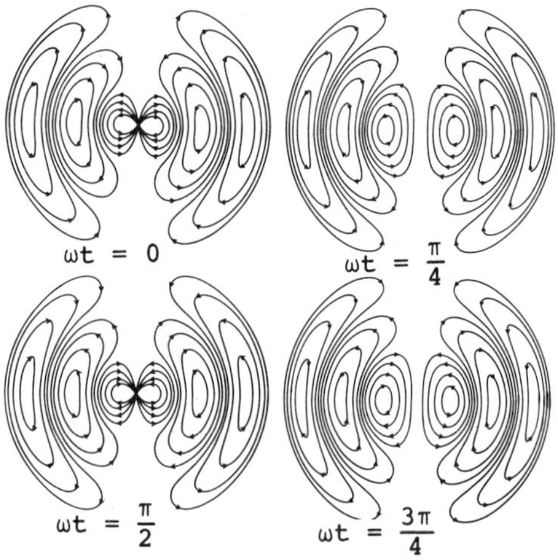

Figure 14-1.3. Electric field lines of a radiating dipole. [Reprinted with permission from Electromagnetic Fields and Waves, Second Edition, by Paul Lorrain and Dale Corson, 1970.]

and the total power crossing a spherical surface of radius r_o is

$$P_{rad} = \oint_S \mathscr{S}_c \cdot d\overline{S} = \int_0^{2\pi} d\phi \int_0^{\pi} \mathscr{S}_c \cdot \overline{a}_r \, r_o^2 \sin\theta \, d\theta$$

$$P_{rad} = \frac{4\omega\pi|C|^2}{3k\mu_o} - \frac{4\pi\omega|C|^2}{j3k^4 r_o^3 \mu_o} \qquad (14\text{-}1.26)$$

The real part of P_{rad} gives the average power radiated; the imaginary part is the reactive component of power. Observe that the real power is independent of the radius of the surface enclosing the dipole whereas the reactive power does depend on the radius r_o. For the case of the very thin antenna, we can easily find the *radiation resistance* of the antenna and also its reactance. We need merely compare Eq. (14-1.26) with the general relation for power

$$P_{rad} = I_{rms}^2 R_{rad} + jI_{rms}^2 X_c$$

from which we identify

$$R_{rad} = \frac{4\omega\pi|C|^2}{3\mu_o k\, I_{rms}^2}; \qquad X_c = \frac{4\omega\pi|C|^2}{3\mu_o k^4 r^3 I_{rms}^2} \qquad (14\text{-}1.27)$$

Since C varies as k, then X_c varies as $1/\omega$ which means that the reactance of the infinitesimal dipole is capacitive, an expected behavior since the field near the antenna is predominantly an electric field.

b. The power directivity pattern: The plot of the time-average Poynting's vector as a function of angle is called the *power radiation pattern*. For the infinitesimal dipole

$$\overline{P}_r = \text{Re}\,\langle\mathscr{S}_c\rangle = \text{Re}\left\langle \frac{\overline{E}\times\overline{H}^*}{2}\right\rangle = \frac{1}{2}\frac{\omega|C|^2\sin^2\theta}{\mu_o k r^2}\,\overline{a}_r \ \frac{\text{Watt}}{\text{m}^2} \qquad (14\text{-}1.28)$$

The general features of the radiation pattern are shown in Fig. 14-1.4. The angular width to the half-power points is called the beamwidth of the radiator. For the infinitesimal dipole the beamwidth (power) is 78 degrees.

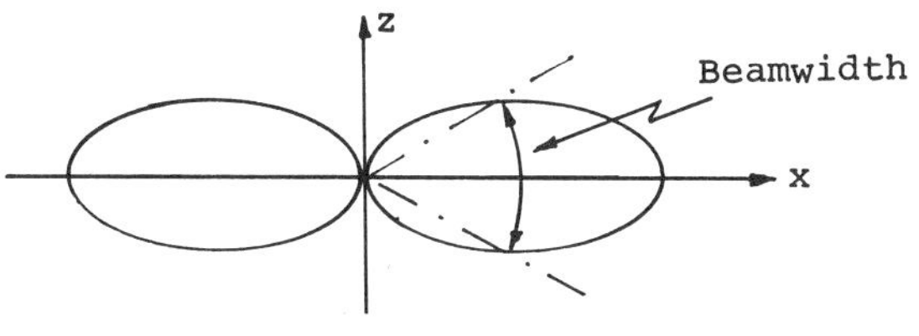

Figure 14-1.4. Power radiation pattern of an infinitesimal dipole.

c. Radiation intensity: We begin with Eq. (14-1.28) and select r^2 times the power pattern in order to obtain a function that is independent of the radius. This resulting relation

$$\bar{a}_R P_i = r^2 \, \mathrm{Re} \, \langle \mathcal{S}_c \rangle \quad \text{Watt/unit solid angle} \tag{14-1.29}$$

is known as the *radiation intensity*, and $\bar{a}_R$ is a unit vector along the Poynting vector $\mathcal{S}_c$. The *normalized antenna power pattern* is the ratio of the power pattern divided by its maximum value.

d. Directivity: The *directivity* D of an antenna is defined as the ratio of the maximum radiation intensity to the average radiation intensity per unit solid angle. That is,

$$D = \frac{P_{i\,max}}{P_{i\,av}} \tag{14-1.30}$$

and

$$P_{i\,av} = \frac{1}{4\pi} \oint_S P_i \, d\Omega \quad \text{Watt/steradian} \tag{14-1.31}$$

The function $P_{i\,av}$ represents the radiation intensity that would be produced by an isotropic radiator radiating the same total power P_r

$$\oint_S P_i \, d\Omega = P_r \tag{14-1.31a}$$

But the total radiated power is

$$P_r = 4\pi \, P_{i\,av} \tag{14-1.31b}$$

and Eq. (14-1.30) assumes the form

$$D = \frac{4\pi \, P_{i\,max}}{P_r} = \frac{4\pi(\text{maximum radiation intensity})}{\text{power radiated}} \tag{14-1.32}$$

e. Gain: Directivity is based entirely on the shape of the far field pattern, that is, the antenna efficiency is not involved. The gain of an antenna does involve the efficiency. That is, the radiation is not uniform over all spherical angles, and so one defines the *directive gain* $G(\theta,\phi)$ of an antenna as the ratio of the radiated power intensity of the given antenna to the maximum radiation from a reference antenna with the same power input. For standardization purposes two types of antennas are usually used: one is the isotropic radiator, which radiates uniformly in all directions; the second is the half-wave dipole. The direction gain is the maximum value of the gain function. Mathematically the gain function is expressed by

$$G(\theta,\phi) = \frac{P_i(\theta,\phi)}{P_{i\,av}(\theta,\phi)} = \frac{r^2 \operatorname{Re} \langle \mathscr{S}_c(\theta,\phi)\rangle}{\frac{1}{4\pi}\int_0^{2\pi} d\phi \int_0^{\pi} r^2 \operatorname{Re} \langle \mathscr{S}_c(\theta,\phi)\rangle \sin\theta \, d\theta} \tag{14-1.33}$$

This expression becomes, for the isotropic radiator as the reference

$$G(\theta,\phi) = \frac{\operatorname{Re} \langle \mathscr{S}_c(\theta,\phi)\rangle}{\left(\frac{P_r}{4\pi r^2}\right)} = \frac{4\pi r^2 \operatorname{Re} \langle \mathscr{S}_c(\theta,\phi)\rangle}{P_r} \tag{14-1.34}$$

where P_r is the total power radiated by the reference antenna.

For the infinitesimal dipole with fields E_θ and H_ϕ given by Eqs. (14-1.21) and (14-1.22), whence using Eq. (14-1.28) we have

$$G(\theta,\phi) = \frac{A \sin^2\theta}{\frac{1}{4\pi}\int_0^{2\pi} d\phi \int_0^{\pi} A \sin^3\theta \, d\theta} = \frac{3}{2}\sin^2\theta \tag{14-1.35}$$

This has the *maximum directional gain* of 3/2.

14-2. Acoustic Radiation from a Pulsating Sphere

As a second example of a radiating source, we consider a simple acoustic radiator, which consists of a thin spherical shell which can expand and contract slightly with an effective radial vibration at an angular frequency ω and a peak amplitude A. Such oscillations can be developed by filling the spherical shell with a fluid that is subjected to a pulsating pressure, as shown in Fig. 14-2.1a. The rate of the fluid flow away from the surface of the sphere is

$$Q(t) = 4\pi a^2 v(t) \quad \frac{m^3}{\text{sec}}$$

where v(t) is the radial velocity. For simplicity, we assume that the source of sound is small and can be replaced by a *distribution* of simple sources, such that

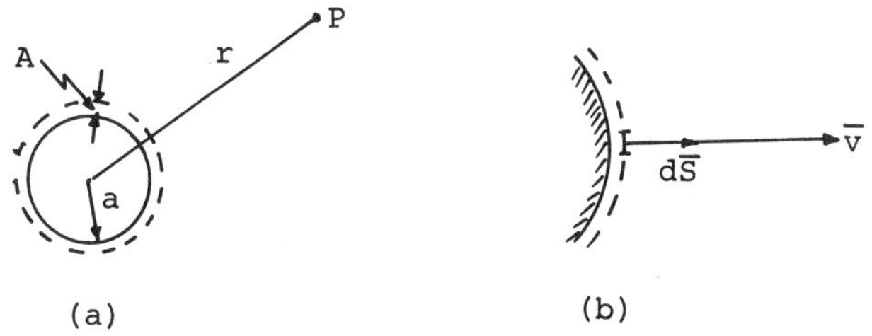

Figure 14-2.1. A pulsating sphere.

the element dV' at (x',y',z') has an equivalent outflow q(x',y',z',t)dV' (m^3/sec). The function q is called the *source function*. Therefore, the configuration here being considered is described by Eq. (8-5.17) but we must add a source term, leading to the controlling equation

$$\nabla^2 p_1 - \frac{1}{c_a^2} \frac{\partial^2 p_1}{\partial t^2} = -\rho_o \frac{\partial q}{\partial t} \tag{14-2.1}$$

The quantity $\rho_o q = \rho_g$ is the rate at which fluid mass is generated per unit volume of the medium. For an harmonic variation, this equation takes on the form

$$\nabla^2 p_1 + k^2 p_1 = -(-j\omega\rho_o q) \tag{14-2.2}$$

where $k^2 = \omega^2/c_a^2$. Equation (14-2.2) is identical in form with Eq. (14-1.2). We can immediately write as the solution [see Eq. (14-1.12)]

$$p_1 = -\frac{j\omega\rho_o}{4\pi} \int_V q(\bar{r}')\, G(\bar{r},\bar{r}')\, dV' \tag{14-2.3}$$

when the field point is at large distances. This equation can be simplified [see Eq. (14-1.15)] and takes the form

$$p_1 = -\frac{j\omega\rho_o}{4\pi} \frac{e^{jkr}}{kr} \{k \int_V q(\bar{r}')\, dV'\} = C \frac{e^{jkr}}{kr} \tag{14-2.4}$$

where C is the constant

$$C = -\frac{j\omega\rho_o}{4\pi} \{k \int_V q(\bar{r}')\, dV'\} \qquad \frac{\text{Kg}}{\text{m-sec}^2} \tag{14-2.5}$$

Using Eq. (14-2.4) and (8-5.32) we obtain for the acoustic potential Φ_a

$$\Phi_a = -\frac{1}{j\omega\rho_o} p_1 = \frac{\{k \int_V q(\bar{r}')\, dV'\}}{4\pi} \frac{e^{jkr}}{kr} = C_1 \frac{e^{jkr}}{kr} \tag{14-2.6}$$

where $C_1 = -C/j\omega\rho_o$. Equation (14-2.6) is similar to the magnetic potential $\bar{A}$ [see Eq. (14-1.15)]. By combining Eqs. (14-2.4) and (8-5.15) we find the velocity of the fluid particles to be

$$v(r) = \frac{C}{j\omega\rho_o} \nabla(\frac{e^{jkr}}{kr}) = -jkC_1 \frac{e^{jkr}}{kr} (1 + \frac{j}{kr}) \tag{14-2.7}$$

This equation is similar to Eq. (14-1.9) for the $\bar{H}$ field of the infinitesimal dipole. This formula shows that one term falls off as 1/r, and this is the radiation field; the second term is out of phase by $\pi/2$ and is more rapidly decaying with distance, and becomes unimportant at large distances.

The time average power density may be formed as follows:

$$\langle P\rangle = \frac{1}{2}\,\text{Re}\,\{pv^*\} = \frac{1}{2}\,\frac{\omega\rho_o k C_1^2}{(kr)^2} \tag{14-2.8}$$

and the total radiated power is

$$P_{rad} = 4\pi r^2 \langle P\rangle$$

It is convenient to introduce the *specific acoustic impedance,* since it proves to be a useful quantity for finding the reaction on a vibrating system. The acoustic impedance is defined as the ratio of velocity to pressure, and for a small source is

$$Z_a = \frac{\langle v\rangle}{\langle p\rangle} = \frac{1 + \frac{j}{kr}}{\rho_o\, c_a} \tag{14-2.9}$$

which is written

$$Z_a = R_a - jX_a = \frac{1}{\rho_o c_a} + j\,\frac{1}{kr\,\rho_o c_a} \tag{14-2.10}$$

The first term on the right is the *specific acoustic resistance,* and the second term is the *specific acoustic reactance.* The imaginary part of the acoustic impedance can be interpreted as the reactance of a frequency dependent mass of magnitude

$$m_r = \frac{1}{\rho_o c_a kr} = \frac{1}{\omega\rho_o r} \tag{14-2.11}$$

This mass represents the mass reaction of the medium to the vibrating sphere. The real part of the wave impedance

$$R_a = \frac{1}{\rho_o c_a} \tag{14-2.12}$$

represents the radiation resistance in the spherical wave.

The volume flow is given by the relation

$$Q = 4\pi r^2 v_r$$

where v_r is the radial velocity. If the source is small compared with the wavelength, i.e., $kr \ll 1$, then $v_r = C_1/kr^2$ and the flow is equal to

$$Q = \frac{4\pi C_1}{k} \tag{14-2.13}$$

14-3. Acoustic Dipoles

In close parallelism with the electric dipole, if a positive sound source and a negative sound source are close together, an acoustic dipole results. Let the distance to the field point from the positive source be r_b, and that from the negative source be r_a as shown in Fig. 14-3.1. The pressure at the field point is given by [see Eq. (14-2.4)]

$$p = C \left(\frac{e^{jkr_b}}{kr_b} - \frac{e^{jkr_a}}{kr_a}\right) \qquad (14\text{-}3.1)$$

For those distances for which r >> d

$$r_a \doteq r + \frac{d}{2} \cos \theta$$

$$r_b \doteq r - \frac{d}{2} \cos \theta$$

and Eq. (14-3.1) approximates to

$$p_1 = \frac{C\, e^{jkr}}{kr} \left[\frac{e^{jk \frac{d}{2} \cos \theta}}{1 - \frac{d}{2r} \cos \theta} - \frac{e^{-jk \frac{d}{2} \cos \theta}}{1 + \frac{d}{2r} \cos \theta}\right] \qquad (14\text{-}3.2)$$

The exponential functions and the denominators of both terms are expanded with terms of the second order or higher being neglected, then

$$p_1 = \frac{Cd\, e^{jkr}}{kr} \cos \theta \left(jk - \frac{1}{r}\right) = \frac{-j\omega\rho_o C_1 d\, e^{jkr}}{kr} \left(jk - \frac{1}{r}\right) \cos \theta$$

$$= k^2 \rho_o c_a \frac{Qd}{4\pi} \frac{e^{jkr}}{r} \cos \theta \left(1 - \frac{1}{jkr}\right) \qquad (14\text{-}3.3)$$

where Q is the volume flow at each source that constitutes the dipole. Also, the moment of the dipole is expressed as

$$D = Qd \qquad (14\text{-}3.4)$$

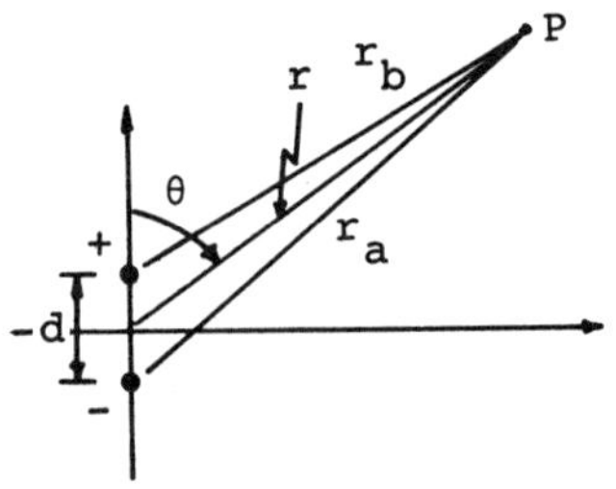

Figure 14-3.1. An acoustic dipole.

For the dipole field the characteristic features are the directivity factor cos θ, and the very small sound radiation whenever the frequency is small or the distance d is small.

The radial velocity for the fluid particles is found to be

$$v_r = \frac{k^2 D}{4\pi} \frac{e^{jkr}}{r} \cos\theta \left(1 - \frac{2}{jkr} + \frac{2}{(jkr)^2}\right) \tag{14-3.5}$$

From a comparison among the spherical acoustic radiator, the acoustic dipole, and the electric dipole, it seems that the spherical acoustic radiator and the electric dipole show a closer similarity than does the acoustic dipole and the electric dipole.

14-4. The Finite Thin Linear Radiator

A more realistic and more practical electromagnetic radiator than the infinitesimal dipole is the linear radiator of the form shown in Fig. 14-4.1a. This figure is that of a linear dipole *center-fed* antenna. In particular, we shall be considering a thin linear antenna of length d that is excited in the center across a very small gap. With this configuration the current along the antenna can be assumed to be sinusoidal in both time and distance, and will be symmetric in the two radiator halves. Further, since the current vanishes at the radiator ends, the current density is written explicitly as

$$\overline{J}(\overline{r}') = \frac{I}{S_0} \sin\left(\frac{kd}{2} - k|z'|\right) \delta(x')\, \delta(y')\, \overline{a}_z \tag{14-4.1}$$

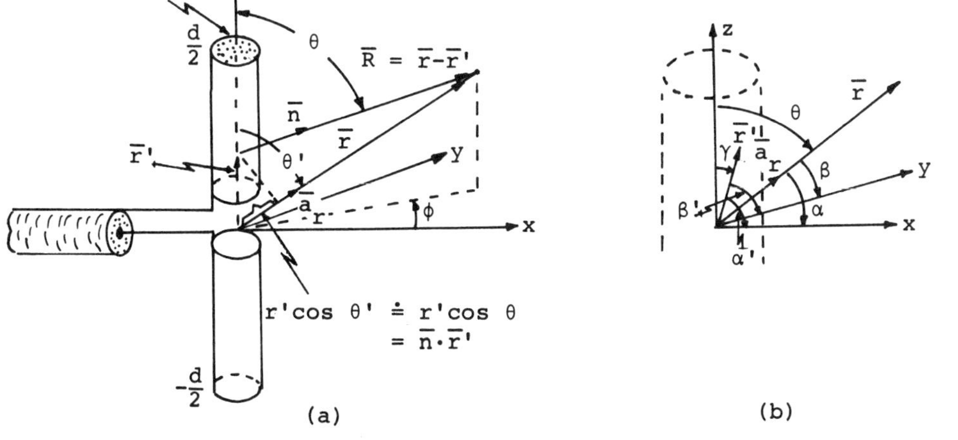

Figure 14-4.1. The center-fed linear dipole.

for $|z| \leq d/2$. With this specified expression for $\overline{J}(\overline{r}')$, we can write for the magnetic vector potential $\overline{A}$ in Eq. (14-1.13)

$$\overline{A}(\overline{r}) = \frac{\mu_o}{4\pi}\int_V \overline{J}(\overline{r}')\,\frac{e^{jk|\overline{r}-\overline{r}'|}}{|\overline{r}-\overline{r}'|}\,dV' \doteq \frac{\mu_o}{4\pi}\int_V \overline{J}(\overline{r}')\,\frac{e^{jkr(1-\frac{\overline{n}\cdot\overline{r}'}{r})}}{r(1-\frac{\overline{n}\cdot\overline{r}'}{r})}\,dV'$$

or

$$\overline{A}(\overline{r}) \doteq \frac{\mu_o e^{jkr}}{4\pi r}\int_V \overline{J}(\overline{r}')\; e^{-jk\overline{n}\cdot\overline{r}'}\; dV' \tag{14-4.2}$$

where we have neglected the term $\overline{n}\cdot\overline{r}'/r$ in the denominator of the amplitude factor, but we have retained the term in the exponential since small variations in distance reflect themselves in large changes in phase. Note that this is one of the critical differences between the infinitesimal dipole and the finite linear dipole. In Eq. (14-4.2) we have also used the following approximations

$$|\overline{r}-\overline{r}'| = [(\overline{r}-\overline{r}')\cdot(\overline{r}-\overline{r}')]^{1/2} = [r^2 - 2\overline{r}\cdot\overline{r}' + r'^2]^{1/2}$$

$$\doteq r\,[1 - 2\,\frac{\overline{r}\cdot\overline{r}'}{r^2}]^{1/2} \doteq r\,(1 - \frac{1}{2}\,(2(\frac{\overline{r}}{r})\cdot\frac{\overline{r}'}{r})) = r(1 - \frac{\overline{n}\cdot\overline{r}'}{r})$$

Since $\overline{a}_r$ and $\overline{n}$ are nearly parallel they can be used interchangeably

We proceed to integrate Eq. (14-4.2) using the current distribution given in Eq. (14-4.1). From Fig. 14-4.1b we obtain the relation

$$\overline{n}\cdot\overline{r}' \doteq \overline{a}_r\cdot\overline{r}' = (\overline{a}_x\cos\alpha + \overline{a}_y\cos\beta + \overline{a}_z\cos\theta)\cdot(\overline{a}_x x'\cos\alpha' + \overline{a}_y y'\cos\beta' + \overline{a}_z z'\cos\gamma')$$

and since for our case $\alpha' = \beta' = \pi/2$ and $\gamma' = 0$, the above relation becomes

$$\overline{n}\cdot\overline{r}' = \overline{a}_z\, z'\cos\theta$$

Introducing the current distribution from Eq. (14-4.1) in this last equation we obtain

$$\overline{A}(\overline{r}) = \overline{a}_z\,\frac{\mu_o I}{4\pi S_o}\,\frac{e^{jkr}}{r}\int_{-d/2}^{d/2} \sin(\frac{kd}{2} - k|z'|)e^{-jkz'\cos\theta}\,dz'\iint_{-\infty}^{\infty}\delta(x')\delta(y')dx'\,dy'$$

Because of the delta function properties, this integral becomes

$$\overline{A}(\overline{r}) = \overline{a}_z\,\frac{\mu_o I}{4\pi S_o}\,\frac{e^{jkr}}{r}\int_{-d/2}^{d/2} \sin(\frac{kd}{2} - k|z'|)e^{-jkz'\cos\theta}dz' \tag{14-4.3}$$

Upon integrating Eq. (14-4.3) we obtain [see Pr. 14-4.1]

$$\overline{A}(\overline{r}) = \overline{a}_z \frac{\mu_0 I}{2\pi S_0} \frac{e^{jkr}}{kr} \left(\frac{\cos(\frac{kd}{2}\cos\theta) - \cos\frac{kd}{2}}{\sin^2\theta}\right) \tag{14-4.4}$$

Using Eqs. (14-4.4) and (14-1.3) in spherical coordinates and proceeding as in Sec. 14-1, we deduce that

$$\overline{H}_\phi = \frac{jI}{2\pi S_0} \frac{e^{jkr}}{r} \left(\frac{\cos(\frac{kd}{2}\cos\theta) - \cos\frac{kd}{2}}{\sin\theta}\right) \overline{a}_\phi \tag{14-4.5}$$

The corresponding electric field vector $\overline{E}$ for large r is found from the relation

$$\overline{E}_\theta = \sqrt{\frac{\mu_0}{\varepsilon_0}}\, \overline{H}_\phi = Z_0 H_\phi \overline{a}_\theta \tag{14-4.6}$$

The time average value of the Poynting vector, which gives a measure of the energy radiated

$$\langle \overline{\mathscr{S}}_{rad} \rangle = \frac{1}{2} \text{Re } [E_\theta H_\phi^*] \overline{a}_r \tag{14-4.7}$$

and the average total power radiated into unit solid angle is

$$P_i(\theta,\phi) = r^2 \langle \overline{\mathscr{S}}_{rad} \rangle \cdot \overline{a}_r = \frac{1}{2} \frac{Z_0 I^2}{4\pi^2 S_0^2} \left(\frac{\cos(\frac{kd}{2}\cos\theta) - \cos\frac{kd}{2}}{\sin\theta}\right)^2 \tag{14.-4.8}$$

Particularly important cases are for selected values of d. If d is a multiple of half wavelengths, then $d = m\lambda/2 = m\pi/k$. The power radiation patterns, and the patterns for E_θ, and for m = 1 and m = 3 are shown in Fig. 14-4.2. The pattern for m = 1 is very similar to that for the infinitesimal dipole [see Fig. 14-1.4].

When an antenna is located over the ground, the field of the antenna sets up currents in the ground which give rise, in turn, to a secondary field. For a perfectly conducting ground, the ground currents may be replaced by a suitable image antenna equally spaced and oriented below the ground-air interface. Hence a $\lambda/4$ vertical antenna on the ground which is fed at the base is the equivalent of a $\lambda/2$ center-fed antenna, when the image radiator is taken into account. Note that most radio broadcast antennas are simple vertical radiators, often in arrays to achieve a given directional pattern.

The average power radiated from a linear antenna is given by [see Eqs. (14-1.31a) and (14-1.29)]

$$P_r = \int_0^{2\pi} d\phi \int_0^{\pi} P_i(\theta,\phi)\sin\theta\, d\phi\, d\theta = 60\, I_{rms}^2 \int_0^{\pi} \frac{(\cos(\frac{kd}{2}\cos\theta) - \cos\frac{kd}{2})^2}{\sin\theta} d\theta \tag{14-4.9}$$

Since $P_r = I_{rms}^2 R$, the radiation resistance R of the thin linear antenna is a func-

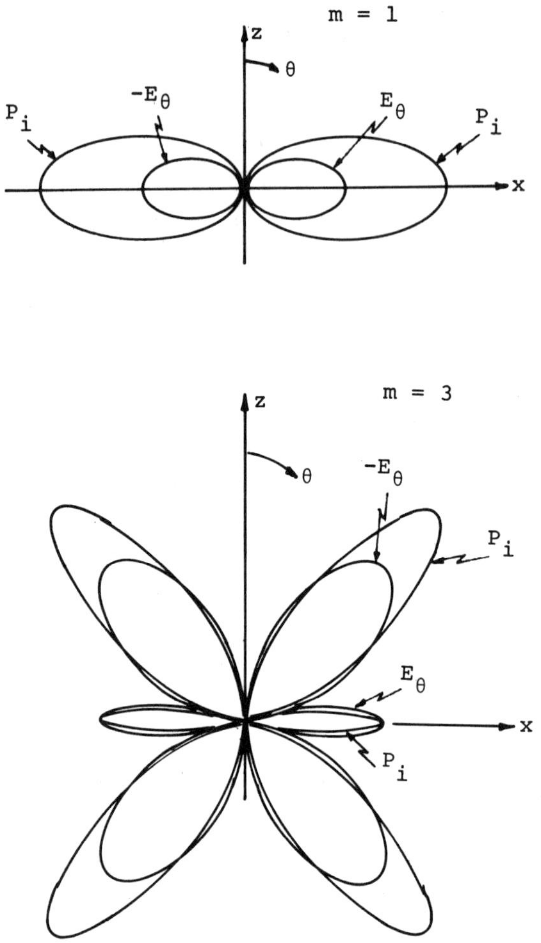

Figure 14-4.2. E_θ and power patterns for dipoles of length $m\,\frac{\lambda}{2}$, with m = 1 and m = 3.

tion of the ratio d/λ. Figure 14-4.3 is a plot of the radiation resistance versus the radiated wavelength.

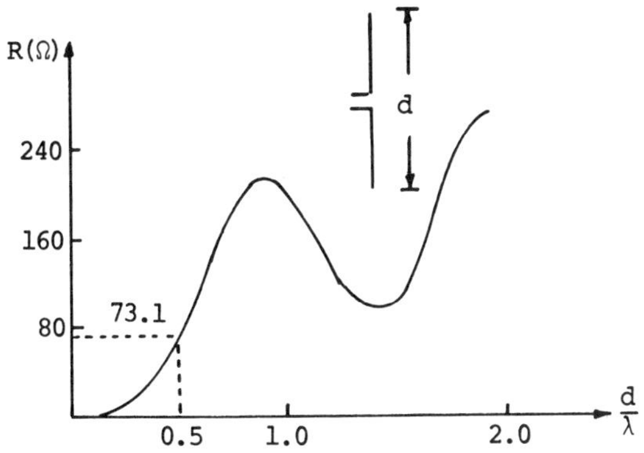

Figure 14-4.3. The radiation resistance R of a thin linear antenna.

14-5. Array of Radiators

Basically, one can achieve a wide variety of patterns using an array of dipoles because the physical spacing of the radiators and the amplitude and phase of the excitation of each radiator are available for adjustment. The resulting field at a given point in space is the superposition of the fields due to each radiator in the array. Initially, therefore, let us consider two identical infinitesimal dipoles arranged in the linear manner shown in Fig. 14-5.1. The field at a distant point due to antenna 1 in the θ-direction is, from Eq. (14-1.22),

$$E_{\theta 1} = -j\omega C \frac{e^{jkr}}{kr} \sin \theta \tag{14-5.1}$$

The field due to antenna 2 has the same general form, but the distance to the field point is R instead of r. By the law of cosines

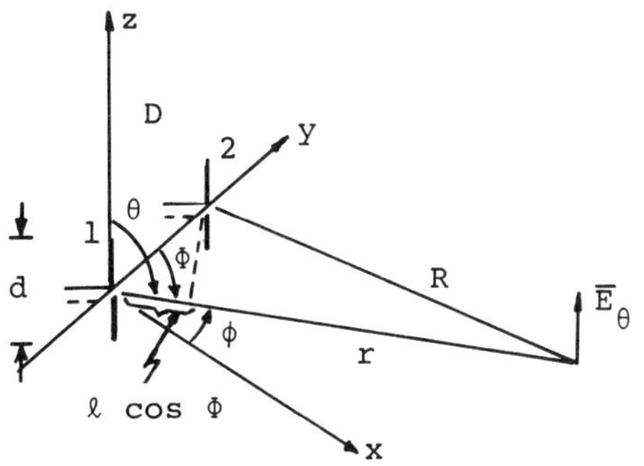

Figure 14-5.1. Array of two colinear infinitesimal dipoles.

$$R = (r^2 + D^2 - 2rD \cos \Phi)^{1/2} = r \left(1 - \frac{2D \cos \Phi}{r} + \frac{D^2}{r^2}\right)^{1/2}$$

Upon expanding this expression by the binomial theorem and retaining the lower order terms since $r >> D$, then

$$R \doteq r - D \cos \Phi$$

With this approximation, the far-zone field due to antenna 2 is

$$E_{\theta 2} = -j\omega C \frac{e^{jk(r - D \cos \Phi)}}{kr} \sin \theta \tag{14-5.2}$$

and the total field at field point P is

$$E_\theta = E_{\theta 1} + E_{\theta 2} = \underbrace{-j\omega C \frac{e^{jkr}}{kr} \sin \theta}_{\text{Antenna Pattern}} \underbrace{(1 + e^{-jkD \cos \Phi})}_{\text{Array Factor}} \tag{14-5.3}$$

A generalization of this formula is possible for a linear array of N dipoles uniformly spaced D meters apart. The total field is given by

$$E_\theta = -j\omega C \frac{e^{jkr}}{kr} \sin \theta \left(1 + \sum_{n=1}^{N-1} e^{-jknD \cos \Phi}\right) = E_1[1 + e^{-jkD \cos \Phi} + (e^{-jkD \cos \Phi})^2 + \ldots]$$

$$= E_1 \frac{(e^{-j\psi})^N - 1}{e^{-j\psi} - 1} = E_1 \frac{e^{-j\frac{N}{2}\psi}}{e^{-j\frac{\psi}{2}}} \frac{e^{-j\frac{N}{2}\psi} - e^{j\frac{N}{2}\psi}}{e^{-j\frac{\psi}{2}} - e^{j\frac{\psi}{2}}}$$

where $E_1 = -j\omega C \sin \theta \, e^{jkr}/kr$, and $\psi = kD \cos \Phi$. The expansion inside the brackets is a geometrical progression. The last expression is written finally in the form

$$E_\theta = E_1 e^{-j\left(\frac{N-1}{2}\right)\psi} \frac{\sin \frac{N\psi}{2}}{\sin \frac{\psi}{2}} \tag{14-5.4}$$

If the phase is referred to the center point of the linear array, the term $\exp[-j((N-1)/2)\psi]$ would have disappeared. When $\psi = 0$, Eq. (14-5.4) is indeterminate. But by applying L'Hospital's rule, we find that $E_\theta\big|_{\psi=0} = NE_1$. Hence the normalized value of the field for a center-point referenced array is

$$\frac{E_\theta}{E_1} = \frac{1}{N} \frac{\sin \frac{N\psi}{2}}{\sin \frac{\psi}{2}} \tag{14-5.5}$$

This expression is known as the *array factor*, and it has the following properties:

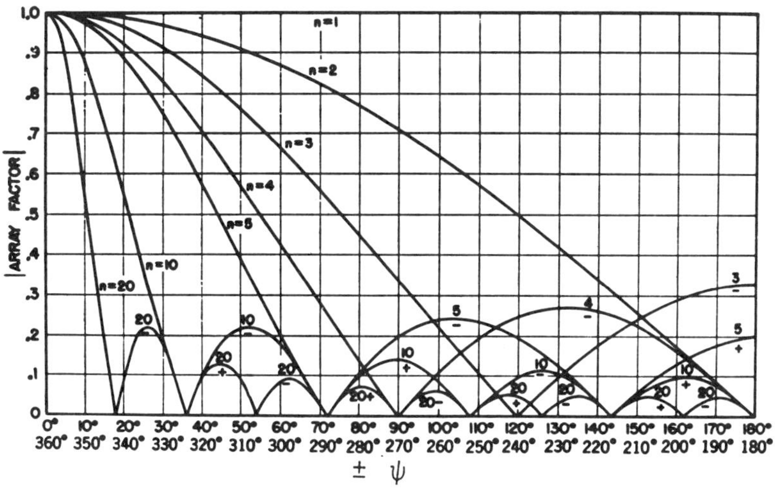

Figure 14-5.2. Array factor for linear arrays of N identical radiators of equal amplitude and spacing. [Reprinted with permission from Antennas, by John D. Kraus, 1950.]

a. The angle $\psi/2 = (kD/2)\cos\Phi$ has its maximum at $\Phi = 0$ and a minimum at $\Phi = \pi$.
b. The array factor is symmetrical about the line of the array.
c. The principal maximum of the array factor occurs at $\psi = 0$.
d. The array factor has zeros (nulls) when the numerator is zero, except when $\psi = 0$. This means that the minimums occur when

$$\frac{n\psi}{2} = m\pi \qquad m = 1,2,3,\ldots$$

The graphical representation of the array factor is given in Fig. 14-5.2. The correspondence between ϕ, Φ, ψ and array factor for N = 2 and N = 3 is given in Table 14-5.1.

Table 14-5.1.

ϕ	Φ	ψ	Array Factor, N = 2	Array Factor, N = 3
90°	0°	180°	0	0.33
0°	90°	0°	1	1
-90°	180°	-180°	0	0.33
-180°	270°	0°	1	1
-270°	360°	180°	0	0.33

The effect of the number of antennas with D = λ/2 on the radiation pattern is shown in Fig. 14-5.3.

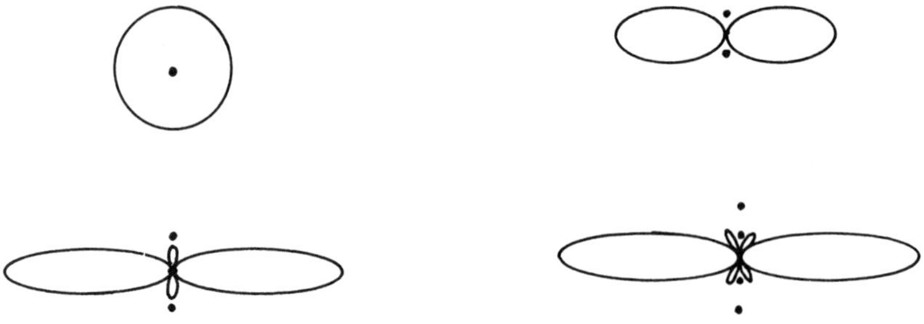

Figure 14-5.3. Radiation patterns of arrays on the xy plane.

Antenna arrays, and these are often one or two dimensional arrays of radiators approximately λ/2 long, are used extensively. The problem is not in calculating the resulting pattern for a specified excitation, but in achieving in practice the specified excitation owing to the mutual coupling that exists among the various antennas of the array. "Tuning" such arrays can often be a very time consuming effort. However, theory has been developed which takes into account the mutual interactions, thereby allowing the dipoles to be fed in a prescribed manner to yield the proper amplitude and phase to achieve the desired resulting pattern.

To investigate the effect of phase difference between input currents as well as their relative magnitudes, we consider two thin linear antennas, distance D apart. The total electric field E_θ at distance r is [see Eq. (14-4.6) and Fig. 14-5.1]

$$E_\theta = E_{\theta_1} + E_{\theta_2} = \frac{jZ_o}{2\pi S_o}\left(\frac{\cos(\frac{kd}{2}\cos\theta) - \cos\frac{kd}{2}}{\sin\theta}\right)\left(I_1\frac{e^{jkr}}{r} + I_2\frac{e^{jkR}}{R}\right)$$

$$= \frac{jZ_o}{2\pi S_o} I_1 \frac{e^{jkr}}{r}\left(\frac{\cos(\frac{kd}{2}\cos\theta) - \cos\frac{kd}{2}}{\sin\theta}\right)\left(1 + \left|\frac{I_2}{I_1}\right| e^{j\Phi_o} e^{-jkD\cos\Phi}\right) \tag{14-5.6}$$

where

Φ_o = phase difference of I_2 with respect to I_1

The absolute value of the electric field in the equitorial plane, θ = π/2, is given by

$$|E_\theta| = \left|\frac{jZ_o}{2\pi S_o} I_1\right| \left|\frac{e^{jkr}}{r}\right| \left|e^{j\frac{\Phi_o - kD\cos\Phi}{2}}\right| \left|\left(e^{-j\frac{\Phi_o - kD\cos\Phi}{2}} + \left|\frac{I_2}{I_1}\right| e^{j\frac{\Phi_o - kD\cos\Phi}{2}}\right)\right|$$

$$= \frac{Z_o I_1}{2\pi S_o}\frac{1}{r}\left[1 + \left|\frac{I_2}{I_1}\right|^2 + 2\left|\frac{I_2}{I_1}\right| \cos(\Phi_o - kD\cos\Phi)\right]^{1/2} \tag{14-5.7}$$

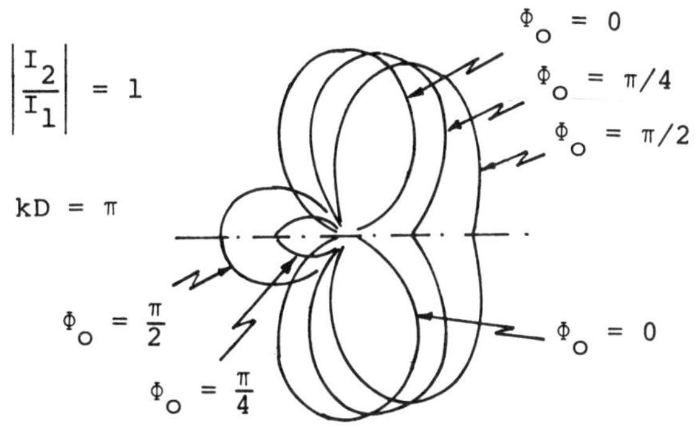

Figure 14-5.4. Variations of the radiation patterns of two thin linear antennas due to the relative phase of their currents.

The power radiation pattern is similar to that given by Eq. (14-5.7) since the E_θ and H_ϕ fields differ by a constant only. The effect of the phase Φ_o, the current ratio $|I_2/I_1|$, and the spacing D are shown in Figs. 14-5.4, 14-5.5, and 14-5.6.

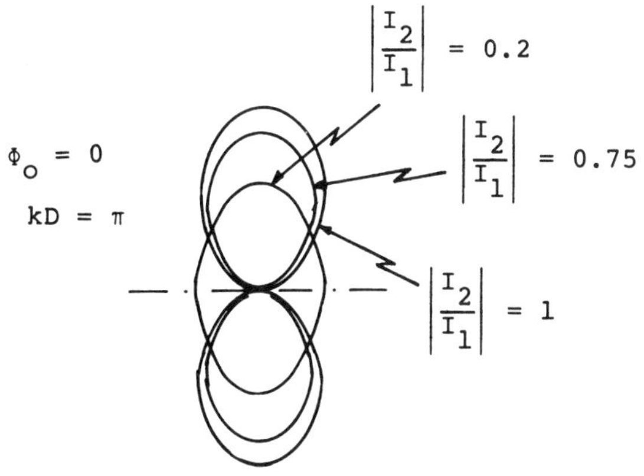

Figure 14-5.5. Variations of the radiation patterns of two thin linear antennas due to the change of the ratio $|I_2/I_1|$.

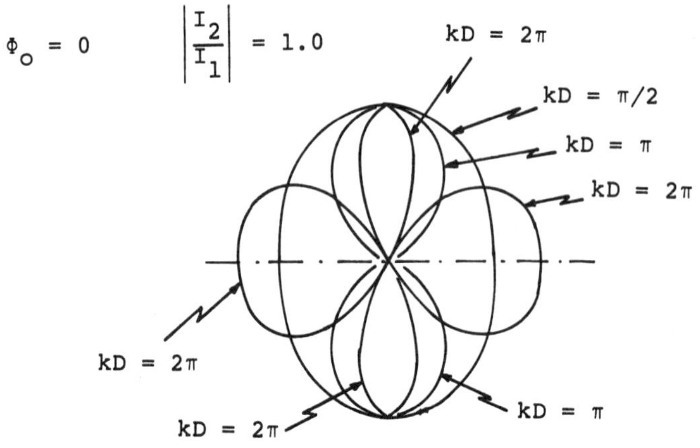

Figure 14-5.6. Variations of the radiation patterns of two thin linear antennas due to the change of the distance D.

14-6. Radiation from Apertures

This section may be considered to be an extension of that in the previous section. Now we shall consider an aperture which is assumed to be excited in a continuous manner so that there is a surface radiating distribution. This problem bears a close relation to diffraction problem that was discussed in Chap. 12. However, we here employ a vector field technique in the solution.

The introduction of fictitious magnetic currents sometimes helps in finding the fields produced by electric charges and currents. Furthermore, using this technique, Maxwell's equations are rendered symmetrical. We first recall that in Chap. 8 we solved the following set of equations - the superscript (e) indicates that the fields are due to electric currents and charges only -

$$\nabla \times \overline{E}^e = j\omega\overline{B}^e \qquad \text{a)}$$

$$\nabla \times \overline{H}^e = -j\omega\varepsilon\, \overline{E}^e + \overline{J} \qquad \text{b)}$$

with

$$\overline{B}^e = \nabla \times \overline{A} \qquad \text{c)} \qquad (14\text{-}6.1)$$

$$\overline{E}^e = \frac{1}{\omega\mu\varepsilon}\nabla(\nabla \cdot \overline{A}) + j\omega\overline{A} \qquad \text{d)}$$

$$\overline{A}(\overline{r}) = \frac{\mu}{4\pi}\int_V \overline{J}(\overline{r})\, \frac{e^{jk|\overline{r}-\overline{r}'|}}{|\overline{r}-\overline{r}'|}\, dV' \qquad \text{e)}$$

If we now introduce a magnetic conduction current density $\overline{N}$ (Volt/m), there will be fields that are due only to these currents. To find these, we must solve the equations

$$\nabla \times \overline{H}^m = -j\omega\varepsilon\overline{E}^m \qquad \text{a)}$$

$$\nabla \times \overline{E}^m = j\omega\mu\overline{H}^m - \overline{N} \qquad \text{b)} \qquad (14\text{-}6.2)$$

The set of magnetic equations may be solved by introducing an electric vector potential $\overline{F}$ such that

$$\varepsilon\overline{E}^m = -\nabla \times \overline{F} \qquad \text{c)}$$

If we compare the last three equations with the first three equations of Eq. (14-6.1) we observe the correspondence shown in the following table.

Table 14-6.1. Correspondence among Parameters in Electric and Magnetic Radiators.

Electric Case	I	$\overline{J}$	$\overline{E}^e$	$\overline{H}^e$	$\overline{A}$	ε	μ	Z
Magnetic Case	K	$\overline{N}$	$\overline{H}^m$	$-\overline{E}_m$	$\overline{F}$	μ	ε	$Z_m = \frac{1}{Z}$

In the light of these analogies, we can write equations of the form given by Eqs. (14-1.6) and (14-1.13), thus

$$\overline{H}^m = \frac{j}{\omega\mu\varepsilon}\nabla(\nabla \cdot \overline{F}) + j\omega\overline{F} \qquad \text{d)}$$

$$\overline{F}(\overline{r}) = \frac{\varepsilon}{4\pi}\int_V \overline{N}(\overline{r})\,\frac{e^{jk|\overline{r}-\overline{r}'|}}{|\overline{r}-\overline{r}'|}\,dV' \qquad \text{e)} \qquad (14\text{-}6.2)$$

These equations give a complete solution to our problem if we know the magnetic current $\overline{N}$. Clearly, when both magnetic and electric currents are present then the electric and magnetic fields are, respectively,

$$\overline{E} = \overline{E}^e + \overline{E}^m$$

$$\overline{H} = \overline{H}^e + \overline{H}^m$$

To proceed requires that we must find the relation which exists between the magnetic current density $\overline{N}$ and the electric field. We can continue by recalling that (see Chap. 8) the tangential components of $\overline{H}$ were discontinuous across an electric current sheet $\overline{J}_s$. The relation that will be found, using Maxwell's equation (14-6.1b) is

$$\overline{J}_s = \overline{n} \times (\overline{H}_1^{\,e} - \overline{H}_2^{\,e}) \qquad (14\text{-}6.3)$$

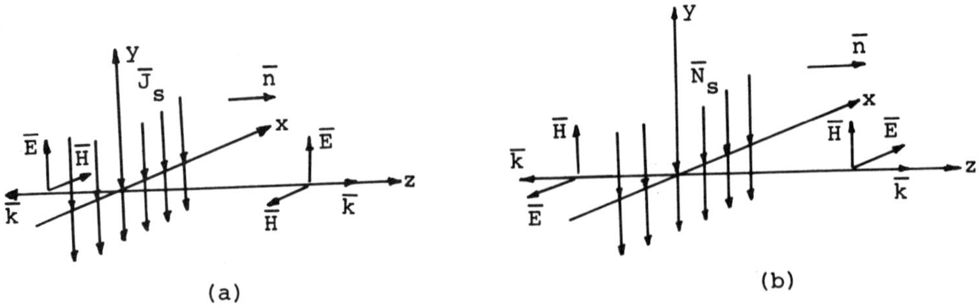

Figure 14-6.1. Excitation of plane waves from an infinite electric and magnetic current sheet.

where $\bar{n}$ points to the side of $\bar{H}_1^e$. Now by comparing Eqs. (14-6.1b) and (14-6.2b) we can write, by analogy,

$$\bar{N}_s = -\bar{n} \times (\bar{E}_1^m - \bar{E}_2^m) \tag{14-6.4}$$

The minus sign results from the minus sign in the magnetic current $\bar{N}$.

If a plane wave travels from minus infinity to plus infinity, then to an observer at $z > 0$, an electric current sheet at $z = 0$ is a completely equivalent source of radiation, as shown in Fig. 14-6.1a. From Eq. (14-6.3) it is apparent that the value of the surface current is twice the magnetic field intensity on the side $z > 0$ [see also Eq. (6-6.6)].

$$\bar{J}_s = 2\bar{n} \times \bar{H} \tag{14-6.5}$$

Similarly, from Eq. (14-6.4) we shall find that

$$\bar{N}_s = -2\bar{n} \times \bar{E} \tag{14-6.6}$$

Example 14-6.1. Find the radiation field from a rectangular aperture as shown in Fig. 14-6.2, if the field over the aperture is uniform.

$$\bar{E}_{ap} = \bar{a}_y E_o \tag{14-6.7}$$

Solution. By Eq. (14-6.6) we can write for the equivalent magnetic current

$$\bar{N}_s = -2\bar{n} \times \bar{E}_{ap} = -2\bar{n} \times \bar{a}_y E_o \tag{14-6.8}$$

This is shown graphically in Fig. 14-6.2b. We next introduce the magnetic current into Eq. (14-6.2e) which then specifies for the magnetic potential

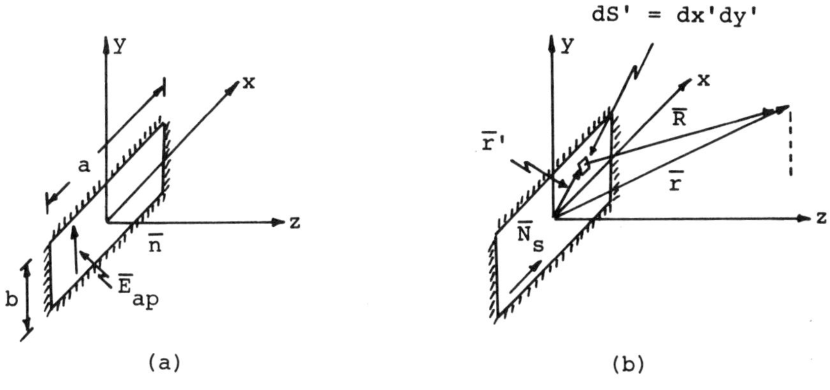

Figure 14-6.2. Aperture electric field and its equivalent magnetic surface current density.

$$F_x = \frac{\varepsilon E_o}{2\pi}\int_{S'} \frac{e^{jk|\overline{r}-\overline{r}'|}}{|\overline{r}-\overline{r}'|}\, dx'dy' \int_{-\infty}^{\infty} \delta(z')\, dz' \tag{14-6.9}$$

To proceed, we apply the usual approximations for $e^{jk|\overline{r}-\overline{r}'|}$ and $|\overline{r}-\overline{r}'|$, namely

$$|\overline{r}-\overline{r}'| = r - (xx' + yy')$$

$$kR = kr - \overline{k}\cdot\overline{r}' = kr - k\overline{a}_r \cdot \overline{r}'$$

and for the denominator we use the simple approximation $|\overline{r}-\overline{r}'| = r$. Equation (14-6.9) becomes

$$F_x = \frac{\varepsilon E_o e^{jkr}}{2\pi r}\int_{-a/2}^{a/2} e^{-jkxx'/r}\, dx' \int_{-b/2}^{b/2} e^{-jkyy'/r}\, dy' \int_{-\infty}^{\infty} \delta(z')\, dz'$$

which integrates to

$$F_x = \frac{\varepsilon E_o e^{jkr} ab}{2\pi r}\;\frac{\sin\left(\frac{kx}{r}\frac{a}{2}\right)}{kx\,\frac{a}{2}}\;\frac{\sin\left(\frac{ky}{r}\frac{b}{2}\right)}{ky\,\frac{b}{2}} \tag{14-6.10}$$

This result should be compared with that obtained in Ex. 14-4.2.

The electric field may be found from Eq. (14-6.2c). For simplicity we shall consider the electric field at the Z-axis only. Since at any point on the Z-axis the magnetic potential is a function of the Z-coordinate only, it is expected that the $\overline{E}$-field will have a Y-component only [see Eq. (14-6.2c)]. The value is given by

$$\overline{E} = -\overline{a}_y \frac{E_o}{2\pi}\left(\frac{jk}{z} - \frac{1}{z^2}\right)e^{jkz} \tag{14-6.11}$$

Clearly, the field at large distances assumes the form of a radiation field, as would be expected. In case the field point is off of the Z-axis, the magnetic potential $\overline{F} = \overline{a}_x F_x(x,y,z)$ is a function of all three coordinates. The curl of $\overline{F}$ gives two components of the $\overline{E}$-field, one is in the Y-direction and the other is in the Z-direction. However, since $\overline{H} = (j/\omega\mu\varepsilon)\ \nabla(\nabla \cdot F) + j\omega\overline{F}$, the magnetic field has all three components.

ΔΔΔ

Example 14-6.2. Find the fields that result from a circular aperture that is illuminated with a uniform electric field

$$\overline{E} = \overline{a}_x E_o \tag{14-6.12}$$

as shown in Fig. 14-6.3.

Solution. We proceed in much the same way that we did in Ex. 14-6.1. Thus we obtain for the magnetic potential

$$\overline{F} = -\overline{a}_y \frac{\varepsilon E_o e^{jkr}}{2\pi r} \int_{S'} e^{jk\left(\frac{xx' + yy'}{r}\right)} dS' \int_{-\infty}^{\infty} \delta(z')\, dz' \tag{14-6.13}$$

To change the integral into spherical coordinates, we observe that

$$x = r \sin\theta \cos\phi \qquad x' = r' \cos\phi'$$

$$y = r \sin\theta \sin\phi \qquad y' = r' \sin\phi'$$

and

$$\frac{xx' + yy'}{r} = r' \sin\theta \cos(\phi - \phi')$$

Introduce these relations into Eq. (14-6.13) to obtain

$$\overline{F} = -\overline{a}_y \frac{\varepsilon E_o e^{jkr}}{2\pi r} \int_0^a \int_0^{2\pi} e^{-jkr' \sin\theta \cos(\phi-\phi')}\, d\phi' r' dr' \tag{14-6.14}$$

By using the integral representation of the Bessel function

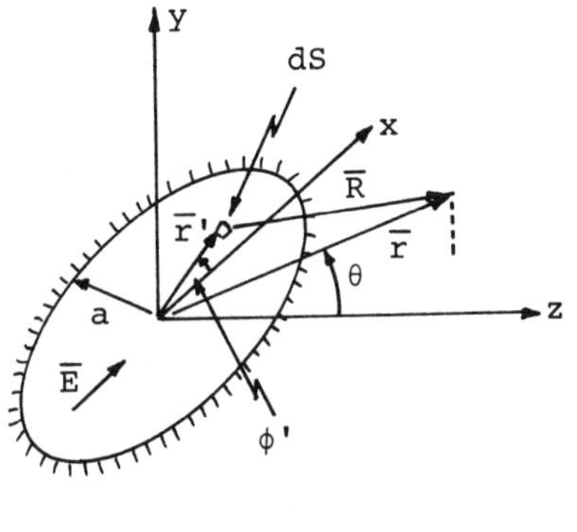

Figure 14-6.3. Radiation from a circular aperture.

$$J_o(x) = \frac{1}{2\pi}\int_0^{2\pi} e^{jx \cos \xi}\, d\xi$$

we obtain

$$\overline{F} = -\overline{a}_y \frac{\varepsilon E_o e^{jkr}}{r}\int_0^a r'\, J_o(kr' \sin \theta)\, dr' \qquad (14\text{-}6.15)$$

Note here that the negative sign in the exponent of the integrand in Eq. (14-6.14) can be incorporated into the cosine function by shifting it by π degrees. Further, since $\cos \phi'$ is periodic, the integral is independent of the constant ϕ and any additional constant that may occur. We integrate Eq. (14-6.15) by making use of Eq. (4-3.19c). The result is

$$\overline{F} = -\overline{a}_y \frac{\varepsilon E_o}{r} e^{jkr}\, a^2 \frac{J_1(ka \sin \theta)}{(ka \sin \theta)} \qquad (14\text{-}6.16)$$

From this we can easily find the electric and magnetic field vectors using procedures that are identical to those developed in the previous example. This solution should be compared with that in Ex. 12-4.2.

ΔΔΔ

14-7. Sound Radiation from a Loud Speaker

We wish to study the sound radiation from a loud speaker with all elements of the radiating surface being free to move. To do this, the radiating surface is considered to be a simple piston, but not necessarily having a rigid face. We proceed by subdividing the surface into small elements dS, as shown in Fig. 14-6.3. The volume flow of air from each of these elements is v dS, and this is equivalent to a sound source of strength dq = v dS which radiates into the half space of solid angle 2π. Further, we assume that each source is infinitesimally small so that dipole and higher-order sound components can be neglected. By Eq. (14-2.4) we can write for the pressure due to an elementary source

$$dp_1 = \frac{-j\omega\rho_o k\, dq}{4\pi} = \frac{-j\omega\rho_o}{4\pi}\frac{e^{jkR}}{kR}(kv\, dS) \qquad (14\text{-}7.1)$$

To find the total pressure, we sum the contributions from all the elementary sources. We thus obtain

$$p_1 = \frac{-j\omega\rho_o k}{4\pi}\int_S v(x',y')\, \frac{e^{jkR}}{kR}\, dS' \qquad (14\text{-}7.2)$$

This integral is a special case of Huygen's principle (see Chap. 12) and specifies that every point on a plane vibrating surface can be considered as the center of an outgoing spherical wave.

For a far field solution [see Ex. 14-6.2; also Eq. (14-6.2)] Eq. (14-7.2) takes the form

$$p_1 = \frac{-j\omega\rho_o k\ e^{jkr}}{4\pi rk} \int_S v(x',y')\ e^{-jk\left(\frac{xx' + yy'}{r}\right)}\ dS' = \frac{-jc_a\rho_o k\ e^{jkr}}{4\pi r}$$

$$\cdot \int_S v(x',y')\ e^{-jk\ [x\ \cos\ (\overline{r},\overline{a}_x)\ +\ y\ \cos\ (\overline{r},\overline{a}_y)]}\ dS' \qquad (14\text{-}7.3)$$

Since the velocity has the same phase at all points (this is not true for a constrained circular membrane having nodal lines) the sound field is a maximum in the direction normal to the vibration. Therefore we can write

$$P_{1max} = \frac{-jk\rho_o c_a\ e^{jkr}}{4\pi r} \int_S v(x',y')dS' = -jk\rho_o c_a \frac{Q_s}{4\pi r}\ e^{jkr} \qquad (14\text{-}7.4)$$

where Q_s is the volume flow into the half space. With this expression, we can now write Eq. (14-7.3) in the form

$$p_1 = p_{1max} \int_S \frac{v(x',y')\ e^{-jk\ [x\ \cos(\overline{r},\overline{a}_x)\ +\ y\ \cos(\overline{r},\overline{a}_y)]}\ dS'}{Q_s}$$

$$= p_{1max}\ \frac{1}{Q_s} \int_S e^{-[\ ]} dQ = p_{1max}\ D \qquad (14\text{-}7.5)$$

where p_{1max} is a known quantity, $dQ = v(x',y')dS'$ is the element of volume flow, and D is the directivity function. Because p_{1max} is known in Eq. (14-7.5) we need be concerned only with D. But for individual sources which are driven in phase, Q can be chosen to be a real quantity. The integral in Eq. (14-7.5) reduces to the sum

$$D = \frac{1}{Q_s} \sum_n Q_n\ e^{jk\ [x\ \cos(\overline{r},\overline{a}_x)\ +\ y\ \cos(\overline{r},\overline{a}_y)]} \qquad (14\text{-}7.6)$$

where

$$Q_s = \sum_n Q_n$$

Example 14-7.1. Find the radiation pattern in the XZ plane, if four equal strength radiators are located on the X-axis, each d meters apart.

Solution. Using a procedure similar to that in Sec. 14-5, the directivity function for four radiators is written

$$D = \frac{1}{4Q}\ [Q + Q\ e^{jkd\ \cos(\overline{r},\overline{a}_x)} + Q\ e^{j2kd\ \cos(\overline{r},\overline{a}_x)} + Q\ e^{j3kd\ \cos(\overline{r},\overline{a}_x)}]$$

If we designate the angle between the Z-axis and r as angle θ, then Eq. (14-7.6) takes the form

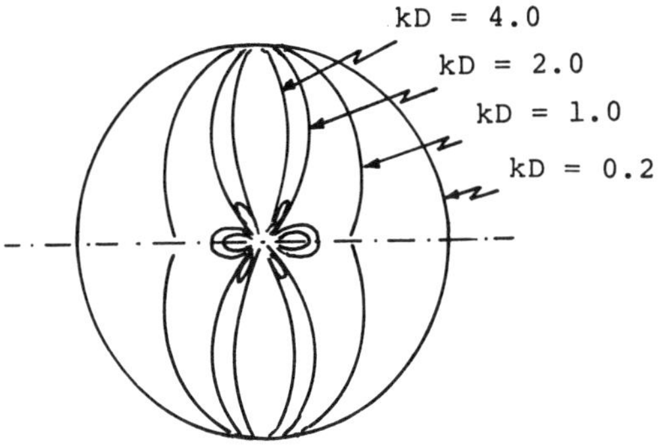

Figure 14-7.1. The directivity pattern of four equal equiphase colinear acoustic radiators.

$$D = \frac{1}{4}\left[1 + e^{j\psi} + e^{j2\psi} + e^{j3\psi}\right] = \frac{1}{4}\,\frac{1 - e^{j4\psi}}{1 - e^{j\psi}} = \frac{1}{4}\,\frac{e^{j2\psi}}{e^{j\frac{\psi}{2}}}\,\frac{(e^{-j2\psi} - e^{j2\psi})}{(e^{-j\frac{\psi}{2}} - e^{j\frac{\psi}{2}})}$$

which becomes

$$D = \frac{1}{4}\, e^{j3\frac{\psi}{2}}\, \frac{\sin 2\psi}{\sin \frac{\psi}{2}}$$

where $\psi = kd \sin\theta$. A plot of $|D|$ versus θ is given in Fig. 14-7.1.

ΔΔΔ

4-8. The Reciprocity Theorem

Before considering the reciprocity theorem in field theory, we review reciprocity in circuit theory, since there is a close relationship between the two. In circuit theory the reciprocity theorem states that the response at any location in the system due to an excitation elsewhere in the system will be the same if the location of the excitation source and response point are interchanged. The situation is illustrated in Fig. 14-8.1. Stated analytically, the reciprocity theorem demands that

$$Z_{21} = Z_{12}$$

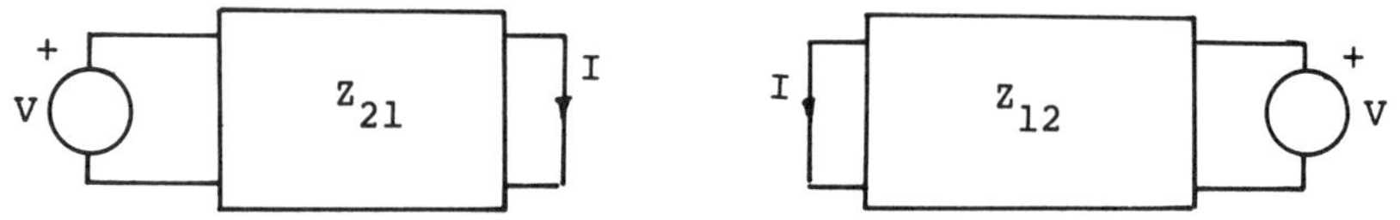

Figure 14-8.1. Reciprocity in network theory.

This result is valid for lumped linear systems without regard to the complexity of the network coupling the excitation and response ports.

In field problems the reciprocity theorem relates the radiation pattern of an antenna array when used in a transmitting mode and in a receiving mode. The theorem states that a given antenna array that is radiating into free space will have the same directional pattern (hence antenna gain) as this antenna array when used as a receiver of radiation from free space into a short circuit. The practical importance of this result is evident since it allows the radiation properties of an antenna array for transmission to be determined using a test range consisting of a low power source and the antenna array in a receiving mode.

To develop the proof, we consider two fields $\overline{E}_1$ and $\overline{H}_1$ and $\overline{E}_2$ and $\overline{H}_2$, each being produced by a different source. By the superposition theorem, the field at a point in space due to the presence of both sources simultaneously will be the fields $\overline{E}_1 + \overline{E}_2$ and $\overline{H}_1 + \overline{H}_2$. For these fields, the controlling Maxwell equations are

$$\begin{aligned} &\nabla \times \overline{E}_1 = j\omega\mu\, \overline{H}_1 && \text{a)} \\ &\nabla \times \overline{H}_1 = \overline{J}_1 - j\omega\varepsilon\, \overline{E}_1 && \text{b)} \\ &\nabla \times \overline{E}_2 = j\omega\mu\, \overline{H}_2 && \text{c)} \\ &\nabla \times \overline{H}_2 = \overline{J}_2 - j\omega\varepsilon\, \overline{E}_2 && \text{d)} \end{aligned} \qquad (14\text{-}8.1)$$

Now dot multiply the second equation by $\overline{E}_2$ and the third by $\overline{H}_1$ and subtract the two resulting equations. There results

$$\overline{H}_1 \cdot \nabla \times \overline{E}_2 - \overline{E}_2 \cdot \nabla \times \overline{H}_1 = \nabla \cdot (\overline{E}_2 \times \overline{H}_1) = j\omega\mu\overline{H}_1 \cdot \overline{H}_2 - \overline{E}_2 \cdot \overline{J}_1 + j\omega\varepsilon\overline{E}_2 \cdot \overline{E}_1 \qquad (14\text{-}8.2)$$

By a systematic interchange of the subscripts of this equation, we obtain the following

$$\overline{H}_2 \cdot \nabla \times \overline{E}_1 - \overline{E}_1 \cdot \nabla \times \overline{H}_2 = \nabla \cdot (\overline{E}_1 \times \overline{H}_2) = j\omega\mu\overline{H}_2 \cdot \overline{H}_1 - \overline{E}_1 \cdot \overline{J}_2 + j\omega\varepsilon\overline{E}_1 \cdot \overline{E}_2 \qquad (14\text{-}8.3)$$

The last two equations are subtracted, which leads to

$$\nabla \cdot (\overline{E}_1 \times \overline{H}_2 - \overline{E}_2 \times \overline{H}_1) = \overline{E}_2 \cdot \overline{J}_1 - \overline{E}_1 \cdot \overline{J}_2 \qquad (14\text{-}8.4)$$

For a point not in the region where the source currents $\overline{J}_1$ and $\overline{J}_2$ exist, Eq. (14-8.4) assumes the form

$$\nabla \cdot (\overline{E}_1 \times \overline{H}_2 - \overline{E}_2 \times \overline{H}_1) = 0 \qquad (14\text{-}8.5)$$

We integrate Eq. (14-8.4) over the volume V, and upon an application of the divergence theorem, we obtain

$$\int_S (\overline{E}_1 \times \overline{H}_2 - \overline{E}_2 \times \overline{H}_1) \cdot \overline{dS} = \int_V (\overline{E}_2 \cdot \overline{J}_1 - \overline{E}_1 \cdot \overline{J}_2)\, dV \qquad (14\text{-}8.6)$$

Let the surface be extended over all space. The waves are nearly plane, and we can employ the plane wave relations of Eq. (10-2.14)

$$\overline{E}_1 = Z\, \overline{H}_1 \times \overline{a}_r \qquad \overline{E}_2 = Z\, \overline{H}_2 \times \overline{a}_r$$

Hence the integral over all space ($r \to \infty$) is

$$\int_S (\overline{E}_1 \times \overline{H}_2 - \overline{E}_2 \times \overline{H}_1) \cdot \overline{a}_r dS = Z \int [(\overline{H}_1 \times \overline{a}_r) \times \overline{H}_2 - (\overline{H}_2 \times \overline{a}_r) \times \overline{H}_1] \cdot \overline{a}_r dS \qquad (14\text{-}8.7)$$

from which, since the vector triple product has the form

$$\overline{A} \times (\overline{B} \times \overline{C}) = (\overline{A} \cdot \overline{C})\overline{B} - (\overline{A} \cdot \overline{B})\overline{C}$$

then

$$\int_S (\overline{E}_1 \times \overline{H}_2 - \overline{E}_2 \times \overline{H}_1) \cdot \overline{a}_r\, dS = 0 \qquad (14\text{-}8.8)$$

We thus have

$$\int_{\text{space}} \overline{E}_1 \cdot \overline{J}_2\, dV = \int_{\text{space}} \overline{E}_2 \cdot \overline{J}_1\, dV \qquad (14\text{-}8.9)$$

This result has the interpretation illustrated in Fig. 14-8.2. For the case of thin antennas of infinite conductivity, Eq. (14-8.9) becomes

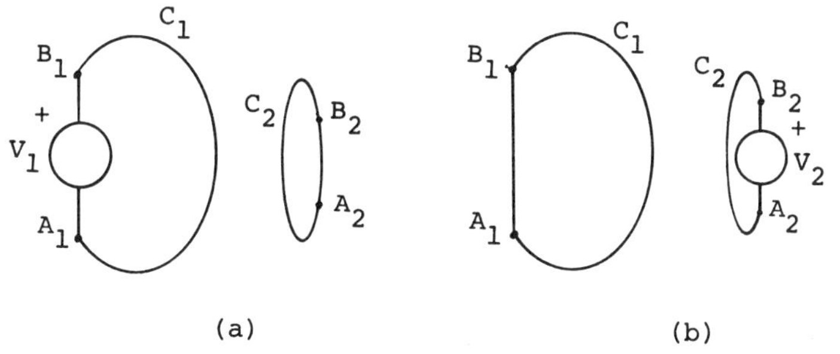

Figure 14-8.2. A pair of antennas illustrating the reciprocity theorem.

$$\int \bar{E}_1 \cdot \bar{J}_2 \, dV = \int_{A_1B_1} \frac{I_{12}}{S} \bar{E}_1 \cdot d\bar{\ell} + \int_{B_1C_1A_1} \frac{I_{12}}{S} \bar{E}_1 \cdot d\bar{\ell} = \frac{I_{12}V_1}{S} + 0$$

$$= \int \bar{E}_2 \cdot \bar{J}_1 dV = \int_{A_2B_2} \frac{I_{21}}{S} \bar{E}_2 \cdot d\bar{\ell} + \int_{B_2C_2A_2} \frac{I_{21}}{S} \bar{E}_2 \cdot d\bar{\ell}$$

$$= \frac{I_{21}V_1}{S} + 0 \quad (4\text{-}8.10)$$

where $\bar{E}_1 \cdot d\bar{\ell} = \bar{E}_2 \cdot d\bar{\ell} = 0$ inside the antenna, $\bar{E}_2 \cdot d\bar{\ell} = 0$ in the short-circuited path, I_{12} is the current in the first antenna due to the second being energized, I_{21} is the current in the second antenna due to the first being energized, and S is the surface area of the wires in which the current was assumed uniform. The volume integral was restricted only to the antennas since $\bar{J}_1$ and $\bar{J}_2$ are zero everywhere else.

In a similar way using Eq. (14-8.9) for the case shown in Fig. 14-8.2b we obtain

$$\int \bar{E}_1 \cdot \bar{J}_2 \, dV = 0 = \int \bar{E}_2 \cdot \bar{J}_1 \, dV = \frac{I_{21}}{S} V_2 = \frac{I_{12}}{S} V_1 \quad (14\text{-}8.11)$$

For the general case when both sources are present, the superposition theorem dictates the addition of the last two equations. Thus we have

$$I_{12} V_1 = I_{21} V_2$$

or

$$\frac{I_{21}}{V_1} = \frac{I_{12}}{V_2} \quad (14\text{-}8.12)$$

which shows that this theorem is concerned only with the ratio I/V.

The foregoing discussion shows that if the mediums are linear, passive and isotropic, then the antenna whether in the radiating or in the receiving mode will have identical patterns. Specifically, our development shows that if we apply a voltage source V_1 to the input terminals of the first antenna, the second antenna will have a short circuit current I_{21}. This current is proportional to the electric field component which is parallel to the linear dipole elements, and therefore to the directivity pattern $D(\theta,\phi)$ of the antenna. But we have that $I_{21}/V_1 = C\,D(\theta,\phi)$, where C is a constant. The reciprocity theorem Eq. (14-8.12) requires that the receiving pattern of the antenna has the same $D(\theta,\phi)$. It is noted, however, that the reciprocity theorem does not provide information about the current distribution of the receiving antenna; nor does it give information about the scattered field. Essentially all that we have done is to calculate lumped properties from the incident fields; the reverse is not possible from reciprocity considerations alone.

REVIEW QUESTIONS

1. What is the difference between the induction and the radiation field of a dipole antenna?
2. How do we find the radiated power of an antenna?
3. What is the directivity pattern of an antenna?
4. Is the radiated power real or complex? If complex what do the real and imaginary parts represent?
5. How do we define the gain of an antenna?
6. Does an acoustic radiating source resemble an antenna radiating electromagnetic fields?
7. For the center-fed linear antenna, what are the parameters which affect its radiation pattern?
8. Why do we use an array of radiators?
9. What antenna constants affect the radiation characteristics of an array?
10. Explain the reciprocity theorem.

PROBLEMS

14-1.1. If $\lambda >> d$ and I is independent of position in the short dipole shown in Fig. 14-1.2, show that the constant $C = (\mu_o/4\pi)k\ Id$.

14-1.2. Show that Eq. (14-1.17) is a solution to the wave equation $\nabla^2 A_z + k^2 A_z = 0$ in which A_z is independent of coordinates θ and ϕ.
[Hint: Write the equation in spherical coordinates.]

14-1.3. Verify Eqs. (14-1.18), (14-8.19), and (14-1.20).

14-1.4. Show that the radiation resistance of a short dipole is $R_{rad} = 80\ \pi^2 (d/\lambda)^2$
[Hint: Use C from Pr. 14-1.1 above.]

14-1.5. Plot the far field $|\overline{E}_o|$ versus θ for a particular ϕ. The resulting plot is known as the *E-field pattern*.

14-2.1. Starting with the continuity equation (8-5.9) prove Eq. (14-2.1).

[Hint: Eqs. (8-5.12) and (8-5.8) in one dimension is $\partial\rho_o v_x/\partial x = -(1/c_a^2)$ $\partial p_1/\partial t + \rho_o g$. Differentiate this with respect to time t and substitute Eq. (8-5.14) after being differentiated with respect to x.]

14-2.2. Show that the circuit analog of radiation specific acoustic impedance of a pulsating sphere is that shown in Fig. P14-2.2.

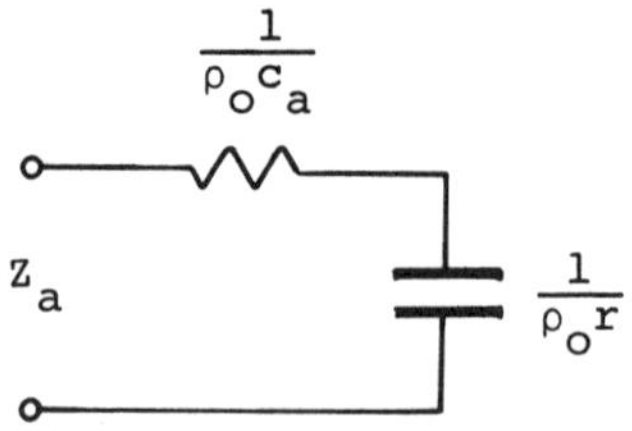

Figure P14-2.2.

14-3.1. Verify Eq. (14-3.5).

14-3.2. Because of the variation of the velocity with θ, the acoustic impedance per unit area has little physical significance. As a result, the impedance for the dipole is defined as the ratio of the axial velocity to the driving force over the spherical surface. Find this mean acoustical impedance Z_{am}.

[Hint: $Z_{am} = v/\int_{-\pi}^{\pi} p_1 \cos\theta \cdot 2\pi r^2 \sin\theta \, d\theta$.]

14-3.3. The circuit analog of the mechanical impedance for an acoustic dipole is shown in the Fig. P14-3.3. Find the values of L_a, C_a and R_a.

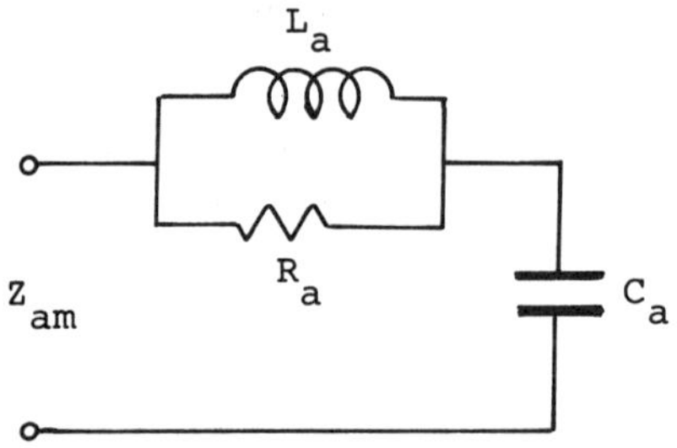

Figure P14-3.3.

14-3.4. For a small pulsating sphere, show that the radiation resistance for a dipole is two orders of magnitude smaller than that of a monopole (a single sphere).

14-4.1. Verify Eq. (14-4.4).

[Hint: $\int_{-d/2}^{d/2} \sin\left(\frac{kd}{2} - k|z|\right) e^{-jkz\cos\theta} dz$

$= \int_{-d/2}^{0} \sin\left(\frac{kd}{2} + kz\right) e^{-jkz\cos\theta} dz + \int_{0}^{d/2} \sin\left(\frac{kd}{2} - kz\right) e^{-jkz\cos\theta} dz$

$= \int_{0}^{d/2} \sin\left(\frac{kd}{2} - kz\right) [e^{jkz\cos\theta} + e^{-jkz\cos\theta}] \, dz$.]

14-4.2. Verify Eq. (14-4.5).

14-4.3. Find $\overline{A}(\overline{r})$ for a linear center-fed antenna whose length d is equal to $\lambda/2$.

[Ans: $\overline{A}(\overline{r}) = \overline{a}_z \dfrac{\mu I}{2\pi S_o} \dfrac{e^{jkr}}{r} \dfrac{\cos(\frac{\pi}{2}\cos\theta)}{\sin^2\theta}$]

14-4.4. Repeat Pr. 14-4.3 for the case of a linear $\lambda/4$ antenna which is on an infinite ground plane of infinite conductivity.

14-4.5. Find the total time-averaged power radiated and the radiation resistance of a half-wave dipole.

[Hint: $\langle P\rangle_{rad} = \oint_S \langle \overline{\mathscr{S}}_{rad}\rangle \cdot d\overline{S}'$; try to approximate the integrand, or use a computer.]

[Ans: $\langle P\rangle_{rad} = 73\,\dfrac{(I/S)^2}{2}$; $R_{rad} = 73\ \Omega$.]

14-5.1. Refer to Eq. (14-5.5).

a. Show that the array has a maximum in the direction $\Phi = 90$ deg when each dipole has a zero phase. This is the condition for a *broadside* array.

b. If the phase of each dipole is proportional to the displacement from dipole and is such that the Nth dipole has a phase $\psi_N = (N-1)kd$, show that the resulting pattern has a maximum in the direction $\Phi = 180$ deg. This is the condition for an *end-fire* array.

14-5.2. a. Determine the equation for the vertical pattern of the isolated colinear array shown in the figure. The elements carry equal currents and in the same phase.

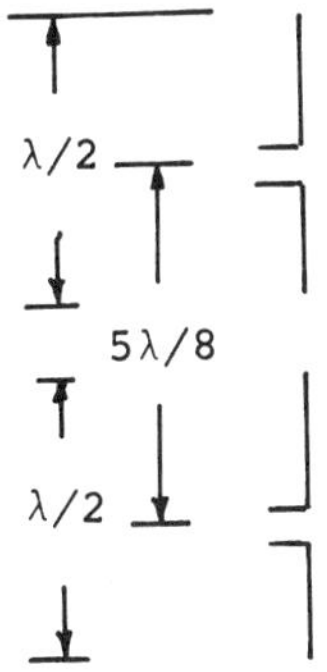

Figure P14-5.2.

b. Sketch the vertical pattern of this array.

c. What is the form of the horizontal pattern? What is the direction of the electric vector?

14-5.3. Two vertical half-wave antennas are located in a horizontal plane. Suppose that antenna 1 has an input current of 2.0 Amp rms and antenna 2 has an input current of 3.0 Amp rms. The phase angle between the currents is 90 deg with the phase of the current in antenna 1 leading that in antenna 2. The separation between antennas is $\lambda/4$.

a. Find an expression for E_θ for the array.
b. For r_2 = 5000 m, f = 10 MHz, ϕ = 45 deg, find the numerical value of E_θ.
c. Determine the magnitude of the magnetic field intensity H_ϕ under the conditions specified in b.

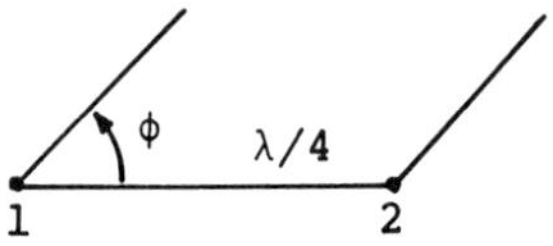

Figure P14-5.3.

14-5.4. A half-wave dipole is oriented vertically at a center distance h = $\lambda/4$ above the ground.

a. Deduce an expression for the field at any point in space.
b. Sketch a curve showing the resulting field pattern.

14-5.5. Repeat Pr. 14-5.4 for the case when the half-wave dipole is oriented horizontally above the ground.

14-5.6. Two $\lambda/4$ vertical radiators are used in an array for transmitting. The spacing between antennas is 0.3λ. The input current to one antenna is 5 Amp rms and the current to the other is 10 Amp rms. The antennas are excited in phase with each other.

a. For an assumed perfectly conducting earth, find the power radiated by this two-antenna array.
b. Sketch the far field radiation pattern for this array.

14-5.7. Consider a two dimensional array of antennas as illustrated.

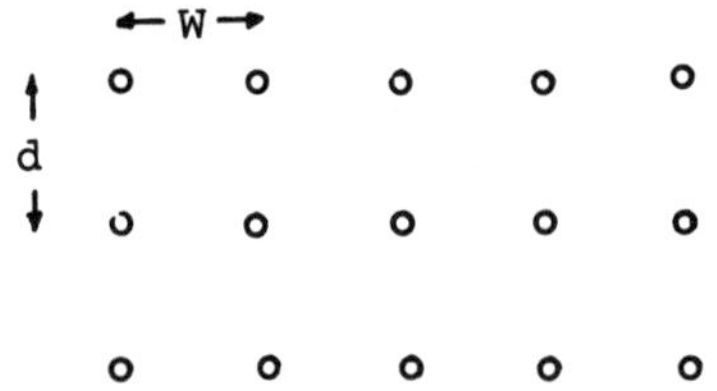

Figure P14-5.7.

Assume that the excitation is such as to provide the same progressive phase shift for each horizontal row and each vertical column. Find an expression for the total pattern of the array and show that it can be written simply as the product of the pattern of the individual dipoles and a two-dimensional array factor, with the two-dimensional array factor being the product of the horizontal and vertical array factors.

14-6.1. Verify Eq. (14-6.9).

14-6.2. Find $\overline{H}$ on the Z axis for the Example 14-6.1; also the average power flowing in the Z-direction.

14-6.3. Find the magnetic potential $\overline{F}$ for the TE_{01} mode ($\overline{E} = \overline{a}_y E_o \cos \pi x/a$) radiating from the open end of a rectangular waveguide with dimensions $a \times b$.

14-6.4. Find the electromagnetic field radiated from the open end of a coaxial line with inner radius a and outer radius b.

[Hint: $E = \overline{a}_{r'} \frac{A}{r'}$; $A = \frac{V}{\ell n \frac{b}{a}}$.]

14-6.5. Find the $\overline{E}$ and $\overline{H}$ field on the Z-axis using the results of Ex. 14-6.2. In addition, find the average power flow in the Z-direction.

14-7.1. Show that the directivity for a circular acoustic radiator with constant velocity across it is given by

$$D = \frac{2\pi a^2}{Q_s} \frac{J_1(ka \sin \theta)}{(ka \sin \theta)} .$$

14-7.2. Find the directivity pattern of a loud speaker for the following four frequencies: kd = 0.1, 0.5, 1.0, 4.0.

14-8.1. Refer to the accompanying figures. Develop the reciprocity theorem when the excitation sources are current sources.
[Ans: $V_{21}/I_1 = V_{12}/I_2$]

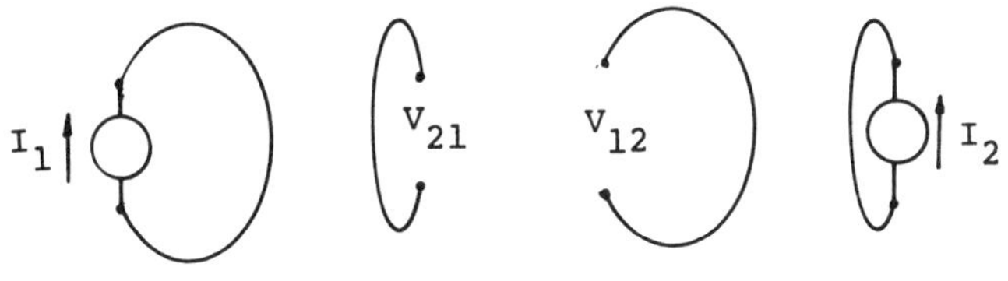

Figure P14-8.1.

CHAPTER 15

SPECIAL METHODS IN FIELD ANALYSIS

A. Variational Principles

In this chapter we shall discuss some techniques which are useful in the approximate formulation or solution of field problems. Many of the methods which are in present day use are related to variational techniques. These include: finite element, Rayleigh-Ritz, among others. We shall develop some basic ideas of this important branch of mathematics.

In our present analysis, we shall accept the *continuum* viewpoint of matter in which the independent variables are the coordinates of space and time. This model is to be contrasted with the Lagrangian viewpoint which treats all matter as an aggregate of individual particles each retaining its identity as it moves through space. Problems of this nature describe the fields of temperature, mass concentration, displacement, stress, electromagnetic and acoustic environments. The analysis and description from these areas lead to equations which are expressed as partial differential equations plus the appropriate boundary conditions.

Important to this study are the contents of Appendix II. It is suggested that this Appendix material be read as part of the present study.

15-1. Functions and Functionals

Variational calculus is a branch of mathematics that deals with *functionals*. We must think of functionals as variable values assumed by different functions belonging to some specified class. We can also look at them as functions of other functions. In mathematical representation we write

$$I[x(t)] = \int_a^b f(x(t))\, dt \tag{15-1.1}$$

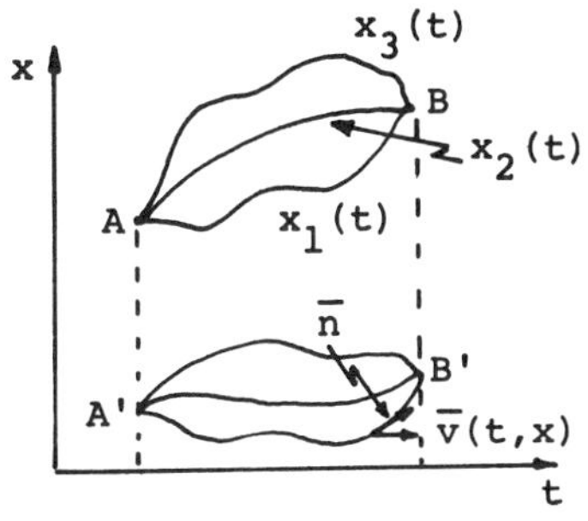

Figure 15-1.1. Alternate paths between two points.

For example, a specific functional might be

$$I[x(t)] = I[x] = \int_a^b (3x^2 + 2\dot{x})dt$$

where the dot means differentiation with respect to the independent variable.

Suppose that we are asked to find the length of the curves between points A and B shown in Fig. 15-1.1. To do this we would write the well-known formula of calculus

$$S[x(t)] = \int_A^B dS = \int_A^B \sqrt{dt^2 + dx^2} = \int_A^B \sqrt{1 + \dot{x}^2}\, dt \tag{15-1.2}$$

where t is a spatial variable. Different values $S_1, S_2, \ldots S_n$ are deduced in general by inserting the form for each x(t) in Eq. (15-1.2). In accordance with the discussion above, the length is a functional, by definition.

As a second illustration, consider the velocity $\bar{v}(t,x)$ (t = spatial variable) of a particle moving from A' to B' shown in Fig. 15-1.1. The time that it takes for the particle to move along an incremental path of length $d\ell$ is

$$d\tau = \frac{d\ell}{\bar{v}(t,x) \cdot \bar{n}} \tag{15-1.3}$$

where $\bar{n}$ is a unit vector parallel to $d\bar{\ell}$. The total time for the particle to move from A' to B' is

$$I[x(t)] = \tau = \int_{A'}^{B'} \frac{\sqrt{1 + \dot{x}^2}}{v[t,x(t)]}\, dt \tag{15-1.4}$$

which indicates that the time, as defined, is also a functional.

An individual function $x_i(t)$ to be admissible must belong to a certain class of functions. They must, for example, be continuous and possess continuous derivatives over the interval of interest. There is, however, a similiarity between

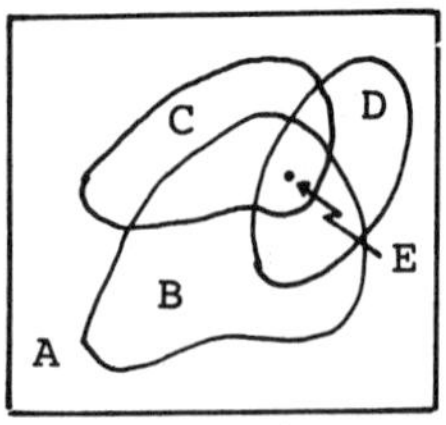

Figure 15-1.2. To illustrate the necessary conditions for functionals. A, set of all admissible curves; B, set of functions that satisfy condition 1; C and D, set of functions that satisfy conditions 2 and 3, respectively; E, element of the set that extremizes the functional.

functions and functionals since in both cases we are interested in finding their maxima or minima. To extremize a given functional, we must impose certain *necessary conditions* which must be satisfied by the extremizing function. Hence the set of functions that can solve a given problem is smaller than the set of functions that satisfy the necessary conditions. This results because not all of the functions that belong to the admissible set extremize the functional.

Figure 15-1.2 shows graphically different sets and the elements which satisfy all the necessary conditions and at the same time extremizes the functional. We must continue to add more necessary conditions until we eliminate all the functions but the one that solves the problem. This is a rather unending routine; hence we seek other properties which, if they are satisfied by a function, insures that it is the one which was sought. These properties are the *sufficient conditions*. However, we shall restrict ourselves only to necessary conditions since we can then use various successive approximation algorithms to obtain the function which extremizes the functional which otherwise would be possible only using the necessary conditions.

In order to understand how functionals are used, it is instructive to compare their properties with those of ordinary functions with which we are more familiar. This is undertaken by the presentation below.

Function and Functional

I. To each value of the independent variable t of its domain, we associate a certain value for the dependent function x(t), as illustrated in Fig. 15-1.3a.

Ia. To each function x(t) of its class we associate a number for the functional I[x(t)] which has the function x(t) as the independent variable. See Fig. 15-1.3b.

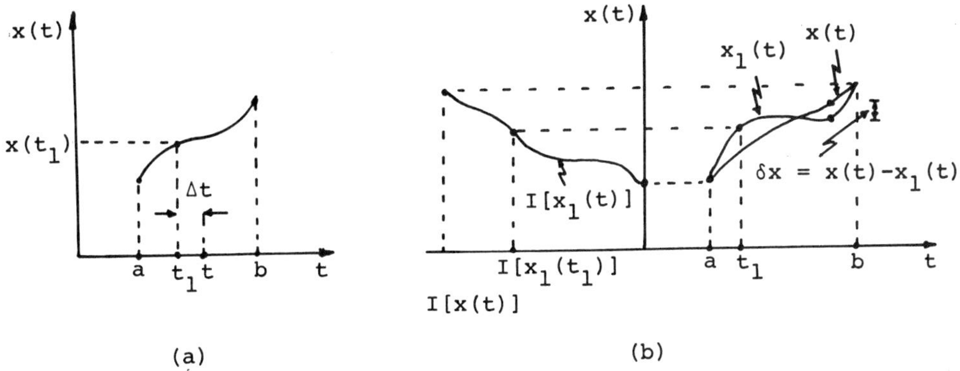

Figure 15-1.3. Illustrations of functions and functionals.

II. The difference $\Delta t = t - t_1$ of the independent variable is called the increment of the ordinary function x(t) (see Fig. 15-1.3a).

IIa. The difference $\delta x = x(t) - x_1(t)$ is the variation of the argument of a functional I[x(t)] where x(t) and $x_i(t)$ $i = 1,2,3,\dots,n$ belong to the same class of functions (see Fig. 15-1.3b).

III. The function x(t) is continuous *at a point* $t = t_1$ if for each positive number ε there exists a quantity $\delta > 0$ such that $|x(t)-x_1(t)| < \varepsilon$ whenever $|t-t_1| < \delta$. In general it is understood that a function x(t) is continuous when a small variation of its independent variable results in a small variation of the function (see Fig. 15-1.4a).

IIIa. A functional is continuous *on a curve* $x = x(t)$ if for an arbitrary positive number ε there exists a number $\delta > 0$ such that $|I[x(t)] - I[x_1(t)]| < \varepsilon$ whenever $|x(t)-x_1(t)| < \delta$ (see Fig. 15-1.4b). The closeness of functionals is of order greater than one if, in addition to $|x(t)-x_1(t)| < \delta$ the following inequalities are also true: $|\dot{x}(t)-\dot{x}_1(t)| < \delta$, $|\ddot{x}(t)-\ddot{x}_1(t)| < \delta, \dots$

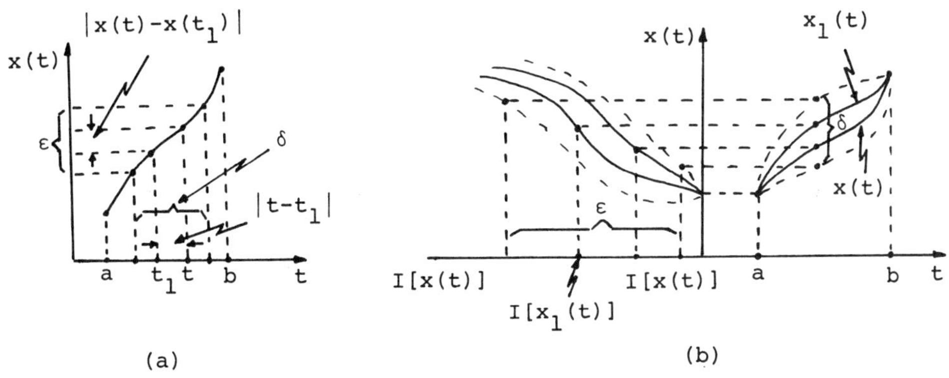

Figure 15-1.4. To illustrate continuity of functions and functionals.

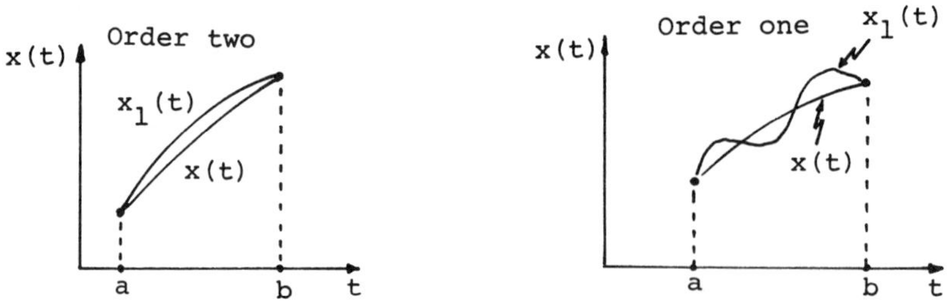

Figure 15-1.5. To illustrate functions of different order.

Figure 15-1.5 shows two functions, one of order 2 and one of order 1.

IV. The finite difference Δx of the function x(t) is given by the equality $\Delta x = x(t+\delta t) - x(t) = \dot{x}(t)\delta t + \beta(t,\delta t)\delta t$, where $\beta \to 0$ when $t \to 0$. The differential of the function x(t) is defined by the linear part of the above relation $dx(t) = \dot{x}\, dt$ (see Fig. 15-1.6a).

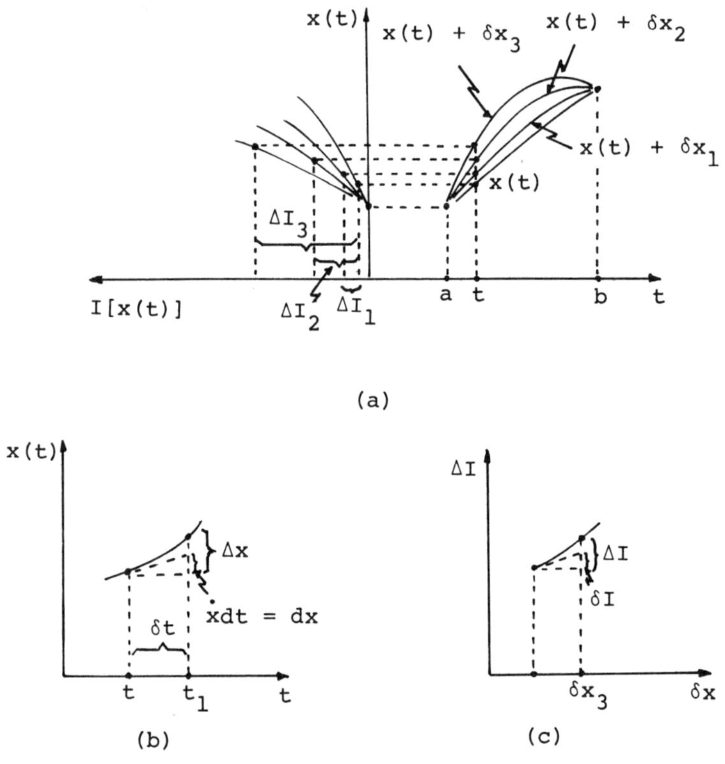

Figure 15-1.6. To illustrate the differentials of functions and functionals.

IVa. If the difference $\Delta I[x(t)] = I[x(t) + \delta x(t)] - I[(x(t)]$ of a functional can be written in a form which has a linear part, then that part is called the *variation* of the functional and it is designed by δI. In mathematical form, we write $\Delta I = \delta I[x,\delta x] + \beta(x,\delta x) \max |\delta x|$ where $\beta \to 0$ whenever $\max|\delta x| \to 0$; (see Fig. 15-1.6b).

Whenever we can represent a functional by a linear part and an additional term of order higher than one relative to δx, we say that the functional is *differentiable*.

V. If a function $x(t)$ is differentiable in an interval $[a,b]$ and takes an extremum value at some point $a \leq t_1 \leq b$, then $dx(t)$ at t_1 is equal to zero. This is a necessary condition for the function $x(t)$ to possess an extremum within the interval.

Va. Theorem 15-1.1. A necessary condition for a functional to have an extremum *along a curve x(t)* is that its variation $\delta I[x,\delta x]$ (the linear part of the functional difference $\Delta I[x(t)] = I[x(t) + \delta x(t)] - I[x(t)]$) vanishes along the same curve for all admissible δx.

Proof: Suppose the functional $I[x(t)]$ has a minimum along the curve $x(t)$. Assuming $|\delta x| \to 0$ implies that the nonlinear part of ΔI goes to zero, the linear part $\delta I[\delta x]$ takes on both positive and negative values, depending on the values given to δx. For a negative δx, δI is negative and thus ΔI is also negative. This cannot be true because $\Delta I \geq 0$ on $x(t)$, and the inequality is true for any variation δx if we have $\delta I = 0$.

VI. The differential of a function $x(t)$ is given by

$$\frac{\partial}{\partial \alpha} x(t + \alpha\delta t)\bigg|_{\alpha=0} = \dot{x}(t)dt = dx \tag{15-1.5}$$

To find this identity, we must consider the appropriate limiting process involving the difference $\Delta x(t)$. The quantity $\Delta x(t)$ becomes

$$\Delta x(t) = x(t + \alpha\delta t) - x(t) = \dot{x}(t)\alpha\delta t + \beta(t,\alpha\delta t)\alpha\delta t$$

In the limit

$$\lim_{\alpha\to 0} \frac{\Delta x(t)}{\alpha} = \dot{x}(t)\delta t = dx(t)$$

since for $\delta t \to 0$, $\beta \to 0$.

VIa. Similarly for the functional, we can find its variation by using the identity

$$\delta I[x,\alpha\delta x] = \frac{\partial}{\partial \alpha} I[x(t) + \alpha\delta x(t)]\bigg|_{\alpha=0} \tag{15-1.6}$$

15-2. A Fundamental Lemma

One of the fundamental lemmas which will help us develop the Euler equation for the minimization of an important functional for our subsequent use is the following:

Lemma 15-2.1. If a function f(x,t) is continuous in a domain D of the (x,t) plane, and if

$$\iint_D f(x,t)g(x,t)\,dx\,dt = 0 \tag{15-2.1}$$

for any continuously differentiable function g which vanishes on the boundary C of D, then f(x,t) = 0 throughout this domain.

Proof: Let us assume that $f(x,t) \neq 0$ in a region D' of the domain D; also let $f(x,t) > 0$ in D', and refer to Fig. 15-2.1. The function g is defined as follows

$$g(x,t) = \begin{cases} 0 & x_a \le x \le x_1 \quad t_a \le t \le t_1 \\ (x-x_1)^2(x-x_2)^2(t-t_1)^2(t-t_2)^2 & x_1 \le x \le x_2 \quad t_1 \le t \le t_2 \\ 0 & x_2 \le x \le x_b \quad t_2 \le t \le t_b \end{cases} \tag{15-2.2}$$

This function satisfies the boundary conditions, and it is continuously differentiable. Therefore the integral in Eq. (15-2.1) is equal to a positive number. But this contradicts the hypothesis, and hence f(x,t) = 0.

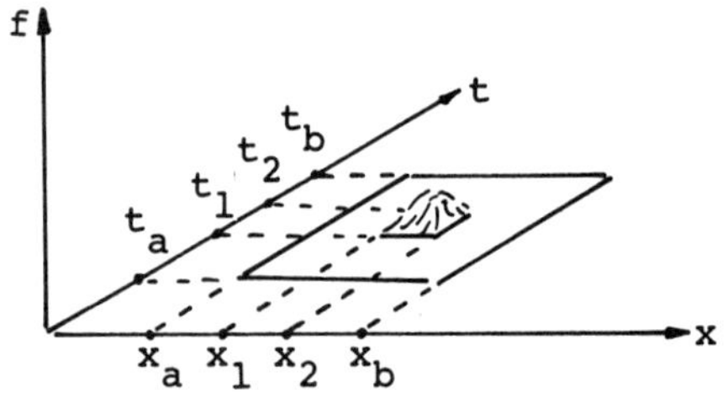

Figure 15-2.1. To illustrate the domain D for Lemma 15-2.1.

15-3. Euler's Equation

(a) One Dependent Variable. Euler's equation is a second order differential equation which extremizes a functional appropriate to a physical system. Specifically, we consider the functional

$$I[x(t)] = \int_a^b f(t,x,\dot{x})\,dt \tag{15-3.1}$$

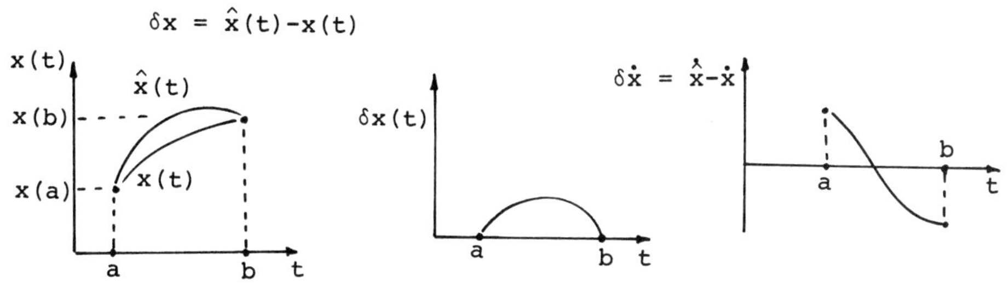

Figure 15-3.1. To illustrate the extremizing, the comparison curve, and the differential δx.

defined on the class of functions which have continuous first derivatives in the closed interval [a,b] and which satisfies the requisite boundary conditions. We now consider:

Theorem 15-3.1. A necessary condition for the functional of Eq. (15-3.1) to possess a weak extremum is that the function x(t) must satisfy Euler's equation

$$\frac{\partial f}{\partial x} - \frac{d}{dt}\frac{\partial f}{\partial \dot{x}} = 0 \tag{15-3.2}$$

Proof: Consider the curve x(t) to be an extremizing curve. Let us create a one-parameter family of curves (see Fig. 15-3.1) using the relation

$$x(t,\alpha) = x(t) + \alpha\delta x = x(t) + \alpha[\hat{x}(t) - x(t)] \tag{15-3.3}$$

The family of curves shown contains as its members the extremizing curve x(t) (set $\alpha = 0$) and the comparison curve $\hat{x}(t)$ (set $\alpha = 1$). Substitute Eq. (15-3.3) into Eq. (15-3.1) to find the relation

$$I[\alpha] = \int_a^b f(t,x(t,\alpha),\dot{x}(t,\alpha))\,dt \tag{15-3.4}$$

This becomes an extremum value by Theorem 15-1.1 and Eq. (15-1.6) if its variation at $\alpha = 0$ vanishes. Therefore we must have that

$$\delta I[x,\alpha\delta x] = \left.\frac{\partial I[\alpha]}{\partial\alpha}\right|_{\alpha=0} = \left.\frac{\partial}{\partial\alpha}\int_a^b f(t,x(t,\alpha),\dot{x}(t,\alpha))dt\right|_{\alpha=0}$$

$$= \left.\int_a^b \left(\frac{\partial f}{\partial x}\frac{\partial x(t,\alpha)}{\partial\alpha} + \frac{\partial f}{\partial\dot{x}}\frac{\partial\dot{x}(t,\alpha)}{\partial\alpha}\right)dt\right|_{\alpha=0} = 0 \tag{15-3.5}$$

We also have the following relations

$$\frac{\partial}{\partial\alpha} x(t,\alpha) = \frac{\partial}{\partial\alpha} [x(t) + \alpha\delta x] = \delta x \qquad \text{a)}$$

$$\frac{\partial}{\partial\alpha} \dot{x}(t,\alpha) = \frac{\partial}{\partial\alpha} [\frac{\partial}{\partial t} [x(t) + \alpha\delta x]] = \delta\dot{x} \qquad \text{b)} \qquad (15\text{-}3.6)$$

When these are introduced into Eq. (15-3.5) there results

$$\delta I[x] = \int_a^b [\frac{\partial f}{\partial x} \delta x + \frac{\partial f}{\partial \dot{x}} \delta\dot{x}] \, dt = 0 \qquad (15\text{-}3.7)$$

Integrate the second term by parts to yield the expression

$$\int_a^b [\frac{\partial f}{\partial x} \delta x] dt + \frac{\partial f}{\partial \dot{x}} \delta x \Big|_a^b - \int_a^b \frac{d}{dt}(\frac{\partial f}{\partial \dot{x}}) \delta x \, dt = \int_a^b [\frac{\partial f}{\partial x} - \frac{d}{dt}(\frac{\partial f}{\partial \dot{x}})] \delta x dt = 0 \qquad (15.3\text{-}8)$$

where $(\partial f/\partial x)\delta x = 0$ at $t = a$ and $t = b$ since $\delta x = 0$ at these points. The function δx has the same properties as the g function in Lemma 15-2.1. This leads to the Euler equation given in Eq. (15-3.2).

Another method of deducing Eq. (15-3.8) involves the use of Taylor's expansion theorem. We begin with the relation

$$x(t) + \rho(t) \qquad (15\text{-}3.9)$$

to denote a slightly varied extremizing curve, where $\rho(t)$ denotes the small incremental function with zero values at the boundary points $t = a$ and $t = b$, i.e., such that the boundary conditions $x(t)\big|_{t=a} = A$ and $x(t)\big|_{t=b} = B$ are satisfied. Figure 15-3.2 illustrates one of the many possible relations of the specified form. The desired variation is the linear part of the following functional relation

$$\begin{aligned}
\Delta I &= I[x(t)+\rho(t)] - I[x(t)] \\
&= \int_a^b f(t,x(t)+\rho(t), \dot{x}(t)+\dot{\rho}(t))dt - \int_a^b f(t,x(t),\dot{x}(t))dt \\
&= \int_a^b \{f(t,x(t)+\rho(t), \dot{x}(t)+\dot{\rho}(t))dt - f(t,x(t),\dot{x}(t))\} \, dt \\
&= \int_a^b \{\frac{\partial f}{\partial x}(t,x(t),\dot{x}(t))\rho(t) + \frac{\partial f}{\partial \dot{x}}(t,x(t),\dot{x}(t))\dot{\rho}\} \, dt + \left\{\begin{matrix}\text{terms of higher order} \\ \text{in } \rho(t) \text{ and } \dot{\rho}(t)\end{matrix}\right.
\end{aligned} \qquad (15\text{-}3.10)$$

This latter expression was obtained by using the Taylor expansion in two variables,

$$f(x,y) = f(a,b) + ((x-a)\frac{\partial}{\partial x} + (y-b)\frac{\partial}{\partial y})f(x,y)\Big|_{\substack{x=a\\y=b}} + \frac{1}{2!}((x-a)\frac{\partial}{\partial x} + (y-b)\frac{\partial}{\partial y})^2 f(x,y)\Big|_{\substack{x=a\\y=b}} + \cdots$$

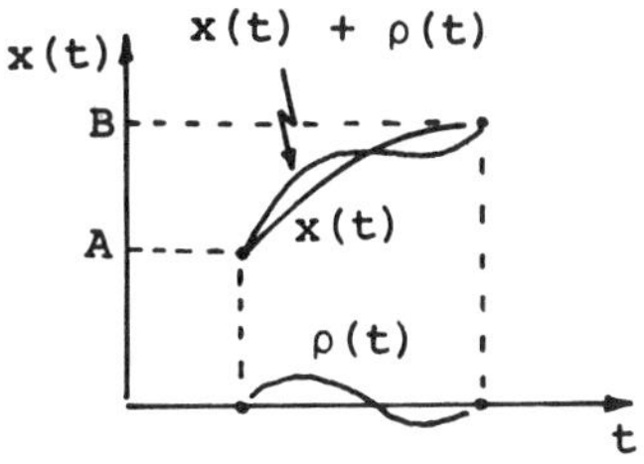

Figure 15-3.2. To illustrate the relation x(t) + ρ(t).

In this particular case, it is observed that $x \triangleq x(t)$, $y \triangleq \dot{x}(t)$, $x-a \triangleq x(t) + \rho(t) - x(t) = \rho(t)$ and $y-b \triangleq \dot{x}(t) - \dot{\rho}(t) - \dot{x}(t) = \dot{\rho}(t)$. The linear part of Eq. (15-3.10) is similar to Eq. (15-3.7), and it may be written

$$\delta I[x] = \int_a^b \left(\frac{\partial f}{\partial x}\rho + \frac{\partial f}{\partial \dot{x}}\dot{\rho}\right)dt \tag{15-3.11}$$

Now by applying the necessary condition $\delta I[x] = 0$, integrating the second term of Eq. (15-3.11) by parts, and then applying the fundamental Lemma of the Calculus of Variation, the result is the Euler equation. ΔΔΔ

Example 15-3.1. Find the curve on a plane which has the shortest length between two points.

Solution. The element of arc length is given in general by

$$ds = \sqrt{dx^2 + dy^2} = \sqrt{1 + \left(\frac{dy}{dx}\right)^2}\,dx = \sqrt{1 + \dot{y}^2}\,dx$$

From this

$$s = \int_a^b \sqrt{1 + \dot{y}^2}\,dx = \int_a^b f(\dot{y})dx$$

By Eq. (15-3.2) we write

$$\frac{\partial f}{\partial x} - \frac{d}{dx}\left(\frac{\partial f}{\partial \dot{y}}\right) = 0 - \frac{d}{dx}\left(\frac{\dot{y}}{\sqrt{1 + \dot{y}^2}}\right) = 0$$

This can be integrated to give

$$\frac{\dot{y}}{\sqrt{1 + \dot{y}^2}} = \text{const. or} \quad \dot{y} = \text{const.}$$

This indicates that the required curve is the straight line between points a and b, a result that could have been anticipated. ΔΔΔ

(b) Two Dependent and One Independent Variables. This is an extension of the foregoing results for the case of two dependent variables. The functional in this case will be of the form

$$I[x_1,x_2] = \int_a^b f(t,x_1,x_2,\dot{x}_1,\dot{x}_2)\ dt \tag{15-3.12}$$

with the boundary conditions

$$\begin{aligned} &x_1(a) = a_{10} \qquad x_2(a) = a_{20} \qquad &a)\\ &x_1(b) = a_{11} \qquad x_2(b) = a_{22} \qquad &b)\end{aligned} \tag{15-3.13}$$

To find the extremizing function, we shall first maintain one of the two functions constant and vary the other, and then interchange the operations. Thus we first examine the functional $I[x_1]$ which is to be extremized

$$I[x_1] = \int_a^b f(t,x_1(t,\alpha),x_2(t),\dot{x}_1(t,\alpha),\dot{x}_2(t))\ dt \tag{15-3.14}$$

Now keep $x_2(t)$ constant and vary $x_1(t)$ in such a way that its projection on the x_2,t plane remains fixed. As a result, the curve itself remains on the cylinder $x_2 = x_2(t)$ throughout the entire process of variation, as shown in Fig. 15-3.3. A similar situation arises when we maintain $x_1(t)$ constant and vary $x_2(t)$, with an expression that parallels (15-3.14) appropriately modified. But since each functional depends on one variable only, then as shown in the previous analysis, the functional must satisfy an Euler equation for each variable. This leads to the pair of equations

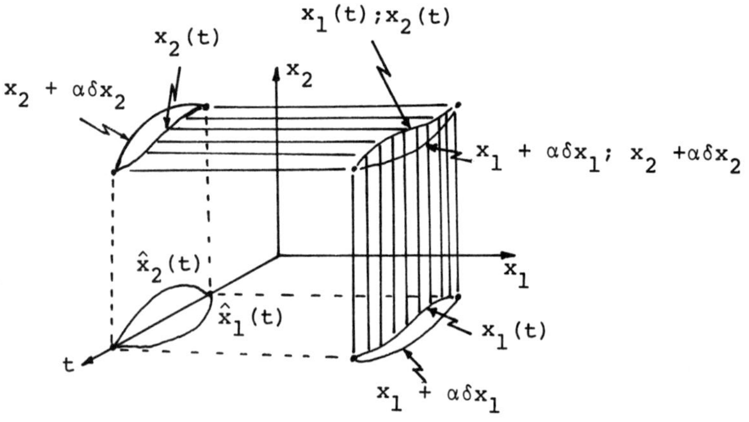

Figure 15-3.3. A functional with two dependent variables.

$$\frac{\partial f}{\partial x_1} - \frac{d}{dt}\frac{\partial f}{\partial \dot{x}_1} = 0 \qquad \text{a)}$$
$$\frac{\partial f}{\partial x_2} - \frac{d}{dt}\frac{\partial f}{\partial \dot{x}_2} = 0 \qquad \text{b)} \qquad (15\text{-}3.15)$$

These conclusions can be extended to a system with n dependent variables. In the general case, therefore, the following system of n Euler equations will apply, which must satisfy the boundary conditions noted

$$\frac{\partial f}{\partial x_i} - \frac{d}{dt}\frac{\partial f}{\partial \dot{x}_i} = 0 \qquad i = 1,2,\ldots,n \qquad \text{a)}$$
$$x_i(a) = a_{i0} \qquad \text{b)} \qquad (15\text{-}3.16)$$
$$x_i(b) = a_{i1} \qquad \text{c)}$$

Example 15-3.2. (Fermat's Principle). Find the path for light waves between two points A and B embedded in a nonhomogeneous medium.

Solution. If the space is filled with a nonhomogeneous medium, the speed of light in this medium is a function of position. The light will follow the curve which has a minimum travel time with respect to any other path. Refer to Fig. 15-3.4. For this problem the functional is

$$I = \int_A^B \frac{ds}{u(t,x_1,x_2)} = \int_A^B \frac{\sqrt{1 + \dot{x}_1^2 + \dot{x}_2^2}}{u(t,x_1,x_2)}\, dt \qquad (15\text{-}3.17)$$

is to be minimized on the curve on which the travel time is the shortest. Since this is a two variable functional, use is made of Eqs. (15-3.15) which yields the expressions

$$\frac{\partial u}{\partial x_1}\frac{(1 + \dot{x}_1^2 + \dot{x}_2^2)^{1/2}}{u^2} + \frac{d}{dt}\frac{\dot{x}_1}{u(1 + \dot{x}_1^2 + \dot{x}_2^2)^{1/2}} = 0 \qquad \text{a)}$$
$$\frac{\partial u}{\partial x_2}\frac{(1 + \dot{x}_1^2 + \dot{x}_2^2)^{1/2}}{u^2} + \frac{d}{dt}\frac{\dot{x}_2}{u(1 + \dot{x}_1^2 + \dot{x}_2^2)^{1/2}} = 0 \qquad \text{b)} \qquad (15\text{-}3.18)$$

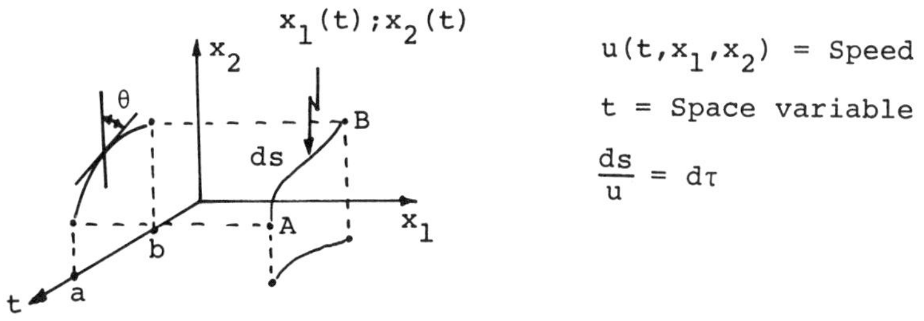

Figure 15-3.4. Fermat's principle in optics.

These determine the desired curve.

For the particular case in which the medium varies only in the x_2-direction and is homogeneous in the x_1 and t directions, the function in the integrand of Eq. (13-5.17) is independent of the independent variable t. The function f thus assumes the form

$$f = \frac{(1 + \dot{x}_2^{\,2})^{1/2}}{u(x_2)} \tag{15-3.19}$$

But since

$$\begin{aligned}\frac{d}{dt}\left(\dot{x}_2 \frac{\partial f}{\partial \dot{x}_2} - f\right) &= \dot{x}_2 \frac{d}{dt}\frac{\partial f}{\partial \dot{x}_2} - \left(\frac{\partial f}{\partial t} + \frac{\partial f}{\partial x_2}\dot{x}_2\right) \\ &= -\dot{x}_2\left[\frac{\partial f}{\partial x_2} - \frac{d}{dt}\frac{\partial f}{\partial \dot{x}_2}\right] - \frac{\partial f}{\partial t} \\ &= -\dot{x}_2\left[\frac{\partial f}{\partial x_2} - \frac{d}{dt}\frac{\partial f}{\partial \dot{x}_2}\right]\end{aligned}$$

where $\partial f/\partial t = 0$, Euler's equation assumes the form

$$\frac{d}{dt}\left(\dot{x}_2 \frac{\partial f}{\partial \dot{x}_2} - f\right) = 0 \tag{15-3.20}$$

This equation implies that

$$\dot{x}_2 \frac{\partial f}{\partial \dot{x}_2} - f = C \tag{15-3.21}$$

where C is an arbitrary constant. By combining Eqs. (15-3.19) and (15-3.21) we obtain

$$\frac{\dot{x}_2^{\,2}}{u(1 + \dot{x}_2^{\,2})^{1/2}} - \frac{(1 + \dot{x}_2^{\,2})^{1/2}}{u} = C$$

or

$$\frac{1}{u(1 + \dot{x}_2^{\,2})} = -C \tag{15-3.22}$$

ΔΔΔ

(c) One Dependent and Two Independent Variables. The foregoing results can be extended to the case of one dependent variable and several independent variables. For the case of two independent variables, the functional of importance is

$$I[x_2(x_1,t)] = \iint_D f(t,x_1,x_2,p,q)\, dt\, dx_1 \tag{15-3.23}$$

where $p = \partial x_2/\partial t$; $q = \partial x_2/\partial x_1$, and the values of the function $x_2(t,x_1)$ on the boundary C of the domain D are specified. Figure 15-3.5 shows the extremizing surface $x_2(t,x_1)$, the increment surface, the domain D and the boundary C. Consequently we write

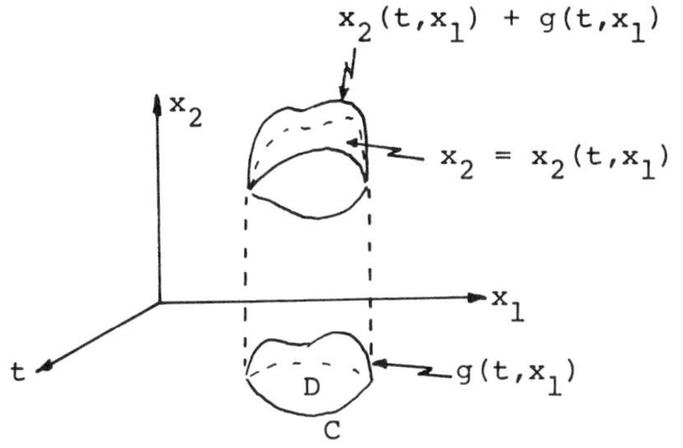

Figure 15-3.5. Two independent variables.

$$\Delta I = I[x_2+g] - I[x_2] = \iint_D \left(f(t,x_1,x_2+g,p + \frac{\partial g}{\partial t}, q + \frac{\partial g}{\partial x_1}) - f(t,x_1,x_2,p,q)\right)dt dx_1$$

$$= \delta I + \ldots = \iint_D \left[\frac{\partial f}{\partial x_2} g + \frac{\partial f}{\partial p}\frac{\partial g}{\partial t} + \frac{\partial f}{\partial q}\frac{\partial q}{\partial x_1}\right] dt\, dx_1 + \ldots \qquad (15\text{-}3.24)$$

where the dots indicate terms of order higher than those relative to g, $\partial g/\partial t$, $\partial g/\partial x_1$. But the last two terms of Eq. (15-3.24) become

$$\iint_D \left(\frac{\partial t}{\partial p}\frac{\partial g}{\partial t} + \frac{\partial f}{\partial q}\frac{\partial g}{\partial x_1}\right)dt dx_1 = \iint_D \left[\frac{\partial}{\partial t}\left(\frac{\partial f}{\partial p} g\right) + \frac{\partial}{\partial x_1}\left(\frac{\partial f}{\partial q} g\right)\right]dt dx_1$$

$$- \iint_D \left[\frac{\partial}{\partial t}\frac{\partial f}{\partial p} + \frac{\partial}{\partial x_1}\frac{\partial f}{\partial q}\right] g\, dt\, dx_1$$

$$= \int_C \left(\frac{\partial f}{\partial p} g\, dx_1 - \frac{\partial f}{\partial q} g\, dt\right) - \iint_D \left[\frac{\partial}{\partial t}\frac{\partial f}{\partial p} + \frac{\partial}{\partial x_1}\frac{\partial f}{\partial q}\right] g\, dt\, dx_1 \qquad (15\text{-}3.25)$$

where Stokes theorem in the form

$$\iint_D \left(\frac{\partial P}{\partial t} - \frac{\partial R}{\partial x_1}\right)dt\, dx_1 = \int_C (P\, dx_1 + R\, dt)$$

has been used. Since $g(t,x_1)$ is zero on the boundary C, Eqs. (15-3.24) and (15-3.25) give

$$\delta I = \iint_D \left(\frac{\partial f}{\partial x_2} - \frac{\partial}{\partial t}\frac{\partial f}{\partial p} - \frac{\partial}{\partial x_1}\frac{\partial f}{\partial q}\right) g(t,x_1)\, dt\, dx_1 \qquad (15\text{-}3.26)$$

The necessary condition $\delta I = 0$ and the fundamental lemma imply that

$$\frac{\partial f}{\partial x_2} - \frac{\partial}{\partial t}\frac{\partial f}{\partial p} - \frac{\partial}{\partial x_1}\frac{\partial f}{\partial q} = 0 \qquad (15\text{-}3.27)$$

This is known as the *Euler-Lagrange* equation, where $p = \partial x_2/\partial t$; $q = \partial x_2/\partial x_1$.

For the case of $\underline{n}$ dependent variables, e.g., a physical field with three spatial and one time independent variables, there exist $\underline{n}$ Euler-Lagrange equations

$$\frac{\partial \mathscr{L}}{\partial \Phi_i} - \sum_{j=1}^{n} \frac{\partial}{\partial x_j} \frac{\partial \mathscr{L}}{\partial(\partial \Phi_i/\partial x_j)} - \frac{\partial}{\partial t}\left(\frac{\partial \mathscr{L}}{\partial(\partial \Phi_i/\partial t)}\right) = 0 \qquad i = 1,2,\ldots,n \tag{15-3.28}$$

where the letter $\mathscr{L}$ has been substituted for f. $\mathscr{L}$ is known as the *Lagrangian density*. Therefore the functional

$$I = \int_V \mathscr{L}\left(\Phi_i, x_j, \frac{\partial \Phi_i}{\partial x_j}\right) dx_1\, dx_2\, dx_3\, dt \tag{15-3.29}$$

is extremized if $\mathscr{L}$ satisfies Eq. (15-3.28).

We introduce the *Lagrangian function* L given by

$$L = \int_V \mathscr{L}\left(t, \Phi_i, \nabla\Phi_i, \frac{\partial \Phi_i}{\partial t}\right) dx_1\, dx_2\, dx_3 \tag{15-3.30}$$

and the stationary property can be expressed in the form

$$\delta \int_{t_o}^{t_o+\tau} L\, dt = 0 \tag{15-3.31}$$

which is analogous to Hamilton's principle in dynamics.

(d) Hamilton's Principle. As an alternate view of the extremum calculation, we shall here adopt the fairly customary development of Hamilton's principle from considerations of particle dynamics. It is important to note, however, that the principle is considerably more general than the development would indicate, and it provides the starting point for the discussion of dynamical systems in general.

Consider a system of particles which is described by d'Alembert's principle which is written, for a point mass system,

$$\sum_{i=1}^{N} (m_i \ddot{\bar{r}}_i - f_i) \cdot \delta\bar{r}_i = 0 \tag{15-3.32}$$

where $\delta\bar{r}_i$ denotes a virtual displacement which is consistent with the equations of condition. This means that the displacement is assured to be one that would be possible by a physical system acting under natural physical laws. It is noted that

$$\frac{d^2\bar{r}_i}{dt^2} \cdot \delta\bar{r}_i = \frac{d}{dt}\left(\frac{d\bar{r}_i}{dt} \cdot \delta\bar{r}_i\right) - \frac{d\bar{r}_i}{dt} \cdot \frac{d}{dt}\delta\bar{r}_i$$

or

$$= \frac{d}{dt}\left(\frac{d\bar{r}_i}{dt} \cdot \delta\bar{r}_i\right) - \frac{d\bar{r}_i}{dt} \cdot \delta\left(\frac{d\bar{r}_i}{dt}\right) \tag{15-3.33}$$

so that

$$\ddot{\bar{r}}_i \cdot \delta\bar{r}_i = \frac{d}{dt}\left(\frac{d\bar{r}_i}{dt} \cdot \delta\bar{r}_i\right) - \delta\frac{1}{2}\left(\frac{d\bar{r}_i}{dt}\right)^2 \tag{15-3.34}$$

This result allows us to write

$$\sum_{i=1}^{N} m_i\ddot{\bar{r}}_i \cdot \delta\bar{r}_i = \sum_{i=1}^{N} [m_i \frac{d}{dt}(\frac{d\bar{r}_i}{dt} \cdot \delta\bar{r}_i) - \delta \frac{m_i}{2}(\frac{d\bar{r}_i}{dt})^2] = \sum_{i=1}^{N} \bar{f}_i \cdot \delta\bar{r}_i \qquad (15\text{-}3.35)$$

If there is an applied force that is derivable from a potential energy function V, then

$$\sum_{i=1}^{N} \bar{f}_i \cdot \delta\bar{r}_i; \quad \bar{f}_i = -\bar{a}_{x1}\frac{\partial V}{\partial x_{i1}} - \bar{a}_{x2}\frac{\partial V}{\partial x_{i2}} - \bar{a}_{x3}\frac{\partial V}{\partial x_{i3}} \qquad (15\text{-}3.36)$$

and Eq. (15-3.35) can be written

$$\sum_{i=1}^{N} m_i \frac{d}{dt}(\frac{d\bar{r}_i}{dt} \cdot \delta\bar{r}_i) = \delta(T - V) \qquad (15\text{-}3.37)$$

where $T = \Sigma_{i=1}^{N}(m_i/2)(d\bar{r}_i/dt)^2$ is the kinetic energy. This expression is now integrated over a time interval τ from an initial time t_0. This gives

$$\int_{t_0}^{t_0+\tau} \sum_{i=1}^{N} m_i \frac{d}{dt}(\frac{d\bar{r}_i}{dt} \cdot \delta\bar{r}_i)dt = \int_{t_0}^{t_0+\tau} \delta(T-V)\, dt$$

But all virtual displacements will vanish at times t_0 and $t_0+\tau$ as these end positions are specified. Hence

$$\sum_{i=1}^{N} m_i \frac{d\bar{r}_i}{dt} \cdot \delta\bar{r}_i \Big|_{t_0}^{t_0+\tau} = \int_{t_0}^{t_0+\tau} \delta(T-V)\, dt = 0 \qquad (15\text{-}3.38)$$

from which it follows that

$$\delta \int_{t_0}^{t_0+\tau} (T-V)dt = 0 \qquad (15\text{-}3.39)$$

since the sum of a number of variations is equal to the variation of the sum. This is *Hamilton's principle* for conservative systems. The quantity (T-V) is the Lagrangian function, which is often written $L \equiv (T-V)$.

Hamilton's principle states that if a system of mass particles moves under natural laws from a given configuration to another configuration at time $t_0 + \tau$, then the time integral of the difference between the kinetic and potential energies of the system is stationary for the natural path of the system between the two given configurations. This implies that the integral along the natural path is less than that along an infinitely near, but nonnatural path, between the same terminal configurations. As a practical matter, since Hamilton's principle involved no reference to any coordinate system, it is suited as a starting point in general dynamical investigations.

Hamilton's principle is broader than the principle of energy since V may be a function of time as well as the coordinates. It is true even for non-conservative systems if one writes $\bar{f} \cdot \delta\bar{r}$, or more generally $P_1\delta q_1 + \dots + P_m\delta q_m$ for V, where

P_i is the generalized force tending to change the generalized coordinate δq_i.

(e) Lagrange's Equations. We are now in a position to investigate the integral

$$I = \int_{t_o}^{t_o+\tau} L\,dt \tag{15-3.40}$$

where the Lagrangian L is a function of time t, the coordinates x_i, and the derivatives $\dot{x}_i$ with respect to time. Now consider the variation

$$\hat{x}_i = x_i(t) + \varepsilon g_i(t) \qquad i = 1,2,\ldots N \tag{15-3.41}$$

where $g_i(t)$ are any set of functions satisfying the conditions

$$g_i(t_o) = g_i(t_o+\tau) = 0 \qquad i = 1,2,\ldots N \tag{15-3.42}$$

and ε is an infinitesimal variable. By combining this with Eq. (15-3.40), we can write

$$\delta I = \int_{t_o}^{t_o+\tau} L(x_i+\varepsilon g_i,\dot{x}_i+\varepsilon\dot{g}_i,t)dt - \int_{t_o}^{t+\tau} L(x_i,\dot{x}_i,t)\,dt$$
$$= \varepsilon \int_{t_o}^{t_o+\tau} \sum_{i=1}^{N} \left(\frac{\partial L}{\partial x_i} g_i + \frac{\partial L}{\partial \dot{x}_i}\dot{g}_i\right)dt + \text{higher order terms} = 0$$

However, the term

$$\int_{t_o}^{t_o+\tau} \frac{\partial L}{\partial \dot{x}_i}\dot{g}_i\,dt = \frac{\partial L}{\partial \dot{x}_i} g_i \Bigg|_{t_o}^{t_o+\tau} - \int_{t_o}^{t_o+\tau} \frac{d}{dt}\left(\frac{\partial L}{\partial \dot{x}_i}\right)g_i dt = -\int_{t_o}^{t_o+\tau} \frac{d}{dt}\left(\frac{\partial L}{\partial \dot{x}_i}\right)g_i\,dt$$

and the variation δI takes the form

$$\delta I = \varepsilon \int_{t_o}^{t_o+\tau} \sum_{i=1}^{N} \left[\frac{\partial L}{\partial x_i} - \frac{d}{dt}\left(\frac{\partial L}{\partial \dot{x}_i}\right)\right]g_i\,dt = 0 \tag{15-3.43}$$

Since the g_i's are independent of each other, it follows from the fundamental lemma that

$$\frac{\partial L}{\partial x_i} - \frac{d}{dt}\left(\frac{\partial L}{\partial \dot{x}_i}\right) = 0 \qquad i = 1,2,\ldots N \tag{15-3.44}$$

This shows that the Lagrange function obeys the Euler equation.

We now introduce generalized momenta variables of the form

$$p_i = \frac{\partial L}{\partial \dot{x}_i} \qquad i = 1,2,\ldots N \tag{15-3.45}$$

Then the Lagrange equations take the form

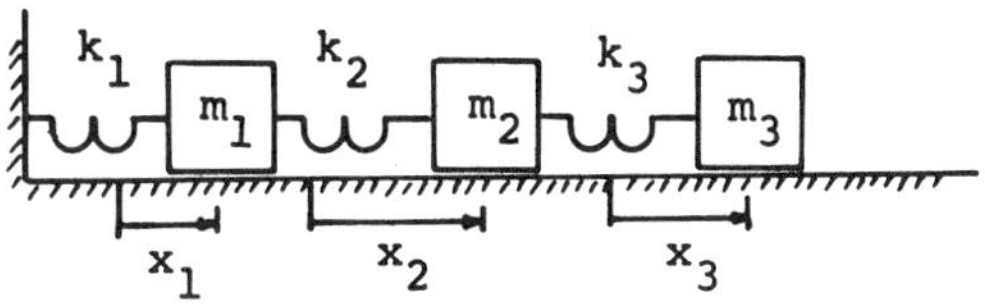

Figure 15-3.6. A system of three masses on a frictionless surface.

$$\dot{p}_i = \frac{\partial L}{\partial x_i} \qquad i = 1,2,\ldots N \tag{15-3.46}$$

Note that a parallel development could be accomplished in terms of a Hamiltonian formulation with

$$H = H(p_i, q_i, t) = \sum_{i=1}^{N} p_i \dot{x}_i - L \tag{15-3.47}$$

where H is the *Hamiltonian* function, which is expressed in terms of x_i, p_i and t.

Example 15-3.3. Find the differential equations which govern the system shown in Fig. 15-3.6.

Solution. If x_1, x_2 and x_3 are the respective displacements from their positions of equilibrium of masses m_1, m_2 and m_3, the kinetic and potential energies are written

$$T = \frac{1}{2}(m_1\dot{x}_1^{\,2} + m_2\dot{x}_2^{\,2} + m_3\dot{x}_3^{\,2})$$

$$V = \frac{1}{2}k_1x_1^{\,2} + \frac{1}{2}k_2(x_2-x_1)^2 + \frac{1}{2}k_3(x_3-x_2)^2$$

where k_1, k_2 and k_3 are the spring constants. Since L = T - V, Eq. (15-3.44) gives the following system of equations

$$m_1\ddot{x}_1 + k_1x_1 - k_2(x_2-x_1) = 0$$

$$m_2\ddot{x}_2 + k_2(x_2-x_1) - k_3(x_3-x_2) = 0$$

$$m_3\ddot{x}_3 + k_3(x_3-x_2) = 0$$

These may be solved, subject to specified initial conditions $x_1(0)$, $x_2(0)$, $x_3(0)$, $\dot{x}_1(0)$, $\dot{x}_2(0)$, $\dot{x}_3(0)$ at time t = 0. ΔΔΔ

Example 15-3.4. Deduce the differential equations which govern the system of particles shown in Fig. 15-3.7 (see also Sec. 8-3).

Solution. The change in length Δd_i for small angles is

$$\Delta d_i = \left(\frac{d_i}{\cos\theta_i} - d_i\right) = \left(\frac{1}{\cos\theta_i} - 1\right)d_i \doteq \frac{d_i\theta_i^{\,2}}{2}$$

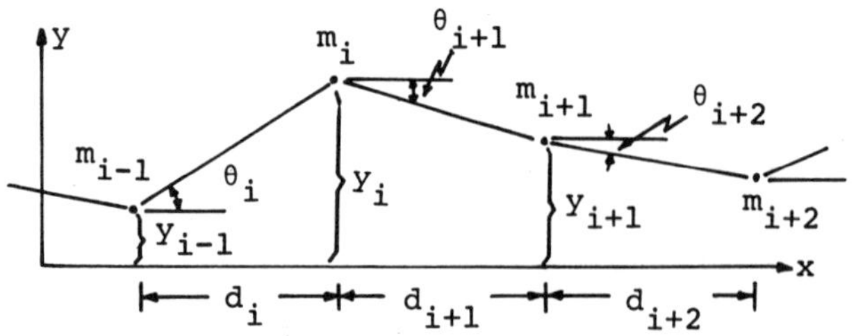

Figure 15-3.7. Vibration of equal point masses joined with massless flexible strings.

The potential energy is the tension T_ℓ multiplied by the increase in length Δd_i. But approximately

$$\theta_i \doteq \frac{y_i - y_{i-1}}{d_i}, \quad \theta_{i+1} \doteq \frac{y_{i+1} - y_i}{d_{i+1}}, \ldots$$

and assuming interaction between the nearest neighbors,

$$V = \frac{T_\ell}{2}\left[\frac{(y_i - y_{i-1})^2}{d_i} + \frac{(y_{i+1} - y_i)^2}{d_{i+1}}\right] \doteq \frac{T_\ell}{2d}\left[(y_i - y_{i-1})^2 + (y_{i+1} - y_i)^2\right]$$

where it is assumed that $\ldots d_i = d_{i+1} = d_{i+2} + \ldots = d$. The kinetic energy of the i-th mass is $T = \frac{1}{2} m_i y_i^2$.

An application of Lagrange's equations gives

$$m_i \ddot{y}_i = \frac{T_\ell}{d}(y_{i-1} + y_{i+1} - 2y_i)$$

which is identical with Eq. (8-3.1). ΔΔΔ

Example 15-3.5. Find the Lagrangian function for a charged particle in an electromagnetic field.

Solution. We employ the known relation between the electric field $\overline{E}$, the vector potential $\overline{A}$ ($\overline{B} = \nabla \times \overline{A}$), and the scalar potential Φ_e given by Eq. (8-9.3)

$$\overline{E} = -\nabla\Phi_e - \frac{\partial \overline{A}}{\partial t} \qquad (15\text{-}3.48)$$

Also, the force on a moving charged particle in an electromagnetic field is given by the Lorentz equation, Eq. (6-1.6),

$$\overline{F} = q(\overline{E} + \overline{v} \times \overline{B}) \qquad (15\text{-}3.49)$$

This equation can be written

$$\overline{F} = q[-\nabla\Phi_e - \frac{\partial\overline{A}}{\partial t} + \overline{v} \times (\nabla \times \overline{A})] = q[-\nabla\Phi_e - \frac{\partial\overline{A}}{\partial t} + \nabla(\overline{v}\cdot\overline{A}) - \overline{v}\cdot\nabla\overline{A}]$$

$$= q[-\nabla\Phi_e - \frac{d\overline{A}}{dt} + \nabla(\overline{v}\cdot\overline{A})] \qquad (15\text{-}3.50)$$

where

$$\frac{d\overline{A}}{dt} = \frac{\partial\overline{A}}{\partial t} + \overline{v}\cdot\nabla\overline{A} \qquad (15\text{-}3.51)$$

If we assume the existence of a generalized potential Φ, the x-component of the generalized force is found to be given by the equation

$$F_x = \frac{d}{dt}\left(\frac{\partial\Phi}{\partial\dot{x}}\right) - \frac{\partial\Phi}{\partial x} \qquad (15\text{-}3.52)$$

If we set

$$\Phi = q(\Phi_e - \overline{v}\cdot\overline{A}) \qquad (15\text{-}3.53)$$

we will obtain the components of the force F_x, F_y and F_z as specified by Eq. (15-3.50). This means that the Lagrangian of a charged particle in an electromagnetic field is

$$L = T - \Phi = T - q\Phi_e + q\overline{v}\cdot\overline{A} \qquad (15\text{-}3.54)$$

where T is the kinetic energy of the particle. ΔΔΔ

(f) Lagrange Multipliers. Let us consider the extremization of the function

$$F(x_1,x_2,\lambda) = f(x_1,x_2) + \lambda g(x_1,x_2) \qquad (15\text{-}3.55)$$

which, as shown, is a function of the three variables x_1, x_2, λ. The necessary conditions for a stationary value are

$$\frac{\partial F}{\partial x_1} = \frac{\partial f}{\partial x_1} + \lambda\frac{\partial g}{\partial x_1} = 0$$

$$\frac{\partial F}{\partial x_2} = \frac{\partial f}{\partial x_2} + \lambda\frac{\partial g}{\partial x_2} = 0$$

$$\frac{\partial F}{\partial \lambda} = g(x_1,x_2) = 0$$

These equations are combined in a way to eliminate λ. The result is found to be

$$\frac{\partial f}{\partial x_1}\frac{\partial g}{\partial x_2} - \frac{\partial f}{\partial x_2}\frac{\partial g}{\partial x_1} = 0 \qquad \text{a)}$$

$$g(x_1,x_2) = 0 \qquad \text{b)}$$

(15-3.56)

This method is known as the method of Lagrange multipliers, and the quantity is called the *Lagrange multiplier.*

Example 15-3.6. Find the minimum distance from the plane specified by $x_1 + 2x_2 + 3x_3 + 4 = 0$ to the origin.

Solution. The distance square from the origin to a point on a plane is $f(x_1,x_2,x_3) = x_1^2 + x_2^2 + x_3^2$. Furthermore, the given point satisfies the equation $g(x_1,x_2,x_3) = x_1 + 2x_2 + 3x_3 + 4 = 0$. By the method of Lagrange multipliers applied to the function

$$F(x_1,x_2,x_3,\lambda) = x_1^2 + x_2^2 + x_3^2 + \lambda(x_1 + 2x_2 + 3x_3 + 4)$$

the necessary conditions are

$$\frac{\partial F}{\partial x_1} = 2x_1 + \lambda = 0 \qquad \frac{\partial F}{\partial x_2} = 2x_2 + 2\lambda = 0$$

$$\frac{\partial F}{\partial x_3} = 2x_3 + 3\lambda x_3 = 0 \qquad \frac{\partial F}{\partial \lambda} = x_1 + 2x_2 + 3x_3 + 4 = 0$$

Upon solving for λ (λ =-2/3) and back-substituting into the above equations, these can be solved to yield the coordinates of the point

$$x_1 = \frac{1}{3}; \qquad x_2 = -\frac{2}{3}; \qquad x_3 = -\frac{17}{9}$$

The minimum distance is then found to be $\sqrt{334}/3$.

ΔΔΔ

15-4. Field Equations

We shall consider a number of examples that will employ variational methods to deduce applicable field equations.

Example 15-4.1. If Φ is a function of the spatial coordinates x_1,x_2,x_3 (or equivalently x,y,z) what type of equation is obtained if the following Lagrangian density is used

$$\mathscr{L} = \frac{1}{2}(\nabla\Phi)^2 = \frac{1}{2}\nabla\Phi\cdot\nabla\Phi = \frac{1}{2}\sum_{j=1}^{3}\left(\frac{\partial\Phi}{\partial x_j}\right)^2 \tag{15-4.1}$$

Solution. The Euler-Lagrange Eq. (15-3.28) becomes

$$\frac{\partial\frac{1}{2}(\nabla\Phi)^2}{\partial\Phi} + \frac{\partial}{\partial x_1}\frac{\partial}{\partial(\partial\Phi/\partial x_1)}\left[\frac{1}{2}\sum_{j=1}^{3}\left(\frac{\partial\Phi}{\partial x_j}\right)^2\right] + \frac{\partial}{\partial x_2}\frac{\partial}{\partial(\partial\Phi/\partial x_2)}\left[\frac{1}{2}\sum_{j=1}^{3}\left(\frac{\partial\Phi}{\partial x_j}\right)^2\right]$$

$$+ \frac{\partial}{\partial x_3}\frac{\partial}{\partial(\partial\Phi/\partial x_3)}\left[\frac{1}{2}\sum_{j=1}^{3}\left(\frac{\partial\Phi}{\partial x_j}\right)^2\right] = 0$$

or

$$\frac{\partial}{\partial x_1}\left(\frac{2}{2}\frac{\partial\Phi}{\partial x_1}\right)+\frac{\partial}{\partial x_2}\left(\frac{2}{2}\frac{\partial\Phi}{\partial x_2}\right)+\frac{\partial}{\partial x_3}\left(\frac{2}{2}\frac{\partial\Phi}{\partial x_3}\right)=\nabla^2\Phi=0 \tag{15-4.2}$$

The result is seen to be Laplace's equation. ΔΔΔ

Example 15-4.2. Find the Lagrangian function and the Lagrangian density for an electrostatic field.

Solution. For a volume distribution of charge with density ρ, the energy associated with the system is given by Eq. (5-9.6)

$$W=\frac{1}{2}\int_V \rho\Phi\, dV \tag{15-4.3}$$

where $\overline{E} = -\nabla\Phi$. Using the Gauss equation $\nabla \cdot \overline{E} = \rho/\varepsilon_o$, we also find [see Eq. (5-9.9)] that

$$W=\frac{\varepsilon_o}{2}\int_{\text{space}} (\nabla\Phi)^2 dV \tag{15-4.4}$$

We employ Eqs. (15-4.3) and (15-4.4) to write the energy associated with the volume charge at any point in space. We refer to this as the mutual electrical energy function,

$$W_e=\int_V \left[\rho\Phi-\frac{\varepsilon_o}{2}(\nabla\Phi)^2\right] dV \tag{15-4.5}$$

This integral is equivalent to Poisson's equation which describes the electrostatic field, since it is a minimum for the correct potential Φ of the known distribution of charges. If we were to pick a function $\hat{\Phi}$ where $\hat{\Phi} = \Phi + \phi$ which is the sum of the correct field Φ plus a small deviation ϕ, then the first order deviation δW_e will be zero if $\nabla^2\Phi = -\rho/\varepsilon_o$. Hence if we take $W_e = L$ as the Lagrangian function, the Lagrangian density is given by

$$\mathscr{L}=-\frac{\varepsilon_o}{2}(\nabla\Phi)^2+\rho\Phi \tag{15-4.6}$$

By an application of Eq. (15-3.28), Poisson's equation is again obtained. ΔΔΔ

Example 15-4.3. Consider the vibrating string of Sec. 8-2. Employ Hamilton's principle in establishing the system characteristics for the physical system.

Solution. Refer to Fig. 8-2.1b which illustrates an element of the string. We can write the energy functions directly.

a. Kinetic energy function

$$T=\int_\ell \frac{1}{2}\rho_\ell dx\left(\frac{\partial y}{\partial t}\right)^2 \tag{15-4.7}$$

b. Potential energy function: this specifies the energy in the string due to its change in length. If the stretched string length is ℓ', then

$$V = \int_{\ell'} T_e \, d\ell - T_e \ell$$

where T_e is the tension. But

$$d\ell = \sqrt{dx^2 + dy^2} = dx\sqrt{1 + (\frac{dy}{dx})^2}$$

and so

$$V = \int_{\ell'} T_e \sqrt{1 + (\frac{dy}{dx})^2}\, dx - T_e \ell$$

But the total change in length is very small. This allows us to expand the integrand in a binomial expansion and to retain only the first two terms. Therefore with $\ell' \doteq \ell$

$$V \doteq \int_{\ell} T_e \,[1 + \frac{1}{2}(\frac{dy}{dx})^2]dx - T_e \ell$$

so that finally

$$V = \int_{\ell} \frac{T_e}{2} (\frac{dy}{dx})^2 \, dx \tag{15-4.8}$$

By Hamilton's principle

$$\delta \int_{t_o}^{t_o+\tau} (T-V)dt = 0 = \delta \int_{t_o}^{t_o+\tau} \{\int_{\ell} [\frac{\rho_\ell}{2}(\frac{\partial y}{\partial t})^2 - \frac{T_e}{2}(\frac{\partial y}{\partial x})^2]dx\}dt$$

The Lagrangian density is

$$\mathscr{L} = \frac{\rho_\ell}{2} (\frac{\partial y}{\partial t})^2 - \frac{T_e}{2} (\frac{\partial y}{\partial x})^2$$

An application of the Euler-Lagrange equation, Eq. (15-3.28), or the Lagrange equation (15-3.44) yields the expression

$$-\rho_\ell \frac{\partial}{\partial t} (\frac{\partial y}{\partial t}) + T_e \frac{\partial}{\partial x} (\frac{\partial y}{\partial x}) = 0$$

from which it follows that

$$\frac{\partial^2 y}{\partial x^2} = \frac{\rho_\ell}{T_e} \frac{\partial^2 y}{\partial t^2} \tag{15-4.9}$$

which is Eq. (8-2.5).

ΔΔΔ

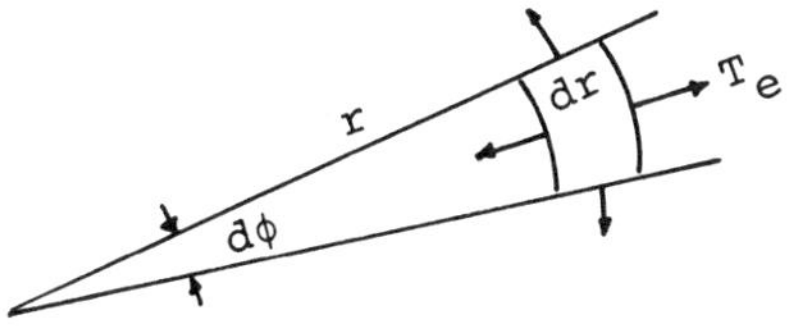

Figure 15-4.1. An elementary section of the circular diaphragm.

Example 15-4.4. Use Hamilton's principle to deduce the controlling equation for the stretched circular diaphragm. This is the circular counterpart of the rectangular drumhead of Sec. 8-4.

Solution. We write the necessary energy functions. These are:

a. Kinetic energy function

$$T = \int \rho_s \frac{dr\ r\ d\phi}{2} \left(\frac{\partial x}{\partial t}\right)^2 \tag{15-4.10}$$

b. Potential energy function. Refer to Fig. 15-4.1 for an elementary section of the circular diaphragm. The potential energy function can be written as a logical extension of the development that leads to Eq. (15-4.8). The result is

$$V = \int \frac{T_e}{2} \left[\left(\frac{\partial z}{\partial r}\right)^2 + \left(\frac{\partial z}{r\partial \phi}\right)^2\right] r\ dr\ d\phi \tag{15-4.11}$$

The Hamilton's principle expression is

$$\delta \int_{t_o}^{t_o+\tau} \left\{\int_r \int_\phi \left[\frac{\rho_s}{2} r\left(\frac{\partial z}{\partial t}\right)^2\right] + \frac{T_e r}{2} \left[\left(\frac{\partial z}{\partial r}\right)^2 + \left(\frac{\partial z}{r\partial \phi}\right)^2\right]^2 dr\ d\phi\right\} dt = 0$$

By the Euler-Lagrange condition, Eq. (15-3.28),

$$\rho_s \frac{\partial}{\partial t} \left(\frac{\partial z}{\partial t}\right) - T_e \left[\frac{1}{r} \frac{\partial}{\partial r} \left(r \frac{\partial z}{\partial r}\right) + \frac{1}{r} \frac{\partial}{\partial \phi} \left(\frac{\partial z}{r\partial \phi}\right)\right] = 0$$

from which

$$\rho_s \frac{\partial^2 z}{\partial t^2} = T_e \left[\frac{\partial^2 z}{\partial r^2} + \frac{1}{r} \frac{\partial z}{\partial r} + \frac{\partial^2 z}{r^2 \partial \phi^2}\right]$$

which is written

$$\frac{\partial^2 z}{\partial r^2} + \frac{1}{r} \frac{\partial z}{\partial r} + \frac{1}{r^2} \frac{\partial^2 z}{\partial \phi^2} = \frac{1}{c^2} \frac{\partial^2 z}{\partial t^2} \tag{15-4.12}$$

where $c = \sqrt{T_e/\rho_s}$.

ΔΔΔ

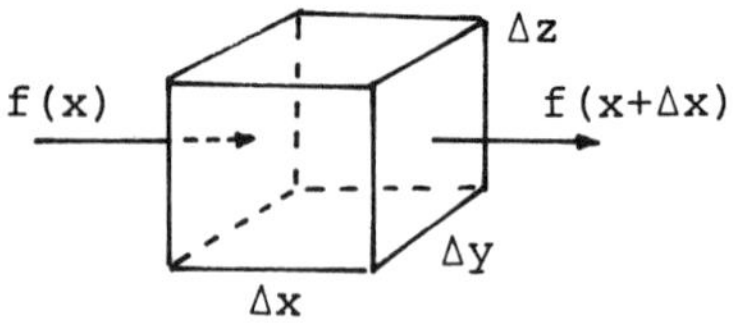

Figure 15-4.2. The control volume in a gas.

Example 15-4.5. Consider the question of acoustic waves in a fluid, a matter that was examined in Sec. 8-5. Deduce the energy functions and the controlling equations for acoustic wave propagation.

Solution. Consider a control volume in the field and suppose that changes occur only in the X-direction. As discussed in Sec. 8-5, it will be supposed that the change in density owing to a volume change will be an adiabatic one. Suppose that a compressional wave is applied to the gas. The resulting change in volume, and so in density, results in the transfer of energy to the gas, with a resulting potential energy storage in the gas. The potential energy is the work done in bringing the given volume at equilibrium pressure to a new volume and density. To find this, we must consider the change in work done on the gas due to the changes in density.

Refer to Fig. 15-4.2 which shows the situation before the compressional wave arrives. The compression causes a change ξ in the X-dimension measured from the equilibrium position. The work done in this change of dimension is given by the expression

$$dW = [f(x+\Delta x+\xi) - f(x+\xi)]\frac{\partial}{\partial x}(\Delta x + \xi)\Delta x - [f(x+\Delta x) - f(x)]\Delta x$$

which expands to

$$dW = \frac{\partial f}{\partial x}(1 + \frac{\partial \xi}{\partial x})\Delta x - \frac{\partial f}{\partial x}\Delta x$$

which reduces to the expression

$$dW = \frac{\partial f}{\partial x}\frac{\partial \xi}{\partial x}\Delta x \qquad (15\text{-}4.13)$$

This is written in terms of a change in pressure Δp

$$\langle dW \rangle = \frac{1}{2}(\Delta p \Delta y \Delta z)\frac{\partial \xi}{\partial x}\Delta x \qquad (15\text{-}4.14)$$

The factor 1/2 has been introduced to take account of the fact that the force will vary between zero and some maximum, and it is the average value that is here required, with the special brackets to denote the time average.

To find the pressure change, we proceed from considerations of the change in volume which results because the X-dimension changes by an amount Δx. But we can write, as above,

$$\xi(x+\Delta x,y,z) = \xi(x,y,z) + \frac{\partial \xi}{\partial x}\Delta x$$

so that the volume changes by the amount

$$\Delta V = (1 + \frac{\partial \xi}{\partial x})\Delta x\Delta y\Delta z - \Delta x\Delta y\Delta z = \frac{\partial \xi}{\partial x}\Delta x\Delta y\Delta z = \frac{\partial \xi}{\partial x} V_o$$

From the equation of state given in Eq. (8-5.4), this expression becomes

$$\frac{\Delta V}{V_o} = \frac{\partial \xi}{\partial x} = \frac{1}{\gamma p_o}\Delta p = \frac{1}{\gamma p_o} p_1 \qquad (15\text{-}4.15)$$

where p_1 is the small change in pressure from the mean p_o caused by the acoustic wave. Thus the potential energy is written

$$\langle dW\rangle = \frac{1}{2}\gamma p_o (\frac{\partial \xi}{\partial x})^2 \, dx\, dy\, dz \qquad (15\text{-}4.16)$$

The kinetic energy for the change in the differential volume is

$$dT = \rho_v \frac{dx\, dy\, dz}{2}(\frac{\partial \xi}{\partial t})^2 \qquad (15\text{-}4.17)$$

Hamilton's principle yields

$$\delta \int_{t_o}^{t_o+\tau} [\int \{\frac{\rho_v}{2}(\frac{\partial \xi}{\partial t})^2 - \frac{1}{2}\gamma p_o (\frac{\partial \xi}{\partial x})^2\} dx\, dy\, dz] dt = 0 \qquad (15\text{-}4.18)$$

and by Eq. (15-3.28), the Euler-Lagrange equation, we obtain

$$-\rho_v \frac{\partial^2 \xi}{\partial t^2} + \gamma p_o \frac{\partial^2 \xi}{\partial x^2} = 0$$

This can be written in the form

$$\frac{\partial^2 \xi}{\partial x^2} = \frac{\rho_v}{\gamma p_o}\frac{\partial^2 \xi}{\partial t^2} \qquad (15\text{-}4.19)$$

It is customary to write this expression in terms of the pressure change. By Eq. (15-4.15)

$$\frac{\partial^2 \xi}{\partial x^2} = \frac{1}{\gamma p_o}\frac{\partial p_1}{\partial x}$$

and Eq. (15-4.19) becomes

$$\frac{\partial}{\partial x}\left(\frac{\partial^2 \xi}{\partial x^2}\right) = \frac{\rho_v}{\gamma p_o}\frac{\partial^2}{\partial t^2}\left(\frac{\partial \xi}{\partial x}\right)$$

or

$$\frac{\partial}{\partial x}\left(\frac{1}{\gamma p_o}\frac{\partial p_1}{\partial x}\right) = \frac{\rho_v}{\gamma p_o}\frac{\partial^2}{\partial t^2}\left(\frac{1}{\gamma p_o}p_1\right)$$

Hence finally

$$\frac{\partial^2 p_1}{\partial x^2} = \frac{\rho_v}{\gamma p_o}\frac{\partial^2 p_1}{\partial t^2} \tag{15-4.20}$$

which is Eq. (8-5.17).

ΔΔΔ

Example 15-4.6. As a special case of Ex. 15-4.5, consider a horn with a slow, though not necessarily linear, taper. Let S(x) denote the horn cross-section at a distance x from the origin. Find an expression for the pressure distribution in the horn.

Solution. Refer to Fig. 15-4.3. Consider the lamina specified by Sdx. The mass contained in the lamina is

$$dm = \rho_v \; S \; dx$$

As in Ex. 15-4.5, let ξ denote the change in x measured from the equilibrium position due to a change in pressure. By a simple extension of Eqs. (15-4.16) and (15-4.17) we write

$$\begin{aligned} T &= \int \frac{\rho_v S}{2}\left(\frac{\partial \xi}{\partial t}\right)^2 dx \\ W &= \int \frac{\gamma p_o}{2} S \left(\frac{\partial \xi}{\partial x}\right)^2 dx \end{aligned} \tag{15-4.21}$$

Hamilton's principle becomes

$$\delta \int_{t_o}^{t_o+\tau} \int \left[\frac{\rho_v S}{2}\left(\frac{\partial \xi}{\partial t}\right)^2 - \frac{\gamma p_o S}{2}\left(\frac{\partial \xi}{\partial x}\right)^2\right] dx\, dt = 0$$

This yields, by the Euler-Lagrange equations,

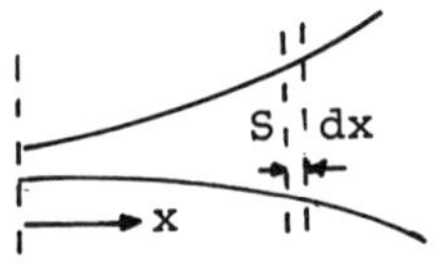

Figure 15-4.3. A horn with a slow taper.

$$-\rho_v S \frac{\partial}{\partial t}(\frac{\partial \xi}{\partial t}) + \gamma p_o \frac{\partial}{\partial x}(S \frac{\partial \xi}{\partial x}) = 0$$

from which it follows that

$$\frac{1}{S}\frac{\partial}{\partial x}(S \frac{\partial \xi}{\partial x}) = \frac{\rho_v}{\gamma p_o}\frac{\partial^2 \xi}{\partial t^2} = \frac{1}{c^2}\frac{\partial^2 \xi}{\partial t^2} \tag{15-4.22}$$

This is expanded to

$$\frac{\partial^2 \xi}{\partial x^2} + \frac{1}{S}\frac{\partial S}{\partial x}\frac{\partial \xi}{\partial x} = \frac{1}{c^2}\frac{\partial^2 \xi}{\partial t^2}$$

which can be written in the form

$$\frac{\partial^2 \xi}{\partial x^2} + (\frac{\partial}{\partial x}\log S)\frac{\partial \xi}{\partial x} = \frac{1}{c^2}\frac{\partial^2 \xi}{\partial t^2} \tag{15-4.23}$$

We now proceed in the manner that led from Eq. (15-4.19) to (15-4.20). We note from Eq. (15-4.15) that

$$\frac{\partial \xi}{\partial x} = \frac{1}{\gamma p_o} p_1$$

so that

$$\frac{\partial^2 \xi}{\partial x^2} = \frac{1}{\gamma p_o}\frac{\partial p_1}{\partial x}$$

Now differentiate Eq. (15-4.23) with respect to x

$$\frac{\partial}{\partial x}(\frac{\partial^2 \xi}{\partial x^2}) + \frac{\partial}{\partial x}[(\frac{\partial}{\partial x}\log S)\frac{\partial \xi}{\partial x}] = \frac{1}{c^2}\frac{\partial^2}{\partial t^2}(\frac{\partial \xi}{\partial x})$$

Hence, finally,

$$\frac{\partial^2 p_1}{\partial x^2} + (\frac{\partial}{\partial x}\log S)\frac{\partial p_1}{\partial x} = \frac{1}{c^2}\frac{\partial^2 p_1}{\partial t^2} \tag{15-4.24}$$

where it has been assumed that $\partial^2/\partial x^2(\log S)$ is very small since (log S) is a slowly varying function.

ΔΔΔ

B. Approximate Solutions to Field Problems

In Part A of this chapter we introduced some basic ideas of the Calculus of Variations, and how to use these techniques to find special functionals, which in turn were to be maximized by functions obeying well-known differential equations. In this portion of this chapter we shall present methods which are useful in finding approximate solutions to boundary value problems, often for examples that cannot be solved by the methods previously studied.

There are many methods available for the solution of differential equations. These can be categorized into two broad groups: (a) direct integration - exact solutions, such as those considered in Chap. 4 and throughout this text, and (b) approximate solutions. This second category includes a number of mathematical techniques, only some of which will be examined: power series, perturbation methods, Monte Carlo methods, finite difference techniques, method of weighted residuals (MWR), Ritz method, Galerkin's method, variational method, finite element method. We shall show that close relationships exist among some of these methods.

Often continuum problems have apparently rather different formulations, although these formulations are essentially equivalent. Examples are problems that are formulated in differential form with specified boundary conditions, with the integration of these equations providing the solution. In the variational formulation, it is required to find functions which extremize functionals subject to the same given boundary conditions. These functions are the expected solutions since they also satisfy the differential equations that describe the problem. Furthermore, we may sometimes have to maximize one functional and at the same time to minimize another. In such a case we are actually finding upper and lower bounds on the functionals, a bounding procedure that many times has significant engineering value.

15-5. Boundary Value Problems

We shall initially consider two theorems which provide the mathematical means for finding functionals. These functionals in turn are minimized by functions that satisfy the desired equations. We state without proof:

Theorem 15-5.1. If an operator A is positive definite (see Appendix II) then the equation

$$Au = f \tag{15-5.1}$$

has only one solution.

ΔΔΔ

Theorem 15-5.2. If an operator A is positive definite and Eq. (15-5.1) has a solution, then the functional

$$I[u] = (Au,u) - 2(u,f) = \int_V (uAu - 2uf)\, dV \tag{15-5.2}$$

is minimized by a function which satisfies Eq. (15-5.1).

ΔΔΔ

Consider the well-known Sturm-Liouville differential equation

$$Au = -\frac{d}{dx}\left[p(x)\frac{du}{dx}\right] + r(x)u = f(x) \tag{15-5.3}$$

with boundary conditions

$$u(a) = 0 \qquad u(b) = 0 \qquad \text{a)}$$

$$\left.\frac{du}{dx}\right|_{x=a} = 0 \qquad \left.\frac{du}{dx}\right|_{x=b} = 0 \qquad \text{b)} \qquad (15\text{-}5.4)$$

$$u(a) = u(b); \quad p(a)\left.\frac{du}{dx}\right|_{x=a} = p(b)\left.\frac{du}{dx}\right|_{x=b} \qquad \text{c)}$$

The operator A under these conditions is self-adjoint and positive definite (see Appendix II). We must impose the following assumptions on the problem:

a. $p(x)$, $dp(x)/dx$, and $r(x)$ are continuous over the range $a \le x \le b$,
b. within the range $p(x) \ge 0$ and $r(x) \ge 0$
c. the function can vanish at a finite number of points, provided that the integral

$$I = \int_a^b \frac{1}{p(x)}\, dx$$

has a finite value.

Example 15-5.1. Find the functional defined for Eq. (4-9.1), namely

$$\frac{d^2\Phi}{dx^2} = -\frac{\rho(x)}{\varepsilon} \qquad (15\text{-}5.5)$$

with $\Phi(0) = \Phi(1) = 0$, which describes the potential function between two grounded plates for which a specified volume charge distribution exists.

Solution. Eq. (15-5.5) is of the Sturm-Liouville type, with $p(x) = 1$, $r(x) = 0$, $f(x) = \rho(x)/\varepsilon$, and $A = -d^2/dx^2$. Hence the desired functional becomes

$$I[\Phi] = \int_0^1 [-\Phi \frac{d^2\Phi}{dx^2} - 2\Phi \frac{\rho(x)}{\varepsilon}]dx = -\Phi \left.\frac{d\Phi}{dx}\right|_0^1 + \int_0^1 [(\frac{d\Phi}{dx})^2 - 2\Phi \frac{\rho(x)}{\varepsilon}]dx$$

Employing the specified boundary conditions, the result is

$$I[\Phi] = \int_0^1 [(\frac{d\Phi}{dx})^2 - 2\Phi \frac{\rho(x)}{\varepsilon}]\, dx \qquad (15\text{-}5.6)$$

$\Delta\Delta\Delta$

The Ritz Method. Following Ritz, we construct a linear combination of $\underline{n}$ independent functions

$$u_n = \sum_{i=1}^{n} a_i \phi_i \qquad (15\text{-}5.7)$$

where a_i are arbitrary numerical coefficients. The functions ϕ_i are known as *expansion*, *basis*, or *trial*, functions and are selected in such a manner that u_n

satisfies the boundary conditions. By substituting Eq. (15-5.7) into Eq. (15-5.2), the functional takes the following form

$$I[u_n] = \left(\sum_{i=1}^{n} a_i A\phi_i, \sum_{j=1}^{n} \phi_j a_j\right) - 2\left(\sum_{i=1}^{n} a_i\phi_i, f\right)$$

$$= \sum_{i,j=1}^{n} (A\phi_i,\phi_j)a_i a_j - 2\sum_{i=1}^{n} (\phi_i, f)a_i \qquad (15\text{-}5.8)$$

The next step is to select the a_i's so that $I[u_n]$ becomes a minimum. The necessary condition which must be satisfied for this minimum is that

$$\frac{\partial I[u_n]}{\partial a_i} = 0 \qquad i = 1,2,\ldots n \qquad (15\text{-}5.9)$$

Eq. (15-5.9) gives n linear algebraic equations which can be solved for the unknown constants a_i.

Example 15-5.2. Use the Ritz method to find the approximate solution to Ex. 15-5.1, with $\rho(x) = x^2$ and $\varepsilon = 1$.

Solution. We write as a trial function

$$\Phi_2 = a_1\phi_1 + a_2\phi_2 = a_1(x-x^2) + a_2(x^2-x^3); \quad \phi_n = x^n - x^{n+1} \qquad (15\text{-}5.10)$$

Then Eq. (15-5.8) becomes

$$I[\Phi_2] = (A\phi_1,\phi_1)a_1a_1 + (A\phi_1,\phi_2)a_1a_2 + (A\phi_2,\phi_1)a_2a_1 + (A\phi_2,\phi_2)a_2a_2$$
$$- 2(\phi_1,f)a_1 - 2(\phi_2,f)a_2 \qquad (15\text{-}5.11)$$

An application of Eq. (15-5.9) yields the following two equations

$$2(A\phi_1,\phi_1)a_1 + [(A\phi_1,\phi_2) + A(\phi_2,\phi_1)]a_2 = 2(\phi_1,f)$$

$$[(A\phi_1,\phi_2) + (A\phi_2,\phi_1)]a_1 + 2(A\phi_2,\phi_2)a_2 = 2(\phi_2,f)$$

But $(A\phi_1,\phi_2) = (A\phi_2,\phi_1)$ and the system of equations becomes

$$\begin{aligned}(A\phi_1,\phi_1)a_1 + (A\phi_2,\phi_1)a_2 &= (\phi_1,f)\\ (A\phi_1,\phi_2)a_1 + (A\phi_1,\phi_2)a_2 &= (\phi_2,f)\end{aligned} \qquad (15\text{-}5.12)$$

However,

$$(A\phi_1,\phi_1) = \int_0^1 -[\frac{d^2}{dx^2}(x-x^2)](x-x^2)dx = \frac{1}{3};\quad (A\phi_2,\phi_1) = \int_0^1 -[\frac{d^2}{dx^2}(x^2-x^3)](x-x^2)dx = \frac{1}{6}$$

$$(A\phi_2,\phi_2) = \frac{2}{15};\qquad (\phi_1,f) = \frac{1}{20};\qquad (\phi_2,f) = \frac{1}{30}$$

The solution of Eq. (15-5.12) yields the constants a_1 and a_2. Thus

$$a_1 = \frac{\begin{vmatrix} \frac{1}{20} & \frac{1}{6} \\ \frac{1}{30} & \frac{2}{15} \end{vmatrix}}{\begin{vmatrix} \frac{1}{3} & \frac{1}{6} \\ \frac{1}{6} & \frac{2}{15} \end{vmatrix}} = \frac{1}{5};\qquad a_2 = \frac{1}{6}$$

The solution to the second order function is then

$$\Phi_2 = \frac{1}{5}(x-x^2) + \frac{1}{6}(x^2-x^3) \tag{15-5.13}$$

The first order solution can be obtained by using Eq. (15-5.12a); this is

$$\Phi_1 = \frac{3}{20}(x-x^2) \tag{15-4.14}$$

where $a_1 = (\phi_1,f)/(A\phi_1,\phi_1) = 3/20$. The exact solution is readily obtained, and is

$$\Phi = \frac{1}{2}(x-x^4) \tag{15-5.15}$$

The three solutions are given in Table 15-5.1.

ΔΔΔ

Table 15-5.1. Exact and approximate solutions of the specified problem.

	Exact	Ex. 15-5.2.		Ex. 15-5.3.	Ex. 15-5.6.
x	Φ	Φ_1	Φ_2	Φ_2	Φ_3
0.0	0.0	0.0	0.0	0.0	0.0
0.1	0.008325	0.013500	0.007500	0.006500	0.009480
0.2	0.016533	0.024000	0.016000	0.014222	0.019012
0.3	0.024325	0.031500	0.024500	0.022166	0.027728
0.4	0.031200	0.036000	0.032000	0.029333	0.034762
0.5	0.036458	0.037500	0.037500	0.034722	0.039246
0.6	0.039200	0.036000	0.040000	0.037333	0.040313
0.7	0.038325	0.031500	0.038500	0.036166	0.037097
0.8	0.032533	0.024000	0.032000	0.030222	0.028731
0.9	0.020325	0.013500	0.019500	0.018500	0.014347
1.0	0.0	0.0	0.0	0.0	-0.006920

We return to Eq. (15-5.12) which we write in the following forms

(a) In matrix form

$$\begin{bmatrix} (\phi_1, A\phi_1) & (\phi_1, A\phi_2) \\ (\phi_2, A\phi_1) & (\phi_2, A\phi_2) \end{bmatrix} \begin{bmatrix} a_1 \\ a_2 \end{bmatrix} = \begin{bmatrix} (\phi_1, f) \\ (\phi_2, f) \end{bmatrix} \tag{15-5.16}$$

or, in general,

$$[A_{ij}][a_j] = [f_i] \tag{15-5.17}$$

(b) In functional form

$$(\phi_i, \sum_j a_j A\phi_j) = (\phi_i, f) \tag{15-5.18}$$

Method of Weighted Residuals. Consider the inhomogeneous equation

$$Au = f \tag{15-5.19}$$

where A is a linear, positive definite operator, and f is a known function. Let u be represented by a set of functions u_i belonging in the domain of the operator A in the form

$$u_n = \sum_{i=1}^{n} a_i u_i \qquad i = 1,2,\ldots n \tag{15-5.20}$$

where the a_i's are unknown constants. Substitute Eq. (15-5.20) into Eq. (15-5.19), multiply by another set of functions w_i, and integrate over the given dimensions. When this is accomplished, we obtain the following set of equations

$$(w_i, \sum_{j=1}^{N} a_j Au_j) = (w_i, f) \tag{15-5.21}$$

or equivalently

$$\begin{aligned} (w_1, Au_1)a_1 + (w_1, Au_2)a_2 + \ldots + (w_1, Au_N)a_N &= (w_1, f) \\ (w_2, Au_1)a_1 + (w_2, Au_2)a_2 + \ldots + (w_2, Au_N)a_N &= (w_2, f) \\ &\vdots \\ (w_N, Au_1)a_1 + (w_N, Au_2)a_2 + \ldots + (w_N, Au_N)a_N &= (w_N, f) \end{aligned} \tag{15-5.22}$$

This set of equations is conveniently written in matrix form

$$[A_{ij}][a_j] = [f_i] \tag{15-5.23}$$

where

$$[A_{ij}] = \begin{bmatrix} (w_1,Au_1) & (w_1,Au_2) & \cdots & (w_1,Au_N) \\ (w_2,Au_1) & (w_2,Au_2) & \cdots & (w_2,Au_N) \\ \vdots & & & \\ (w_N,Au_1) & (w_N,Au_2) & & (w_N,Au_N) \end{bmatrix} \quad \text{(a)}$$

$$[a_j] = \begin{bmatrix} a_1 \\ a_2 \\ \vdots \\ a_N \end{bmatrix} \quad \text{(b)} \qquad [f_i] = \begin{bmatrix} (w_1,f) \\ (w_2,f) \\ \vdots \\ (w_N,f) \end{bmatrix} \quad \text{(c)} \qquad (15\text{-}5.24)$$

The solution of the system of equations in Eq. (15-5.22) is equivalent to the matrix representation

$$[a_j] = [A_{ij}]^{-1}[f_i]$$

where the inversion of the matrix $[A_{ij}]^{-1}$ exists, if it is nonsingular.

The w_i functions are known as *weighting* or *testing* functions. For the particular choice $w_i = u_i$ the method is known as *Galerkin's* method. It is also known as the *point matching* or *collocation* method when the testing functions are delta functions. While it may appear that the Ritz and the Galerkin methods are identical, this is not always true.

Example 15-5.3. Repeat Ex. 15-5.1 which is now expressed: find the potential distribution between two grounded plates with a charge distribution $\rho(x)/\varepsilon = x^2$ and with $\delta(x-x_i)$ as testing functions.

Solution. We assume the approximate solution

$$\Phi_2 = a_1(x-x^2) + a_2(x^2-x^3) \qquad (15\text{-}5.25)$$

Introduce this solution into the differential equation (15-5.5) to obtain

$$-a_1 \frac{d^2(x-x^2)}{dx^2} - a_2 \frac{d^2(x^2-x^3)}{dx^2} = x^2 \qquad (15\text{-}5.26)$$

The appropriate testing functions are deduced by setting

$$x_i = \frac{i}{j+1}; \quad \text{or} \quad x_1 = \frac{1}{3}, \quad x_2 = \frac{2}{3} \qquad (15\text{-}5.27)$$

since i = 1,2,...j for the basis functions. Now multiply Eq. (15-5.26) by $\delta(x-1/3)$ and integrate over the domain [0,1]. This yields

$$-a_1 \int_0^1 \frac{d^2(x-x^2)}{dx^2}\,\delta(x-\tfrac{1}{3})dx - a_2 \int_0^1 \frac{d^2(x^2-x^3)}{dx^2}\delta(x-\tfrac{1}{3})dx = \int_0^1 x^2\delta(x-\tfrac{1}{3})dx \qquad (15\text{-}5.28)$$

from which

$$a_1 = \frac{1}{18}$$

Similarly, by multiplying Eq. (15-5.26) by $\delta(x-2/3)$ and integrating over the same domain, there results

$$a_2 = \frac{1}{6}$$

Hence the second order solution is given by

$$\Phi_2 = \frac{1}{18}(x-x^2) + \frac{1}{6}(x^2-x^3) \tag{15-5.29}$$

This solution is contained in column 5 of Table 15-5.1.

ΔΔΔ

Example 15-5.4. A square region shown in Fig. 15-5.2 is covered with a constant charge density $\rho = -4$, with the boundaries being grounded. Find the potential over the surface.

Solution. This problem requires the solution to the Poisson equation

$$\nabla^2\Phi = -4 \tag{15-5.30}$$

subject to the boundary conditions

$$\Phi(x,0) = \Phi(x,1) = \Phi(0,y) = \Phi(2,y) = 0 \tag{15-5.31}$$

We consider as an expansion function the following

$$\Phi_2(x,y) = xy(2-x)(1-y)[a_1 + a_2(x^2+y^2)] = a_1\phi_1 + a_2\phi_2 \tag{15-5.32}$$

which is seen to satisfy the boundary conditions. Now proceed as in Ex. 15-5.2 to deduce the values of the two unknown constants a_1 and a_2.

ΔΔΔ

When nonhomogeneous boundary conditions are given, say of the form

$$u(0) = \rho_1(x) \qquad u(1) = \rho_2(x) \tag{15-5.33}$$

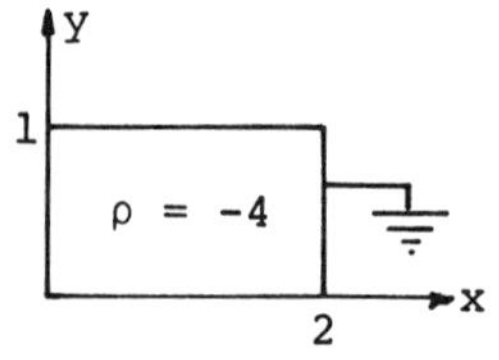

Figure 15-5.2. A potential problem in two dimensions.

then the functional to be extremized for the Poisson equation

$$-\frac{d^2u}{dx^2} = f(x)$$

is given by

$$I[x] = \int [(\frac{du}{dx})^2 - 2uf]\, dx \qquad (15\text{-}5.34)$$

Now one adopts an expansion function of the form

$$u_i = \psi(x) + \sum_1 a_i\phi_i \qquad a)$$

with

$$\psi(0) = \rho_1(x) \qquad \psi(1) = \rho_2(x) \qquad b) \qquad (15\text{-}5.35)$$

$$\phi_i(0) = 0 \qquad \phi_i(1) = 0 \qquad c)$$

The accepted domain $0 \leq x \leq 1$ is not restrictive since any other given domain $0 \leq x \leq x_1$ can always be transformed to the domain $0 \leq x \leq 1$. For example, for the equation

$$\frac{d^2\Phi}{dx'^2} = 0, \qquad \Phi(0) = \Phi_0, \qquad \Phi(x_0) = \Phi_1$$

we can set $\Phi = (\Phi-\Phi_0)/(\Phi_1-\Phi_0)$ and $x = x'/x_0$ and obtain the equivalent equation

$$\frac{d^2\Phi}{dx^2} = 0; \qquad \Phi(0) = 0, \qquad \Phi(1) = 1$$

Example 15-5.5. Determine the potential distribution between two conducting plates with charge distribution $\rho(x) = x^2$, $\varepsilon = 1$, and boundary conditions $\Phi(0) = 1$, $\Phi(0) = 10$.

Solution. Consider the following second order expansion function

$$\Phi_2 = (1 + 9x^2) + a_1(x-x^2) + a_2(x^2-x^3) \qquad (15\text{-}5.36)$$

Next, substitute Eq. (15-5.36) into Eq. (15-5.34), to get

$$I[\Phi_2] = \int_0^1 [(18)^2x^2 + a_1^2(1-2x)^2 + a_2^2(2x-3x^2)^2 + 36a_1x(1-2x) + 36a_2x(2x-3x^2)$$

$$+ 2a_1a_2(1-2x)(2x-3x^2) - 2x^2[1 + 9x^2 + a_1(x-x^2) + a_2(x^2-x^3)]dx \qquad (15\text{-}5.37)$$

From this it follows

$$\frac{\partial I[\Phi_2]}{\partial a_1} = 0 = \int_0^1 [2a_1(1-2x)^2 + 36x(1-2x) + 2a_2(1-2x)(2x-3x^2) - 2x^2(x-x^2)]dx$$

$$= \frac{2}{3} a_1 + \frac{1}{3} a_2 - \frac{61}{10}$$

and

$$\frac{\partial I[\Phi_2]}{\partial a_2} = 0 = \int_0^1 [2a_2(2x-3x^2)^2 + 36x(2x-3x^2) + 2a_1(1-2x)(2x-3x^2) - 2x^2(x^2-x^3)]dx$$

$$= \frac{1}{3} a_1 + \frac{4}{15} a_2 - \frac{46}{15}$$

This pair of equations is solved for the values of a_1 and a_2, which have the values $a_1 = 136/15$ and $a_2 = 1/6$. The second order solution becomes

$$\Phi_2 = (1 + 9x^2) + \frac{136}{15}(x-x^2) + \frac{1}{6}(x^2-x^3) \tag{15-5.38}$$

ΔΔΔ

When more than one dimension is involved, the functional to be extremized is

$$I[u] = \int_V [(\nabla u)^2 - 2uf]dV \qquad \text{a)}$$

with (15-5.39)

$$\psi(\bar{r})\Big|_S = g(\bar{r}) \qquad \text{b)}$$

where S is the surface enclosing the domain V, and $\psi(r)$ obeys the same boundary conditions as the unknown function $u(r)\big|_S = g(r)$.

For the case when the Poisson equation

$$-\nabla^2 u(\bar{r}) = f(\bar{r}) \qquad \text{a)}$$

is associated with the boundary condition (15-5.40)

$$\frac{\partial u}{\partial n} + \sigma u\Big|_S = g(\bar{r}) \qquad \text{b)}$$

where σ is positive and is a continuous function on the boundary, and $\partial/\partial n$ indicates a derivative normal to the surface S, the functional to be extremized is of the form

$$I[u] = \int_V [(\nabla u)^2 - 2uf]dV + \int_S (\sigma u^2 - 2ug)dS \tag{15-5.41}$$

For the case when the functions u_j and w_i do not obey the boundary conditions, we define another operator, called the extended operator A^e which is such that $(w_i, A^e u_j) = (u_j, A^e w_i)$. To accomplish this, we set

$$(w_i, A^e u_j) = \int_0^1 w_i A u_j \, dx - u_j \frac{dw_i}{dx}\Big|_0^1 \tag{15-5.42}$$

The right hand side is equal to

$$-u_j \frac{dw_i}{dx}\bigg|_0^1 + u_j \frac{dw_i}{dx}\bigg|_0^1 - w_i \frac{du_j}{dx}\bigg|_0^1 + \int_0^1 u_j\left(-\frac{d^2w_i}{dx^2}\right)dx = (u_j, A^e w_i) - w_i \frac{du_j}{dx}\bigg|_0^1$$

This result implies that A^e is self-adjoint, independently of the boundary conditions. The following example illustrates the procedure.

Example 15-5.6. Find the solution to Ex. 15-5.2 using the extended operator technique.

Solution. We assume, in the present case, the following function

$$w_i = u_i = x^i \qquad i = 1,2,3$$

The individual elements of the matrix $[A_{ij}]$ of Eq. (15-5.24a) are:

$$A_{11} = \int_0^1 x\left(-\frac{d^2(x)}{dx^2}\right)dx - x\frac{d(x)}{dx}\bigg|_0^1 = -1$$

$$A_{12} = \int_0^1 x\left(-\frac{d^2(x^2)}{dx^2}\right)dx - x^2\frac{d(x)}{dx}\bigg|_0^1 = -2$$

$$A_{13} = \int_0^1 x\left(-\frac{d^2(x^3)}{dx^2}\right)dx - x^3\frac{d(x)}{dx}\bigg|_0^1 = -3$$

Proceeding in this manner, we also find the following matrix elements

$$A_{21} = -2,\quad A_{22} = -\frac{8}{3},\quad A_{23} = -\frac{7}{2},\quad A_{31} = -3,\quad A_{32} = -\frac{7}{2},\quad A_{33} = -\frac{21}{5}$$

To deduce the elements of the matrix $[f_i]$ of Eq. (15-5.24c)

$$f_1 = \int_0^1 x\cdot x^2\,dx = \frac{1}{4},\qquad f_2 = \int_0^1 x^2\cdot x^2\,dx = +\frac{1}{5},\qquad f_3 = \int_0^1 x^3\cdot x^2\,dx = \frac{1}{6}$$

Eq. (15-5.23) for this case assumes the form

$$\begin{bmatrix} -1 & -2 & -3 \\ -2 & -8/3 & -7/2 \\ -3 & -7/2 & -21/5 \end{bmatrix} \begin{bmatrix} a_1 \\ a_2 \\ a_3 \end{bmatrix} = \begin{bmatrix} 1/4 \\ 1/5 \\ 1/6 \end{bmatrix} \tag{15-5.44}$$

The solution of this system of equations for the a's leads to the following values

$$a_1 = 0.09166,\qquad a_2 = 0.04591,\qquad a_3 = -0.14449$$

The potential function is then written

$$\Phi_3 = 0.09166x + 0.04591x^2 - 0.14449x^3 \tag{15-5.45}$$

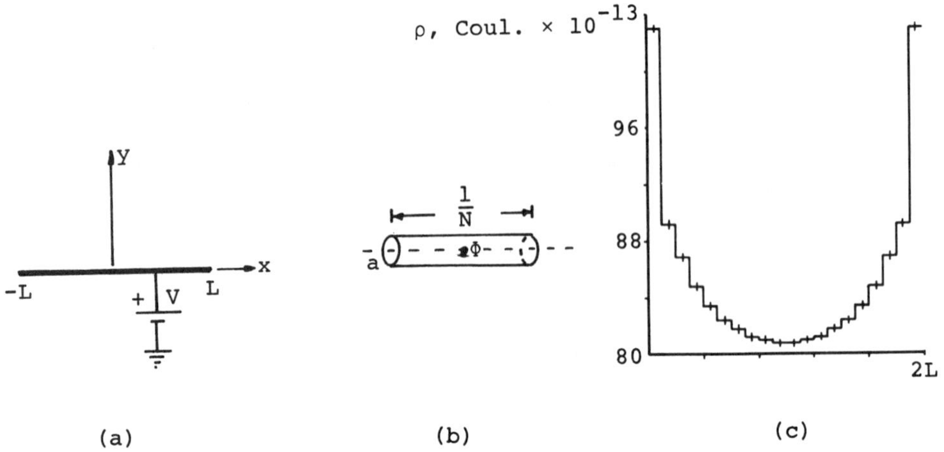

Figure 15-5.3. (a) Conducting wire maintained at constant potential; (b) The dimensional characteristics of the wire; (c) Numerical results. [Reprinted with permission from IEEE Trans. on Education, Vol. E-21, p. 17, Leonard L. Tsai and Charles E. Smith, "Moment Methods in Electromagnetics for Undergraduates", 1978.]

The values of Φ_3 versus the independent variable x are contained in Table 15-5.1.

ΔΔΔ

Some of the ideas that have been discussed above for the approximate solution of field problems that have been formulated in differential equation form can also be adapted to the evaluation of integral equations. We shall show the procedure by means of two examples.

Example 5-5.7. A straight thin wire shown in Fig. 15-5.3 of length 2L is situated in free space and is maintained at a constant potential $\Phi = V$. Determine the charge distribution on the wire.

Solution. Begin with Eq. (4-6.6), the potential integral,

$$\Phi(\overline{r}) = \frac{1}{4\pi\varepsilon_0} \int_V \frac{\rho(\overline{r}')}{|\overline{r}-\overline{r}'|}\, dV' \qquad (15\text{-}5.46)$$

which relates the potential with the charge distribution. Since the potential is known on the X-axis, and with the assumption that the wire is thin, Eq. (15-5.46) is written in the form

$$V = \frac{1}{4\pi\varepsilon_0} \int_{-L}^{L} \frac{\rho(x')}{|x-x'|}\, dx' \qquad (15\text{-}5.47)$$

This is an integral equation (Fredholm integral of the first kind). We seek a numerical solution to this problem.

We observe that Eq. (15-5.47) applies for the field point everywhere along the wire. Consider, therefore, explicitly, the fixed point x_m on the wire. Hence we shall consider the integral

$$V = \frac{1}{4\pi\varepsilon_0} \int_{-L}^{L} \frac{\rho(x')}{|x_m - x'|}\, dx' \qquad (15\text{-}5.48)$$

which is a function of x' only. The problem now is to deduce this functional dependence in algebraic form. To accomplish this, divide the length 2L into N increments, each of length Δx_n. Further, it is assumed that the charge is uniformly distributed in each incremental length. Now introduce the relation

$$\rho(x) \doteq \sum_{n=1}^{N} \rho_n \qquad (15\text{-}5.49)$$

into Eq. (15-5.48). This yields the equation

$$V = \sum_{n=1}^{N} \ell_{mn}\rho_n \qquad m = 1,2,\ldots N \qquad (15\text{-}5.50)$$

where

$$\ell_{mn} = \int_{\Delta x_n} \frac{dx'}{4\pi\varepsilon_0 |x_m - x'|} \qquad (15\text{-}5.51)$$

For numerical results, choose L = 1, and it is noted that the lengths Δx_n are all equal, with $\Delta x_n = 2/N$. The potential at the center of Δx_n due to unit charge uniformly distributed in Δx_n is given by

$$\ell_{nn} = \int_{-1/N}^{1/N} \frac{dx}{4\pi\varepsilon_0 x} \qquad (15\text{-}5.52)$$

The same formula can be used to calculate the potential at the center of Δx_m due to unit charge over Δx_n. But the idea is used that the charge over Δx_n is concentrated at point x_n. Equation (15-5.51) becomes

$$\ell_{mn} \doteq \frac{2/N}{4\pi\varepsilon_0 |x_m - x_n|} \qquad (15\text{-}5.53)$$

The values given by the last two equations are then introduced into Eq. (15-5.50) which constitutes a set of N linear equations with N unknowns ρ_N's.

$$\begin{aligned}
\ell_{11}\rho_1 + \ell_{12}\rho_2 + \cdots + \ell_{1N}\rho_N &= 4\pi\varepsilon_0 V \\
\ell_{21}\rho_1 + \ell_{22}\rho_2 + \cdots + \ell_{2N}\rho_N &= 4\pi\varepsilon_0 V \\
\vdots \qquad\qquad\qquad & \qquad \vdots \\
\ell_{N1}\rho_1 + \ell_{N2}\rho_2 + \cdots + \ell_{NN}\rho_N &= 4\pi\varepsilon_0 V
\end{aligned} \qquad (15\text{-}5.54)$$

It is found, however, that the integrand in Eq. (15-5.52) contains a singularity. To avoid this, we must take the thickness of the wire into consideration. It is recalled that for a charged conductor that the charge is distributed over the surface of the conductor, with charge density ρ_s, which is assumed to be constant over Δx_n. Refer to Fig. 15-5.3b, and consider the potential integral which becomes

$$\Phi = \frac{1}{4\pi\varepsilon_o}\int_0^{2\pi}\int_{-1/N}^{1/N}\frac{\rho_s\ a\ d\phi dx}{\sqrt{a^2+x^2}} = \frac{2\pi a\rho_s}{4\pi\varepsilon_o}\ \ell n\ (x+\sqrt{x^2+a^2})\Bigg|_{-1/N}^{1/N}$$

$$= \frac{\rho_n}{4\rho\varepsilon_o}\ \ell n\ \frac{\frac{1}{N}+\sqrt{(\frac{1}{N})^2+a^2}}{-\frac{1}{N}+\sqrt{(\frac{1}{N})^2+a^2}} \doteq \frac{2\rho_n}{4\pi\varepsilon_o}\ \ell n\ (\frac{2}{aN}) \tag{15-5.55}$$

where $\rho_n = 2\pi a\rho_s$, with $\underline{a}$ assumed to be less than the length Δx_n.

The numerical results for the wire of length 2L = 1 and diameter 1 mm are shown graphically in Fig. 15-5.3c.

The capacitance of the wire can be found from the relation

$$C = \frac{Q}{V} \doteq \frac{1}{V}\sum_{n=1}^{N}\rho_n \tag{15-5.56}$$

ΔΔΔ

Example 15-5.8. A square plane of side 2L is situated in free space. It is maintained at constant potential Φ = V, as shown in Fig. 15-5.4. Determine the charge distribution and the capacitance of the plate.

Solution. The two dimensional form of Eq. (15-5.46) at the plate is

$$\Phi(x,y) = V = \int_{-L}^{L} dx' \int_{-L}^{L} \frac{\rho(x',y')}{4\pi\varepsilon_o\sqrt{(x-x')^2+(y-y')^2}}\,dy' \tag{15-5.57}$$

Set

$$\rho(x,y) \doteq \sum_{n=1}^{N}\rho_n \tag{15-5.58}$$

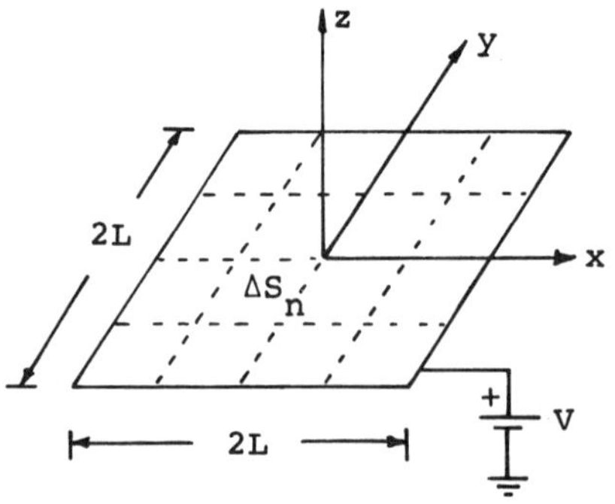

Figure 15-5.4. A conducting plane maintained at a constant potential.

where it is assumed that ρ_n is constant and uniformly distributed over the element ΔS_n. The procedure followed in the previous example is followed, and it is required to evaluate

$$\ell_{mn} = \int_{\Delta x_n} dx' \int_{\Delta y_n} \frac{1}{4\pi\varepsilon_0 \sqrt{(x_m - x')^2 + (y_m - y')^2}} dy' \tag{15-5.59}$$

to be used in the expression

$$V = \sum_{n=1}^{N} \ell_{mn}\rho_n \tag{15.5.60}$$

The potential at the center of the ΔS_n square due to the unit charge density uniformly distributed over its surface is

$$\begin{aligned} \ell_{nn} &= \int_{-1/N}^{1/N} dx \int_{-1/N}^{1/N} \frac{1}{4\pi\varepsilon_0 \sqrt{x^2 + y^2}} dy \qquad m = n \\ &= \frac{2}{N\pi\varepsilon_o} \ln(1 + \sqrt{2}) = \frac{2}{N\pi\varepsilon_0} 0.8814 \end{aligned} \tag{15-5.61}$$

Similarly, the off-diagonal elements are obtained by using the formula

$$\ell_{mn} \doteq \frac{\Delta S_n}{4\pi\varepsilon_0 |\bar{r}_m - \bar{r}_n|} = \frac{(1/N)^2}{4\pi\varepsilon_0 \sqrt{(x_m - x_n)^2 + (y_m - y_n)^2}} \qquad m \neq n \tag{15-5.62}$$

as was done in the previous example.

The set of equations to be solved are exactly the same as those in Eq. (15-5.54) except that the constants ℓ_{mn} must be evaluated from Eqs. (15-5.61) and (15-5.62). ΔΔΔ

For further studies using this approach, which is known as the method of moments, the reader should consult the work of Harrington (see Bibliography).

15-6. Eigenvalue Problems

In Appendix II we present the very important concept in mathematics and physics of *eigenvalue* and *eigenfunctions*. The eigenvalues and eigenfunctions of an equation are related to the permitted vibrational frequencies of clamped strings, membranes, short-circuited transmission lines, etc., and to the particular physical configurations of these vibrating systems. A general equation of the type discussed is

$$Au - \lambda Bu = 0 \tag{15-6.1.}$$

where A and B are linear operators and λ is a constant. The wave equation $\nabla^2\bar{E} + k^2\bar{E} = 0$ is of the type given in Eq. (15-6.1), where $A = -\nabla^2$, $\lambda = k^2$, $B = 1$. Further, to each characteristic value λ (eigenvalue), there corresponds a nontrivial solution function u (eigenfunction). In addition, boundary conditions are also given for eigenvalue problems. The boundary conditions were discussed in Chap. 4, and were described as Dirichlet, Neumann, or mixed conditions.

Given an eigenvalue equation having a discrete spectrum, we can find the eigenvalues, approximately, using the Ritz method. For Eq. (15-6.1), let us choose a set of expansion functions ϕ_i, and let

$$u_n = \sum_{i=1}^{n} a_i\phi_i \tag{15-6.2}$$

where a_i are constant coefficients. Substitute Eq. (15-6.2) into Eq. (15-6.1) and use the linearity property of the operators A and B. Then

$$\sum_{i=1}^{n} a_i[(A\phi_i - \lambda B\phi_i] = 0 \tag{15-6.3}$$

The inner product of this equation with ϕ_j gives the set of equations

$$\sum_{i=1}^{n} a_i[(A\phi_i,\phi_j) - \lambda(B\phi_i,\phi_j)] = 0 \qquad j = 1,2,\ldots n \tag{15-6.4}$$

This can be written in the following matrix form

$$\begin{bmatrix} (A\phi_1,\phi_1) & (A\phi_2,\phi_1) & \cdots & (A\phi_n,\phi_1) \\ (A\phi_1,\phi_2) & (A\phi_2,\phi_2) & \cdots & (A\phi_n,\phi_2) \\ \vdots & \vdots & & \vdots \\ (A\phi_1,\phi_n) & (A\phi_2,\phi_n) & \cdots & (A\phi_n,\phi_n) \end{bmatrix} \cdot \begin{bmatrix} a_1 \\ a_2 \\ \vdots \\ a_n \end{bmatrix} = \lambda \begin{bmatrix} (B\phi_1,\phi_1)\ldots B(\phi_n,\phi_1) \\ (B\phi_1,\phi_2)\ldots B(\phi_n,\phi_2) \\ \vdots \\ (B\phi_1,\phi_n)\ldots B(\phi_n,\phi_n) \end{bmatrix} \begin{bmatrix} a_1 \\ a_2 \\ \vdots \\ a_n \end{bmatrix} \qquad \text{a)}$$

or in compact form

$$[\alpha_{mn}][a_n] = \lambda[\beta_{mn}][a_n] \qquad \text{b)} \tag{15-6.5}$$

A solution to this equation exists if the determinant of the system is zero. This gives a polynomial in λ whose roots

$$|\alpha_{mn} - \lambda\beta_{mn}| = 0 \tag{15-6.6}$$

are the approximate eigenvalues λ_i of the eigenvalue problem.

Specifically, consider the Helmholtz equation for waves

$$\nabla^2\Phi(\bar{r}) + k^2\Phi(\bar{r}) = 0 \tag{15-6.7}$$

together with its boundary conditions. This equation is of the form in Eq. (15-6.1), with $A = -\nabla^2$, $\lambda = k^2$, and $B = 1$. Now multiply by $\Phi(\bar{r})$ and integrate over the volume V. This yields for the eigenvalue

$$\lambda = k^2 = \frac{-\int_V \Phi(\bar{r})\,\nabla^2\Phi(\bar{r})\,dV}{\int \Phi^2(\bar{r})\,dV} \tag{15-6.8}$$

This equation is transformed into a form which is sometimes more suitable for use in numerical calculations. With this end in mind, consider the expression

$$\nabla \cdot (\Phi\nabla\Phi) = \Phi\nabla^2\Phi + \nabla\Phi \cdot \nabla\Phi \tag{15-6.9}$$

It follows that

$$\begin{aligned}\int \Phi\nabla^2\Phi\,dV &= \int_V \nabla \cdot (\Phi\nabla\Phi)dV - \int_V (\nabla\Phi)^2 dV \\ &= \int_S \Phi\nabla\Phi\,dS - \int_V (\nabla\Phi)^2 dV\end{aligned} \tag{15-6.10}$$

where the divergence theorem was used to transform the first term on the right. When this expression is combined with Eq. (15-6.9) it follows that

$$\lambda = \frac{\int_V (\nabla\Phi)^2 dV - \int_S \Phi\nabla\Phi\,dS}{\int_V \Phi^2\,dV} \tag{15-6.11}$$

For the case of homogeneous boundary conditions

$$\Phi(\bar{r})\Big|_S = 0 \qquad \text{(Dirichlet)}$$

$$\frac{\partial\Phi(\bar{r})}{\partial n}\Big|_S = 0 \qquad \text{(Neumann)}$$

Eq. (15-6.11) becomes

$$\lambda = \frac{\int_V (\nabla\Phi(\bar{r}))^2 dV}{\int_V (\Phi(\bar{r}))^2 dV} \tag{15-6.12}$$

For mixed type boundary conditions of the form

$$\frac{\partial\Phi(r)}{\partial n} + \alpha\Phi(r) = 0$$

the ratio assumes the form

$$\lambda = \frac{\int_V [\nabla\Phi(\bar{r})]^2 dV + \int_S \alpha\Phi^2(\bar{r})dS}{\int_V \Phi^2(\bar{r})dV} \tag{15-6.13}$$

If λ_0 is the lower bound of the functional given by Eq. (15-6.13) and if there exists a function Φ_0 such that $\lambda = \lambda_0$, then λ_0 is the lowest eigenvalue of Eq. (15-6.8) and Φ_0 is the corresponding eigenfunction of the equation. This implies that any other admissible function Φ will give a larger value for the eigenvalue.

Example 15-6.1. Find the approximate value (upper bound) of the lowest eigenvalue for the rectangular membrane of dimensions 1,2 for the x,y directions which is clamped at all edges.

Solution. Since the membrane is clamped at its edges, the Dirichlet boundary conditions apply. In this case, Eq. (15-6.12) is the suitable form. We select as a trial function a form that will satisfy the boundary conditions. Such a function is

$$\Phi(x,y) = (2x-x^2)(y-y^2)$$

From this it follows

$$(\nabla\Phi)^2 = (2-2x)^2(y-y^2)^2 + (2x-x^2)(1-2y)^2$$

and so

$$\lambda = \frac{\omega^2}{c_d^2} = \frac{\int_0^2 (2-2x^2)dx \int_0^1 (y-y^2)dy + \int_0^2 (2x-x^2)dx \int_0^1 (1-2y)^2 dy}{\int_0^2 (2x-x^2)^2 dx \int_0^1 (y-y^2)^2 dy} = 12.5$$

The exact value is [see Eq. (13-5.10)]

$$\lambda = \frac{\omega^2}{c_d^2} = (\frac{\pi}{2})^2 + (\frac{\pi}{1})^2 = 12.337$$

The difference between these two values is only 1.3 percent. ΔΔΔ

15-7. Stationary Formulas for Vector Fields

Consider an electromagnetic cavity filled with a nonhomogeneous dielectric of permittivity $\varepsilon(r)$ and formed by a perfect conductor, with its consequent boundary condition $\overline{n} \times \overline{E} = 0$. The wave equation is given by

$$\nabla \times \nabla \times \overline{E} - \omega^2\mu\varepsilon\, \overline{E} = 0 \tag{15-7.1}$$

for μ constant. Scalarly multiply this equation by $\overline{E}$ and integrate over the volume V of the cavity. The result is the following expression for the frequency of resonance

$$\omega_r^2 = \frac{\int_V \bar{E} \cdot (\nabla \times \nabla \times \bar{E})dV}{\mu \int_V \varepsilon E^2 \, dV} \tag{15-7.2}$$

Now use the vector identity $\nabla \cdot (\bar{A} \times \bar{B}) = \bar{B} \cdot (\nabla \times \bar{A}) - \bar{A} \cdot (\nabla \times \bar{B})$ and impose the boundary condition $\bar{n} \times \bar{E} = 0$. Equation (15-7.2) assumes the form

$$\omega_r^2 = \frac{\int_V (\nabla \times \bar{E}) \cdot (\nabla \times \bar{E})dV}{\mu \int_V \varepsilon E^2 \, dV} \tag{15-7.3}$$

Note that Eq. (15-7.3) retains its variational character if the trial fields do not satisfy the boundary conditions if it is written

$$\omega_r^2 = \frac{\int_V (\nabla \times \bar{E})\cdot(\nabla \times \bar{E})dV + 2\int_S [(\nabla \times \bar{E}) \times \bar{E}] \cdot d\bar{S}}{\mu \int_V \varepsilon E^2 \, dV} \tag{15-7.4}$$

Example 15-7.1. Find the approximate value of the resonant frequency for the TE_{101} mode in a rectangular cavity filled with a medium of constant permittivity (see Sec. 13-7).

Solution. Suppose that the electric field is assumed to be of the form

$$\bar{E} = \bar{a}_y \, x(1-x)z(2-z)$$

Eq. (15-7.3) becomes, in this case

$$\omega_r^2 = \frac{\int_0^b dy \int_0^1 (x-x^2)dx \int_0^2 (2-2z)^2 dz + \int_0^b dy \int_0^1 (1-2x)^2 dx \int_0^2 (2z-z^2)^2 dz}{\mu\varepsilon \int_0^b dy \int_0^1 (x-x^2)^2 \int_0^2 (2z-z^2)^2 dz} = \frac{12.5}{\mu\varepsilon}$$

This result is only 1.3% above the exact value $12.337/\mu\varepsilon$. ΔΔΔ

Now consider the vector wave equation of the form

$$\nabla^2\bar{A} + k^2\bar{A} = 0 \tag{15-7.5}$$

The Rayleigh-Ritz method leads to the relation

$$k_0^2 \leq \frac{\int_V \bar{A} \cdot \nabla^2\bar{A} \, dV}{\int_V \bar{A}\cdot\bar{A} \, dV} \tag{15-7.6}$$

where k_0 is the lowest eigenvalue.

To prove this result, a scalar function Φ will be defined in terms of approximating functions ϕ which are solutions of the scalar wave equation. Begin with

$$\Phi = \sum_i a_i\phi_i = a_0\phi_0 + a_1\phi_1 + \dots \tag{15-7.7}$$

so that

$$\nabla^2\Phi = a_0\nabla^2\phi_0 + a_1\nabla^2\phi_1 + \cdots \qquad (15\text{-}7.8)$$

Since the ϕ_i's satisfy the scalar wave equation, Eq. (15-7.8) now assumes the form

$$\nabla^2\Phi = -a_0 k_0^2\phi_0 - a_1 k_1^2\phi_1 - \cdots \qquad (15\text{-}7.9)$$

It can be shown, by direct substitution, that the function

$$\bar{A} = \bar{a}\Phi$$

satisfies the vector wave equation. We can thus write

$$\nabla^2\bar{A} = \nabla^2(\bar{a}\sum_i a_i\phi_i) = \bar{a}\sum_i a_i\nabla^2\phi_i = -\bar{a}\,\Sigma a_i k_i^2\phi_i$$

It follows that the integral

$$\int_V \bar{A}\cdot\nabla^2\bar{A}\,dV = -\int_V \sum_i\sum_j a_i a_j k_i^2\phi_i\phi_j\,dV$$
$$= -\int_V \sum_i a_i^2 k_i^2\phi_i^2\,dV = -\sum_i a_i^2 k_i^2$$

because of orthogonality of the wave functions. The integral

$$\int_V \bar{A}\cdot\bar{A}\,dV = \int_V \sum_i a_i^2\phi_i^2\,dV = \sum_i a_i^2$$

The ratio is

$$\frac{\int_V \bar{A}\cdot\nabla^2\bar{A}\,dV}{\int_V \bar{A}\cdot\bar{A}\,dV} = \frac{\sum_i a_i^2 k_i^2}{\sum_i a_i^2}$$

Since the consecutive eigenvalues can be arranged in the form $k_0 < k_1 < k_2 \quad \cdots$ the ratio

$$\frac{\sum_1 a_i^2 k_i^2}{\sum_i a_i^2} = k_0^2\,\frac{1 + (\frac{a_1k_1}{a_0k_0})^2 + (\frac{a_2k_2}{a_0k_0})^2 + \cdots}{1 + (\frac{a_1}{a_0})^2 + (\frac{a_2}{a_0})^2 + \cdots} \geq k_0^2$$

which proves Eq. (15-7.6).

An important class of cavities are those which possess rotational symmetry about an axis, such as the cavity shown in Fig. 15-7.1. The resonators used in klystron tubes have shapes approximately like those shown in Fig. 15-7.1. The vector Rayleigh-Ritz method is readily transformed into a form which is particularly

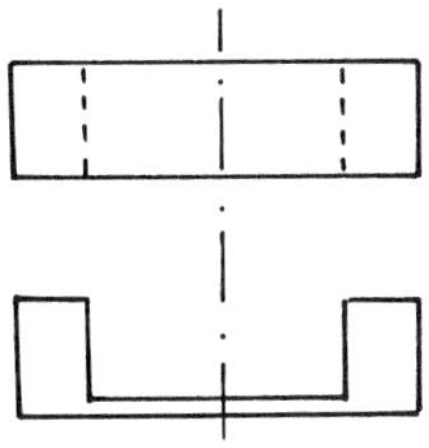

Figure 15-7.1. The approximate form of a klystron cavity.

convenient for such resonators. The transformation is possible because the magnetic vector possess rotational symmetry and has no nodal planes in the ϕ-direction. This suggests a field of the form

$$\overline{B} = \overline{a}_\phi\ f(r,z) \tag{15-7.10}$$

But the wave equation in $\overline{B}$ can be written in terms of three scalar wave equations

$$\nabla^2 B_x + k^2 B_x = 0$$

$$\nabla^2 B_y + k^2 B_y = 0$$

$$\nabla^2 B_z + k^2 B_z = 0$$

However, the Z-component of the magnetic field is zero. The complete solution to the vector wave equation in B will be given in terms of the field components

$$\begin{aligned} B_x &= f(r,z)\cos\phi \\ B_y &= f(r,z)\sin\phi \\ B_z &= 0 \end{aligned} \tag{15-7.11}$$

Consider the X-component of the integral in Eq. (15-7.6). This becomes, for $\overline{A} = \overline{B}$

$$\int_V \overline{A}\cdot\nabla^2\overline{A}\ dV\Big|_x = \int_V (f\cos\phi)\nabla^2(f\cos\phi)dV$$

For the Laplacian in cylindrical coordinates, this becomes

$$\int_V \overline{A}\cdot\nabla^2\overline{A}\ dV\Big|_x = \int \cos^2\phi\ d\phi \iint\left[\frac{1}{r}\frac{\partial}{\partial r}\left(r\frac{\partial f}{\partial r}\right) - \frac{f}{r^2} + \frac{\partial^2 f}{\partial z^2}\right] fr\ dr\ dz$$

A similar expression results when the Y-component is used. Consequently, the resulting form for the Rayleigh-Ritz method becomes

$$k_o^2 \leq \frac{\iint [\frac{1}{r}\frac{\partial}{\partial r}(r\frac{\partial f}{\partial r}) + \frac{\partial^2 f}{\partial z^2} - \frac{f}{r^2}]\ fr\ dr\ dz}{\iint f^2 r\ dr\ dz} \tag{15-7.12}$$

A reasonable question to raise at this point is how one proceeds to select the trial functions since, in general, it is quite possible to find functions of many different types which will satisfy the boundary conditions. Actually there is no general rule for choosing these functions. For the most part, it is necessary to guess solutions and to look for functions which may possess the following qualities: (a) functions that are easy to integrate, (b) functions that satisfy Laplace's equation over most of the region of the resonator, and (c) functions which satisfy the wave equation, but for which the value of k is unknown.

Example 15-7.2. Use the vector Rayleigh-Ritz method to find the upper bound of the lowest eigenvalue k of a cylindrical resonator filled with a homogeneous dielectric (see Sec. 13-7c).

Solution. It is known that for this resonator, the excitation is in the mode for which the field has the form illustrated (see Eq. (13-7.16)). Suppose that the field distribution in the cavity is chosen of the form shown in Fig. 15-7.2c. That is, it is assumed that the fields in the two regions can be described by linear segments

Region I $(r < \alpha)$ $f = r/\alpha$

Region II $(r > \alpha)$ $f = \alpha/r$

where α is an unknown distance that must be determined. It is noted that these two functions satisfy the Laplace equation, thus satisfying one of the guidelines for selecting the field. They also satisfy the boundary conditions. Further, in the two regions it is found that $(1/r)\,\partial/\partial r\,(r\,\partial f/\partial r) - f/r^2$ is zero so that Eq. (15-7.2) becomes zero. This indicates that the contribution to the integral occurs mainly

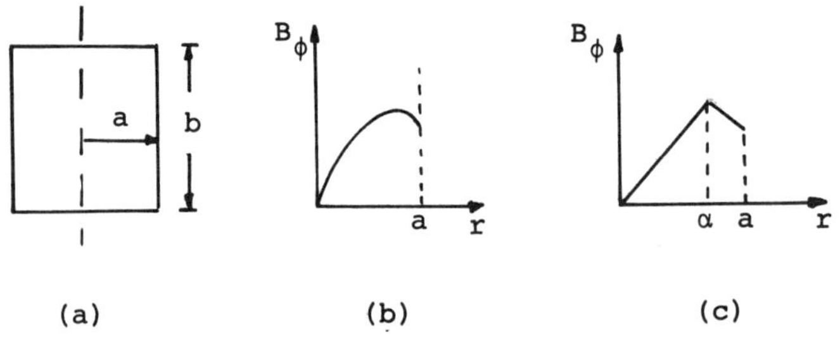

Figure 15-7.2. (a) A cylindrical cavity; (b) The field in a cylindrical cavity; (c) The approximate field distribution.

from a small region in the neighborhood of the discontinuity between regions I and II.

To evaluate the integral in the neighborhood of the discontinuity, it is noted that

$$\int \frac{f}{r}\frac{\partial}{\partial r}\left(r\frac{\partial f}{\partial r}\right)r\,dr \doteq \int \frac{\partial}{\partial r}\left(r\frac{\partial f}{\partial r}\right)dr$$

since r does not vary appreciably in that region. As a result

$$\int_{I-II} \frac{\partial}{\partial r}\left(r\frac{\partial f}{\partial r}\right)dr \doteq r\frac{\partial f}{\partial r}\bigg|_{I}^{II} = -2$$

In addition, it is seen that

$$\int_{I-II} \frac{f}{r^2}\,fr\,dr = \int_{I-II} \frac{f^2}{r}\,dr = -\int_{\alpha+\tau} \frac{f^2}{r}\,dr + \int_{\alpha-\tau} \frac{f^2}{r}\,dr = 0$$

The integral for the rest of the two regions can be evaluated to give

$$\int_0^a f^2 r\,dr = \int_0^{\alpha} \frac{r^3}{\alpha^2}\,dr + \int_{\alpha}^{a} \frac{\alpha^2}{r}\,dr = \frac{\alpha^2}{4} + \alpha^2 \ln\frac{a}{\alpha}$$

It is not necessary to evaluate the simple integral in z because the results appear in both the numerator and in the denominator, and cancel each other. With these results, Eq. (15-7.12) becomes

$$k_o^2 \le \frac{2}{\dfrac{\alpha^2}{4} + \alpha^2 \ln\dfrac{a}{\alpha}}$$

or

$$k_o^2 a^2 \le \frac{2a^2/\alpha^2}{\dfrac{1}{4} + \ln\dfrac{a}{\alpha}} = \frac{2q^2}{\dfrac{1}{4} + \ln q}$$

where $q = a/\alpha$.

The next step is to evaluate the constant α that appears in these equations. Since we are looking for the smallest value of the fraction, a simple procedure is to plot $k_o^2a^2$ versus q. From this plot the minimum value is found to be 6.59 for $k_o^2a^2$. Using this value

$$k_o a = \sqrt{6.59} = 2.57$$

This value is 6.7% higher than the exact value of 2.4048.

ΔΔΔ

REVIEW QUESTIONS

1. What is the difference between functions and functionals?
2. Define the variation of the functional.
3. Do we associate the notion of differentiability to functionals?
4. What is the difference of continuity in functions and continuity in functionals.
5. What is the necessary condition for a functional to have an extremum along a curve?
6. Write Euler's equation in one dependent variable.
7. What is the physical interpretation of the integral

$$\delta \int_{t_o}^{t_o+\tau} (T-V)dt = \delta \int_{t_o}^{t_o+\tau} L\, dt = 0$$

7. What is the relation between the Lagrangian function and the Lagrangian density?
8. Name some approximate methods for boundary value problems.
9. If an operator A is positive definite, what type of solution does the equation $Au = f$ have?
10. What is the relation between the functions which solve the equation $Au = f$ ($A \equiv$ positive definite) and those that extremize the functional $I[u] = \int_V [uAu - 2uf]dV$?
11. Is the equation $d^2\Phi/dx^2 = -\rho(x)/\varepsilon$ with its boundary conditions $\Phi(0) = \Phi(1) = 0$ a Sturm-Liouville equation?
12. When does one use the method of the extended operator?
13. Does the ration $\int_V (\nabla\Phi)^2 dV / \int_V \Phi^2 dV$ yield the upper or the lower bound of the lowest eigenvalue?

PROBLEMS

15-3.1. Verify Eq. (15-3.22) and show that the same equation is obtained using Snell's law for finely stratified mediums.
[Hint: $\sin\theta_1/u_1 = \sin\theta_2/u_2 = \text{const.}$]

15-3.2. Find the differential equations which are the result of extremizing the functional (two dependent variables)

$$I[x_1,x_2] = \int_a^b (2x_1x_2 - 2x_1^2 - \dot{x}_1^2 - \dot{x}_2^2)dt$$

[Ans: $x_2 - 2x_1 - \ddot{x}_1 = 0$; $x_1 + \ddot{x}_2 = 0$]

15-3.3. Find the minimum distance from a plane $ax_1 + bx_2 + cx_3 + d = 0$ to the origin. [Ans: $d/\sqrt{a^2+b^2+c^2}$]

15-4.1. Show that the equation that is obtained by using Eq. (15-4.6) is the Poisson equation $\nabla^2\Phi = -\rho/\varepsilon_o$.

15-4.2. Verify Eq. (15-4.9).

15-4.3. Verify Eq. (15-4.12).

15-4.4. Use the same procedure as in Example 15-4.4 to find that Eq. (8-4.5) is satisfied by a rectangular diaphragm.

15-4.5. Verify Eq. (15-4.19).

15-4.6. Find the Lagrangian density as a function of the acoustic potential, Eq. (8-5.18), and show that it satisfies the equation

$$\frac{\partial^2\Phi_a}{\partial x^2} = \frac{1}{c_a^2}\frac{\partial^2\Phi_a}{\partial t^2}$$

15-5.1. Find the third order solution for the case given in Ex. 15-5.2 and compare its numerical values $0 \leq x \leq 1$ with the exact solution.

15-5.2. Find the values of a_1 and a_2 for Ex. 15-5.4 and write the first order solution.

15-5.3. Use the collocation method for Ex. 15-5.4 and compare the values found from Probs. 15-5.2 and 15-5.3 at the point (1,1.5).

15-5.4. Find the first and third order solutions for the case given in Ex. 15-5.4.

15-5.5. Find the temperature along a linear rod, given $K = 1$, $\rho(x) = x + x^3$ $\Phi(0) = 10$ and $\Phi(2) = 15$ [see Eq. (2-6.2)].

15-5.6. Find the charge distribution on a wire segment having the shape shown in Fig. P15-5.6; given L = 2 m, a = radius = 1 mm, V = 10 Volt, and N = elements = 6.

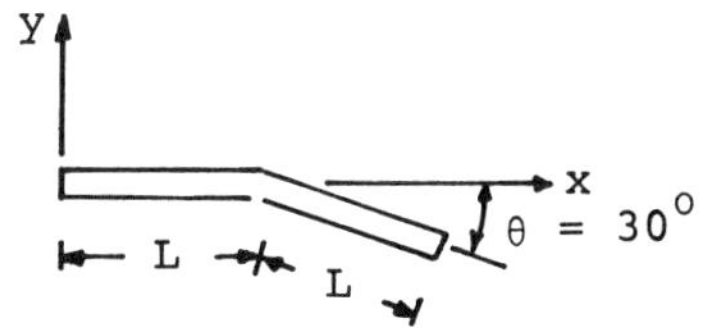

Figure P15-5.6.

15-5.7. Find the charge distribution and capacitance of a charged conducting plate; given: $2L \times 2L = 4\ m^2$, V = 10 Volt, and M = N = number of elements = 6×6.

15-6.1. Find approximate values for the eigenvalues of a short-circuited lossless transmission line, using a third order expansion. Compare the approximate with the exact eigenfunctions by plotting them.
[Ans: $\lambda_i = (i\pi)^2$ $i = 1,2,3,\ldots$ are the exact values]

15-6.2. Find the approximate eigenvalues for an open-ended transmission line: (b) for a clamped string.

15-6.3. Deduce the approximate eigenvalue for a circular clamped membrane of radius $a = 1$.
[Ans: Exact value $\lambda_c = 5.7832$]

15-7.1. Verify Eq. (15-7.3).

15-7.2. Determine the resonant frequency for the TM_{010} mode in a cylindrical cavity using the following trial fields: (a) $\bar{E} = \bar{a}_z(1 - \rho/a)$:
(b) $\bar{E} = \bar{a}_z(1 - \rho^2/a^2)$
[Ans: Exact value $\omega_r^2 = 5.78306/\mu\varepsilon a^2$)]

APPENDIX I

VECTOR ANALYSIS

A. Vector Algebra

I-1. Vectors and Two Vector Operations

Vectors are represented geometrically by means of straight lines with arrow heads, the arrow pointing in the direction of the vector, the length being proportional to its magnitude. They are represented in our work by letters with bars above them.

The sum of two vectors $\bar{A}$ and $\bar{B}$ is another vector $\bar{C}$, where

$$\bar{C} = \bar{A} + \bar{B} \tag{I-1.1}$$

as shown in Fig. I-1.1.

Since $\bar{C}$ is the diagonal of the parallelogram, the commutative law applies to vectors, and

$$\bar{A} + \bar{B} = \bar{B} + \bar{A} \tag{I-1.2}$$

In addition, the associative law also applies, and we have

$$(\bar{A}+\bar{B}) + \bar{C} = \bar{A} + (\bar{B}+\bar{C}) \tag{I-1.3}$$

Referring to Fig. I-1.1, we see that we can express the vector $\bar{A}$ in terms of the sum of three vectors parallel to the rectangular (orthogonal) axes,

$$\bar{A} = \bar{a}_x A_x + \bar{a}_y A_y + \bar{a}_z A_z \tag{I-1.4}$$

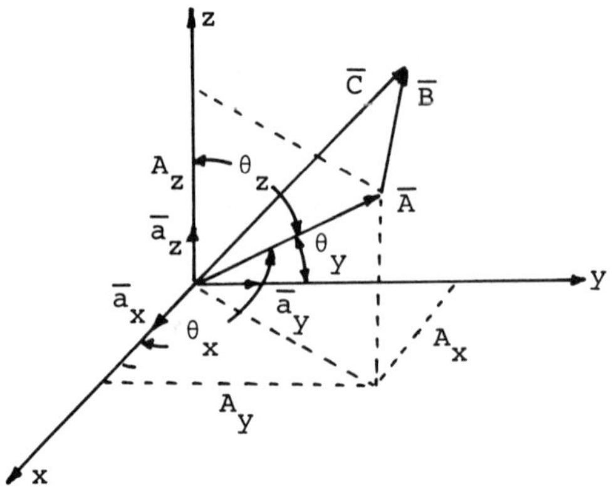

Figure I-1.1. The addition of vectors.

where $\bar{a}_x$, $\bar{a}_y$, $\bar{a}_z$ are unit vectors in the X,Y,Z direction, respectively. In this expression there appears the product of a vector and a scalar. Such a product is defined as a vector having a magnitude equal to the product of the scalar and the magnitude of the vector (unity in this case), and having a direction that is the direction of the original vector. The scalars A_x, A_y, A_z are the components of $\bar{A}$ and are given by

$$\begin{aligned} A_x &= A \cos \theta_x \\ A_y &= A \cos \theta_y \\ A_z &= A \cos \theta_z \end{aligned} \tag{I-1.5}$$

where θ_x, θ_y, θ_z are the angles between $\bar{A}$ and the positive directions of the axis, where A is the magnitude of $\bar{A}$ (see Fig. I-1.1).

To find the vector sum of two vectors $\bar{A}$ and $\bar{B}$ requires that each vector be referred to the same set of axes. Thus for two vectors having the three components

$$\bar{A} + \bar{B} = (A_x\bar{a}_x + A_y\bar{a}_y + A_z\bar{a}_z) + (B_x\bar{a}_x + B_y\bar{a}_y + B_z\bar{a}_z)$$

or (I-1.6)

$$\bar{A} + \bar{B} = (A_x + B_x)\bar{a}_x + (A_y + B_y)\bar{a}_y + (A_z + B_z)\bar{a}_z$$

This equation follows directly from the associative property of vector addition, as in Eq. (I-1.3).

Consider now the product of two vectors. There are two types of product, the *scalar* product and the *vector* product. These names serve to indicate that the result of the respective multiplication in the first case is a scalar and in the second case is a vector. Other operations such as a scalar product of a vector with the vector product of two other vectors may also be formed.

By definition, the scalar or *dot* product of two vectors $\bar{A}$ and $\bar{B}$ is a scalar quantity and is the product of the magnitudes of the vectors and the cosine of the angle between them, thus

$$\bar{A} \cdot \bar{B} = AB \cos(\bar{A},\bar{B}) = \bar{B} \cdot \bar{A} \qquad \text{(I-1.7)}$$

From this we have the following

$$\bar{A} \cdot \bar{A} = A^2$$

and

$$\bar{A} \cdot \bar{B} = 0$$

if $\bar{A}$ is perpendicular to $\bar{B}$. The scalar product of $\bar{A}$ and $\bar{B}$ given by Eq. (I-1.7) may be expressed in terms of their rectangular components, thus

$$\begin{aligned}\bar{A} \cdot \bar{B} &= (A_x\bar{a}_x + A_y\bar{a}_y + A_z\bar{a}_z) \cdot (B_x\bar{a}_x + B_y\bar{a}_y + B_z\bar{a}_z) \\ &= A_xB_x + A_yB_y + A_zB_z \qquad \text{(I-1.8)}\end{aligned}$$

since

$$\bar{a}_x \cdot \bar{a}_x = \bar{a}_y \cdot \bar{a}_y = \bar{a}_z \cdot \bar{a}_z = 1; \quad \bar{a}_x \cdot \bar{a}_y = \bar{a}_y \cdot \bar{a}_z = \bar{a}_z \cdot \bar{a}_x = 0$$

The vector or *cross* product of two vectors is quite different from the dot product of two vectors. By definition, the cross product of two vectors $\bar{A}$ and $\bar{B}$ is a new vector the magnitude of which is the product of the magnitudes of the two vectors and the sine of the angle between them; the direction of the resultant vector is normal to the plane of the two vectors and in the direction of advance of a right-handed screw which is turned from the first vector to the second. The situation is shown in Fig. I-1.2. By definition, therefore

$$\bar{A} \times \bar{B} = AB \sin(\bar{A},\bar{B})\, \bar{n} \qquad \text{(I-1.9)}$$

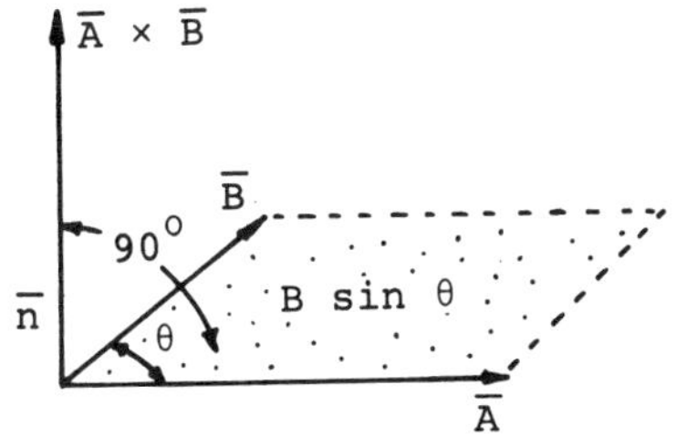

Figure I-1.2. The vector product $\bar{A} \times \bar{B}$.

where $\overline{n}$ is a unit vector which is obtained as specified in the definition. It is of some interest to note that the cross product specifies the cross-hatched area shown in Fig. I-1.2, the direction of the area being specified by the unit vector $\overline{n}$. Another fact of importance follows by considering the vector product $\overline{B} \times \overline{A}$, which is the cross product of the two vectors in reverse order. From the definition, the magnitude is the same as before, but the direction of the area is opposite to that above; hence

$$\overline{A} \times \overline{B} = -\overline{B} \times \overline{A} \qquad \text{(I-1.10)}$$

This shows that the vector product of two vectors is *not* commutative. Clearly, the vector product of a vector with itself or with a parallel vector is zero, since the angle between the two vectors is zero, and the sine of the angle is therefore zero.

Example I-1.1. Find the cross product of two vectors in rectangular coordinates.

Solution. Since the following relations obviously apply

$$\overline{a}_x \times \overline{a}_x = \overline{a}_y \times \overline{a}_y = \overline{a}_z \times \overline{a}_z = 0$$

$$\overline{a}_x \times \overline{a}_y = \overline{a}_z \qquad \overline{a}_y \times \overline{a}_z = \overline{a}_x \qquad \overline{a}_z \times \overline{a}_x = \overline{a}_y$$

it is easily found that

$$\overline{A} \times \overline{B} = \overline{a}_x(A_yB_z-A_zB_y) + \overline{a}_y(A_zB_x-A_xB_z) + \overline{a}_z(A_xB_y-A_yB_x) \qquad \text{(I-1.11)}$$

This result is often written in determinant form

$$\overline{A} \times \overline{B} = \begin{vmatrix} \overline{a}_x & \overline{a}_y & \overline{a}_z \\ A_x & A_y & A_z \\ B_x & B_y & B_z \end{vmatrix} \qquad \text{(I-1.12)}$$

I-2. Vector Identities

A number of useful vector identities are included for general reference.

$$\overline{A} \cdot (\overline{B}\times\overline{C}) = \overline{B} \cdot (\overline{C}\times\overline{A}) = \overline{C} \cdot (\overline{A}\times\overline{B})$$

$$\overline{A} \times (\overline{B}\times\overline{C}) = \overline{B}(\overline{A}\cdot\overline{C}) - \overline{C}(\overline{A}\cdot\overline{B})$$

$$(\overline{A}\times\overline{B}) \cdot (\overline{C}\times\overline{D}) = (\overline{A}\cdot\overline{C})(\overline{B}\cdot\overline{D}) - (\overline{B}\cdot\overline{C})(\overline{A}\cdot\overline{D})$$

$$(\overline{A}\times\overline{B}) \times (\overline{C}\times\overline{D}) = (\overline{A}\times\overline{B}\cdot\overline{D})\overline{C} - (\overline{A}\times\overline{B}\cdot\overline{C})\overline{D}$$

$$\nabla(\Phi_1+\Phi_2) = \nabla\Phi_1 + \nabla\Phi_2$$

$$\nabla(\Phi_1\Phi_2) = \Phi_1\nabla\Phi_2 + \Phi_2\nabla\Phi_1$$

$$\nabla(\overline{A}\cdot\overline{B}) = (\overline{A}\cdot\nabla)\overline{B} + (\overline{B}\cdot\nabla)\overline{A} + \overline{A} \times (\nabla\times\overline{B}) + \overline{B} \times (\nabla\times\overline{A})$$

$$\nabla \cdot (\overline{A}+\overline{B}) = \nabla \cdot \overline{A} + \nabla \cdot \overline{B}$$

$$\nabla \cdot (\Phi\overline{A}) = \overline{A} \cdot \nabla\Phi + \Phi\nabla \cdot \overline{A}$$

$$\nabla \cdot (\overline{A}\times\overline{B}) = \overline{B} \cdot \nabla \times \overline{A} - \overline{A} \cdot \nabla \times \overline{B}$$

$$\nabla \cdot \nabla \times \overline{A} = 0$$

$$\nabla \cdot \nabla\Phi = \nabla^2\Phi$$

$$\nabla \times (\overline{A}+\overline{B}) = \nabla \times \overline{A} + \nabla \times \overline{B}$$

$$\nabla \times (\Phi\overline{A}) = \nabla\Phi \times \overline{A} + \Phi\nabla \times \overline{A}$$

$$\nabla \times (\overline{A}\times\overline{B}) = \overline{A}\nabla \cdot \overline{B} - \overline{B}\nabla \cdot \overline{A} + (\overline{B}\cdot\nabla)\overline{A} - (\overline{A}\cdot\nabla)\overline{B}$$

$$\nabla \times (\nabla\times\overline{A}) = \nabla(\nabla\cdot\overline{A}) - \nabla^2\overline{A}$$

$$(\nabla\times\overline{A}) \cdot (\nabla\times\overline{B}) = \nabla \cdot (\overline{B}\times\nabla\times\overline{A}) + \overline{B} \cdot (\nabla\times\nabla\times\overline{A})$$

$$\nabla \times \nabla\Phi = 0$$

$$\nabla \cdot \overline{r} = 3$$

$$\nabla \times \overline{r} = 0$$

$$\nabla r = \overline{r}/r$$

$$\nabla(1/r) = -\overline{r}/r^3$$

$$\int_V \nabla\Phi dV = \int_S \Phi\, \overline{n}\, dS$$

$$\int_V \nabla \cdot \overline{A} dV = \oint_S \overline{A} \cdot \overline{n}\, dS$$

$$\int_V \nabla \times \overline{A}\, dV = \oint_S \overline{n} \times \overline{A}\, dS$$

$$\int_S \overline{n} \times \nabla\Phi\, dS = \oint_C \Phi d\overline{\ell}$$

$$\int_S \nabla \times \overline{A} \cdot \overline{n}\, dS = \int_C \overline{A} \cdot d\overline{\ell}$$

B. Coordinate Systems: Vector Identities

Because of particular symmetries in physical problems, it is often convenient to use coordinate systems other than the rectangular system. Of particular interest are the cylindrical and the spherical coordinate systems. We shall, therefore, establish important relations among these three coordinate systems. In addition, a set of vector identities is also included in this appendix.

I-3. Transformation of Vectors Among Coordinate Systems

It is sometimes desirable to transform a vector field from one coordinate system to another. To illustrate the procedure, we shall consider the transformation of a vector from cartesian coordinates to spherical coordinates. Refer to Fig. I-3.1 which shows a vector $\overline{A}$ in a cartesian and spherical system of coordinates. A given vector $\overline{A}$ in the two systems is written respectively by

$$\overline{A} = A_x\overline{a}_x + A_y\overline{a}_y + A_z\overline{a}_z \tag{I-3.1}$$

$$\overline{A} = A_r\overline{a}_r + A_\theta\overline{a}_\theta + A_\phi\overline{a}_\phi \tag{I-3.2}$$

To change the independent variables, we first consider the end point of the vector $\overline{A}$ which, in rectangular coordinates, is specified by (x,y,z) or equivalently, we can say that $A_x = x$, $A_y = y$, and $A_z = z$. In the spherical system for the same point we find from Fig. I-3.1b the following relations

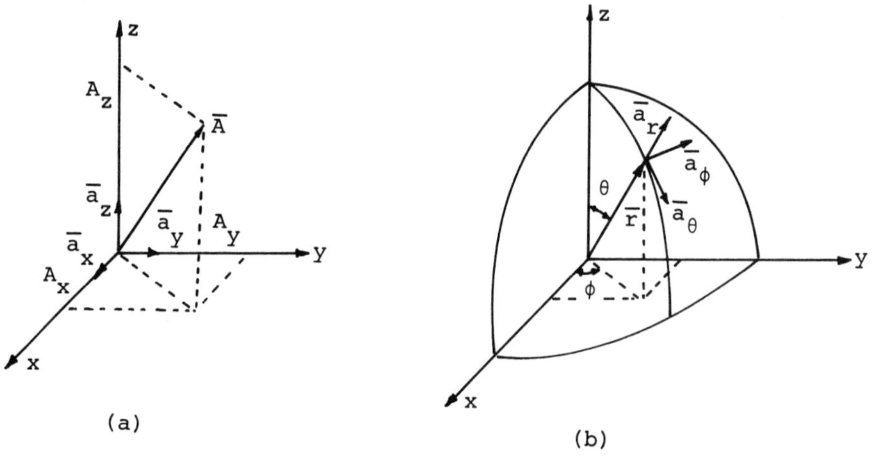

Figure I-3.1. Cartesian and spherical coordinate systems.

$$x = r \sin\theta \cos\phi$$
$$y = r \sin\theta \sin\phi \qquad \text{(I-3.3)}$$
$$z = r \cos\theta$$

Conversely, we can solve these three equations for the unknowns r, θ, φ to yield a set of relations which change the spherical coordinates to cartesian coordinates. These are

$$r = \sqrt{x^2 + y^2 + z^2}$$
$$\theta = \cos^{-1} \frac{z}{\sqrt{x^2 + y^2 + z^2}} \qquad \text{(I-3.4)}$$
$$\phi = \tan^{-1} \frac{y}{x}$$

Suppose that we now effect the scalar multiplication of Eqs. (I-3.1) and (I-3.2) with $\bar{a}_r$, $\bar{a}_\theta$, and $\bar{a}_\phi$. We obtain the following identities

$$A_r = A_x\bar{a}_x\cdot\bar{a}_r + A_y\bar{a}_y\cdot\bar{a}_r + A_z\bar{a}_z\cdot\bar{a}_r$$
$$A_\theta = A_x\bar{a}_x\cdot\bar{a}_\theta + A_y\bar{a}_y\cdot\bar{a}_\theta + A_z\bar{a}_z\cdot\bar{a}_\theta \qquad \text{(I-3.5)}$$
$$A_\phi = A_x\bar{a}_x\cdot\bar{a}_\phi + A_y\bar{a}_y\cdot\bar{a}_\phi + A_z\bar{a}_z\cdot\bar{a}_\phi$$

The requisite scalar products are easily found from Fig. I-3.1, and are

$$\bar{a}_x\cdot\bar{a}_r = \sin\theta\cos\phi; \quad \bar{a}_y\cdot\bar{a}_r = \sin\theta\sin\phi; \quad \bar{a}_z\cdot\bar{a}_r = \cos\theta$$
$$\bar{a}_x\cdot\bar{a}_\theta = \cos\theta\cos\phi; \quad \bar{a}_y\cdot\bar{a}_\theta = \cos\theta\sin\phi; \quad \bar{a}_z\cdot\bar{a}_\theta = -\sin\theta \qquad \text{(I-3.6)}$$
$$\bar{a}_x\cdot\bar{a}_\phi = -\sin\phi \quad ; \quad \bar{a}_y\cdot\bar{a}_\phi = \cos\phi \quad ; \quad \bar{a}_z\cdot\bar{a}_\phi = 0$$

Example I-3.1. Represent the vector field $\bar{E} = (x+1)\bar{a}_x + \bar{a}_y + y\bar{a}_z$ in spherical coordinates.

Solution. This problem is a special adaptation of the relationships above, with $A_x = x+1$, $A_y = 1$ and $A_z = y$. Using Eqs. (I-3.3), (I-3.5) and (I-3.6) we obtain

$$\begin{aligned}\bar{A} = {} & [(r \sin\theta \cos\phi+1)\sin\theta\cos\phi + \sin\theta\sin\phi + r \sin\theta\sin\phi\cos\theta]\bar{a}_r \\ & + [(r \sin\theta\cos\phi+1)\cos\theta\cos\phi + \cos\theta\sin\phi - r \sin\theta\sin\phi\sin\theta]\bar{a}_\theta \qquad \text{(I-3.7)} \\ & + [-(r \sin\theta\cos\phi+1)\sin\phi + \cos\phi]\bar{a}_\phi\end{aligned}$$

Table I-3.1. Transformation of Variables

Cartesian to Cylindrical	Cylindrical to Cartesian
$x = r\cos\phi$	$r = (x^2 + y^2)^{1/2}$
$y = r\sin\phi$	$\phi = \tan^{-1} y/x$
$z = z$	$z = z$
$A_r = A_x\cos\phi + A_y\sin\phi$	$A_x = A_r \frac{x}{(x^2+y^2)^{1/2}} - A_\phi \frac{y}{(x^2+y^2)^{1/2}}$
$A_\phi = -A_x\sin\phi + A_y\cos\phi$	$A_y = A_r \frac{y}{(x^2+y^2)^{1/2}} + A_\phi \frac{x}{(x^2+y^2)^{1/2}}$
$A_z = A_z$	$A_z = A_z$
Cartesian to Spherical	**Spherical to Cartesian**
$x = r\sin\theta\cos\phi$	$r = (x^2+y^2+z^2)^{1/2}$
$y = r\sin\theta\sin\phi$	$\theta = \cos^{-1}\frac{z}{(x^2+y^2+z^2)^{1/2}}$
$z = r\cos\theta$	$\phi = \tan^{-1} y/x$
$A_r = A_x\sin\theta\cos\phi + A_y\sin\theta\sin\phi + A_z\cos\theta$	$A_x = A_r\frac{x}{(x^2+y^2+z^2)^{1/2}} + A_\theta\frac{xz}{[(x^2+y^2)(x^2+y^2+z^2)]^{1/2}} - A_\phi\frac{y}{(x^2+y^2)^{1/2}}$
$A_\theta = A_x\cos\theta\cos\phi + A_y\cos\theta\sin\phi - A_z\sin\theta$	$A_y = A_r\frac{y}{(x^2+y^2+z^2)^{1/2}} + A_\theta\frac{yz}{[(x^2+y^2)(x^2+y^2+z^2)]^{1/2}} + A_\phi\frac{x}{(x^2+y^2)^{1/2}}$
$A_\phi = -A_x\sin\phi + A_y\cos\phi$	$A_z = A_r\frac{z}{(x^2+y^2+z^2)^{1/2}} - A_\theta\frac{(x^2+y^2)^{1/2}}{(x^2+y^2+z^2)^{1/2}}$

Proceeding as above, we can relate the cartesian and the cylindrical system of coordinates, which is shown in Fig. I-3.2. Table I-3.1 gives the transformation of vectors among the cartesian and the other two polar coordinate systems.

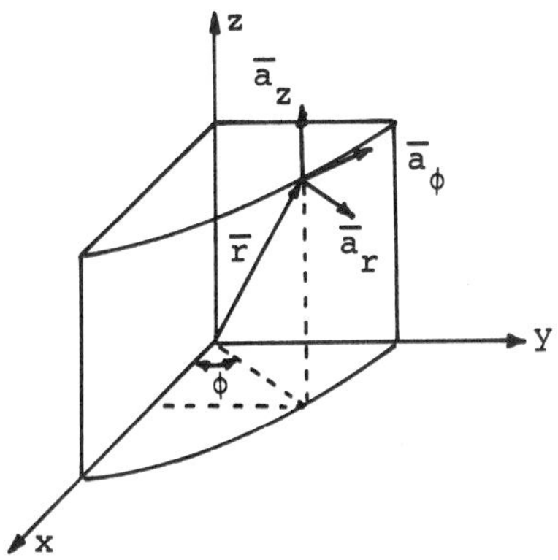

Figure I-3.2. Cylindrical coordinate system.

I-4. Transformation in Curvilinear Coordinates

In this section we develop the form of the operators ∇, $\nabla\cdot$, $\nabla\times$ and ∇^2 in general curvilinear coordinates and from these we shall express the results in rectangular, cylindrical and spherical coordinates. We note that when an incremental change occurs in the cartesian system of coordinate variables, it is proportional to a magnitude of the spatial coordinate. This property does not exist generally in other orthogonal systems. For example, an incremental change $d\phi$ in the cylindrical variable ϕ, is an angle, it is not a distance. However, $r d\phi$ is the magnitude of the displacement. This suggests that it may be necessary to multiply the increment of a coordinate variable by a factor which itself may be a function of all three variables. This fact will become evident in considering the general orthogonal curvilinear coordinates.

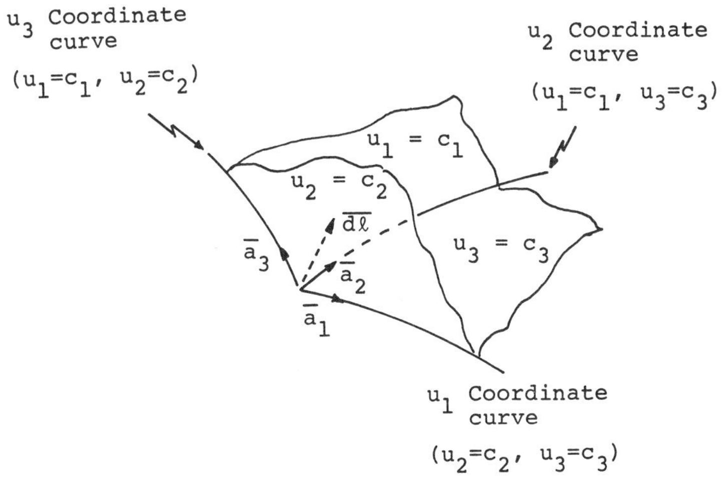

Figure I-4.1. The orthogonal curvilinear coordinate system.

Refer to Fig. I-4.1 which illustrates the orthogonal curvilinear coordinates. Here u_1, u_2 and u_3 are three orthogonal coordinates, and $u_1 = c_1$, $u_2 = c_2$ and $u_3 = c_3$ are three coordinate surfaces which intersect each other normally, as shown. The coordinates of the incremental length $d\bar{\ell}$ along the three unit vectors $\bar{a}_1$, $\bar{a}_2$ and $\bar{a}_3$ can be written

$$\begin{aligned} d\bar{\ell}_1 &= \bar{a}_1 h_1(u_1u_2u_3)du_1 \\ d\bar{\ell}_2 &= \bar{a}_2 h_2(u_1u_2u_3)du_2 \\ d\bar{\ell}_3 &= \bar{a}_3 h_3(u_1u_2u_3)du_3 \end{aligned} \tag{I-4.1}$$

where h_i (for i = 1,2,3) is the transformation parameter which relates the change in the coordinate u_i to the real displacement in the direction of increasing u_i. The length of $d\bar{\ell}$ is easily found to be

$$|d\bar{\ell}|^2 = d\bar{\ell}\cdot d\bar{\ell} = (h_1du_1)^2 + (h_2du_2)^2 + (h_3du_3)^2 \tag{I-4.2}$$

Further, the three elemental surfaces and volume are given by

$$\begin{aligned} d\bar{S}_1 &= h_2h_3du_2du_3\bar{a}_1 \\ d\bar{S}_2 &= h_1h_3du_1du_3\bar{a}_2 \\ d\bar{S}_3 &= h_1h_2du_1du_2\bar{a}_3 \\ dV &= h_1h_2h_3du_1du_2du_3 \end{aligned} \tag{I-4.3}$$

To find the exact values for the h's for specific orthogonal coordinate systems, we must refer to the detailed configuration. Refer to Fig. I-4.2 for the cylindrical and spherical coordinate systems.

The length $d\bar{\ell}$ in cylindrical coordinates is given by

$$|d\bar{\ell}|^2 = d\bar{\ell}\cdot d\bar{\ell} = (dr)^2 + (rd\phi)^2 + (dz)^2$$

which, by comparison with Eq. (I-2.2) shows that

$$h_1 = 1 \qquad h_2 = r \qquad h_3 = 1 \tag{I-4.4}$$

In addition for the cylindrical coordinate system, the $\bar{a}_i$'s and the u_i's are respectively

$$\bar{a}_1 = \bar{a}_r,\ \bar{a}_2 = \bar{a}_\phi,\ \bar{a}_3 = \bar{a}_z; \qquad u_1 = r,\ u_2 = \phi,\ u_3 = z \tag{I-4.5}$$

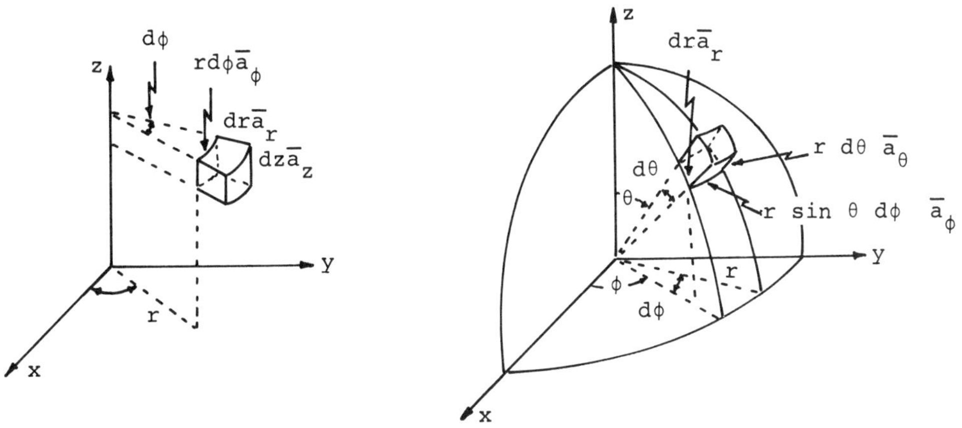

Figure I-4.2. Illustrating the elemental lengths in cylindrical and in spherical coordinates.

The various relations for the cylindrical and spherical coordinate systems are given in Table I-4.1.

Table I-4.1. Coordinate Transformations

Cylindrical Coordinates		Spherical Coordinates	
$x = r\cos\phi$	$r = u_1$	$x = r\cos\theta\cos\phi$	$r = u_1$
$y = r\sin\phi$	$\phi = u_2$	$y = r\cos\theta\sin\phi$	$\theta = u_2$
$z = z$	$z = u_3$	$z = r\sin\theta$	$\phi = u_3$
$d\bar{\ell}_1 = d\bar{\ell}_r = \bar{a}_r dr$		$d\bar{\ell}_1 = d\bar{\ell}_r = \bar{a}_r dr$	
$d\bar{\ell}_2 = d\bar{\ell}_\phi = \bar{a}_\phi r d\phi$		$d\bar{\ell}_2 = d\bar{\ell}_\theta = \bar{a}_\theta r d\theta$	
$d\bar{\ell}_3 = d\bar{\ell}_z = \bar{a}_z dz$		$d\bar{\ell}_3 = d\bar{\ell}_\phi = \bar{a}_\phi r\sin\theta\, d\phi$	
$h_1 = 1,\ h_2 = r,\ h_3 = 1$		$h_1 = 1,\ h_2 = r,\ h_3 = r\sin\theta$	
$d\bar{S}_1 = d\bar{S}_r = \bar{a}_r\, r d\phi\, dz$		$d\bar{S}_1 = d\bar{S}_r = \bar{a}_r\, r^2\sin\theta\, d\theta d\phi$	
$d\bar{S}_2 = dS_\phi = \bar{a}_\phi\, dr dz$		$d\bar{S}_2 = d\bar{S}_\theta = \bar{a}_\theta\, r\sin\theta\, dr d\phi$	
$d\bar{S}_3 = dS_z = \bar{a}_z\, r dr d\phi$		$d\bar{S}_3 = d\bar{S}_\phi = \bar{a}_\phi\, r d\theta d\phi$	
$dV = r dr d\phi\, dz$		$dV = r^2\sin\theta\, dr d\theta d\phi$	

a. Gradient. To find the greatest rate of change of a function Φ along the direction of the $\bar{a}_i$'s we must write

$$\nabla\Phi = \frac{\partial\Phi}{\partial\ell_1}\bar{a}_1 + \frac{\partial\Phi}{\partial\ell_2}\bar{a}_2 + \frac{\partial\Phi}{\partial\ell_3}\bar{a}_3$$
$$= \frac{\partial\Phi}{\partial u_1}\frac{\partial u_1}{\partial\ell_1}\bar{a}_1 + \frac{\partial\Phi}{\partial u_2}\frac{\partial u_2}{\partial\ell_2}\bar{a}_2 + \frac{\partial\Phi}{\partial u_3}\frac{\partial u_3}{\partial\ell_3}\bar{a}_3 \tag{I-4.6}$$

We substitute the values for the $du_i/d\ell_i$ from Eq. (I-4.1) from which we obtain

$$\nabla\Phi = \frac{1}{h_1}\frac{\partial\Phi}{\partial u_1}\bar{a}_1 + \frac{1}{h_2}\frac{\partial\Phi}{\partial u_2}\bar{a}_2 + \frac{1}{h_3}\frac{\partial\Phi}{\partial u_3}\bar{a}_3 \tag{I-4.7}$$

To write the gradient in cylindrical and spherical coordinates, we combine this equation with the appropriate results from Table I-4.1. The results are

rectangular $$\nabla\Phi = \frac{\partial\Phi}{\partial x}\bar{a}_x + \frac{\partial\Phi}{\partial y}\bar{a}_y + \frac{\partial\Phi}{\partial z}\bar{a}_z \tag{I-4.8a}$$

cylindrical $$\nabla\Phi = \frac{\partial\Phi}{\partial r}\bar{a}_r + \frac{1}{r}\frac{\partial\Phi}{\partial\phi}\bar{a}_\phi + \frac{\partial\Phi}{\partial z}\bar{a}_z \tag{I-4.8}$$

spherical $$\nabla\Phi = \frac{\partial\Phi}{\partial r}\bar{a}_r + \frac{1}{r}\frac{\partial\Phi}{\partial\theta}\bar{a}_\theta + \frac{1}{r\sin\theta}\frac{\partial\Phi}{\partial\phi}\bar{a}_\phi \tag{I-4.9}$$

b. Divergence. To derive the divergence of a vector field $\bar{F}$ in general curvilinear coordinates, we express it in its generalized form by writing

$$\bar{F}(u_1,u_2,u_3) = \bar{a}_1F_1(u_1,u_2,u_3) + \bar{a}_2F_2(u_1,u_2,u_3) + \bar{a}_3F_3(u_1,u_2,u_3) \tag{I-4.10}$$

Physically, as discussed in Chap. 2 the divergence of a vector field is a measure of the net outflow per unit volume of the flux of the vector as the incremental volume approaches zero. Refer to Fig. I-4.3 which shows an elementary volume. We observe that the flux of the vector field at the mid-point between the two surfaces is given by

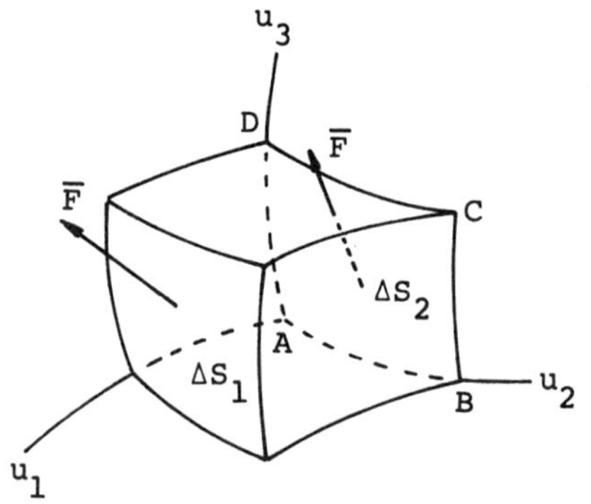

Figure I-4.3. To determine the divergence in curvilinear coordinates.

$$F_1(u_1,u_2,u_3)h_2h_3du_2du_3$$

The value of the function at the surfaces ΔS_2 can be determined using a Taylor expansion, which, to first order is

$$\text{Flux } \Delta S_2 = F_1(u_1,u_2,u_3)h_2h_3du_2du_3 + \frac{1}{2}\frac{\partial}{\partial u_1}[F_1(u_1,u_2,u_3)h_2h_3]du_1du_2du_3$$

where the factors h_2 and h_3 have been incorporated inside the derivative sign because they are functions of the u_i's. Correspondingly, the flux through the surfac ΔS_1 is given by

$$\text{Flux } \Delta S_1 = -[F_1(u_1,u_2,u_3)h_2h_3du_2du_3 - \frac{1}{2}\frac{\partial}{\partial u_1}(F_1(u_1,u_2,u_3)h_2h_3)du_1du_2du_3]$$

Adding the last two equations gives us the net flux through the surfaces ΔS_1 and ΔS_2, namely

$$\text{Net Flux} = \frac{\partial}{\partial u_1}(F_1h_2h_3)du_1du_2du_3$$

We can proceed in an identical manner to find the contribution to the net flux from the two additional pairs of faces. The total net flux is then

$$\text{Total net flux} = [\frac{\partial}{\partial u_1}(F_1h_2h_3) + \frac{\partial}{\partial u_2}(F_2h_1h_3) + \frac{\partial}{\partial u_3}(F_3h_1h_2)]du_1du_2du_3$$

Using the definition of divergence (see Chap. 2) we thus find that in generalized coordinates

$$\nabla \cdot \bar{F} = \lim_{\Delta V \to 0} \frac{\oint \bar{F} \cdot d\bar{S}}{\Delta V} = \frac{1}{h_1h_2h_3}[\frac{\partial}{\partial u_1}(h_2h_3F_1) + \frac{\partial}{\partial u_2}(h_1h_3F_2) + \frac{\partial}{\partial u_3}(h_1h_2F_3)] \quad \text{(I-4.12)}$$

For the specific case of cylindrical and spherical coordinates, the divergence assumes the form

rectangular $$\nabla \cdot \bar{F} = \frac{\partial F_x}{\partial x} + \frac{\partial F_y}{\partial y} + \frac{\partial F_z}{\partial z} \quad \text{(I-4.13a)}$$

cylindrical $$\nabla \cdot \bar{F} = \frac{1}{r}\frac{\partial}{\partial r}(rF_r) + \frac{1}{r}\frac{\partial F_\phi}{\partial \phi} + \frac{\partial F_z}{\partial z} \quad \text{(I-4.13)}$$

spherical $$\nabla \cdot \bar{F} = \frac{1}{r^2}\frac{\partial}{\partial r}(r^2F_r) + \frac{1}{r \sin\theta}(F_\theta \sin\theta) + \frac{1}{r \sin\theta}\frac{\partial F_\phi}{\partial \phi} \quad \text{(I-4.14)}$$

c. The Curl. The component of curl $\overline{F}$ in the u_1 direction is (see Eq. (2-2.1))

$$(\nabla \times \overline{F}_i) = \lim_{\Delta S_i = 0} \frac{\oint \overline{F} \cdot d\overline{\ }}{\Delta S_i} \tag{I-4.15}$$

If we choose the point (u_1,u_2,u_3) at the center of the contour in Fig. I-4.3 labeled ABCD then the components of the field can be expanded in Taylor series about that point. The contributions from the paths AB and CD are

$$\int_A^B F_2 d\ell_2 + \int_C^D F_2 d\ell_2 = \int_A^B F_2 h_2 du_2 + \int_C^D F_2 h_2 du_2$$

$$= [F_2h_2 - \frac{\partial(F_2h_2)}{\partial u_3}\frac{du_3}{2}]\, du_2 - [F_2h_2 + \frac{\partial(F_2h_2)}{\partial u_3}\frac{du_3}{2}]du_2 = - \frac{\partial(F_2h_2)}{\partial\partial u_3}\, du_2du_3$$

where the minus sign in the second parenthesis takes into consideration that the line integration carries a directional sense. Similarly, the contributions from the paths DA and BC is $(\partial/\partial u_2)(F_2h_3)du_2du_3$. Thus

$$(\nabla \times F)_i = \frac{1}{h_2h_3}\, [\frac{\partial}{\partial u_2}(F_3h_3) - \frac{\partial}{\partial u_3}(F_2h_2)] \tag{I-4.16}$$

Adding the contributions from similar paths on the surfaces u_1u_3 and u_1u_2, we find that the curl of $\overline{F}$ is given by

$$\nabla \times \overline{F} = \frac{\overline{a}_1}{h_2h_3}\, [\frac{\partial}{\partial u_2}(F_3h_3) - \frac{\partial}{\partial u_3}(F_2h_2)] + \frac{\overline{a}_2}{h_1h_3}\, [\frac{\partial}{\partial u_3}(F_1h_1) - \frac{\partial}{\partial u_1}(F_3h_3)]$$

$$+ \frac{\overline{a}_3}{h_1h_2}\, [\frac{\partial}{\partial u_1}(F_2h_2) - \frac{\partial}{\partial u_2}(F_1h_1)] \tag{I-4.17}$$

This equation is conveniently written in determinantal form

$$\nabla \times \overline{F} = \frac{1}{h_1h_2h_3} \begin{vmatrix} h_1\overline{a}_1 & h_2\overline{a}_2 & h_3\overline{a}_3 \\ \frac{\partial}{\partial u_1} & \frac{\partial}{\partial u_2} & \frac{\partial}{\partial u_3} \\ h_1F_1 & h_2F_2 & h_3F_3 \end{vmatrix} \tag{I-4.18}$$

Using Eq. (I-4.17) we can write for the curl in rectangular, cylindrical and spherical coordinates

rectangular $\nabla \times \overline{F} = \overline{a}_x(\frac{\partial F_z}{\partial y} - \frac{\partial F_y}{\partial z}) + \overline{a}_y(\frac{\partial F_x}{\partial z} - \frac{\partial F_z}{\partial x}) + \overline{a}_z(\frac{\partial F_y}{\partial x} - \frac{\partial F_x}{\partial y})$

cylindrical $\nabla \times \overline{F} = \overline{a}_r(\frac{1}{r}\frac{\partial F_z}{\partial \phi} - \frac{\partial F_\phi}{\partial z}) + \overline{a}\, (\frac{\partial F_r}{\partial z} - \frac{\partial F_z}{\partial r}) + \overline{a}_z(\frac{1}{r}\frac{\partial (rF_\phi)}{\partial r} - \frac{1}{r}\frac{\partial F_r}{\partial \phi})$

(I-4.19)

spherical $$\nabla \times \overline{F} = \frac{\overline{a}_r}{r \sin\theta}\left[\frac{\partial}{\partial\theta}(F_\phi \sin\theta) - \frac{\partial F_\theta}{\partial\phi}\right] + \frac{\overline{a}_\theta}{r}\left[\frac{1}{\sin\theta}\frac{\partial F_r}{\partial\phi} - \frac{\partial}{\partial r}(rF_\phi)\right] + \frac{\overline{a}_\phi}{r}\left[\frac{\partial}{\partial r}(rF_\theta) - \frac{\partial F_r}{\partial\theta}\right] \qquad \text{(I-4.20)}$$

d. The Laplacian. Noting that $\nabla^2\Phi = \nabla \cdot \nabla\Phi$, we can use Eqs. (I-4.7) and (I-4.12) to write the Laplacian in generalized coordinates. The resulting expression is

$$\nabla^2\Phi = \nabla\cdot\nabla\Phi = \frac{1}{h_1h_2h_3}\left[\frac{\partial}{\partial u_1}\left(\frac{h_2h_3}{h_1}\frac{\partial\Phi}{\partial u_1}\right) + \frac{\partial}{\partial u_2}\left(\frac{h_3h_1}{h_2}\frac{\partial\Phi}{\partial u_2}\right) + \frac{\partial}{\partial u_3}\left(\frac{h_1h_2}{h_3}\frac{\partial\Phi}{\partial u_3}\right)\right] \qquad \text{(I-4.21)}$$

The specific form of the Laplacian in cylindrical and spherical coordinates follow:

rectangular $$\nabla^2\Phi = \frac{\partial^2\Phi}{\partial x^2} + \frac{\partial^2\Phi}{\partial y^2} + \frac{\partial^2\Phi}{\partial z^2} \qquad \text{(I-4.22)}$$

cylindrical $$\nabla^2\Phi = \frac{1}{r}\frac{\partial}{\partial r}\left(r\frac{\partial\Phi}{\partial r}\right) + \frac{1}{r^2}\frac{\partial^2\Phi}{\partial\phi^2} + \frac{\partial^2\Phi}{\partial z^2} \qquad \text{(I-4.23)}$$

spherical $$\nabla^2\Phi = \frac{1}{r^2}\frac{\partial}{\partial r}\left(r^2\frac{\partial\Phi}{\partial r}\right) + \frac{1}{r^2\sin\theta}\frac{\partial}{\partial\theta}\left(\sin\theta\frac{\partial\Phi}{\partial\theta}\right) + \frac{1}{r^2\sin^2\theta}\frac{\partial^2\Phi}{\partial\phi^2} \qquad \text{(I-4.24)}$$

PROBLEMS

I-1. Given two vectors $\overline{A}$ and $\overline{B}$ defined by: $\overline{A} = 3\overline{a}_x + 2\overline{a}_y - \overline{a}_z$, $\overline{B} = \overline{a}_x + 4\overline{a}_y + \overline{a}_z$, determine the following: $\overline{A}+\overline{B}$; $\overline{A}-\overline{B}$; $|\overline{A}|$; $|\overline{B}|$; $\measuredangle(\overline{A},\overline{B})$; θ_x, θ_y, θ_z for both vectors; $\overline{A}\cdot\overline{B}$; $\overline{A} \times \overline{B}$.

I-2. Find the magnitude of the vectors given below and the unit vectors along their direction:

a. $3\overline{a}_x$ b. $3\overline{a}_x + 4\overline{a}_y$ c. $2x\overline{a}_x + 3y\,\overline{a}_y$

d. $\overline{r}-\overline{r}'$ e. $-2\overline{a}_x + 3\overline{a}_y - 2\overline{a}_z$ f. $-\overline{a}_x - \overline{a}_y - \overline{a}_z$

I-3. Find the angle between the following vectors

a. $3\overline{a}_x + 2\overline{a}_y$ and $2\overline{a}_x + 14\overline{a}_y$ b. $3\overline{a}_x + 2\overline{a}_y - \overline{a}_z$ and $-2\overline{a}_x + 3\overline{a}_y + 8\overline{a}_z$ c. $\overline{a}_x + \overline{a}_y$ and $-\overline{a}_y + 2\overline{a}_z$

I-4. Given three vectors, $\overline{A}$, $\overline{B}$ and $\overline{C}$ defined by: $\overline{A} = 3\overline{a}_x + \overline{a}_y - 2\overline{a}_z$, $\overline{B} = \overline{a}_x + 2\overline{a}_y + \overline{a}_z$, and $\overline{C} = \overline{a}_x + \overline{a}_y + \overline{a}_z$, determine the angle between the two vectors which start from the tip of the vector $\overline{A}$ and end at the tips of $\overline{B}$ and $\overline{C}$, respectively.

I-5. Find the vector which extends from the point (2,1,3) to (1,2,-1).

I-6. Find a vector which is perpendicular to $\overline{A} = 2\overline{a}_x + 4\overline{a}_y + \overline{a}_z$.

I-7. Find and sketch to *scale* the magnitude and direction of the vector field $\overline{A} = \sqrt{x}\, y\overline{a}_x + y^2\overline{a}_y$ at the following points: (0,0), (1,0), (2,0), (0,1), (0,2), (1,0.5), (2,1), (1,1), (2,2), (0.5,1), (1,2).

I-8. Find the sum and the difference of the following vectors:

a. $3x\overline{a}_x + 2\overline{a}_y$, $\overline{a}_x + \overline{a}_z$

b. $3\overline{a}_x + 2\overline{a}_y + 4\overline{a}_z$, $3x\overline{a}_x + 2y\overline{a}_y + 4z\overline{a}_z$

c. $-\overline{a}_x - \overline{a}_y - \overline{a}_z$, $-\overline{a}_x - \overline{a}_y - \overline{a}_z$

I-9. Find the vectors which must be added to the following vectors so that the resulting vectors are equal to $\overline{a}_z$:

a. $3\overline{a}_x + 2\overline{a}_y$ b. $3x\overline{a}_x + 2yx\overline{a}_y + 8x\overline{a}_z$ c. $\overline{a}_x$

I-10. Find the unit vector which is parallel to the vector $\overline{B} = 3\overline{a}_x + 7\overline{a}_y + 2\overline{a}_z$.

I-11. Find the unit vectors which are perpendicular to the following vectors and the X-axis:

a. $3\overline{a}_x + 4\overline{a}_y + \overline{a}_z$ b. $3x\overline{a}_x + 4yx\overline{a}_y - x\overline{a}_z$

c. $-3\overline{a}_x + 2\overline{a}_y - 3\overline{a}_z$ d. $2\overline{a}_x - 2\overline{a}_y - 4\overline{a}_z$

I-12. Show that $\overline{A} \times (\overline{B}\times\overline{C}) = \overline{B}(\overline{A}\cdot\overline{C}) - \overline{C}(\overline{A}\cdot\overline{B})$.
(Hint: Expand independently the two sides of the identity.)

I-13. If $\overline{A} = \overline{a}_x + \overline{a}_y - \overline{a}_z$, $\overline{B} = -\overline{a}_x - \overline{a}_y + \overline{a}_z$, and $\overline{C} = 2\overline{a}_x + 2\overline{a}_y + 2\overline{a}_z$, find:
(a) $\overline{A} \cdot (\overline{B}\times\overline{C})$; (b) $\overline{B}(\overline{A}\cdot\overline{C})$; and (c) $\overline{C}(\overline{A}\cdot\overline{B})$.

I-14. Calculate the value of α such that the two vectors $\overline{A} = \alpha\,\overline{a}_x + 2\overline{a}_y + 2\overline{a}_z$ and $\overline{B} = \overline{a}_x + \alpha\,\overline{a}_y + \overline{a}_z$ are perpendicular to each other.

I-15. Prove the cosine rule for triangles $[c^2 = a^2 + b^2 - 2ab\cos(a,b)]$ using the vectors representing the three sides of a triangle.

I-16. Let the potential change by +3 V/m in the X-direction and by -2 V/m in the Y-direction. Find the electric field $\overline{E}$.
(Ans: $3.6/\underline{146^\circ\ 19'}$ with respect to the positive X-axis.)

APPENDIX II

SPACES AND OPERATORS

II-1. Linear Spaces

When we are studying set theory, we are concerned with abstract sets, where no structure in the set is used or assumed. Because we are interested in using linear spaces, we must introduce special structures; the most convenient one is to use the notion of nearness for each pair of elements belonging to the set (space). In addition, most sets that are useful in applications have both *algebraic* and *metric* structures. Primiarly, we are interested in sets whose elements are real or complex continuous functions defined in an open domain D. To deal with such spaces we must introduce the concept of *operator* and *functional*.

Definition II-1.1. An *operator* A is defined on a set of functions belonging to the set X if there exists a law according to which a new set of functions belonging to the set Y is defined such that to each function in X there is one and only one function in Y. The set X is called the domain D_A of the operator A and the set Y is called the range R_A of the operator. The name operator is also used interchangeably with the terms *function, transformation,* and *mapping*. If the mapping of X does not cover all Y, we call the mapping X *into* Y. If X is mapped in all Y we call the mapping X *onto* Y, and if two elements in X always have different images in Y we call it a *one-to-one* mapping. A graphical representation of an operator is given in Fig. II-1.1.

Definition II-1.2. If an operator A defined on a set of functions generates for each function a constant (real or complex), the operator is called a *functional*.

Example II-1.1. One of the most common functionals is the definite integral $A = \int_a^b dt$. If we operate on any integrable function f defined in the interval [a,b] the result is a number. Thus A is a functional on f. The brackets [ ] indicate that the end point of the interval a,b are included.

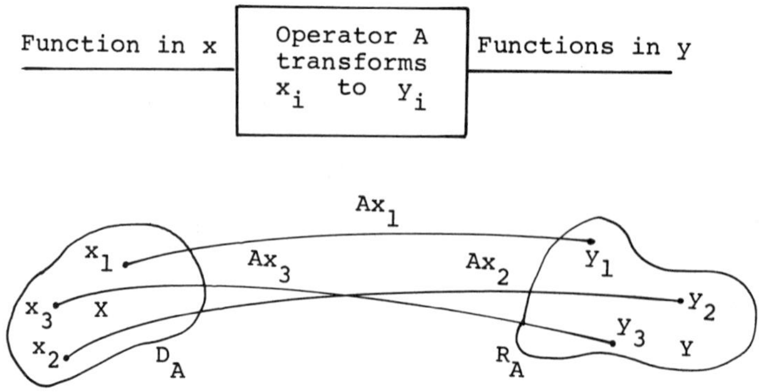

Figure II-1.1. Illustration of operator mappings.

The basic *algebraic* quality of a function space is its linearity; there are the following definitions:

Definition II-1.3. A function space is linear if the following properties are true:

1. To every pair of functions x_1 and x_2 there corresponds another function $x_1 + x_2$ with the properties

a. $x_1 + x_2 = x_2 + x_1$

b. $x_1 + [x_2+x_3] = [x_1+x_2] + x_3$

c. $x + 0 = x$ for every x in the space

d. $\alpha(\beta x) = \alpha\beta x$ where α and β are real or complex numbers

e. $(\alpha+\beta)x = \alpha x + \beta x$

f. $\alpha(x_1+x_2) = \alpha x_1 + \alpha x_2$

g. $1x = x$

When we have only real elements the space is real; when we have complex quantities involved, we imply that the space is complex. The space, real or complex, will be easily identified from the context of its description.

The above have been concerned with the algebraic structure of sets. We now address ourselves to the *metric* structure of sets. We thus consider:

Definition II-1.4. The collection of elements $x_1, x_2, \ldots$ constitutes a *metric space* if to each pair x_i, x_j there corresponds a real number $d[x_i,x_j]$, which is called the *metric* and which satisfies the properties:

a. $d[x_i,x_j] = d[x_j,x_i]$

b. $d[x_i,x_j] \geq 0$ $\quad (d[x_i,x_j] = 0$ iff $x_i = x_j = 0)$

c. $d[x_i,x_k] \leq d[x_i,x_j] + d[x_j,x_k]$ (triangular inequality)

Example II-1.2. Consider the space $C(t_0,t_1)$ of all real-valued continuous functions x defined in the interval $t_0 \leq t \leq t_1$ and having the metric

$$d[x_i,x_j] = \max_{t_0 \leq t \leq t_1} |x_i - x_j|$$

The properties a. and b. of Definition II-1.4 are automatically satisfied. To see that property c. is also satisfied, we write the metric as follows

$$d[x_i,x_k] = \max_{t_0 \leq t \leq t_1} |(x_i - x_j) + (x_j - x_k)|$$

Using the property of the absolute value of two quantities, we have

$$d[x_i,x_k] \leq \max_{t_0 \leq t \leq t_1} |x_i - x_j| + \max_{t_0 \leq t \leq t_1} |x_i - x_k|$$

or

$$d[x_i,x_k] \leq d[x_i,x_j] + d[x_j,x_k]$$

Therefore we have shown that the space with the given metric is a metric space. $\Delta\Delta\Delta$

Another property which characterizes a space is its *completeness*. If, for example, the $\lim_{i,j\to\infty} d[x_i,x_j] = 0$, we call such a space *complete*.

One of the most useful spaces is that proposed by Hilbert. A linear complete space with bounded functions defined in a domain D is a *Hilbert* space if for each pair of functions x_i,x_j belonging to the same space a number (x_i,x_j) called the scalar product is generated which satisfies the following axioms:

I. $(x_i,x_j) = (x_j,x_i)^*$

II. $(a_i x_i + a_j x_j, x_k) = a_i(x_i,x_k) + a_j(x_j,x_k)$ $[a_i,a_j$ are constants$]$

III. $(x_i,x_i) > 0$ when $x_i \neq 0$; $(x_i,x_i) = 0$ when $x_i = 0$

The quantity (x_i,x_j) is defined by

$$(x_i,x_j) = \int_V x_i(p)\, x_j^*(p)\, dV \tag{II-1.1}$$

where V is multidimensional volume. If, for example, the functions x_i and x_j have two independent variables y and z, then Eq. (II-1.1) assumes the form

$$(x_i(p),x_j(p)) = (x_i(y,z),x_j(y,z)) = \int_{y_0}^{y_1}\int_{z_0}^{z_1} x_i(y,z)y_j^*(y,z)dydz \tag{II-1.2}$$

The non-negative number $(x_i,x_i)^{1/2} = \|x\|$ is called the *norm* of the element x_i and it characterizes the metric qualities of the Hilbert space.

The properties of the Hilbert space H are

I. The space H is *linear*

II. The *scalar product* of any two elements x_i, x_j is defined in H as (x_i, x_j) and it is equal to a number

III. H is *infinite-dimensional* space

IV. H is *complete*

V. H is *separable*. This means that there exists a sequence of elements of H (subset) which is everywhere dense in H. That is, for each element x in H we can find an element x_i of the subset such that $d[x, x_i] < \varepsilon$ for any ε.

II-2. Linear Operators

Earlier in this section we stated the definition of an operator over an abstract set of functions. We now wish to develop some specific concepts of linear operators defined on a separable Hilbert space.

Definition II-2.1. An operator A is called linear if to each element in H the following is true

$$A(a_1x_1 + a_2x_2 + \dots + a_nx_n) = a_1Ax_1 + a_2Ax_2 + \dots + a_nAx_n \tag{II-2.1}$$

where n is any integer; $a_1, a_2, \dots, a_n$ are constants, and the x_i's belong to H.

If an operator generates an element belonging to the space of its definition and identical to itself, it is called an *identity operator*. Also an operator which generates zero from any element in the space of its definition is called a *null* operator. Some different types of operators are given in the following examples.

Example II-2.1. The first order differential operator d/dx is defined on the set L^2 of continuous and square integrable functions having first derivatives, whereas the second order differential operator d^2/dx^2 is defined on the set L^2 of continuous and square integrable functions having second derivatives. In the case of differential operators, we must bear in mind that the result of a differentiation may create an element which does not belong to the L^2.

ΔΔΔ

Example II-2.2. Another class of operators are the integral operators in L^2 space; the simplest one is the Fredholm operator

$$Ax = \int_a^b K(t,\xi)\, x(\xi)d\xi$$

where the kernel $K(t,\xi)$ is any continuous function of t and ξ.

ΔΔΔ

Definition II-2.2. An operator A is called *symmetric* if the following identity is true:

$$(Ax_1,x_2) = (x_1,Ax_2) \tag{II-2.2}$$

where x_1 and x_2 are continuous functions defined in the closed domain of A and the generated functions Ax_1 and Ax_2 have finite norms.

Example II-2.3. If an operator defined in $t \in [0,1]$ is the first order differential operator d/dt, then the function 1/t is outside the field of definition of the operator because at t = 0 x(t) becomes infinite. The function $x(t) = t^2$ is an acceptable function because x(t) is defined at zero and its norm is finite.

$$\left\|\frac{dx}{dt}\right\| = \left[\left(\frac{dx}{dt}, \frac{dx}{dt}\right)\right]^{1/2} = \left[\int_0^1 2t^2 dt\right]^{1/2} = \sqrt{2/3}$$

In addition, using Eq. (II-2.2) we find that

$$(Ax,y) - (x,Ay) = \int_0^1 \frac{dx}{dt} y\, dt - \int_0^1 x \frac{dy}{dt} dt = xy\Big|_0^1 - 2\int_0^1 x \frac{dy}{dt} dt$$

which implies that if the functions x(t) and y(t) satisfy the relation

$$x(1)y(1) - x(0)y(0) = 2\int_0^1 x \frac{dy}{dt} dt$$

our operator is symmetric. ΔΔΔ

Definition II-2.3. A symmetric operator A is *positive definite* if the inequality

$$(Ax,x) > 0 \tag{II-2.3}$$

holds for any function x in its field of definition.

Example II-2.4. Let us take as our operator the derivative $-d^2/dt^2$, and select our functions such that x(0) = x(1) = 0 in the domain $t \in [0,1]$. Then

$$(Ax,x) = -\int \frac{d^2x}{dt^2} x\, dt = -x \frac{dx}{dt}\Big|_0^1 + \int_0^1 \left(\frac{dx}{dt}\right)^2 dt$$

If

$$-x \frac{dx}{dt}\Big|_{t=1} + x \frac{dx}{dt}\Big|_{t=0} = 0$$

then

$$(Ax,x) = \int_0^1 \left(\frac{dx}{dt}\right)^2 dt > 0$$

and the operator is positive definite.

ΔΔΔ

Physically, we can associate the quantity (Ax,x) with the energy of a system. The positive definiteness of the operator indicates that we must always supply energy if we wish to change the configuration of the system.

Definition II-2.4. A symmetric operator A is called *positive-bounded-below* if the inequality

$$(Ax,x) \geq C \, \|x\|^2 \qquad \text{(II-2.4)}$$

holds, where C is a positive constant, and x belongs in the domain of A. The smallest number C in this inequality is called the norm of A and is denoted $\|A\|$.

Example II-2.5. Consider the two-dimensional Laplacian operator $A = -(\partial^2/\partial t^2)-(\partial^2/\partial s^2)$ defined on the domain $t \in [0,1]$ and $s \in [0,1]$, with the boundary conditions

$$x(t,s)\Big|_{t=0} = x(t,s)\Big|_{s=0} = x(t,s)\Big|_{t=1} = x(t,s)\Big|_{s=1} = 0$$

Since $x(0,s_1) = 0$ we can write

$$x(t_1,s_1) = \int_0^{t_1} \frac{\partial x(t,s_1)}{\partial t} \, dt$$

If we now apply Schwartz (Cauchy) inequality, we have

$$x^2(t_1,s_1) = [\int_0^{t_1} (1) \frac{\partial x(t,s_1)}{\partial t} \, dt]^2 \leq \int_0^{t_1} 1^2 dt \int_0^{t_1} [\frac{\partial x(t,s_1)}{\partial t}]^2 \, dt$$

However, since $t_1 \leq 1$, the last inequality is written in the form

$$x^2(t_1,s_1) \leq \int_0^1 [\frac{\partial x(t,s_1)}{\partial t}]^2 \, dt$$

Next, we integrate the inequality over the domain $t \in [0,1]$, $s \in [0,1]$, with the result

$$\iint x^2(t_1,s_1) dt_1 ds_1 \leq \int_0^1\int_0^1\int_0^1 [\frac{\partial x(t,s_1)}{\partial t}]^2 \, dt_1 dt \, ds_1$$

$$= (1) \int_0^1\int_0^1 [\frac{\partial x(t,s_1)}{\partial t}]^2 \, dt \, ds_1 \leq \int_0^1\int_0^1 [(\frac{\partial x}{\partial t})^2 + (\frac{\partial x}{\partial s})^2] \, dt \, ds$$

Now we observe that the expression

$$(Ax,x) = \int_0^1 \int_0^1 [(\frac{\partial x}{\partial t})^2 + (\frac{\partial x}{\partial s})^2] \, dt \, ds$$

implies that

$$(Ax,x) \geq 1 \int_0^1 \int_0^1 x^2(t,s)\, dt\, ds = 1\, \|x\|^2$$

This has the same form as Eq. (II-2.4) with the constant C = 1. This shows that the Laplacian operator is positive-bounded-below. ΔΔΔ

Definition II-2.5. A linear operator $\tilde{A}$ is the *adjoint* of the operator A if, for all elements x_i and x_j in the domain of A

$$(x_i, Ax_j) = (\tilde{A}x_i, x_j) \tag{II-2.5}$$

If $\tilde{A} = A$, then A is said to be *self-adjoint*.

Example II-2.6. Show that the operator $-d^2/dt^2$ defined on $t \in [0,1]$ with the boundary conditions $x_i(0) = x_j(0) = x_i(1) = x_j(1) = 0$ is self-adjoint.

Solution. Applying Def. (II-2.5) we have

$$\begin{aligned}(x_i, Ax_j) &= -\int_0^1 x_i \frac{d^2x_j}{dt^2}\, dt = -x_i \left.\frac{dx_j}{dt}\right|_{t=0}^{1} + \int_0^1 \frac{dx_i}{dt} \frac{dx_j}{dt}\, dt \\ &= -x_i \left.\frac{dx_j}{dt}\right|_{t=0}^{1} + x_j \left.\frac{dx_i}{dt}\right|_{t=0}^{1} - \int_0^1 \frac{d^2x_i}{dt^2} x_j\, dt \\ &= (\tilde{A}x_i, x_j)\end{aligned}$$

where $\tilde{A} = A = -d^2/dt^2$. ΔΔΔ

II-3. Operators for Second-Order Ordinary Differential Equations

The general linear differential operator A associated with the second-order differential equation is given by

$$A = a(x) \frac{d^2}{dx^2} + b(x) \frac{d}{dx} + c(x) \tag{II-3.1}$$

To define the operator A completely we must specify (a) a linear vector space L^2 of square integrable functions such that Au(x) belongs to L^2, and (b) the following linear independent boundary conditions

$$B_1(u) = \alpha_{10}u(a) + \alpha_{11} \frac{du(a)}{dx} + \beta_{10}u(b) + \beta_{11} \frac{du(b)}{dx} = \gamma_1 \tag{II-3.2a}$$

$$B_2(u) = \alpha_{20}u(a) + \alpha_{21} \frac{du(a)}{dx} + \beta_{20}u(b) + \beta_{21} \frac{du(b)}{dx} = \gamma_2 \tag{II-3.2b}$$

where α's, β's, and γ's are given constants.

To find the *formal adjoint* operator $\tilde{A}$ of A, we integrate the product vAu over a specified domain. Integrating vAu by parts repeatedly, we obtain

$$\int_a^b vAu\,dx = \int_a^b va\frac{d}{dx}\left(\frac{du}{dx}\right)dx + \int_a^b vb\frac{du}{dx}dx + \int_a^b vcu\,dx$$

$$= \left(va\frac{du}{dx} + vbu\right)\Bigg|_a^b - \int_a^b \frac{d(va)}{dx}\frac{du}{dx}dx - \int_a^b \frac{d(vb)}{dx}udx + \int_a^b vcu\,dx$$

$$= \left(av\frac{du}{dx} - \frac{d(av)}{dx}u + bvu\right)\Bigg|_a^b + \int_a^b u\left(\frac{d^2(av)}{dx^2} - \frac{d(bv)}{dx} + cv\right)dx \qquad \text{(II-3.3)}$$

Making use of Eq. (II-2.2) we thus observe that

$$\tilde{A} = a(x)\frac{d^2}{dx^2} + \left(2\frac{da}{dx} - b\right)\frac{d}{dx} + \left(\frac{d^2a}{dx^2} - \frac{db}{dx} + c\right)$$

With respect to operators, their adjoints and boundary conditions, we observe the following three cases.

I. If $A \neq \tilde{A}$ and boundary conditions of A $\neq$ boundary conditions of $\tilde{A}$, then we call $\tilde{A}$ *formal adjoint*.

II. If $A = \tilde{A}$ and boundary conditions of A $\neq$ boundary conditions of $\tilde{A}$, then we call $\tilde{A}$ *formally self-adjoint*.

III. If $A = \tilde{A}$ and the boundary conditions of A = boundary conditions of $\tilde{A}$, then we call $\tilde{A}$ *self-adjoint*.

With concern for the differential equations and their boundary conditions, we note the following cases:

A. Homogeneous differential equations with *homogeneous* boundary conditions:

$Au = 0 \qquad B_1(u) = 0 \qquad B_2(u) = 0$

B. Homogeneous differential equations with *non-homogeneous* boundary conditions:

$Au = 0 \qquad B_1(u) = \gamma_1 \qquad B_2(u) = \gamma_2$

C. Non-homogeneous differential equations with *homogeneous* boundary conditions:

$Au = f(x) \qquad B_1(u) = 0 \qquad B_2(u) = 0$

D. Non-homogeneous differential equations with *non-homogeneous* boundary conditions:

$Au = f(x) \qquad B_1(u) = \gamma_1 \qquad B_2(u) = \gamma_2$

In the course of our studies, we will meet examples of each of these cases.

PROBLEMS

II-1. Show that the operator $-d^2/dt^2$ defined in the domain $t \in [0,1]$ is symmetric if

$$\left(\frac{dx}{dt} y - x \frac{dy}{dt}\right)\Bigg|_0^1 = 0.$$

II-2. Find the conditions such that the operator d^2/dt^2 is positive definite if the functions which belong in the field of definition of the operator satisfy the boundary conditions

$$\frac{dx(0)}{dt} + \alpha x(0) = 0; \qquad \frac{dx(1)}{dt} + \beta x(1) = 0$$

II-3. Show that d^4/dt^4 is self-adjoint in the domain [0,1] if the functions belong to L^2, possess fourth derivatives, and the following conditions are met:

$$x(0) = x(1) = \frac{dx(0)}{dt} = \frac{dx(1)}{dt} = \frac{d^2x(0)}{dt^2} = \frac{d^2x(1)}{dt^2} = 0.$$

II-4. Find the adjoint of A if it is a 3 × 3 matrix. [Hint: $\tilde{A} = A^T$]

II-5. Verify the following for any bounded operators A and B and a real scalar a: $\tilde{\tilde{(A)}} = A$; $(\widetilde{A+B}) = \tilde{A}+\tilde{B}$; $(aA) = aA$; $(AB) = BA$.

II-6. Let x_i and x_j be twice-differentiable functions which are defined in the domain of A. If we have the relation

$$(x_i, Ax_j) = \int_0^1 \left(x_i a_0 \frac{d^2x_j}{dt^2} + x_i a_1 \frac{dx_j}{dt} + x_i a_2 x_j\right) dt$$

find the adjoint of A (formally adjoint). Under what condition does A become self-adjoint?

[Hint: Remember that the operator you seek is inside the integral.]

APPENDIX III

ENERGY AND POWER IN OPTICAL SYSTEMS

III-1. Energy and Power in Linear Optical Systems

In the field of optics, two types of energy units are common. These are: radiometric (physical) and photometric (psychophysical). The radiometric units are given in Table III-1.1.

Table III-1.1. Radiometric Units

Name	Symbol	Units	Description
Radiant energy	Q_e	Joule	The total energy associated with optical radiation
Radiant energy density	W_e	Joule/m^3	The radiant energy per unit volume
Radiant flux	$\Phi_e = \frac{dQ_e}{dt}$	Watt	The time rate of flow of radiant energy
Radiant existence	$M_e = \frac{d\Phi_e}{dA}$	Watt/m^2	The ratio of the radiant flux leaving an infinitesimal area to the elemental area
Irradiance	$E_e = \frac{d\Phi_e}{dA}$	Watt/m^2	The ratio of the radiant flux incident on an infinitesimal area to the elemental area
Radiant intensity	$I_e = \frac{d\Phi_e}{d\Omega}$	Watt/ster	The quotient of the radiant flux leaving a surface in an elemental solid angle by that angle
Radiance	$L_e = \frac{d^2\Phi_e}{d\Omega dA\cos\theta} = \frac{dI_e}{dA\cos\theta} = \frac{dE_e}{d\Omega}$	$\frac{\text{Watt}}{m^2\text{ster}}$	The radiance in a given direction or the radiant flux per unit solid angle per unit projected area

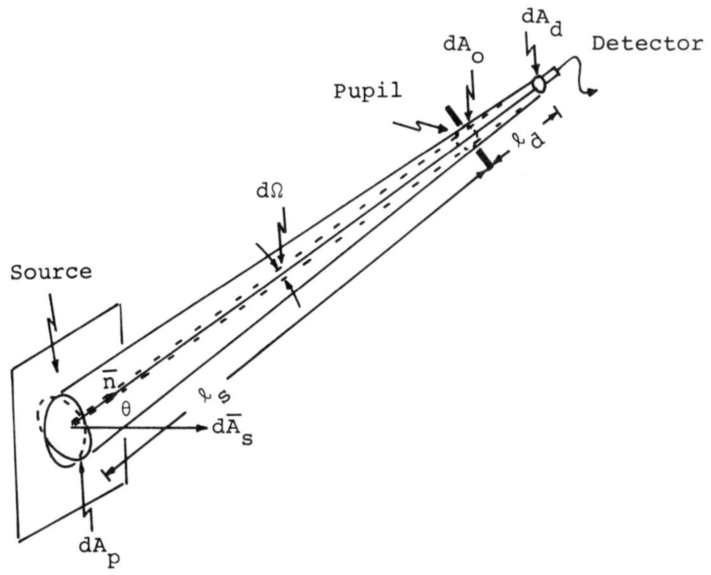

Figure III-1.1. Determination of the radiance of a source.

If a frequency dependence exists, the quantities Q_e, W_e and Φ_e are given respectively by

$$Q_e = \int_0^\infty Q_e(\lambda)d\lambda \qquad W_e = \int_0^\infty W_e(\lambda)d\lambda \qquad \Phi_e = \int_0^\infty \Phi_e(\lambda)d\lambda \tag{III-1.1}$$

The following examples will help understand the radiometric quantities.

Example III-1.1. Find the radiance of a source, assuming the use of a detector with 100 percent efficiency.

Solution. As shown in Fig. III-1.1, the area dA_p is related to the pupil area at the source by the relation $dA_p = dA_o(\ell_s + \ell_d)^2/\ell_d^2$. The solid angle subtended by the detector to the source is $d\Omega = dA_d/(\ell_s + \ell_d)^2$. From these relations we find that $dA_p d\Omega = dA_o dA_d/\ell_d^2$. From the definition of radiance L_e and assuming that the detector is calibrated to read radiant flux, in Watt, we obtain

$$L_e = \frac{d^2\Phi_e}{dA_p\ d\Omega} = \frac{d^2\Phi_e}{dA_s\ \cos\theta\ d\Omega} = \frac{d^2\Phi_e\ \ell_d^2}{dA_o\ dA_d} \tag{III-1.2}$$

Example III-1.2. A detector is located in front of a source, as shown in Fig. III-1.2. Find the radiant flux reaching the detector.

Solution. From the figure we find that $dA_s = \Delta h\ dy$ and the radiant flux $d^2\Phi_e$ reaching the detector is (see Table III-1.1)

$$d^2\Phi_e = L_e\ d\Omega\ dA_s\ \cos\theta = L_e \frac{dA_d}{r^2} dA_s \cos\theta = L_e \frac{dA_d}{r^2} \Delta h\ dy\ \cos\theta$$

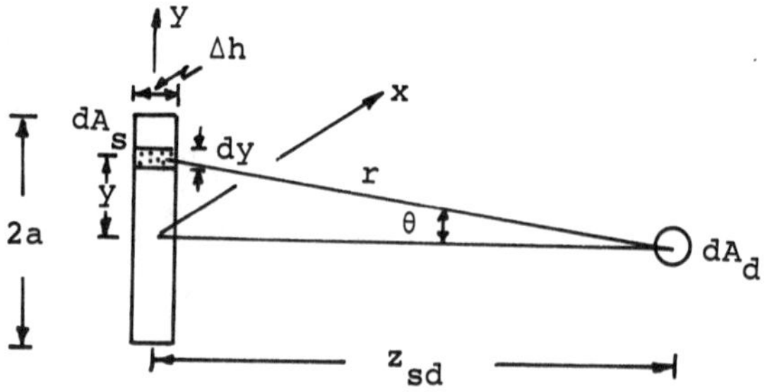

Figure III-1.2. Determination of collected radiant flux

Now use the relations $y^2 + z_{sd}^2 = r^2$ and $\cos\theta = z_{sd}/r = z_{sd}/(z_{sd}^2 + y^2)^{1/2}$. The total flux reaching the detector is given by

$$d\Phi_e = L_e \Delta h \, dA_d \, z_{sd} \int_{-a}^{a} \frac{dy}{(z_{sd}^2 + y^2)^{3/2}} = 2L_e \Delta h \, dA_d \, a \frac{1}{z_{sd}(a^2 + z_{sd}^2)^{1/2}}$$

From this, the incident irradiance is

$$E_e = \frac{d\Phi_e}{dA_d} = \frac{2L_e \Delta h a}{z_{sd}(a^2 + z_{sd}^2)^{1/2}}$$

For large values of z_{sd} we have, approximately

$$E_e = \frac{L_e(\text{Area})}{z_{sd}^2} = \frac{I_e}{z_{sd}^2}$$

where I_e is the radiant intensity (Watt/ster.).

ΔΔΔ

The photometric units parallel exactly the radiometric ones. Now, however, their establishment entails decisions by human observers who are to compare optical sources. Since no two people will have exactly the same optical resonse to different wavelengths, a *standard luminosity curve* has been accepted. This curve

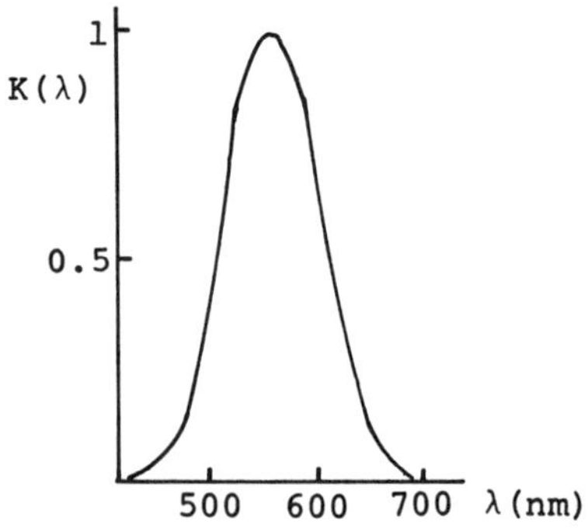

Figure III-1.3. The standard luminosity curve.

expresses the functional form $K(\lambda) = K_m V(\lambda)$, and this is given in Fig. III-1.3. The basic photometric units are the following:

a. Luminous energy $Q_v = K_m \int V(\lambda) Q_e(\lambda) d\lambda$ (Talbot)

b. Luminous density W_v (Talbot/m^3)

c. Luminous flux $\Phi_v = K_m \int V(\lambda) \Phi_e(\lambda) d\lambda$ (Lumen)

d. Luminous exitance $M_v = d\Phi_v/dA$ (Lumen/m^2)

e. Illuminance $E_v = d\Phi_v/dA = K_m \int E_e(\lambda) V(\lambda) d\lambda$ (Lumen/m^2 or Lux or m-Candle)

f. Luminous Intensity $I_v = d\Phi_v/d\Omega$ (Lumen/ster. or Candle)

g. Luminance $L_v = d^2\Phi_v/d\Omega dA \cos\theta$ (Lumen/m^2-ster; Candle/m^2; nit)

PROBLEMS

III-1. Find the radiant flux reaching the detector from a disk source of radius a, as shown in Fig. PIII-1.1.
[Ans: $d\Phi_e = \pi L_e dA_d z_{sd}^2[(1/z_{sd}^2 - 1/(z_{sd}^2 + a^2)]]$

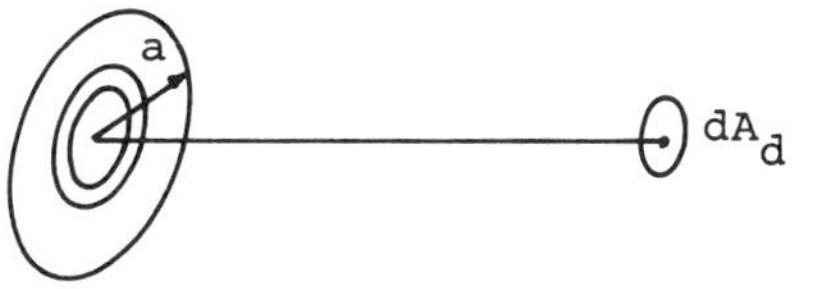

Figure PIII-1.1.

III-2. Find the radiant flux falling on the detector from a small source dA_s.
[Ans: $d^2\Phi_e = (L_e dA_s \cos\theta\, dA_d \cos\phi)/z_{sd}^2$]

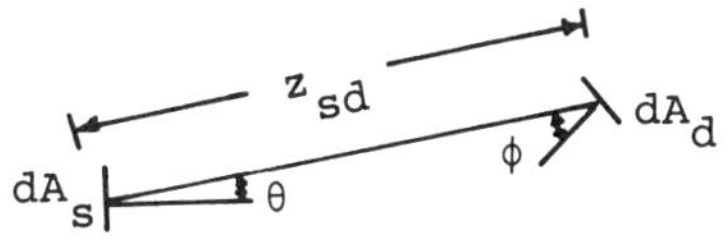

Figure PIII-1.2.

APPENDIX IV

FOURIER AND LAPLACE TRANSFORMS

A. Fourier Transforms

IV-1. One Dimensional Fourier Transforms

Fourier transforms constitute one of the very powerful mathematical techniques for the solution of physical problems. Because of this, they play an important role in mathematical analysis. The Fourier transform pair is given by the formulas

$$\mathscr{F}[f(t)] = F(\omega) = \int_{-\infty}^{\infty} f(t)e^{-j\omega t}\,dt$$

$$f(t) = \mathscr{F}^{-1}[F(\omega)] = \frac{1}{2\pi}\int_{-\infty}^{\infty} F(\omega)e^{j\omega t}d\omega = \int_{-\infty}^{\infty} F(2\pi f)e^{j2\pi ft}df \quad \text{b)} \qquad \text{(IV-1.1)}$$

where the following conditions must be fulfilled:

a. the function f(t) must be square integrable over the full range $(-\infty,+\infty)$.
b. the function f(t) must have only a finite number of discontinuities and a finite number of maximums and minimums in any finite range.
c. the function f(t) must have a finite number of singularities.

The following are some of the most fundamental and useful properties of Fourier transforms:

1. Linearity

$$\mathscr{F}[a_1f_1(t) + a_2f_2(t)] = a_1\mathscr{F}[f_1(t)] + a_2\mathscr{F}[f_2(t)]$$

2. Time Shifting

$$\mathscr{F}[f(t-t_o)] = e^{-j\omega t_o}\mathscr{F}[f(t)] = e^{-j\omega t_o} F(\omega)$$

3. Time Scaling

$$\mathcal{F}[f(at)] = \frac{1}{|a|} F(\frac{\omega}{a}) \qquad a = \text{real constant}$$

4. Frequency Shifting

$$\mathcal{F}[e^{j\omega_0 t} f(t)] = F(\omega-\omega_0)$$

5. Parseval's relation

$$\int_{-\infty}^{\infty} |f(t)|^2 dt = \frac{1}{2\pi}\int_{-\infty}^{\infty} |F(\omega)|^2 d\omega$$

6. Time Convolution

$$\mathcal{F}[\int_{-\infty}^{\infty} f_1(\tau)f_2(t-\tau)d\tau] = F_1(\omega)F_2(\omega)$$

7. Frequency Convolution

$$\mathcal{F}[f_1(t)f_2(t)] = \frac{1}{2\pi}\int_{-\infty}^{\infty} F_1(x)F_2(\omega-x)dx$$

8. Autocorrelation

$$\mathcal{F}[\int_{-\infty}^{\infty} f(\tau)f^*(\tau-t)d\tau] = F(\omega)F^*(\omega) = |F(\omega)|^2$$

$$\mathcal{F}[f(t)f^*(t)] = \frac{1}{2\pi}\int_{-\infty}^{\infty} F(x)F^*(x+\omega)dx$$

9. Time Differentiation

$$\mathcal{F}[\frac{d^n f(t)}{dt^n}] = (j\omega)^n F(\omega), \qquad \text{zero initial conditions}$$

10. Cosine Fourier Transform

$$\mathcal{F}_c[f(t)] = 2\int_0^{\infty} f(t)\cos\omega t\, dt = F(\omega)$$

$$\mathcal{F}_c^{-1}[F(\omega)] = \frac{1}{\pi}\int_0^{\infty} F(\omega)\cos\omega t\, d\omega = f(t)$$

11. The Complex Conjugate Fourier Transform

$$\mathcal{F}[f^*(t)] = [\int_{-\infty}^{\infty} f(t)e^{j\omega t}dt]^* = [\int_{-\infty}^{\infty} f(t)e^{-t(-\omega)}dt]^* = F(-\omega)^*$$

If $f(t)$ is a real function, $F(-\omega) = F^*(\omega)$.

Example IV-1.1. Find the Fourier transform of the function

$$f(t) = e^{-at}\, u_{-1}(t)$$

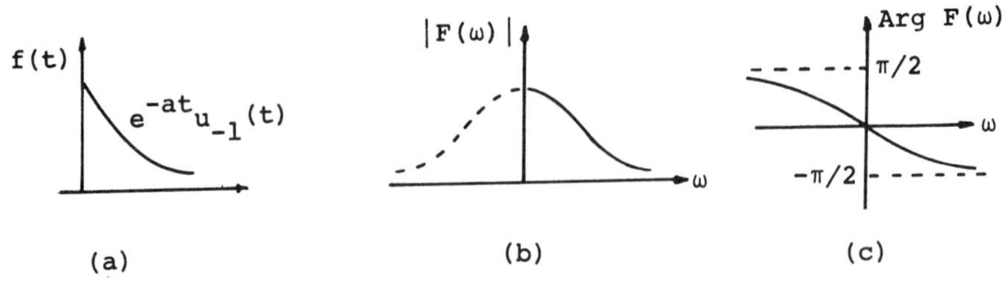

Figure IV-1.1. (a) Time function, (b) The magnitude and its Fourier transform, (c) The argument of its Fourier transform.

Solution. Apply the definition, Eq. (II-1.1a) to obtain

$$F(\omega) = \int_{-\infty}^{\infty} e^{-at}u_{-1}(t)e^{-j\omega t}dt = \int_{0}^{\infty} e^{-(a+j\omega)t}\, dt$$

$$= -\frac{1}{a+j\omega} e^{-(a+j\omega)t}\Big|_0^{\infty} = \frac{1}{a+j\omega} \qquad a > 0$$

Fig. IV-1.1 shows the function and its Fourier representation. ΔΔΔ

Example IV-1.2. Find the Fourier transform of the pulse function $p_\tau(t)$ shown in Fig. IV-1.2a.

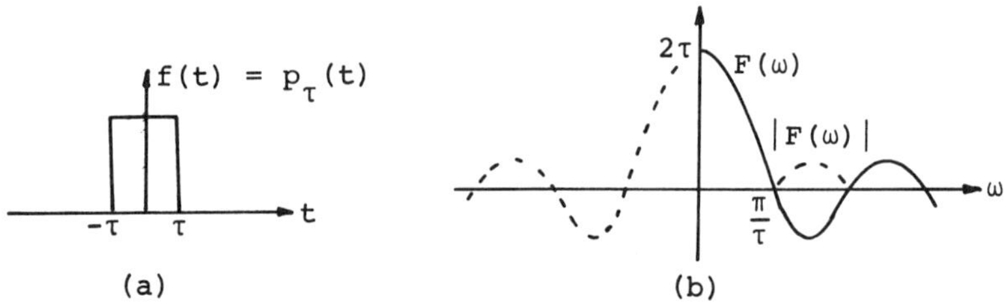

Figure IV-1.2. (a) Time function, (b) its Fourier transform.

Solution.

$$F(\omega) = \int_{-\infty}^{\infty} p_\tau(t)e^{-j\omega t}dt = \int_{-\tau}^{\tau} e^{-j\omega t}dt = 2\,\frac{\sin \omega\tau}{\omega} = 2\tau\,\frac{\sin \omega\tau}{\omega\tau}$$

ΔΔΔ

Example IV-1.3. Find the Fourier transform of the delta function $\delta(t)$.

Solution. From the definition of the delta function we have the relation

$$F(\omega) = \int_{-\infty}^{\infty} \delta(t)e^{-j\omega t}dt = e^{-j\omega\cdot 0} = 1$$

By the inverse transform relation, we obtain

$$\delta(t) = \frac{1}{2\pi}\int_{-\infty}^{\infty} 1\cdot e^{j\omega t}d\omega \quad \text{or} \quad 2\pi\delta(t) = \int_{-\infty}^{\infty} e^{j\omega t}d\omega$$

With the help of this last relation, we write

$$\int_{-\infty}^{\infty} e^{j\omega t}dt = 2\pi\delta(\omega) \qquad \text{or} \qquad \int_{-\infty}^{\infty} e^{-j(-\omega)t}dt = 2\pi\delta(-\omega) = 2\pi\delta(\omega)$$

which shows that $\delta(t)$ is an even function.

Also, we have the relation

$$\mathscr{F}[e^{j\omega_o t}] = \int_{-\infty}^{\infty} e^{j\omega_o t}\,e^{-j\omega t}dt = \int_{-\infty}^{\infty} e^{-j(\omega-\omega_o)t}dt = 2\pi\delta(\omega-\omega_o) = 2\pi\delta(\omega_o-\omega)$$

ΔΔΔ

Example IV-1.4. Prove Parseval's relation.

Solution. Begin with the relation

$$\frac{1}{2\pi}\int_{-\infty}^{\infty} F(\omega)F^*(\omega)d\omega = \frac{1}{2\pi}\int_{-\infty}^{\infty} [\iint_{-\infty}^{\infty} f(t)f^*(t')e^{-j\omega(t-t')}dt\ dt']d\omega$$

$$= \iint_{-\infty}^{\infty} f(t)f^*(t')\ [\frac{1}{2\pi}\int_{-\infty}^{\infty} e^{-j\omega(t-t')}d\omega]dt\ dt'$$

$$= \iint_{-\infty}^{\infty} f(t)f^*(t')\delta(t-t')dt\ dt' = \int_{-\infty}^{\infty} |f(t)|^2dt$$

ΔΔΔ

Example IV-1.5. Prove the convolution property.

Solution. We write directly

$$\int_{-\infty}^{\infty} [\int_{-\infty}^{\infty} f_1(\tau)f_2(t-\tau)d\tau]e^{-j\omega t}dt = \int_{-\infty}^{\infty} f_1(\tau)[\int_{-\infty}^{\infty} f_2(t-\tau)e^{-j\omega t}dt]d\tau$$

$$= \int_{-\infty}^{\infty} f_1(\tau)e^{-j\omega\tau}F_2(\omega)d\tau = F_1(\omega)F_2(\omega)$$

ΔΔΔ

A number of important Fourier transform pairs are contained in Tables IV-1 and IV-2.

Table IV-1.1.

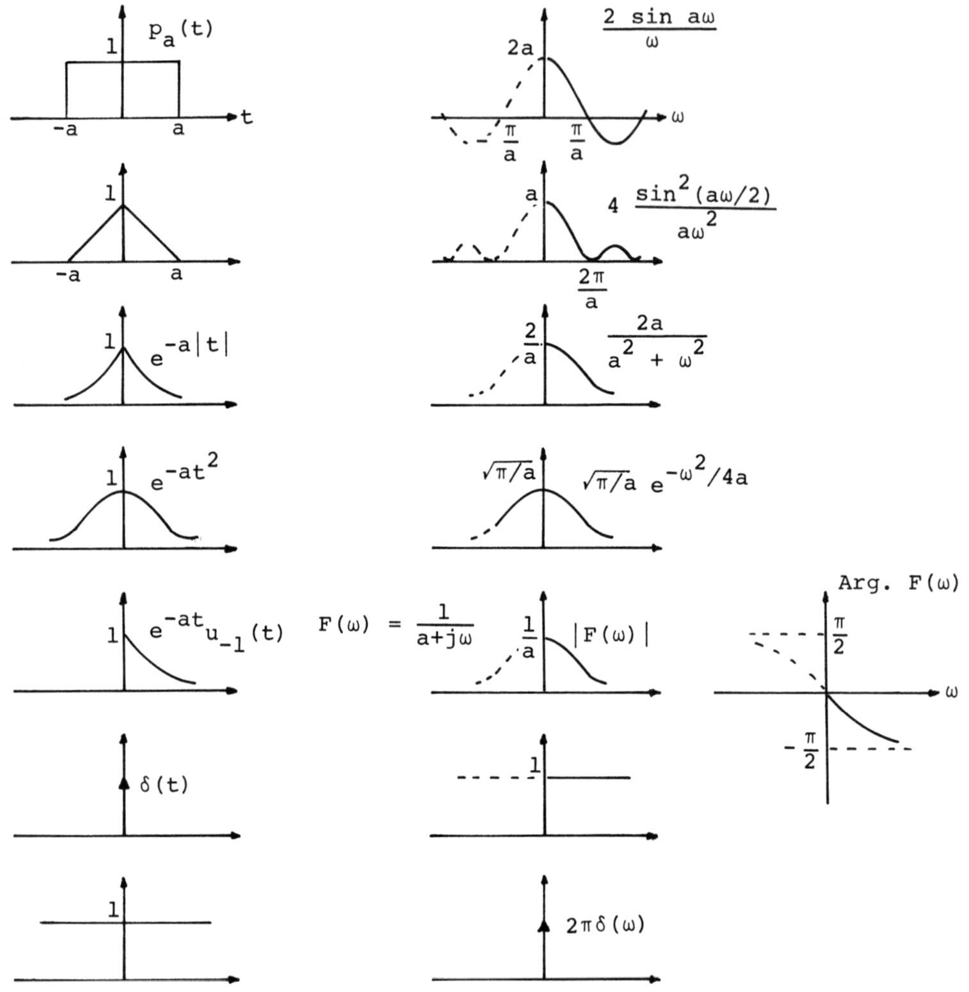

$p_a(t)$
1
-a
a
t
2a
$\frac{2 \sin a\omega}{\omega}$
$\frac{\pi}{a}$
$\frac{\pi}{a}$
ω
1
-a
a
a
$4 \frac{\sin^2(a\omega/2)}{a\omega^2}$
$\frac{2\pi}{a}$
1
$e^{-a|t|}$
$\frac{2}{a}$
$\frac{2a}{a^2 + \omega^2}$
1
e^{-at^2}
$\sqrt{\pi/a}$
$\sqrt{\pi/a}\ e^{-\omega^2/4a}$
1
$e^{-at}u_{-1}(t)$
$F(\omega) = \frac{1}{a+j\omega}$
$\frac{1}{a}$
$|F(\omega)|$
Arg. F(ω)
$\frac{\pi}{2}$
ω
$-\frac{\pi}{2}$
δ(t)
1
1
2πδ(ω)

Table IV-1.2.

Time Function, f(t)	Fourier Transform, F(ω)
1. $e^{-at}u(t)$	$\frac{1}{a + j\omega}$
2. $te^{-at}u(t)$	$(\frac{1}{a + j\omega})^2$
3. $g_T(t) = \begin{cases} 1, & \lvert t\rvert < T/2 \\ 0, & \text{otherwise} \end{cases}$	$T\,\frac{\sin(\omega T/2)}{\omega T/2} = T \text{ sinc } (\frac{\omega T}{2})$
4. $\begin{cases} A(1- \frac{\lvert t\rvert}{T}), & \lvert t\rvert < T \\ 0, & \lvert t\rvert > T \end{cases}$	$AT \text{ sinc}^2(\frac{\omega T}{2})$
5. $e^{-a\lvert t\rvert}$	$\frac{2a}{a^2 + \omega^2}$
6. $e^{-at} \sin \omega_0 t\ u(t)$	$\frac{\omega_0}{(a + j\omega)^2 + \omega_0^2}$
7. $e^{-at} \cos \omega_0 t\ u(t)$	$\frac{a + j\omega}{(a + j\omega)^2 + \omega_0^2}$
8. e^{-at^2}	$\frac{\pi}{a}\, e^{-\omega^2/4a}$
9. $\frac{t^{n-1}}{(n - 1)!}\, e^{-at}u(t)$	$\frac{1}{(j\omega + a)^n}$
10. $\frac{1}{a^2 + t^2}$	$\frac{\pi}{a}\, e^{-a\lvert\omega\rvert}$
11. $\frac{\cos bt}{a^2 + t^2}$	$\frac{\pi}{2a}[e^{-a\lvert\omega-b\rvert} + e^{-a\lvert\omega+b\rvert}]$
12. $\frac{\sin bt}{a^2 + t^2}$	$\frac{\pi}{2aj}\,[e^{-a\lvert\omega-b\rvert} - e^{-a\lvert\omega+b\rvert}]$
13. $\cos \omega_0 t[u(t+ \frac{T}{2})-u(t- \frac{T}{2})]$	$\frac{T}{2}[\text{sinc}(\frac{(\omega-\omega_0)}{2}\, T) + \text{sinc}(\frac{(\omega+\omega_0)}{2}\, T)]$

IV-2. Two Dimensional Fourier Transforms

The Fourier transform, Eq. (IV-1.1b) may be considered to express the function f(t) as an infinite sum (the integral) of elementary functions $e^{j\omega t}$ (an infinite number of sine and cosine functions) each of which is weighted by an amount $F(\omega)$. In a similar fashion, we can consider the two-dimensional Fourier transform

$$F(\omega_x,\omega_y) = \iint_{-\infty}^{\infty} f(x,y)\, e^{-j(\omega_x x+\omega_y y)}\, dx\, dy \qquad \text{a)}$$

$$f(x,y) = \mathscr{F}^{-1}[F(\omega_x,\omega_y)] = \frac{1}{(2\pi)^2}\iint_{-\infty}^{\infty} F(\omega_x,\omega_y) e^{j(\omega_x x+\omega_y y)}\, d\omega_x d\omega_y \qquad \text{b)} \qquad \text{(IV-2.1)}$$

The function f(x,y) can be thought of as the result of the addition of an infinite number of elementary functions $e^{j(\omega_x x+\omega_y y)}$ each of which is weighted by $F(\omega_x,\omega_y)$ at frequencies ω_x and ω_y. We observe that $e^{j(\omega_x x+\omega_y y)}$ resembles the phase factor of a propagating wave $e^{j\bar{k}\cdot\bar{r}} = e^{j(k_x x+k_y y)}$ traveling in the $\bar{k}$ direction. This suggests that the function $e^{j(\omega_x x+\omega_y y)}$ at each pair of the spatial frequencies ω_x and ω_y can be represented in the XY plane as a sinusoidal amplitude variation inclined at an angle θ, as shown in Fig. IV-2.1. The spectrum $F(\omega_x,\omega_y)$ is then a weighting factor to the elementary function $e^{j(\omega_x x+\omega_y y)}$ such that when all (infinite number) the elementary weighted functions are summed, we synthesize the desired function f(x,y).

The following lists some of the basic properties of the two-dimensional Fourier transforms:

1. Linearity

$$\mathscr{F}[af_1(x,y) + bf_2(a,y)] = a\mathscr{F}[f_1(x,y)] + b\mathscr{F}[f_2(x,y)]$$

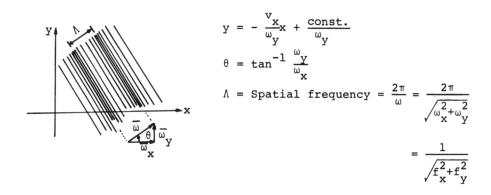

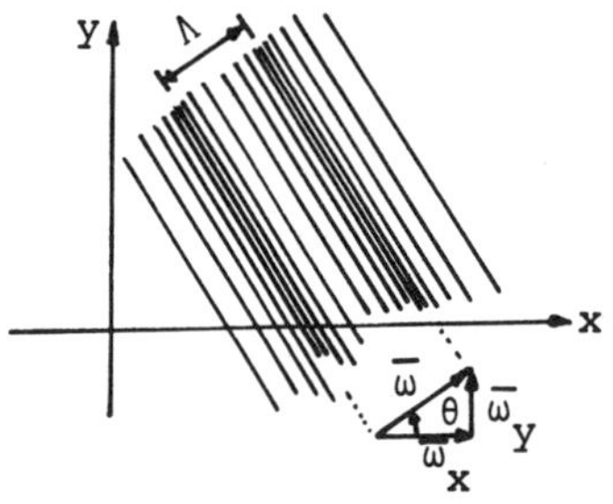

$$y = -\frac{v_x}{\omega_y}x + \frac{\text{const.}}{\omega_y}$$

$$\theta = \tan^{-1}\frac{\omega_y}{\omega_x}$$

$$\Lambda = \text{Spatial frequency} = \frac{2\pi}{\omega} = \frac{2\pi}{\sqrt{\omega_x^2+\omega_y^2}}$$

$$= \frac{1}{\sqrt{f_x^2+f_y^2}}$$

Figure IV-2.1. Two dimensional elementary function.

2. Spatial shifting

$$\mathscr{F}[f(x-a,y-b)] = e^{-j(\omega_x a+\omega_y b)} F(\omega_x,\omega_y)$$

3. Spatial scaling

$$\mathscr{F}[f(ax,by)] = \frac{1}{|ab|} F(\frac{\omega_x}{a}, \frac{\omega_y}{b})$$

4. Spatial frequency shifting

$$\mathscr{F}[e^{j(\omega_{xo}x+\omega_{yo}y)} f(x,y)] = F(\omega_x-\omega_{xo},\omega_y-\omega_{yo})$$

5. Parseval's relation

$$\iint_{-\infty}^{\infty} |f(x,y)|^2 dx\, dy = \iint_{-\infty}^{\infty} f(x,y)f^*(x,y)dx\, dy = \frac{1}{(2\pi)^2}\iint_{-\infty}^{\infty} |F(\omega_x,\omega_y)|^2 d\omega_x d\omega_y$$

6. Spatial Convolution

$$[\iint_{-\infty}^{\infty} f_1(\xi,\eta)f_2(x-\xi,y-\eta)d\xi d\eta] = F_1(\omega_x,\omega_y)F_2(\omega_x,\omega_y)$$

7. Spatial Frequency convolution

$$\mathscr{F}[f_1(x,y)f_2(x,y)] = \frac{1}{(2\pi)^2}\iint_{-\infty}^{\infty} F_1(\omega_x-\xi)F_2(\omega_y-\eta)d\xi\, d\eta$$

8. Autocorrelation

$$\mathscr{F}[\iint_{-\infty}^{\infty} f(\xi,\eta)f^*(\xi-x,\eta-y)d\xi d\eta] = |F(\omega_x,\omega_y)|^2$$

9. Separable Functions

$$\mathscr{F}[f(x,y)] = \mathscr{F}[f_1(x)f_2(y)] = \mathscr{F}[f_1(x)]\mathscr{F}[f_2(y)]$$

10. Differentiation (zero initial conditions)

$$\mathscr{F}[(\frac{\partial}{\partial x})^m(\frac{\partial}{\partial y})^n f(x,y)] = (j\omega_x)^m(j\omega_y)^n F(\omega_x,\omega_y)$$

The reader should refer to Chap. 12 for examples that involve the two dimensional Fourier transform.

B. Laplace Transforms

IV-3. Laplace Transforms

The one-sided Laplace transform is defined for functions which start at a finite time, i.e., the functions are zero for $t < 0$, and satisfy the integrability condition

$$\int_{-\infty}^{\infty} |f(t)|dt = \text{finite} \tag{IV-3.1}$$

To improve this condition, we consider instead the function

$$f_1(t) = e^{-\sigma t} f(t)u_{-1}(t) \tag{IV-3.2}$$

where $\sigma > 0$ and is real, and such that the integral

$$\int_0^{\infty} e^{-\sigma t} f(t)dt \tag{IV-3.3}$$

converges. We introduce Eq. (IV-3.2) into the Fourier integral representation of a function, with the result

$$f_1(t) = \frac{1}{2\pi}\int_{\infty}^{\infty} e^{j\omega t}d\omega \int_0^{\infty} e^{-\sigma t} f(t)e^{-j\omega t}dt$$

or

$$f(t)e^{-\sigma t} = \frac{1}{2\pi}\int_{-\infty}^{\infty} e^{j\omega t}d\omega \int_0^{\infty} f(t)e^{-(\sigma+j\omega)t}dt = \frac{1}{2\pi}\int_{-\infty}^{\infty} e^{j\omega t}d\omega \int_0^{\infty} f(t)e^{-st}dt$$

or

$$f(t) = \frac{1}{2\pi}\int_{-\infty}^{\infty} e^{(\sigma+j\omega)t}d\omega\, F(s)$$

We write $s = \sigma + j\omega$, and $ds = j\, d\omega$

$$f(t) = \frac{1}{2\pi j}\int_{\sigma-j\infty}^{\sigma+j\infty} e^{(\sigma+j\omega)t}F(s)d(\sigma+j\omega) = \frac{1}{2\pi j}\int_{\sigma-j\infty}^{\sigma+j\infty} F(s)e^{st}\, ds$$

The Laplace transform pair has the form

$$F(s) = \mathscr{L}[f(t)] = \int_0^{\infty} f(t)e^{-st}\, dt \qquad \text{a)}$$

$$f(t) = \mathscr{L}^{-1}[F(s)] = \frac{1}{2\pi j}\int_{\sigma-j\infty}^{\sigma+j\infty} F(s)e^{st}\, ds \qquad \text{b)} \tag{IV-3.4}$$

The following are some of the most useful properties of Laplace transforms:

1. Linearity

$$\mathscr{L}[af_1(t) + bf_2(t)] = aF_1(s) + bF_2(s)$$

2. Shifting

$$\mathscr{L}[e^{at}f(t)] = F(s - a)$$

3. Time Convolution

$$\mathscr{L}[\int_0^{\infty} f_1(\tau)f_2(t-\tau)d\tau] = F_1(s)F_2(s)$$

4. First Order Derivative

$$\mathscr{L}[\frac{df}{dt}] = s\mathscr{L}[f(t)] - f(0) = sF(s) - f(0)$$

5. Second Order Derivative

$$\mathscr{L}[\frac{d^2f}{dt^2}] = s^2F(s) - sf(0) - \frac{df(0)}{dt}$$

6. Integral

$$\mathscr{L}[\int_0^t f(\xi)d\xi] = \frac{1}{s}F(s) + \frac{\left.\int_{-\infty}^t f(\xi)d\xi\right|_{t=0}}{s}$$

Example IV-3.1. Find the Laplace transform of the function $f(t) = e^{-at}u_{-1}(t)$.

Solution. Apply Eq. (IV-3.4a) to obtain

$$F(s) = \int_0^{\infty} e^{-at}e^{-st}\,dt = \int_0^{\infty} e^{-(s+a)t}dt = \frac{1}{s+a}$$

ΔΔΔ

Example IV-3.2. Find the Laplace transform of the differential equation

$$\frac{d^2v(t)}{dt^2} + 3\,\frac{dv(t)}{dt} + 4v(t) = \delta(t)$$

with zero initial conditions.

Solution. We do this on a term by term basis.

From property 5: $\mathscr{L}[\frac{d^2v(t)}{dt^2}] = s^2F(s) - s\cdot 0 - 0 = s^2F(s)$

From property 4: $\mathscr{L}[3\,\frac{dv(t)}{dt}] = 3[sF(s) - 0] = 3sF(s)$

By Eq. (IV-3.4a): $\int_0^{\infty} \delta(t)e^{-st}dt = e^{-s\cdot 0} = 1.$

Therefore the Laplace transform of the given differential equation becomes

$$s^2F(s) + 3sF(s) + 4F(s) = 1$$

from which

$$F(s) = \frac{1}{s^2 + 3s + 4}$$

In the next section we shall learn how to invert already transformed functions without the use of Eq. (IV-3.4b). ΔΔΔ

Table IV-3.1 contains important Laplace transform pairs:

Table IV-3.1.

$F(s) = \mathscr{L}\{f(t)\}$	$f(t)$
$F(s - a)$	$e^{at}f(t)$
$F(as)$	$\frac{1}{a} f(\frac{t}{a})$
$F(as + b)$	$\frac{1}{a} \exp(-\frac{bt}{a}) f(\frac{t}{a})$
$\frac{1}{s} e^{-cs}, \quad c > 0$	$\alpha(t - c) = 0, \; 0 \leq t < c,$ $= 1, \; t \geq c$
$e^{-cs}F(s), \; c > 0$	$f(t - c)\alpha(t - c)$
$F_1(s)F_2(s)$	$\int_0^t f_1(\beta)f_2(t - \beta)d\beta$
$\frac{1}{s}$	1
$\frac{1}{s^{n+1}}$	$\frac{t^n}{n!}$
$\frac{1}{s^{x+1}}, \quad x > -1$	$\frac{t^x}{\Gamma(x + 1)}$
$s^{-1/2}$	$(\pi t)^{-1/2}$
$\frac{1}{s + a}$	e^{-at}
$\frac{1}{(s + a)^{n+1}}$	$\frac{t^n e^{-at}}{n!}$
$\frac{k}{s^2 + k^2}$	$\sin kt$

$F(s) = \mathscr{L}\{f(t)\}$	$f(t)$
$\frac{s}{s^2 + k^2}$	$\cos kt$
$\frac{k}{s^2 - k^2}$	$\sinh kt$
$\frac{s}{s^2 - k^2}$	$\cosh kt$
$\frac{2k^3}{(s^2 + k^2)^2}$	$\sin kt - kt \cos kt$
$\frac{2ks}{(s^2+k^2)^2}$	$t \sin kt$
$\frac{1}{s} \exp(-c\sqrt{s}), \quad c > 0$	$\operatorname{erfc}(\frac{c}{2\sqrt{t}})$
$\frac{1}{s\sqrt{s+1}}$	$\operatorname{erf}(\sqrt{t})$
$\ln(1 + \frac{1}{s})$	$\frac{1 - e^{-t}}{t}$
$\ln \frac{s + k}{s - k}$	$\frac{2 \sinh kt}{t}$
$\ln(1 - \frac{k^2}{s^2})$	$\frac{2}{t}(1 - \cosh kt)$
$\ln(1 + \frac{k^2}{s^2})$	$\frac{2}{t}(1 - \cos kt)$
$\arctan \frac{k}{s}$	$\frac{\sin kt}{t}$
$\frac{1}{s} \exp(-\frac{x}{s})$	$J_0(2\sqrt{xt})$
$\frac{1}{s^{n+1}} \exp(-\frac{x}{s})$	$(\frac{t}{x})^{(1/2)n} J_n(2\sqrt{xt})$
$\frac{1}{\sqrt{s^2 + x^2}}$	$J_0(xt)$
$1 - \frac{s}{\sqrt{s^2 + x^2}}$	$xJ_1(xt)$

IV-4. Inverse Laplace Transform

Often in our studies we must obtain the inverse transform of a rational fraction N(s)/D(s), where the numerator and denominator are polynomials in s, and the degree of D(s) is higher than the degree of N(s). A convenient approach is to expand the rational fraction into partial fraction form. This permits us to replace a complicated problem with a set of simpler problems.

Example IV-4.1. Obtain the inverse transform of

$$\mathscr{L}^{-1}\left[\frac{s - 4}{s^3 + 4s^2 + 3s}\right]$$

Solution. We expand this function in partial fraction form as follows:

$$\frac{s - 4}{s^3 + 4s^2 + 3s} = \frac{s - 4}{s(s+3)(s+1)} = \frac{A}{s} + \frac{B}{s+1} + \frac{C}{s+3}$$

$$= \frac{A(s+1)(s+3) + Bs(s+3) + Cs(s+1)}{s^3 + 4s^2 + 3s}$$

This establishes the identity

$$s - 4 = A(s+1)(s+3) + Bs(s+3) + Cs(s+1)$$

To determine the constants A, B and C, we set s = 0, s = -1 and s = -3 successively. When this is done we obtain

for s = 0 we find $\quad -4 = A\cdot 1\cdot 3 = 3A$

for s = -1 $\quad -5 = B\cdot(-1)\cdot 2 = -2B$

for s = -3 $\quad -7 = C\cdot(-3)\cdot(-2) = 6C$

From these we find that A = -4/3; B = 5/2; C = -7/6. Therefore

$$\frac{s - 4}{s^3 + 4s^2 + 3s} = -\frac{4}{3}\cdot\frac{1}{5} + \frac{5}{2}\frac{1}{s+1} - \frac{7}{6}\frac{1}{s+3}$$

The inverse is easily found by using Table IV-3.1. The result is

$$\mathscr{L}^{-1}\left[\frac{s - 4}{s^3 + 4s^2 + 3s}\right] = -\frac{4}{3} + \frac{5}{2}e^{-t} - \frac{7}{6}e^{-3t}$$

ΔΔΔ

Example IV-4.2. Obtain

$$\mathscr{L}^{-1}\left[\frac{s^2 - s + 1}{s^3(s+1)^2}\right]$$

Solution. Since the denominator has multiple roots, we expand it into the following form

$$\frac{s^2 - s + 1}{s^3(s+1)^2} = \frac{A_1}{s} + \frac{A_2}{s^2} + \frac{A_3}{s^3} + \frac{B_1}{s+1} + \frac{B_2}{(s+1)^2}$$

From this, we obtain the identity

$$s^2 - s + 1 = A_1 s^2(s+1)^2 + A_2 s(s+1)^2 + A_3(s+1)^2 + B_1 s^3(s+1) + B_2 s^3$$

We require five equations for determining the unknown constants. By the proper selection of values for s, we obtain the equation set

$$\begin{array}{ll} s = 0 & 1 = A_3 \\ s = -1 & 3 = -B_2 \\ s = 1 & 1 = 4(A_1 + A_2 + A_3) + 2B_1 + B_2 \\ s = 2 & 3 = 36A_1 + 18A_2 + 9A_3 + 24B_1 + 8B_2 \\ s = -2 & 7 = 4A_1 - 2A_2 + A_3 + 8B_1 - 8B_2 \end{array}$$

These equations are readily solved for the unknown constants. ΔΔΔ

Example IV-4.3. Obtain

$$\mathscr{L}^{-1}\left[\frac{s + 1}{s(s^2+4)^2}\right]$$

Solution. The quadratic factors require the corresponding partial fraction terms to have linear numerators, the expansion assumes the form

$$\frac{s + 1}{s(s^2+4)^2} = \frac{A}{s} + \frac{B_1 s + C_1}{s^2 + 4} + \frac{B_2 s + C_2}{(s^2+4)^2}$$

from which the following identity is found

$$s+1 = A(s^2+4)^2 + (B_1 s+C_1)s(s^2+4) + (B_2 s+C_2)s$$

The remaining steps parallel those given in Ex. IV-4.1. ΔΔΔ

APPENDIX V

DIFFERENCE EQUATIONS

Some aspects of difference equations occur in Chap. 3 in connection with numerical approximation solutions to differential equations. Other aspects of difference equations appear in Chap. 11 in conjunction with the study of systems of lenses. In simple terms, a difference equation is a relation among the values of r at various points of the set S of consecutive integers for which the difference equation is defined. The range of values of the integer must be specified for each equation. We first consider:

Definition V-1. A difference equation over the set S of consecutive integers is linear over S if it can be written in the form

$$f_0(n)r_{n+k} + f_1(n)r_{n+k-1} + \cdots + f_{k-1}(n)r_{n+1} + f_k(n)r_n = h(n) \tag{V-1}$$

where f_0, f_1, ..., f_k and h are each functions of n defined for all values of n in the set.

Definition V-2. A linear difference equation, written in the form of Eq. (V-1) is of order k over S if both f_0 and f_k are different from zero at each point of S.

We shall continue our discussion with specific reference to Eq. (11-9.9) which, if we raise each index by 1, is an equation of the form

$$r_{n+2} - ar_{n+1} + br_n = 0$$

which shows that the equation is of second order. As specific examples, we note the following difference equations, which are linear with constant coefficients

$$r_{n+2} + 3r_{n+1} + 2r_n = 2n \qquad \text{(order 2)}$$

$$r_{n+2} + r_{n+1} = 4n \qquad \text{(order 1)} \qquad \text{(V-2)}$$

$$r_{n+2} - 3r_n = 0 \qquad \text{(order 2)}$$

Refer again to Eq. (V-1). We assume that $f_0(n) \neq 0$, and the equation can be written in the form

$$r_{n+k} + a_1 r_{n+k-1} + \ldots + a_{k-1} r_{n+1} + a_k r_n = h_n \qquad \text{(V-3)}$$

where $a_1, a_2, \ldots, a_k$ are constants (with $a_k \neq 0$) and where h_n is an arbitrary function of n which is defined for $n = 0,1,2,\ldots$. If $h_n = 0$, then Eq. (V-3) will assume the form

$$r_{n+k} + a_1 r_{n+k-1} + \ldots + a_k r_n = 0 \qquad \text{(V-4)}$$

This is called the *homogeneous* difference equation corresponding to the *non-homogeneous* difference equation (V-3). Appropriate forms corresponding to Eq. (V-2) can readily be developed.

To proceed, we consider the following theorem:

Theorem V-1. If $r^{(1)}$ and $r^{(2)}$ are any two solutions of the linear homogeneous difference equation (V-4) then $r^h = C_1 r^{(1)} + C_2 r^{(2)}$ is also a solution, with C_1 and C_2 being arbitrary constants.

Proof: Let us take the second order difference equation, (k = 2)

$$r_{n+2} + a_1 r_{n+1} + a_2 r_n = 0 \qquad \text{(V-5)}$$

We must show that if $r^{(1)}$ and $r^{(2)}$ are solutions of Eq. (V.5) then $C_1 r^{(1)} + C_2 r^{(2)}$ is also a solution. Introduce the linear combination of the solutions into Eq. (V-5), to obtain

$$[C_1 r_{n+2}^{(1)} + C_2 r_{n+2}^{(2)}] + a_1 [C_1 r_{n+1}^{(1)} + C_2 r_{n+1}^{(2)}] + a_2 \, [C_1 r_n^{(1)} + C_2 r_n^{(2)}] = 0$$

or

$$C_1 \, [r_{n+2}^{(1)} + a_1 r_{n+1}^{(1)} + r_n^{(1)}] + C_2 \, [r_{n+2}^{(2)} + a_1 r_{n+1}^{(2)} + r_n^{(2)}] = 0 \qquad \text{(V-6)}$$

which is an identity, and it is true for any $n = 0,1,2,\ldots$. This is so because the quantities inside the brackets are zero since $r^{(1)}$ and $r^{(2)}$ are solutions of Eq. (V-5).

Theorem V-2. If r^h is a solution of the homogeneous equation (V.4) and r^p is a solution of the non-homogeneous equation (V-3) then $r^h + r^p$ is a solution of Eq. (V-3).

Proof: By hypothesis for a second order equation, we have

$$r_{n+2}^{h} + a_1 r_{n+1}^{h} + a_2 r_n^{h} = 0$$
$$r_{n+2}^{p} + a_1 r_{n+1}^{p} + a_2 r_n^{p} = h_n \qquad \text{(V-7)}$$

Upon addition of these two equations, we obtain

$$(r_{n+2}^{h} + r_{n+2}^{p}) + a_1(r_{n+1}^{h} + r_{n+1}^{p}) + a_2(r_n^{h} + r_n^{p}) = h_n \qquad \text{(V-8)}$$

which is the expected solution.

Example V-1. Find the solution to the first order homogeneous difference equation

$$r_{n+1} + a_1 r_n = 0 \qquad n = 0,1,2,\ldots \qquad \text{(V-9)}$$

Solution. We assume a solution of the form

$$r_n^{h} = C(-a_1)^n \qquad \text{(V-10)}$$

where C is a constant. Now introduce Eq. (V-10) into Eq. (V-9) to find the relation

$$C(-a_1)^{n+1} + Ca_1(-a_1)^n = C(-a_1)^n(-a_1 + a_1) = 0$$

which proves that the relation assumed is an appropriate form. Suppose also that an initial condition

$$r_o = C_o \qquad \text{(V-11)}$$

had been given. We can find the constant C from the relation

$$r_o^{h} = C_o = C(-a_1)^o = C \qquad \text{(V-12)}$$

Thus the solution of Eq. (V-9) with the initial condition (V-11) is given by

$$r_n^{h} = C_o(-a_1)^n \qquad \text{(V-13)}$$

ΔΔΔ

Example V-2. Find the solution to the difference equation

$$r_{n+1} - 2r_n = -n \qquad \text{(V-14)}$$

with the initial condition $r_o = 2$.

Solution. This problem is of the form specified in Eq. (V-9), but here the equation is non-homogeneous. For the homogeneous equation, by Eq. (V-13), the solution is

$$r_n^h = C(2)^n \tag{V-15}$$

To find the particular solution, we adopt tentatively as a solution

$$r_n^p = n + 1 \tag{V-16}$$

The validity of this can be verified by direct substitution. Hence the complete solution is given by

$$r_n = r_n^h + r_n^p = C(2)^n + n + 1 \tag{V-17}$$

By applying the initial condition, we find that

$$r_o = 2 = C(2)^o + 0 + 1 \qquad \therefore \quad C = 1 \tag{V-18}$$

and the solution to Eq. (V-14) is

$$r_n = 2^n + n + 1 \tag{V-19}$$

ΔΔΔ

We are now in a position to investigate the general solution of the second order homogeneous equation. We assume that

$$r_n = m^n \tag{V-20}$$

where m is some suitably chosen constant, different from zero. If we substitute this trial solution into Eq. (V-5) we obtain

$$m^2 + a_1 m + a_2 = 0 \tag{V-21}$$

which is known as the *auxiliary equation*. If m satisfies this equation, then Eq. (V-20) is the solution to Eq. (V-21). Clearly, since the auxiliary equation is a quadratic algebraic equation, it has two roots in m, say m_1 and m_2. Three cases are possible: (1) m_1 and m_2 distinct and real; (2) $m_1 = m_2$ and real; (3) m_1 and m_2 complex conjugates of each other. For the case when the roots are real and distinct, the solution to the homogeneous equation is

$$r_n^h = C_1 m_1^n + C_2 m_2^n \tag{V-22}$$

Example V-3. Find the solution to the following homogeneous equation

$$r_{n+2} - 3r_{n+1} + 2r_n = 0 \tag{V-23}$$

Solution. The auxiliary equation is readily found to be

$$m^{n+2} - 3m^{n+1} + 2m^n = m^n(m^2 - 3m + 2) = 0$$

For a non-trivial solution $m \neq 0$, and then

$$m = -\frac{3 \pm \sqrt{9-8}}{2} \qquad \therefore \quad m_1 = 1, \quad m_2 = 2$$

Hence the general solution is given by

$$r_n^h = C_1(1)^n + C_2(2)^n = C_1 + C_2 2^n \tag{V-24}$$

When the roots are real and equal, then the solutions $r^{(1)}$ and $r^{(2)}$ are not independent. To obtain a solution, we proceed in a manner that parallels the case of equal roots in differential equations. We retain as a solution $r^{(1)} = m_1^n$, but we now set $r^{(2)} = nm_1^n$. The solution is then

$$r_n^h = C_1 m_1^n + C_2 n m_1^n = (C_1 + C_2 n) m_1^n \tag{V-25}$$

ΔΔΔ

Example V-4. Find the solution to the difference equation

$$r_{n+2} + 2r_{n+1} + r_n = 0 \tag{V-26}$$

Solution. The two roots of the auxiliary equation are found to be $m_1 = m_2 \equiv 1$ and the general solution of Eq. (V-26) is given by

$$r_n^h = (C_1 + C_2 n)(-1)^n \tag{V-27}$$

which can be verified by direct substitution into the given difference equation.

The third possibility for the roots is that they form a complex conjugate pair. Since the value of our solution r_n^h must be a real number, it is implied that the unknown constant C_1 and C_2 must be complex conjugates. Thus we set

$$m_1 = Re^{j\theta}, \quad m_2 = Re^{-j\theta}, \quad C_1 = Ce^{j\phi}, \quad C_2 = Ce^{-j\phi} \tag{V-28}$$

and we obtain

$$r_n^h = C_1 m_1^n + C_2 m_2^n = 2CR^n \cos(n\theta + \phi) = AR^n \cos(n\theta + \phi) \qquad \text{(V-29)}$$

where A and B are arbitrary constants. ΔΔΔ

Example V-5. Find the solution of the equation

$$r_{n+2} + 4r_n = 0 \qquad \text{(V-30)}$$

Solution. The auxiliary equation

$$m^2 + 4 = 0$$

has the roots $m_1 = 2j$ and $m_2 = -2j$. In polar form these roots are

$$m_1 = 2e^{j\frac{\pi}{2}} \qquad m_2 = 2e^{-j\frac{\pi}{2}}$$

The solution is given by

$$r_n^h = A2^n \cos(n\,\frac{\pi}{2} + \phi) \qquad \text{(V-31)}$$

If, in addition, the initial conditions are $r_0^h = 0$ and $r_1^h = 1$, we shall find the following identities

$$0 = A2^0 \cos\phi = A\cos\phi$$

$$1 = A2^1 \cos\,(\frac{\pi}{2} + \phi)$$

from which we find that $\phi = \pi/2$ and $A = -1/2$. Thus the solution is

$$r_n^h = -\frac{1}{2}\,2^n \cos(n\,\frac{\pi}{2} + \frac{\pi}{2}) = 2^{n-1} \sin\frac{n\pi}{2} \qquad \text{(V-32)}$$

ΔΔΔ

PROBLEMS

V-1. Find the general solution to each of the following homogeneous difference equations:

a. $r_{n+2} - 4r_n = 0$

b. $r_{n+2} + 16r_n = 0$

c. $r_{n+2} + 2r_{n+1} + 2r_n = 0$

d. $r_{n+2} + 3r_{n+1} - 4r_n = 0.$

APPENDIX VI

MATRIX EIGENVALUE PROBLEM

This Appendix will examine certain features and methods of finding the eigenvalues and eigenvectors of a system of equations. These concepts will be found useful in our discussions of optical resonators.

When a matrix operates on a vector (column matrix), the resultant will be altered in both its magnitude and direction. However, when associated with certain matrixes, the result can be vectors whose magnitudes alone have changed. We call such vectors the "eigenvectors," and these are the solutions of the following eigenvalue problem

$$[A]\ [r] = \lambda\, [r]$$

or

$$\begin{bmatrix} a_{11} & a_{12} \\ a_{21} & a_{22} \end{bmatrix} \cdot \begin{bmatrix} r_1 \\ r_2 \end{bmatrix} = \lambda \begin{bmatrix} r_1 \\ r_2 \end{bmatrix} \tag{VI-1}$$

for the simple case of a two dimensional problem. The results can be extended easily to problems of higher dimensions. The complex value λ is the *eigenvalue*. Note that since $[r]^{*T}\lambda^{*}\lambda[r] = |\lambda|^2|[r^2]|$ the magnitude $|\lambda|$ of the complex eigenvalue λ determines the expansion or the contraction of the vector. The vector $[r]^T$ is the row vector (transpose) of $[r]$.

The eigenvalue problem of Eq. (VI-1) assumes the form

$$([A] - \lambda\, [I])\ [r] = 0 \tag{VI-2}$$

where $[I]$ is the identity matrix. For a nontrivial solution to exist, we must have

$$|[A] - \lambda[I]| = \begin{vmatrix} a_{11}-\lambda & a_{12} \\ a_{21} & a_{22}-\lambda \end{vmatrix} = 0 \quad \text{(VI-3)}$$

from which

$$\lambda^2 + (-a_{11}-a_{22})\lambda + (a_{11}a_{22}-a_{21}a_{12}) = \lambda^2 + a_1\lambda + a_2 = 0 \quad \text{(VI-4)}$$

Clearly, Eq. (VI-4) has two roots which we designate λ_1 and λ_2 (here assumed to be distinct). By making use of the roots, we write the expression

$$(\lambda-\lambda_1)\ (\lambda-\lambda_2) = \lambda^2 + (-\lambda_1-\lambda_2)\lambda + \lambda_1\lambda_2 \quad \text{(VI-5)}$$

By comparing this with Eq. (VI-4) we write

$$\begin{aligned} a_1 &= -(\lambda_1+\lambda_2) = -\ \text{Trace}\ [A] \\ a_2 &= \lambda_1\lambda_2 = \text{Det}\ [A] \end{aligned} \quad \text{(VI-6)}$$

In dealing with this type of problem, we must first find the eigenvalues and then the corresponding eigenvectors. This requires that we seek the non-singular matrix [Q] which reduces a given matrix [A] to diagonal form under the similarity transformation

$$[A]' = [Q]^{-1}\ [A]\ [Q] \quad \text{(VI-7)}$$

This presupposes that the eigenvalues are distinct. If we choose [A]' to be diagonal (hence that the eigenvalues are distinct) then Eq. (VI-7) becomes

$$\begin{bmatrix} a_{11} & a_{12} \\ a_{21} & a_{22} \end{bmatrix} \begin{bmatrix} q_{11} & q_{12} \\ q_{21} & q_{22} \end{bmatrix} = \begin{bmatrix} q_{11} & q_{12} \\ q_{21} & q_{22} \end{bmatrix} \begin{bmatrix} a_1' & 0 \\ 0 & a_2' \end{bmatrix} \quad \text{(VI-8)}$$

which shows that the product of [A] and each column of [Q] is equal to the product of [Q] and each column of [A]'. That is, for the indicated equality

$$[A] \begin{bmatrix} q_{11} \\ q_{21} \end{bmatrix} = a_1' \begin{bmatrix} q_{11} \\ q_{21} \end{bmatrix}; \qquad [A] \begin{bmatrix} q_{12} \\ q_{22} \end{bmatrix} = a_2' \begin{bmatrix} q_{12} \\ q_{22} \end{bmatrix}$$

or

$$[[A] - a_1'[I]] \begin{bmatrix} q_{11} \\ q_{21} \end{bmatrix} = 0; \qquad [[A] - a_2'[I]] \begin{bmatrix} q_{12} \\ q_{22} \end{bmatrix} = 0 \quad \text{(VI-9)}$$

This set has nontrivial solutions if

$$|[A] - a_1'[I]| = 0; \qquad |[A] - a_2'[I]| = 0$$

This indicates that $a_1' = \lambda_1$ and $a_2' = \lambda_2$ [see Eq. (VI-2)]. It can be shown that [Q] is nonsingular and therefore $[Q]^{-1}$ exists, so that we can always diagonalize [A] having distinct eigenvalues by a similarity transformation using a matrix whose column vectors are the eigenvectors of [A].

To obtain the eigenvectors, we proceed as follows. We equate each column matrix of Eq. (VI-9) to an arbitrary column vector $[Y]^{(1)}$ whose first element is non-zero, with all of the remaining entries being zero. That is, we write

$$\begin{bmatrix} a_{11}-\lambda_1 & a_{12} \\ a_{21} & a_{22}-\lambda_1 \end{bmatrix} \begin{bmatrix} q_{11} \\ q_{21} \end{bmatrix} = \begin{bmatrix} y_1^{(1)} \\ 0 \end{bmatrix}; \qquad \begin{bmatrix} a_{11}-\lambda_2 & a_{12} \\ a_{21} & a_{22}-\lambda_2 \end{bmatrix} \begin{bmatrix} q_{12} \\ q_{22} \end{bmatrix} = \begin{bmatrix} y_1^{(2)} \\ 0 \end{bmatrix}$$

or

$$\begin{bmatrix} q_{11} \\ q_{21} \end{bmatrix} = \begin{bmatrix} a_{11}-\lambda_1 & a_{12} \\ a_{21} & a_{22}-\lambda_1 \end{bmatrix}^{-1} \begin{bmatrix} y_1^{(1)} \\ 0 \end{bmatrix}; \qquad \begin{bmatrix} q_{12} \\ q_{22} \end{bmatrix} = \begin{bmatrix} a_{11}-\lambda_2 & a_{12} \\ a_{21} & a_{22}-\lambda_2 \end{bmatrix}^{-1} \begin{bmatrix} y_1^{(2)} \\ 0 \end{bmatrix}$$

For convenience, we denote the elements of the inverse matrixes $b_{ik}^{(1)}$ and $b_{ik}^{(2)}$; then the equation given yields

$$q_{11} = b_{11}^{(1)} y_1^{(1)} \qquad q_{12} = b_{11}^{(2)} y_1^{(2)}$$

$$q_{21} = b_{21}^{(1)} y_1^{(1)} \qquad q_{22} = b_{21}^{(2)} y_1^{(2)}$$

Now eliminate the y-parameters, and this specifies the required ratios

$$\frac{q_{11}}{q_{21}} = \frac{b_{11}^{(1)}}{b_{21}^{(1)}} \qquad \frac{q_{12}}{q_{22}} = \frac{b_{11}^{(2)}}{b_{22}^{(2)}} \tag{VI-11}$$

As a matter of detail, to find the inverse of a square matrix $[A] = [a_{ij}]$, we first find the cofactor matrix $[A]^c$ having the elements $a_{ij}{}^c$, where $a_{ij}{}^c$ is the cofactor of the element a_{ij} in the determinant $|a_{ij}|$. Next we take the transpose of the matrix $[A]^c$ and divide the resulting matrix by the determinant of $|[A]|$, that is,

$$[A]^{-1} = \frac{\text{adj } [A]}{|[A]|} = \frac{[A]^{cT}}{|[A]|} \qquad (|[A]| \neq 0) \tag{VI-12}$$

Example VI-1. Find the inverse of a third order matrix A, where

$$A = \begin{bmatrix} a_{11} & a_{12} & a_{13} \\ a_{21} & a_{22} & a_{23} \\ a_{31} & a_{32} & a_{33} \end{bmatrix}$$

Solution. The cofactor matrix of A is the following:

$$[A]^c = \begin{bmatrix} \begin{vmatrix} a_{22} & a_{23} \\ a_{32} & a_{33} \end{vmatrix} & -\begin{vmatrix} a_{21} & a_{23} \\ a_{31} & a_{33} \end{vmatrix} & \begin{vmatrix} a_{21} & a_{22} \\ a_{31} & a_{32} \end{vmatrix} \\ -\begin{vmatrix} a_{12} & a_{13} \\ a_{32} & a_{33} \end{vmatrix} & \begin{vmatrix} a_{11} & a_{13} \\ a_{31} & a_{33} \end{vmatrix} & -\begin{vmatrix} a_{11} & a_{12} \\ a_{31} & a_{32} \end{vmatrix} \\ \begin{vmatrix} a_{12} & a_{13} \\ a_{22} & a_{23} \end{vmatrix} & -\begin{vmatrix} a_{11} & a_{13} \\ a_{21} & a_{23} \end{vmatrix} & \begin{vmatrix} a_{11} & a_{12} \\ a_{21} & a_{22} \end{vmatrix} \end{bmatrix} = \begin{bmatrix} a_{11}^c & a_{12}^c & a_{13}^c \\ a_{21}^c & a_{22}^c & a_{23}^c \\ a_{31}^c & a_{32}^c & a_{33}^c \end{bmatrix} \tag{VI-13}$$

The transpose of A^c is given by

$$[A]^{cT} = \begin{bmatrix} a_{11}^c & a_{21}^c & a_{31}^c \\ a_{12}^c & a_{22}^c & a_{32}^c \\ a_{13}^c & a_{23}^c & a_{33}^c \end{bmatrix}$$

This result, in conjunction with Eq. (VI-12) gives the desired form.

APPENDIX VII

CONVERSION UNITS AND PHYSICAL CONSTANTS

VII-1. Units and Dimensions

For a self-consistent system the unit of current in the m.k.s. system is the Ampere and the unit of resistance the Ohm. When one Ampere passes through a resistance of one Ohm in one second the heat dissipated is equal to one Joule, or

$$W = I^2Rt \qquad \text{Joule} \tag{VII-1.1}$$

From this equation we obtain

$$1 \text{ Ohm} = 1 \frac{\text{Watt}}{\text{Ampere}^2} = 1 \frac{\text{kilogram-meter}^2}{\text{Coulomb}^2\text{-second}} \tag{VII-1.2}$$

Since $R = \ell/\sigma S$ (see Ex. 5-11.1) the dimension of the conductivity σ is given by

$$1 \frac{\text{mho}}{\text{meter}} = \frac{1}{\text{Ohm-meter}} = 1 \frac{\text{Coulomb}^2\text{-second}}{\text{kilogram-meter}^3} \tag{VII-1.3}$$

The Volt is defined as 1 Watt/Ampere, or

$$1 \text{ Volt} = 1 \frac{\text{Watt}}{\text{Ampere}} = 1 \frac{\text{kilogram-meter}^2}{\text{Coulomb-second}^2} \tag{VII-1.4}$$

From Eq. (1-10.2) we have the relation $J = \sigma E = 1$ Ampere/meter^2 and, thus,

$$1 \text{ unit of } E = 1 \frac{\text{Watt}}{\text{Ampere-meter}} = 1 \frac{\text{Volt}}{\text{meter}} = 1 \frac{\text{kilogram-meter}}{\text{Coulomb-second}^2}$$

The product of charge and electric field intensity E has the dimension of force, therefore

$$1 \text{ Coulomb} \times 1 \frac{\text{Volt}}{\text{meter}} = 1 \frac{\text{Joule}}{\text{meter}} = 1 \frac{\text{kilogram-meter}}{\text{second}^2} = \text{Newton} \qquad \text{(VII-1.5)}$$

The magnetic flux is given by (see Eq. 6-2.13)

$$\psi = \text{magnetic flux} = \int_S \overline{B} \cdot d\overline{S} \quad \text{Weber} \qquad \text{(VII-1.6)}$$

From Faraday's law $\int_C \overline{E} \cdot d\overline{\ell} = -d\psi/dt$ then

$$1 \text{ Volt} = 1 \frac{\text{Weber}}{\text{second}} \qquad \text{(VII-1.7)}$$

or equivalently

$$1 \text{ Weber} = 1 \text{ Volt} \times 1 \text{ second} = 1 \frac{\text{Joule}}{\text{Ampere}} = 1 \frac{\text{kilogram-meter}^2}{\text{Coulomb-second}} \qquad \text{(VII-1.8)}$$

Since $Q = \text{Coulomb} = \oint \varepsilon_o \varepsilon_r \overline{E} \cdot d\overline{S}$ we have the following dimensions for ε_o

$$\text{dimensions of } \varepsilon_o = \frac{\text{Coulomb}}{\text{Volt-meter}} = \frac{\text{Farad}}{\text{meter}} \qquad \text{(VII-1.9)}$$

The dimension for μ_o are:

$$\text{dimensions of } \mu_o = \frac{\text{Volt-second}}{\text{Ampere-meter}} = \frac{\text{Henry}}{\text{meter}} \qquad \text{(VII-1.10)}$$

VII-2. Units and Their Abbreviations

Table VII-2.1.

Term	Unit	Abbreviation
Electric current, I	Ampere	A
Magnetic field strength, H	Ampere/meter	A/m
Electric charge, Q	Coulomb	$C \triangleq A\text{-}s$
Capacitance, C	Farad	$F \triangleq A\text{-}s/V$
Inductance, L	Henry	$H \triangleq V\text{-}s/A$
Frequency, f	Hertz	$Hz \triangleq s^{-1}$
Force,	Newton	$N \triangleq (kg\text{-}m)/s^2$
Pressure, P	Newton/meter^2	N/m^2
Electric resistance, R	Ohm	Ω
Magnetic flux density	Teslar	$T \triangleq Wb/m^2$
Voltage	Volt	$V \triangleq W/A$

VII-3. Physical Constants

Table VII-3.1.

Quantity	Symbol	Value
Boltzmann constant	K	1.380662×10^{-23} JK^{-1}
Electron charge	e	$-1.602189 \times 10^{-19}$ C
Electron rest mass	m_e	9.109534×10^{-31} kg
Light velocity	c	2.997924×10^{8} m sec^{-1}
Permeability of vacuum	μ_o	$4\pi \times 10^{-7}$ Hm^{-1}
Permittivity of vacuum	ε_o	8.854187×10^{-12} Fm^{-1}
Planck's constant	h	6.626176×10^{-34} JHz^{-1}
Proton rest mass	m_H	1.672648×10^{-27} kg
Impedance of space	Z_o	376.7304 Ω

SELECTED BIBLIOGRAPHY

1. Abraham, M., and Becker, R., *The Classical Theory of Electricity and Magnetism*, Second Edition, Hafner Publishing Co., 1949.

2. Adler, R. B., Chu, L. J., and Fano, R. H., *Electromagnetic Energy Transmission and Radiation*, John Wiley & Sons, Inc., 1960.

3. Baker, B. B., and Copson, E. T., *The Mathematical Theory of Huygens' Principle*, Oxford at the Clarendon Press, 1969.

4. Born, M., and Wolf, E., *Principles of Optics*, Third Edition, Pergamon Press, 1965.

5. Bradshaw, M. D., and Byatt, W. J., *Introductory Engineering Field Theory*, Prentice-Hall Inc., 1967.

6. Brekhovskikh, L. M., *Waves in Layered Media*, Academic Press, 1960.

7. Budden, K. G., *Radio Waves in the Ionosphere*, Cambridge University Press, 1961.

8. Cairo, L., and Kahan, T., *Variational Techniques in Electromagnetism*, Gordon and Breach, 1965.

9. Collin, R. E., *Field Theory of Guided Waves*, McGraw-Hill Book Co., 1960.

10. Courant, R., and Hilbert, D., *Methods of Mathematical Physics*, Vol. I and II. Interscience Publishers, 1962.

11. Croxton, C. A., *Introductory Eigenphysics*, John Wiley and Sons, 1974.

12. Elmore, W. C., and Heald, M. A., *Physics of Waves*, McGraw-Hill Book Co., 1969.

13. Elsgolc, L. E., *Calculus of Variations*, Pergamon Press, 1962.

14. Feynman, R. C., Leighton, R. B., and Sands, M., "*The Feynman Lectures on Physics*," Addison-Wesley Publ. Co., Inc., 1964.

15. Forsythe, G. E., and Wasow, W. R., *Finite-Difference Methods for Partial Differential Equations*, John Wiley & Sons, Inc., 1965.

16. Foster, K., and Anderson, R., *Electromagnetic Theory Problems and Solutions*, Butterworth (London), 1969.

17. Fowles, G. R., *Introduction to Modern Optics,* Holt, Rinehart & Winston Inc., 1968.

18. French, A. P., *Vibrations and Waves,* W. W. Norton and Company, Inc., 1971.

19. Friedman, B., *Principles and Techniques of Applied Mathematics,* John Wiley & Sons Inc., 1956.

20. Gaskill, J. D., *Linear Systems, Fourier Transforms and Optics,* Notes, to be published by John Wiley & Sons, Inc.

21. Goldberg, S., *Introduction to Difference Equations,* John Wiley & Sons Inc., 1958.

22. Goodman, J. W., *Introduction to Fourier Optics,* McGraw-Hill Book Co., 1968.

23. Greenberg, M. D., *Application of Green's Functions in Science and Engineering,* Prentice-Hall Inc., 1971.

24. Harrington, R. F., *Time-Harmonic Electromagnetic Fields,* McGraw-Hill Book Co., 1961.

25. Harrington, R. F., *Field Computation by Moment Methods,* The Macmillan Co., 1968.

26. Hecht, E., and Zajac, A., *Optics,* Addison-Wesley Publishing Co., 1974.

27. Hildebrand, F. B., *Methods of Applied Mathematics,* Ninth Printing, Prentice-Hall Inc., 1963.

28. Jackson, J. D., *Classical Electrodynamics,* John Wiley & Sons, Inc., 1962.

29. Javid, M., and Brown, P. M., *Field Analysis and Electromagnetics,* McGraw-Hill Book Co., Inc., New York, 1963.

30. Johnk, C. T. A., *Engineering Electromagnetic Fields and Waves,* John Wiley & Sons, New York, 1975.

31. Jordan, E. C., and Balmain, K. G., *Electromagnetic Waves and Radiating Systems,* Second Edition, Prentice-Hall, Inc., 1968.

32. Kapany, N. S., and Burke, J. J., *Optical Waveguides,* Academic Press, 1972.

33. Kittel, C., *Introduction to Solid State Physics,* John Wiley & Sons, Inc., 1967.

34. Klein, M. V., *Optics,* John Wiley & Sons, Inc., New York, 1970.

35. Kraus, J. D., and Carver, K. R., *Electromagnetics,* Second Edition, McGraw-Hill Book Co., 1973.

36. Kraus, J. D., *Antennas,* McGraw-Hill Book Co., 1950.

37. Lamb, H., *The Dynamical Theory of Sound,* Dover Publications Inc., 1960.

38. Langmuir, R. V., *Electromagnetic Fields and Waves,* McGraw-Hill Book Co., 1961.

39. Lorrain, P., and Corson, D. R., *Electromagnetic Fields and Waves,* Second Edition, W. H. Freeman and Co., San Francisco, 1970.

40. Marcuse, D., *Theory of Dielectric Optical Waveguides,* Academic Press, 1974.

41. Marion, J. B., *Classical Electromagnetic Radiation,* Academic Press, New York, 1965.

42. McLachlan, N. W., *Bessel Functions for Engineers*, Second Edition, Oxford at the Clarendon Press, 1955.

43. Mikhlin, S. G., *Variational Methods in Mathematical Physics*, Pergamon Press, 1964.

44. Moiseiwitsch, B. L., *Variational Principles*, John Wiley & Sons, 1966.

45. Moore, R. K., *Wave and Diffusion Analogies*, McGraw-Hill Book Co., 1964.

46. Morse, P. M., and Ingard, K. V., *Theoretical Acoustics*, McGraw-Hill Book Co., 1968.

47. Officer, C. B., *Introduction to the Theory of Sound Transmission with Applications to the Ocean*, McGraw-Hill Co. Inc., 1958.

48. O'Neill, E. L., *Introduction to Statistical Optics*, Addison-Wesley Publishing Co., Inc., 1963.

49. Page, L., and Adams, N. I., *Electrodynamics*, Dover Publications Inc., 1965.

50. Pain, H. J., *The Physics of Vibrations and Waves*, John Wiley & Sons LTD., 1971.

51. Panofsky, W. K. H., and Phillips, M., *Classical Electricity and Magnetism*, Second Edition, Addison-Wesley Publishing Co., Inc., 1962.

52. Papoulis, A., *Systems and Transforms with Application in Optics*, McGraw-Hill Book Co., 1968.

53. Papoulis, A., *The Fourier Integral and its Applications*, McGraw-Hill Book Co., 1962.

54. Paris, D. T., and Hurd, F. K., *Basic Electromagnetic Theory*, McGraw-Hill Book Co., 1969.

55. Parrent, G. B., and Thompson, B. J., *Physical Optics Notebook*, Society of Photo-optical Instrumentation Engineers, 1971.

56. Plonsey, R., and Collin, R. E., *Principles and Applications of Electromagnetic Fields*, McGraw-Hill Book Co., Inc., 1961.

57. Ramo, S., Whinnery, J. R., and Van Duzer, T., *Fields and Waves in Communication Electronics*, John Wiley & Sons, Inc., New York, 1965.

58. Rayleigh, J. W. S., *The Theory of Sound*, Dover Publications Inc., 1945.

59. Seely, S., *Introduction to Electromagnetic Fields*, McGraw-Hill Book Co., 1958.

60. Shedd, P. C., *Fundamentals of Electromagnetic Waves*, Prentice-Hall Inc., 1954.

61. Siegman, A. E., *An Introduction to Lasers and Masers*, McGraw-Hill Book Co. , 1971.

62. Skudrzyk, E., *The Foundation of Acoustics*, Springer-Verlag, 1971.

63. Smith, G. D., *Numerical Solution of Partial Differential Equations*, Oxford University Press, 1965.

64. Sneddon, I. N., *Elements of Partial Differential Equations*, McGraw-Hill Book Co., 1957.

65. Sommerfeld, A., *Mechanics of Deformable Bodies*, Academic Press, 1964.

66. Sommerfeld, A., *Optics*, Academic Press, 1964.

67. Stix, T. H., *The Theory of Plasma Waves*, McGraw-Hill Book Co., 1962.

68. Stratton, J. A., *Electromagnetic Theory*, McGraw-Hill Book Co., 1941.

69. Tai, C. T., *Dyadic Green's Functions in Electromagnetic Theory*, Intext Educational Publishers, 1971.

70. Tanenbaum, B. S., *Plasma Physics*, McGraw-Hill Book Co., 1967.

71. Tsai, L. L., and Smith, C. E., "*Moment Methods in Electromagnetics for Undergraduates*," IEEE Trans. On Educ., E-21, p. 14, 1978.

72. Tyras, G., *Radiation and Propagation of Electromagnetic Waves*, Academic Press, 1969.

73. Van Bladel, J., *Electromagnetic Fields*, McGraw-Hill Book Co., 1964.

74. Yariv, A., *Introduction to Optical Electronics*, Second Edition, Holt, Rinehart & Winston, 1976.

75. Yu, F. T. S., *Introduction to Diffraction, Information Processing, and Holography*, The MIT Press, 1973.

INDEX

D

P

Q

R